PEARSON EDEXCEL A

BIOLOGY

MARTIN ROWLAND
ED LEES
C.J. CLEGG

In order to ensure that this resource offers high-quality support for the associated Pearson qualification, it has been through a review process by the awarding body. This process confirms that this resource fully covers the teaching and learning content of the specification or part of a specification at which it is aimed. It also confirms that it demonstrates an appropriate balance between the development of subject skills, knowledge and understanding, in addition to preparation for assessment.

Endorsement does not cover any guidance on assessment activities or processes (e.g. practice questions or advice on how to answer assessment questions), included in the resource nor does it prescribe any particular approach to the teaching or delivery of a related course.

While the publishers have made every attempt to ensure that advice on the qualification and its assessment is accurate, the official specification and associated assessment guidance materials are the only authoritative source of information and should always be referred to for definitive guidance.

Pearson examiners have not contributed to any sections in this resource relevant to examination papers for which they have responsibility.

Examiners will not use endorsed resources as a source of material for any assessment set by Pearson.

Endorsement of a resource does not mean that the resource is required to achieve this Pearson qualification, nor does it mean that it is the only suitable material available to support the qualification, and any resource lists produced by the awarding body shall include this and other appropriate resources.

Orders: please contact Bookpoint Ltd, 130 Park Drive, Milton Park, Abingdon, Oxon OX14 4SE. Telephone: +44 (0)1235 827827. Fax: +44 (0)1235 400401. Email education@bookpoint.co.uk Lines are open from 9 a.m. to 5 p.m., Monday to Saturday, with a 24-hour message answering service. You can also order through our website: www.hoddereducation.co.uk

ISBN: 978 1 5104 6993 8

Edexcel A level Biology Student Book 1 published in 2015

Edexcel A level Biology Student Book 2 published in 2015

This combined edition published in 2019 by
Hodder Education,
An Hachette UK Company
Carmelite House
50 Victoria Embankment
London EC4Y 0DZ
www.hoddereducation.co.uk

Impression number 10 9 8 7 6 5 4 3 2 1

Year 2023 2022 2021 2020 2019

Cover photo © Mustafa Öztürk / Blackdiamond67 / 500px - stock.adobe.com

Typeset in India by Aptara Inc.

Printed in India

A catalogue record for this title is available from the British Library.

Contents

Origins of genetic variation

Control systems

Ecosystems

Appendix

Go to www.hoddereducation.co.uk/EdexcelBiology to find the answers and extended glossaries

Get the most from this book

Welcome to the **Pearson Edexcel A level Biology (Year 1 and Year 2) Student's Book**. This book covers all content for the Pearson Edexcel A level Biology specification and the Pearson Edexcel AS Biology specification.

The following features have been included to help you get the most from this book.

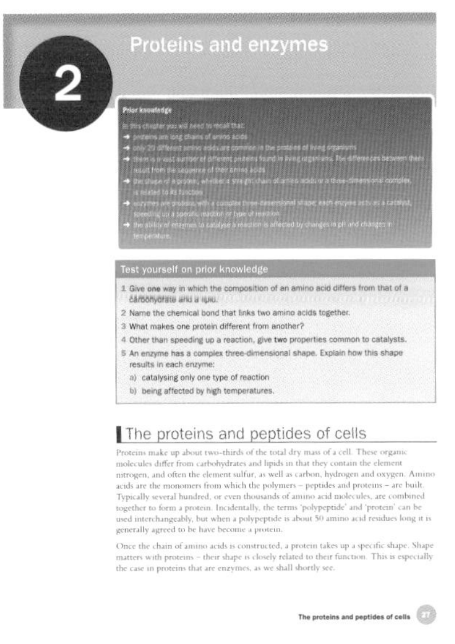

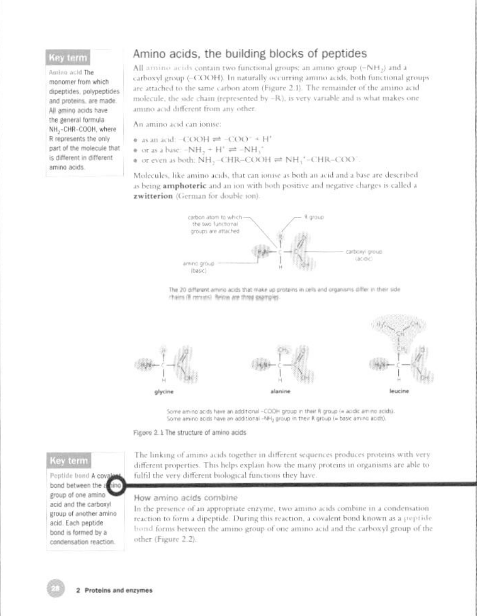

Key terms and formulae

These are highlighted in the text and definitions are given in the margin to help you pick out and learn these important concepts.

Examples

Examples of questions and calculations feature full workings and sample answers.

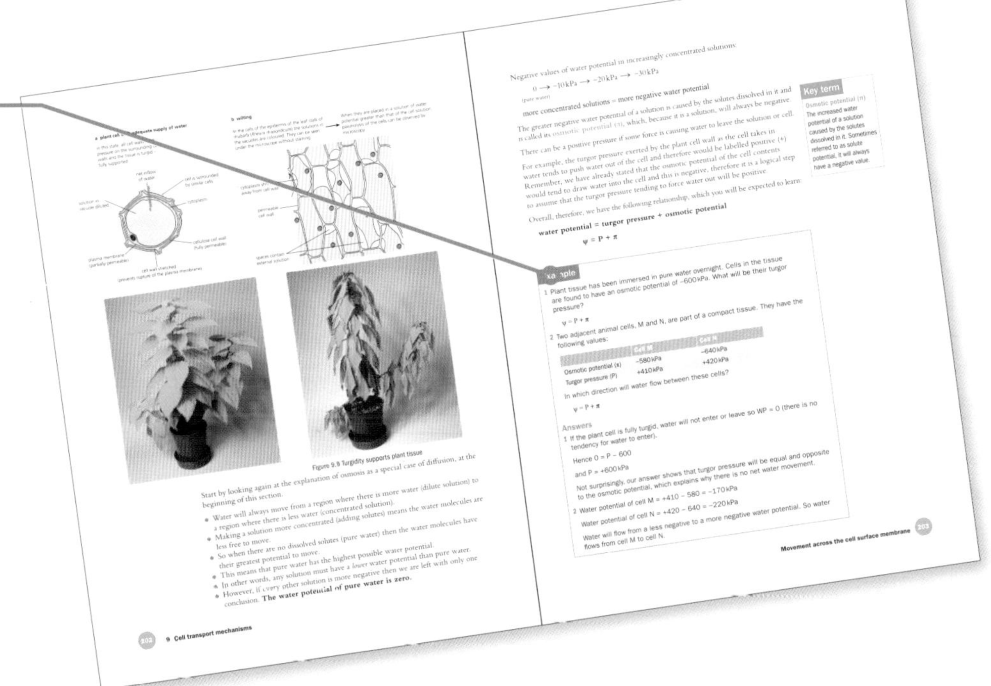

Test yourself questions

These short questions, found throughout each chapter, are useful for checking your understanding as you progress through a topic.

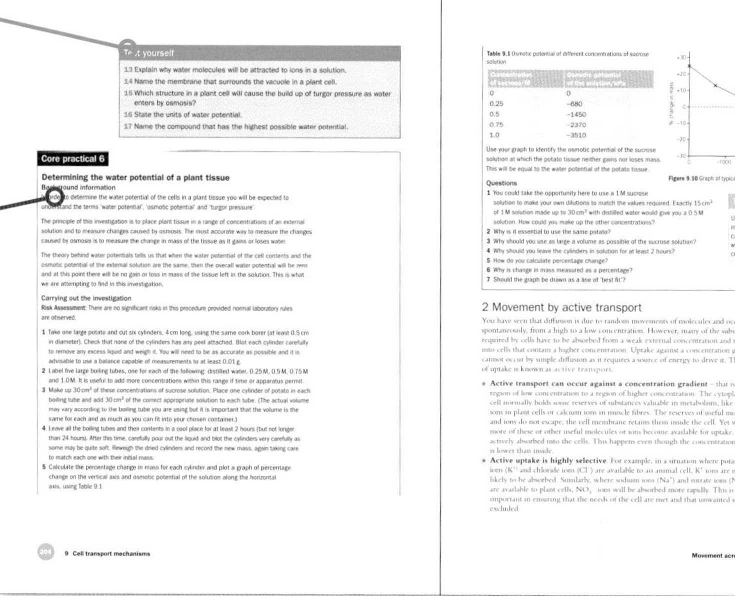

Activities and Core practicals

These practical-based activities will help consolidate your learning and test your practical skills. Edexcel's Core practicals are clearly highlighted.

In this edition the authors describe many important experimental procedures to conform to recent changes in the A level curriculum. Teachers should be aware that, although there is enough information to inform students of techniques and many observations for exam purposes, there is not enough information for teachers to replicate the experiments themselves, or with students, without recourse to CLEAPSS Hazcards or Laboratory worksheets which have undergone a risk assessment procedure.

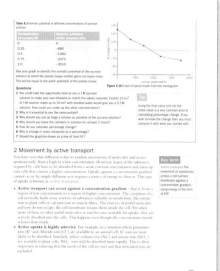

Exam practice questions

You will find Exam practice questions at the end of every chapter. These follow the style of the different types of questions you might see in your examination and are colour coded to highlight the level of difficulty. Test your understanding even further with Maths questions and Stretch and challenge questions.

Practice questions

1 The graph shows the effect of temperature on the rate of an enzyme-catalysed reaction.

Which of the following statements is true about the graph?

A The enzyme starts to become denatured at point W.

B The enzyme starts to become denatured at point X.

C The enzyme starts to become denatured at point Y.

D The enzyme starts to become denatured at point Z. (1)

2 Denaturation involves breakage of which types of bond?

A Hydrogen bonds, ionic bonds and peptide bonds

B Disulfide bonds, hydrogen bonds and peptide bonds

C Disulfide bonds, ionic bonds and peptide bonds

D Disulfide bonds, hydrogen bonds and ionic bonds (1)

3 Which of the following statements is true about an amino acid in a weakly acidic solution?

A It will not ionise.

B It will ionise as an anion.

C It will ionise as a cation.

D It will ionise as a zwitterion. (1)

4 Collagen and haemoglobin are two different proteins. Explain **one** way in which the structure of each molecule is adapted for its function. (4)

5 The diagrams represent four different types of molecule important in biology. Identify each type of molecule. (4)

Tip: Question 4 tests recall with understanding (AO1). Note that the command word is 'explain'; a simple description of each molecule will not gain full marks.

Tip: Question 5 tests recall with understanding (AO1) from Chapters 1 and 2.

Tips

These highlight important facts, common misconceptions and signpost you towards other relevant topics.

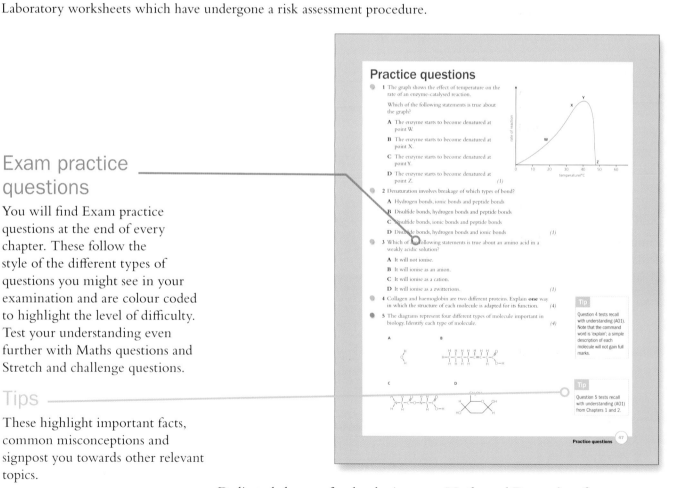

Dedicated chapters for developing your **Maths** and **Preparing for your exam** are also included in this book.

Introduction

Welcome to *Pearson Edexcel A level Biology (Year 1 and Year 2)*. This book has been written to cover the content of the Pearson Edexcel Level 3 Advanced GCE in Biology B (9BI0). Since the subject content is the same, it also covers the content of the Pearson Edexcel Level 3 Advanced Subsidiary GCE in Biology B (8BI0).

The main 26 chapters cover the essential concepts, facts, principles and terminology of the A level qualification. The first 12 chapters only are needed if studying the AS qualification. The two chapters in the Appendix contain advice about developing skills that are assessed in your final examinations. Since you will need to put into practice the principles they contain, you are advised to read these final chapters at the start of your course. You will also find it useful to dip into them during the course, especially when preparing your examination strategy.

The biological content of each chapter has been written to ensure you cover everything that you can be expected to recall with understanding in your examinations. To help you and to encourage you to take an active part in your learning, the chapters contain the following features.

- Clear definitions of technical terms that you will be expected to understand and use correctly.
- Tips that offer reminders, hints or warnings.
- Regularly spaced Test yourself questions that encourage recall and understanding.
- Activities that encourage you to apply your knowledge, analyse information and make judgements.

At the end of each chapter you will find a series of Exam Practice Questions. By simulating the types of questions that you will encounter in your examinations, these questions will help you to develop, and maintain, the skills that will be assessed. To help you further, these questions have been graded to indicate their accessibility level (● = AS/A level grade E–C, ● = AS grade C–A/A level grade C and ● = AS grade A/A level grade C–A). In addition, each chapter contains Stretch and challenge questions. Some of these are similar to questions in an A level paper that are targeted at the more able students. Others encourage you to use the learning resource centre in your college or school to carry out further research. Don't feel you have to do this alone; group research will develop your skills and can be more satisfying than working alone.

Practical work is an essential part of science. The Pearson Edexcel Biology specification contains core practicals that you are expected to carry out and on which you can be tested in examinations. This book covers these core practicals in a way that will encourage you to think about what you are doing, make comments on, or develop practical procedures, analyse results and make judgements. Again, these are all skills that can be assessed in your examinations.

Above all else, Biology is a fascinating subject which we hope you enjoy. We hope that some of our own enjoyment of Biology is reflected in this book and in the supporting material.

Acknowledgements

This book is an extensively revised, restructured and updated version of the Edexcel Biology for AS and A level books by C J Clegg. We have relied heavily on the original books and are most grateful that C J Clegg has encouraged us to build on his work. We would also like to acknowledge the value of the detailed comments and suggestions from Liz Jones. The team at Hodder Education, led initially by Hanneke Remsing and then by Emma Braithwaite, has made an extremely valuable contribution to the development of the book and the website resources. In particular, we would like to thank Abigail Woodman, the project manager, for her expert advice and encouragement. We are also grateful for the skilful work on the print and electronic resources by Lydia Young.

Ed Lees and Martin Rowland

January 2019

1 Introducing the chemistry of life

Prior knowledge

In this chapter you will need to recall that:

- carbohydrates contain the chemical elements carbon, hydrogen and oxygen in the ratio $C_x(H_2O)_y$
- carbohydrates include simple sugars, such as glucose, and complex carbohydrates, such as cellulose and starch
- simple sugars are used in respiration; complex carbohydrates might be glucose stores (starch) or structural components of cells (cellulose)
- lipids also contain the chemical elements carbon, hydrogen and oxygen, but there is much less oxygen in lipids than in carbohydrates
- lipids can be useful storage compounds and can also be structural components of cells
- inorganic ions are present in the cytoplasm of cells and in body fluids; each type of ion has a specific function
- water is essential for life and most of the mass of an organism comprises water
- water is a reactant in many cell reactions; these reactions also occur in solution in water.

Test yourself on prior knowledge

1 Give **one** way in which the composition of a carbohydrate molecule is similar to that of a lipid and **one** way in which it is different from that of a lipid.

2 Name **one** type of carbohydrate used for energy storage in an animal and **one** used for energy storage in a plant.

3 How do animal lipids differ from plant lipids at room temperature?

4 Give **two** functions of lipids.

5 Calcium ions are essential for healthy growth in animals and plants. Give **one** function of calcium ions in humans and **one** function of calcium ions in plants.

6 In cells, water is a reactant in hydrolysis reactions and in condensation reactions. Describe the difference between these two types of reaction.

Some basic concepts

Chemical elements are the units of pure substance that make up our world. The Earth is composed of about 92 stable elements; living things are built from some of them. Table 1.1 shows a comparison between the most common elements in the Earth's crust and in us. You can see that the bulk of the Earth is composed of the elements oxygen, silicon, aluminium and iron. Of these, only oxygen is a major component of our cells.

Table 1.1 Most common elements

Earth's crust		Human body	
Element	**% of atoms**	**Element**	**% of atoms**
Oxygen	47.0	Hydrogen	63.0
Silicon	28.0	Oxygen	25.5
Aluminium	7.9	Carbon	9.5
Iron	4.5	Nitrogen	1.4
Calcium	3.5	Calcium	0.3
Sodium	2.5	Phosphorus	0.2

In fact, about 16 elements are required to build up all the molecules of the cell, and are therefore essential for life. Consequently, the full list of essential elements is a relatively short one. Furthermore, about 99 per cent of living matter consists of just four elements: carbon, hydrogen, oxygen and nitrogen.

The elements carbon, hydrogen and oxygen predominate because living things contain large quantities of water, and also because most other molecules present in cells and organisms are compounds of carbon combined with hydrogen and oxygen, including the carbohydrates and lipids. We will examine the structures and roles of carbohydrates and lipids shortly.

The element nitrogen is combined with carbon, hydrogen and oxygen in compounds called amino acids, from which proteins are constructed (Chapter 2). First, we will introduce some inorganic ions essential for organisms, and then discuss water.

Atoms, molecules and ions

The fundamental unit of chemical structure is the **atom**. Atoms group together to form molecules and molecules are the smallest part of most elements or compounds that can exist alone under normal conditions. For example, both oxygen and nitrogen naturally combine with another atom of the same type to form a molecule (O_2 and N_2, respectively).

If an atom gains or loses an electron, an **ion** is formed. Depending on their charge, ions migrate to the poles of an electric field. Positively charged ions migrate to the negative pole (cathode) and so are called **cations**. In contrast, negatively charged ions migrate to the positive pole (anode) and so are called **anions**.

Key terms

Atom The smallest part of an element that can take part in a chemical change.

Ions Charged particles formed when atoms gain or lose electrons. **Cations** are positively charged, whereas **anions** are negatively charged.

Acid A compound that releases hydrogen ions in solution. Acidic solutions have a pH value below 7.

Acids and bases

An **acid** is a compound that releases hydrogen ions in solution. We are familiar with the sharp taste that acids such as lemon juice or vinegar give to the tongue. These are relatively weak acids, weak enough to use on foods. The stronger the acid the more dangerous and corrosive it is, and the more hydrogen ions it releases. An example of a strong acid is hydrochloric acid. In water, this acid dissociates completely. The word dissociate means 'separates into its constituent ions':

$$HCl \rightarrow H^+ + Cl^-$$

hydrochloric acid → hydrogen ion (proton) + chloride ion

With organic acids such as citric acid (present in lemon juice) and ethanoic acid (found in vinegar), which we recognise as weak acids, relatively few molecules dissociate, and few hydrogen ions are present:

CH_3COOH	$\rightleftharpoons$	CH_3COO^-	+	H^+
ethanoic acid		ethanoate ion		hydrogen ion (proton)

> **Key term**
>
> **Base** A compound that can take up hydrogen ions in solution. Basic solutions have a pH value above 7.

A **base** is a compound that can take up hydrogen ions in solution. In doing so it can neutralise an acid, forming a salt and water in the process. Many bases are insoluble in water. Those that are soluble in water are called alkalis. Examples of strong bases (that are also alkalis) are sodium hydroxide and potassium hydroxide. Strong alkalis, like strong acids, are completely dissociated in water:

$NaOH$	$\rightarrow$	Na^+	+	OH^-
sodium hydroxide		sodium ion		hydroxide ion

> **Tip**
>
> Remember when dealing with logarithmic values that a value of 2 ($\log_{10} 100$) is ten times greater than a value of 1 ($\log_{10} 10$), not two times greater.

pH and buffers

pH is a measure of the acidity or alkalinity of a solution. Strictly, pH is a measure of the hydrogen ion concentration. Since these concentrations involve a very large range of numbers, the pH scale uses logarithms:

$$pH = -\log_{10} H^+ \text{ concentration}$$

The pH value of pure water is 7. A solution with a pH value less than 7 is acidic; strong acids have a pH value of 0 to 2. A solution with a pH value more than 7 is alkaline; strong alkalis have a pH value of 12 to 14.

pH can be measured experimentally, either using an indicator solution or a pH meter. For example, universal pH indicator is a mixture of several different indicators, and changes colour with the pH, as shown in Figure 1.1.

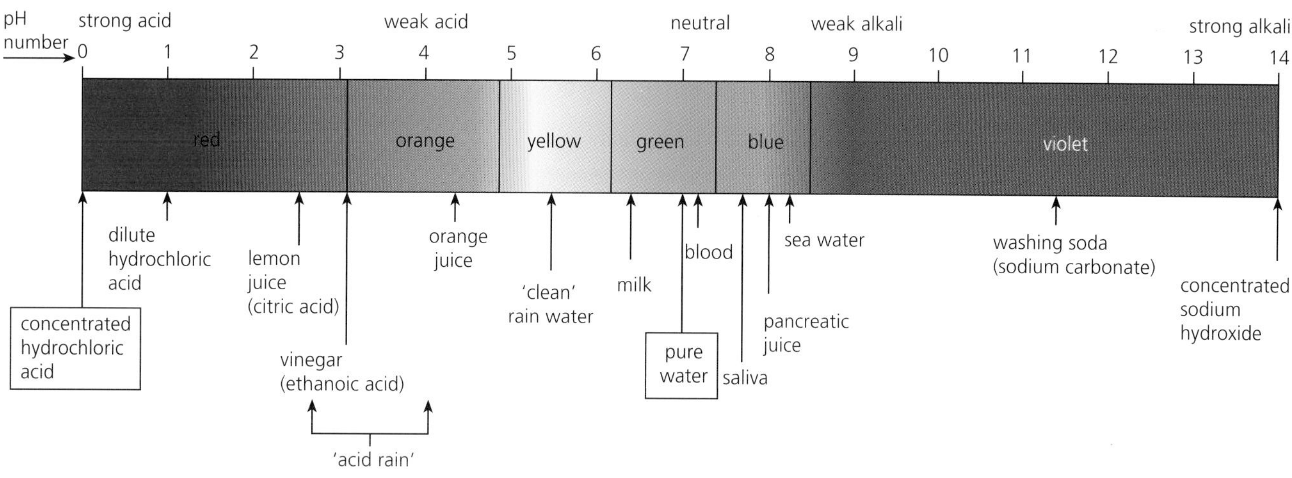

Figure 1.1 The pH scale of universal pH indicator solution

pH is very important in living organisms, largely because pH affects the shape of enzymes, almost all of which are proteins (page 35). In a mammal's body there are mechanisms that stabilise pH at a value just slightly above pH 7.0. If the pH varies much from this value this lack of stabilisation is quickly fatal. For plants that obtain essential mineral ions from the soil solution, the pH of the soil affects the availability of the ions for absorption.

Key term

Buffer solution A solution that resists changes in pH; usually a mixture of a weak acid and one of its soluble salts.

A **buffer solution** is one that will resist pH change when diluted, or if a little acid or alkali is added. Many buffers used in laboratory experiments contain a weak acid (such as ethanoic acid and one of its soluble salts, for example sodium ethanoate). In this case, if acid is added, the excess hydrogen ions are immediately removed by being combined with ethanoate ions to form undissociated ethanoic acid. Alternatively, if alkali is added, the excess hydroxyl ions immediately combine with hydrogen ions, forming water. At the same time, more of the ethanoic acid dissociates, adding more hydrogen ions to the solution. The pH does not change in either case.

In the body of a mammal, the blood is very powerfully buffered by the presence of a mixture of phosphate ions, hydrogencarbonate ions and blood proteins (page 236). The blood is held between pH 7.35 and 7.45.

Test yourself

1 Distinguish between a sodium atom and a sodium ion.

2 A pH value is calculated as $-\log_{10}$ hydrogen ion concentration. By how many times is the concentration of hydrogen ions in a solution with a pH value of 2 greater than one with a pH value of 8?

3 Explain the importance of using buffer solutions during investigations into the rate of enzyme-controlled reactions.

4 Explain the meaning of the term *dissociation*.

5 Explain why a positively charged ion is called a cation.

Inorganic ions used by plants

Key term

Metabolism All the chemical reactions that occur within an organism.

Metabolism involves a range of inorganic ions, in addition to those mentioned above. Table 1.2 shows four inorganic ions whose roles in plants you are required to know.

Table 1.2 The role of selected ions in plants

Inorganic ion	Role in plants
Nitrate (NO_3^-)	Used to synthesise the nitrogenous bases in DNA and RNA nucleotides and to synthesise the amino groups of amino acids.
Calcium (Ca^{2+})	Used to synthesise calcium pectate, which exists as a layer, called the middle lamella, between the walls of adjacent plant cells.
Magnesium (Mg^{2+})	Used to synthesise the photosynthetic pigment, chlorophyll.
Phosphate (PO_4^{3-})	Used to synthesise adenosine triphosphate (ATP) from adenosine diphosphate (ADP) and to synthesise DNA and RNA

Water

Living things are typically solid, substantial objects, yet water forms the bulk of their structures – between 65 and 95 per cent by mass of most multicellular plants and animals (about 80 per cent of a human cell consists of water). Despite this, and the fact that water has some unusual properties, it is a substance that is often taken for granted.

Water is composed of atoms of the elements hydrogen and oxygen. One atom of oxygen and two atoms of hydrogen combine by sharing of electrons in an arrangement known as a **covalent bond** (see Figure 1.2). The large nucleus of the oxygen atom draws electrons (negatively charged) away from the smaller hydrogen nuclei (positively charged) with an interesting consequence. Although overall the water molecule is electrically neutral, there is a weak negative charge (represented by δ^-) on the oxygen atom and a weak positive charge (represented by δ^+) on each hydrogen atom. In other words, the water molecule carries an unequal distribution of electrical charge within it. This arrangement is known as a **polar molecule**.

> **Key terms**
>
> **Covalent bond** A relatively strong chemical link between two atoms in which electrons are shared between them.
>
> **Polar molecule** A molecule that contains weak positive charges (represented by δ^+) and weak negative charges (represented by δ^-)

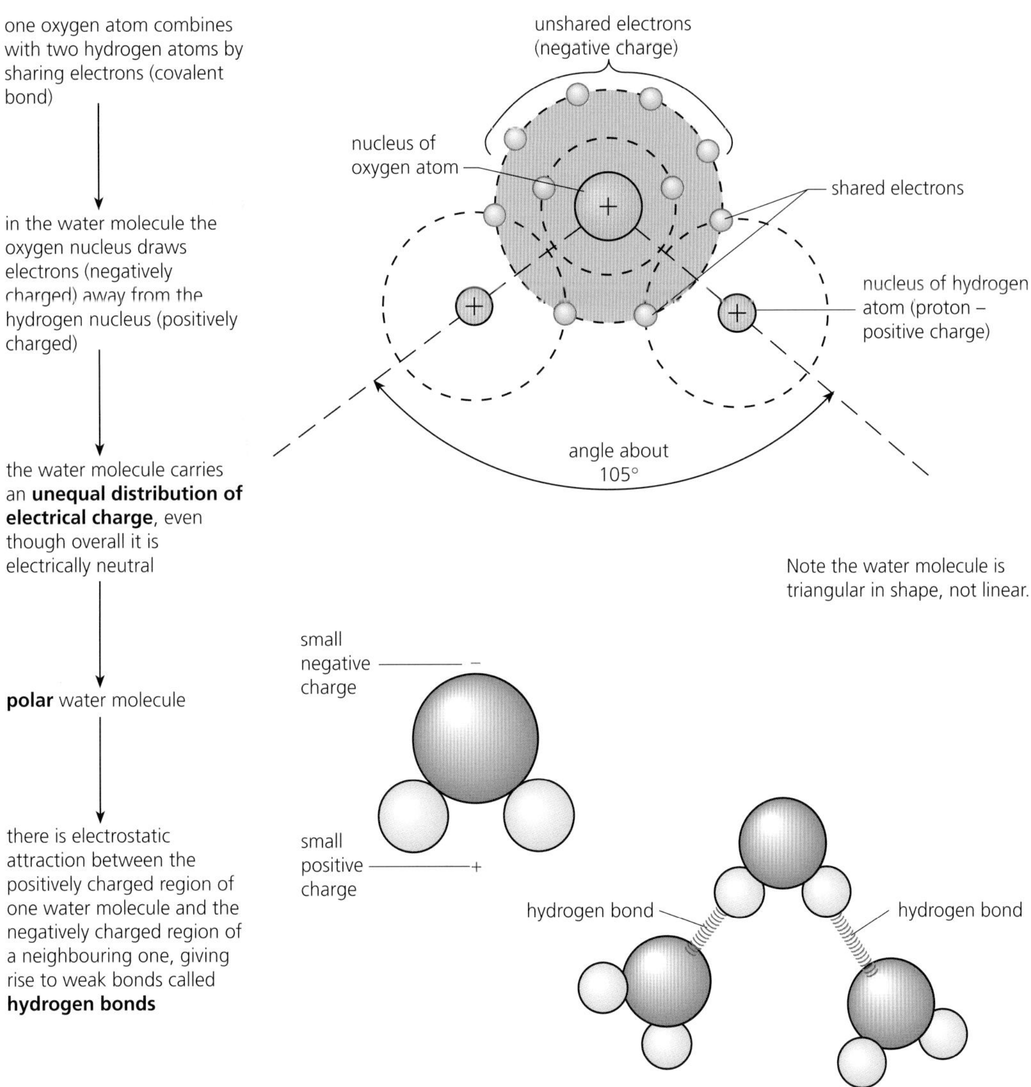

one oxygen atom combines with two hydrogen atoms by sharing electrons (covalent bond)
in the water molecule the oxygen nucleus draws electrons (negatively charged) away from the hydrogen nucleus (positively charged)
the water molecule carries an **unequal distribution of electrical charge**, even though overall it is electrically neutral
polar water molecule
there is electrostatic attraction between the positively charged region of one water molecule and the negatively charged region of a neighbouring one, giving rise to weak bonds called **hydrogen bonds**
unshared electrons (negative charge)
nucleus of oxygen atom
shared electrons
nucleus of hydrogen atom (proton – positive charge)
angle about 105°
Note the water molecule is triangular in shape, not linear.
small negative charge
small positive charge
hydrogen bond
hydrogen bond

Figure 1.2 A water molecule and the hydrogen bonds it forms

Hydrogen bonds

The positively charged hydrogen atoms of one molecule are attracted to negatively charged oxygen atoms of nearby water molecules by forces called **hydrogen bonds**. These are weak bonds compared with covalent bonds, yet they are strong enough to hold water molecules together. This is called **cohesion**; it not only attracts water molecules to each other but also to another charged particle or charged surface. In fact, hydrogen bonds largely account for the unique properties of water, which are examined next.

> **Key terms**
>
> **Hydrogen bond** A relatively weak link between two atoms in which a weakly negative atom attracts another weakly positive atom.
>
> **Cohesion** The force by which hydrogen bonds hold polar molecules together, or to a charged surface.

Solvent properties of water

Because water molecules are polar, water is a powerful solvent for other polar substances (Figure 1.3). These include:

- ionic substances like sodium chloride (Na^+ and Cl^-). All ions become surrounded by a shell of orientated water molecules (Figure 1.3)
- carbon-containing (organic) molecules with ionised groups, such as the carboxyl group ($-COO^-$) and amino group ($-NH_3^+$). Soluble organic molecules like sugars dissolve in water due to the formation of hydrogen bonds with their slightly charged hydroxyl groups ($-OH^-$).

Once they have dissolved, the **solute** molecules are free to move around in water (the **solvent**) and, as a result, are more chemically reactive than when in the undissolved solid state.

Key terms

Hydrophilic Refers to substances that will mix with water.

Hydrophobic Refers to substances that will not mix with water.

Polar substances that can dissolve in, or mix in, water are termed **hydrophilic** (water-loving). On the other hand, non-polar substances are repelled by water, as in the case of oil on the surface of water. Non-polar substances are **hydrophobic** (water-hating).

Ionic compounds like NaCl dissolve in water:

$NaCl \rightleftharpoons Na^+ + Cl^-$

with a group of orientated water molecules around each ion.

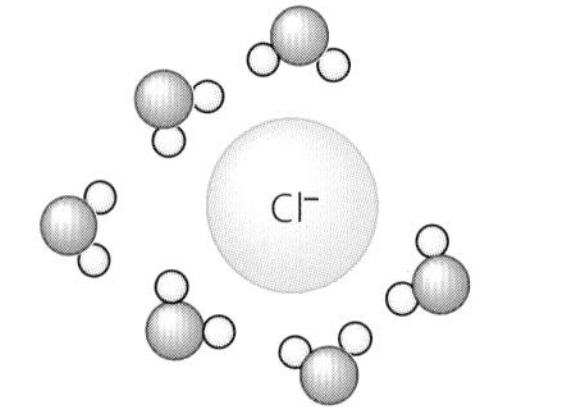

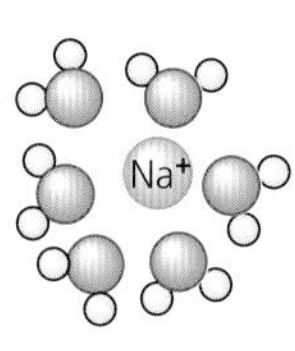

Sugars and alcohols dissolve due to hydrogen bonding between polar groups in their molecules (e.g. –OH) and the polar water molecules.

Figure 1.3 Water as universal solvent

Tip

The specific heat capacity of water given in the text is $4.184\,kJ\,kg^{-1}\,°C^{-1}$. You need to be confident in using compound units. In this case, the unit means that it takes 4.184 kJ of heat to increase the temperature of 1 kg of water by 1 degree Celsius.

High specific heat capacity of water

A lot of heat is required to raise the temperature of water. This is because heat is needed to break the hydrogen bonds between water molecules. This property of water is its **specific heat capacity**. The specific heat capacity of water is extremely high ($4.184\,kJ\,kg^{-1}\,°C^{-1}$). Consequently, the temperature of aquatic environments like streams and rivers, ponds, lakes and seas is very slow to change when the surrounding air temperature changes. Aquatic environments have much more stable temperatures than do terrestrial (land) environments.

Another consequence is that the temperature of cells and the bodies of organisms does not change readily. Bulky organisms, particularly, tend to have a stable temperature in the face of a fluctuating surrounding temperature, whether in extremes of heat or cold.

Surface tension of water

Compared with other liquids, water has extremely strong adhesive and cohesive properties.

As we saw earlier, cohesion is the force by which charged molecules stick together. Water molecules are held together by hydrogen bonding. In practice, these bonds continually break and reform with other surrounding water molecules but, at any one moment, a large number are held together by their hydrogen bonds.

Figure 1.4 A pond skater moving over the water surface

At an air–water interface, cohesion between water molecules results in **surface tension**. The outermost molecules of water form hydrogen bonds with water molecules below them. This gives a very high surface tension to water, which you can see being exploited by the pond skater in Figure 1.4. This insect has a waxy cuticle that prevents wetting of its body and its mass is not great enough to break the surface tension of the water.

Incompressibility of water

Water is essentially incompressible. Incompressibility is a common property of liquids but water is especially so. There is much less distance between the molecules in a liquid than in a gas, and the intermolecular force of the hydrogen bonds aids this property. Because of this incompressibility, a water-filled cavity within an organism can act as a hydrostatic skeleton.

Maximum density of water at 4 °C

Most liquids contract on cooling, reaching maximum density at their freezing point. Water is unusual in reaching its maximum density at 4 °C (Figure 1.5). So as water freezes, the ice formed is less dense than the cold water around it. As a consequence, ice floats on top of very cold water. The floating layer of ice insulates the water below. The consequence is that lakes rarely freeze solid; aquatic life can generally survive freezing temperatures.

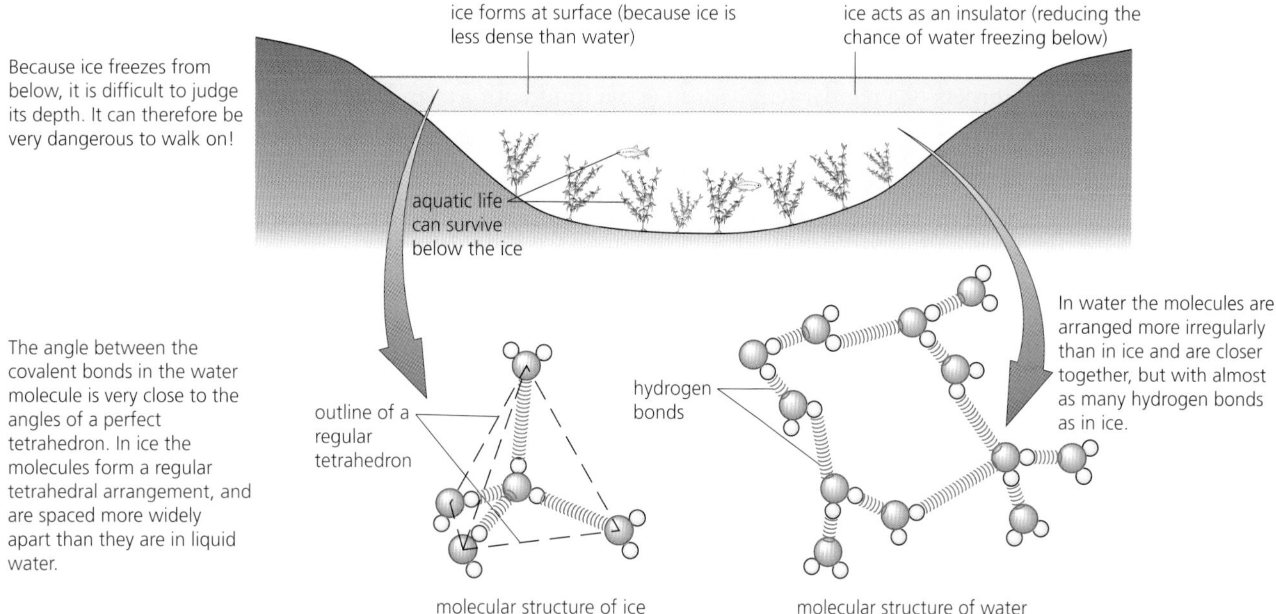

ice forms at surface (because ice is less dense than water)
ice acts as an insulator (reducing the chance of water freezing below)
Because ice freezes from below, it is difficult to judge its depth. It can therefore be very dangerous to walk on!
aquatic life can survive below the ice
The angle between the covalent bonds in the water molecule is very close to the angles of a perfect tetrahedron. In ice the molecules form a regular tetrahedral arrangement, and are spaced more widely apart than they are in liquid water.
outline of a regular tetrahedron
hydrogen bonds
In water the molecules are arranged more irregularly than in ice and are closer together, but with almost as many hydrogen bonds as in ice.
molecular structure of ice
molecular structure of water

Figure 1.5 Ice forms on the surface of water

Test yourself

6 Suggest what symptoms would be shown by a plant growing in magnesium-deficient soil. Explain your answer.

7 What is meant by the term *metabolism*?

8 The text includes five properties of water that make it essential in biology. Use your knowledge of metabolism to suggest a sixth property.

9 Water that evaporates from the leaves of a flowering plant is replaced when a water column is pulled up the plant in xylem tissue. This water column is under negative pressure (tension). Explain why this does *not* cause the water column to break.

10 Explain why the pond skater shown in Figure 1.4 can walk on water but you cannot.

Introducing the carbon of organic compounds

Key term

Organic compound
A compound in which carbon atoms are linked by covalent bonds to each other and to hydrogen molecules. The molecules of organic compounds can be very large and can exist as chains or rings of carbon atoms.

Carbon is a relatively uncommon element of the Earth's crust but, as Table 1.1 showed, in cells and organisms it is the third most abundant element. The majority of the carbon compounds found in living organisms are relatively large molecules in which many carbon atoms are linked together and to hydrogen and oxygen atoms by covalent bonds. They are known as **organic compounds**.

Some carbon-containing compounds are not like this – for example, the gas carbon dioxide (CO_2) and hydrogencarbonate ions (HCO_3^-) are not organic forms of carbon.

The properties of carbon

Carbon has remarkable properties. It has a relatively small atom, but it is able to form four strong, stable, covalent bonds. As you can see in Figure 1.6, these bonds point to the corners of a regular tetrahedron (a pyramid with a triangular base). This is because the four pairs of electrons that form the covalent bonds repel each other and so position themselves as far away from each other as possible.

Carbon atoms are able to react with each other to form extended chains. The resulting carbon 'skeletons' can be straight chains, branched chains or rings. Carbon also bonds covalently with other atoms, such as oxygen, hydrogen, nitrogen and sulfur, forming different groups of organic molecules with distinctive properties.

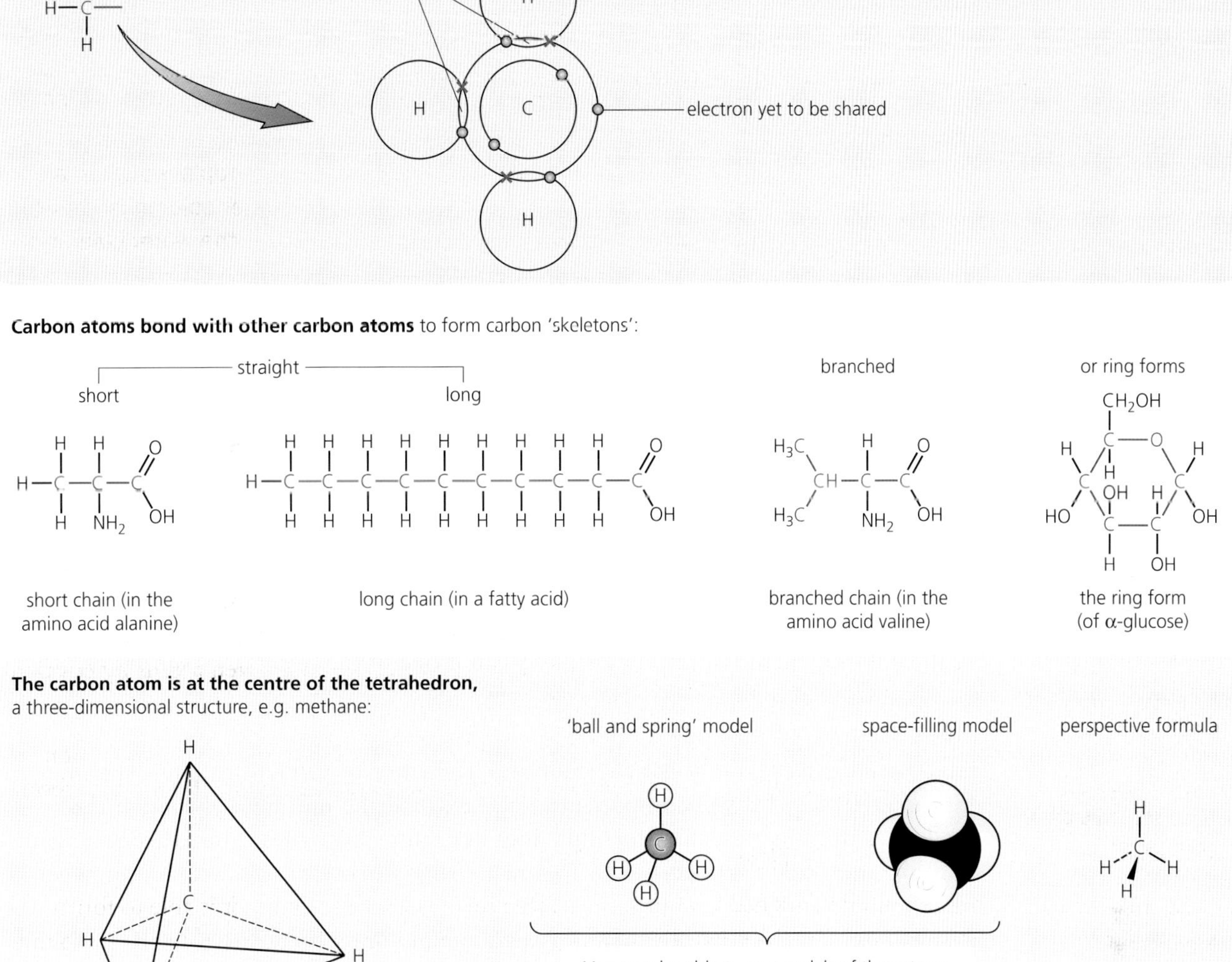
Covalent bonds are formed by sharing of electrons, one from the carbon atom and one from the neighbouring atom it reacts with:
shared electrons
electron yet to be shared
Carbon atoms bond with other carbon atoms to form carbon 'skeletons':
straight
short
long
branched
or ring forms
short chain (in the amino acid alanine)
long chain (in a fatty acid)
branched chain (in the amino acid valine)
the ring form (of α-glucose)
The carbon atom is at the centre of the tetrahedron, a three-dimensional structure, e.g. methane:
'ball and spring' model
space-filling model
perspective formula
You may be able to see models of these types in your school or college chemistry laboratory.

Figure 1.6 A tetrahedral carbon atom, its covalent bonds and the carbon 'skeletons' it can form

One inevitable outcome of these features is that there are vast numbers of organic compounds – more than the total of known compounds made from other elements, in fact. Biologists think the diversity of organic compounds has made possible the diversity of life. Fortunately, very many of the organic chemicals of living things fall into one of four discrete groups or 'families' of chemicals with many common properties, one of which is the carbohydrates. We will consider this family of molecules first before looking at a second family, the lipids.

Carbohydrates

Carbohydrates include sugars, starch, glycogen and cellulose. They contain only three elements: carbon, hydrogen and oxygen, in the ratio $C_x(H_2O)_y$. Table 1.3 summarises features of the three types of carbohydrates you should recognise.

Table 1.3 Carbohydrates of cells and organisms.

Type of carbohydrate	Features
Monosaccharides	Simple sugars, including: • trioses ($C_3H_6O_3$), which you will learn more about in Year 2 • pentoses ($C_5H_{10}O_5$), e.g. ribose and deoxyribose (see Chapter 3) • hexoses ($C_6H_{12}O_6$), e.g. glucose, fructose, galactose.
Disaccharides	Two simple sugars chemically linked by a glycosidic bond during a condensation reaction, e.g. • sucrose = glucose + fructose • lactose = glucose + galactose • maltose = glucose + glucose.
Polysaccharides	Very many simple sugars chemically linked by glycosidic bonds, e.g. • starch (a fuel store in plants) • glycogen (a fuel store in animals) • cellulose (a major component of plant cell walls).

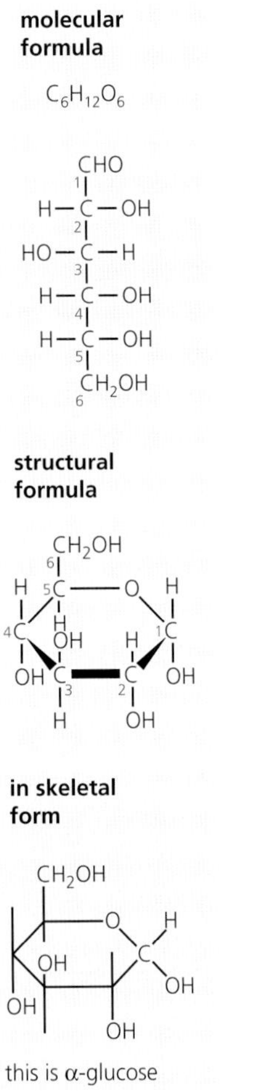

molecular formula

$C_6H_{12}O_6$

structural formula

in skeletal form

this is α-glucose

Figure 1.7 The structure of alpha glucose

Monosaccharides – the simple sugars

Monosaccharides are carbohydrates with relatively small molecules. They are soluble in water and taste sweet. In biology, glucose is an especially important monosaccharide because:

- all green leaves manufacture glucose using light
- all cells use glucose in respiration – we call it one of the respiratory substrates.

The structure of glucose

Glucose is a hexose, i.e. it has a **molecular formula** of $C_6H_{12}O_6$. This type of formula tells us what the component atoms are, and the numbers of each in the molecule. But the molecular formula does not tell us how these atoms are arranged within a molecule. You can see in Figure 1.7 that glucose can be written on paper as a linear molecule. It does not exist in this form because, as you saw in Figure 1.6, the four bonds in each of its carbon atoms are arranged into a tetrahedron; the molecule cannot be 'flat'. Rather, glucose is folded, taking a ring or cyclic form. Figure 1.7 also shows the **structural formula** of glucose.

The carbon atoms of an organic molecule can be numbered. This allows us to identify which atoms are affected when the molecule reacts and changes shape. For example, as the glucose ring forms, the oxygen on carbon atom 5 (carbon-5) becomes linked to that on carbon atom 1 (carbon-1). As a result, the glucose ring contains five carbon atoms and an oxygen atom; again, you can see this in Figure 1.7.

Isomers of glucose

Molecules with the same molecular formula but different structural formulae are known as **isomers**. Many organic compounds exist in isomeric forms, and so it is often important to know the structure of an organic compound as well as its composition.

In the ring structure of glucose the positions of –H and –OH that are attached to carbon-1 can lie in one of two directions, giving rise to two isomers, known as **alpha-glucose** (α-glucose) and **beta-glucose** (β-glucose). You can see these isomers in Figure 1.8. The significance of the differences between them will become apparent when we compare the structures of starch, glycogen and cellulose (pages 13–16).

Key terms

Molecular formula Shows the nature and number of atoms in a molecule, for example $C_5H_{10}O_5$.

Structural formula Shows the way in which the atoms within a molecule are arranged in space.

Isomers Two or more different structural formulae of the same molecular formula.

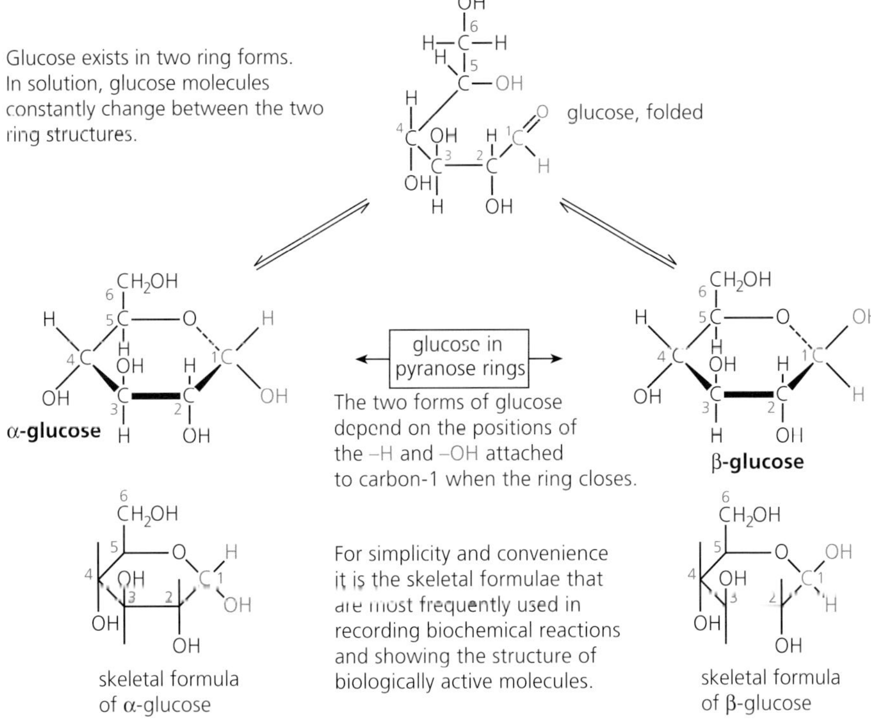

Glucose exists in two ring forms. In solution, glucose molecules constantly change between the two ring structures.
glucose, folded
α-glucose
glucose in pyranose rings
The two forms of glucose depend on the positions of the –H and –OH attached to carbon-1 when the ring closes.
β-glucose
skeletal formula of α-glucose
For simplicity and convenience it is the skeletal formulae that are most frequently used in recording biochemical reactions and showing the structure of biologically active molecules.
skeletal formula of β-glucose

Figure 1.8 Alpha and beta glucose

A test for the presence of glucose, a 'reducing sugar'

Glucose and some other sugars are known as 'reducing sugars'. This is because, when they are heated with an alkaline solution of copper(II) sulfate (a blue solution, called Benedict's solution), the carbonyl group (–C=O) that their molecule contains (known as an aldehyde group) reduces Cu^{2+} ions of copper(II) sulfate to Cu^{+} ions, which then form a brick-red precipitate of copper(I) oxide. In the process, the aldehyde group is oxidised to a carboxyl group (–COOH).

This reaction is used to test for reducing sugar, and is known as **Benedict's test** (Figure 1.9). If no reducing sugar is present the solution remains blue after heating. The colour change observed depends on the concentration of reducing sugar. The greater the concentration the more precipitate is formed, and the more the colour changes:

blue → green → yellow → brown → red

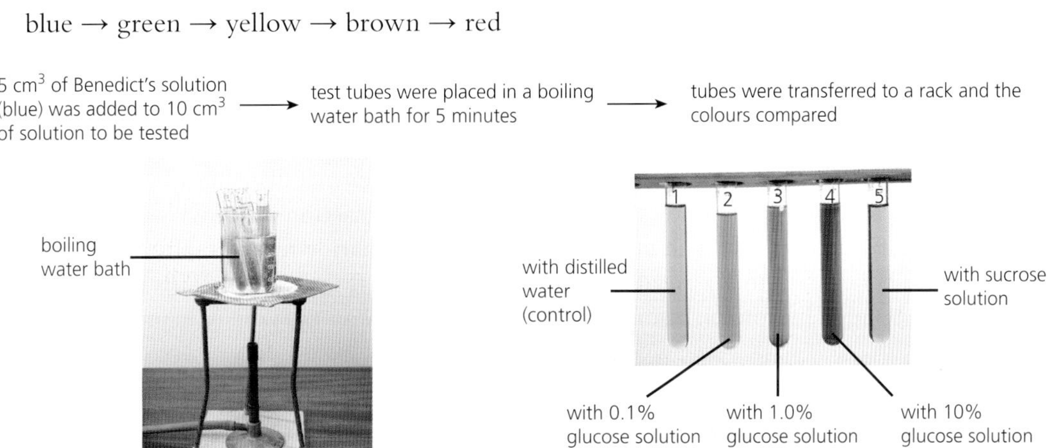

5 cm^3 of Benedict's solution (blue) was added to 10 cm^3 of solution to be tested
test tubes were placed in a boiling water bath for 5 minutes
tubes were transferred to a rack and the colours compared
boiling water bath

with 0.1% glucose solution
with 1.0% glucose solution
with 10% glucose solution

Figure 1.9 The test for reducing sugar. Wear eye protection when performing this test

Other monosaccharides of importance in living cells

Glucose, fructose and galactose are examples of hexose sugars commonly occurring in cells and organisms, but it is only the structure of α- and β-glucose that you need to know. Other monosaccharide sugars produced by cells and used in metabolism include a 3-carbon sugar (Table 1.4), and two 5-carbon sugars (**pentoses**), namely ribose and deoxyribose. These pentoses are components of the nucleic acids and you will learn about their structure in Chapter 3.

Table 1.4 Other monosaccharides important in cell chemistry

Length of carbon chain	Name of sugar	Molecular formula	Formula	Roles
3C = triose	glyceraldehyde	$C_3H_6O_3$	H–C=O H–C–OH CH_2OH	intermediate in respiration and photosynthesis
5C = pentoses	ribose	$C_5H_{10}O_5$	H–C=O H–C–OH H–C–OH H–C–OH CH_2OH ring: CH_2OH, O, OH, HO, OH	in RNA, ATP and hydrogen acceptors NAD and NADP
	deoxyribose	$C_5H_{10}O_4$	H–C=O H–C–H H–C–OH H–C–OH CH_2OH ring: CH_2OH, O, OH, HO	in DNA

Key terms

Condensation reaction A reaction in which two molecules are chemically linked together with the elimination of a molecule of water.

Glycosidic bond A covalent bond between two monosaccharides.

Hydrolysis reaction A reaction in which a molecule of water is used in breaking a chemical bond (the reverse of a condensation reaction).

Disaccharides

A disaccharide is a carbohydrate made of two monosaccharides linked together. For example, sucrose is formed from a molecule of glucose and a molecule of fructose chemically linked together.

Condensation and hydrolysis reactions

When two monosaccharide molecules are combined to form a disaccharide, a molecule of water is also formed as a product, and so this type of reaction is known as a **condensation reaction**. The bond between monosaccharide residues, after the removal of H–O–H between them, is called a **glycosidic bond** (Figure 1.10). This is a strong, covalent bond. The condensation reaction is catalysed by an enzyme (Chapter 2).

In the reverse process, disaccharides are 'digested' to their component monosaccharides in a **hydrolysis reaction**. Of course this reaction involves adding a molecule of water ('*hydro-*') as splitting ('*-lysis*') of the glycosidic bond occurs. It is catalysed by an enzyme, too, but it is a different enzyme from the one that brings about the condensation reaction.

Apart from sucrose, other disaccharide sugars produced by cells and used in metabolism include:

- maltose, formed by a condensation reaction of two molecules of glucose
- lactose, formed by a condensation reaction of galactose and glucose.

sucrose + water $\underset{\text{condensation}}{\overset{\text{hydrolysis}}{\rightleftharpoons}}$ glucose + fructose

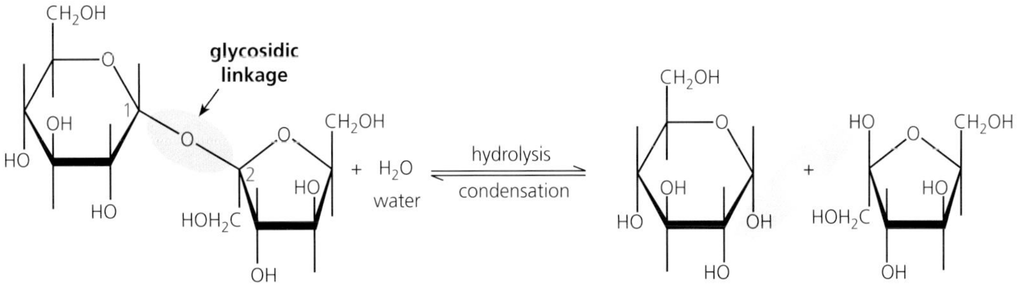

This structural formula shows us how the glycosidic linkage forms/breaks.

maltose + water $\underset{\text{condensation}}{\overset{\text{hydrolysis}}{\rightleftharpoons}}$ glucose + glucose

lactose + water $\underset{\text{condensation}}{\overset{\text{hydrolysis}}{\rightleftharpoons}}$ galactose + glucose

Figure 1.10 Sucrose, a disaccharide, and the monosaccharides that form it

Polysaccharides

A polysaccharide is built from many monosaccharides linked by glycosidic bonds formed during condensation reactions. '*Poly*' means many, and in fact thousands of saccharide (sugar) units make up a polysaccharide. So a polysaccharide is a giant molecule, a macromolecule. Normally each polysaccharide contains only one type of **monomer**. A chemist calls this a **polymer** because it is constructed from a huge number of *identical* monomers.

Some polysaccharides function as fuel stores. Both glycogen and starch are examples, as we shall shortly see. On the other hand, some polysaccharides, such as cellulose, have a structural role. Cellulose has huge molecules that are not so easily hydrolysed by enzyme action.

Starch

Starch is a mixture of two polysaccharides, both of which are polymers of α-glucose:

- **amylose** – an unbranched chain of α-glucose residues
- **amylopectin** – branched chains of α-glucose residues.

The glycosidic bonds between α-glucose residues in starch bring the molecules together in such a way that a helix forms. The whole starch molecule is then stabilised by countless hydrogen bonds between parts of the component glucose **residues**.

> **Key terms**
>
> **Polymer** A large molecule comprising repeated, identical smaller molecules (**monomers**) linked together by chemical bonds.
>
> **Residues** When monomers are linked together in a polymer, we can no longer refer to them as molecules. Instead, we can call them residues.

Starch is the major storage carbohydrate of most plants. It is laid down as compact grains. It is useful because its molecules are both compact and insoluble, but are readily hydrolysed to form sugar when required. Of course, enzymes are involved in this reaction, too.

We sometimes see 'soluble starch' as an ingredient of manufactured foods. Here the starch molecules have been broken down into short lengths, making them dissolve more easily.

A test for the presence of starch

We test for starch by adding a solution of iodine in potassium iodide. Iodine molecules fit neatly into the centre of a starch helix, creating a blue-black colour (Figure 1.11).

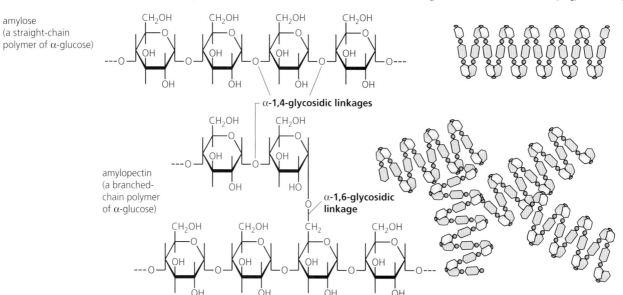

amylose (a straight-chain polymer of α-glucose)

CH_2OH O OH OH ---O– –O– –O– –O– –O---

α-1,4-glycosidic linkages

amylopectin (a branched-chain polymer of α-glucose)

CH_2OH O OH OH HO

α-1,6-glycosidic linkage

CH_2

In the test for starch with iodine in potassium iodide solution, the blue-black colour comes from a starch/iodine complex:

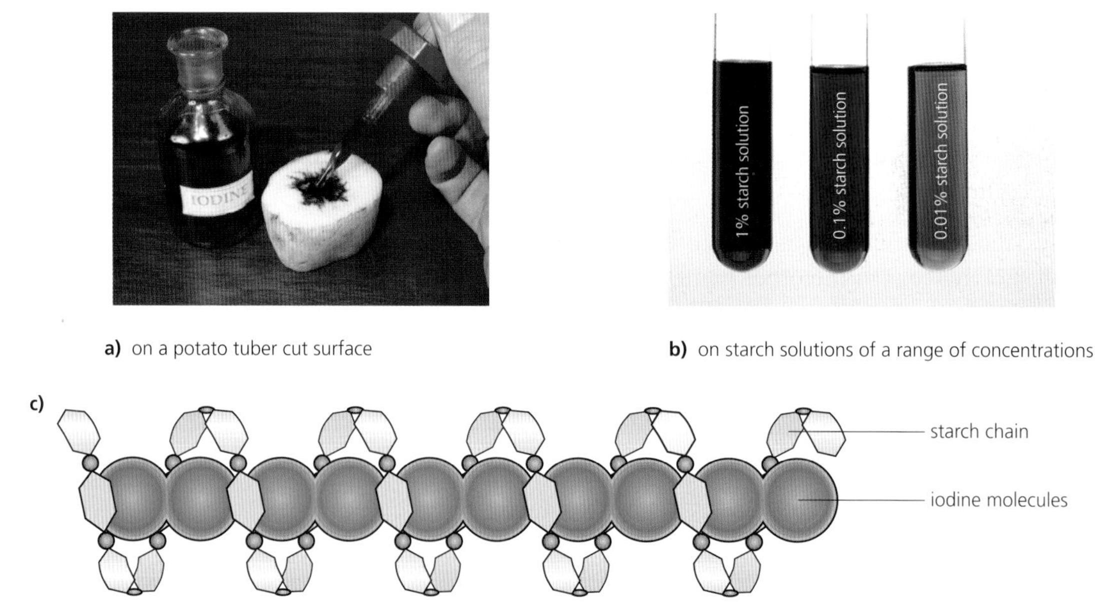

a) on a potato tuber cut surface

b) on starch solutions of a range of concentrations

c)

Figure 1.11 Starch

Glycogen

Glycogen is also a polymer of α-glucose. It is chemically very similar to amylopectin, although larger and more highly branched. Granules of glycogen are seen in liver cells and muscle fibres when observed by the electron microscope, but they occur throughout the human body, except in the brain cells (where there are virtually no carbohydrate reserves). During prolonged and vigorous exercise we draw on our glycogen reserves first. Only when these are exhausted does the body start to metabolise stored fat.

Structural formula

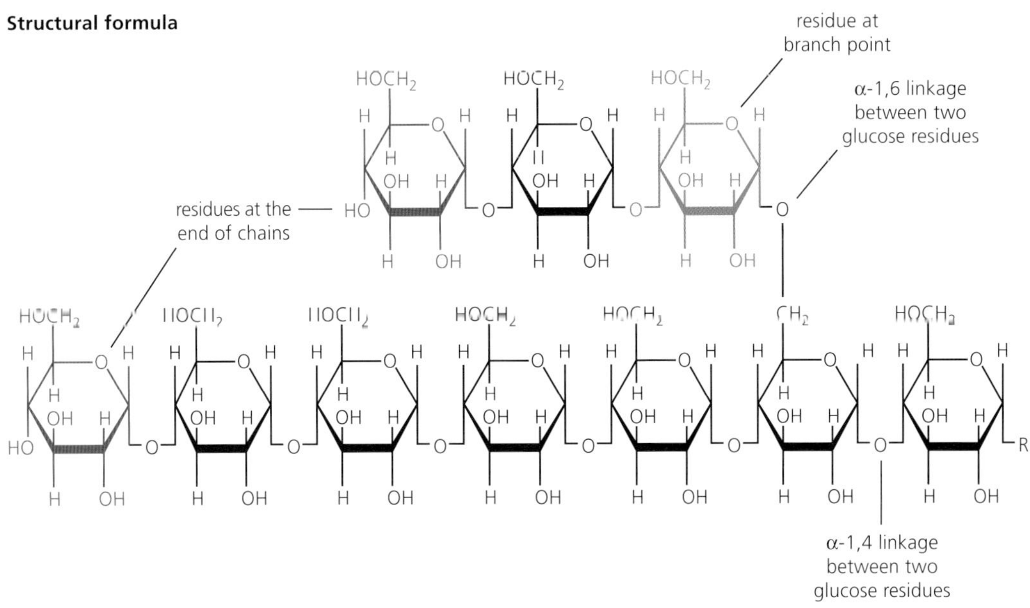

TEM of a liver cell (x7000)

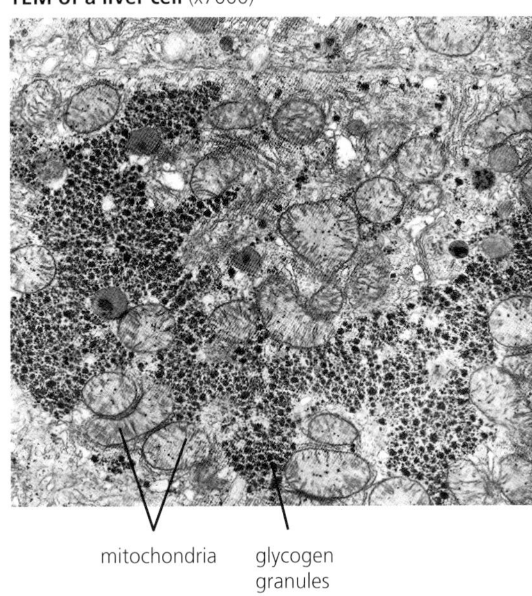

Diagram to show the branching pattern of a glycogen molecule

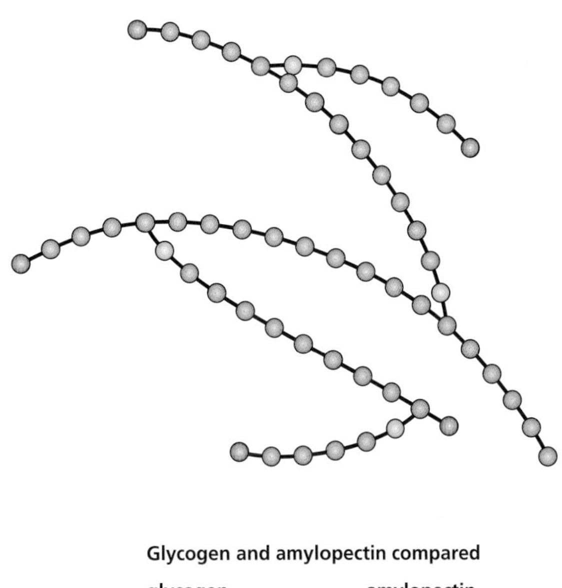

Glycogen and amylopectin compared

glycogen	amylopectin
branch point every 10 glucose residues	branch point every 30 glucose residues

Figure 1.12 Glycogen

Cellulose

Cellulose is a polymer of around 2000 to 3000 units of beta-glucose (β-glucose). Look back to Figure 1.8, which shows the difference in structure between α-glucose and β-glucose.

Can you spot what it is?

The only difference between the two molecules is the way in which the –H and –OH groups are bonded to carbon-1. In α-glucose the –H group is uppermost whereas in β-glucose the –OH group is uppermost. Although this might seem trivial, it has a big effect when molecules of β-glucose become linked together. As Figure 1.13 shows, the way glycosidic bonds form causes adjacent β-glucose units to be upside down with respect to each other. These glycosidic bonds are referred to as β-1,4 glycosidic bonds. This arrangement leads to cellulose molecules being long, straight-chains.

About 200 of these chains naturally become packed into fibres, held together by hydrogen bonds (Figure 1.13). The strength of plant cell walls results from the combined effect of the bonds between β-glucose monomers, the hydrogen bonds within and between these chains of β-glucose and the way in which the fibres are arranged in different directions.

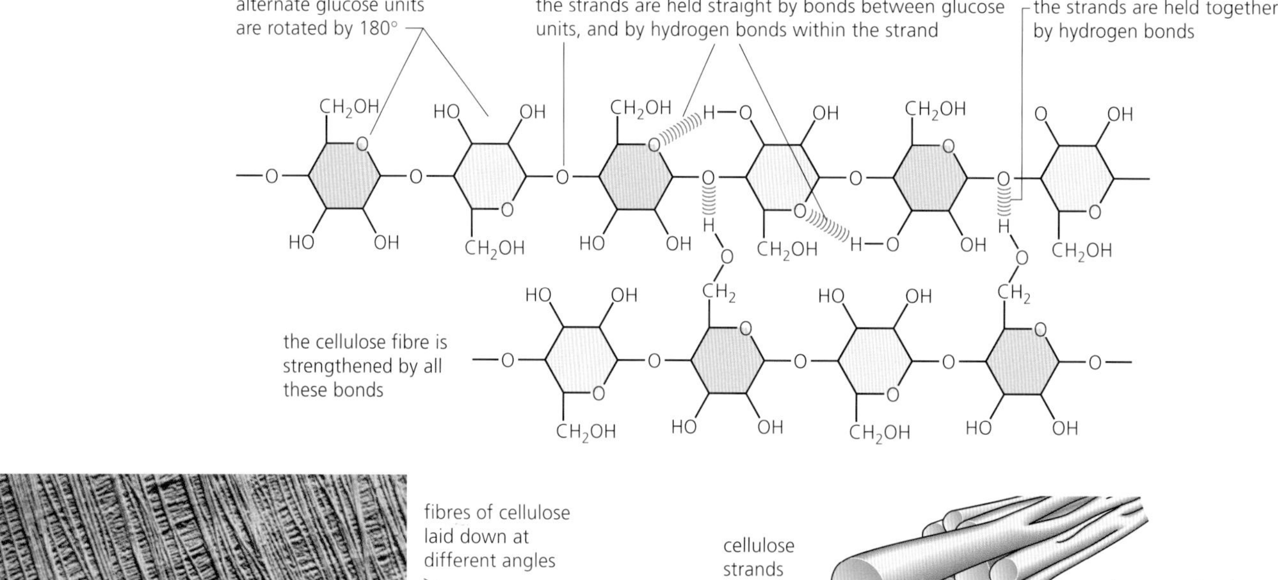

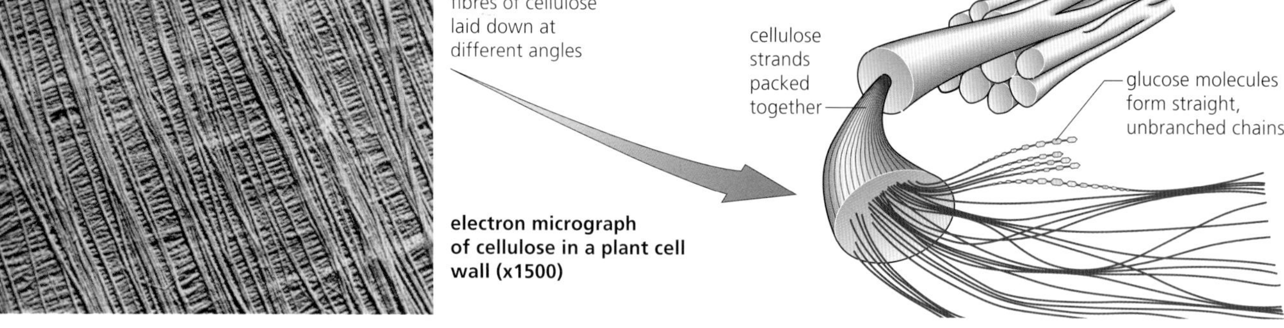

Figure 1.13 The chemistry and structure of cellulose

Test yourself

11 Explain the difference between a molecular formula and a structural formula.

12 α-glucose and β-glucose are isomers. Explain what this means.

13 What is the difference between a pentose and a hexose sugar?

14 Lactose is a disaccharide found in milk. Into which monosaccharides is it broken down in your intestines?

15 Starch is a polymer. What is meant by a *polymer*?

16 Both starch and glycogen can be broken down to provide glucose, used in respiration. Name the type of reaction by which both are broken down.

17 The reaction by which amylose and amylopectin are hydrolysed produces disaccharides.

a) Name the disaccharide formed.

b) Which compound, amylase or amylopectin, would you expect to be hydrolysed faster? Explain your answer.

Lipids

The second 'family' of organic molecules to consider here is the lipids. These occur in mammals as fats and in plants as oils. Fats and oils appear to be rather different substances, but the basic difference between them is that, at about 20 °C (room temperature), oils are liquid and fats are solid. Like the carbohydrates, lipids also contain the elements carbon, hydrogen and oxygen, but in lipids the proportion of oxygen is much less.

Lipids are insoluble in water, i.e. are hydrophobic. However, lipids can be dissolved in organic solvents such as alcohol (for example ethanol).

Key term

Ester bond The bond formed during a condensation reaction between a fatty acid and glycerol.

Here we will consider only two types of lipid: triglycerides and phospholipids.

Triglycerides

Triglycerides are formed during condensation reactions between glycerol (an alcohol) and three fatty acids. The bonds formed are known as **ester bonds**.

Fatty acids are long hydrocarbon chains, anything between 14 and 22 carbon atoms long.

The structures of a fatty acid commonly found in cells and that of glycerol are shown in Figure 1.14 and the steps to triglyceride formation in Figure 1.15. Enzymes catalyse the condensation reactions by which triglycerides are formed.

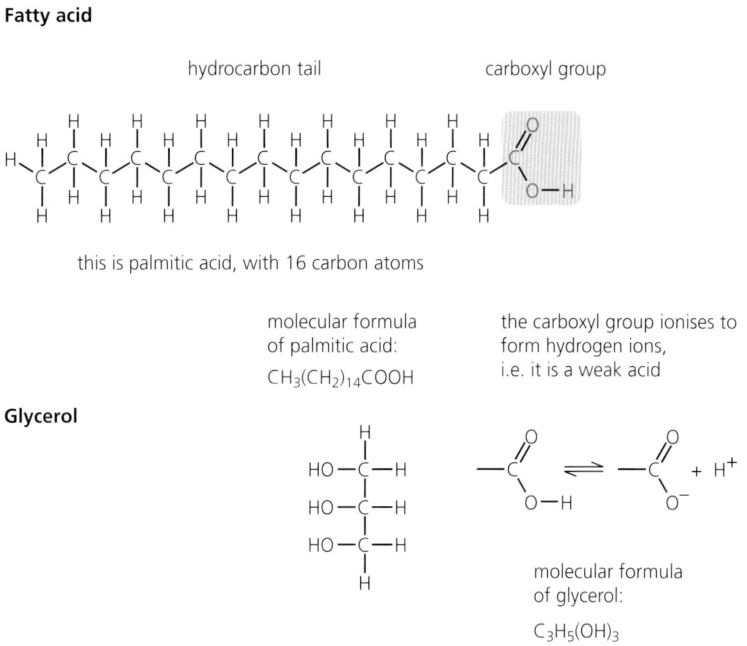

Figure 1.14 Fatty acids and glycerol, the building blocks of lipids

The hydrophobic properties of triglycerides are caused by the hydrocarbon chains of the component fatty acids. A molecule of triglyceride is quite large, but relatively small when compared with macromolecules such as starch. However, because of their hydrophobic properties, triglyceride molecules clump together (aggregate) into huge globules in the presence of water, making them appear to be macromolecules.

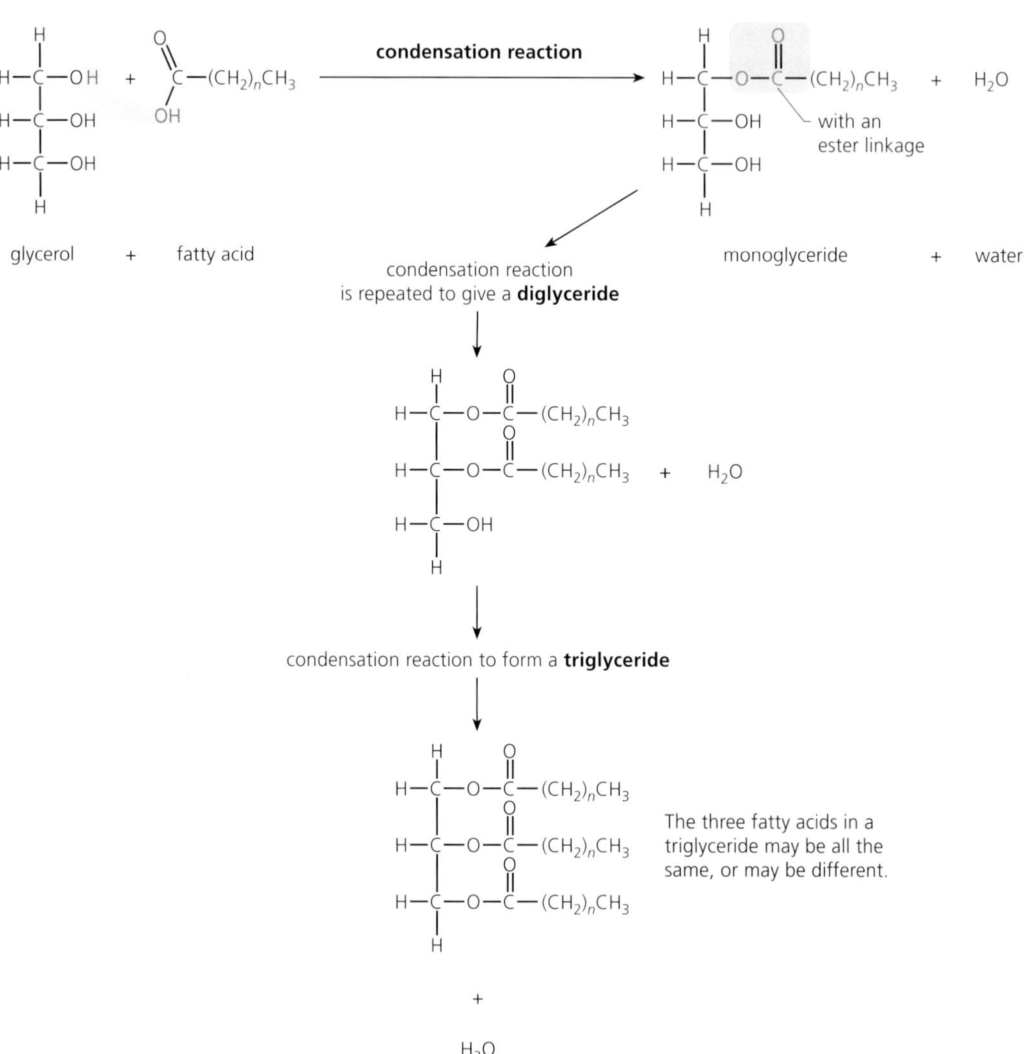

Figure 1.15 Formation of triglyceride

Saturated and unsaturated lipids

We have seen that the length of the hydrocarbon chains is different from fatty acid to fatty acid. These chains can differ in another way, too. To understand this latter difference, we need to note another property of carbon atoms and the ways they can combine together in chains. This concerns the existence of double covalent bonds (Figure 1.16).

a **double bond** is formed when two pairs of electrons are shared
space-filling model
C=C
e.g. in ethene
(ethene is a plant growth regulator)

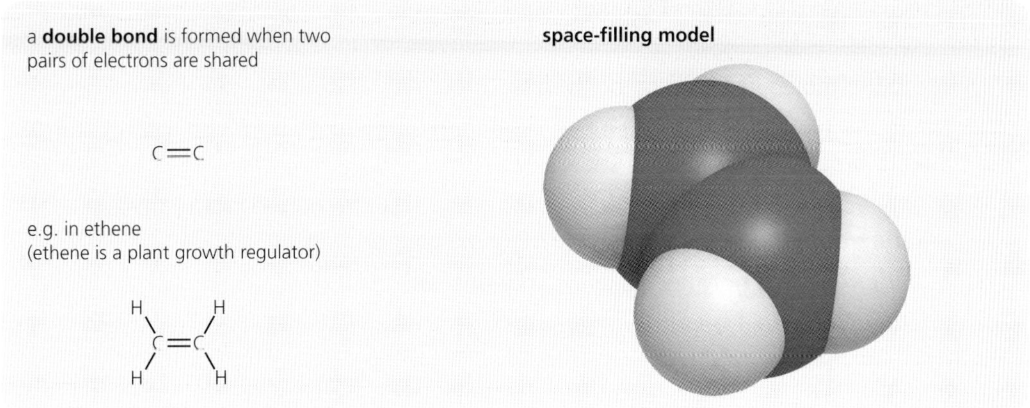

Figure 1.16 A carbon-carbon double covalent bond

A double covalent bond is formed when adjacent carbon atoms share *two pairs* of electrons, rather than the single electron pair shared in a single covalent bond. Carbon compounds that contain double carbon–carbon bonds are known to chemists as **unsaturated** compounds. On the other hand, when all the carbon atoms of the hydrocarbon tail of an organic molecule are combined together by single bonds, the compound is described as **saturated**. This difference is illustrated in Figure 1.17.

Key terms

Unsaturated fatty acid A fatty acid in which one or more pairs of adjacent carbon atoms in the hydrocarbon chain are linked by a double covalent bond (represented as C=C).

Saturated fatty acid One in which all the bonds between carbon atoms in the hydrocarbon chain are single covalent bonds (represented as C–C).

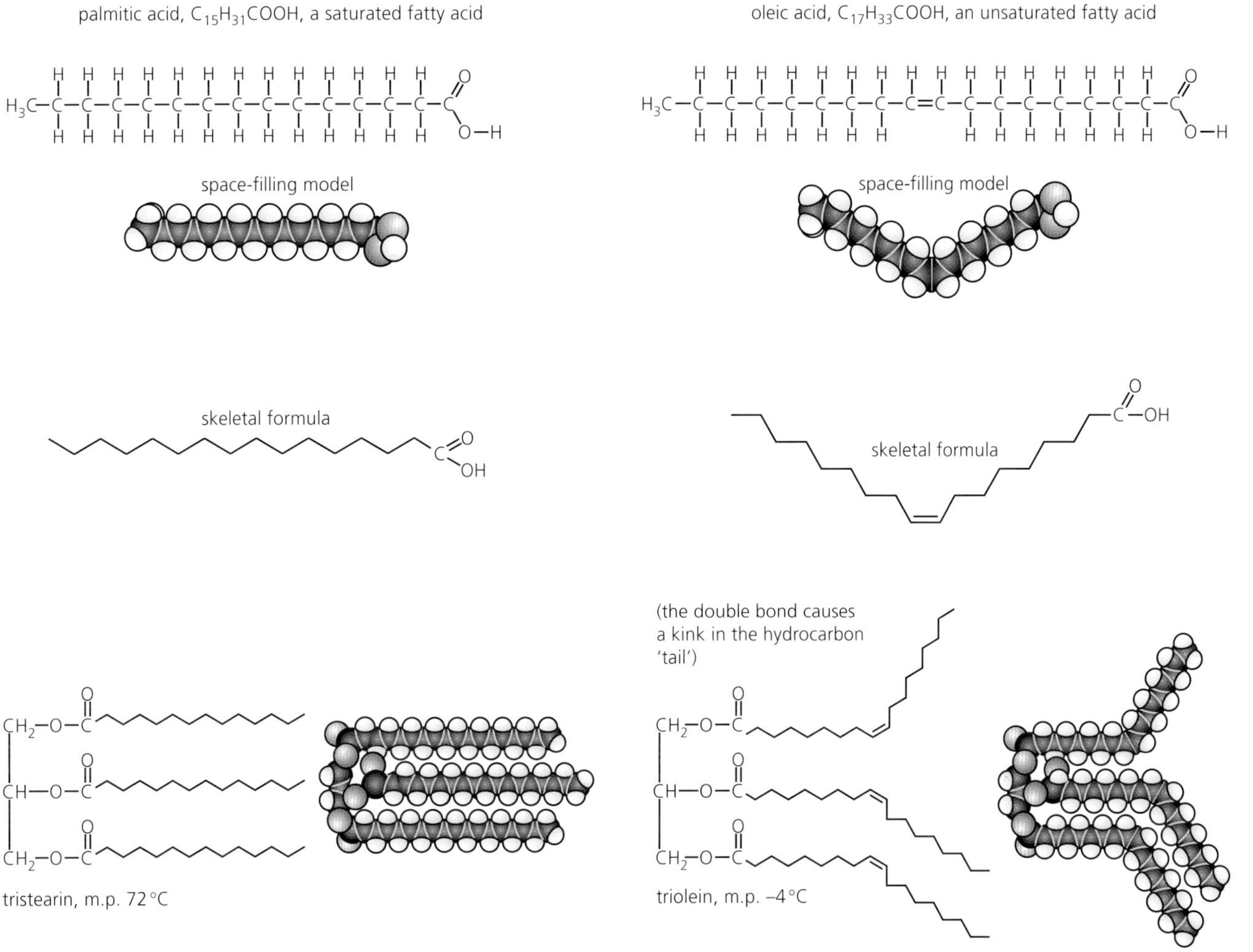

palmitic acid, $C_{15}H_{31}COOH$, a saturated fatty acid
oleic acid, $C_{17}H_{33}COOH$, an unsaturated fatty acid
space-filling model
space-filling model
skeletal formula
skeletal formula
(the double bond causes a kink in the hydrocarbon 'tail')
tristearin, m.p. 72 °C
triolein, m.p. –4 °C

Figure 1.17 Saturated and unsaturated fatty acids and triglycerides formed from them

Test yourself

18 State the molecular formula of glycerol.

19 Name the type of bond formed by the condensation of glycerol and a single fatty acid to produce a monoglyceride.

20 A fatty acid can be represented as $CH_3–(CH_2)_n–COOH$. Would this represent a saturated or unsaturated fatty acid? Explain your answer.

21 Is a triglyceride a polymer? Explain your answer.

22 What makes a triglyceride hydrophobic?

The roles of lipids in living organisms

You need to be familiar with three ways in which the structure of lipids relates to their role in living organisms.

Energy storage

When triglycerides are oxidised during respiration, energy is released. Some is lost to the environment as heat but some is used to make ATP – the energy currency of cells, introduced in Chapter 9. Mass for mass, when fully respired, lipids release more than twice as much energy as do carbohydrates (Table 1.5). Lipids, therefore, form a more 'concentrated' energy store than do carbohydrates.

A fat store is especially typical of animals that endure long unfavourable seasons in which they survive on reserves of food stored in the body. Oils are often a major energy store in the seeds and fruits of plants, and it is common for fruits and seeds to be used commercially as a source of edible oils for humans, for example maize, olives and sunflower.

Table 1.5 Lipids and carbohydrates as energy stores – a comparison

Feature	Lipids	Carbohydrates
Energy released on complete breakdown / $kJ\,g^{-1}$	~37	~17
Ease of breakdown	Not easily hydrolysed – energy released slowly	More easily hydrolysed – energy released quickly
Solubility	Hydrophobic, so do not cause osmotic water uptake by cells	Sugars are highly soluble in water, so can cause osmotic water uptake by cells
Production of metabolic water	A great deal of metabolic water produced on oxidation	Less metabolic water produced on oxidation

Waterproofing

Since lipids are hydrophobic, they repel water.

Oily secretions from the sebaceous glands, found in the skin of mammals, act as a water repellent, preventing fur and hair from becoming waterlogged when wet. Birds have a preen gland that fulfils the same function for feathers. You might have seen birds preening – they use their beaks to spread lipids from this gland over their feathers.

Insulation

Lipids are poor conductors of both heat and hydrophilic ions.

Triglycerides are stored in mammals as adipose tissue, typically under the skin, where it is known as subcutaneous fat. Fat reserves like these have a restricted blood supply (Figure 1.18) so little body heat is distributed to the fat under the skin. In these circumstances, the subcutaneous fat functions as a heat insulation layer.

Myelin is a lipid found in the surface membranes of cells that wrap around the long fibres of nerve cells in animals (Chapter 22). Over much of its length, the many layers of myelin insulate the fibre, preventing the passage of sodium and potassium ions that are essential for the conduction of the nerve impulse. As a result, nerve impulses travel along nerve fibres surrounded by myelin much faster than along those that are not surrounded by myelin.

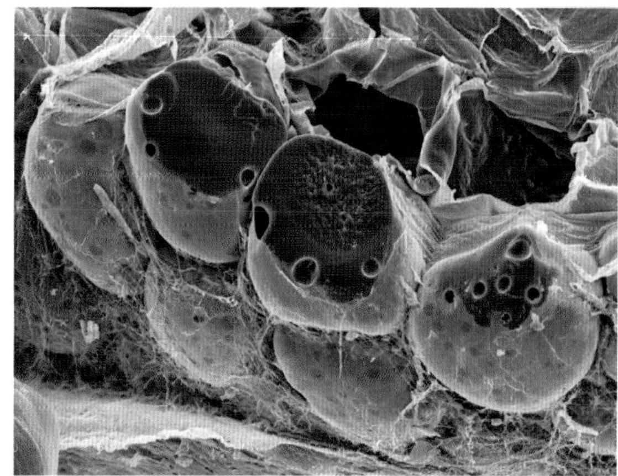

Figure 1.18 Adipose tissue

Phospholipids

A phospholipid has a similar chemical structure to a triglyceride, except one of the fatty acid groups is replaced by a phosphate group.

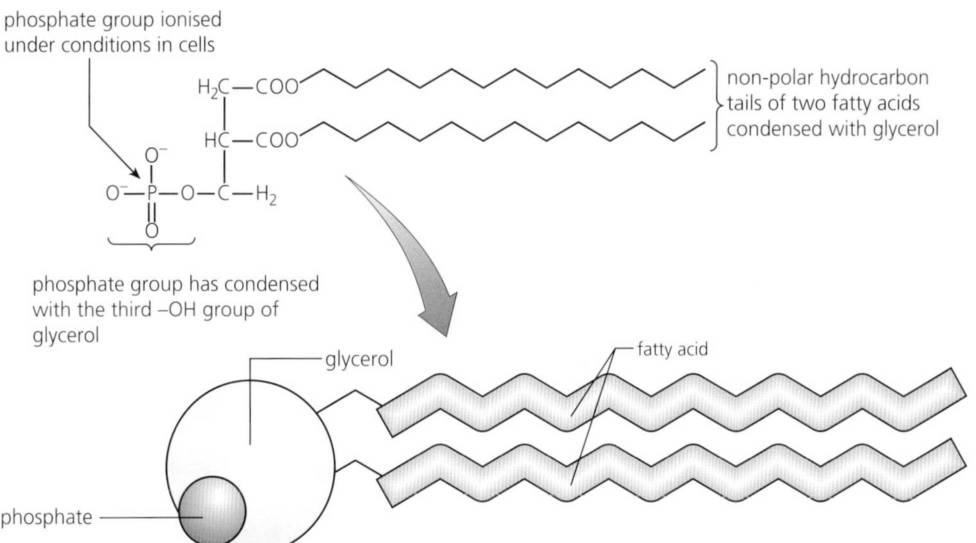

Figure 1.19 Phospholipid

You can see from Figure 1.19 that a phospholipid molecule has a 'head' composed of a glycerol to which is attached an ionised phosphate group. Since hydrogen bonds readily form between this phosphate group and water molecules, this part of the molecule has hydrophilic properties. The remainder of a phospholipid consists of two long, fatty acid residues, comprising hydrocarbon chains. As we have seen above, these 'tails' have hydrophobic properties.

So phospholipid molecules are unusual in being partly hydrophilic and partly hydrophobic. The effect of this is that a small quantity of phospholipid in contact with water will float, with the hydrocarbon tails exposed above the water. It forms a single layer (monolayer) of phospholipids (Figure 1.20).

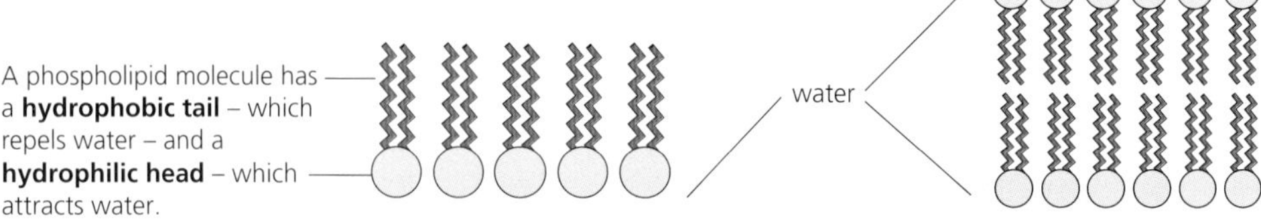

Phospholipid molecules **in contact with water** form a **monolayer**, with heads dissolved in the water and the tails sticking outwards.
When **mixed with water**, phospholipid molecules arrange themselves into a **bilayer**, in which the hydrophobic tails are attracted to each other.
A phospholipid molecule has a **hydrophobic tail** – which repels water – and a **hydrophilic head** – which attracts water.
water

Figure 1.20 Phospholipid molecules and water

> **Key term**
>
> **Bilayer** A single structure made of two layers of molecules, usually used to describe the arrangement of phospholipids in a cell membrane.

When slightly more phospholipid is added the molecules arrange themselves as a **bilayer**, with the hydrocarbon 'tails' facing together, away from the water, and the hydrophilic heads in the water (Figure 1.20). Their hydrophobic/hydrophilic nature and their ability to form a bilayer are two extremely important properties of phospholipids, as you will see when we consider cell surface membranes in Chapter 9.

Test yourself

23 Some people believe that a camel stores water in its hump. In fact, the hump is a lipid store. Use information in Table 1.5 to suggest how this lipid store is an adaptation to living in desert conditions.

24 Explain how the structure of triglycerides results in their waterproofing properties.

25 How does a molecule of triglyceride differ from a molecule of phospholipid?

26 When mixed with water, phospholipids often form micelles – small droplets with the fatty acid 'tails' on the inside and the 'heads' on the outside. Suggest why.

Chapter summary

Basic chemistry

- An atom is the smallest part of an element.
- When atoms gain electrons, they become negatively charged ions, called anions. When atoms lose electrons, they become positively charged ions, called cations.
- An acid is a compound that loses hydrogen ions (protons) in solution. In contrast, a base is a compound that can take up hydrogen ions in solution.
- pH is a measure of the acidity or alkalinity of a solution. Its value spans a scale of 0 (very acid) to 14 (very alkaline), calculated as pH = $-\log_{10}$ hydrogen ion concentration.
- A buffer solution resists pH changes.

Ions and water

- Inorganic ions are important components of cytoplasm. Plants use nitrate (NO_3^-), calcium (Ca^{2+}), magnesium (Mg^{2+}) and phosphate (PO_4^{3-}) ions when producing amino acids, the middle lamella of their cell walls, chlorophyll, and ADP/ATP, respectively.
- Water has properties that are important to living organisms:
  - Because its molecules are polar (i.e., have a positively charged and a negatively charged region), water is a powerful solvent for other polar molecules.
  - Hydrogen bonds between water molecules cause strong cohesion between water molecules. This results in strong surface tension, incompressibility and a high specific heat capacity.

Monomers and polymers

- Long chain molecules (polymers), such as polysaccharides and polypeptides, are made by condensation reactions between smaller units (monomers).
- Hydrolysis reactions release monomers from polymers.

Carbohydrates

- Monosaccharides are the smallest carbohydrates. Trioses ($C_3H_6O_3$) are important intermediates in respiration and photosynthesis. Deoxyribose and ribose are pentoses ($C_5H_{10}O_5$) that are components of nucleic acids.
- Glucose, fructose and galactose are hexoses ($C_6H_{12}O_6$). Glucose has two isomers (molecules with the same number but different arrangements of atoms), α-glucose and β-glucose. Alpha glucose is used in cells as a respiratory substrate.
- Condensation reactions between two monosaccharides produce disaccharides ($C_{12}H_{22}O_{11}$). The monomers are held together by glyosidic bonds. Sucrose is a disaccharide that is an important transport substance in plants.
- Condensation reactions between many monomers produce polysaccharides. Large, globular polysaccharides, like starch and glycogen, act as insoluble stores of α-glucose. Cellulose is a polymer of β-glucose. It forms fibres that add flexibility and strength to the cell walls of plants and algae.

Lipids

- Triglycerides are a type of lipid, comprising one molecule of glycerol attached by ester bonds to three molecules of fatty acid. They can act as a fuel store. Their hydrophobic nature also gives them waterproofing and insulation properties.
- A phospholipid is like a triglyceride, with an inorganic phosphate group (PO_4^{3-}) in the place of a terminal fatty acid. The phosphate group produces a hydrophilic end to this molecule, which is important in forming the bilayer of biological membranes.

Practice questions

1 The general formula for a carbohydrate is:

A $C_6H_{12}O_6$

B $C_6(H_2O)_6$

C $C_n(H_2O)_{2n}$

D $C_x(H_2O)_y$

2 Sucrose is a disaccharide formed by the condensation of:

A glucose and fructose

B glucose and glucose

C glucose and galactose

D fructose and galactose

3 Phospholipids are mainly

A used as an energy store

B found in plasma membranes

C used for waterproofing

D hormones

4 Copy and complete the table to show similarities and differences between glycogen and starch. *(4)*

Feature	Glycogen	Starch
Found in cells of which group of organisms?		
Formed from which monomer?		
Name of polymer(s)		
Degree of branching		

5 The structure of biological molecules is related to their function. Explain **two** ways in which the structure of glycogen is related to its function and **two** ways in which the structure of a triglyceride is related to its function. *(4)*

6 Cellulose forms cell walls in plants. Describe the structure of cellulose and explain how its properties contribute to the functions of cell walls. *(6)*

7 The diagram shows a molecule of α-glucose.

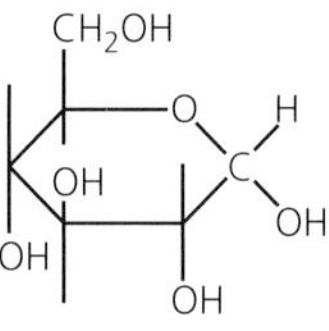

a) How can you tell that this is α-glucose and **not** β-glucose. *(1)*

b) i) Draw a diagram to show a condensation reaction between two molecules of α-glucose. *(2)*

ii) Name the products of this reaction. *(1)*

iii) Explain why the bond linking the two units of glucose is called an α-1,4 glycosidic bond. *(3)*

8 A group of scientists investigated milk production by dairy cattle. For 28 days, they fed one group of cows their normal diet and fed a second group of cows the same diet with added animal fat.

After 28 days, the scientists made several measurements on the cows and on the milk they produced. The table shows their results.

Result calculated by scientists	Cows with normal diet	Cows with normal diet plus added animal fat
Mean body mass/kg	547.9	552.0
Mean concentration of lipid in blood/mg per 100 cm^3	469.1	605.7
Mean milk production/kg per cow per day	14.5	16.1
Mean content of butterfat in milk/%	4.6	4.7

a) Suggest a null hypothesis that the scientists were testing in their investigation. *(1)*

b) Explain the difference in the concentration of lipids in the blood of the two groups of cows. *(3)*

c) Calculate the percentage increase in milk production of the cows with added fat in their diet. *(1)*

d) Can you conclude from the data in the table that adding fat to the diet of the cows resulted in a change in the composition of the milk they produced? Explain your answer. *(4)*

9 Earthworms have a body that is divided into discrete segments. Figure 1 shows a longitudinal section through one segment. The outer region of the body has two layers of muscle surrounding an inner fluid-filled space, called the coelom. The fluid in this coelom (coelomic fluid) is mainly water.

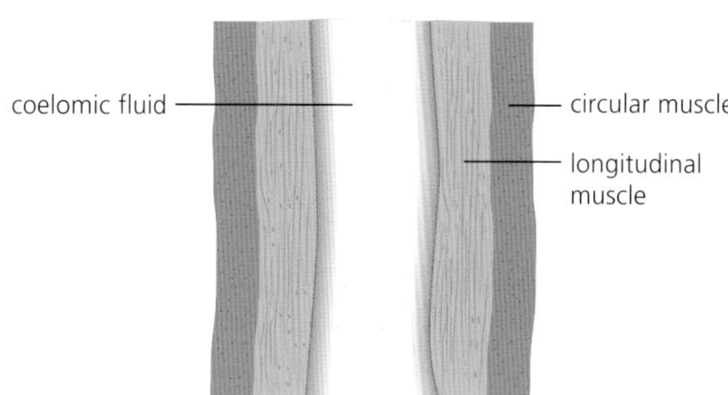

Figure 1

The diagrams in Figure 2 represent different times as an earthworm moves forwards. Contraction of the circular muscle in one body segment causes that segment to become long and thin. Contraction of the longitudinal muscle in one body segment causes that segment to become short and fat.

Earthworms normally live in a burrow in the soil.

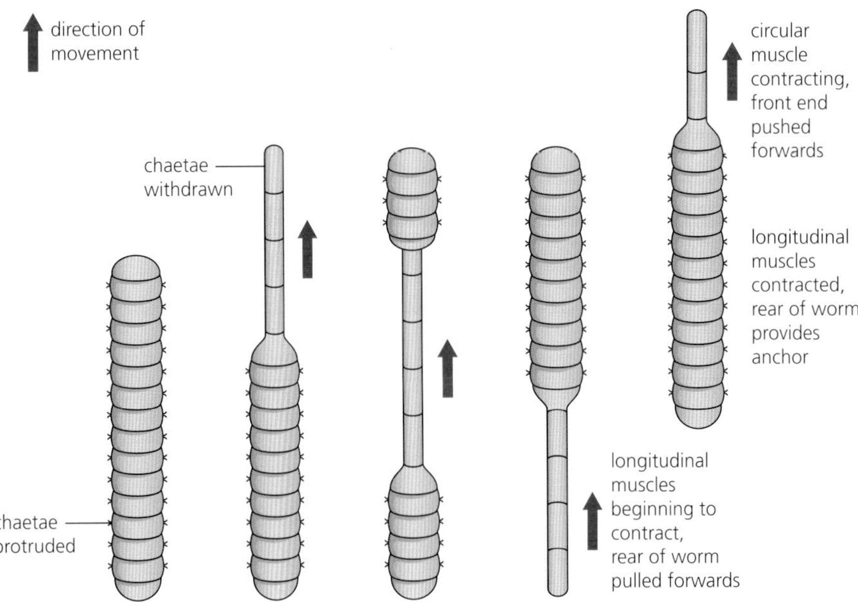

Figure 2

a) Use your knowledge of the properties of water to explain how the coelomic fluid enables the movement of the earthworm shown in Figure 2. *(4)*

b) The chaetae shown in Figure 2 are short, bristle-like structures. Suggest their role in the movement of the earthworm. *(4)*

2 Proteins and enzymes

Prior knowledge

In this chapter you will need to recall that:

- → proteins are long chains of amino acids
- → only 20 different amino acids are common in the proteins of living organisms
- → there is a vast number of different proteins found in living organisms. The differences between them result from the sequence of their amino acids
- → the shape of a protein, whether a straight chain of amino acids or a three-dimensional complex, is related to its function
- → enzymes are proteins with a complex three-dimensional shape; each enzyme acts as a catalyst, speeding up a specific reaction or type of reaction
- → the ability of enzymes to catalyse a reaction is affected by changes in pH and changes in temperature.

Test yourself on prior knowledge

1 Give **one** way in which the composition of an amino acid differs from that of a carbohydrate and a lipid.

2 Name the chemical bond that links two amino acids together.

3 What makes one protein different from another?

4 Other than speeding up a reaction, give **two** properties common to catalysts.

5 An enzyme has a complex three-dimensional shape. Explain how this shape results in each enzyme:

a) catalysing only one type of reaction

b) being affected by high temperatures.

The proteins and peptides of cells

Proteins make up about two-thirds of the total dry mass of a cell. These organic molecules differ from carbohydrates and lipids in that they contain the element nitrogen, and often the element sulfur, as well as carbon, hydrogen and oxygen. Amino acids are the monomers from which the polymers – peptides and proteins – are built. Typically several hundred, or even thousands of amino acid molecules, are combined together to form a protein. Incidentally, the terms 'polypeptide' and 'protein' can be used interchangeably, but when a polypeptide is about 50 amino acid residues long it is generally agreed to be have become a protein.

Once the chain of amino acids is constructed, a protein takes up a specific shape. Shape matters with proteins – their shape is closely related to their function. This is especially the case in proteins that are enzymes, as we shall shortly see.

Key term

Amino acid The monomer from which dipeptides, polypeptides and proteins, are made. All amino acids have the general formula NH_2-CHR-COOH, where R represents the only part of the molecule that is different in different amino acids.

Amino acids, the building blocks of peptides

All **amino acids** contain two functional groups: an amino group ($-NH_2$) and a carboxyl group (–COOH). In naturally occurring amino acids, both functional groups are attached to the same carbon atom (Figure 2.1). The remainder of the amino acid molecule, the side chain (represented by –R), is very variable and is what makes one amino acid different from any other.

An amino acid can ionise:

- as an acid: $-COOH \rightleftharpoons -COO^- + H^+$
- or as a base: $-NH_2 + H^+ \rightleftharpoons -NH_3^+$
- or even as both: $NH_2-CHR-COOH \rightleftharpoons NH_3^+-CHR-COO^-$.

Molecules, like amino acids, that can ionise as both an acid and a base are described as being **amphoteric** and an ion with both positive and negative charges is called a **zwitterion** (German for double ion).

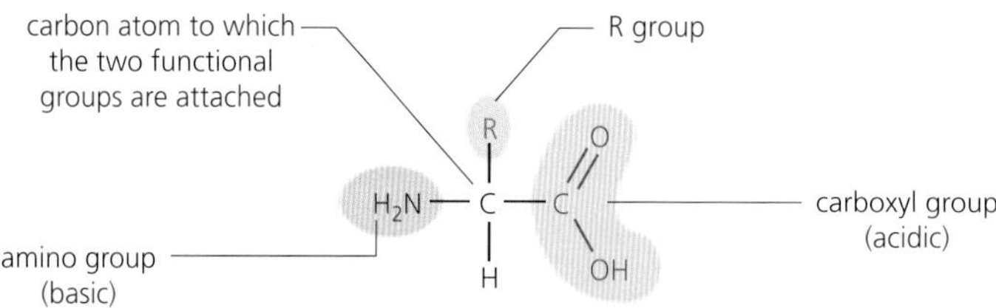

The 20 different amino acids that make up proteins in cells and organisms differ in their side chains (R groups). Below are three examples.

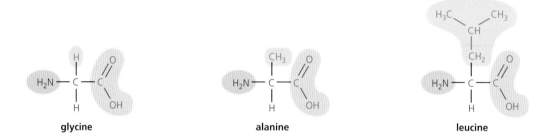

glycine

alanine

leucine

Some amino acids have an additional –COOH group in their R group (= acidic amino acids).
Some amino acids have an additional $-NH_2$ group in their R group (= basic amino acids).

Figure 2.1 The structure of amino acids

The linking of amino acids together in different sequences produces proteins with very different properties. This helps explain how the many proteins in organisms are able to fulfil the very different biological functions they have.

Key term

Peptide bond A covalent bond between the amino group of one amino acid and the carboxyl group of another amino acid. Each peptide bond is formed by a condensation reaction.

How amino acids combine

In the presence of an appropriate enzyme, two amino acids combine in a condensation reaction to form a dipeptide. During this reaction, a covalent bond known as a **peptide bond** forms between the amino group of one amino acid and the carboxyl group of the other (Figure 2.2).

A further condensation reaction between the dipeptide and another amino acid results in a tripeptide. In this way, long strings of amino acid residues, linked by peptide bonds, are formed. As you will see in Chapter 3, polypeptides are assembled by adding one amino acid at a time.

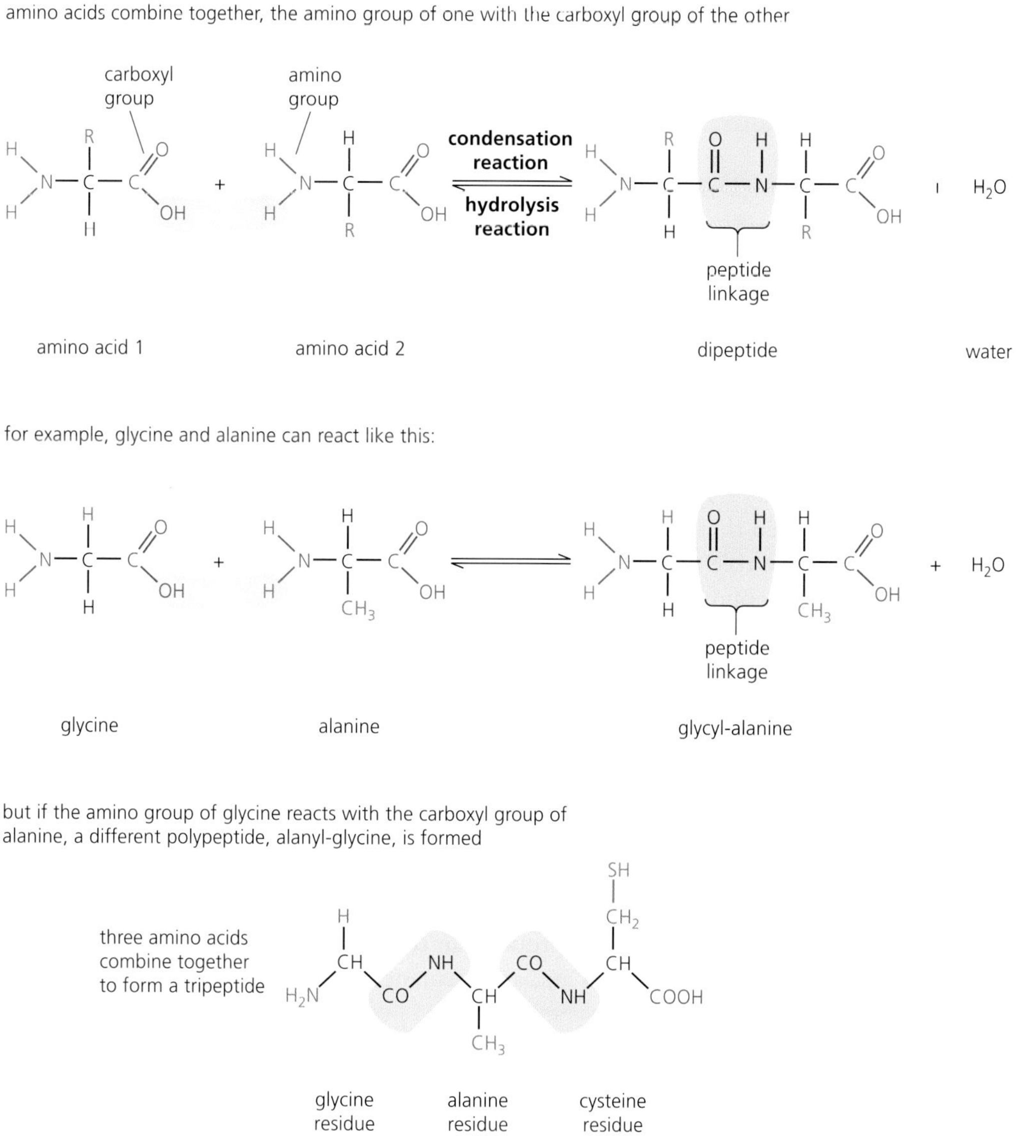

Figure 2.2 Peptide bond formation

Testing for the presence of protein: the biuret test

The biuret test is used as an indicator of the presence of protein because it gives a purple colour in the presence of peptide bonds (–CO–NH–).

We test for the presence of a protein by adding an equal quantity of sodium hydroxide solution to the test solution, followed by a few drops of 0.5% copper(II) sulfate solution. After gentle mixing, the appearance of a distinctive purple colour confirms that protein is present in the test solution (Figure 2.3).

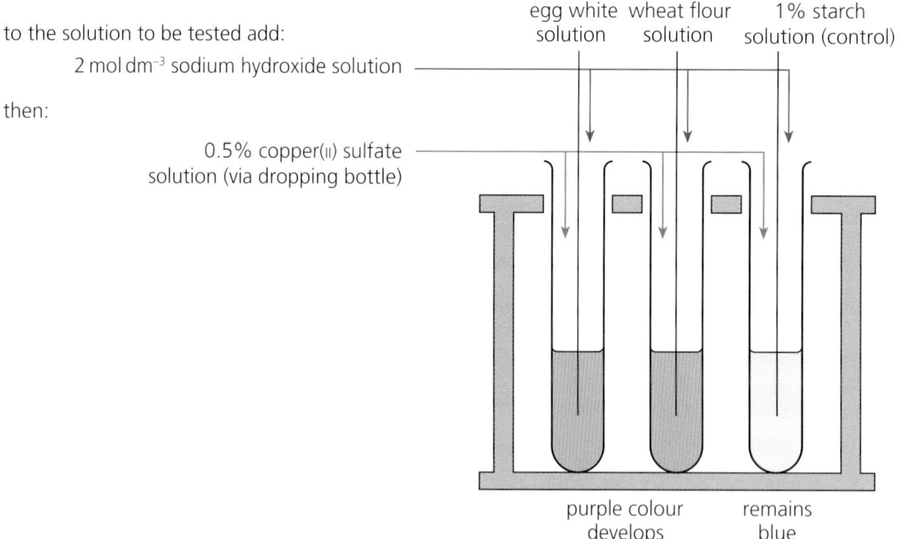

Figure 2.3 The biuret test on protein solutions. Wear goggles when performing this test

The structure of proteins

We have already noted that the shape of a protein molecule is critical in determining the properties and the role that protein has in a cell. There are four levels of protein structure: primary, secondary, tertiary and quaternary.

The **primary structure** of a protein is the sequence of the amino acids in its molecule. As you have seen above, the amino acids are held together by peptide bonds. Proteins differ in the variety, number and order of their constituent amino acids. As you will see in Chapter 3, the order of amino acids in a polypeptide chain is controlled by the DNA of the cell producing it. Just changing one amino acid in the sequence might completely alter the properties of a protein.

The **secondary structure** of a protein develops immediately after its formation when parts of the polypeptide chain become folded or twisted, or both. The most common shapes are formed either by coiling, to produce an α helix, or folding into β sheets. These shapes are shown in Figure 2.4 and are permanent, being held in place by hydrogen bonds.

The **tertiary structure** of a protein is the compact structure, unique to that protein, that arises when the molecule is further folded and held in a particular complex three-dimensional shape. Figure 2.5 shows a polypeptide with a tertiary structure, together with the three types of bond that hold the shape in place – ionic bonds, hydrogen bonds and disulfide bonds.

The **quaternary structure** of a protein arises when two or more polypeptides become held together, forming a complex, biologically active molecule.

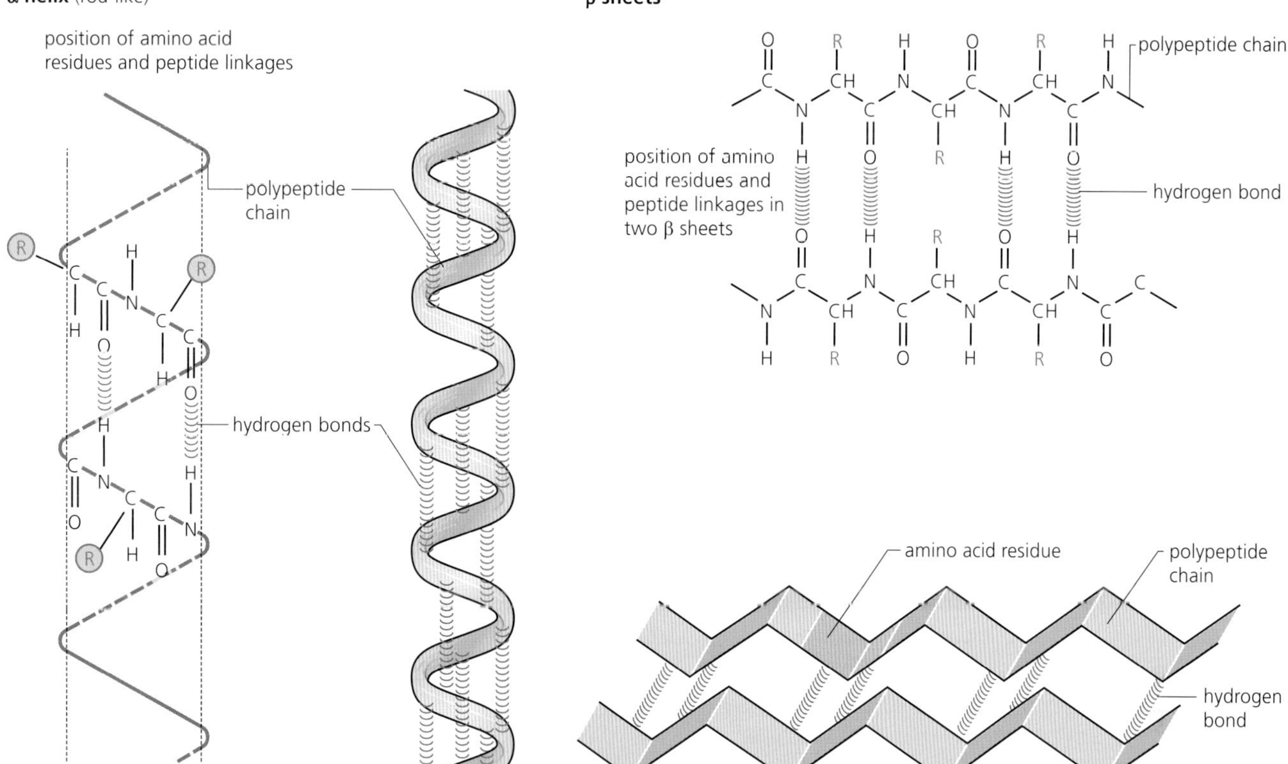

Figure 2.4 The secondary structure of proteins

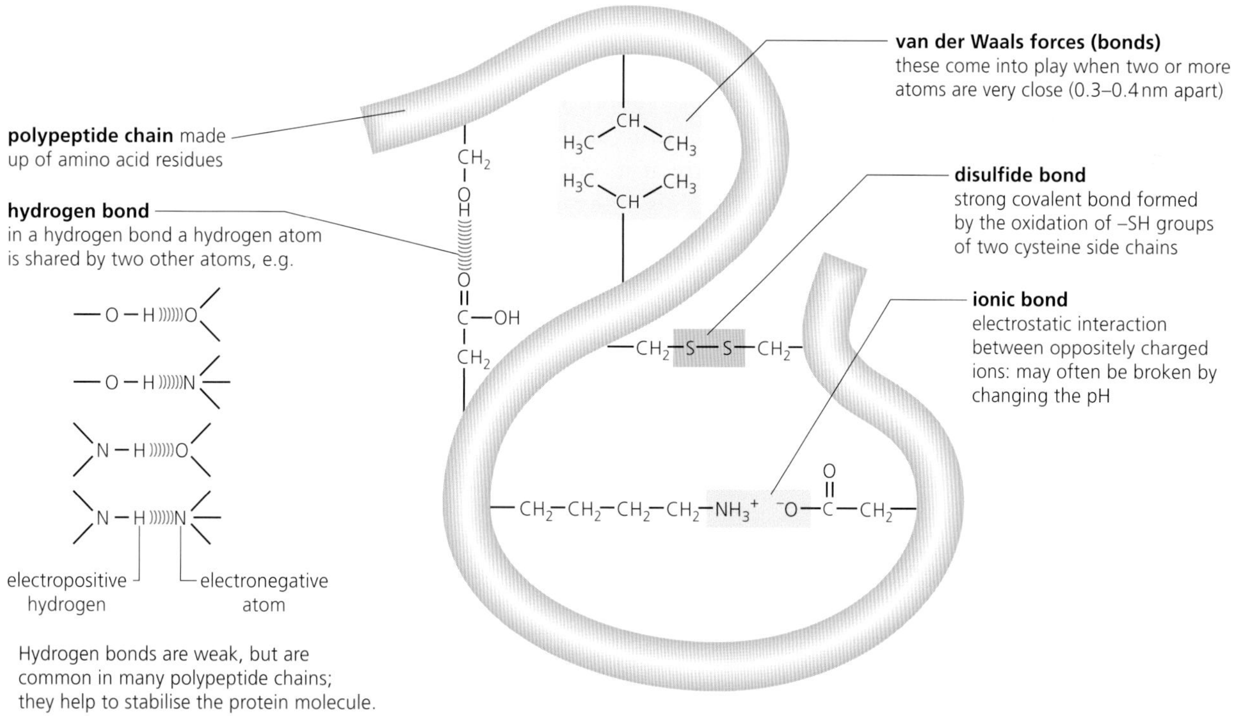

Figure 2.5 The types of bond holding together the tertiary structure of a protein

Fibrous and globular proteins

Collagen and haemoglobin are examples of proteins. Both consist of more than one polypeptide chain, i.e. they both have a quaternary structure. Their shape, however, is quite different. One is fibrous and the other is globular.

Fibrous proteins contain long, coiled polypeptide chains, shaped like a rod or wire. Collagen, a component of bone and tendons, is a fibrous protein. Figure 2.6 shows that a single collagen molecule has three polypeptide chains, held together by covalent bonds and hydrogen bonds, forming a triple helix. This structure makes collagen resistant to denaturing and provides its strength.

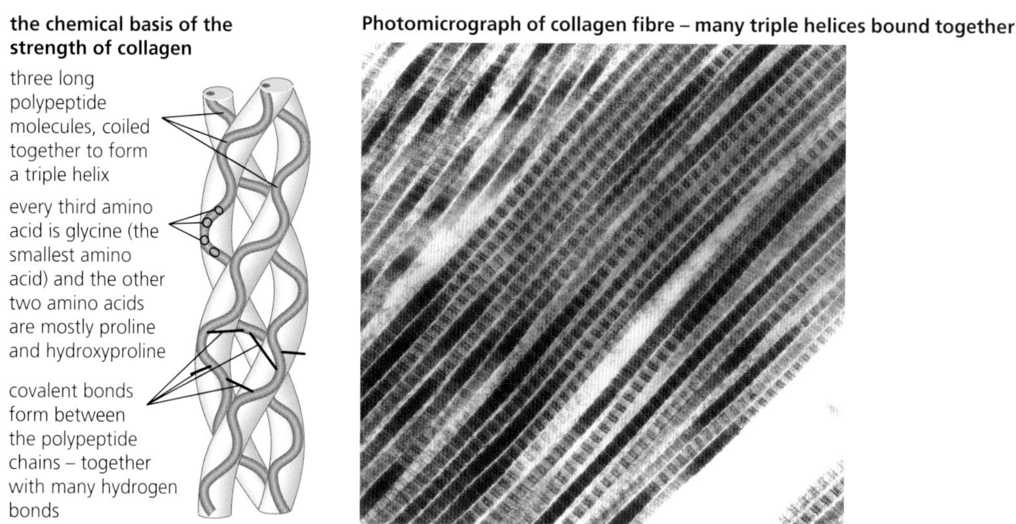
the chemical basis of the strength of collagen
three long polypeptide molecules, coiled together to form a triple helix
every third amino acid is glycine (the smallest amino acid) and the other two amino acids are mostly proline and hydroxyproline
covalent bonds form between the polypeptide chains – together with many hydrogen bonds
Photomicrograph of collagen fibre – many triple helices bound together

Figure 2.6 Collagen – an example of a fibrous protein

Globular proteins are more spherical. Their polypeptide chains wind in such a way that their hydrophilic amino acids are at the surface of the 'sphere' whilst their hydrophobic amino acids are at its core. Haemoglobin, the respiratory pigment found in our red blood cells, is an example of a globular protein. A haemoglobin molecule consists of four polypeptide chains, each bound to an iron-containing haem group (Figure 2.7). The iron in the haem groups binds to oxygen. As the first molecule of oxygen binds to a haem group, it causes a change in the shape of the haemoglobin molecule, making it easier for further oxygen molecules to bind. You will see the effect of this property when you learn about the transport of oxygen in Chapter 10.

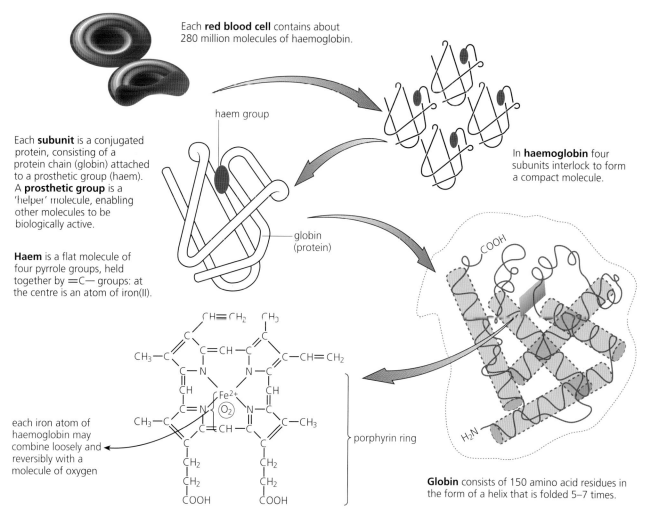

Each **red blood cell** contains about 280 million molecules of haemoglobin.

In **haemoglobin** four subunits interlock to form a compact molecule.

haem group

Each **subunit** is a conjugated protein, consisting of a protein chain (globin) attached to a prosthetic group (haem). A **prosthetic group** is a 'helper' molecule, enabling other molecules to be biologically active.

globin (protein)

Haem is a flat molecule of four pyrrole groups, held together by =C— groups: at the centre is an atom of iron(II).

COOH

H_2N

each iron atom of haemoglobin may combine loosely and reversibly with a molecule of oxygen

porphyrin ring

Globin consists of 150 amino acid residues in the form of a helix that is folded 5–7 times.

Figure 2.7 Haemoglobin: an example of a globular protein

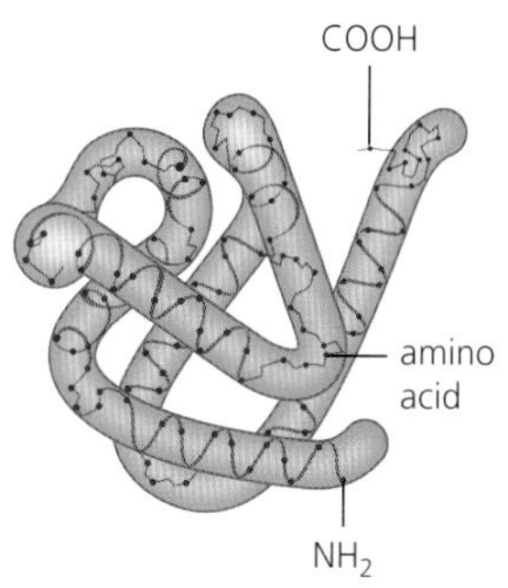

Figure 2.8 A molecule of myoglobin

Test yourself

1 In a chemical reaction, two amino acids join together.
 a) What *type* of chemical reaction occurs when two amino acids join together?
 b) Name the chemical bond that forms between these amino acids.

2 Amino acids can act as buffers, resisting changes in pH. Use your knowledge of amino acids to suggest how amino acids act as buffers.

3 How does the shape of a fibrous protein differ from that of a globular protein?

4 Myoglobin is an oxygen-carrying protein found in skeletal muscle cells. Figure 2.8 shows one molecule of myoglobin.How many levels of protein structure can you see in the diagram? Explain your answer.

5 Are enzyme molecules fibrous proteins or globular proteins?

Denaturation

We have seen the variety of shapes that different protein molecules might have. The different shapes are related to the functions these proteins have in cells and organisms. You will learn about the functions of several proteins throughout your course. For now, some of their important roles, together with their dynamic states, are reviewed in Figure 2.9.

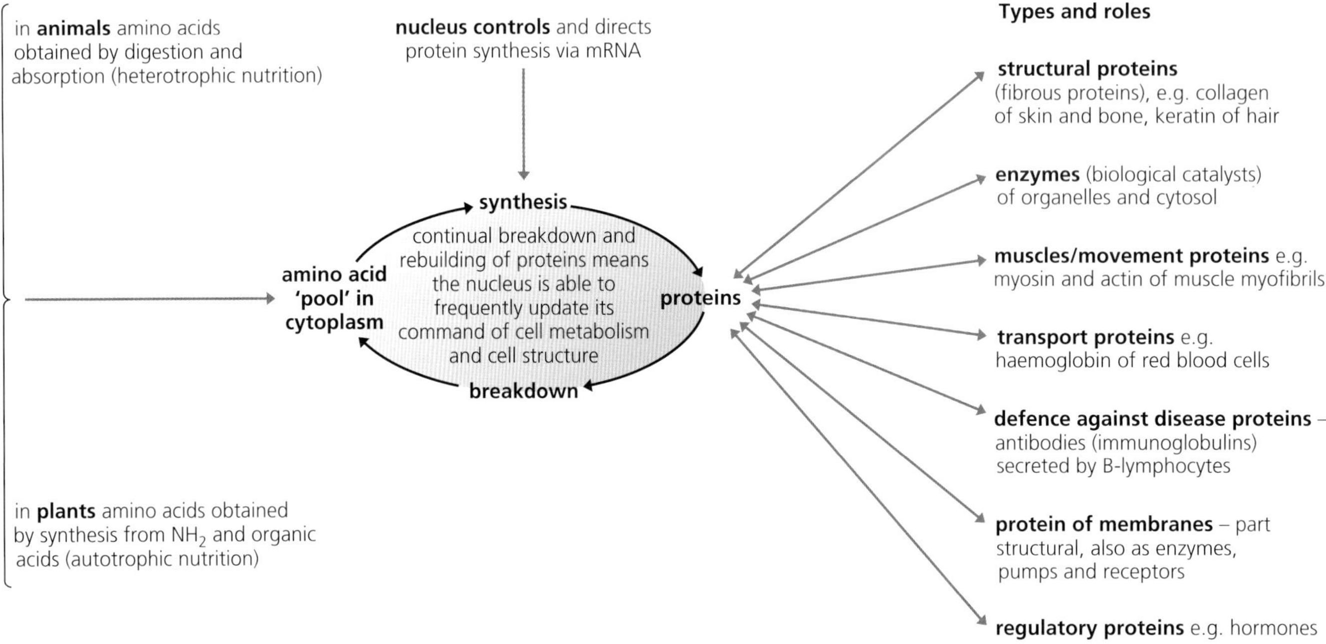

Figure 2.9 Cell proteins – origins, types and roles

> **Key term**
>
> **Denaturation** A change in the shape of a protein that alters, or destroys, the ability of the protein to carry out its function. The change results from the breakage of bonds holding the shape of the protein together.

Look again at the range of bonds that hold the 3-D shape of the tertiary structure of a protein in Figure 2.5. Their roles in maintaining the 3-D shape of the protein are confirmed when any protein loses its specific 3-D shape (we refer to this as **denaturation**). This happens only because these bonds that maintain the 3-D shape of the protein molecule are changed. This change can be caused by exposure to high temperature, to heavy metal ions, and to some organic solvents, but is also triggered by changes in pH and by certain other chemicals. When the shape of a protein changes, the protein may cease to be useful. The biochemistry of cells and organisms is extremely sensitive to conditions that alter proteins in this way.

Incidentally, when high temperature and heavy metal ions cause denaturation, the changes are irreversible, typically causing the protein to become elongated, disorganised strands, which are insoluble in water. This apart, however, it is often the case that proteins will revert back to their former shape, once the conditions that triggered denaturation are removed. This observation led to the idea that it is simply the amino acid sequence of a protein that decides its tertiary structure. This may well be true for many polypeptides and small proteins. However, in most proteins within the cell environment, folding is a speedy process in which some accessory proteins, including enzymes, are normally involved. These might determine the shape as much as, or more than, the primary structure does.

Test yourself

6 Is a protein a polymer? Explain your answer.
7 Name **three** types of chemical bond that might be present in a protein molecule.
8 Pickling is one form of food preservation. It involves immersing food in vinegar, i.e. weak ethanoic acid. Suggest how this slows decomposition of the food.
9 Muscle wastage is one of the symptoms of a protein-deficient diet. Explain why.
10 When a hen's egg is cooked its protein is denatured irreversibly. Is protein denaturation always irreversible?

Enzymes – biological catalysts

There are literally many thousands of chemical reactions taking place within cells and organisms. We saw in Chapter 1 that metabolism is the name we give to these chemical reactions of life. The molecules involved are collectively called **metabolites**. Many of these are made within organisms. Other metabolites have been imported from the environment, for example water and oxygen.

> **Key term**
>
> **Metabolite** The term used to describe any molecule involved in the reactions occurring in cells and organisms (in other words involved in metabolism).

Metabolism actually consists of chains (linear sequences) and cycles of enzyme-catalysed reactions, such as we see in protein synthesis (see Chapter 3), respiration (Chapter 13) and photosynthesis (Chapter 14). These reactions may be classified as one of just two types, according to whether they involve the build-up or breakdown of organic molecules.

- In **anabolic** reactions, larger molecules are built up from smaller molecules. Examples of anabolism are the synthesis of proteins from amino acids and the synthesis of polysaccharides from simple sugars.
- In **catabolic** reactions, larger molecules are broken down. Examples of catabolism are the digestion of complex foods and the breakdown of sugar in respiration.

Overall: **metabolism = anabolism + catabolism**

Introducing catalysis

For a reaction between two molecules to occur there must be successful collisions between them. The molecules must collide with each other at the right angle and with the right velocity. If the angle of collision is not correct, the molecules bounce apart. Only if the molecules are lined up and collide with the correct energies does a reaction occur.

Most chemical reactions do not occur spontaneously. In a laboratory or in an industrial process, chemical reactions can be made to occur by applying high temperatures, high pressures, extremes of pH, and by maintaining high concentrations of the reacting molecules. If these drastic conditions were not applied, very little of the chemical product would be formed quickly.

> **Key term**
>
> **Catalyst** A substance that increases the rate of a chemical reaction. Only a small concentration of the catalyst is required. Additionally, the catalyst is chemically unaffected by the reaction it catalyses and can be recovered once that reaction is complete.

Alternatively, a **catalyst** can be used. You might recall from your GCSE science course the industrial use of a catalyst in the Haber process. If so, you will know that a catalyst (iron in the Haber process) is a substance that increases the rate of a reaction without itself being chemically changed. Chemical reactions in cells and organisms can occur at normal temperatures, under very mild, almost neutral, aqueous conditions and often at low concentrations of reactants, because cells contain many catalysts. We will now see how these catalysts enable reactions to occur in cells and organisms.

Key terms

Enzyme An organic catalyst that speeds up a metabolic reaction in cells and organisms.

Substrate A molecule that binds to the active site of an enzyme to form an enzyme–substrate complex. As a result, the substrate is converted to product and the enzyme remains unchanged.

Active site Enzyme molecules are usually much bigger than their substrate molecules. The active site is the small part of the enzyme molecule that binds to its specific substrate and causes the catalysis.

Induced-fit hypothesis A model used to explain enzyme action. When an enzyme and substrate combine, the enzyme's active site changes shape to become truly complementary to the part of the substrate to which it attaches. Combination with its substrate *induces* the enzyme's active site to *fit*.

Tip

Most enzymes work within cells, in other words they are **intracellular**. Some, like the enzymes of our digestive system or of the microorganisms that cause the recycling of nutrients within an ecosystem (see Chapter 25), are secreted from the cell – they are **extracellular**.

Enzymes as catalysts

The catalysts that are produced in cells are **enzymes**. Most are protein molecules. Like all catalysts, enzymes:

- do not change the nature of the reaction they catalyse
- are effective in small concentrations
- remain chemically unchanged at the end of the reaction.

How enzymes work: the enzyme–substrate complex

An enzyme molecule (**E**) works by binding to a specific substance, known as its **substrate** molecule (**S**), at a specially formed pocket in the enzyme, called its **active site**. As the enzyme and substrate bind, they form an unstable enzyme–substrate complex (**ES**), which immediately breaks down to form the product(s) (**P**), plus the unchanged enzyme. Using these letters, this reaction can be shown as a simple equation:

$$\mathbf{E + S \rightleftharpoons ES \rightleftharpoons P + E}$$

In your GCSE science course, you probably learnt about the 'lock-and-key' model of enzyme action. In this model, the enzyme and substrate molecules have a fixed shape and the substrate fits into the active site of the enzyme just like a key fits into a lock. Further studies show that this model is too simplistic. In fact, an enzyme molecule *does* change shape as a substrate molecule binds to its active site, rather like a glove changes shape as you put your hand into it. Only during this binding of enzyme and substrate does the active site become truly complementary to the part of the substrate molecule to which it attaches. As often happens in science, new evidence disproves or modifies a previously held model or theory. In this case, the new model is called the **induced-fit hypothesis**. You can see how the substrate induces the enzyme to fit in Figure 2.10. Notice in this computer-generated model, how the active site of the enzyme is only a general fit until the substrates combine with it.

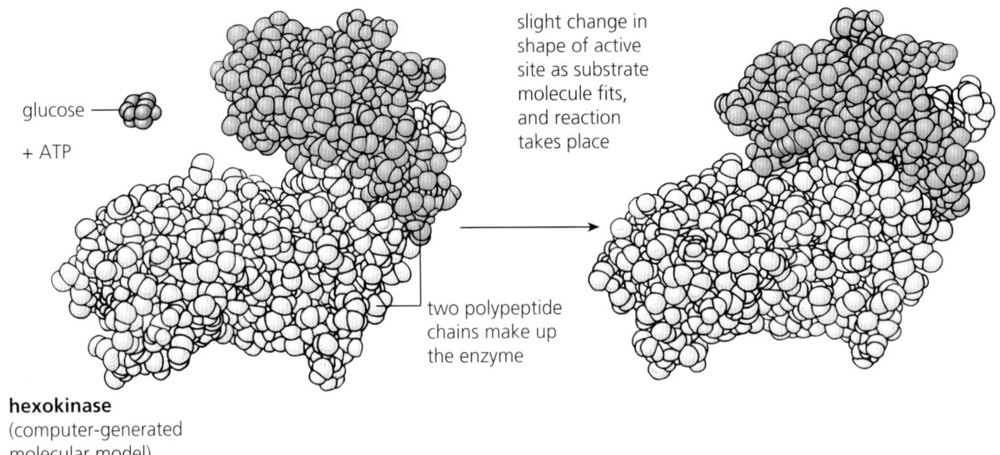

Figure 2.10 The induced-fit hypothesis to explain enzyme action

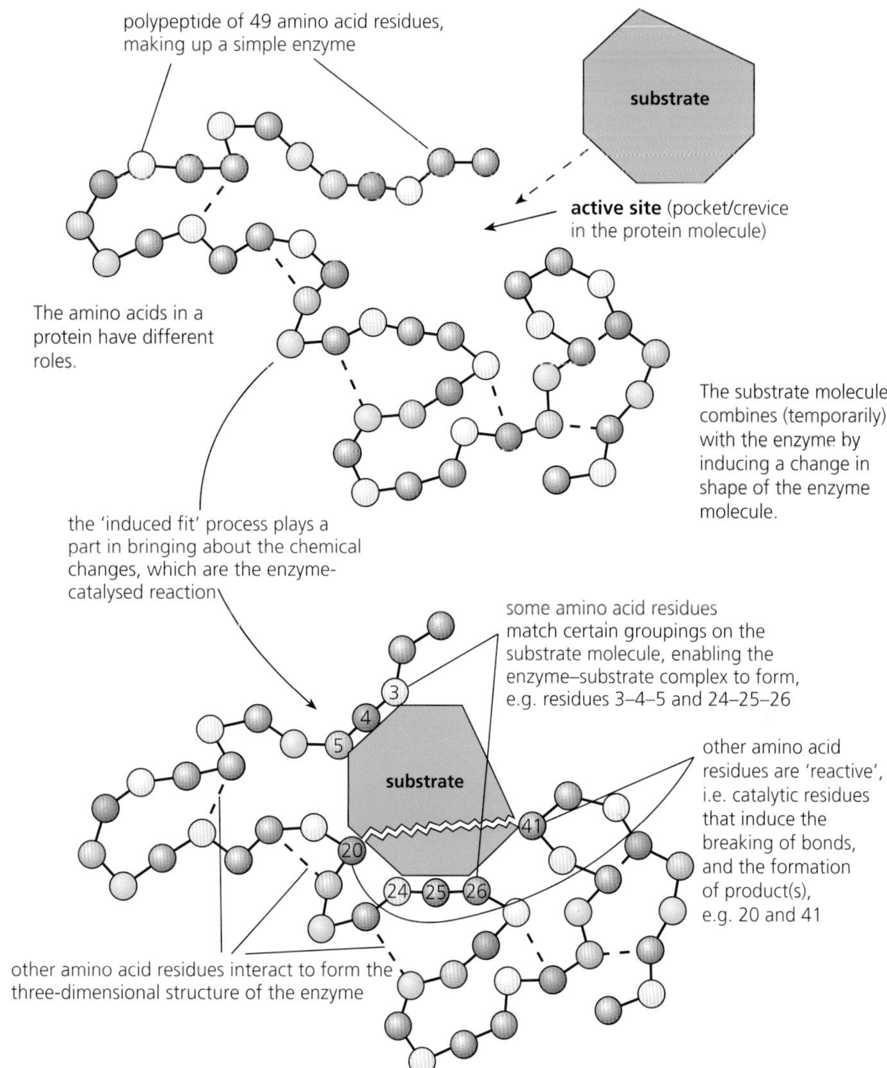
polypeptide of 49 amino acid residues, making up a simple enzyme
substrate
active site (pocket/crevice in the protein molecule)
The amino acids in a protein have different roles.
The substrate molecule combines (temporarily) with the enzyme by inducing a change in shape of the enzyme molecule.
the 'induced fit' process plays a part in bringing about the chemical changes, which are the enzyme-catalysed reaction
some amino acid residues match certain groupings on the substrate molecule, enabling the enzyme–substrate complex to form, e.g. residues 3–4–5 and 24–25–26
3
4
5
substrate
other amino acid residues are 'reactive', i.e. catalytic residues that induce the breaking of bonds, and the formation of product(s), e.g. 20 and 41
41
20
24
25
26
other amino acid residues interact to form the three-dimensional structure of the enzyme

Specificity:

- Some amino acid residues allow a particular substrate molecule to 'fit'
- Some amino acid residues bring about particular chemical changes.

Figure 2.11 The induced-fit hypothesis of enzyme action

An enzyme lowers the activation energy of the reaction it catalyses

As molecules react they become unstable intermediates, but only momentarily whilst in a so-called transition state. Effectively, the products are formed immediately. The amount of energy needed to raise substrate molecules to their transition state is called **activation energy**. This is the energy barrier that has to be overcome before the reaction can happen. As Figure 2.12 shows, like all catalysts, enzymes work by lowering the activation energy of the reactions they catalyse.

Figure 2.12 also shows a simplistic 'model' of the start of a chemical reaction. A boulder represents a substrate perched on a slope, prevented from rolling down by a small hump (representing the activation energy) in front of it. The boulder can be pushed over the hump, or the hump can be dug away (representing a lowering of the activation energy), allowing the boulder to roll and shatter at a lower level (representing formation of products).

Key term

Activation energy The energy barrier that must be overcome before reactants reach their temporary transition state. Enzymes lower the activation energy of the reactions they catalyse, making the reaction occur more readily.

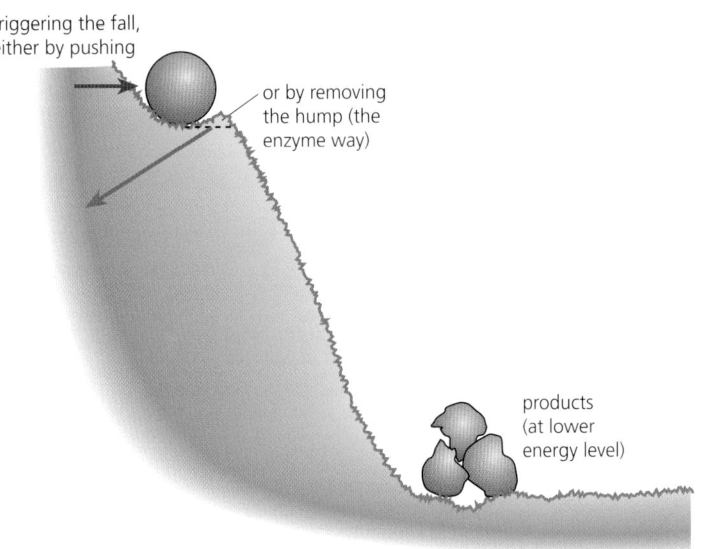

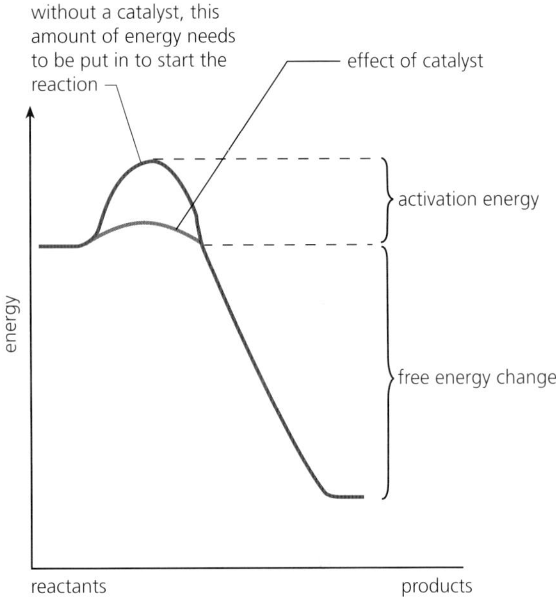

Figure 2.12 Activation energy

Test yourself

11 Distinguish between the terms *anabolism*, *catabolism* and *metabolism*.

12 Give **three** properties shown by all catalysts.

13 Do collisions between an enzyme and its substrate always result in the formation of an enzyme–substrate complex? Explain your answer.

14 Explain the terms *activation energy* and *transition state* in relation to an enzyme-catalysed reaction.

15 What is meant by the term *active site*?

The active site and enzyme specificity

Enzymes are highly specific in their action – they catalyse only one type of reaction or only a very small group of highly similar reactions. This means that an enzyme 'recognises' a very small group of substrate molecules or even only a single type of molecule. This is because the active site to which the substrate molecule binds has a precise shape and distinctive chemical properties (meaning the presence of particular chemical groups and bonds). Only particular substrate molecules, with a shape that is complementary to that of the active site, are attracted to a particular active site and can fit there. All other substrate molecules are unable to fit and so cannot bind.

Tip

The active site of an enzyme has a shape complementary to that of its substrate; it does not have the same shape.

Core practical 1

Investigate a factor affecting the initial rate of an enzyme-controlled reaction

The background to your practical investigation

You can measure the rate of an enzyme-catalysed reaction in one of two ways:

- the amount of substrate that has disappeared from a reaction mixture in a given period of time
- the amount of product that has accumulated from the reaction mixture in a given period of time.

In your college or school laboratory, you will carry out at least one experiment to investigate the effect of an environmental variable on the rate of an enzyme-controlled reaction. It doesn't really matter which factor you investigate or which enzyme you use. Here we use the enzyme catalase as our example to show general features involved in any investigation into the effect of a variable on the rate of an enzyme-catalysed reaction.

Catalase is an enzyme found in many tissues. It catalyses the hydrolysis of hydrogen peroxide, a toxic by-product of some metabolic reactions, to water and oxygen:

$$2H_2O_2 \xrightarrow{\text{catalase}} 2H_2O + O_2$$

Catalse is particularly common in liver tissue but, if you prefer not to handle animal tissue, it is also very common in potato tissue.

Working with catalase, it is easy to measure the rate of reaction by measuring the rate at which the product (oxygen) accumulates. In the experiment illustrated in Figure 2.13, the volume of oxygen that has accumulated at 30-second intervals is recorded in a table of raw data; these data are then processed and plotted on a graph.

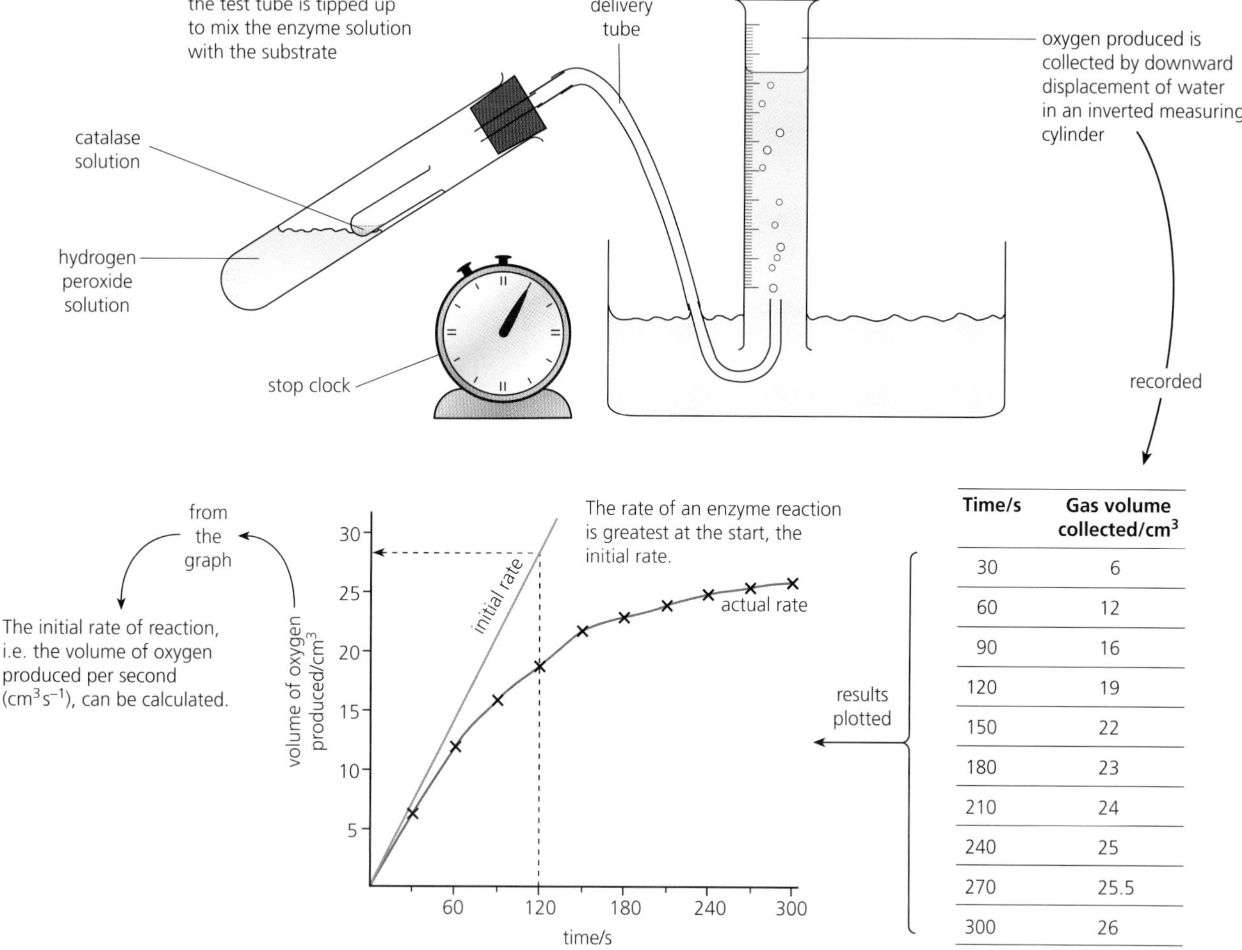

Time/s	Gas volume collected/cm³
30	6
60	12
90	16
120	19
150	22
180	23
210	24
240	25
270	25.5
300	26

Figure 2.13 Measuring the rate of reaction, using catalase. Wear eye protection when performing this experiment

Carrying out the investigation

Look at Figure 2.13, showing how you could measure the initial rate of reaction of a catalase-controlled reaction.

1 The catalase solution is initially placed in a small test tube within the larger test tube containing the hydrogen peroxide solution. Explain why.
2 You measure the volume of oxygen in the measuring cylinder at 30-second intervals. How would you take your measurement to ensure it is **accurate**?
3 Using a measuring cylinder, such as the one in Figure 2.13, how would you estimate your error in taking your readings of volume?
4 When during your investigation would you draw your table for the raw data you collect? What 'rules' would you follow in drawing the table?
5 How could you modify this investigation to measure the effect of temperature on the initial rate of reaction?
6 Which temperatures would you use? Explain your answer.
7 How would you ensure that the temperature in your water bath remained constant?
8 Ideally, you should repeat the procedure at each temperature several times. Explain why.
9 Explain how you would process, and then plot on a graph, your data to show the effect of temperature on the rate of this enzyme-controlled reaction.
10 Why should you place 'Temperature/°C' in the left-hand column of your new table?
11 It would be difficult to determine the optimum temperature for catalase from your graph. Describe how you could obtain a more accurate value for the optimum temperature.

Key term

Accurate Measurement that is close to the true value of what is being measured.

Factors that change the rate of reaction of enzymes

Enzymes are very sensitive to environmental conditions. Here we will consider how temperature, pH, substrate concentration and enzyme concentration affect the activity of enzymes.

Temperature

Figure 2.14 shows typical results of the effect of temperature on the rate of an enzyme-catalysed reaction.

Not all enzymes have the same optimum temperature. For example, the bacteria in hot thermal springs have enzymes with optima in the region 80–100 °C, whilst seaweeds of northern seas and the plants of the tundra have optima closer to 0 °C. Humans have enzymes with optima at or about normal body temperature (37 °C).

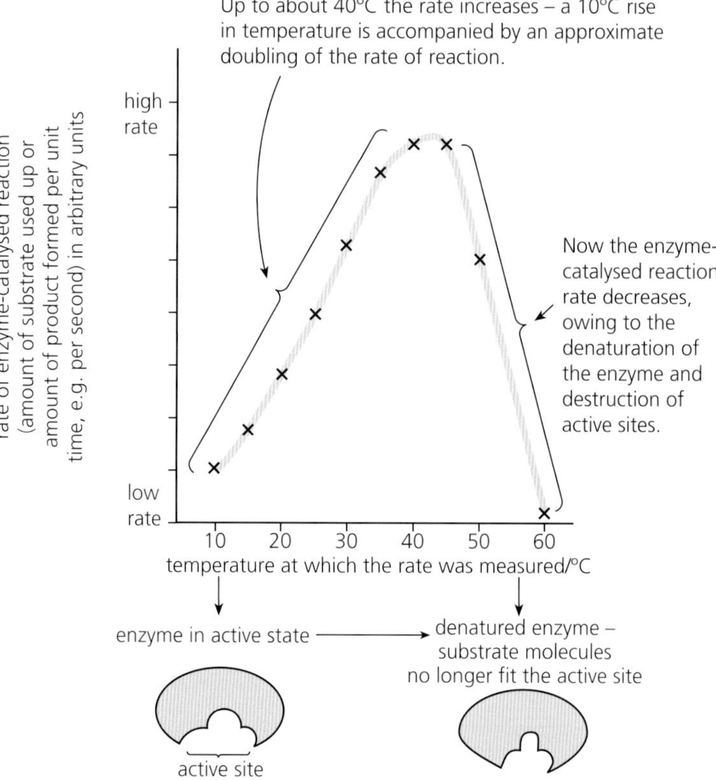

Figure 2.14 The effect of temperature on an enzyme-catalysed reaction

Example

How can we explain the graph in Figure 2.14?

It is tempting to describe the trend or pattern shown by a graph or by data in a table. In an examination, a question requiring this response would use the command word 'Describe'. Here, though, we are looking for an *explanation*. This means we must give *reasons* for the trend or pattern shown by the data; a simple description would not gain credit.

Two concepts are involved in explaining the effect of temperature on the rate of an enzyme-controlled reaction. Increases in temperature cause an increase in:

- the random thermal movement of particles. In other words, the higher the temperature, the more molecules, and the particles within them, move about. If they move about more, collisions between them become increasingly likely
- the rate of denaturation of protein molecules. This happens because high temperatures cause such violent movement of particles within a protein molecule that the bonds holding the protein molecule together (Figure 2.5) break, so its active site loses its critical shape.

Let's apply these two concepts to explain the shape of the curve in Figure 2.14.

Answer

As the temperature increases from 10 °C to 30 °C, the rate of reaction increases *because* the molecules of enzyme and substrate are moving more rapidly and are more likely to collide and react.

As the temperature increases from 45 °C to 60 °C, the rate of reaction slows *because* more and more enzyme molecules have been denatured and so fewer functional enzyme molecules remain available to catalyse the reaction.

At some temperature between 30 °C and 45 °C, a balance is reached between the increased rate of reaction caused by more collisions of enzyme and substrate and the decreased rate of reaction caused by denaturation of the enzyme. This temperature is known as the optimum temperature of that enzyme.

Tip

When asked to 'explain', it might help you remember to give a reason if you develop the habit of including the word 'because' in your answer.

Key terms

Random thermal movement The movement shown by all particles, whether sub-atomic particles, atoms, or molecules, at temperatures above absolute zero. As the temperatures increases, so does the rate of random thermal movement.

Optimum temperature The temperature at which the rate of an enzyme-controlled reaction is fastest. At this point there is a balance between an increase in successful collisions between enzyme and substrate molecules and loss of active enzyme molecules as a result of their denaturation.

Optimum pH The value, or narrow range of values, over which an enzyme-catalysed reaction is fastest.

pH

Each enzyme has a range of pH values, called its optimum pH, in which the rate of the reaction it catalyses is fastest. pH has this effect because the structure of a protein (and therefore the shape of the active site) is maintained by various bonds within the three-dimensional structure of the protein (look back to Figure 2.5 to remind yourself of these bonds). A change in pH from the optimum value alters the bonding patterns. As a result, the shape of the active site of the enzyme molecule is progressively changed.

This is shown in Figure 2.15. At the optimum pH, the active site has the appropriate shape to combine with its substrate. At pH values away from the optimum, the shape of

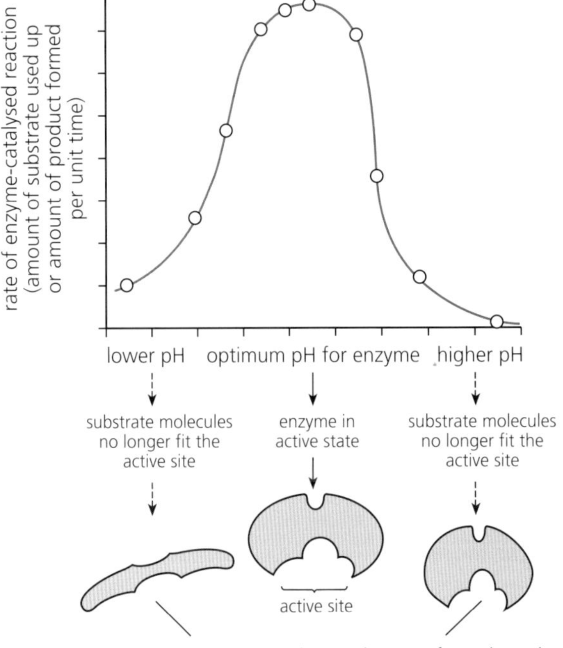

Figure 2.15 The effect of pH on enzyme shape and activity

the active site changes so that it will no longer bind with its substrate. Unlike the effect of temperature, however, the effects of pH on the active site are normally reversible. That is, provided the change in surrounding acidity or alkalinity is not too extreme, as the pH is brought back to the optimum for that enzyme, the active site may reappear.

Substrate concentration

Figure 2.16 shows the effect of increasing substrate concentration on the rate of an enzyme-catalysed reaction. The curve has two phases.

- At lower substrate concentrations, the rate increases in direct proportion to the increase in substrate concentration.
- At higher substrate concentrations, the rate of reaction becomes constant, showing no further increase as the substrate concentration increases.

Figure 2.16 also shows why these two phases occur. At low substrate concentrations, there is effectively an excess of enzyme molecules present. This means there are 'free' enzyme molecules that are available to react with added substrate molecules to form more enzyme–substrate complexes per unit time. We can say that substrate concentration is the **limiting factor** at this stage of the reaction.

As more substrate molecules are added, however, there comes a point at which the concentration of substrate is greater than that of the enzyme. There are no longer 'free' enzyme molecules. Now, in effect, substrate molecules have to 'queue up' for access to an active site. Adding more substrate increases the number of molecules awaiting contact with an enzyme molecule. There is now no increase in the rate of reaction, explaining the plateau in the curve shown in Figure 2.16.

Key term

Limiting factor Any factor that limits the rate at which a reaction, or process, can occur.

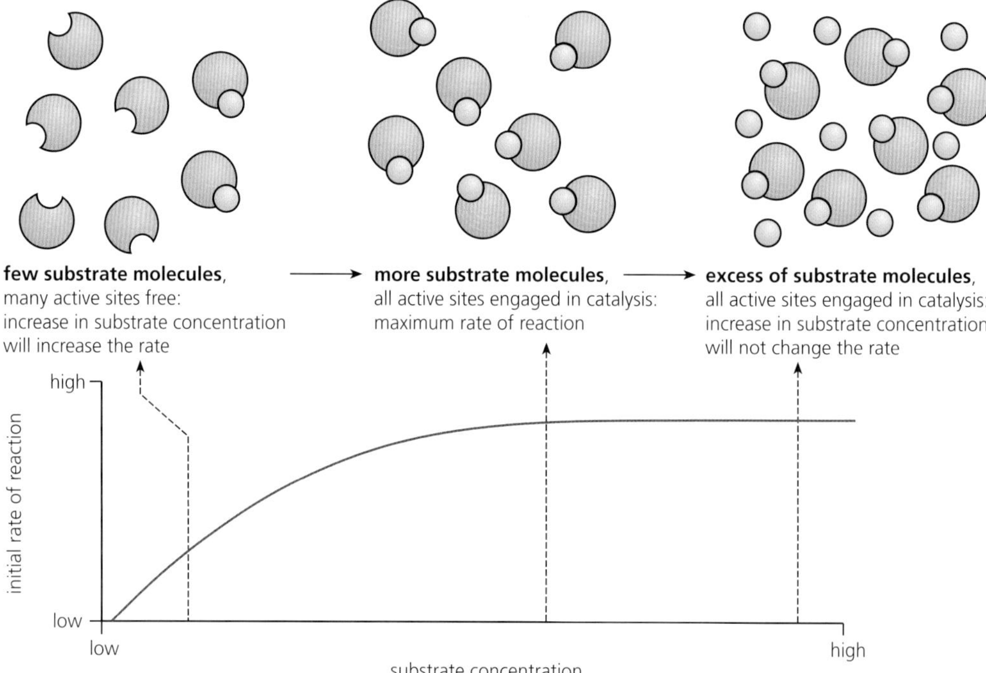
few substrate molecules,
many active sites free:
increase in substrate concentration
will increase the rate
more substrate molecules,
all active sites engaged in catalysis:
maximum rate of reaction
excess of substrate molecules,
all active sites engaged in catalysis:
increase in substrate concentration
will not change the rate
high
initial rate of reaction
low
low
high
substrate concentration

Figure 2.16 The effect of substrate concentration on the rate of an enzyme-catalysed reaction

Enzyme concentration

Figure 2.17 shows the effect of increasing enzyme concentration on the rate of an enzyme-catalysed reaction. This curve also has two phases.

- At lower enzyme concentrations, the rate increases in direct proportion to the increase in enzyme concentration.
- At higher enzyme concentrations, the rate of reaction becomes constant, showing no further increase as the enzyme concentration increases.

Figure 2.17 also shows why these two phases occur. At low enzyme concentrations, there is effectively an excess of substrate molecules present. This means there are no 'free' enzyme molecules available to react with the substrate molecules already there. This time, it is the enzyme concentration that is the limiting factor at this stage of the reaction.

As more enzyme molecules are added, more 'free' active sites become available, so more enzyme-substrate complexes can be formed and the rate of reaction increases. As even more enzyme molecules are added, however, there comes a point at which the concentration of enzyme becomes greater than that of the substrate. There are now 'free' enzyme molecules. Consequently, adding even more enzyme molecules will not increase the rate of reaction, explaining the plateau in the curve shown in Figure 2.17.

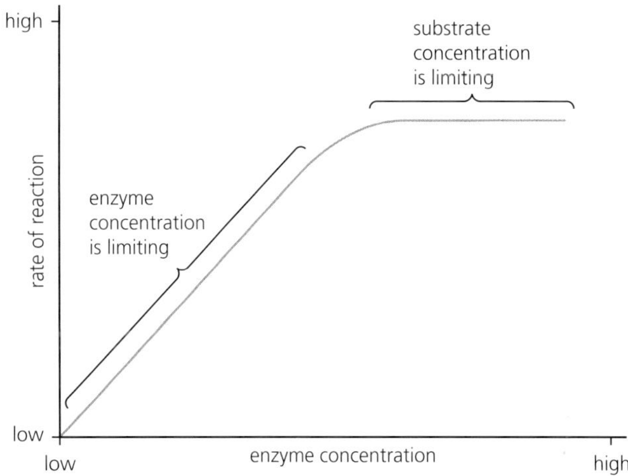

Figure 2.17 The effect of enzyme concentration on the rate of an enzyme-catalysed reaction

Inhibitors of enzymes

Some substances can react with an enzyme, slowing the rate of the reaction it catalyses. These substances are known as **enzyme inhibitors**. Studies of the effects of inhibitors have helped our understanding of:

- the chemistry of the active site of enzymes
- the natural regulation of metabolism
- the ways in which certain commercial pesticides and many drugs work (by inhibiting specific enzymes and preventing particular reactions).

There are two types of enzyme inhibitor with which we need to be familiar. Their effects are summarised in Table 2.1 and in Figure 2.18.

Table 2.1 Competitive and non-competitive inhibition of enzymes compared

Competitive inhibition	Non-competitive inhibition
Inhibitor chemically resembles the substrate molecule and binds with the active site, blocking access to substrate molecules.	Inhibitor chemically unlike the substrate molecule, but by binding to another (allosteric) site, changes the shape of the enzyme molecule, including the active site.
With a low concentration of inhibitor, increasing the concentration of substrate eventually overcomes inhibition as substrate molecules displace inhibitor and enzyme–substrate collisions become more likely than enzyme–inhibitor collisions.	With a low concentration of inhibitor, increasing concentration of substrate can neither displace inhibitor nor prevent binding of further inhibitor molecules.
For example, O_2 competes with CO_2 for the active site of rubisco.	For example, alanine non-competitively inhibits pyruvate kinase.

Key term

Enzyme inhibitor
A substance that slows the rate of an enzyme-controlled reaction by preventing binding of the substrate to the active site of the enzyme.

- Competitive inhibitors bind directly to the enzyme's active site, blocking access by the substrate.
- Non-competitive inhibitors bind to the enzyme at a site other than the active site and, by doing so, cause the shape of the enzyme's active site to change.

When the initial rates of reaction of an enzyme are plotted against substrate concentration, the effects of competitive and non-competitive inhibitors are seen to be different.

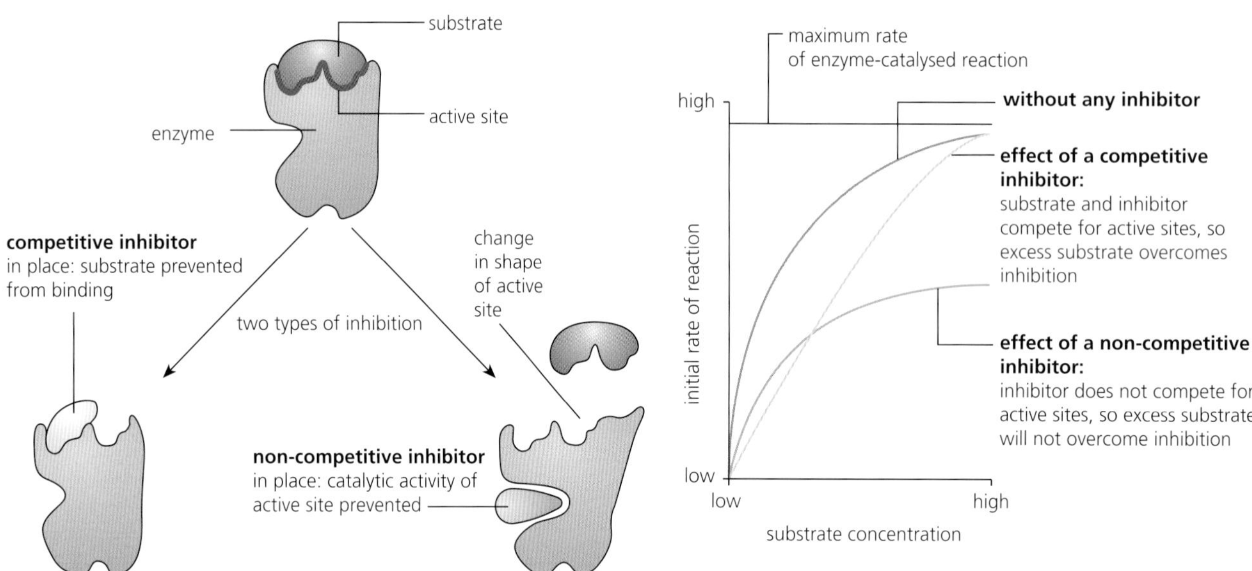

Figure 2.18 Competitive and non-competitive inhibitors – the principles

Competitive inhibitors

The molecules of a competitive inhibitor sufficiently resemble the shape of the true substrate so that they can bind to the active site of the enzyme, forming an enzyme–inhibitor complex. Because these inhibitors are not acted on by the enzyme and turned into 'products' as normal substrate molecules are, the enzyme–inhibitor complex tends to remain intact. However, if the concentration of the substrate molecule is increased, the inhibitor molecules are progressively displaced from the active sites – and become less likely to re-attach.

An enzyme you will meet in year 2, called ribulose bisphosphate carboxylase (or rubisco for short), is one of the most common enzymes on Earth. It catalyses the reaction between carbon dioxide and a 'CO_2-acceptor molecule' during the process of photosynthesis. Oxygen is a competitive inhibitor of this enzyme.

Non-competitive inhibitors

The molecules of a non-competitive inhibitor are quite unlike the true substrate molecule, yet can still combine with the enzyme. In this case, the attachment does not occur at the active site of the enzyme but at another (allosteric) site. As a result of this binding, the shape of the enzyme molecule changes and, with it, the shape of the active site also changes. The active site is no longer complementary to molecules of the substrate and the enzyme loses its ability to bind with substrate molecules. Unlike the case with competitive inhibition, adding more substrate does not dislodge the inhibitor, since the substrate and inhibitor are not competing for the active site of the enzyme. Consequently, non-competitive inhibition is often permanent.

One of the steps in cell respiration that you will meet in year 2 is catalysed by an enzyme called pyruvate kinase. The amino acid alanine is a non-competitive inhibitor of this enzyme. Many poisons are non-competitive inhibitors of enzymes.

End-product inhibition in the control of metabolic pathways

Many metabolic pathways exist as a chain of reactions, each catalysed by a different, specific enzyme. Enzyme inhibition is often involved in the regulation of such pathways.

Figure 2.19 represents a chain of reactions by which a substrate (A) is converted to a useful end product (F). Each reaction in the chain is controlled by a different, specific, enzyme (a to e). The whole process can be regulated because the end product (F) is a non-competitive inhibitor of the first enzyme in the chain (a). As the concentration of end product (F) increases, it inhibits enzyme a, slowing the rate of the first reaction in the series (conversion of A to B) and, hence, slowing the entire pathway. So, in **end-product inhibition**, as the product molecules accumulate, the steps in their production are switched off. But these product molecules may now become the substrates in subsequent metabolic reactions. If so, the accumulated product molecules will be removed, and production of new product molecules will recommence.

> **Key term**
>
> **End-product inhibition** A feature of a chain of enzyme-controlled reactions in which a product of a late reaction in the series inhibits the enzyme controlling an earlier reaction.

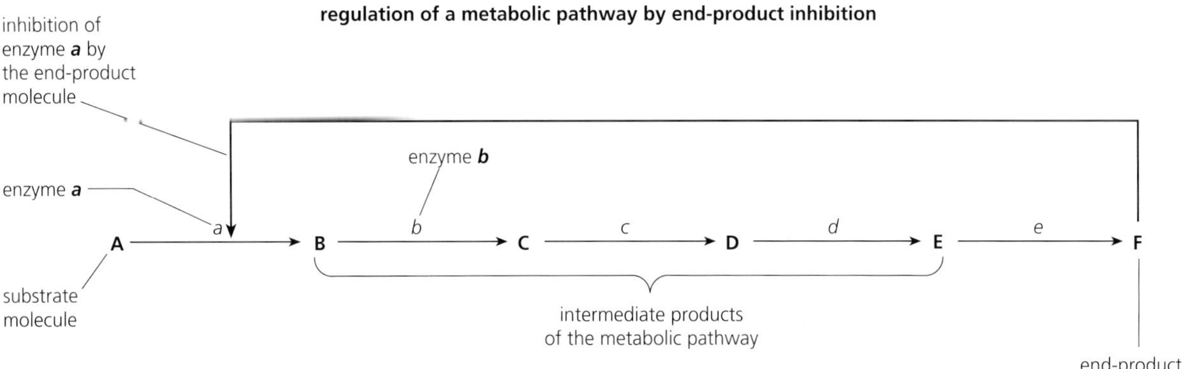

Figure 2.19 End-product inhibition of metabolism

Test yourself

16 Outline the difference between the lock-and-key and the induced-fit models of enzyme action.

17 Explain the difference between the time of reaction and the rate of reaction.

18 Which **one** of the following statements is true? Explain your answer.

- **A** Enzymes only begin to denature when they are heated to boiling.
- **B** Enzymes only begin to denature at temperatures above their optimum temperature.
- **C** Enzymes begin to denature at their optimum temperature.
- **D** Enzymes begin to denature below their optimum temperature.

19 When investigating enzyme-catalysed reactions, scientists usually include a buffer solution in their reaction mixtures. Explain why.

20 Amylase is an enzyme that hydrolyses starch to maltose. It is secreted by the salivary glands of some humans and is also secreted by the pancreas. Amylase from the salivary glands has an optimum pH in the range 4.6 to 5.2, whereas amylase from the pancreas has an optimum pH in the range 6.7 to 7.0.

What can you conclude from this information about the nature of human amylase?

Chapter summary

Amino acids

- Amino acids are the monomers from which polypeptides and proteins are made.
- Every amino acid has two functional groups – an amino group (NH_2) and a carboxyl group (COOH). These groups are attached to the same carbon atom to which is also attached a side chain, labelled R. The nature of the R group makes each amino acid unique.
- An amino acid can be represented by $H_2NCHRCOOH$.
- A condensation reaction between two amino acids produces a dipeptide. The two monomers are held together by a peptide bond.

Proteins

- Polypeptides and proteins are polymers of many amino acids linked by peptide bonds.
- There are four levels of protein structure:
  - Primary – the sequence of amino acids.
  - Secondary – the chain of amino acids folds into helices and/or beta-pleated sheets held in place by hydrogen bonds.
  - Tertiary – the protein folds into a complex three-dimensional globular structure held in place by ionic bonds and disulfide bonds.
  - Quaternary – some proteins contain more than one polypeptide chain; this is the quaternary structure of proteins and is held in place by covalent bonds.
- Collagen and haemoglobin both have a quaternary structure:
  - Collagen is a fibrous protein. It has three polypeptide chains forming a triple helix that provides the strength of, for example, tendons.
  - Haemoglobin is a globular protein. Its four polypeptide chains are bound to iron-containing haem groups that bind to oxygen.

Enzymes

- Enzymes are globular proteins that act as catalysts in extracellular and intracellular reactions.
- Part of the enzyme molecule is an active site. Following appropriate collisions, this active site binds with specific, complementary substrate molecule(s) to form an enzyme-substrate complex.
- Formation of the enzyme-substrate complex reduces the activation energy needed to convert substrate(s) into product(s).
- The induced-fit hypothesis proposes that the active site of an enzyme changes shape as it combines with its substrate(s).
- Any factor that increases the rate at which enzyme molecules bind to their substrates increases the rate of an enzyme-controlled reaction. Consequently, an increase in the concentration of enzyme, an increase in the concentration of substrate and, within a narrow range, an increase in temperature all increase the rate of reaction.
- Any factor that changes the shape of an enzyme's active site will slow the rate of reaction. High temperatures, which denature enzymes, changes in pH or the presence of a non-competitive inhibitor all slow the rate of reaction in this way.
- Competitive inhibitors have a similar shape to an enzyme's true substrate and bind to the enzyme's active site.

Practice questions

1 The graph shows the effect of temperature on the rate of an enzyme-catalysed reaction.

Which of the following statements is true about the graph?

A The enzyme starts to become denatured at point W.

B The enzyme starts to become denatured at point X.

C The enzyme starts to become denatured at point Y.

D The enzyme starts to become denatured at point Z. *(1)*

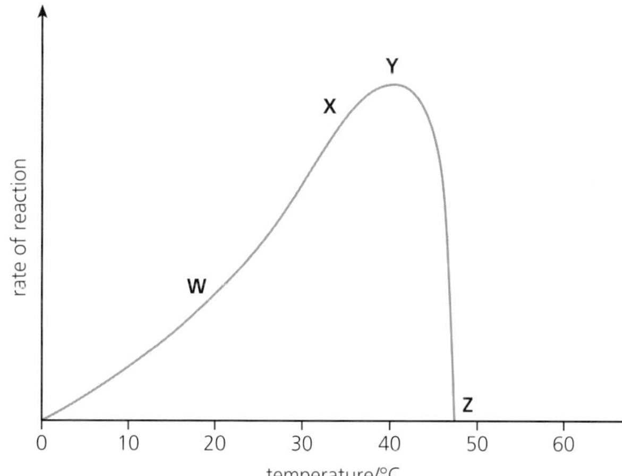

2 Denaturation involves breakage of which types of bond?

A Hydrogen bonds, ionic bonds and peptide bonds

B Disulfide bonds, hydrogen bonds and peptide bonds

C Disulfide bonds, ionic bonds and peptide bonds

D Disulfide bonds, hydrogen bonds and ionic bonds *(1)*

3 Which of the following statements is true about an amino acid in a weakly acidic solution?

A It will not ionise.

B It will ionise as an anion.

C It will ionise as a cation.

D It will ionise as a zwitterion. *(1)*

4 Collagen and haemoglobin are two different proteins. Explain **one** way in which the structure of each molecule is adapted for its function. *(4)*

5 The diagrams represent four different types of molecule important in biology. Identify each type of molecule. *(4)*

A

B

C

D

CH_2OH

Tip

Question 4 tests recall with understanding (AO1). Note that the command word is 'explain'; a simple description of each molecule will not gain full marks.

Tip

Question 5 tests recall with understanding (AO1) from Chapters 1 and 2.

6 The diagram shows a molecule of an amino acid called alanine.

$$H_2N-\overset{\displaystyle CH_3}{\underset{\displaystyle H}{C}}-COOH$$

a) Draw a new diagram to show how two molecules of alanine join together to form a dipeptide. *(2)*

b) What name is given to the type of reaction by which a dipeptide is formed? *(1)*

c) How do other amino acids differ in structure from alanine? *(1)*

d) There are 20 different amino acids found in the proteins in living organisms. Theoretically, how many different dipeptides could exist? *(1)*

7 A student added 1 cm^3 of a dilute solution of catalase to 20 cm^3 of a 5% solution of hydrogen peroxide. She measured the concentration of product formed at regular intervals.

a) Why did the student use a *dilute* solution of catalase? *(2)*

b) Given a 100% solution of hydrogen peroxide, describe how you would produce 20 cm^3 of a 5% solution of hydrogen peroxide. *(1)*

Tip

You might find it helpful to refer to Figure 2.13 when answering Question 7.

The student recorded her results in a table. She used this table to produce the sketch graph of her results, shown here.

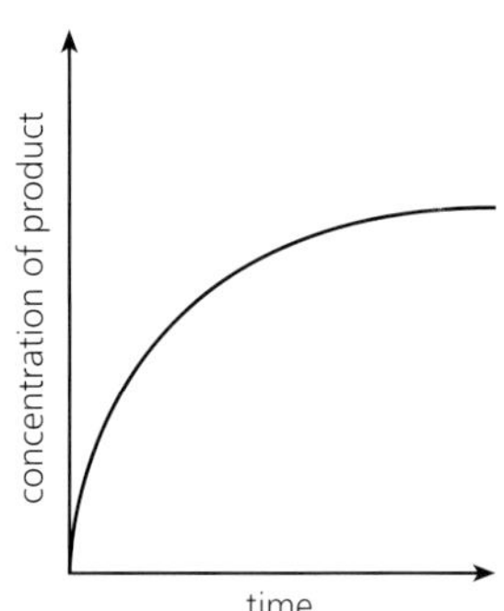

c) Explain why the graph is described as a 'sketch graph'. *(1)*

d) Suggest why the student produced a sketch graph of her results. *(1)*

e) Explain the shape of the curve shown in the graph. *(2)*

f) Add a second curve to the graph to show the results you would expect if this student had repeated her experiment but added a non-competitive inhibitor to the starting mixture. Justify the curve you have drawn. *(3)*

8 Compare and contrast the effects of competitive inhibitors and non-competitive inhibitors. *(5)*

Stretch and challenge

9 Enzyme-catalysed reactions can be analysed quantitatively. Three commonly used measures are the temperature coefficient (Q_{10}), the maximum rate of reaction (V_{max}) and the Michaelis constant (K_m).

a) The temperature coefficient of an enzyme is found by the following equation:

$$Q_{10} = \frac{\text{rate of reaction at temperature } (T + 10)\,°C}{\text{rate of reaction at temperature } T\,°C}$$

Calculate the Q_{10} value for the enzyme-catalysed reaction shown in Figure 1.

b) Figure 2 shows changes in the rate of reaction at different substrate concentrations.

Use information from Figure 2 to answer the following questions:

i) Describe how the Michaelis constant (K_m) is calculated.

ii) Explain how you could use information about the Michaelis constant to determine whether an enzyme-catalysed reaction was affected by a competitive inhibitor or a non-competitive inhibitor.

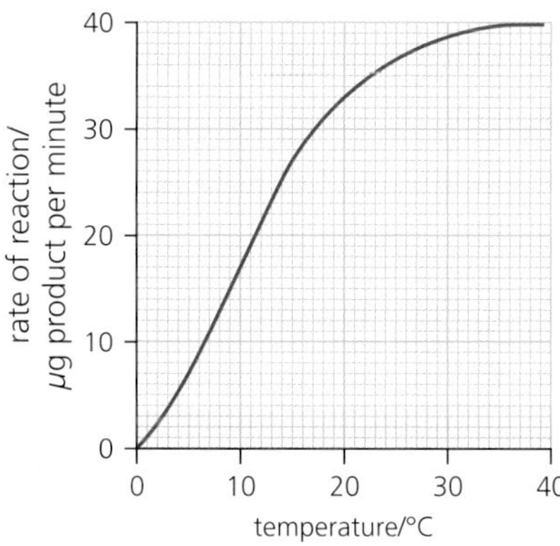

Figure 1

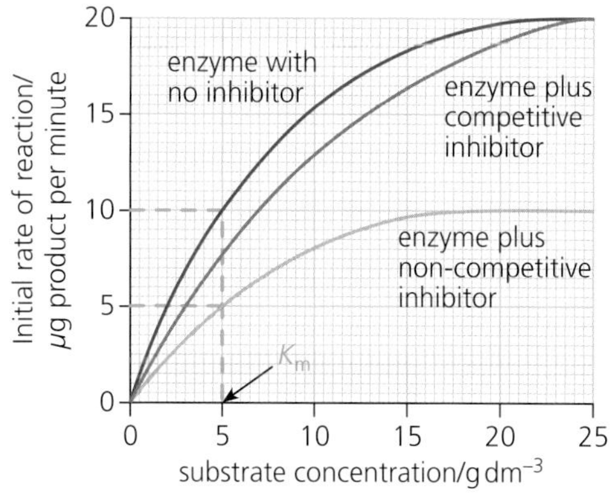

Figure 2

10 Earlier in this chapter, you were told 'The catalysts that are produced in cells are enzymes. Most are protein molecules.'

Clearly, this statement tells you that some enzymes are *not* protein molecules.

Use a search engine or an undergraduate textbook to find which group of enzymes are not proteins.

a) What type of molecule are they?

b) In what reactions are they involved and where?

c) Why do some scientists think these enzymes might have had an important role in the evolution of life on Earth?

d) Suggest why the discoverers of these non-protein enzymes had difficulty publishing their findings.

11 In Year 2 of your course, you will learn about a number of coenzymes. Find out what a coenzyme is and about the general role of coenzymes.

12 You are currently reading a paper-based book. Several enzymes were used in the production of this paper from boiled wood pulp. Carry out the research needed to produce a list of at least four types of enzyme likely to have been used in producing paper from wood pulp and give the function of each.

3 Nucleic acids and protein synthesis

Prior knowledge

In this chapter you will need to recall that:

- ➜ a DNA molecule is made up of two strands forming a double helix
- ➜ each DNA strand is a polymer made from four different nucleotides; each nucleotide consists of a common sugar and phosphate group with one of four different bases attached to the sugar
- ➜ the sequence of bases in a cell's DNA molecule(s) determines the sequence of amino acids in the polypeptides and proteins the cell produces
- ➜ a gene is a sequence of DNA bases that determines the sequence of amino acids of a single protein
- ➜ a change in the sequence of bases within a gene can alter the activity of the protein for which it codes.

Test yourself on prior knowledge

1 A DNA molecule is a polymer of nucleotides.
  a) What is meant by a polymer?
  b) Name the components of a single DNA nucleotide.

2 DNA carries the genetic code for the sequence of amino acids in a protein. In what form is the genetic code carried in a DNA molecule?

3 a) Where is the DNA in a human cell?
  b) Where in a human cell is protein made?

4 What is a gene mutation?

5 Give the role of a messenger RNA molecule in a human cell.

The structure of nucleic acids

Nucleic acids are the 'information molecules' of cells. The 'information' they carry determines the sequence of amino acids in each protein a cell can produce. As you will see, the way in which 'information' about the amino acid sequence is held in nucleic acids – the genetic code – is universal. This means that it is not specific to any one organism or even to a larger group – like mammals or bacteria – alone. It makes sense in all organisms.

Key term

Nucleotide The monomer from which nucleic acids are formed. Each nucleotide comprises a pentose, a phosphate group and a purine or pyrimidine base.

There are two types of nucleic acid, DNA (deoxyribonucleic acid) and RNA (ribonucleic acid). These molecules have roles in the day-to-day control of cells and organisms and in the transmission of genetic information from generation to generation. Before understanding how they do this, we need to look at the **nucleotides** from which nucleic acids are formed.

Structure of nucleotides

A nucleotide is the monomer from which both DNA and RNA are formed.

Each nucleotide consists of three substances combined together (Figure 3.1):

- a pentose (ribose in RNA and deoxyribose in DNA)
- a nitrogenous base, which might be:
  - a double-ringed purine (either adenine or guanine in both DNA and RNA)
  - a single-ringed pyrimidine (either cytosine or thymine in DNA; either cytosine or uracil in RNA)
- phosphoric acid.

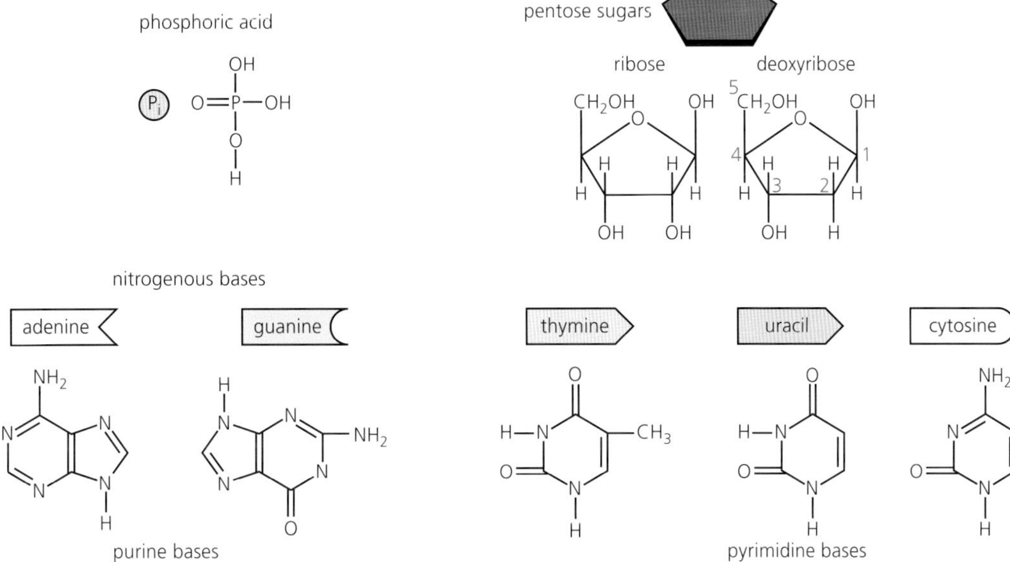

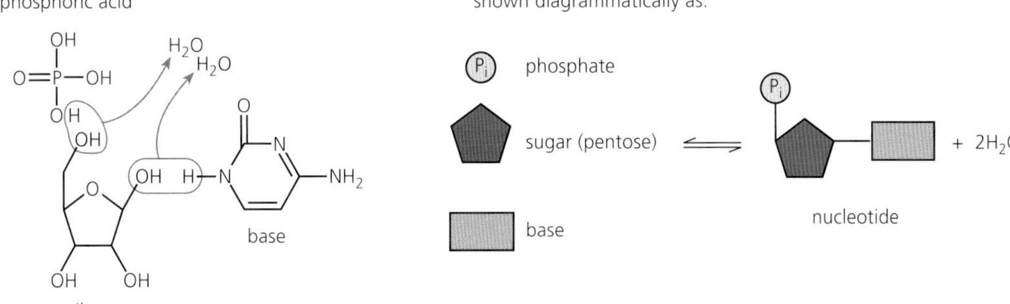

Figure 3.1 The components of nucleotides

Polynucleotide chains

Two nucleotides can be joined together by a condensation reaction, catalysed by an enzyme **DNA polymerase**. Figure 3.2 shows how this reaction results in the formation of a covalent bond, called a **phosphodiester bond**, between adjacent nucleotides. In Figure 3.3, four condensation reactions have produced a chain of five nucleotides.

Key terms

DNA polymerase The enzyme that catalyses the formation of a phosphodiester bond between two nucleotides.

Phosphodiester bond The covalent bond between two nucleotides.

condensation to form a dinucleotide...

...shown diagrammatically as:

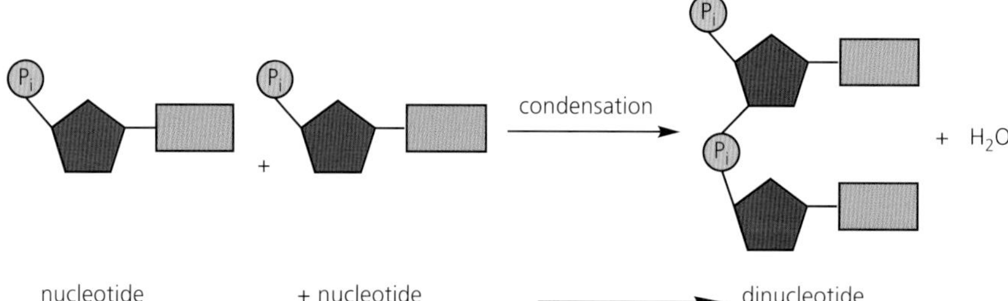

Figure 3.2 A condensation reaction between two nucleotides produces a dinucleotide

Nucleotides become chemically combined together, phosphate to pentose sugar, by covalent bonds, with a sequence of bases attached to the sugar residues. Up to 5 million nucleotides condense together in this way, forming a polynucleotide (nucleic acid).

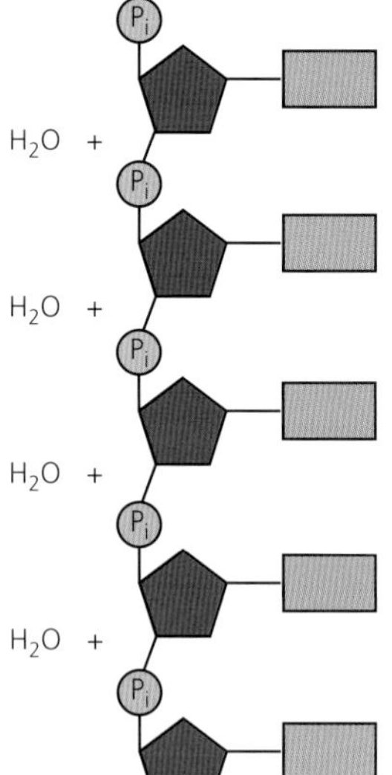

nucleotides are added at this end of the growing polynucleotide

Figure 3.3 How nucleotides make up a polynucleotide chain

Large numbers of nucleotides become condensed together to form huge molecules – the nucleic acids, also known as polynucleotides. A nucleic acid or polynucleotide is a very long, thread-like macromolecule. You can see in Figure 3.3 how alternating sugar and phosphate molecules form the 'backbone' of the polynucleotide, with a nitrogenous base attached to each sugar molecule along the strand. Notice the label that shows where new nucleotides are added to a developing polynucleotide chain. This becomes important when we look at how DNA is copied later in this chapter.

RNA molecules

RNA molecules are relatively short. In fact, RNA molecules tend to be between 100 and thousands of nucleotides long, depending on the particular role they have.

In every RNA nucleotide:

- the pentose is ribose
- the base is cytosine, guanine, adenine or uracil, but never thymine.

This is shown in Figure 3.4, which also shows that RNA molecules are always a single strand of nucleotides.

In the 'information business' of cells there are three functional types of RNA:

- messenger RNA (mRNA) – carries a copy of a single gene to a cell's ribosomes
- transfer RNA (tRNA) – carries individual amino acids to ribosomes during protein synthesis
- ribosomal RNA – forms part of the sub-units of ribosomes.

We will expand on the roles of these RNA molecules later in this chapter.

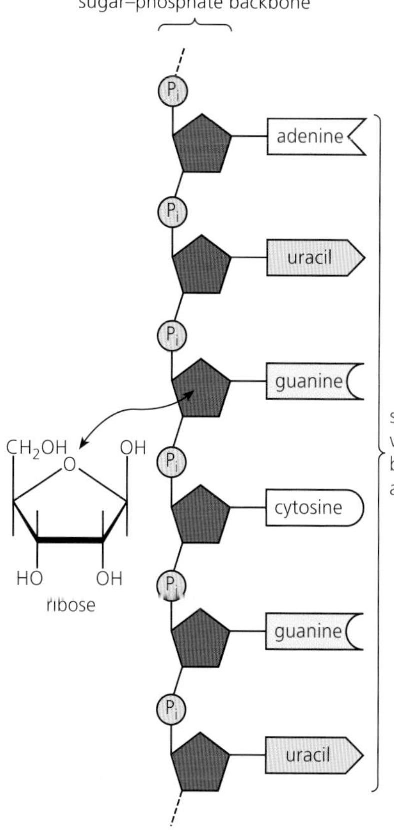

Figure 3.4 RNA structure

DNA molecules

DNA molecules form extremely long strands, of the order of several million nucleotides in length.

In every DNA nucleotide:

- the pentose is deoxyribose
- the base is cytosine, guanine, adenine or thymine, but never uracil.

Unlike RNA, a DNA molecule consists of two polynucleotide strands, held together by hydrogen bonds between its bases. The two strands take the shape of a double helix (Figure 3.5). You can see that the hydrogen bonds that hold the two strands together are formed between specific bases: adenine with thymine; cytosine with guanine. This pairing, known as **complementary base pairing**, is the key to:

- the stability of the DNA double helix (although individual hydrogen bonds are weak, millions of them in a DNA molecule provide strength)
- the way in which genetic information can be transferred from DNA to RNA (mRNA)
- the way amino acids are assembled into polypeptides in the cytoplasm.

The bases of the two strands fit together only if the deoxyribose molecules to which they are attached point in opposite directions. You can see the effect of this in Figure 3.5. Because the two sugar–phosphate backbones point in opposite directions, these DNA strands are said to be **antiparallel**.

Key term

Complementary base pairing A key feature of DNA molecules in which two antiparallel polynucleotide chains are held together by hydrogen bonds between the bases adenine and thymine or the bases cytosine and guanine.

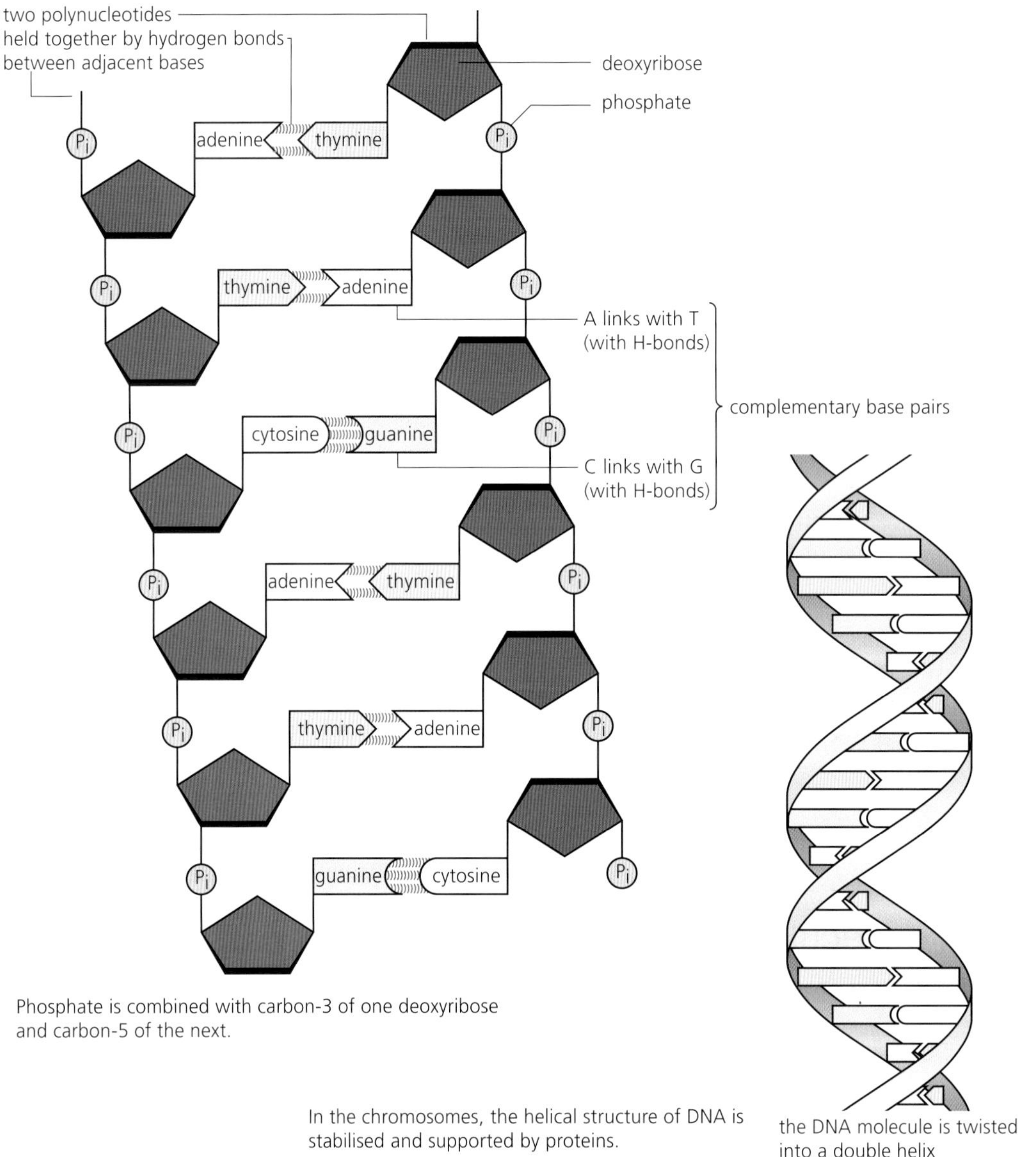
two polynucleotides held together by hydrogen bonds between adjacent bases
deoxyribose
phosphate
adenine
thymine
cytosine
guanine
A links with T (with H-bonds)
C links with G (with H-bonds)
complementary base pairs
Phosphate is combined with carbon-3 of one deoxyribose and carbon-5 of the next.
In the chromosomes, the helical structure of DNA is stabilised and supported by proteins.
the DNA molecule is twisted into a double helix

Figure 3.5 DNA structure

Test yourself

1 Name:
   a) the enzyme that catalyses the condensation of two nucleotides
   b) the name of the product(s) of this condensation reaction
   c) the bond formed between the two nucleotides.

2 How does deoxyribose differ from ribose?

3 Other than the nature of their pentose, give **three** ways in which the structure of RNA is different from that of DNA.

4 Figure 3.3 shows that nucleotides are added only to one end of a growing polynucleotide. Suggest why they can only be added to one end.

5 How does the function of tRNA differ from that of mRNA?

DNA replication – how DNA copies itself

Every time a cell divides, a copy of its DNA passes to each 'daughter' cell formed by the division. This can happen because, prior to dividing, the cell has made accurate copies of each of its DNA molecules. We call this copying process **DNA replication**. As you will see in Chapter 5, in eukaryotic cells, DNA replication takes place in the interphase nucleus, well before the events of nuclear division.

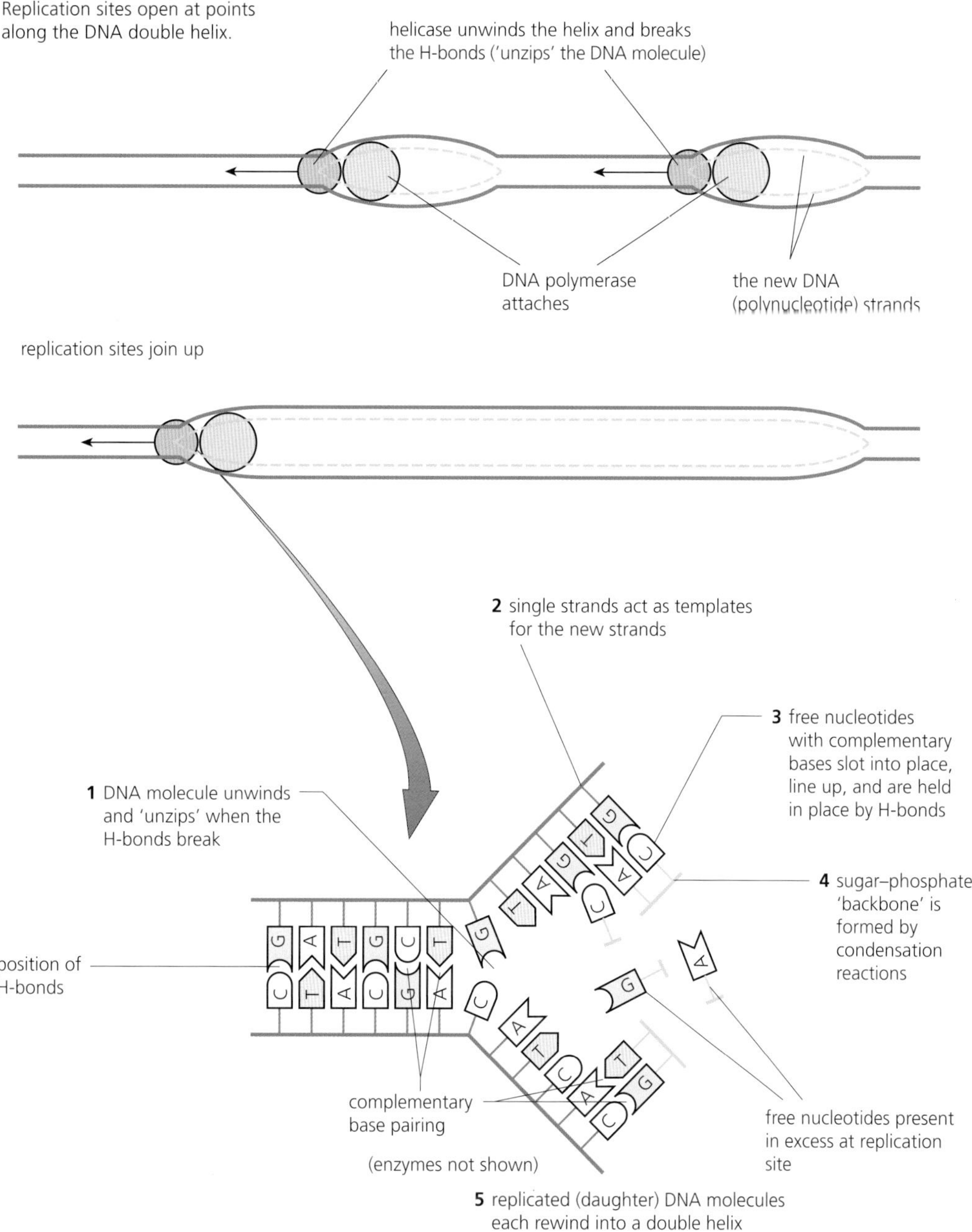

Replication sites open at points along the DNA double helix.
helicase unwinds the helix and breaks the H-bonds ('unzips' the DNA molecule)
DNA polymerase attaches
the new DNA (polynucleotide) strands
replication sites join up
2 single strands act as templates for the new strands
3 free nucleotides with complementary bases slot into place, line up, and are held in place by H-bonds
1 DNA molecule unwinds and 'unzips' when the H-bonds break
4 sugar–phosphate 'backbone' is formed by condensation reactions
position of H-bonds
complementary base pairing
(enzymes not shown)
free nucleotides present in excess at replication site
5 replicated (daughter) DNA molecules each rewind into a double helix

Figure 3.6 DNA replication

The lower diagram in Figure 3.6 provides a simple summary of the process of DNA replication. The steps are outlined in more detail on the next page.

Step 1: the double helix of a DNA molecule unwinds and the hydrogen bonds holding the strands together break. As a result, the bases on both strands become exposed.

Step 2: each of the separated strands of DNA acts as a template for the production of a new polynucleotide strand with a complementary sequence of nucleotide bases.

Step 3: free nucleotides, produced by the cell earlier, are attracted to their complementary exposed bases on each template strand and become held in place by hydrogen bonds.

Step 4: condensation reactions link the new nucleotides together to form the sugar-phosphate backbone of each new strand.

Key term

Semi-conservative replication The process by which two copies of a DNA molecule are made and in which both 'parent' strands remain intact and act as templates for the formation of new, complementary, strands.

Once completed, each daughter DNA molecule rewinds into a double helix. Since one strand of each new double helix was present in the original DNA molecule and the other is a newly synthesised strand, this process is known as **semi-conservative replication**.

Of course, these reactions are catalysed by enzymes. The breakage of the hydrogen bonds and the unwinding of the DNA double helix (Step 1) is catalysed by the enzyme **DNA helicase**. The linking of nucleotides in the developing strands (Step 4) is catalysed by the enzyme **DNA polymerase**.

The upper diagrams in Figure 3.6 add a little more detail to this process. Notice that the points in the DNA molecule at which DNA helicase opens the double helix are called **replication sites**. You can see that more than one replication site occurs in each DNA molecule. This means that new strands of DNA are produced in segments that are then joined together. The joining of these segments is catalysed by another enzyme – **DNA ligase**.

DNA polymerase also has a role in 'proof reading' the new strands. Any 'mistakes' that start to happen (for example, the wrong bases pairing up) are corrected. As a result, each new DNA double helix is an exact copy of the original.

Activity

The evidence for DNA replication

The structure of DNA that you have learnt about above was first proposed by James Watson and Francis Crick in 1953. At the time, they also postulated that DNA replication would be semi-conservative. It was not until 5 years later that Matthew Meselson and Franklin Stahl devised an experiment that would test this hypothesis.

Meselson and Stahl used cultures of a bacterium commonly found in human intestines, called *Escherichia coli*. They planned to allow cells in these cultures to grow and divide and then to extract DNA from these new cells. They knew that the *E. coli* cells in a culture all divide at the same time – every 60 minutes.

1 Suggest why it was important that the cells in a culture of *E. coli* divided at the same time.

The way in which Meselson and Stahl intended to analyse the DNA they collected involved the two isotopes of nitrogen. We came across isotopes in Chapter 1, where we saw that all atoms in an element have the same number of protons and electrons but might contain different numbers of neutrons. The most commonly occurring nitrogen atoms have 14 neutrons in their nuclei but some nitrogen atoms have 15. The atoms with 15 neutrons are called 'heavy' nitrogen and represented as ^{15}N, while the more common atoms with 14 neutrons are called 'light' nitrogen and re-presented as ^{14}N.

2 Which part of DNA nucleotides contain nitrogen?

Since DNA bases contain nitrogen, Meselson and Stahl intended to follow DNA replication by labelling these bases.

They cultured *E. coli* in a medium (food source) where the available nitrogen contained only the 'heavy' nitrogen isotope, ^{15}N. They continued to do this for long enough that they could be sure that all the DNA of the bacteria was entirely 'heavy'.

Now came the clever part. They transferred these bacteria to a medium containing the normal '(light') isotope, ^{14}N, and allowed them to grow for 60 minutes.

3 What would you expect to happen during those 60 minutes?
4 What properties would you expect the new DNA strands produced by the *E. coli* to possess if replication is semi-conservative?
5 What properties would you expect the new DNA strands produced by *E. coli* to possess if the original DNA had remained intact and a completely new copy had been made from it?

Clearly, Meselson and Stahl had worked out in advance how they could detect heavy and light DNA – the differences in mass are too small to use a top-pan balance. They relied on the fact that the two DNA strands – one containing ^{14}N and the other containing ^{15}N – would have different densities. They extracted and purified DNA from bacteria that had only been grown in medium containing ^{15}N and DNA from bacteria that had been allowed to grow for 60 minutes in medium containing ^{14}N. They then placed samples of each type of DNA in separate centrifugation tubes containing a solution of a salt whose density increased from the top of the tube to the bottom of the tube. They then centrifuged the tubes.

6 What would you expect to find after centrifugation if DNA replication is semi-conservative?

Figure 3.7 shows that this is exactly what Meselson and Stahl found. It also shows the results Meselson and Stahl found when they allowed the transferred *E. coli* to divide for a second time in the medium containing ^{14}N.

1 **Meselson and Stahl** 'labelled' nucleic acid (i.e. DNA) of the bacterium *Escherichia coli* with 'heavy' nitrogen (^{15}**N**), by culturing in a medium where the only nitrogen available was as $^{15}NH_4^+$ ions, for several generations of bacteria.

2 When DNA from labelled cells was extracted and centrifuged in a density gradient (of different salt solutions) all the DNA was found to be 'heavy'.

3 In contrast, the DNA extracted from cells of the original culture (before treatment with ^{15}**N**) was 'light'.

4 Then a labelled culture of *E.coli* was switched back to a medium providing unlabelled nitrogen only, i.e. $^{14}NH_4^+$. Division in the cells was synchronised, and:
- after **one generation** all the DNA was of intermediate density (each of the daughter cells contained (i.e. *conserved*) one of the parental DNA strands containing ^{15}**N** alongside a newly synthesised strand containing DNA made from ^{14}N)
- after **two generations** 50% of the DNA was intermediate and 50% was 'light'. This too agreed with semi-conservative DNA replication, given that labelled DNA was present in only half the cells (one strand per cell).

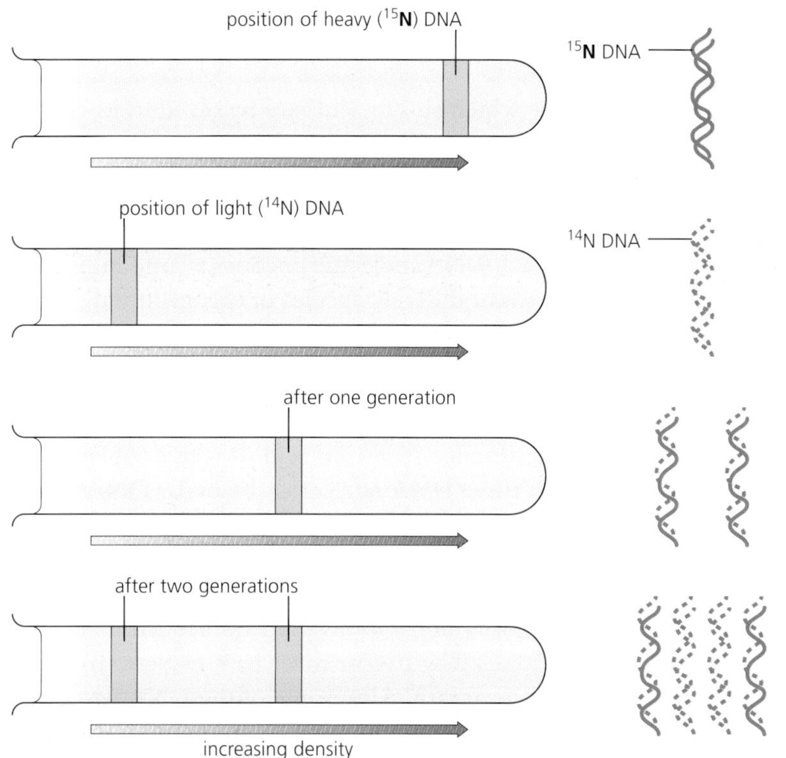

Figure 3.7 A summary of the experiment carried out by Meselson and Stahl

Test yourself

6 Explain why DNA replication is described as semi-conservative.
7 What is the importance of base pairing during DNA replication?
8 What experimental results would you expect after one generation in the Meselson–Stahl experiment in Figure 3.7 if DNA replication had been conservative?
9 What experimental results would you expect if the Meselson–Stahl experiment in Figure 3.7 had continued for three generations?
10 What causes DNA molecules to unwind during replication?

DNA and protein synthesis – the genetic code

Key term

Gene A sequence of DNA nucleotide bases that encodes the sequence of amino acids in a functional polypeptide.

The major role of DNA is to enable a cell to make specific proteins. The huge length of a single DNA molecule codes for a very large number of proteins. Within this extremely long molecule, the relatively short length of DNA that codes for the sequence of amino acids in a single polypeptide chain is called a **gene**. Proteins are very variable in size and, consequently, so are genes. A very few genes are as short as 75–100 nucleotides long. Most are at least 1000 nucleotides in length, and some are more.

Most proteins contain several hundred amino acids condensed together in a linear series. There are only 20 or so amino acids that are used in protein synthesis; all cell proteins are built from them. The unique properties of each protein lie in:

- which amino acids are involved in its construction
- the sequence in which these amino acids are joined.

The genetic code

Key terms

Genetic code A combination of three nucleotide base triplets encodes an individual amino acid. Each combination of base triplets encodes the same amino acid in all organisms, i.e. this code is universal.

Degenerate code – the genetic code is said to be degenerate because some amino acids are encoded by more than one base triplet.

Each DNA molecule encodes a large number of proteins. The DNA molecules in the cells of different species of organism will have different nucleotide base sequences, encoding proteins that are unique to each species. Despite these differences, the basis of the coding is common to all organisms.

This basis of coding – the **genetic code** – is a sequence of three nucleotide bases coding for an amino acid. It is this triplet code that is universal – the same combination of three DNA nucleotide bases (or **DNA base triplet**) codes for the same amino acid in all organisms. With four bases (C, G, A, T) there are 64 possible different triplet combinations ($4 \times 4 \times 4$). As we have already seen, only 20 amino acids are commonly used by cells. In other words, the genetic code has many more different DNA base triplet combinations than are needed to encode 20 amino acids. Many amino acids are encoded by two or three base triplets. To reflect this, we say that the genetic code is **degenerate**. Also, some of the DNA base triplets represent the 'punctuations' of the code – for example, there are 'start' and 'stop' triplets.

You can see the genetic code in Figure 3.8. The table explains the abbreviations used to represent the 20 amino acids commonly present in proteins. The circle is one way of showing the nucleotide base triplets encoding each amino acid. Notice that this code uses RNA bases, rather than a DNA bases – you can see it uses uracil (U) rather than thymine (T). You might wonder why this is. As we will shortly see, the DNA code is transcribed into messenger RNA that is used by the ribosomes to make proteins; a ribosome 'reads' RNA bases. Figure 3.8 also introduces a new term – **codon**. We use this term to describe a nucleotide base triplet on a molecule of mRNA.

Key term

Codon A nucleotide base triplet on messenger RNA that encodes a single amino acid.

The 20 amino acids used in protein synthesis

Amino acids	Abreviations
alanine	Ala
arginine	Arg
asparagine	Asn
aspartic acid	Asp
cysteine	Cys
glutamine	Gln
glutamic acid	Glu
glycine	Gly
histidine	His
isoleucine	Ile
leucine	Leu
lysine	Lys
methionine	Met
phenylalanine	Phe
proline	Pro
serine	Ser
threonine	Thr
tryptophan	Trp
tyrosine	Tyr
valine	Val

The genetic code in circular form

The codons are messenger RNA base triplets (where uracil, U, replaces thymine, T)

Read the code from the centre of the circle outwards along a radius. For example, serine is coded by UCU, UCC, UCA or UCG, or by AGU or AGC.

In addition, some codons stand for 'stop', signalling the end of a peptide or protein chain.

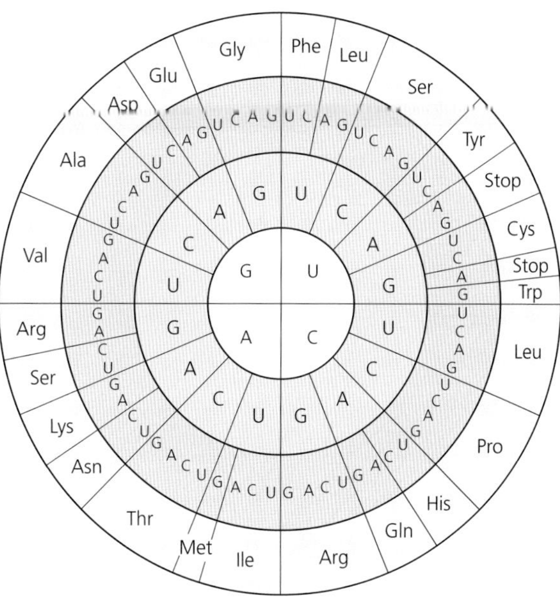

Figure 3.8 The genetic code – a universal code

Test yourself

11 Define the term *gene*.

12 Explain why different genes have different lengths.

13 Explain why the following statement is *not* true.
'The nucleus contains the cell's genetic code.'

14 What is a codon?

15 The sequence of bases in a sample of mRNA was found to be:
GGU, AAU, CCU, UUU, GUU, ACU, CAU, UGU

- **a)** Use Figure 3.8 to give the sequence of amino acids this codes for.
- **b)** Write out the sequence of bases in the antisense strand of DNA from which this mRNA was transcribed.

> **Key terms**
>
> **Antisense strand** The polynucleotide chain in a DNA molecule that is always used as a template to make mRNA, i.e. is transcribed. The order of bases in mRNA determines which amino acids are incorporated into a polypeptide (see Figure 3.8).
>
> **Non-overlapping** The property of the genetic code in which each nucleotide base forms part of only one base triplet.

The process of protein synthesis

Figure 3.9 summarises how a gene controls the production of a polypeptide. On the left-hand side, you can see the two DNA strands held together by hydrogen bonds between complementary base pairs. You can also see that the base sequence is different, depending which of the two polynucleotide chains you look at. Only one of these strands is transcribed into messenger RNA that is used by the ribosomes to make polypeptides. We call it the **antisense strand**. Now look at the right-hand side of Figure 3.9; it shows the antisense DNA code for three amino acids. The first DNA triplet is AGC. This complements the mRNA codon UCG which you can see from Figure 3.8 codes for the amino acid serine. Notice, though, that once AGC has been used the next triplet is GTG. This illustrates another important principle of the genetic code – it is **non-overlapping**. In other words, each base is part of only one triplet code. This means that the DNA base sequence in Figure 3.9 is read, from top to bottom AGC, GTG and CTG and not AGC, GCG, CGT, etc.

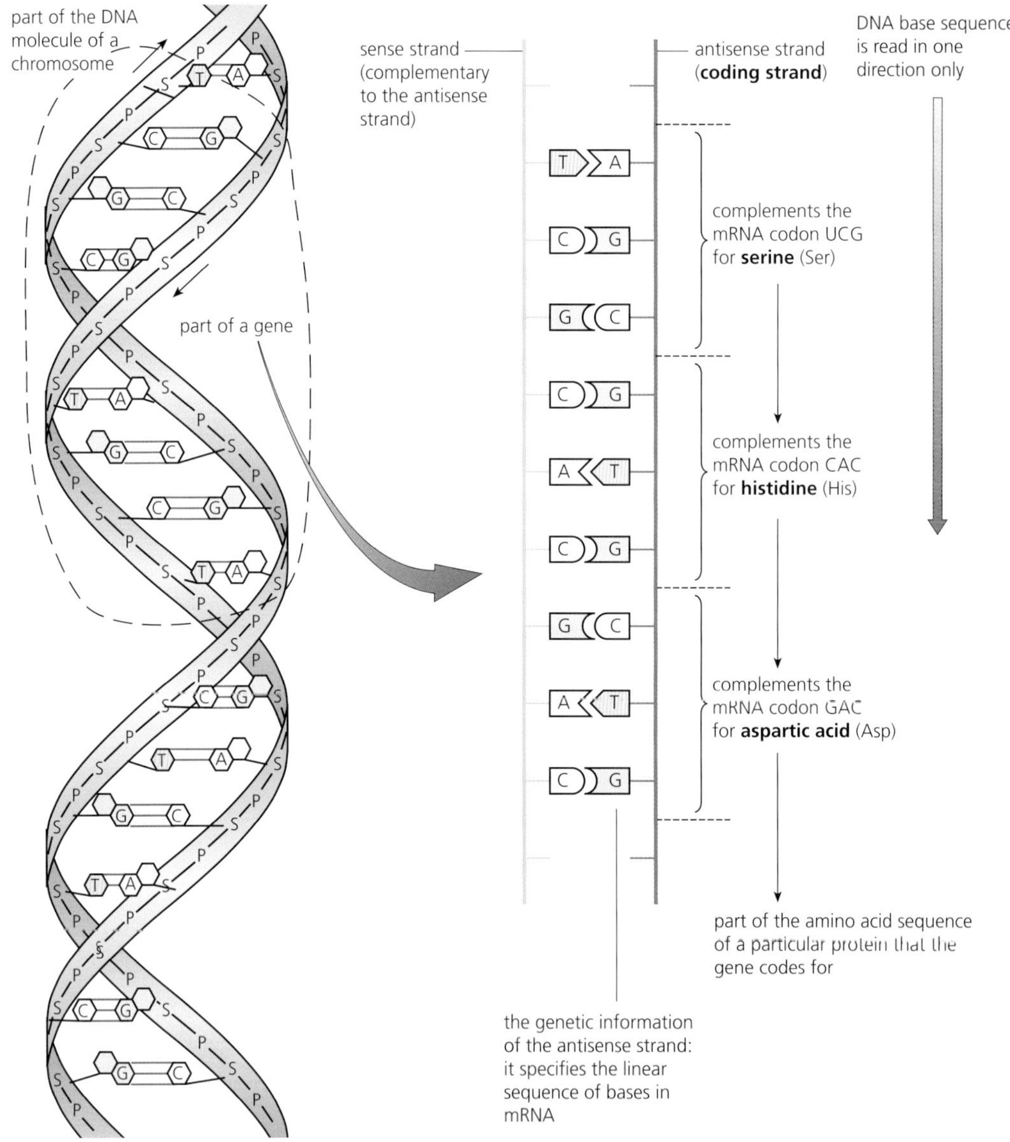

Figure 3.9 Part of a gene and how its DNA codes for amino acids

To aid understanding, we will consider protein synthesis in three stages.

Stage 1 – transcription

Figure 3.10 shows how this stage occurs in the nucleus of a eukaryotic cell and results in a gene being copied into the base sequence of **messenger RNA (mRNA)**, which then leaves the nucleus. This process is called transcription. The following events occur at the point where the gene is to be copied.

- The DNA double helix unwinds, and the hydrogen bonds holding the two strands together break. The enzyme **RNA polymerase** catalyses this reaction.
- One of the separated strands of DNA, the antisense strand, acts as a template for the formation of mRNA.

> **Key term**
>
> **Transcription** The process by which the DNA nucleotide base sequence of a gene is copied into the RNA nucleotide base sequence in a molecule of messenger RNA (mRNA).

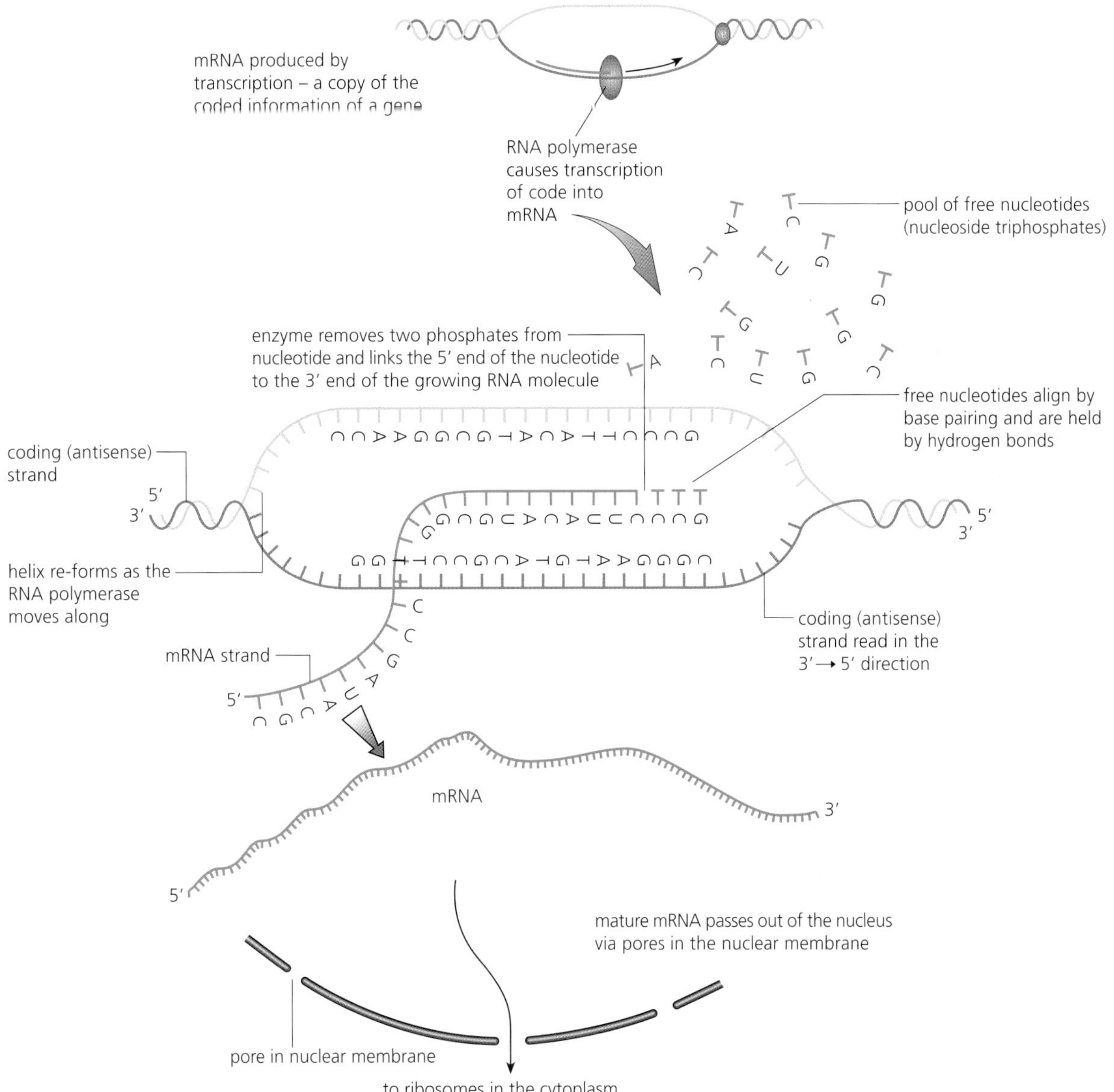

Figure 3.10 Transcription

- Free RNA nucleotides present in the nucleus pair up with the exposed nucleotides on the antisense strand. (Notice in Figure 3.10 that these free RNA nucleotides are referred to as nucleoside triphosphates. These molecules are like nucleotides but have three phosphate groups rather than just the one shown in Figure 3.1. Do not be confused by this, the presence of additional phosphates simply makes the molecules more reactive.).
- Complementary base pairing ensures that cytosine always pairs with guanine and uracil always pairs with adenine.
- **RNA polymerase** catalyses the formation of phosphodiester bonds between the RNA nucleotides, forming a molecule of messenger RNA.

Once the mRNA molecule is formed, it leaves the nucleus through pores in the nuclear membrane (Figure 3.10) and passes to tiny structures in the cytoplasm called **ribosomes** where the information can be 'read' and is used. Once the cell has finished transcribing this gene, this part of the DNA molecule rewinds.

Stage 2 – activation of amino acids

In this stage, the amino acids are activated for protein synthesis by combining with short lengths of a different sort of RNA, called **transfer RNA (tRNA)**. This activation occurs in the cytoplasm.

All molecules of tRNA have the shape of a clover-leaf, but there is a different tRNA for each of the 20 amino acids involved in protein synthesis. At one end of each tRNA molecule is a site where a particular amino acid can be joined (Figure 3.11). At the other end, there is a sequence of three bases called an **anticodon**. This anticodon is complementary to the codon of mRNA that codes for the specific amino acid.

The amino acid is attached to its tRNA by an enzyme. These enzymes are specific to the particular amino acids (and types of tRNA) to be used in protein synthesis. The specificity of the enzymes is a way of ensuring the correct amino acids are used in the right sequence.

Each amino acid is linked to a specific transfer RNA (tRNA) before it can be used in protein synthesis. This is the process of amino acid activation. It takes place in the cytoplasm.
tRNA specific for amino $acid_1$
point of amino acid attachment
+ amino $acid_1$ + ATP
$enzyme_1$
specific enzyme
tRNA–amino $acid_1$ complex
amino $acid_1$
+ AMP + $2P_i$
anticodon specific for amino $acid_1$
anticodon = three consecutive bases in tRNA, complementary to a codon on the mRNA, e.g. AAA is complementary to UUU

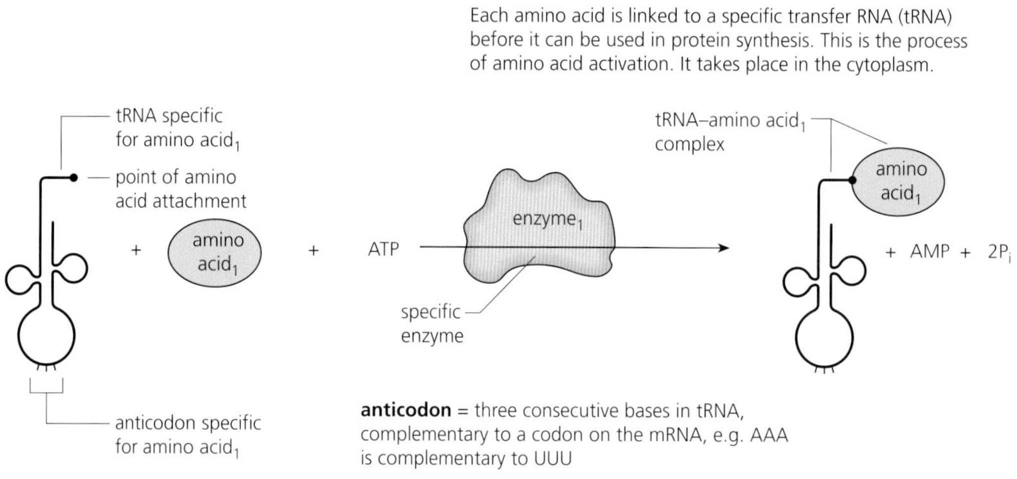

Figure 3.11 Amino acid activation

Stage 3 – translation

In this stage, a protein chain is assembled, one amino acid residue at a time (Figure 3.12). Tiny organelles called ribosomes move to the messenger RNA and move along it, 'reading' the codons from a 'start' codon. As we saw earlier in this chapter, ribosomes themselves contain RNA. In the ribosome, complementary anticodons on the amino acid–tRNAs slot into place and are temporarily held in position by hydrogen bonds. While held there, the amino acids of neighbouring amino

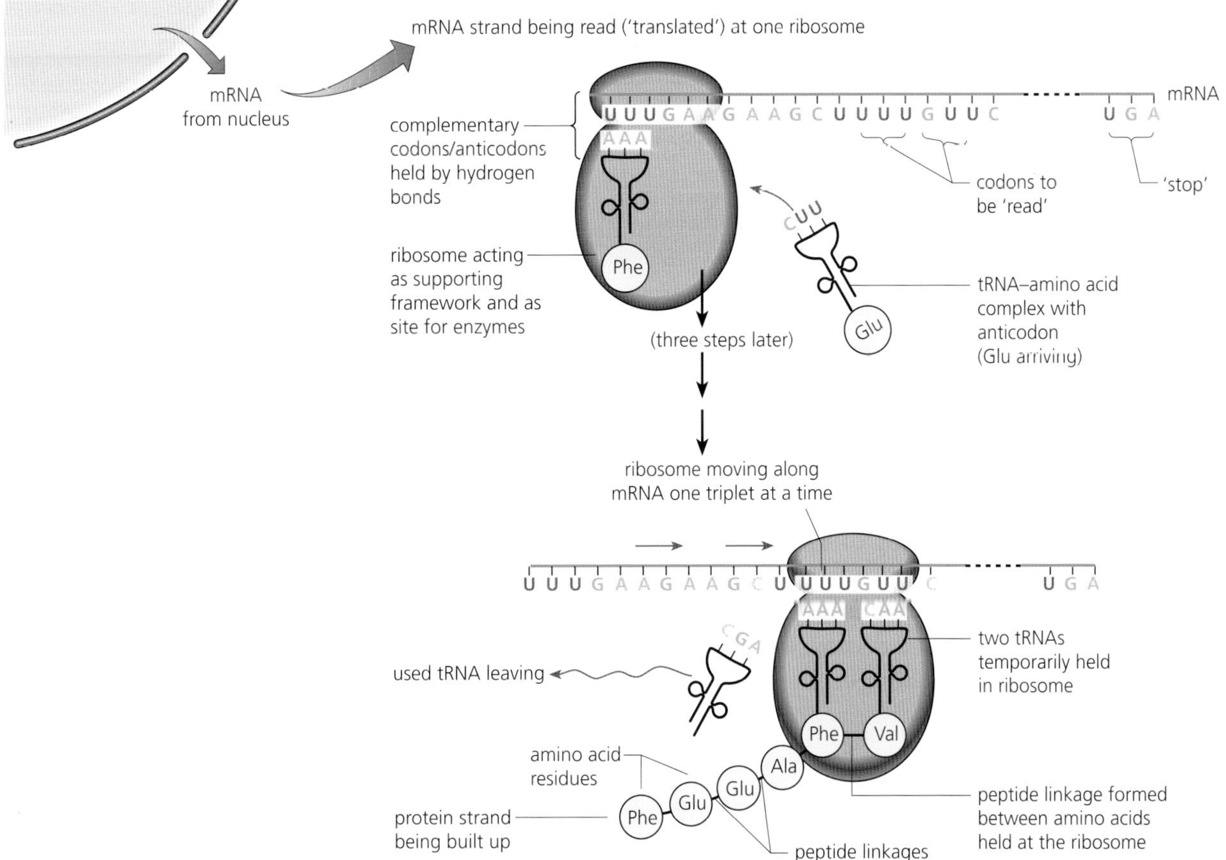

Figure 3.12 Translation

acid–tRNAs are joined by peptide bonds. This frees the first tRNA, which moves back into the cytoplasm for re-use. Once this is done, the ribosome moves on to the next mRNA codon. The process continues until a 'stop' codon occurs.

Key terms

Introns DNA base sequences within a gene that do not code for the amino acid sequence of a polypeptide. Although copied to RNA during DNA transcription, these introns are edited out of the mRNA before it leaves the nucleus.

Exons DNA base sequences within a gene that code for the amino acid sequence of a polypeptide.

Not all DNA codes for protein: mRNA editing

The DNA of eukaryotic cells (those with a nucleus – see Chapter 4) contains many non-coding sections of DNA, called **introns**. As Figure 3.12 shows, these introns lie between coding sections of DNA, called **exons**.

The mRNA first produced during transcription includes RNA copies of the introns. Before leaving the nucleus, this **pre-mRNA** is edited to remove these introns. Figure 3.13 shows how this is done.

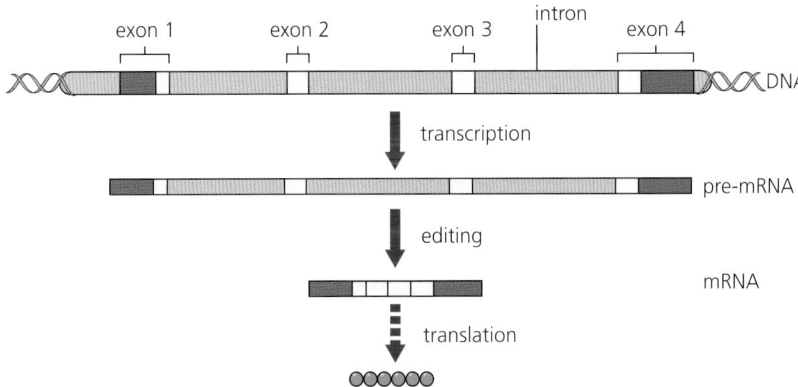

Figure 3.13 Editing of pre-mRNA in eukaryotic cells

During splicing the mRNA copies of the exons can be assembled in different orders. In this way, it is possible for a single gene to give rise to mRNA molecules with different nucleotide base sequences. This enables such a gene to code for more than one polypeptide and explains, for example, how we are able to manufacture a vast number of antibody molecules from a small number of genes.

Since the DNA of prokaryotic cells (cells without a nucleus – see Chapter 4) does not contain introns, this mRNA-editing process does not occur in these cells.

DNA can change: gene mutations

We have seen that a gene is a sequence of nucleotide bases that codes for the sequence of amino acids in a polypeptide. Normally, the sequence of nucleotides in DNA is maintained without changing but, very occasionally, it does change.

Key terms

Gene mutation A random and unpredictable change in the number, or sequence, of bases in a single gene.

Point mutation A gene mutation involving deletion, insertion or substitution of a single base.

A **gene mutation** involves a change in the number, or sequence, of bases in a particular gene. We have already noted that the enzyme machinery that brings about the building of a complementary DNA strand also 'proof reads' and corrects most errors. However, gene mutations can and do occur spontaneously during this step. Certain chemicals can also cause change to the DNA sequence of bases. So do some forms of radiation, such as X-rays. Factors that increase the chances of a mutation are called **mutagens**.

More than one type of gene mutation is possible. They include:

- **base deletion** – one or more bases lost from the sequence
- **base insertion** – one or more bases added to the sequence
- **base substitution** – one or more bases changed for a different base.

If a gene mutation involves only one base, it is described as a **point mutation**. Table 3.1 shows the effect of point mutations using English words, rather than DNA base triplets. Notice how in some cases a nonsense message is produce but in other cases a message with a new meaning is produced. With gene mutations, this could result in a non-functional polypeptide or a polypeptide with a different function.

Table 3.1 Changes in the sense of sentences using three-letter English words to represent the effect of point mutations on the code carried by DNA base triplets

Type of mutation	Effect on 'triplet code'
Normal code (no mutation)	Did you get the car
Deletion (base lost)	Did yog ett hec ar
Insertion (base added)	Did you age tth eca r
Substitution (base changed)	Did you wet the car

Sickle cell anaemia: an example of a point mutation

Sickle cell anaemia is a condition that is common among people originating from areas where malaria is endemic. It results from a point mutation in the gene that codes for the amino acid sequence of a part of the respiratory pigment haemoglobin, found in our red cells (its structure was shown in Figure 2.7). In this case, the point mutation is a base substitution – adenine replaces thymine in one base triplet – causing valine, instead of glutamic acid, to be incorporated into the polypeptide chain (Figure 3.14). The resulting, abnormal haemoglobin tends to clump together and form long fibres that distort the red cells into sickle shapes. In this condition they cannot transport oxygen efficiently and the cells may block smaller capillaries.

Anaemia is a disease typically due to a deficiency in healthy red cells in the blood.

Haemoglobin occurs in red cells – each contains about 280 million molecules of haemoglobin. A molecule consists of two α-haemoglobin and two β-haemoglobin subunits, interlocked to form a compact molecule.

The **mutation** that produces sickle cell haemoglobin (**Hg^S**) is in the gene for β-haemoglobin. It results from the substitution of a single base in the sequence of bases that make up all the codons for β-haemoglobin.

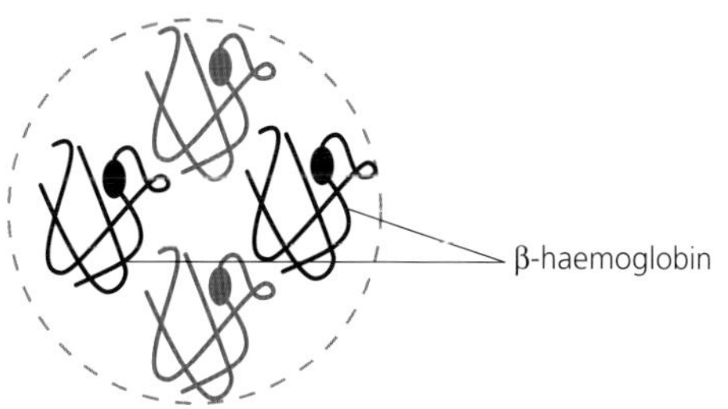

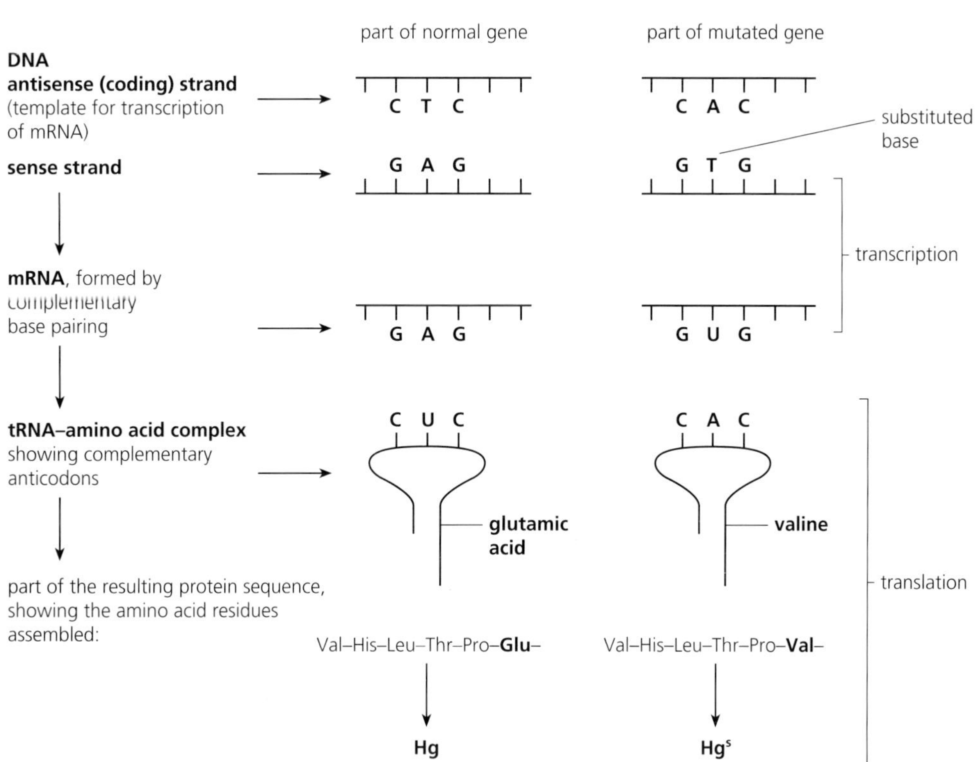

drawing based on a photomicrograph of a blood smear, showing blood of a patient with sickle cells present among healthy red cells

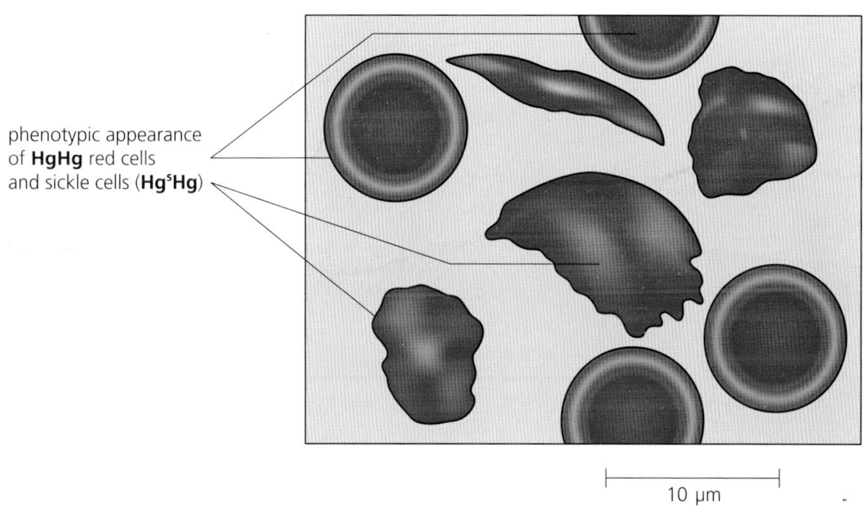

Figure 3.14 Sickle cell anaemia: an example of a point mutation

Test yourself

16 The genetic code is described as degenerate and non-overlapping. Explain what this means.

17 Distinguish between the terms *transcription* and *translation*.

18 During protein production, tRNA molecules carry amino acids to a ribosome. What ensures that the tRNA molecules are used in the correct order?

19 Explain why the RNA produced during transcription is modified before leaving a cell's nucleus.

20 What is a point mutation?

Chapter summary

Nucleotides

- Nucleotides are the monomers from which nucleic acids are made.
- Each nucleotide contains a phosphate group (PO_4^{3-}), a pentose and a nitrogen-containing organic base.
- The organic bases adenine and guanine are purines; each consists of two hydrocarbon rings. The organic bases cytosine, thymine and uracil are pyrimidines; each consists of only one hydrocarbon ring.
- In a ribonucleic acid (RNA) nucleotide, the pentose is ribose and the base is one of adenine, cytosine, guanine or uracil.
- In a deoxyribonucleic acid (DNA) nucleotide, the pentose is deoxyribose and the base is one of adenine, cytosine, guanine or thymine.
- A condensation reaction between two nucleotides forms a dinucleotide. The reaction is catalysed by an enzyme called DNA ligase.
- In a dinucleotide, the two nucleotides are linked by a phosphodiester bond between the phosphate group on carbon atom 5 of one nucleotide and a hydroxyl group attached to carbon atom 3 of the second nucleotide.

RNA molecules

- RNA molecules are single-stranded polymers of RNA nucleotides. They range from 75 nucleotides to a few thousand nucleotides in length.
- There are three types of RNA molecule. Messenger RNA (mRNA) carries a copy of a single gene to a cell's ribosomes. Transfer RNA (tRNA) carries specific individual amino acids to ribosomes during protein synthesis. Ribosomal RNA (rRNA) forms part of the structure of ribosomes.

DNA molecules

- A DNA molecule contains two polymers of DNA nucleotides. Each polymer is several million nucleotides in length.
- The two polynucleotide chains in each DNA molecule are held together by hydrogen bonds between base pairs.
- The base pairs are specific: adenine and thymine pair; cytosine and guanine pair.
- The two polynucleotide strands form a double helix.
- The sequence of bases in one of the DNA strands encodes the amino acid sequence of many polypeptides.
- A sequence of three DNA bases – a base triplet – encodes one amino acid. This is referred to as the genetic code.
- The genetic code is universal, degenerate and non-overlapping.

DNA replication

- DNA replication occurs before cells divide.
- Replication is semi-conservative. Neither strand breaks down; instead each acts as a template for the production of a new complementary strand.
- DNA helicase catalyses the breakage of hydrogen bonds and unwinding of the DNA helix. Free nucleotides form new base pairs.
- DNA polymerase catalyses the formation of two new strands of nucleotides.
- DNA ligase attaches fragments of new strands together.

DNA and protein synthesis

- Protein synthesis occurs in two stages.
- During transcription, the DNA base sequence encoding a polypeptide (i.e., a gene) is copied into molecules of mRNA.
- During translation, ribosomes 'read' the base sequence of mRNA, three bases (a codon) at a time, and join the encoded amino acids together.
- Individual amino acids are brought to ribosomes by molecules of tRNA.
- A change in the base sequence of a gene, for example, the deletion, insertion or substitution of a nucleotide, is a mutation that can affect the amino acid sequence of the encoded protein.

Practice questions

1 Which of the following statements is true of base pairing in a molecule of DNA?

A Adenine always pairs with cytosine

B Adenine always pairs with guanine

C Adenine always pairs with thymine

D Adenine always pairs with uracil *(1)*

2 Which of the following statements is true of human cells?

A The number of bases in a gene is the same as the number of amino acids in the polypeptide it codes for.

B The number of bases in a gene bears no direct relation to the number of amino acids in the polypeptide it codes for.

C The number of bases in a gene is three times the number of amino acids in the polypeptide it codes for.

D The number of bases in a gene is 64 times the number of amino acids in the polypeptide it codes for. *(1)*

3 DNA is described as a stable, information-carrying molecule.

a) What makes a DNA molecule stable? *(2)*

b) How does a DNA molecule carry 'information'? *(2)*

4 The diagram represents part of a molecule of DNA during replication. The letter C on the diagram represents the organic base cytosine and the letter T represents the organic base thymine.

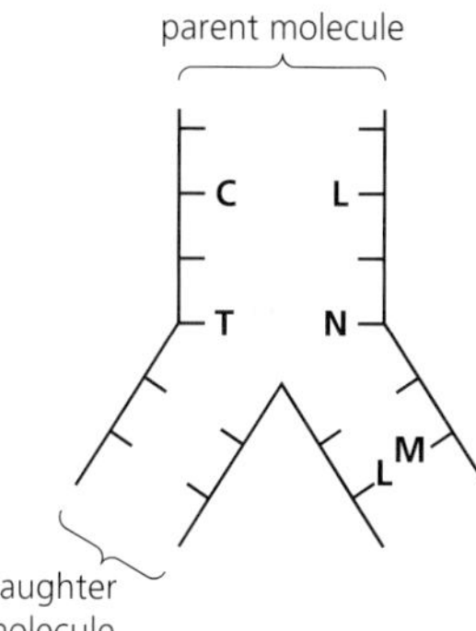

a) The letters L, M and N represent unknown organic bases. Use information in the diagram to name each. *(3)*

b) Explain what caused the parent molecule to split. *(3)*

5 The DNA in a bacterial cell is held in a single, circular molecule of DNA. A scientist analysed the bases in the DNA of a bacterial cell. The table shows her results.

DNA strand	Percentage of each base in each DNA strand			
	A	C	G	T
1	22			
2	15		33	

a) Give two ways in which the DNA of a bacterial cell is different from that of a human cell. *(2)*

b) Explain how you could find the missing values to complete the table. *(3)*

6 The diagram shows a DNA trinucleotide.

a) Explain how you can tell that this trinucleotide is from a DNA molecule. *(2)*

b) Draw a circle around one nucleotide that contains a purine. *(2)*

c) To which end of the molecule would a fourth nucleotide be added if this were a growing DNA strand? Explain your answer. *(3)*

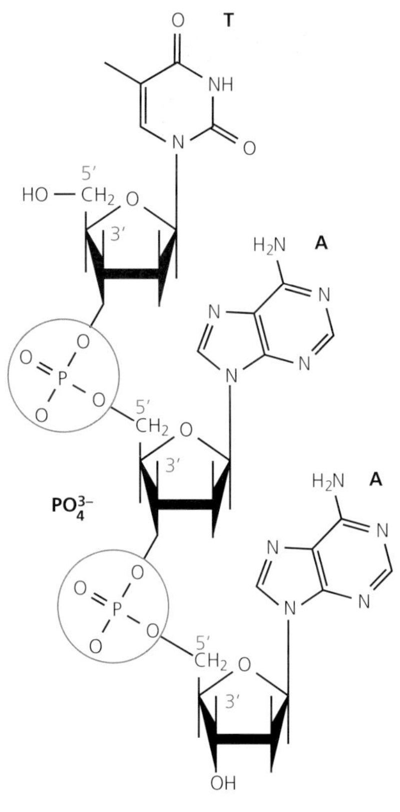

★7 Describe the roles of different types of RNA molecule during the process of translation. *(5)*

Stretch and challenge

8 The diagram represents part of a DNA molecule during DNA replication.

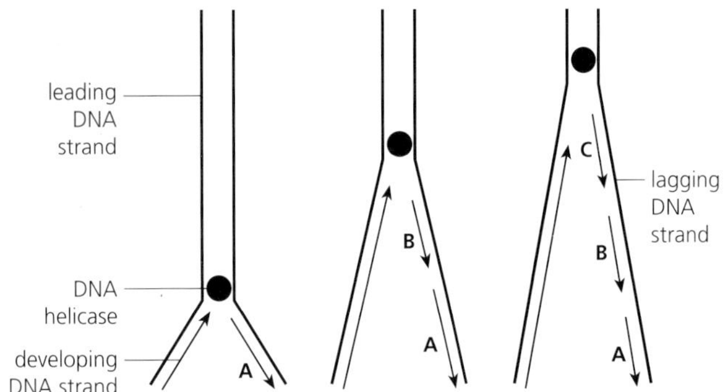

Use your knowledge of enzyme action to explain:

a) the different patterns of replication shown in the two strands of the DNA molecule

b) how the fragments A, B and C become a single strand again.

9 The process of replication you have learnt about in this chapter is catalysed by an enzyme often referred to as DNA-dependent DNA polymerase. Carry out research to find why this name is used and how the action of this enzyme differs from that of RNA-dependent DNA polymerase.

Cell structure and viruses

Prior knowledge

In this chapter you will need to recall that:

- ➜ there are two types of living cell – eukaryotic and prokaryotic
- ➜ a eukaryotic cell has a cell surface membrane surrounding cytoplasm in which there is a nucleus containing the genetic material. The nucleus is separated from the cytoplasm by a membrane, called the nuclear envelope
- ➜ some eukaryotic cells have a cell wall outside their cell surface membrane
- ➜ the cytoplasm of a eukaryotic cell contains organelles. Some of these are surrounded by membrane, including mitochondria and chloroplasts. The aerobic stages of respiration take place in mitochondria; photosynthesis occurs in chloroplasts
- ➜ a prokaryotic cell has a cell wall and a cell surface membrane surrounding its cytoplasm. It does not have a nucleus; instead its genetic material is a single, circular molecule of DNA
- ➜ some prokaryotic cells also have smaller, circular DNA molecules, called plasmids
- ➜ a virus is not a living organism. It is a particle that contains genetic material surrounded by a protein coat. It infects other cells and depends on these cells to produce more virus particles
- ➜ electron microscopy has increased our understanding of sub-cellular structures.

Test yourself on prior knowledge

1 Name **two** groups of organisms that have a cell wall.

2 Name the structures that contain the genetic material in a eukaryotic cell.

3 A eukaryotic cell is surrounded by a cell surface membrane and many of its organelles are surrounded by membranes. Do these membranes have the same structure?

4 Plants have eukaryotic cells; bacteria have prokaryotic cells. Give **two** ways in which the structure of a plant cell and a bacterial cell are:

a) similar

b) different.

5 What is the function of a mitochondrion?

6 Some cells have a cell wall. Give **one** advantage of possessing a cell wall.

Introducing cells

Key term

Cell theory Cells are the fundamental unit of structure, function and organisation in all living organisms.

In the last chapter, we came across a unifying theory in biology, which stated that the genetic code – the base triplets encoding each amino acid – is the same in all organisms. Here we come across a second: the **cell theory**. Put simply, the cell theory states that:

- cells are the smallest unit of living organisms
- all cells are derived from the division of other (pre-existing) cells
- within cells are the sites of all the chemical reactions of life (metabolism).

Key term

Unicellular Composed of a single cell.

Some organisms are made of a single cell; they are called **unicellular** organisms. Figure 4.1 shows three different unicellular organisms. You can see that the three look quite unalike. Among the differences are their size, and the possession or absence of a nucleus and a cell wall. One feature they all have in common is a plasma membrane surrounding their cytoplasm. We will examine these similarities and differences later in this chapter.

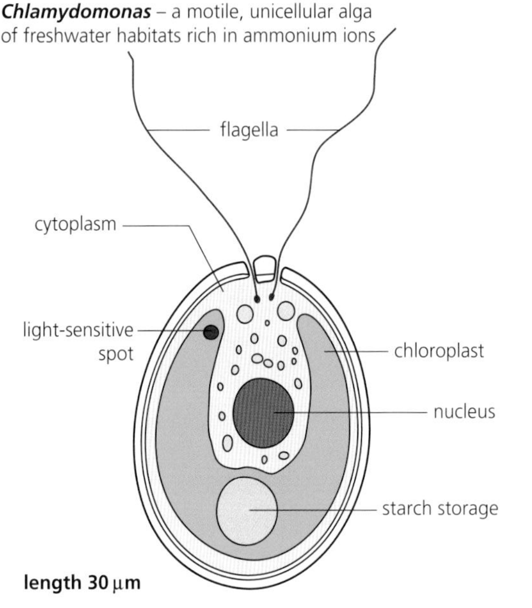

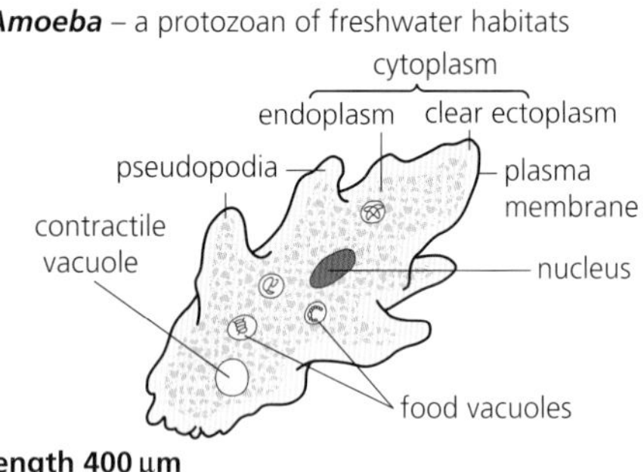

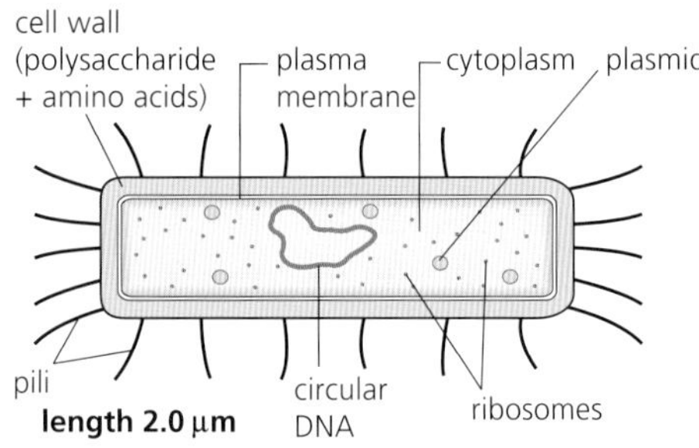

Figure 4.1 Introducing unicellular organisation

Key terms

Multicellular Composed of many cells. Usually the cells differentiate and become arranged into tissues, organs and systems, carrying out different functions.

Differentiation The developmental process by which the structure of the cells of a multicellular organism specialise, becoming adapted for a specific function.

Tissue A group of cells that have a common origin and a similar structure that work together to perform a single function.

Organ A structure, made of more than one type of tissue, that has a specific function.

System A group of organs and tissues that, collectively, perform a particular function.

Other organisms are made of many cells, and are known as **multicellular** organisms. Much of the biology in this book is about multicellular organisms, including humans, and the processes that go on in these organisms. But remember, unicellular organisms carry out all the essential functions of life too, all within the confines of a single cell.

A feature of multicellular organisms is that, after formation, their cells develop differently; they become specialised for the functions they carry out. We call this process **differentiation**. A common outcome of this is that many fully specialised cells are no longer able to divide. But as a consequence of specialisation, cells show great variety in shape and structure, as we will see.

The cells of a multicellular organism are not arranged at random. Instead, cells with a common origin, that have differentiated to perform a particular function, group together as a **tissue**. Blood is an example of an animal tissue; you will look at blood in more detail in Chapter 11. Xylem is an example of a plant tissue; you will look at xylem in more detail in Chapter 12.

Sometimes, many tissues work together to perform a particular function. For example the heart, which pumps the blood around the body of a mammal (Chapter 11), contains epithelial tissue, muscle tissue, connective tissue and nervous tissue. A structure that performs a particular function but is made of more than one tissue is called an **organ**. As you know, the heart, together with blood vessels and blood, forms the circulatory **system**. This general pattern in which complex, multicellular organisms are organised is shown in Figure 4.2.

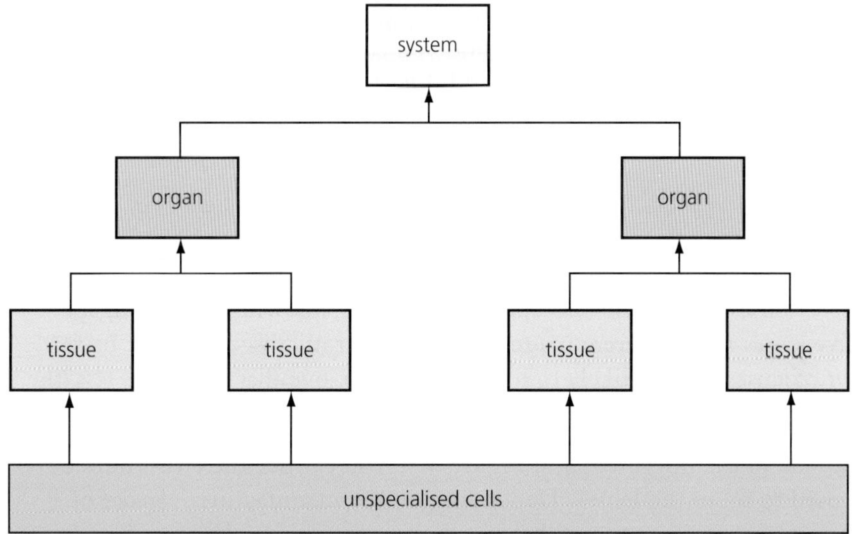

Figure 4.2 The specialised cells of complex multicellular organisms are arranged into tissues, organs and systems

Studying cells

Before going any further, we need to consider how we can study cells. Although a few are just large enough to be seen with the naked eye, cells are extremely small. To study their structure, we need to magnify them. In your college or school laboratory, you will use a compound light microscope. It is called a light microscope because it uses light to view an object. It is called a compound microscope because each of its 'lenses' contains more than one glass lens. Figure 4.3 shows an example of a compound light microscope. The ones in your college or school laboratory might be different from this, but they will have similar features.

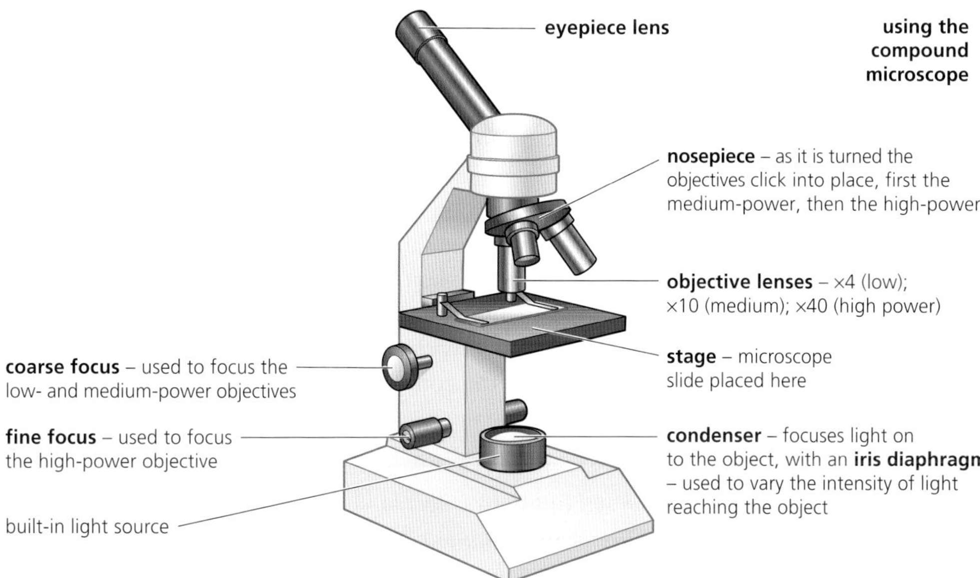

Figure 4.3 A compound light microscope

First, look at the three sets of lenses. One set focuses light before it hits the specimen to be viewed. It is called the **condenser lens** and you can see it near the base of the microscope. The microscope in Figure 4.3 has a built-in light within the condenser. Yours might be the same or you might have a concave mirror there instead. If so, you will need to use light from a window or from a bench lamp.

The other two sets of lenses focus light after it has passed through the specimen to be viewed. The one you will look down is called the **eyepiece lens**. Lower down the microscope is a second set of lenses, called the **objective lenses**. In Figure 4.3, you can see three objectives lenses housed on a nosepiece that rotates, allowing you to engage different objective lenses with different magnifications. Your microscope might have a different number of lenses but it is likely to have at least two: one that magnifies less (the low-power objective lens) and one that magnifies more (the high-power objective lens).

Now look at the side of the microscope in Figure 4.3. You can see the two knurled screws that are used to focus the lenses. Depending on the manufacturer's make of microscope, when you turn these you either move the stage or the objective lenses up and down. The upper one allows a coarse focus; if you turn this, the stage or the objective lens moves a greater distance than if you turn the lower, fine-focus screw.

Finally, there is the stage of the microscope. You will place the specimen to be viewed here and use the two clips to hold it in place. Because light passes through the specimens you view, they must be very thin. You achieve this either by cutting very thin slices of tissue or by squashing tissue. The surface you use to support these thin preparations must also allow light to pass through, so you use glass slides. (Remember to wear eye protection when using glass slides and coverslips.) There are two types of preparation you can view using a light microscope:

- A **temporary preparation**. This involves placing tissue on a glass slide, covering it with a water-based liquid to prevent it drying out, and putting an extremely thin glass **coverslip** over it.
- A **permanent preparation**. In this type of preparation, the water has been removed from the tissue and been replaced by a firmer substance. The coverslip is held in place by a resin.

Cells are usually translucent. To help you to see their structures, chemicals are added that react with cell components. They are called **stains** and, since they colour parts of the cell, staining is a key process to help you identify cell structures.

Figure 4.4 shows two cells viewed using a compound light microscope. One is a plant cell, the other a human cell. For reasons we will examine shortly, you can see very little cell detail. Cell walls and chloroplasts are visible in the plant cells. A nucleus and granules are visible in the human cell. You cannot see a membrane surrounding either cell, though we assume it must be there, and you cannot see much within the cytoplasm. Before examining why so little detail is visible, let's look at one of the core practicals you must carry out.

Test yourself

1 In biology, differentiation has a unique meaning. Explain what it means.
2 Is your stomach a tissue, an organ or a system? Explain your answer.
3 What is the function of the condenser lens in a compound microscope?
4 Why do biologists stain tissue to be viewed using a microscope?
5 How do you avoid trapping air bubbles when you are making a temporary mount of tissue?

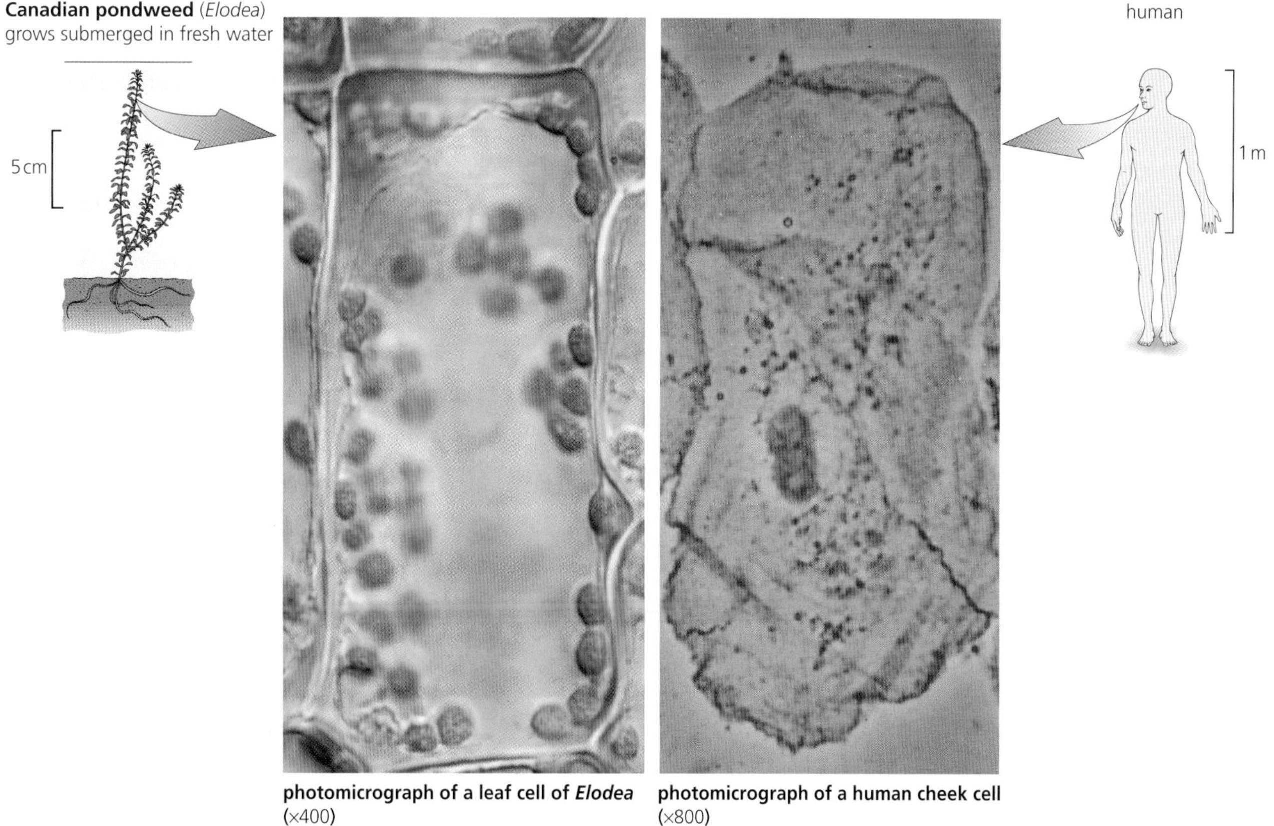

Figure 4.4 Animal and plant cells

Core practical 2

Use of the light microscope, including simple stage and eyepiece micrometers and drawing small numbers of cells from a specialised tissue

This core practical involves three skills: using a compound light microscope safely, measuring the actual size of cells observed using a compound light microscope and drawing a small number of these cells. Let's deal with them in that order.

Using the microscope safely

Although it looks robust, the microscope is very delicate. A slight knock might damage the alignment of the lenses within the eyepiece or objective lens arrangements. Consequently, you should treat the microscope with care.

1. If you are carrying a microscope from a storage area to your bench, use both hands - one supporting the base and the other holding the arm of the microscope.
2. Place the microscope on the bench so that its base is flat and it is far enough away from the edge of the bench to reduce the risk of it falling off. Adjust your seating so that you can comfortably adjust the focusing screws and look down the eyepiece.
3. Ensure the built-in lamp is set at its minimum setting before plugging in the power cable. Then adjust the lamp to about two-thirds of maximum setting.
4. Select a low-power objective lens by rotating the nosepiece. When the lens is correctly in place, you will hear a 'click'.
5. Look at a prepared slide to locate the specimen. Then put the slide onto the stage so that the coverslip is facing upwards and the specimen is located centrally below the objective lens.

Tip

The objective lenses of a compound microscope are very expensive. It is critical you do not push one into the specimen to be viewed when you are turning a focus screw. To avoid this, if you are looking down the eyepiece lens, only ever turn the screw to move an objective lens *away* from the specimen. If you need to move the objective lens towards the specimen, watch the bottom of the objective lens from the side of the microscope, so you can be certain it does not touch the specimen.

6 View the specimen by looking down the eyepiece lens. Focus the image of the specimen, first using the coarse focus control and then the fine focus control. To avoid eyestrain, try to keep both eyes open while looking down the eyepiece lens.
7 Notice that the image of the specimen is upside down and back-to-front compared with looking at the specimen directly. The same will be true when you move the slide around. If you push it to your left, the image will move to your right and vice versa.
8 Focus the condenser by placing a sharp object, such as a mounted needle, on the centre of the light source. Adjust the condenser lens until the specimen and the sharp object are in focus together. You are now ready to use the microscope.

Measuring the actual size of cells

Look at Figure 4.5, which summarises the method you used for measuring the size of cells. In this case, the specimen is a blood smear, but the principles are the same whatever specimen you used.

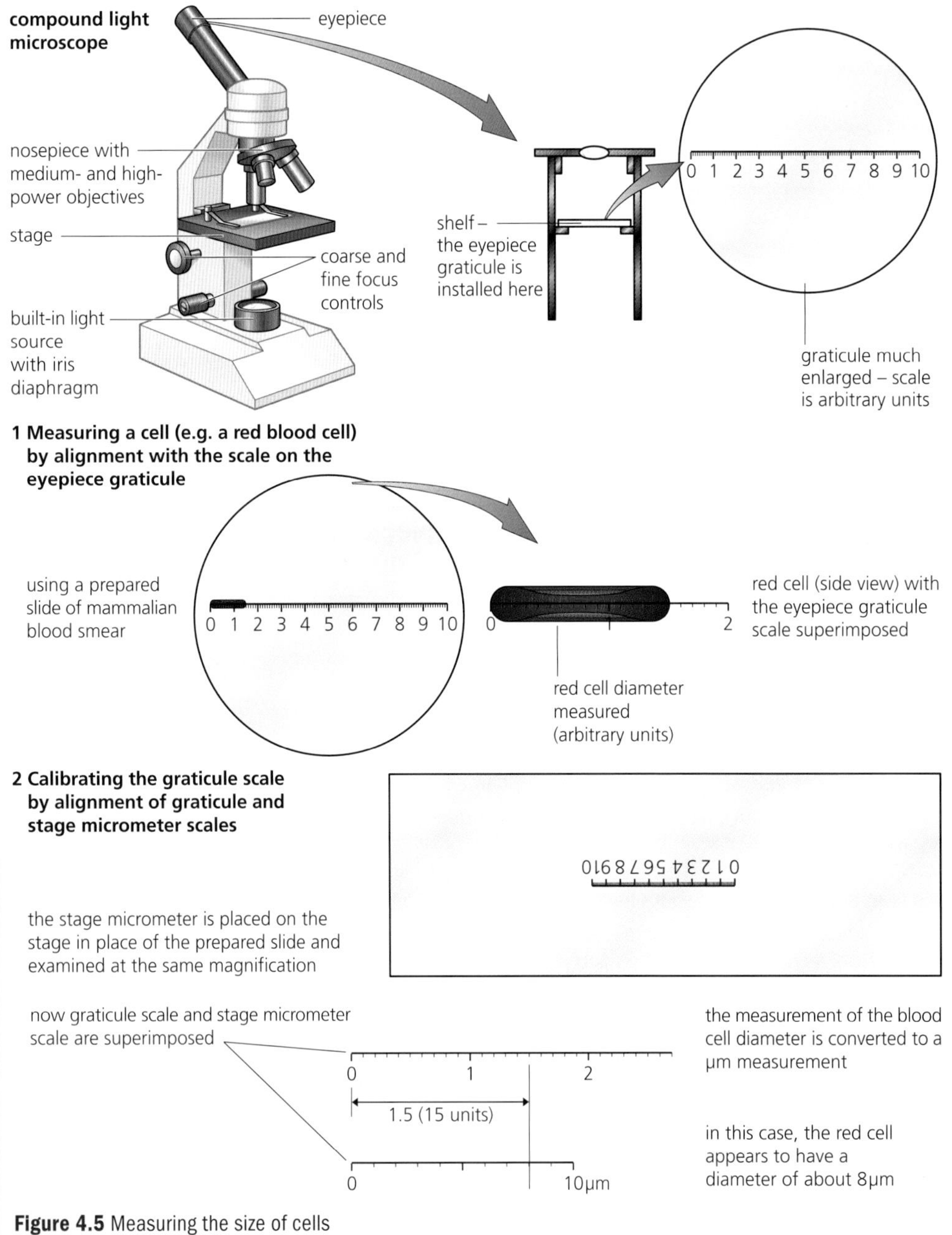

Figure 4.5 Measuring the size of cells

The first step involves inserting a graticule into the eyepiece lens.

1 Describe how you did this. Include in your description any precautions you took.
2 The graticule has a graduated line across it. How did you ensure this appeared horizontal when you placed the eyepiece back into the microscope and viewed cells?
3 Figure 4.5 shows a single red blood cell against the graticule. What can you deduce about the size of this cell?
4 How did you calibrate your graticule?
5 What is the actual diameter of the red blood cell in Figure 4.5?

Drawing small numbers of cells

view (phase contrast) of the layer of the cells (epithelium) lining the stomach wall

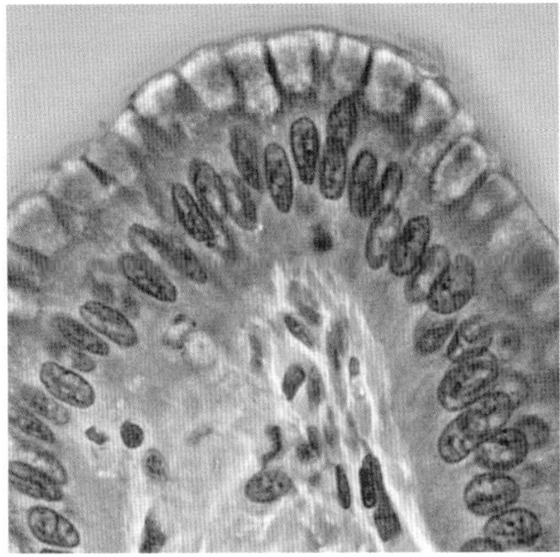

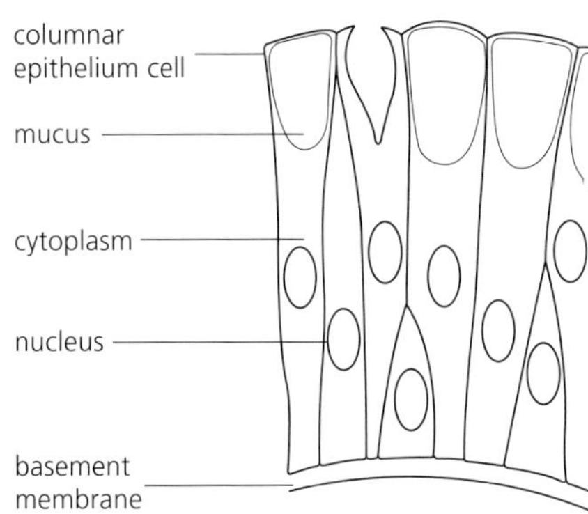
The lining of the stomach consists of columnar epithelium. All cells secrete mucus copiously.
columnar epithelium cell
mucus
cytoplasm
nucleus
basement membrane

Figure 4.6 Recording cell structure by drawing

6 How did your drawings to show the distribution of tissues differ from your drawings to show cell structure?
7 Describe how you ensured that your drawings of a small group of cells accurately represented what you saw using a light microscope.

Digital microscopy

These days, scientists rarely draw the cells and tissues they observe under a microscope. Instead they use a digital microscope or, alternatively, connect an appropriate camera using a microscope coupler or eyepiece adaptor that replaces the standard microscope eyepiece. Images can be displayed directly on a VDU monitor or saved to a computer hard drive, from which they can be retrieved and printed. This technique of **digital microscopy** is shown in Figure 4.7.

Test yourself

6 What is the function of a cell's nucleus?
7 Biologists use a basic stain when staining nuclei. Suggest why.
8 Within a multicellular organism cells show great variety in shape and structure. Explain why.
9 A cell is reported to be 0.000 38 m long. Express this measurement using a more suitable unit of length.
10 The cell theory is a unifying theory in biology. In your own words, give **three** of its component statements.

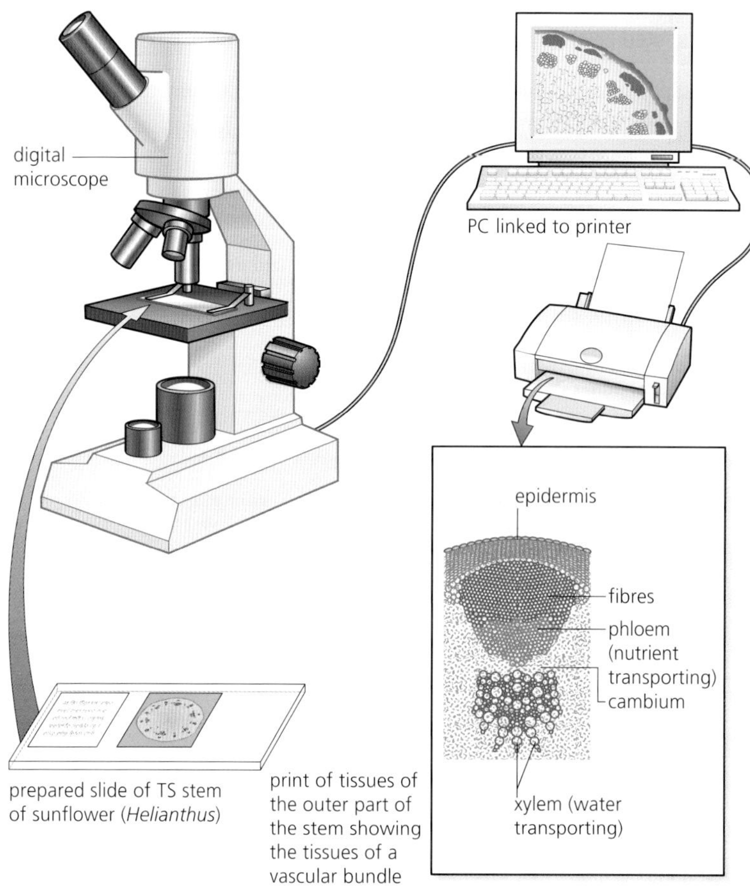

Figure 4.7 Digital microscopy in action

Key term

Magnification The extent to which an object has been enlarged by a microscope, in a drawing or in a photograph.

Tip

You need to be confident in converting units. It might help you remember how to convert units of length if you work in steps of 1000 (10^3). Thus, 1 m = 10^3 mm = 10^6 µm = 10^9 nm. This series (milli, micro and nano) is also true for other units, such as units of mass and volume. Notice that if you follow this advice, you will not measure length in centimetres (cm).

Magnification and resolution of an image

We can now return to our earlier observation regarding Figure 4.4, namely, that we could not see much detail of the cell structure. You might think we could overcome this by increasing the **magnification**, in other words the number of times larger an image is than the specimen. The magnification obtained with a compound microscope depends on which of the lenses you use. For example, using a ×10 eyepiece and a ×10 objective lens, the image is magnified 100 times (10 × 10). When you switch to the ×40 objective lens with the same eyepiece lens, the magnification becomes 400 times (10 × 40). These are the most likely orders of magnification you will use in your laboratory work.

Theoretically, there is no limit to magnification. For example, if a magnified image is photographed, further enlargement can be made photographically. This is what usually happens with photomicrographs shown in books and articles. We can find the magnification using the formula:

$$\text{magnification} = \frac{\text{size of image}}{\text{size of specimen}}$$

For example, suppose a plant cell with a diameter of 150 µm is photographed with a microscope and its image enlarged photographically so that its diameter on the print is 150 mm diameter (150 000 µm). The magnification is:

$$\frac{150\,000}{150} = 1000 \text{ times}$$

If a further enlargement is made, to show the same cell at 300 mm diameter (300 000 μm), the magnification would be:

$$\frac{300\,000}{150} = 2000 \text{ times}$$

In this case, the image size has been doubled but the detail will be no greater. You will not be able to see, for example, details of cell membrane structure, however much the image is enlarged. This is because the layers making up a cell's membrane are too thin to be seen as separate structures using the light microscope.

Example

Using scale bars to determine actual size and magnification

photomicrograph of *Amoeba proteus* (living specimen) – phase contrast microscopy

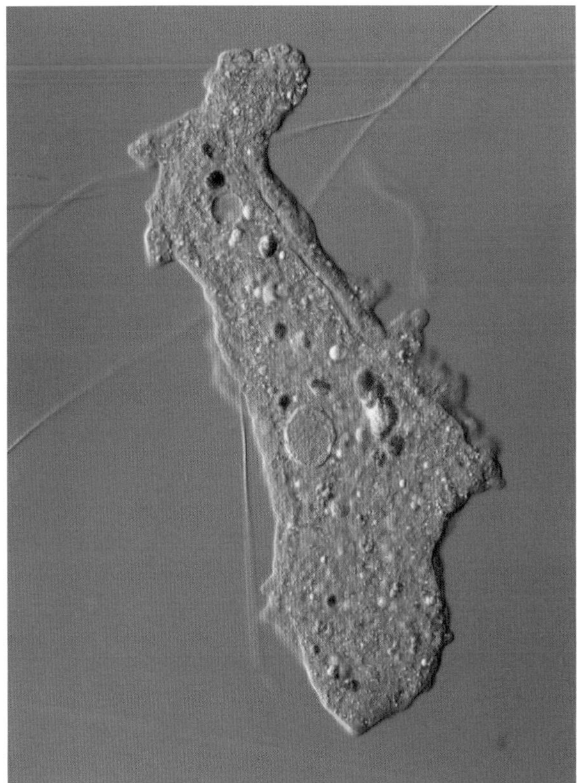

interpretive drawing

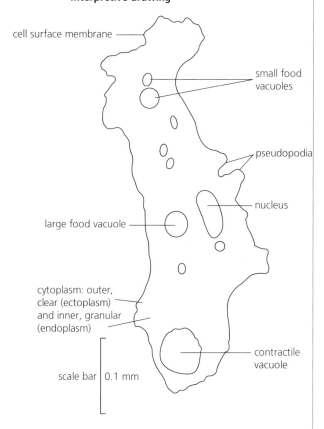

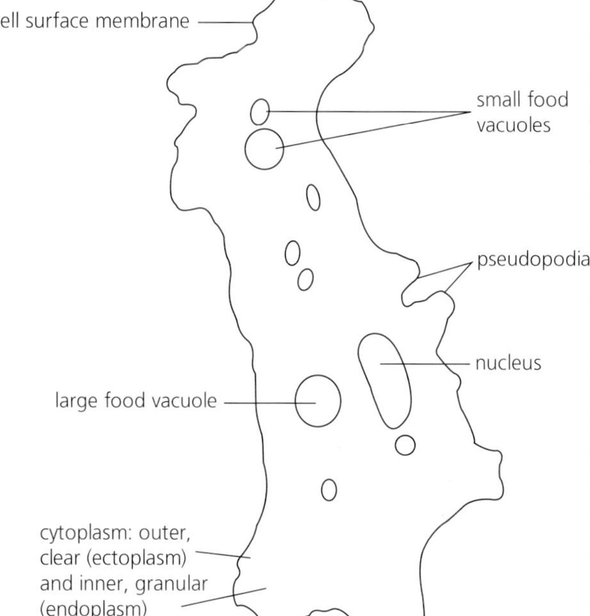

Figure 4.8 Using a scale bar to record size

Once the size of a cell has been measured, a scale bar line may be added to a micrograph or drawing to record the actual size of the structure. This has been done in the photomicrograph and drawing of a single-celled organism called *Amoeba proteus* in Figure 4.8.

1 What is the length of the scale bar in Figure 4.8?

2 What is the length of the drawing of the cell shown in Figure 4.8?

3 Use both your measurements to calculate the actual length of the cell in Figure 4.8.

4 Now calculate the magnification of the drawing in Figure 4.8, using the formula:

$$\text{magnification} = \frac{\text{size of image}}{\text{size of specimen}}$$

Answers

1 Using a rule with millimetre divisions, you should have measured the length of the scale bar as 20 mm.

2 You should have found that the cell is 100 mm long.

3 The actual length is $\frac{100}{20} \times 0.1 = 0.5\,\text{mm}$.

4 The magnification is $\frac{100}{0.5} = \times 200$.

Key term

Resolution The ability to distinguish between points that are very close together. The limit of resolution for a light microscope is about 2 µm (2000 nm) whereas that of a transmission electron microscope is about 5 nm.

Although we could, theoretically, increase magnification indefinitely, doing so would not show us more detail of cell structure. The problem is not magnification but the nature of light itself. Look around the room. How can you distinguish between objects within it? Apart from different colours or textures, you can see space between them. This is fine with large objects but not with tiny ones that are extremely close together. The wavelength of light is such that it cannot pass between these tiny objects. The ability to distinguish tiny objects that are extremely close together is termed resolving power, or **resolution**. If two separate objects cannot be resolved they will be seen as one object. Merely enlarging them will not separate them. Using a light microscope, the limit of resolution is about 0.2 µm. This means that two objects less than 0.2 µm apart will always be seen as one object however much we magnify them using a light microscope.

So, how can we see greater detail of cell structure? The answer is to use radiation with a shorter wavelength than light. Most commonly, we use electrons in an electron microscope. Because an electron beam has a much shorter wavelength than light rays, the resolving power of an electron microscope is much greater than the best light microscopes. Used with biological materials, the limit of resolution in transmission electron microscopy is about 5 nm. Look at Figure 4.9 where the detailed structure of the chloroplast can be seen using a transmission electron microscope. This amount of detail cannot be seen with a light microscope.

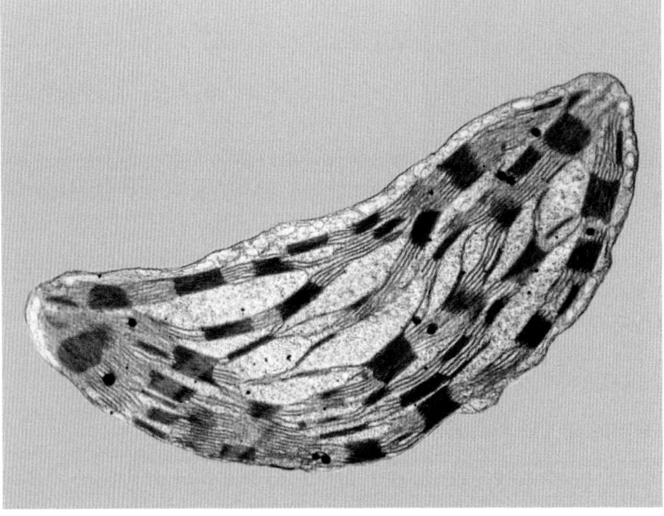

Figure 4.9 Chloroplast enlarged (× 6000) from a transmission electron micrograph

Electron microscopy – the discovery of cell ultrastructure

In an electron microscope, a beam of electrons is used to produce a magnified image in much the same way as the optical microscope uses light. The electron beam is generated by an electron gun and is focused using electromagnets, rather than glass lenses. Since we cannot see electrons, the electron beam is focused onto a fluorescent screen for viewing, or onto a photographic plate for permanent recording. You can see these features in Figure 4.10. Notice the outlet to a vacuum pump in the diagram. Electrons would be deflected by molecules in the air, so the large red column you can see in Figure 4.10 holds the specimen inside a vacuum.

With a **transmission electron microscope**, the electron beam is passed through an extremely thin section of material. Membranes and other structures present are stained with heavy metal ions, making them electron-opaque, so they stand out as dark areas in the image. You can see a technician using a transmission electron microscope in Figure 4.10.

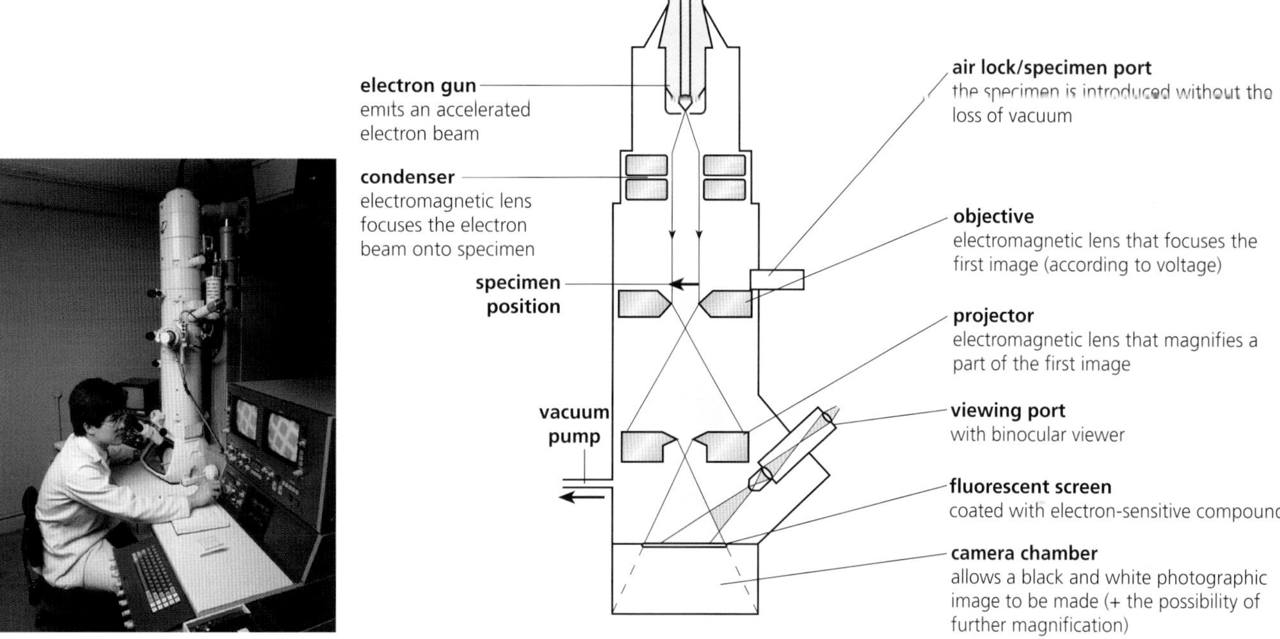

Figure 4.10 A transmission electron microscope

Only transmission electron microscopes can resolve the fine detail of the contents of cells, the organelles and cell membranes, known as **cell ultrastructure** and shown in Figure 4.11. Note that the photograph of a specimen viewed using a transmission electron microscope is called a transmission electron micrograph (TEM).

Key term

Cell ultrastructure The structure of cells seen using a microscope with a high degree of resolution, usually a transmission electron microscope.

Test yourself

11 A student is using a compound microscope to study plant tissue at an institution that does not have graticules or stage micrometers. Suggest how this student could use a ruler to estimate the length of a plant cell in the tissue he is viewing.

12 An *Amoeba proteus* is shown in Figure 4.8.

a) What is the evidence that this organism is *not* a plant?

b) In fact, *Amoeba proteus* is a eukaryotic unicell. Explain the meaning of 'eukaryotic' and 'unicell'.

13 Explain the advantage of using a transmission electron microscope rather than a compound light microscope to study cell structure.

TEM of liver cells (×15 000)

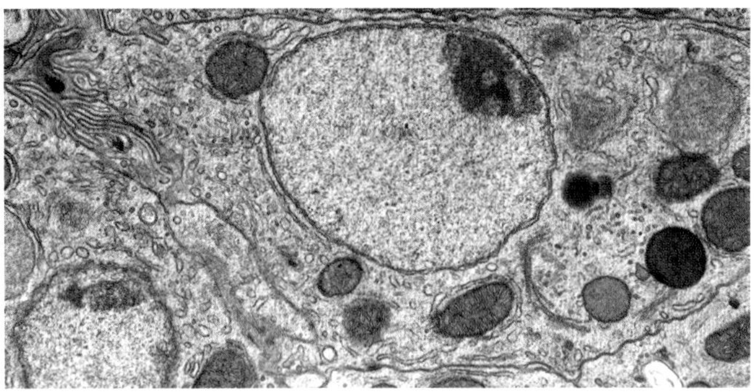

interpretive drawing

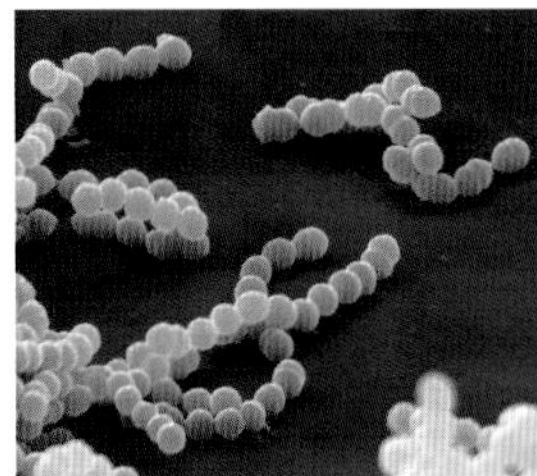

Figure 4.12 A scanning electron micrograph (SEM)

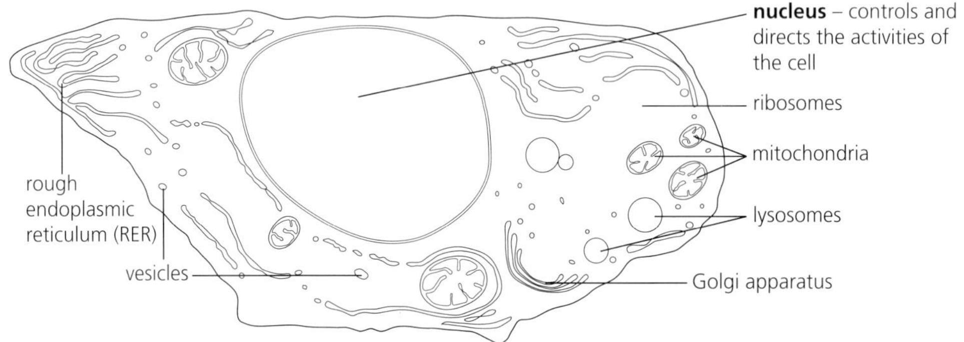

Figure 4.11 Transmission electron micrograph (TEM) of mammalian liver cells with an interpretative drawing

Tip

To answer Question 15 you need to convert micrometres (μm) to nanometres (nm).

With a scanning electron microscope, a narrow electron beam is scanned back and forth across the surface of the specimen. Electrons that are reflected or emitted from this surface are detected and converted into a three-dimensional image, such as the one in Figure 4.12.

Test yourself

14 Suggest **one** disadvantage of using a transmission electron microscope rather than a compound light microscope to study cells.

15 The resolving power of a light microscope is given as 2 μm and that for a transmission electron microscope as 5 nm. How many times greater is the resolving power of the electron microscope than the light microscope? Show your working.

The discovery of two types of cell organisation

Electron microscopy has disclosed two entirely different types of cellular organisation, based on the presence or absence of a nucleus.

The cells of animals, fungi, plants and protoctists have a large, obvious nucleus. The surrounding cytoplasm contains many different membrane-bound organelles. These cells are called **eukaryotic cells** (meaning cells with a 'true nucleus'). We will examine this type of cell organisation first.

In contrast, bacteria contain no nucleus and their cytoplasm does not have any membrane-bound organelles. They are called **prokaryotic cells** (meaning cells 'before the nucleus'). Another key difference between the cells of the prokaryotes and eukaryotes is their size. Prokaryote cells are exceedingly small – about the size of individual mitochondria or chloroplasts found in the cells of eukaryotes. We will return to prokaryotic cells later in this chapter.

Key terms

Eukaryotic cell A cell with a nucleus and membrane-bound organelles in its cytoplasm.

Prokaryotic cell A cell that does not (and never did) have a nucleus or membrane-bound organelles. Bacteria are prokaryotic.

The ultrastructure of eukaryotic cells

Today, the eukaryotic cell is seen as a 'bag' of **organelles**, most of which are made of membranes. The fluid around the organelles is an aqueous solution of chemicals, called the **cytosol**. The cytosol and organelles are contained within a special membrane, the **cell surface membrane**. The detailed structure of this membrane, and the processes by which it is crossed by all the metabolites that move between the cytosol and the environment of the cell, will be discussed in Chapter 9.

Our picture of the arrangement of organelles enclosed by the cell surface membrane of a cell has been built up by the examination of numerous transmission electron micrographs (TEMs). This detailed picture, referred to as the ultrastructure of cells, is represented diagrammatically in Figure 4.13. TEMs of an animal and plant cell, together with an interpretive drawing, are shown in Figure 4.14.

> **Key term**
>
> **Organelle** A structure within the cytoplasm of eukaryotic cells that performs a discrete function. With the exception of ribosomes, organelles are surrounded by at least one layer of membrane, in other words they are membrane-bound.

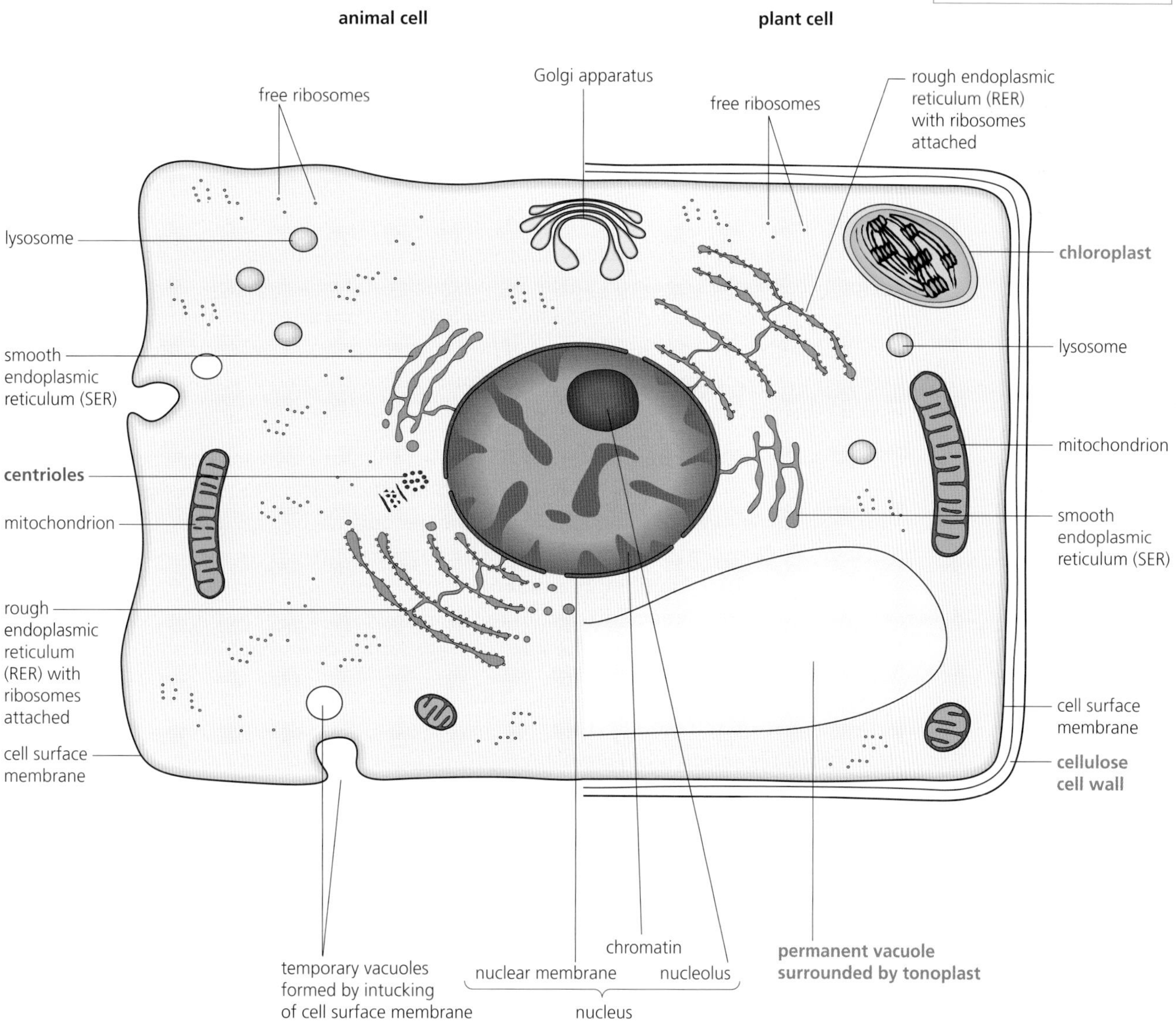

Figure 4.13 The ultrastructure of an animal and plant cell

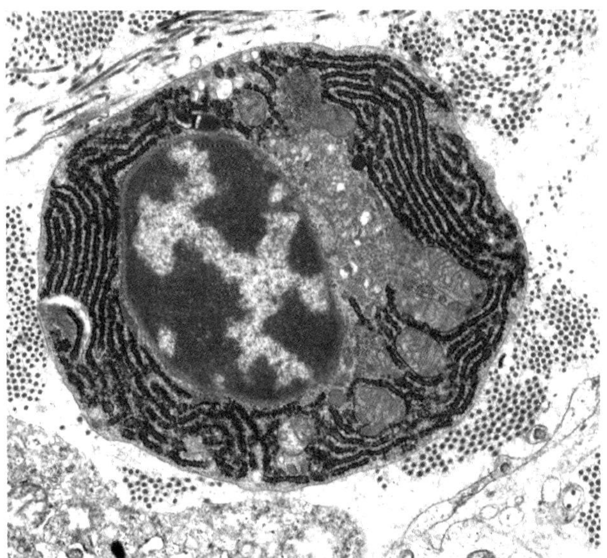
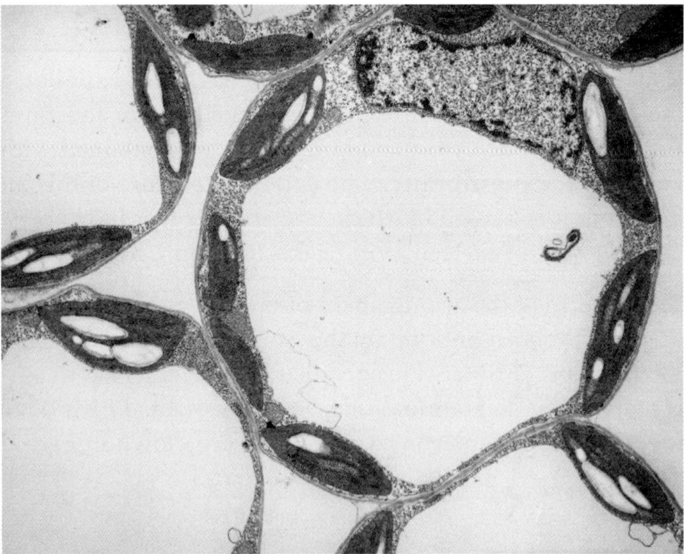

Figure 4.14 TEMs of a mammalian plasma cell and a plant palisade mesophyll cell

Introducing the organelles

Nucleus

The everyday role of the nucleus in protein synthesis has already been described in Chapter 3. It is the largest organelle in the eukaryotic cell, typically 10–20 μm in diameter. It is surrounded by a double **nuclear membrane** that contains many pores, each only about 100 nm in diameter. These nuclear pores allow movement of molecules between the cytoplasm and the nucleus, for example the movement of mRNA that you saw in Chapter 3.

The nucleus contains **chromosomes**. Figure 4.15 shows how each chromosome contains a long strand of DNA wound around beads of histone, a type of protein. The chromosomes are visible using a light microscope only at the time the nucleus divides (Chapter 5). At other times, the chromosomes appear dispersed as a diffuse network, called **chromatin**. One or more **nucleoli** (singular nucleolus) may be present in the nucleus. These rounded, dark-staining bodies are the site of ribosome synthesis. Chromatin, chromosomes and the nucleolus are visible only if stained with certain dyes.

Most eukaryotic cells contain one nucleus but there are interesting exceptions. For example, mature red blood cells of mammals (Chapter 11) and mature sieve tube elements in the phloem of flowering plants (Chapter 12) are both without a nucleus; they lose it as they mature. Voluntary muscle cells and the thin, thread-like mycelia of fungi contain cytoplasm with many nuclei (they are multinucleate).

Key term

Crista One of the many folds of the inner membrane of a mitochondrion, where the chemicals involved in ATP synthesis during aerobic respiration are located.

Mitochondria

Mitochondria are rod-shaped organelles, typically 0.5–1.5 μm diameter, and 3.0–10.0 μm long. Like nuclei, each mitochondrion has a double membrane. You can see in Figure 4.16 (page 84) that the outer membrane forms a smooth boundary whereas the inner membrane is infolded to form cristae (singular crista). The interior of the mitochondrion contains an aqueous solution of metabolites and enzymes, called the **matrix**. Small circular molecules of DNA are also located in the matrix.

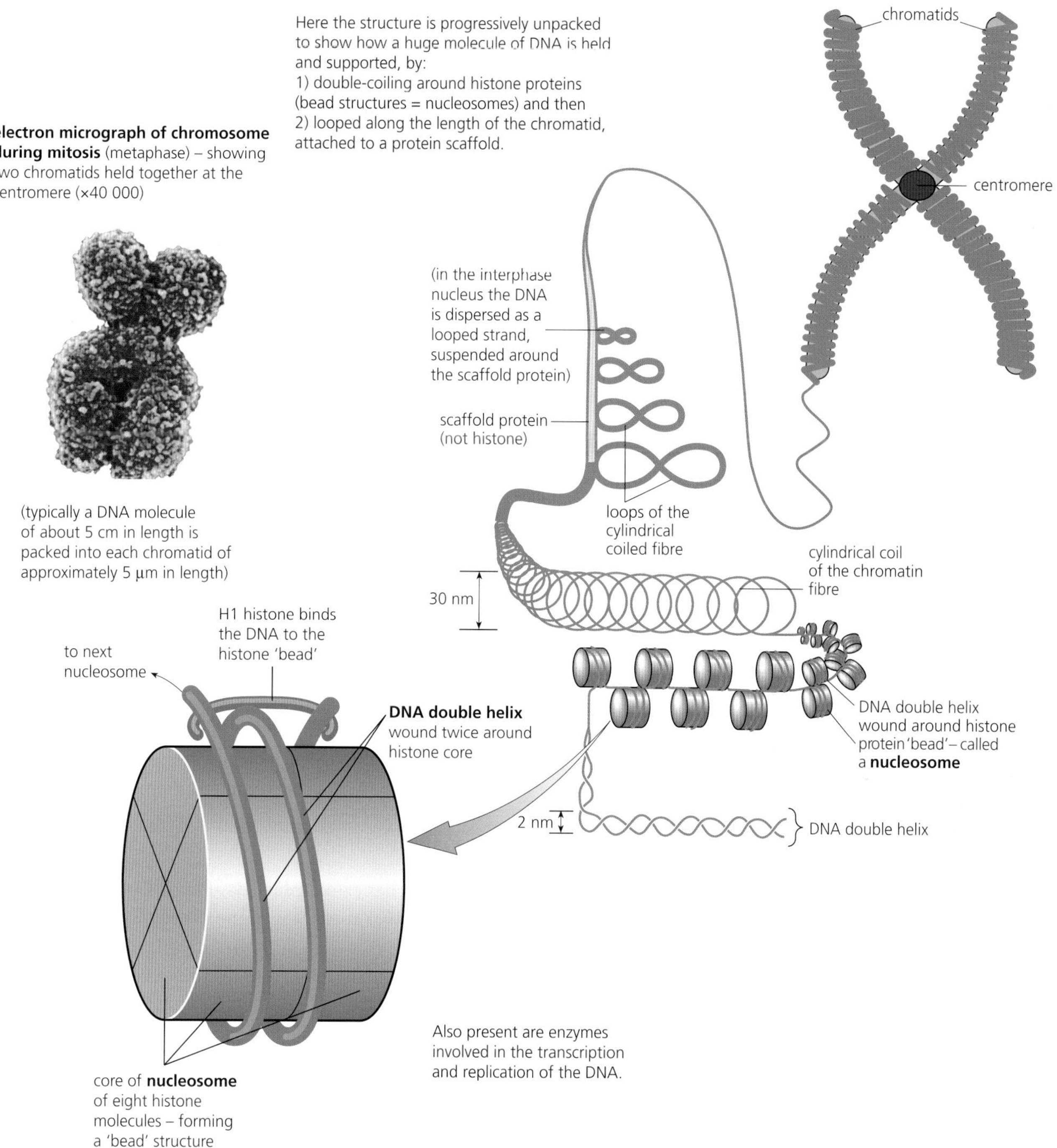
drawing of the chromosome showing the packaging of DNA
chromatids
centromere
Here the structure is progressively unpacked to show how a huge molecule of DNA is held and supported, by:
1) double-coiling around histone proteins (bead structures = nucleosomes) and then
2) looped along the length of the chromatid, attached to a protein scaffold.
electron micrograph of chromosome during mitosis (metaphase) – showing two chromatids held together at the centromere (×40 000)
(in the interphase nucleus the DNA is dispersed as a looped strand, suspended around the scaffold protein)
scaffold protein (not histone)
loops of the cylindrical coiled fibre
(typically a DNA molecule of about 5 cm in length is packed into each chromatid of approximately 5 μm in length)
cylindrical coil of the chromatin fibre
30 nm
H1 histone binds the DNA to the histone 'bead'
to next nucleosome
DNA double helix wound twice around histone core
DNA double helix wound around histone protein 'bead' – called a nucleosome
2 nm
DNA double helix
Also present are enzymes involved in the transcription and replication of the DNA.
core of nucleosome of eight histone molecules – forming a 'bead' structure

Figure 4.15 The packaging of DNA in the chromosomes of eukaryotic cells

Mitochondria are the site of the aerobic stages of respiration (Chapter 13) and where most ATP is produced in cells. Not surprisingly cells that are metabolically very active, such as muscle fibres, contain very large numbers of mitochondria in their cytoplasm.

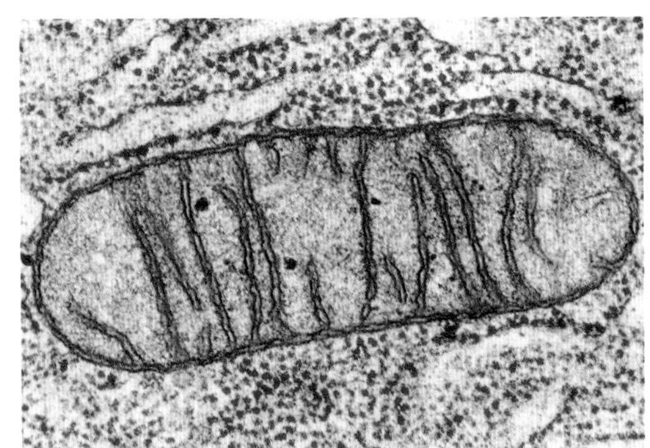

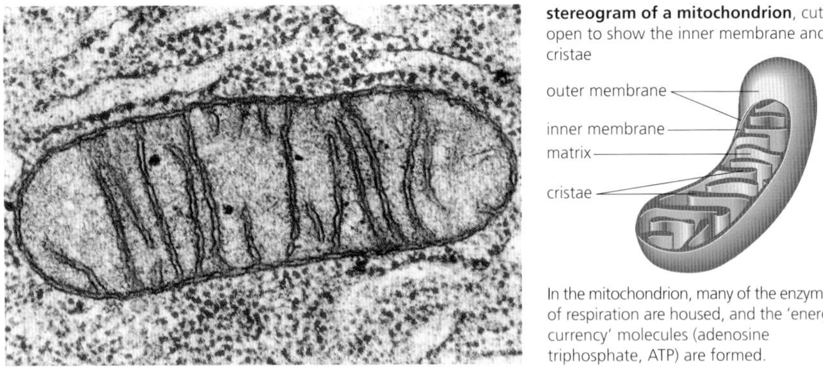

stereogram of a mitochondrion, cut open to show the inner membrane and cristae

outer membrane
inner membrane
matrix
cristae

In the mitochondrion, many of the enzymes of respiration are housed, and the 'energy currency' molecules (adenosine triphosphate, ATP) are formed.

Figure 4.16 The structure of a mitochondrion

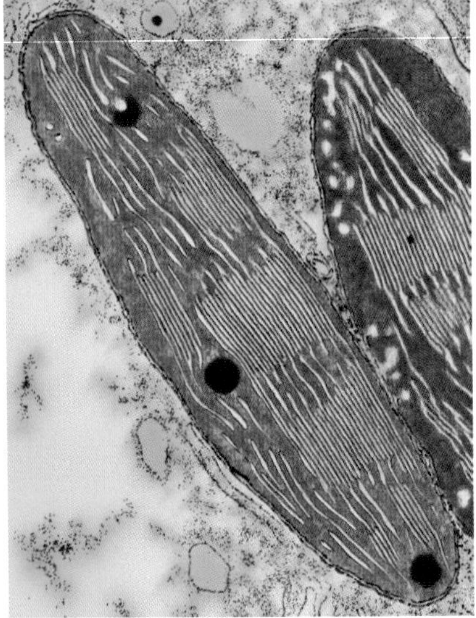

Figure 4.17 The structure of a chloroplast

Chloroplasts

Chloroplasts are biconvex in shape, typically about 4–10 μm long and 2–3 μm wide. They are found in the cells of green plants and photosynthetic protoctists. In plants, most chloroplasts occur in the mesophyll cells of leaves (page 225), where one cell may be packed with 50 or more chloroplasts. Chloroplasts are the site of photosynthesis, the process in which light is used to synthesise sugars from carbon dioxide and water.

Look at the chloroplasts in the TEM in Figure 4.17. Hopefully, you will be able to make out the double membrane around the chloroplast on the right. The outer layer of the membrane is a smooth continuous boundary, but the inner layer becomes in-tucked to form a system of branching membranes called lamellae or **thylakoids**. In the interior of the chloroplast, the thylakoids are arranged in flattened circular piles called **grana** (singular granum). In Figure 4.17 these look a little like a stack of coins. It is here that the chlorophylls and other pigments involved in light capture are located. There are a large number of grana present. Between them the branching membranes are very loosely arranged in an aqueous environment, containing enzymes and often containing small starch grains. This part of the chloroplast is called the **stroma**. Small circular molecules of DNA are also located in the stroma.

Key term

Thylakoids The folded inner membranes of a chloroplast.

Chloroplasts are one of a larger group of organelles called **plastids**. Plastids are found in many plant cells but never in animals. The other members of the plastid family are **amyloplasts** (colourless plastids) in which starch is stored, and **chromoplasts** (coloured plastids), containing non-photosynthetic pigments such as carotene, and occurring in flower petals and the root tissue of carrots.

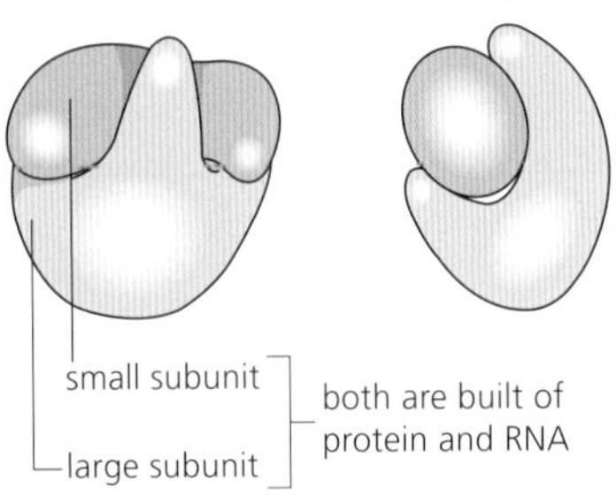

front view
side view
small subunit
large subunit
both are built of protein and RNA

Figure 4.18 The structure of ribosomes

Ribosomes

We saw in Chapter 3 that ribosomes are the site of protein synthesis. The size of minute objects such as ribosomes is often recorded in **Svedberg** units (symbol, S). This is a measure of their rate of **sedimentation** during **centrifugation** under standardised conditions, rather than their actual size. Ribosomes in the cytoplasm of eukaryotic cells have a sedimentation rate of 80S (an actual size of about 25 nm diameter). As we will see later, those of prokaryotic cells (and of those found within both mitochondria and chloroplasts) are slightly smaller, with a sedimentation rate of 70S.

Figure 4.18 shows that ribosomes are built of two sub-units, and do not have membranes as part of their structures. Chemically, they consist of protein and the nucleic acid RNA. Ribosomes are found free in the cytoplasm and also bound to endoplasmic reticulum to form rough endoplasmic reticulum.

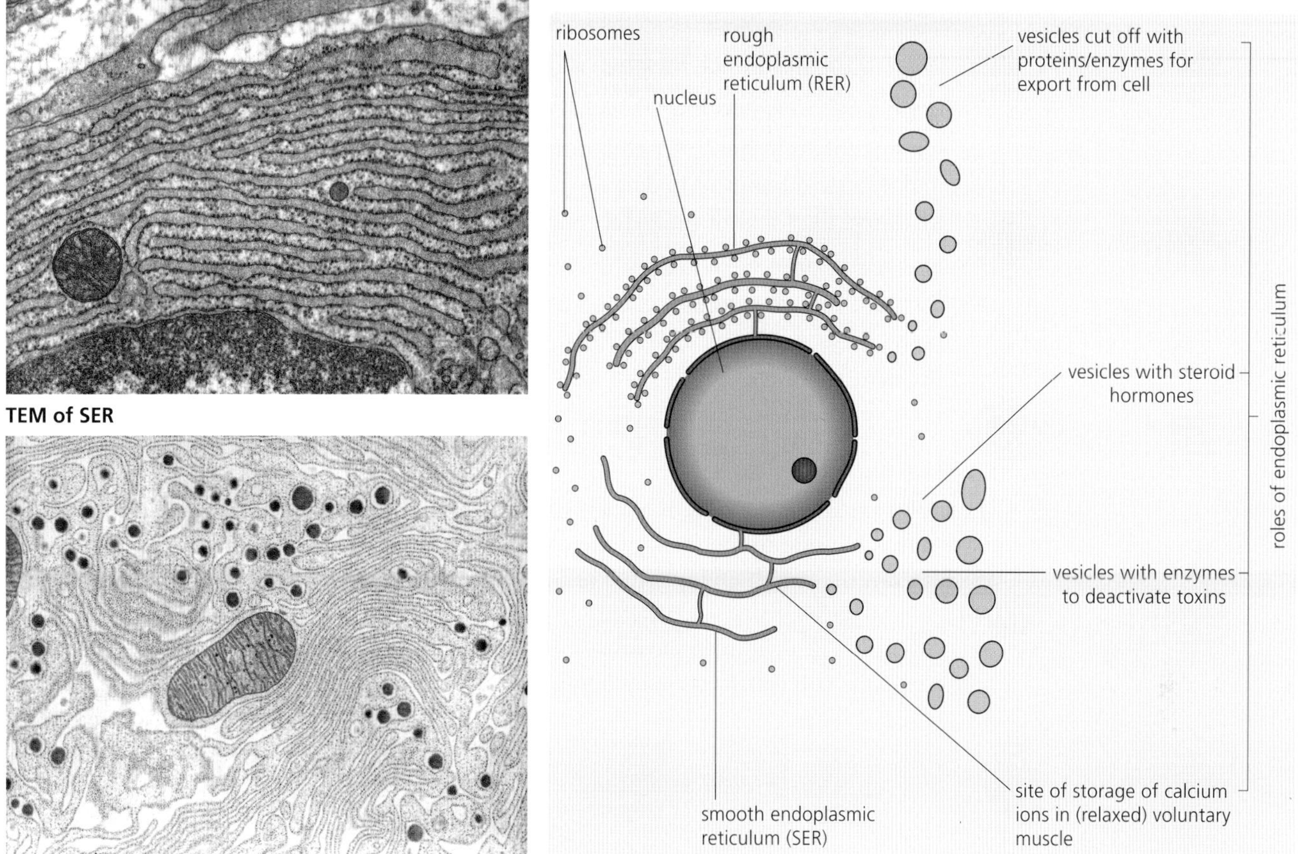

Figure 4.19 Rough endoplasmic reticulum and smooth endoplasmic reticulum

Endoplasmic reticulum

Endoplasmic reticulum consists of networks of folded single membranes forming interconnected sheets, tubes or sacs. The cytoplasm of metabolically active cells is commonly packed with endoplasmic reticulum. Figure 4.19 shows the two distinct, and separate, types of endoplasmic reticulum found in cells.

- **Rough endoplasmic reticulum** is continuous with the outer membrane surrounding the nucleus. It is called 'rough' because it has ribosomes attached to its outer surface (the surface in contact with the cytosol). You know from Chapter 3 that ribosomes link amino acids together to form polypeptide chains. In addition, the rough endoplasmic reticulum develops the tertiary and quaternary shapes of proteins that you learnt about in Chapter 2. It is in the lumen of the rough endoplasmic reticulum that, for example, the critical shape of enzyme molecules is formed. Often proteins are transferred from the rough endoplasmic reticulum to the Golgi apparatus. Sometimes this occurs by direct contact; sometimes it occurs when vesicles are formed from swellings at the margins of the rough endoplasmic reticulum that become pinched off. A vesicle is a small, spherical organelle bounded by a single membrane, which is used to store and transport substances around the cell.
- **Smooth endoplasmic reticulum (SER)** is separate from the rough endoplasmic reticulum and is not usually found near a cell's nucleus. It is called 'smooth' because it has no ribosomes attached to it. Smooth endoplasmic reticulum synthesises lipids, phospholipids and steroids. In the cytoplasm of voluntary muscle fibres, a special form of smooth endoplasmic reticulum is the site of storage of calcium ions, which have an important role in the contraction of muscle fibres.

Key term

Vesicle A small sac of cytoplasm enclosed by membrane. Although they are much smaller than vacuoles, there is no difference between the two structures.

Test yourself

16 What is the difference between a *double membrane* and a *lipid bilayer*?

17 Distinguish between the terms *nucleus* and *nucleolus*.

18 A mitochondrion has a smooth outer membrane and an inner membrane thrown into a large number of foldings.

a) Name the folds of the inner membrane.

b) Suggest **one** advantage of this folding.

19 Suggest why amyloplasts are so called.

20 Ribosomes are made within the nucleus of a cell. Suggest how they get to the cytoplasm.

Golgi apparatus

The Golgi apparatus consists of a stack-like collection of flattened membranous sacs, called **cisternae**. One side of the stack of membranes is formed by the fusion of membranes of vesicles from the rough endoplasmic reticulum. At the opposite side of the stack, vesicles are formed from swellings at the margins that become pinched off. These vesicles might remain within the cell or, in secretory cells, fuse with the cell surface membrane, releasing their contents. You can see vesicles being pinched off from Golgi apparatus in Figure 4.20.

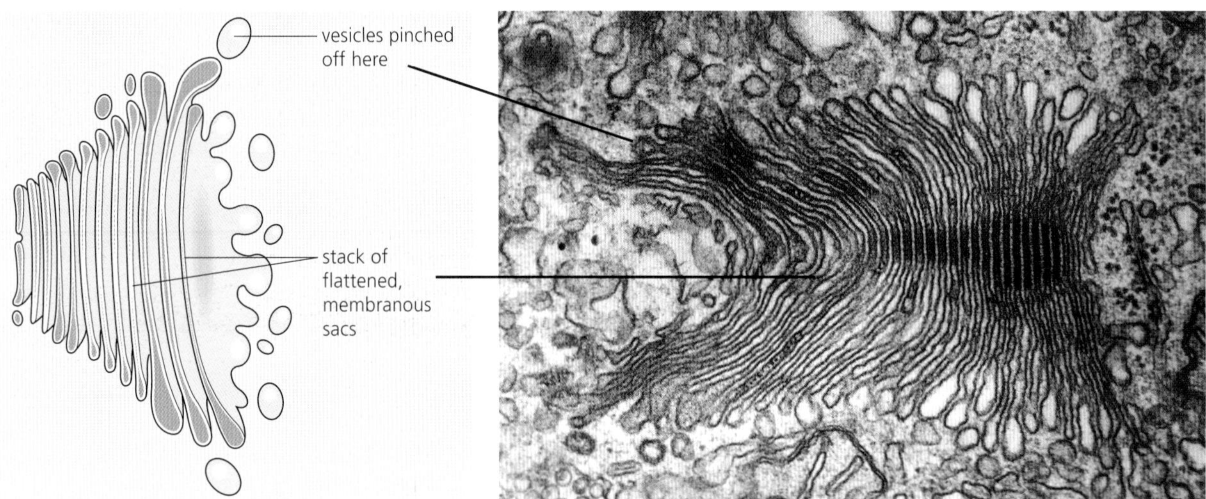

Figure 4.20 The Golgi apparatus

The Golgi apparatus occurs in all cells, but it is especially prominent in metabolically active cells, such as secretory cells. These cells produce a large number of different polymers. The Golgi apparatus is responsible for sorting, modifying and packaging these polymers for secretion or for use within the cell.

Lysosomes

Lysosomes are small spherical vesicles bound by a single membrane. They contain a concentrated mixture of about 50 hydrolytic enzymes, which are produced by the rough endoplasmic reticulum and modified in the Golgi apparatus.

Lysosomes are involved in the breakdown of imported food vacuoles, old organelles and harmful bacteria that have invaded the body and been engulfed by one of the body's defence cells. As Figure 4.21 shows, once engulfed into a larger vacuole, lysosomes fuse with the vacuole and release their hydrolytic enzymes into it. As a result, the food, organelle or bacterium is digested and the products of digestion escape into the cytosol. When an organism dies, the hydrolytic enzymes in the lysosomes of its cells escape into the cytoplasm and cause self-digestion (autolysis).

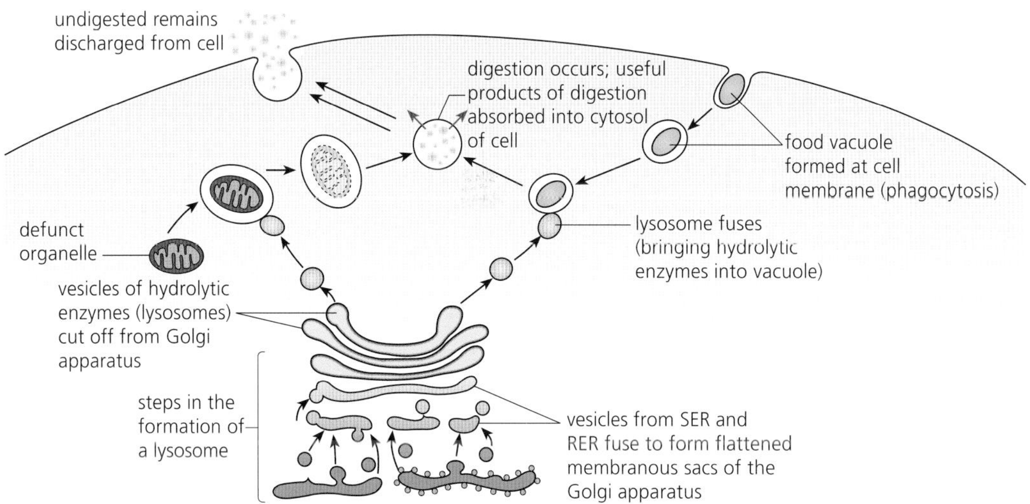

Figure 4.21 The role of lysosomes

Centrioles

Although the cytosol has been described above as an aqueous solution, it is not structureless. **Microtubules** of a globular protein, called tubulin, are often present, forming a network of unbranched, hollow cylinders. These microtubules are involved in moving organelles around in the cytoplasm. They also form the **centrioles**, found in animal cells.

The centrioles occur in pairs – you can see one pair of centrioles in Figure 4.22, which also shows how they normally lie at right angles to each other, just outside the cell's nucleus. Each centriole is composed of nine bundles of microtubules. During cell division the centrioles move apart, creating the spindle (Chapter 5).

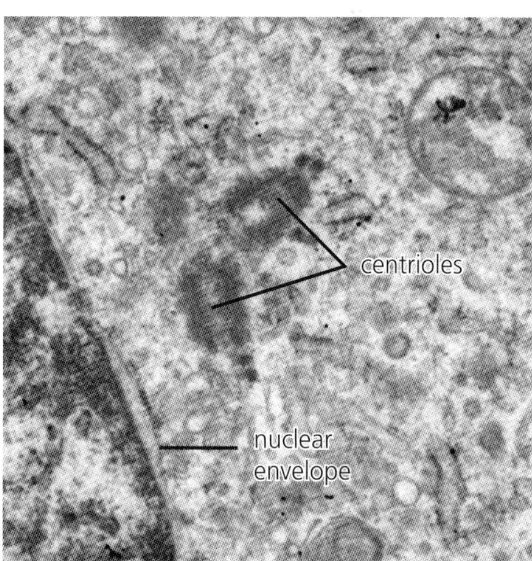

Figure 4.22 A pair of centrioles lying at right angles to each other just outside the nucleus of an animal cell

Plant cell wall

The cells of plants are surrounded by a cell wall. Strictly, the plant cell wall is not an organelle, but it is produced by the actions of organelles. The wall is composed of long, straight fibres of cellulose held together by hydrogen bonds (look back to Figure 1.13 to remind yourself of the structure of cellulose). Because these bundles are laid down at different angles, the cell wall is able to resist stretching in any direction. This prevents plant cells bursting when placed in dilute solutions (see Chapter 9). The cell wall does, however, contain spaces between the bundles of cellulose. These spaces allow the movement of water from cell wall to cell wall – the so-called **apoplast** pathway that you will learn more about in Chapter 12.

Figure 4.23 shows that when a plant cell divides, the first boundary between new cells is a gel-like layer of calcium pectate, called the **middle lamella**. Some of the endoplasmic reticulum of the parent cell becomes trapped in the gaps in this middle lamella. This trapped reticulum persists when the cellulose wall is laid down, forming plasmodesmata.

Key term

Plasmodesmata
Cytoplasmic connections between plant cells through gaps in their cell walls. They are part of the symplast pathway through which, for example, inorganic ions are able to pass from cell to cell without having to pass through cell walls or cell surface membranes.

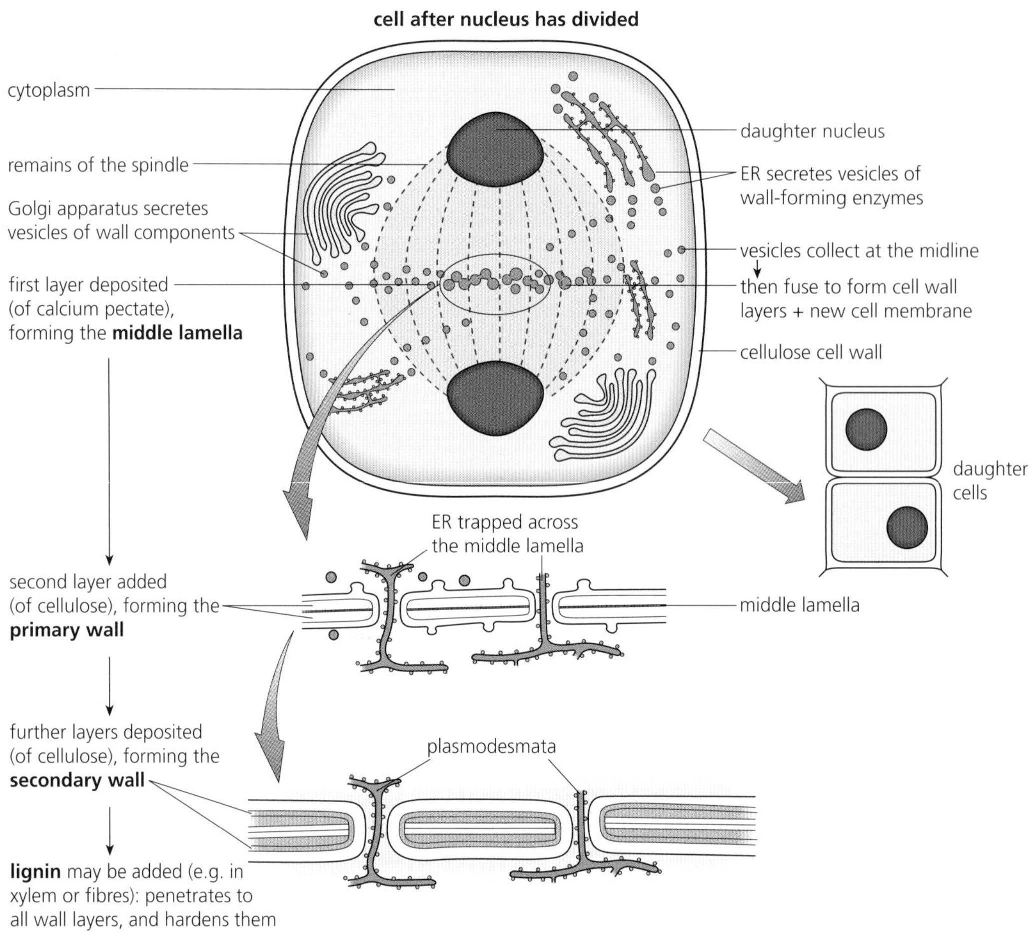

Figure 4.23 Plasmodesmata develop as new cell walls form between plant cells

> **Key term**
>
> **Tonoplast** The membrane surrounding the large, fluid-filled vacuole found in plant cells.

Permanent vacuole of plant cells and the tonoplast

The cytoplasm and cell surface membrane of a plant cell are pressed firmly against its cell wall by a large, permanent, fluid-filled vacuole, which takes up the bulk of the cell. You can see in Figure 4.24 that this vacuole is surrounded by a specialised membrane, the **tonoplast**. This is the barrier between the fluid contents of the vacuole (sometimes called 'cell sap') and the cytoplasm.

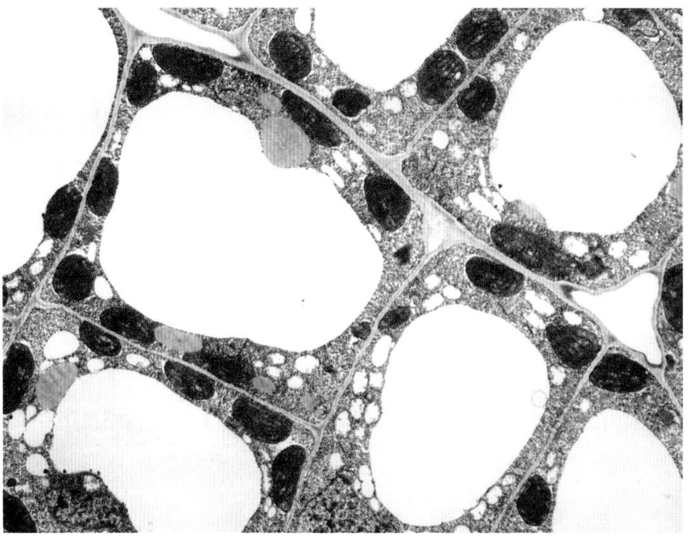

Figure 4.24 TEM of plant cells showing vacuoles and tonoplasts

The ultrastructure of prokaryotic cells

The **prokaryotes** are the bacteria and cyanobacteria (photosynthetic bacteria). These microorganisms, typically unicellular, have a fundamentally different cell structure from the cells of eukaryotes.

Figure 4.25 shows a scanning electron micrograph of a prokaryotic cell, in this case the intestinal bacterium *Escherichia coli*. The drawing summarises the generalised features of prokaryotic cells. Note the following distinctive features.

- Size: prokaryotic cells are exceedingly small – about the size of mitochondria and chloroplasts of eukaryotic cells.
- Absence of a nucleus: a prokaryotic cell lacks a membrane-bound nucleus. Prokaryotic cells have a single, circular DNA molecule in their cytoplasm, referred to as a nucleoid. Unlike a eukaryotic chromosome, the DNA of the nucleoid is not associated with protein.

Key term

Nucleoid The circular DNA molecule found in prokaryotic cells. We do not refer to this as a chromosome because the DNA is neither linear nor associated with histones.

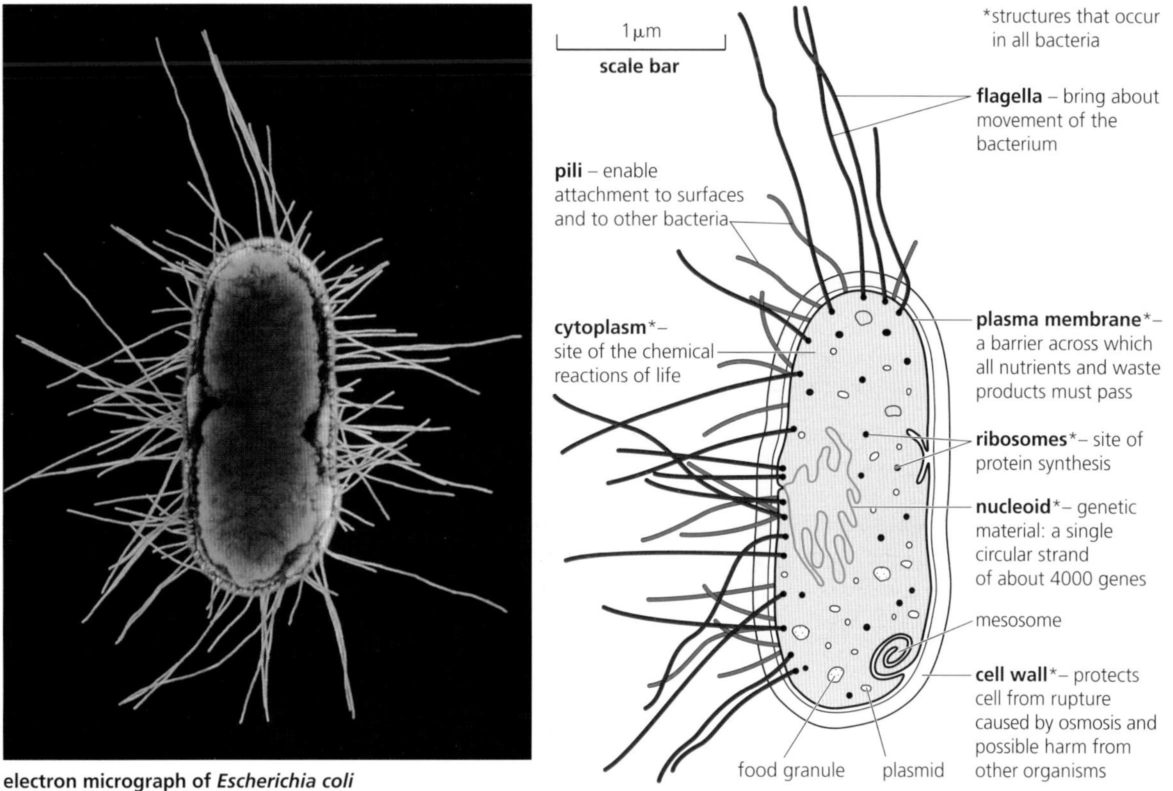

Figure 4.25 A scanning electron micrograph of a prokaryotic cell – the bacterium *Escherichia coli* – together with an interpretive drawing of its structure

- Plasmids: in addition to the nucleoid, some prokaryotic cells have small, circular DNA molecules in their cytoplasm. These plasmids usually contain only a few genes; often they include genes conferring resistance to specific antibiotics.
- 70 S ribosomes: although these ribosomes are involved in protein synthesis, they are smaller than the 80 S ribosomes found in eukaryotic cells.
- Absence of membrane-bound organelles: the cytoplasm of prokaryotic cells lacks the range of organelles found in eukaryotes, for example mitochondria, chloroplasts, Golgi apparatus and endoplasmic reticulum.

Key term

Artefact Something seen in a specimen being viewed using a microscope that was not present in the living cell. Artefacts result from damage caused by the processing of tissue for examination in light microscopes and electron microscopes.

- Cell wall: all prokaryotic cells have a cell wall. Like those of plant cells, the cell walls of prokaryotic cells prevent cells bursting when in dilute solutions. Unlike those of plant cell walls, they are not made of cellulose. Instead, they are made of **peptidoglycan**.
- Pili and flagella: where they occur, pili help prokaryotic cells to attach to surfaces or to each other and flagella help the cells to move about.

Notice that a structure called a mesosome is also shown in Figure 4.25. Many functions were proposed for these modest in-tuckings of the cell surface membrane; they have since been shown to be artefacts – caused by the chemical fixation techniques used to prepare prokaryotic cells for electron microscopy.

Wall structure in bacteria

The rigid wall of a bacterium gives a permanent shape to the cell. It also protects the cell contents against rupture due to osmosis, for example, and it helps to protect some bacteria against harm from other organisms.

Bacterial cell walls contain polymers of amino acids and sugars, called **peptidoglycan**. All bacteria have walls of this substance, but some have additional layers on the outer surface of their wall, and these additional layers change the staining property of the wall. Figure 4.26 summarises the steps in the staining procedure that distinguishes between bacteria and explains the differences in the cell wall chemistry of the two categories of cell.

- **Gram positive** bacteria have thick walls made almost entirely of peptidoglycan. This wall becomes purple when stained by crystal violet.
- **Gram negative** bacteria have thin walls of peptidoglycan with an additional outer membrane. The high lipid content of this outer membrane prevents the crystal violet stain getting to the cell wall, so these bacteria do not become purple.

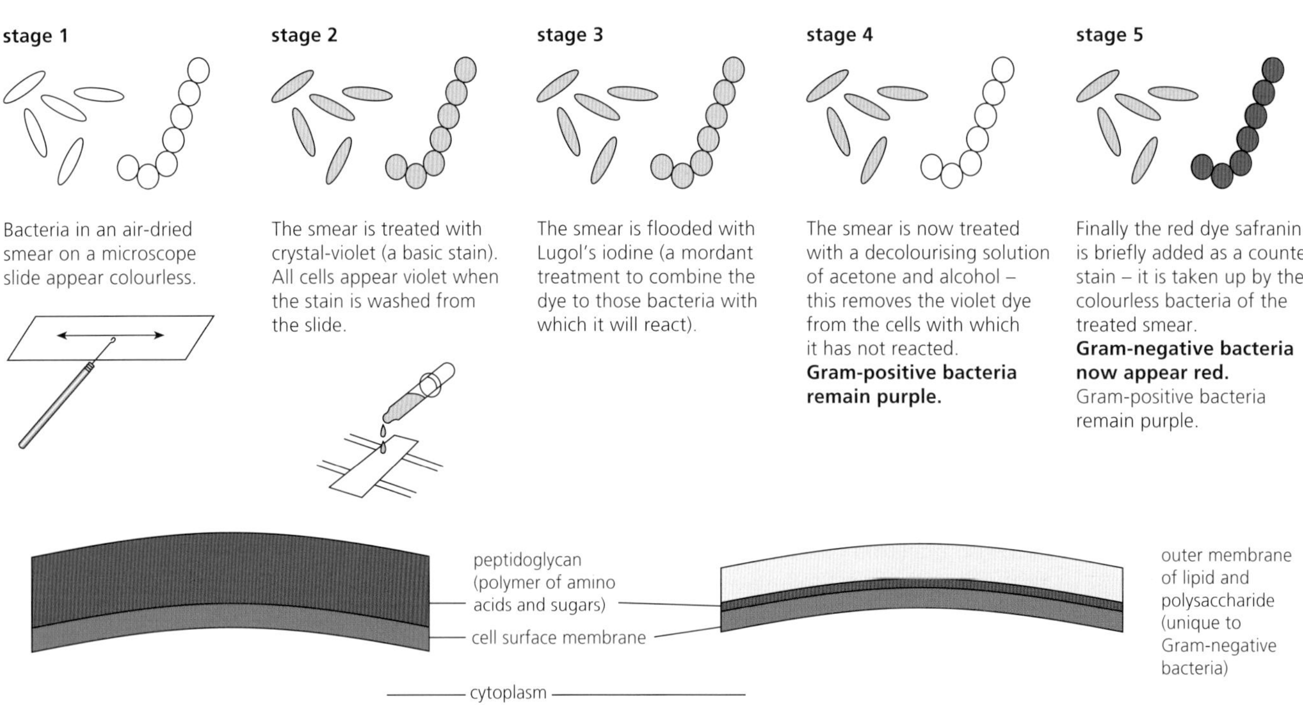

stage 1
Bacteria in an air-dried smear on a microscope slide appear colourless.
stage 2
The smear is treated with crystal-violet (a basic stain). All cells appear violet when the stain is washed from the slide.
stage 3
The smear is flooded with Lugol's iodine (a mordant treatment to combine the dye to those bacteria with which it will react).
stage 4
The smear is now treated with a decolourising solution of acetone and alcohol – this removes the violet dye from the cells with which it has not reacted.
Gram-positive bacteria remain purple.
stage 5
Finally the red dye safranin is briefly added as a counter-stain – it is taken up by the colourless bacteria of the treated smear.
Gram-negative bacteria now appear red.
Gram-positive bacteria remain purple.
peptidoglycan (polymer of amino acids and sugars)
cell surface membrane
outer membrane of lipid and polysaccharide (unique to Gram-negative bacteria)
cytoplasm
section of walls of Gram-positive and Gram-negative bacteria

Figure 4.26 Gram staining and the difference between Gram positive and Gram negative bacteria

The stain is called Gram stain after the Dane, Hans Gram who, in 1884, devised the staining test to distinguish the two types of bacteria. The difference in the properties of these cell walls extends beyond their ability to take up the crystal violet stain. The most important is the effect of antibiotics on these two types of bacteria. The outer, lipid-rich, membrane of Gram negative bacteria is relatively impermeable to antibiotics. As a result, Gram negative bacteria are resistant to many types of antibiotic, including penicillin. Gram positive bacteria are susceptible to penicillin.

Test yourself

21 Identify **two** structures present in prokaryotic cells that are also present in all eukaryotic cells.

22 Biologists believe that mitochondria and chloroplasts evolved from free living prokaryotic organisms that formed mutually beneficial relationships with eukaryotic cells millions of years ago.

Give **two** ways in which mitochondria and chloroplasts are similar to prokaryotes.

23 A mature red blood cell lacks a nucleus and membrane-bound organelles but is not considered to be a prokaryotic cell. Explain why.

24 Other than the evolution of antibiotic resistance, give one reason why antibiotics are not effective against all pathogenic bacteria.

Viruses

Although they are disease-causing agents, viruses are not regarded as living organisms. The reason for this is that they lack a metabolism of their own. Their replication depends entirely on the metabolism of cells they infect. All viruses have:

- a core of nucleic acid, around which is
- a protein coat, called a **capsid**.

Some viruses have an additional external envelope of membrane made of lipids and proteins (for example the human immunodeficiency virus, HIV, that causes acquired immunodeficiency syndrome, AIDS, in humans).

Because they lack any metabolism of their own, viral infections are difficult to treat.

Where effective antivirals have been developed, they must work by inhibiting viral replication by the host cells.

Where antivirals have not been developed, disease control must rely on preventing the spread of the virus. In the absence of an effective antiviral, control of the 2013–15 outbreak of Ebola in the West African countries of Guinea, Sierra Leone, Liberia, Senegal and Nigeria relied entirely on attempts to prevent spread of the virus.

Their inert status also makes the classification of viruses complex. Most systems of classifying them rely on features such as the nature and method of copying their nucleic acid core, the nature of their capsid, their shape and the organisms they infect. Table 4.1 shows some of these features of four viruses.

Table 4.1 Four types of virus

Name of virus	Feature				
	Host	Structure	Size/nm	Nature of nucleic acid core	Copying of nucleic acid core
λ (lambda) bacteriophage	Bacterium *Escherichia coli*	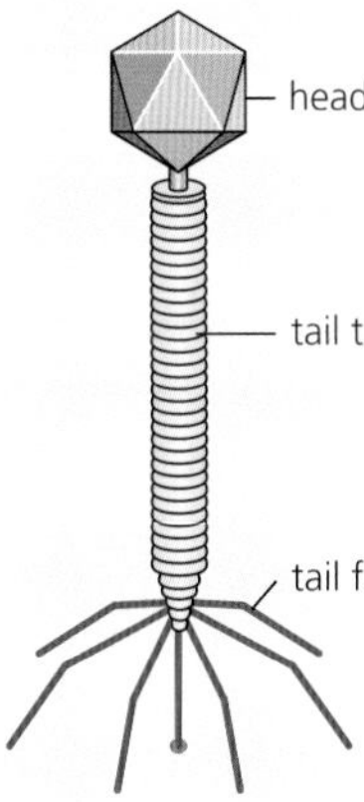 head tail tube tail fibre	Head diameter ~ 50–60 Tail length ~ 150	Double-stranded DNA	Double-stranded DNA transcribed to mRNA
Tobacco mosaic virus	Plants, especially those of the tobacco family	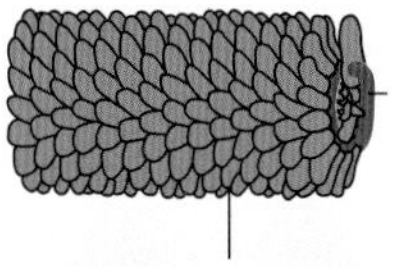 position of RNA protein coat (capsid) of polypeptide building blocks arranged in a spiral around the canal containing RNA	Diameter ~ 18 Length ~ 300	Single-stranded RNA	RNA copied directly to form mRNA
Ebola virus	Humans (especially endothelial cells, liver cells, immune cells and dendritic cells)	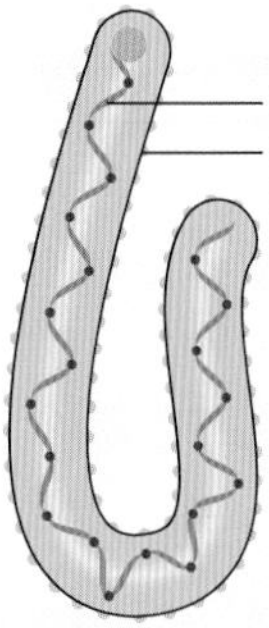 RNA outer protein coat	Diameter ~ 80 Length ~ 130 000	Single-stranded RNA	RNA copied directly to form mRNA
Human immunodeficiency virus	Humans (T helper lymphocytes)	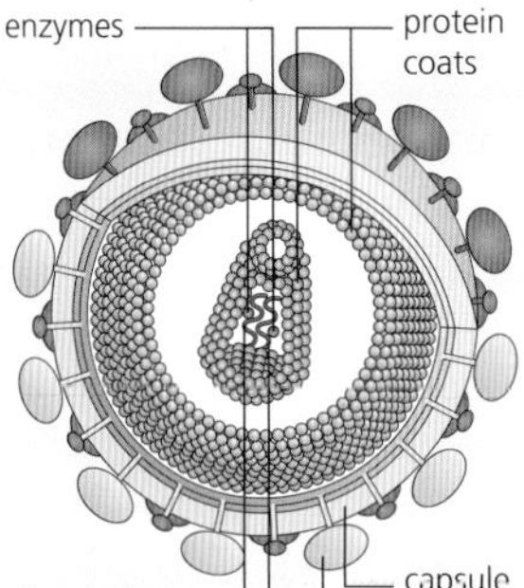 enzymes protein coats single-stranded RNA capsule glycoprotein	Diameter ~ 120	Single-stranded RNA	RNA 'reverse transcribed' into double-stranded DNA, which is incorporated into the host cell's DNA and later transcribed to form mRNA

The lytic cycle

We have seen above that viruses lack any metabolism of their own; instead they rely on the metabolism of the cells they infect to produce more virus particles. Most studies of viruses have been carried out using bacteriophages – viruses that infect bacteria. Figure 4.27 shows the 'life cycle' of a bacteriophage, often referred to simply as a 'phage'. Notice that the phage infects the bacterial cell by injecting its own nucleic acid; the capsid remains outside the bacterial cell. The infected bacterium then produces more phage particles by replicating the phage nucleic acid and producing new capsids.

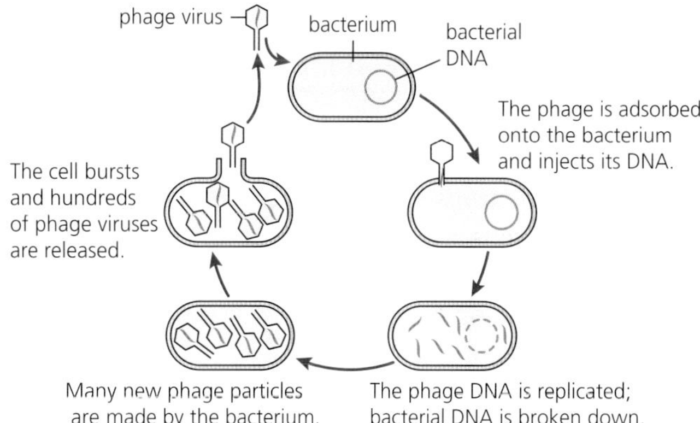

Figure 4.27 The lytic cycle of a lambda (λ) bacteriophage

Eventually, the bacterial cell releases new phages that are free to infect other cells. Because the release of new phages follows lysis of the bacterial cell, this 'life cycle' is called the **lytic cycle**.

Similar events occur in other organisms when they become infected by viruses. Some pathogenic viruses, however, can undergo a period of latency. During this period, the virus does not take over the metabolism of the infected cell but remains dormant (latent) within an infected host cell. There are two types of **viral latency**.

- episomal latency – the viral nucleic acid remains inactive but free in the cytoplasm or nucleus of the infected cell
- proviral latency – the viral nucleic acid becomes incorporated into the DNA of the infected host cell. It is now termed a provirus but, as with episomal latency, the viral nucleic acid can be reactivated at any time.

You might have suffered a disease called chickenpox when you were a child. It is a contagious, but relatively harmless disease caused by a virus, *Varicella zoster*. If you did suffer chickenpox, you will have recovered but the nucleic acid of the virus will have remained in some of your nerve cells. This is an example of episomal latency. Although the viral DNA is inactive, any sudden stress can reactivate it, resulting in a disease called shingles. Normal aging increases the risk of shingles: in the UK, a new policy has been introduced to vaccinate elderly people against shingles, starting with those who are in their 80th year.

Key term

Viral latency A period in which, under the control of specific latency genes, a pathogenic virus remains dormant. During this time the virus, or its nucleic acid, is present inside an infected cell but does not control the cell's activities.

Test yourself

25 What is meant by the following statement: 'Viruses are inert'?

26 The human immunodeficiency virus (HIV) is classed as a retrovirus. Use information in Table 4.1 to suggest why.

27 What is the generic name given to viruses that infect bacteria?

28 Doctors are advised not to prescribe antibiotics to people suffering viral infections. Explain why.

29 Cold sores are caused by the herpes simplex virus (HSV-1). Some people suffer recurrent outbreaks of cold sores. Suggest what this shows about the way that HSV-1 infects sufferers.

Chapter summary

Cell theory

- The cell theory is a unifying concept in biology. It states that cells are a fundamental unit of structure, function and organisation in all living organisms.
- Microscopes are needed to study cell structure. The resolution of electron microscopes allows much finer detail – cell ultrastructure – to be seen.

Prokaryotic cell structure

- Bacteria have prokaryotic cells.
- These cells have a cell surface membrane but lack protein-bound chromosomes and a membrane-bound nucleus.
- The DNA of prokaryotic cells is located in:
  - one large, circular nucleoid
  - many small, circular plasmids.
- The cytoplasm of prokaryotic cells contains ribosomes that are smaller (70S) (Svedberg units) than those in eukaryotic cells (80S).
- All bacteria have a cell wall made of polymers of peptidoglycan.
- Some bacteria also have a lipid-rich membrane outside their cell wall. This changes their ability to take up a Gram stain, so they are termed Gram-negative bacteria. Those without this outer layer take up Gram stain and are called Gram-positive bacteria.
- The outer membrane of Gram-negative bacteria is relatively impermeable to antibiotics, such as penicillin, to which Gram-positive bacteria are susceptible.

Eukaryotic cell structure

- Like prokaryotic cells, eukaryotic cells have an outer cell surface membrane surrounding the cytoplasm.
- Unlike prokaryotic cells, eukaryotic cells have a nucleus that contains chromosomes – linear DNA bound to histone proteins. It is separated from the cell's cytoplasm by a nuclear membrane.
- Within the nucleus is a densely staining region called the nucleolus. It contains DNA, RNA and proteins and is responsible for assembling the subunits of ribosomes.
- The cytoplasm of eukaryotic cells contains a variety of organelles, each with a specific function.
- Mitochondria produce ATP in a process called aerobic respiration.
- Endoplasmic reticulum forms a series of membrane-bound tubes running through the cytoplasm.
  - Rough endoplasmic reticulum is studded with ribosomes.
  - Smooth endoplasmic reticulum has no ribosomes. It is involved in the synthesis of lipids and in the folding, modification and transport of proteins.
- 80S ribosomes synthesise proteins.
- The Golgi apparatus packages proteins into smaller vesicles for transport to their destination.
- Lysosomes are small, spherical vesicles that contain hydrolytic enzymes.
- Centrioles form microtubules that help separate chromosomes during cell division in animal cells.
- Chloroplasts are present in many plant cells and are the site of photosynthesis.
- Plant cells also have a fluid-filled permanent vacuole surrounded by a tonoplast membrane.
- Plants and fungi have cell walls outside their surface membranes. Plant cell walls are formed from cellulose; fungal cell walls from chitin.
- In complex organisms, eukaryotic cells of a single specialised type are organised into tissues, different tissues into organs and different organs into systems.

Viruses

- Viruses are non-living parasites of cells. They are classified according to cell structure and nucleic acid type.
- Many viruses show a lytic cycle that includes a latent period.
- Although antivirals are effective in treating viral infections, preventing the spread of viruses is key to their control.

Practice questions

1 Which one, or more, of the following statements is true?

A Prokaryotic cells have only 70 S ribosomes.

B Prokaryotic cells have 70 S and 80 S ribosomes.

C Eukaryotic cells have only 80 S ribosomes.

D Eukaryotic cells have 70 S and 80 S ribosomes. *(1)*

2 In a photomicrograph, a cell has a diameter of 5 cm. If the magnification is 400 times, the actual size of diameter of the cell is:

A 12.5 μm

B 20.0 μm

C 125.0 μm

D 200.0 μm *(1)*

3 A cell specialised to secrete a steroid hormone is likely to have:

A a large amount of smooth endoplasmic reticulum

B a large amount of rough endoplasmic reticulum

C a large nucleus

D few mitochondria *(1)*

4 The diagram shows the structure of a bacterial cell.

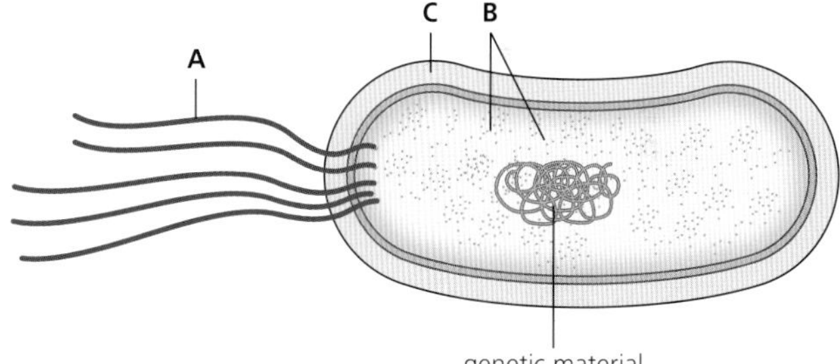

a) Name the structures labelled **A**, **B** and **C**. *(3)*

b) Give one difference between the genetic material of a bacterial cell and that of a eukaryotic cell. *(1)*

c) Other than a difference in their genetic material, give two features that are characteristic of prokaryotes. *(2)*

5 Copy and complete the table showing features of different type of cells by putting a tick (✓) in an empty box if the feature is present and a cross (✗) if it is not. *(5)*

Feature	Animal cell	Bacterial cell	Plant cell
Cell surface membrane			
Cell wall			
Tonoplast			
Ribosome			
Mitochondrion			

6 The following diagram was drawn from a photograph of a cell observed using a transmission electron microscope.

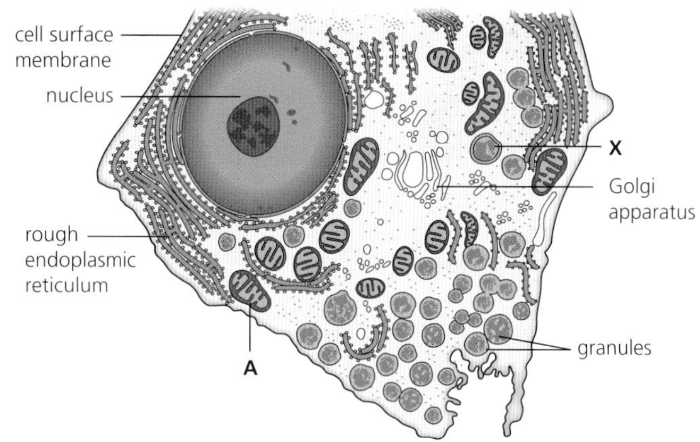

a) Give the evidence from the diagram that this cell was observed using a transmission electron microscope. *(3)*

b) Name the structure labelled **A**. *(1)*

c) The actual diameter of the granule labelled **X** is 1.5 μm. Calculate the magnification of this drawing. Show your working. *(2)*

7 A scientist grew cells in a tissue culture solution. After several hours, she added a small volume of a solution containing radioactively labelled amino acids. At regular intervals, she killed a sample of the cells and measured the level of radioactivity in different parts of the cells in her samples. Some of her results are shown in the table.

Time after adding radioactive amino acids/minutes	Percentage of total radioactivity found in each part of cell		
	Ribosomes	Golgi apparatus	Secretory vesicles
0	80	16	4
120	16	30	11
240	14	8	42
360	16	8	46

a) Why did the scientist add radioactively labelled amino acids several hours after starting to grow the cells in culture solution? *(2)*

b) Use your knowledge of cell structure and function to explain the data in the table. *(3)*

c) Suggest why the percentages at 360 minutes do not add up to 100 percent. *(1)*

Stretch and challenge

8 During much of the twentieth century, biologists assumed that proteins were the hereditary material; DNA was thought to be too simple. In 1952, Alfred Hershey and Martha Chase conducted a series of experiments to investigate whether protein or DNA was the hereditary material. They used bacteriophages in their experiments. Use a search engine to find how they utilised knowledge of the lytic cycle to investigate the nature of the hereditary material.

9 The cell theory is a unifying concept in biology. Use a search engine to discover how this theory was developed.

Tip

When quantitative data are shown in a table, it is often easier to see a trend or pattern in these data by drawing a sketch graph – unlabelled axes and roughly drawn curves.

The eukaryotic cell cycle and cell division

Prior knowledge

In this chapter you will need to recall that:

- ➜ all cells arise from the division of a pre-existing cell
- ➜ the chromosomes of a eukaryotic cell contain its genetic information
- ➜ prior to cell division, a cell makes a copy of each of its chromosomes
- ➜ there are two types of cell division in eukaryotic cells – mitosis and meiosis
- ➜ mitosis is a type of cell division that occurs during growth and during the repair and replacement of cells
- ➜ a cell that divides by mitosis produces two daughter cells that are genetically identical to each other and to itself, in other words produces clones
- ➜ a cell that divides by meiosis divides twice and produces four daughter cells that are not genetically identical to itself or to each other
- ➜ the four daughter cells produced by meiosis have half the number of chromosomes as the parent cell. Each also contains a combination of alleles that is different from the other three daughter cells.

Test yourself on prior knowledge

1 Name the process by which copies of chromosomes are produced.

2 Name **one** place in your body where mitosis regularly occurs.

3 Read the following statements about mitosis. One or more of them are false. Identify the true statements.

   A All cells can undergo mitosis.

   B The number of chromosomes is the same in a cell after mitosis as it was before mitosis.

   C Copies of chromosomes are made during mitosis.

   D Copies of chromosomes are separated during mitosis.

4 In Question 3 you identified one or more statements as false. Explain why they are false.

5 Where in your body does meiosis occur?

Chromosomes, cell division and the cell cycle

As you saw when considering the cell theory in Chapter 4, new cells arise by division of existing cells. Prior to cell division, a cell's DNA is copied by semi-conservative replication, as described in Chapter 3. When the cell then divides, each daughter cell receives one copy of the replicated DNA.

- In prokaryotic cells, cell division occurs by a process known as **binary fission**.
- In eukaryotic cells, cell division is part of a regulated process called the **cell cycle**. It consists of three main stages: interphase, mitosis and cytokinesis.

The cell cycle in unicellular organisms: asexual reproduction

Unicellular eukaryotic organisms, such as yeast or amoeba (Figure 4.8, page 77) grow quickly under favourable conditions. They then divide in two. Since this division results in the production of new organisms, it is a form of reproduction. As no formation or fusion of gametes is involved, it is called **asexual reproduction**. This cycle of growth and division is repeated rapidly, at least whilst conditions remain supportive.

Key terms

Asexual reproduction The formation of new organisms that does not involve the fusion of gametes.

Centromere A narrow region occupying a specific position on each chromosome. This is the only site on each chromosome to which the microfibres of the spindle can attach during mitosis. Following DNA replication, the centromere temporarily holds together the two copies of each chromosome (the chromatids).

Somatic cell Any cell in the body of a multicellular organism other than a germ cell (one that gives rise to gametes) or undifferentiated stem cell.

Homologous chromosomes A pair of chromosomes in a diploid cell that have the same shape and size. More importantly, they carry the same genes in the same order, although not necessarily the same alleles of each gene.

Diploid A eukaryotic cell is said to be diploid (represented as **2*n***) if it contains two copies of each chromosome. In sexually reproducing organisms, one copy comes from each parent.

The cell cycle in multicellular organisms: growth and repair

In multicellular organisms, the life cycle of individual cells is more complex. Here, life begins as a single cell that grows and divides, forming many cells. These new cells allow the organism to grow, eventually making up the adult organism. Only certain of these cells, however, retain the ability to grow and divide throughout life. Even when growth has stopped, these cells are able to replace old or damaged cells. Most of the cells of multicellular organisms, however, become specialised and are then unable to divide further.

Chromosomes – a reminder

As you saw in Chapter 3, the genetic information the nucleus holds in its chromosomes exists as a sequence of nucleotide bases in deoxyribonucleic acid (DNA). We considered the structure of chromosomes in Chapter 4. Look back to Figure 4.15 (page 83) to remind yourself of this structure. Most of the time, chromosomes are long, thin structures that cannot be resolved by light microscopes. Instead, they appear as a diffuse network called chromatin. At the time a nucleus divides, however, the chromosomes become highly coiled. Only in this **condensed** state can they be resolved by light microscopes.

Whilst we will consider other processes occurring during the cell cycle, the behaviour of the chromosomes is so important that we will first concentrate on them. There are five features of chromosomes that it is helpful to note at the outset.

1 **The shape of a chromosome is characteristic**

Each chromosome has a particular, fixed length. Somewhere along the length of the chromosome there is a characteristically narrow region called the **centromere**. A centromere can occur anywhere along the chromosome but it is always in the same position on any given chromosome. The position of the centromere, as well as the length of a chromosome, enables us to identify individual chromosomes in photomicrographs. You can see that the centromere in Figure 5.1 is at the mid-point of its chromosome.

2 **Chromosomes occur in homologous pairs**

The chromosomes of a **somatic cell** occur in pairs of **homologous chromosomes**. They are called *homologous* because the two chromosomes have the same shape and, more importantly, have the same genes in the same order. You can see a pair of homologous chromosomes represented in Figure 5.1. During sexual reproduction, one of each pair came originally from the gamete of one parent and the second from the gamete of the other parent. So, for example, your somatic cells have 23 pairs of homologous chromosomes. At the moment of fertilisation, you inherited one copy of each from your mother's egg cell and the other copy of each from your father's sperm cell. Cells in which the chromosomes are in homologous pairs are described as **diploid**. We represent this as **2*n***, where the symbol '***n***' represents one set of chromosomes.

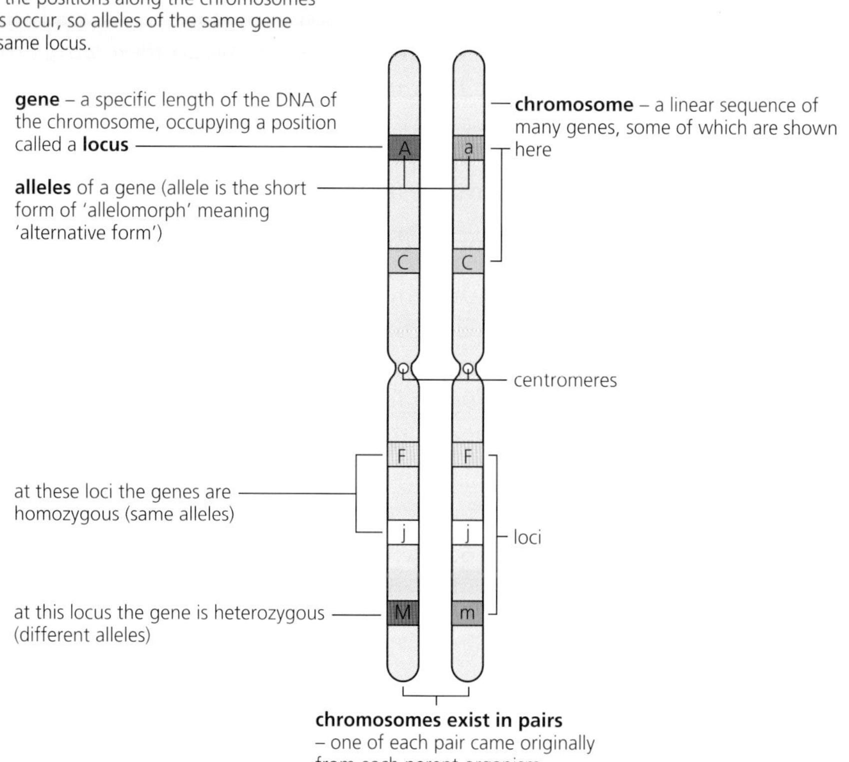
The **loci** are the positions along the chromosomes where genes occur, so alleles of the same gene occupy the same locus.
gene – a specific length of the DNA of the chromosome, occupying a position called a **locus**
alleles of a gene (allele is the short form of 'allelomorph' meaning 'alternative form')
chromosome – a linear sequence of many genes, some of which are shown here
A
a
C
C
centromeres
F
F
j
j
M
m
at these loci the genes are homozygous (same alleles)
loci
at this locus the gene is heterozygous (different alleles)
chromosomes exist in pairs – one of each pair came originally from each parent organism

Figure 5.1 The loci of a pair of homologous chromosomes

3 **For each species, the number of chromosomes is fixed**

For any one species, the number of chromosomes in each somatic cell is normally constant. For example: in the somatic cells of a human there are 46 chromosomes; in a mouse, 40; in an onion, 16; and in a sunflower, 34. Note that these characteristic chromosome numbers are all even numbers; this must be the case because the chromosomes are present in homologous pairs (feature 2).

Combining these first three features, we refer to the characteristic shape and number of chromosomes in a cell as its **karyotype**.

4 **Homologous chromosomes might not carry the same alleles of genes**

In Chapter 3, a gene was defined as a sequence of DNA nucleotide bases that encodes the sequence of amino acids in a functional polypeptide. We noted above that a diploid cell has homologous pairs of chromosomes. Thus, in each diploid cell, there are two copies of each gene. These copies lie in the same positions, or loci (singular **locus**), on the two homologous chromosomes. This is shown in Figure 5.1. Two or more different copies of a gene are called **alleles**. They are different because the order of nucleotide bases differs by one or more bases.

The two genes at any one locus in a diploid cell might have the same nucleotide base sequence. If so, this cell would be described as **homozygous** for this gene. Alternatively, the two genes might have different base sequences, in other words they would be two different alleles of the same gene. If so, the cell would be described as **heterozygous** for this gene. We can refer to diploid organisms as homozygous or heterozygous for a particular gene as well.

Key terms

Karyotype The number and shape of chromosomes in the somatic cell of an organism.

Locus (plural **loci**) The position that a particular gene occupies on a specific chromosome.

Allele One of two or more different forms of the same gene. Different alleles of the same gene have slightly different nucleotide base sequences.

Homozygous Diploid cells have two copies of each gene. If the two copies are the same allele of the gene, the cell is said to be homozygous for this gene.

Heterozygous In a diploid cell, if the two copies of a gene are different alleles, the cell is said to be heterozygous for this gene.

Let's use Figure 5.1 to put features 1, 2 and 4 into context. If you look at Figure 5.1, you can see an imaginary pair of homologous chromosomes (feature 2). As you would expect, they have the same shape – their centromeres are in the same position so that the lengths of their 'arms' is the same (feature 1). The diagram also represents five loci, in other words the positions of five genes. The chemical nature of the gene at each locus is represented by a single letter. At the loci C, F and J, the genes are the same: these loci are homozygous. In contrast, loci A and M are heterozygous (feature 4).

Key term

Chromatid Following DNA replication, a cell has two copies of each of its chromosomes. When these become visible during cell division and can be seen to be held together by their centromeres, they are briefly called chromatids.

5 Chromosomes are copied prior to division, so appear double

Between nuclear divisions, while the chromosomes are still uncoiled and cannot be resolved by light microscopes, a cell makes a copy of each chromosome. Chapter 3 described the semi-conservative replication of DNA – the process by which this copying occurs. Until separated during nuclear division, the two identical copies of each chromosome are held together by their centromeres. While held together, they are referred to as **chromatids**; after their separation during nuclear division, they are referred to as chromosomes again.

Look at the left-hand side of Figure 5.2, which puts all the above features into context. The photomicrograph shows the condensed chromosomes of a somatic cell from a human male.

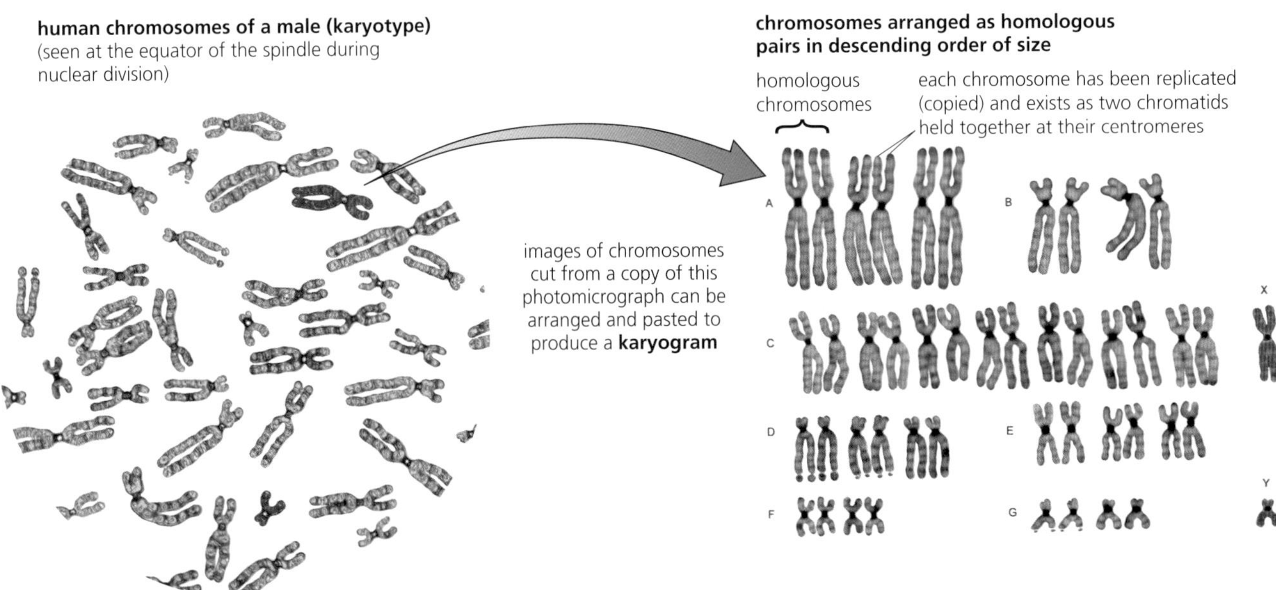
human chromosomes of a male (karyotype)
(seen at the equator of the spindle during nuclear division)
images of chromosomes cut from a copy of this photomicrograph can be arranged and pasted to produce a karyogram
chromosomes arranged as homologous pairs in descending order of size
homologous chromosomes
each chromosome has been replicated (copied) and exists as two chromatids held together at their centromeres
A
B
C
D
E
F
G
X
Y

Figure 5.2 Karyogram of a human male

You saw in point 5 above that, prior to cell division, DNA replication results in the formation of two chromatids held together by a centromere. Take any of the chromosomes in Figure 5.2 and you will see this to be true.

You saw in point 3 above that each cell has a fixed number of chromosomes. As this is a human cell, can you count 46 chromosomes?

You saw in point 2 above that the chromosomes in a somatic cell occur as homologous pairs. *Can you find any homologous pairs in the left-hand image Figure 5.2?*

If not, in the right-hand image of Figure 5.2, the pairs have been sorted for you by cutting each chromosome from a second copy of the photograph, pairing them together, arranging them in descending order of size and numbering them. A photograph (or drawing) like this is called a **karyogram**. Any karyogram of a normal human male you will ever see has these chromosomes arranged and numbered in the same way. It could be used by genetic counsellors (in conjunction with other techniques) to detect the presence of abnormalities in a patient's chromosomes, for example Down's syndrome.

You saw in point 1 above that each chromosome has a characteristic shape. Look at the chromosomes in group A in Figure 5.2. The two chromatids held together in each chromosome, as well as the two chromosomes, are the same size: their centromeres are in the same position, so that the length of their 'arms' is the same. This is not just true of chromosome pairs in *this* human male; it is true of the chromosomes of every human male and, indeed, of every human female. Exactly the same is true of the chromosomes in groups B to G.

Now look at the final pair. You can see that it is not numbered. Rather, one is labelled **X** and the other **Y**. These are known as the **sex chromosomes**, since the **Y** chromosome determines the development of male characteristics. We will return to this issue later. All the other chromosomes (pairs in groups A to G) are called **autosomes**.

Key terms

Sex chromosome A chromosome that carries genes that determine the sex of an organism. In mammals, the **Y** chromosome determines maleness.

Autosome Any chromosome other than a sex chromosome.

Test yourself

1 Sister chromatids and homologous chromosomes both carry the same genes in the same order. Explain the difference between them.
2 What is meant by the term 'allele'?
3 Give **two** functions of a centromere.
4 Explain why the chromosomes within a cell cannot normally be seen using a compound light microscope.
5 What does the karyotype tell you about a cell?

The cell cycle

Although the process of cell division is continuous, it is often described as a series of discrete stages. Figure 5.3 shows how one cell cycle of a eukaryotic cell can be described as:

- **interphase** – the time between divisions
- **mitosis** – separation of the chromatids of each chromosome to form two new nuclei
- **cytokinesis** – division of the cytoplasm.

The length of this cycle depends partly upon conditions external to the cell, such as temperature, supply of nutrients and of oxygen. Its length also depends upon the type of cell. In cells at the growing point of a young stem or of a developing human embryo, the cycle is completed in less than 24 hours. The epithelial cells that line your intestine typically divide every 10 hours, whereas your liver cells divide every year or so. Nerve cells do not normally divide after they have differentiated. In specialised cells such as these, the genes needed to initiate and control cell division are 'switched off', so they cannot divide.

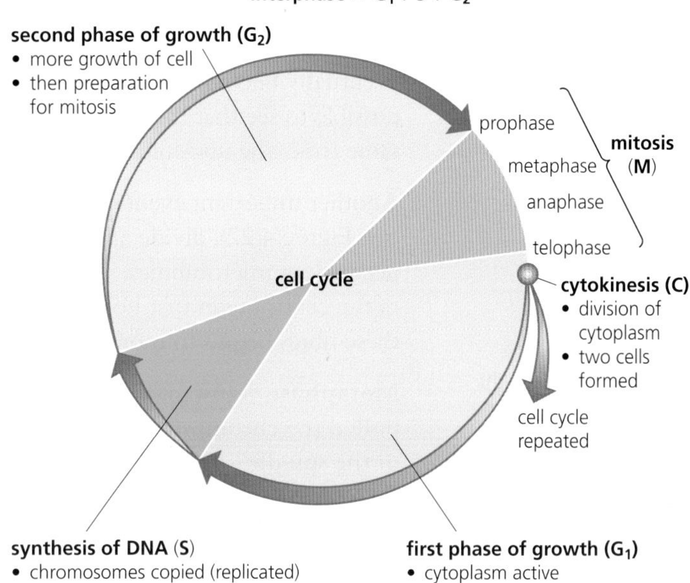

Figure 5.3 The stages of the cell cycle

Interphase

Interphase is always the longest part of the cell cycle, but is of extremely variable length. It is recognisable in light micrographs because no clear chromosomes can be seen in the nucleus. The chromatin results in a diffuse staining of the nucleus. At first glance, the nucleus appears to be 'resting', but this is not the case at all. Table 5.1 summarises the intense activity occurring in a cell during interphase.

Table 5.1 The 'stages' of interphase

G_1 – the 'first growth' phase	In the nucleus, some genes are 'switched on' and their base sequence is transcribed to pre-mRNA molecules. Editing of pre-mRNA to mature mRNA is also occurring. The cytoplasm increases in volume (grows) by producing new proteins and cell organelles, including mitochondria and endoplasmic reticulum.
S – synthesis	In the nucleus, the semi-conservative replication of DNA occurs. New histones are synthesised and attach to the replicated DNA in the nucleus. Each chromosome becomes two chromatids attached at the centromere Growth of the cell continues.
G_2 – the 'second growth' phase	In the nucleus, replicated DNA is 'double checked' for errors and corrected if any errors are found. If correction is not possible, the cell cycle is normally halted at this G2 phase. Cell growth continues by further synthesis of proteins and cell organelles.

Nuclear division – mitosis

When cell division occurs, the nucleus divides first. In mitosis, the chromosomes, present as the chromatids formed during interphase, are separated and distributed to two daughter nuclei.

Figure 5.4 presents mitosis in an animal cell as a process in four phases, but this is for convenience of description only. Mitosis is always one continuous process with no breaks between the phases.

In **prophase**, the chromosomes increasingly shorten and thicken by a process of super-coiling (look back to Figure 4.15 to remind yourself of this coiling). As a result, they eventually become visible as long, thin threads. Only towards the end of prophase is it possible to see that they consist of two chromatids held together at the centromere. At the same time, the nucleolus gradually disappears and the nuclear membrane breaks down.

Another important event occurs during prophase. The centrioles, described in Chapter 4 (see Figure 4.22), divide and move to opposite ends of the cell. As they do so, they radiate a network of microtubules, called the **spindle**. Some of the spindle fibres attach to each side of the centromeres that hold together the chromatids in each chromosome. Contraction of these fibres begins to move the chromosomes apart.

Tip

When examining light micrographs of cells undergoing mitosis, first look for those cells in metaphase. These are easiest to spot because the chromosomes are neatly lined up on the equator of the spindle.

Metaphase is instantly recognisable in light micrographs as the spindle fibres have now pulled the chromosomes into the centre of the cell, where they line up on the equator of the spindle.

In **anaphase**, the centromere of each chromosome divides; the spindle fibres attached to them shorten, resulting in the two chromatids being pulled by their centromeres to opposite poles of the spindle. Once separated, the chromatids are referred to as chromosomes again. In Figure 5.4, you can see an early part of anaphase; the chromatids have only just left the equator of the spindle.

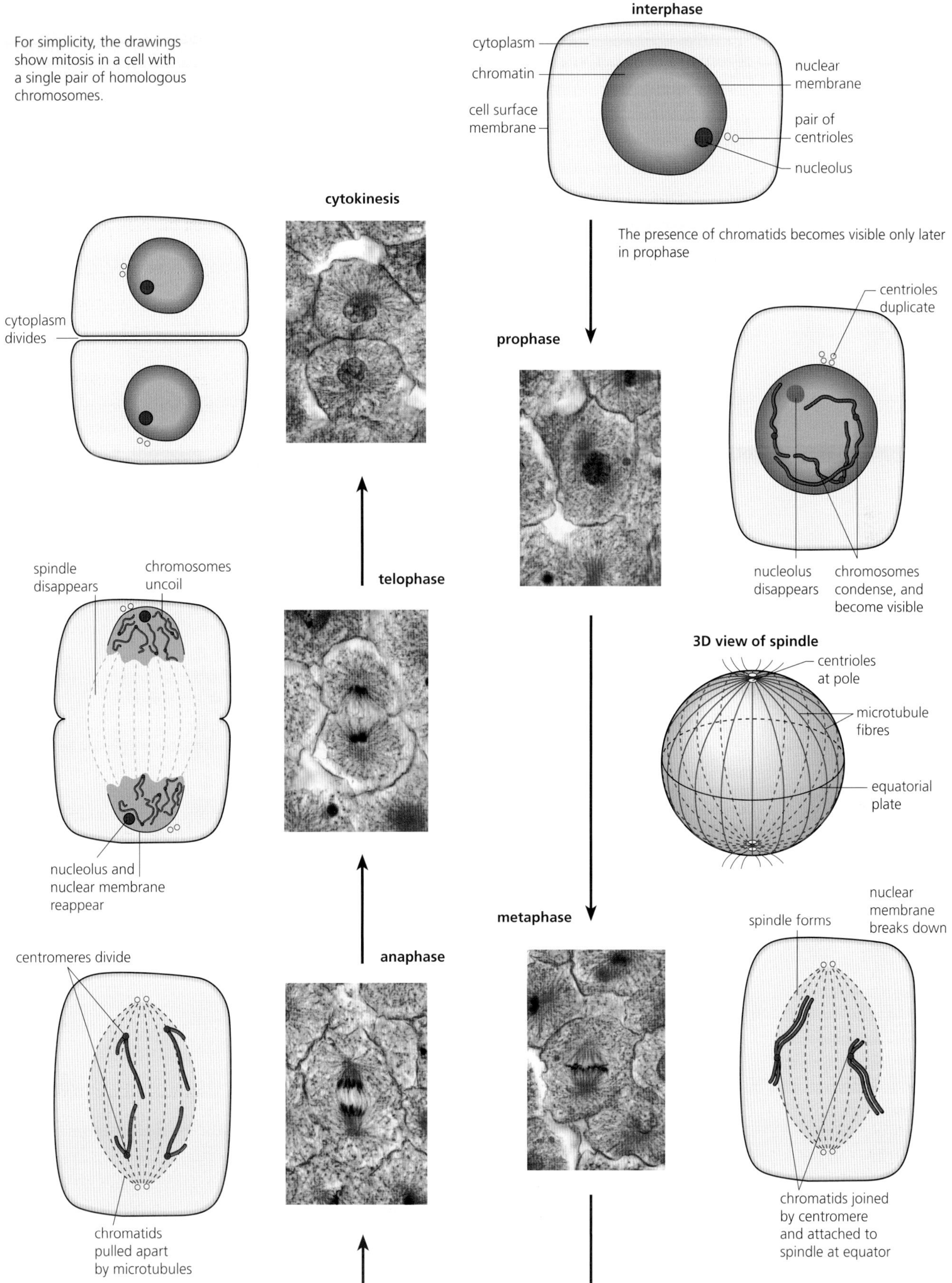
For simplicity, the drawings show mitosis in a cell with a single pair of homologous chromosomes.
interphase
cytoplasm
chromatin
cell surface membrane
nuclear membrane
pair of centrioles
nucleolus
The presence of chromatids becomes visible only later in prophase
prophase
centrioles duplicate
nucleolus disappears
chromosomes condense, and become visible
3D view of spindle
centrioles at pole
microtubule fibres
equatorial plate
metaphase
spindle forms
nuclear membrane breaks down
chromatids joined by centromere and attached to spindle at equator
anaphase
centromeres divide
chromatids pulled apart by microtubules
telophase
spindle disappears
chromosomes uncoil
nucleolus and nuclear membrane reappear
cytokinesis
cytoplasm divides

Figure 5.4 Mitosis in an animal cell

In **telophase**, a nuclear membrane reforms around both groups of chromosomes at opposite ends of the cell. The chromosomes 'de-condense' by uncoiling, becoming chromatin again. You can see this uncoiling has already begun in telophase in Figure 5.4. One or more nucleoli reform in each nucleus.

Cytokinesis

Division of the cytoplasm, known as **cytokinesis**, usually follows telophase. Vesicles from the Golgi apparatus are involved in cytokinesis in both animal and plant cells, but in different ways.

During cytokinesis in animal cells, a **cleavage furrow** (pinch) develops in the middle of the cell. You can see this in Figure 5.4. Contraction of this cleavage 'pinches' the cytoplasm in half. As this happens, cell organelles become distributed between the two developing cells.

This 'pinching' does not happen during cytokinesis in plant cells. Instead, as you can see in Figure 5.5, vesicles from the Golgi apparatus collect along the line of the equator of the spindle, known as the cell plate. These vesicles secrete a gel-like layer of calcium pectate, called the **middle lamella** (see Figure 4.23, page 88). Onto this, they secrete transverse layers of microfibres of cellulose, forming the primary cell wall. Subsequently, more layers are added, often at right angles, forming the secondary cell wall. Many cell walls also become impregnated with lignin. You will see the importance of lignin in Chapter 12.

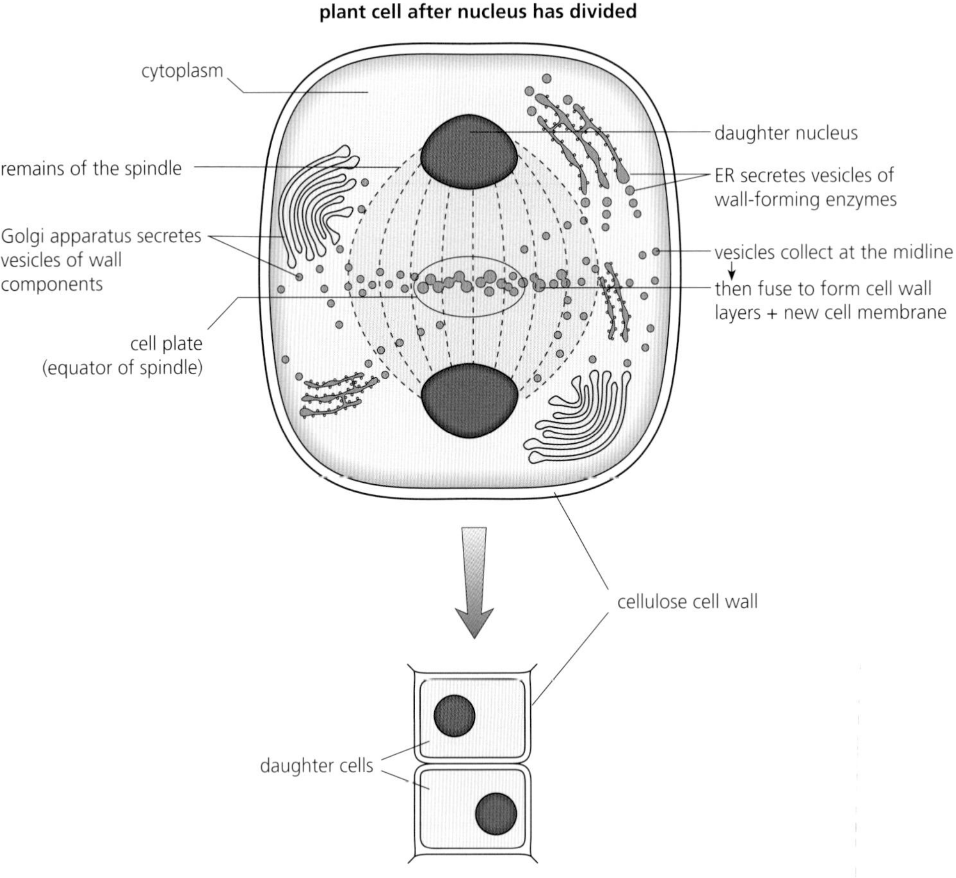

Figure 5.5 Cytokinesis in a plant cell

The significance of mitosis

The 'daughter' cells produced by mitosis are **clones**. This means that they are genetically identical to each other and to the parent cell from which they were formed. This occurs because:

- an exact copy of each chromosome is made by accurate DNA replication during interphase, when two chromatids are formed
- the two chromatids remain attached by their centromeres during prophase of mitosis, when each becomes attached to a spindle fibre
- when the centromeres divide during anaphase, the chromatids of each pair are pulled apart to opposite poles of the spindle. Thus, one copy of each chromosome moves to each pole of the spindle
- the chromosomes at the poles form the new nuclei – two to a cell at this point
- two cells are then formed by division of the cytoplasm at the mid-point of the cell, each with an exact copy of the original nucleus.

Key term

Clones Two or more cells, or organisms, that are genetically identical to each other. In eukaryotic organisms, clones are produced by mitosis.

Test yourself

6 Look back to the drawing and photograph of a eukaryotic cell in Chapter 4 (page 80). In which part of the cell cycle is it all depicted? Explain your answer.

7 Precisely in which part of the cell cycle does DNA replication occur?

8 In which part of the cell cycle are the products of DNA replication separated?

9 Early in mitosis, a chromosome is seen as two chromatids. At the end of mitosis the same chromosome is single. Is there any difference between these two structures? Explain your answer.

10 Plant cells lack centrioles, yet they produce a spindle during mitosis. Use your knowledge of cell structure to suggest how.

Where mitosis is commonly observed

You have seen above that asexual reproduction in some eukaryotic unicells involves mitosis. Consequently, you could observe mitosis by examining cultures of these unicells growing in favourable conditions.

Alternatively, you could examine tissues of multicellular organisms that are actively growing. In mammals, these tissues include epithelial tissues, such as the skin and the lining of the intestine. In flowering plants, these tissues are found at **mersitems** – the actively growing tips of shoots and roots – and the **cambium** within the vascular bundles (Chapter 12). For this reason, our core practical examines mitosis in actively growing root tips of a flowering plant.

Key term

Meristem A group of plant cells that are able to divide by mitosis. Primary meristems are found at the tips of growing shoots and roots. Secondary meristems develop in woody plants, leading to an increase in diameter of roots and shoots.

Core practical 3

Making a temporary squash preparation of a root tip to investigate the stages of mitosis under a microscope

Mitosis can be observed in any tissue that is actively dividing. A tissue in which it is easy to observe mitosis is the growing tip of a plant root. Any plant root will do; onion and garlic bulbs are commonly used in the laboratories of colleges and schools.

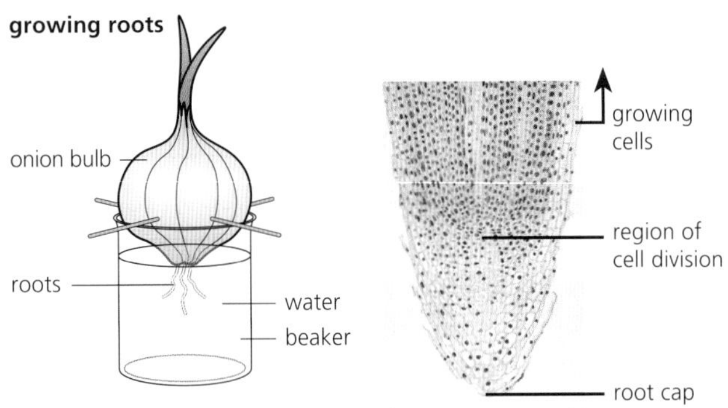

Figure 5.6 The tip of a growing root

Before reading on, follow the steps in the protocol below which describes how to prepare plant tissue for examination under a light microscope, starting off with an onion bulb.

Risk assessment

The two stains most commonly used for this experiment are toluidine blue and orcein, both of which are low hazard. Toluidine blue is used in a simple and low hazard aqueous solution, whereas corrosive carboxylic acids (acetic or proprionic) are required for the orcein stain to adhere to the chromosomes.

Even though its use is more hazardous, orcein is often used in preference to toluidine blue, because the stain produces greater definition of chromosome structure.

The hazards of using the acetic orcein stain can be very much reduced by dispensing a small volume of the stain into a stoppered bottle. Containment of the stain prevents spillage.

The bottle should be firmly stoppered until it needs to be opened. The bottle should always be placed on an impervious surface when it is being handled.

Procedure

1 Onion or garlic cloves are suspended over water, until roots can be seen growing from the "blunt" surface. The roots must be no longer than 1 cm, and must still be growing when the roots are harvested. The roots will, therefore, have lots of dividing cells in a meristem region.

2 Fill a small bottle with 1 M hydrochloric acid, and place it in a thermostatically controlled water bath set at 55 °C. Leave the bottle for 15 minutes, so that the acid warms to the temperature of the water bath.

> **Tip**
>
> Heating the root tips in hydrochloric acid increases the permeability of the cell, so allowing the stain to penetrate more easily.

Place a garlic clove in the bottle, so that the roots are submerged in the 55 °C hydrochloric acid. Leave the roots in the acid for 5 minutes.
When the garlic clove has been in the 55 °C hydrochloric acid for 5 minutes, take it out and rinse the roots thoroughly in tap water. This can be done by either by rinsing under the tap, or by immersing the roots in a beaker of water.

3 Label a small bottle or vial, including a hazard warning.
Place a pinprick hole in the bottle's cap, to prevent the lid popping off when the bottle/vial is heated.
Place a small volume of the stain in the bottle.
There should be enough for a layer of fluid; this is approximately 2 mm in depth.

4 Use a pair of sharp scissors on the garlic clove to cut off the root tips (5–10 mm at the pointed end) so they fall, or can be placed, in the acetic orcein.
Use the scissors to make sure that the root tips are immersed in the stain. Then place the lid on the vial.
Place the acetic orcein vial in the 55 °C water bath. Leave it there for 5 minutes.

> **Tip**
>
> The time and temperature of staining are important. The stain requires 5 minutes at 55 °C for the stain to diffuse into the cell and bind with the chromosomes. In an open watch glass, the acetic acid will often evaporate before the stain has penetrated the cells.
>
> The stopper in the container used in this method means that the acetic acid does not evaporate.

5 After the root tips have been in the stain for 5 minutes, use forceps to take them out of the vial, and place them on a microscope slide.

> **Tip**
>
> Squashing the root spreads the cells, so that there is just a single layer to be seen under the microscope. This makes the individual cells easier to see.

Add a drop of water to the root tip on the slide. Tease the root tip with needles, to spread out the cells. Place a cover slip over the root tip.

Wrap the slide in several layers of a thick paper towel. Use your thumbs to gently press on the slide and cover slip through the paper towel. You should be just able to feel the glass through the towel. Remove the paper towel.

6 Place the slide onto the stage of the microscope, and view the slide under the high power objective lens.

Questions

1 What safety precautions did you take when using the scalpel?

2 In step 2, the root tip is heated in hydrochloric acid. What was achieved by doing this?

3 When examining a temporary preparation, how did you recognise an air bubble trapped under the cover slip?

4 Explain why lateral movements should be avoided in Step 5.

5 Why is paper towel placed between the thumb and the cover slip during Step 5.

6 Assuming that the condenser lens of the microscope (if present) is already focused, list the steps you followed to view the plant tissue using the high-power objective lens.

7 If you pushed the slide to your left, which way did cells in the tissue appear to move?

8 Explain why the preparation is called a 'temporary squash' preparation.

9 Suppose you wish to adapt the method described to find the number of cells in each of the stages of mitosis. How would you adapt the method to ensure that the values you find are accurate?

10 How could you determine an appropriate number of fields of view to observe?

Meiosis – a different type of nuclear division

Meiosis is a type of nuclear division with quite different outcomes from mitosis. Figure 5.7 illustrates three differences.

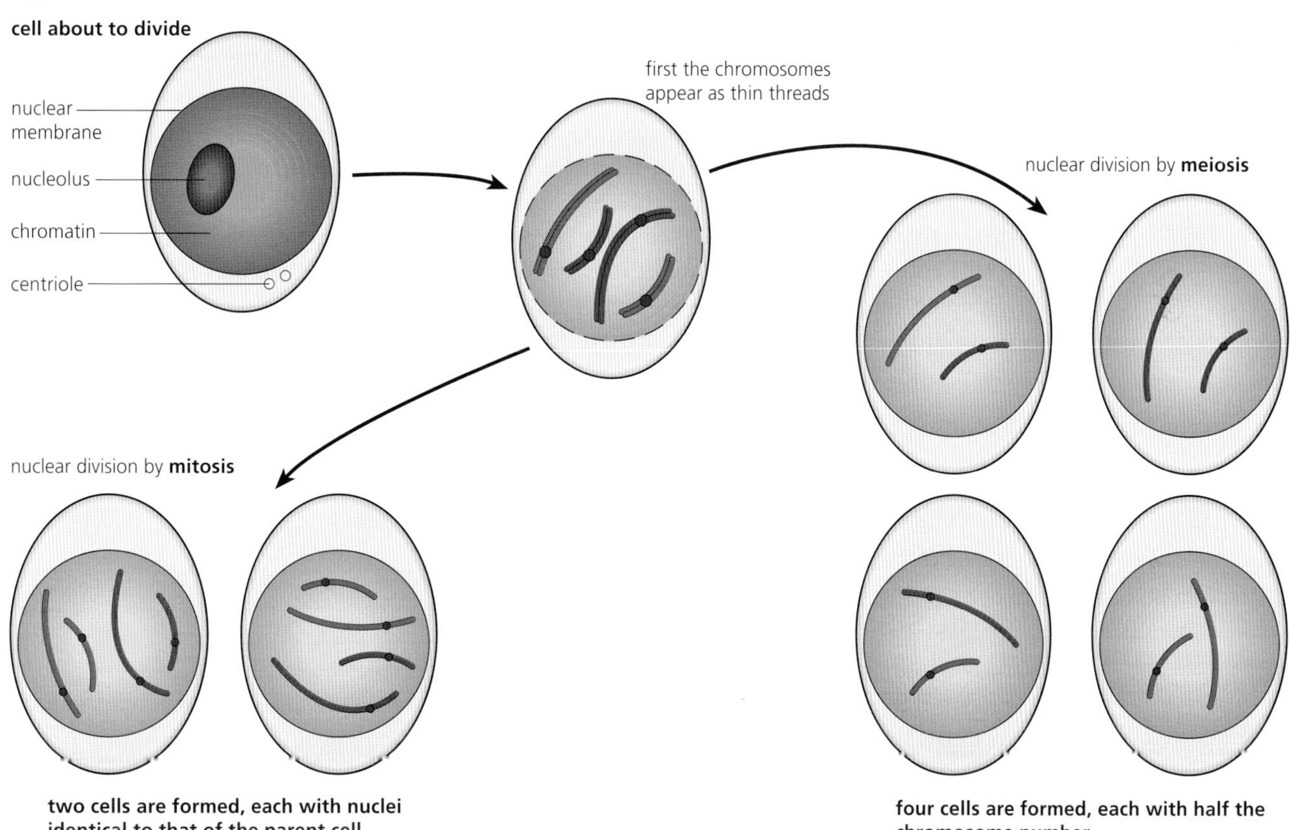
cell about to divide
nuclear membrane
nucleolus
chromatin
centriole
first the chromosomes appear as thin threads
nuclear division by meiosis
nuclear division by mitosis
two cells are formed, each with nuclei identical to that of the parent cell
four cells are formed, each with half the chromosome number

Figure 5.7 Mitosis and meiosis – the significant differences in outcome

- Meiosis normally produces four daughter cells whereas mitosis produces two.
- Meiosis produces daughter cells that have half the number of chromosomes as the parent cell, whereas mitosis produces daughter cells that have the same chromosome complement as the parent cell.
- Meiosis produces daughter cells that are genetically different, whereas mitosis produces daughter cells that are genetically identical to each other and to the parent cell, in other words are clones.

Meiosis occurs at some point in the life cycle of all organisms that reproduce sexually. In humans, for example, meiosis occurs in the gonads – testes and ovaries – and results in the formation of haploid **gametes** that fuse at fertilisation to form a diploid **zygote** (Chapter 6). This is not universally true of all organisms, however. In most fungi, for example, the parent cell is haploid and gametes are formed by mitosis.

Key term

Haploid A eukaryotic cell is haploid (represented by '*n*') if it contains only one chromosome from each of its homologous pairs.

An overview of meiosis

Meiosis involves two divisions of the nucleus, known as **meiosis I** and **meiosis II**.

Look at Figure 5.8, which provides an overview of what happens during both these divisions. To make the diagram simple to understand, Figure 5.8 shows only a single pair of homologous chromosomes.

Start with the first two diagrams at the top of Figure 5.8. You can see that, like mitosis, during the interphase that precedes meiosis, the chromosomes have been replicated to form two chromatids held together by their centromeres. The third diagram, however, shows that in meiosis the homologous chromosomes then pair up. By the end of meiosis I, shown in the fifth diagram in Figure 5.8, homologous chromosomes have been separated into two new cells. Notice, though, that each chromosome still consists of two chromatids, held together at their centromere. It is during meiosis II that these chromatids are separated.

To summarise, meiosis consists of two nuclear divisions but only one replication of the chromosomes. The important points to remember are that:

- in **meiosis I**, homologous chromosomes are separated
- in **meiosis II**, the chromatids of each chromosome are separated.

Meiosis – the detail

As with mitosis, once meiosis starts it usually proceeds as a continuous process. Figure 5.9 provides a more detailed version of meiosis, showing the stages you need to know. Again, to make things simpler to follow, the diagrams show only one pair of homologous chromosomes. The separate steps in Figure 5.9 relate to stages seen in tissue that has been killed, stained and examined under a light microscope. The stages have the same names and sequence as those in mitosis – prophase, metaphase, anaphase and telophase.

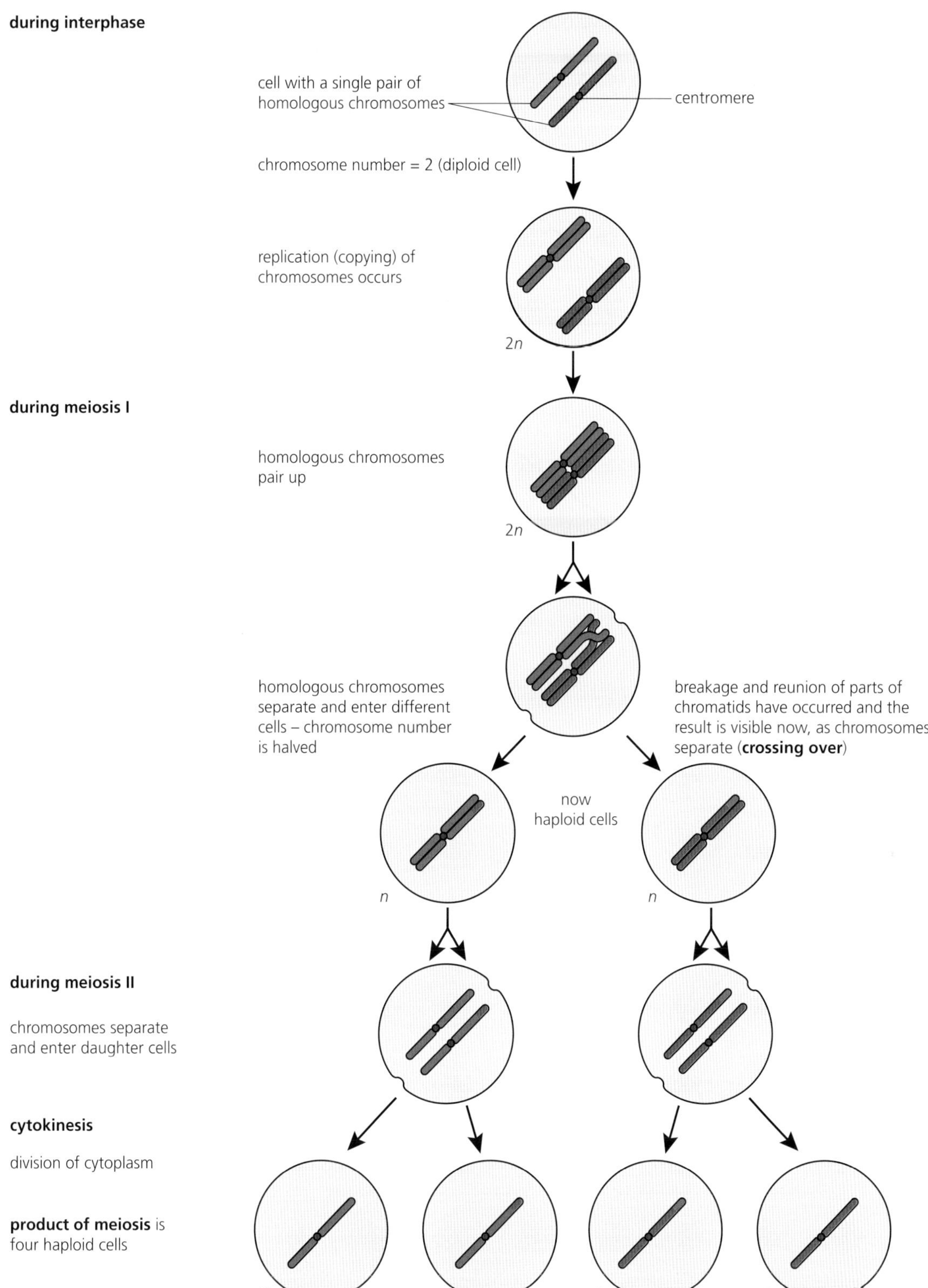
during interphase
cell with a single pair of homologous chromosomes
centromere
chromosome number = 2 (diploid cell)
replication (copying) of chromosomes occurs
2n
during meiosis I
homologous chromosomes pair up
2n
homologous chromosomes separate and enter different cells – chromosome number is halved
breakage and reunion of parts of chromatids have occurred and the result is visible now, as chromosomes separate (crossing over)
now haploid cells
n
n
during meiosis II
chromosomes separate and enter daughter cells
cytokinesis
division of cytoplasm
product of meiosis is four haploid cells
n
n
n
n

Figure 5.8 An overview of meiosis

MEIOSIS I

prophase I (early)
During interphase the chromosomes replicate into chromatids held together by a centromere (the chromatids are not visible). Now the chromosomes condense (shorten and thicken) and become visible.

prophase I (mid)
Homologous chromosomes pair up (becoming **bivalents**) as they continue to shorten and thicken. Centrioles duplicate.

prophase I (late)
Homologous chromosomes repel each other. Chromosomes can now be seen to consist of chromatids. Sites where chromatids have broken and rejoined, causing crossing over, are visible as chiasmata.

metaphase I
Nuclear membrane breaks down. Spindle forms. Bivalents line up at the equator, attached by centromeres.

anaphase I
Homologous chromosomes separate. Whole chromosomes are pulled towards opposite poles of the spindle, centromere first (dragging along the chromatids).

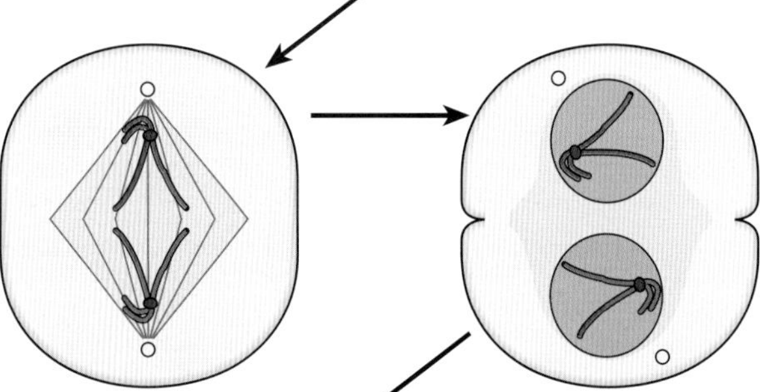

telophase I
Nuclear membrane re-forms around the daughter nuclei. The chromosome number has been halved. The chromosomes start to decondense.

there is no interphase between **MEIOSIS I** and **MEIOSIS II**

MEIOSIS II

prophase II
The chromosomes condense and the centrioles duplicate.

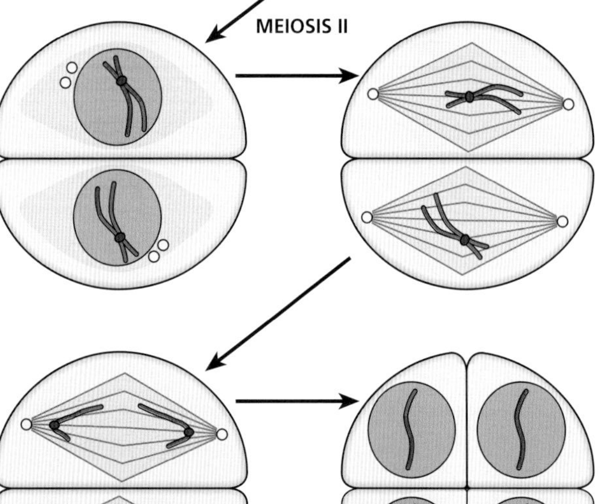

metaphase II
The nuclear membrane breaks down and the spindle forms. The chromosomes attach by their centromere to spindle fibres at the equator of the spindle.

anaphase II
The chromatids separate at their centromeres and are pulled to opposite poles of the spindle.

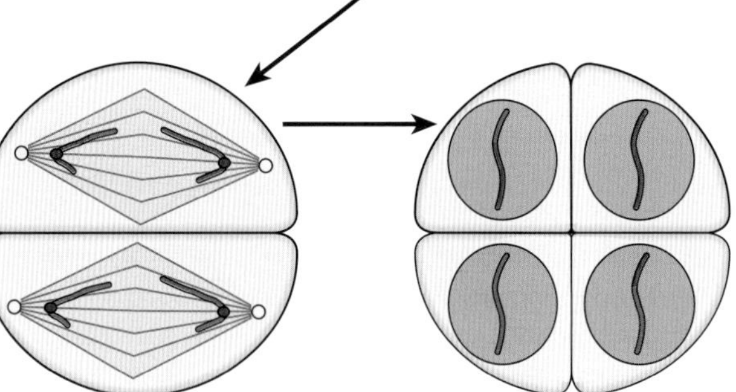

telophase II
The chromatids (now called chromosomes) decondense. The nuclear membrane re-forms. The cells divide.

Figure 5.9 The stages of meiosis

Meiosis I

In **prophase I**, the chromosomes become visible as they condense. At the same time, the two members of each pair of homologous chromosomes pair up. Remember, members of a homologous pair of chromosomes have the same linear sequence of genes. Gene-by-gene, the pairing is very precise. When we see them like this, we refer to each pair as a **bivalent**.

As members of each bivalent continue to shorten, their chromatids often become entangled, causing a stress on the DNA molecules. As a result of this stress within a bivalent, individual chromatids frequently break. The broken ends rejoin more or less immediately. When **non-sister chromatids** from homologous chromosomes break and rejoin they do so at exactly corresponding sites, so that a cross-shaped structure called a **chiasma** is formed at one or more places along a bivalent. In the fourth and fifth diagrams in Figure 5.8, you can see the effect of one chiasma. As a result of breakage, one portion of a blue chromatid and the corresponding portion of a red chromosome have broken and joined the 'wrong' chromatid. This event is known as a **crossing over** because lengths of genes have been exchanged between chromatids. Remember that, although homologous chromosomes have the same loci in the same order, the loci might have different alleles of the same gene. Thus, new combinations of alleles can be produced as a result of crossing over.

Next the spindle forms. As in mitosis, chromatids become attached by their centromeres to the fibres of the spindle. As they contract, these fibres pull the chromosomes, still held together in their homologous pairs, until they come to lie at the equatorial plate of the spindle: this is **metaphase I**.

During **anaphase I**, further contraction of the spindle fibres pulls the homologous chromosomes apart, one to each pole of the spindle. At this stage, however, the sister chromatids remain attached by their centromeres. The pairing between them has started to break down and so, as you can see in Figure 5.9, they both become clearly visible. You can see the outcome of this in the fifth diagram in Figure 5.9.

Telophase I then follows. Two new nuclei are formed and the spindle breaks down. We now have two new cells, each with two nuclei containing a single set of condensed chromosomes, still made of two chromatids. These new cells do not go into interphase, but rather continue smoothly into meiosis II.

Key terms

Bivalent The name given to the two homologous chromosomes in a diploid cell when they are seen paired together during meiosis I. As each chromosome is currently present as two chromatids, there are four chromatids in a single bivalent.

Non-sister chromatids Chromatids on the two different members of a homologous pair of chromosomes.

Chiasma (plural chiasmata) A point seen during meiosis I at which the non-sister chromatids appear interlocked. A chiasma is the result of non-sister chromatids within a bivalent becoming entwined, breaking and re-joining to the fragment from the non-sister chromatid earlier in prophase I.

Crossing over The process by which non-sister chromatids exchange genes following formation of a chiasma

Meiosis II

During **prophase II**, two new spindles form at right angles to the old one. Contraction of the fibres in each spindle pulls the chromosomes to the centre of their respective spindles to reach **metaphase II**. Following division of the centromeres, further contraction of the spindle fibres pulls individual chromatids to opposite poles of their respective spindle during **anaphase II**. Now there are four groups of chromosomes, each with half the number of the original parent cell. During **telophase II**, new nuclei form around these groups of chromosomes. The chromosomes become long and thin again, the nuclear membranes reform and the cytoplasm divides to form new cells.

Test yourself

11 A diploid cell has 20 pairs of homologous chromosomes. How many chromosomes will be present in a cell produced from this cell by:

a) mitosis

b) meiosis?

12 In which of the two divisions of meiosis are sister chromatids separated?

13 Describe how you could distinguish between a cell in metaphase of mitosis and a cell in metaphase I of meiosis.

14 The X and Y chromosomes in Figure 5.2 look very different but are able to pair together during meiosis. What does this suggest about their nature?

Test yourself

15 Look at Figure 5.10, which depicts meiosis without crossing over.

a) The cell depicted in Figure 5.10 has two pairs of homologous chromosomes. Without crossing over, how many genetically different daughter cells could it produce?

b) Use your answer to part a) to devise a formula that will enable you to calculate the number of genetically different daughter cells that could be produced by a cell in which the number of pairs of homologous chromosomes is n.

c) Use the formula you have derived to represent the number of genetically different egg or sperm cells that could result from meiosis in a human.

Independent assortment is illustrated in a parent cell with two pairs of homologous chromosomes (four bivalents). The more bivalents there are, the more variation is possible. In humans, for example, there are 23 pairs of chromosomes giving over 8 million combinations.

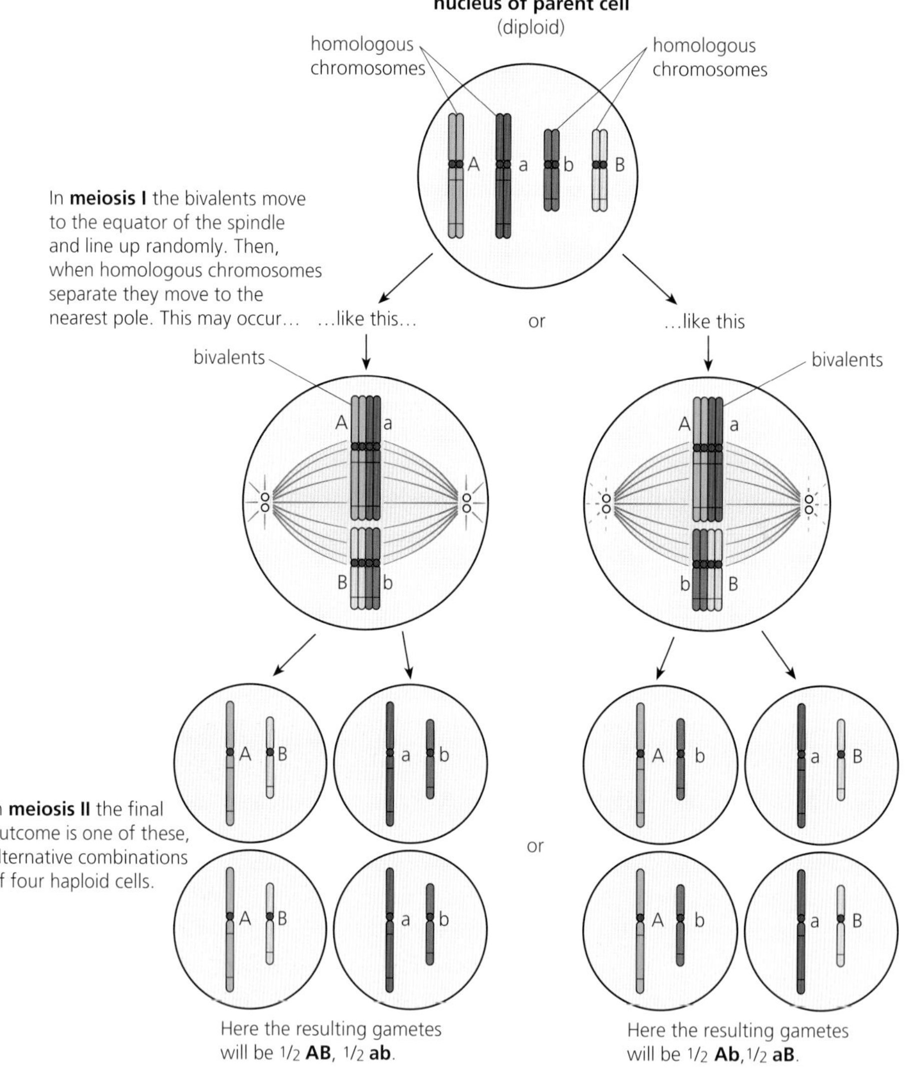

Figure 5.10 Genetic variation resulting from the independent assortment of homologous chromosomes

Meiosis and genetic variation

You have seen that mitosis produces clones – genetically identical cells. Meiosis does not and is a major source of genetic variation in organisms. The cells produced by meiosis are genetically different for two reasons.

There is **independent assortment** of homologous chromosomes. This happens because the bivalents line up at the equator of the spindle in meiosis I entirely at random. As a result, which chromosome of a given pair is pulled to which pole is unaffected by (independent of) the behaviour of the chromosomes in other homologous pairs. Look at Figure 5.10, which represents independent assortment in a parent cell with a diploid number of four chromosomes. To make the process easier to follow, the pairs of homologous chromosomes have been coloured differently. You can see that, depending on which way the two pairs of homologous chromosomes are pulled apart can result in completely different combinations of chromosomes in the daughter cells. We see that independent assortment *alone*, generates a huge amount of variation in the coded information carried by the different haploid cells produced by meiosis.

As described above, there is **crossing over** of segments of the non-sister chromatids of the members of a pair of homologous chromosomes. Figure 5.11 shows more detail of this crossing over. Using letters to represent the alleles of three genes, it also shows how two crossover events result in new combinations of alleles on the chromosomes of the haploid cells produced.

Finally in the random fusion of gametes that occurs during fertilisation, further genetic variation is generated, but that is an issue for later chapters.

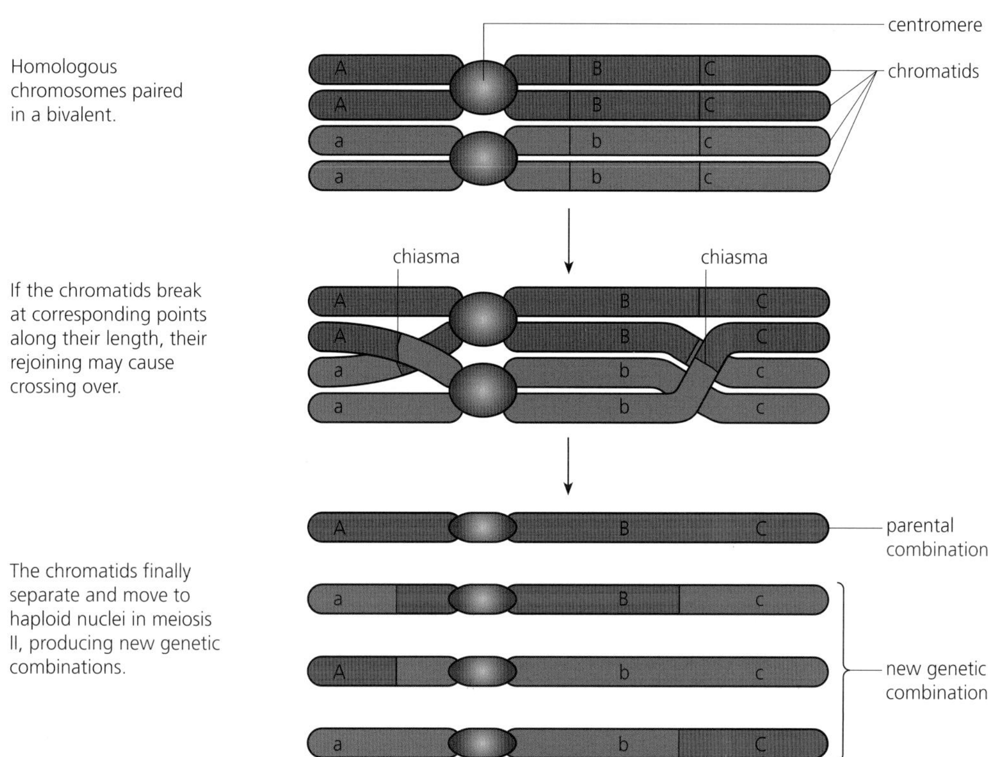

Figure 5.11 Genetic variation due to crossing over between non-sister chromatids

Chromosome mutations

You looked at gene mutations in Chapter 3 (page 64). Chromosome mutations can also occur.

In a **chromosome mutation**, a change in the number or the sequence of genes can be brought about in a number of different ways. They include:

- **chromosome translocation**, in which part of a chromosome breaks and rejoins a completely different chromosome. Although these translocations are usually harmless in humans, carriers have an increased risk of producing gametes with unbalanced translocations that might, after fertilisation, result in miscarriages. About 5 per cent of Down's syndrome cases are caused by gametes in which part of the long arm of chromosome 21 has broken away and re-joined chromosome 14 (a partial chromosome translocation)
- **chromosome non-disjunction**, in which the members of a homologous pair fail to be separated during meiosis. Look at the lower part of Figure 5.12. It illustrates what happens if one pair of chromosomes, in this case the longer pair, fails to separate during meiosis. You can see how the two upper daughter cells in Figure 5.12 contain two copies of this longer chromosome whilst the two lower daughter cells contain no copy of that chromosome at all. If these cells are gametes that fuse with a normal gamete, fertilisation could produce:
  - either a zygote with more copies of this chromosome than usual (**polysomy**)
  - or a zygote with only one copy of this chromosome (**monosomy**).

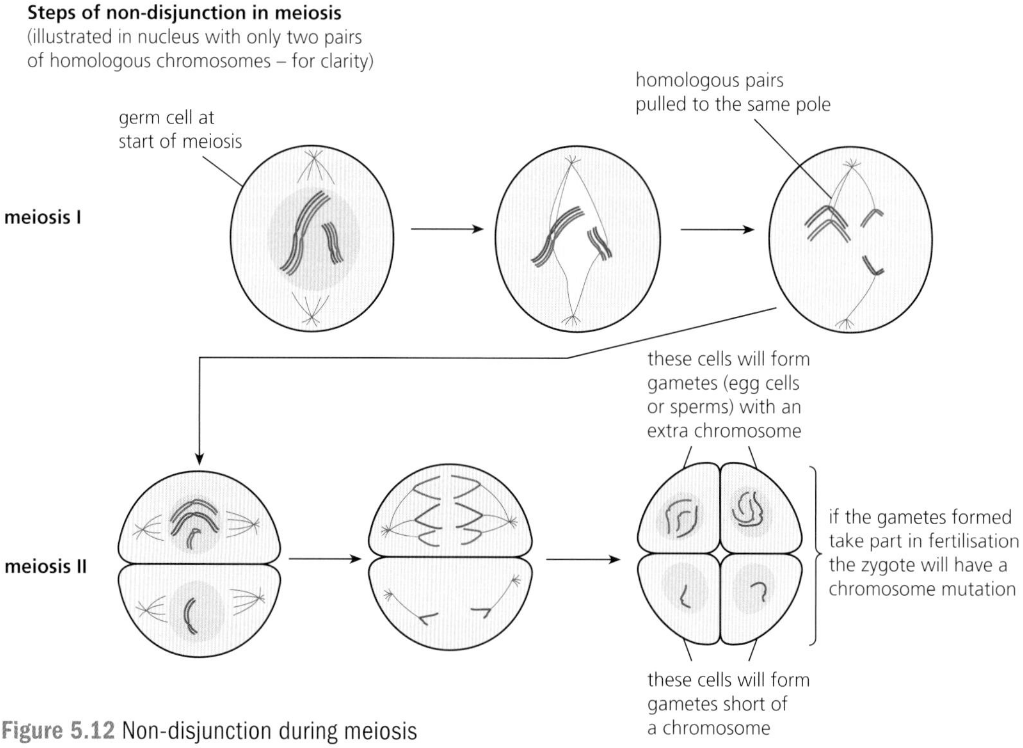

Steps of non-disjunction in meiosis
(illustrated in nucleus with only two pairs of homologous chromosomes – for clarity)

meiosis I
germ cell at start of meiosis
homologous pairs pulled to the same pole

meiosis II
these cells will form gametes (egg cells or sperms) with an extra chromosome
if the gametes formed take part in fertilisation the zygote will have a chromosome mutation
these cells will form gametes short of a chromosome

Figure 5.12 Non-disjunction during meiosis

Key terms

Chromosome non-disjunction The failure of homologous chromosomes to separate properly during the first division of meiosis. It results in daughter cells (gametes) with too many, or too few, chromosomes.

Polysomy A term used to describe a diploid cell, or diploid organism, with more than two copies of a particular chromosome.

Monosomy A term used to describe a diploid cell, or diploid organism, with only one copy of a particular chromosome.

Turner's syndrome – an example of monosomy in humans

In humans, monosomy is usually partial, in other words only part of a chromosome is lost. Full monosomy, that is, lack of one complete chromosome, is usually lethal. Only one case of full monosomy is known in humans – **Turner's syndrome**. Women with Turner's syndrome have only one X chromosome (often represented **XO**), rather than the normal two (represented **XX**). In the UK, about 1 in 2000 girls is affected by this condition. There is a wide range of symptoms associated with Turner's syndrome but in almost all cases, the women have undeveloped ovaries, resulting in a lack of periods and infertility.

Down's syndrome – an example of polysomy in humans

Polysomy is also rare. In the UK, about 750 babies are born each year with **Down's syndrome** and an estimated 60 000 people in the UK live with this condition. Most cases of Down's syndrome result from the non-disjunction of chromosome 21 during gamete production. The resulting zygote inherits three copies of chromosome 21, giving them a total of 47 chromosomes. You can see this in the karyogram of a person with Down's syndrome in Figure 5.13. As with Turner's syndrome, the symptoms of Down's syndrome are variable.

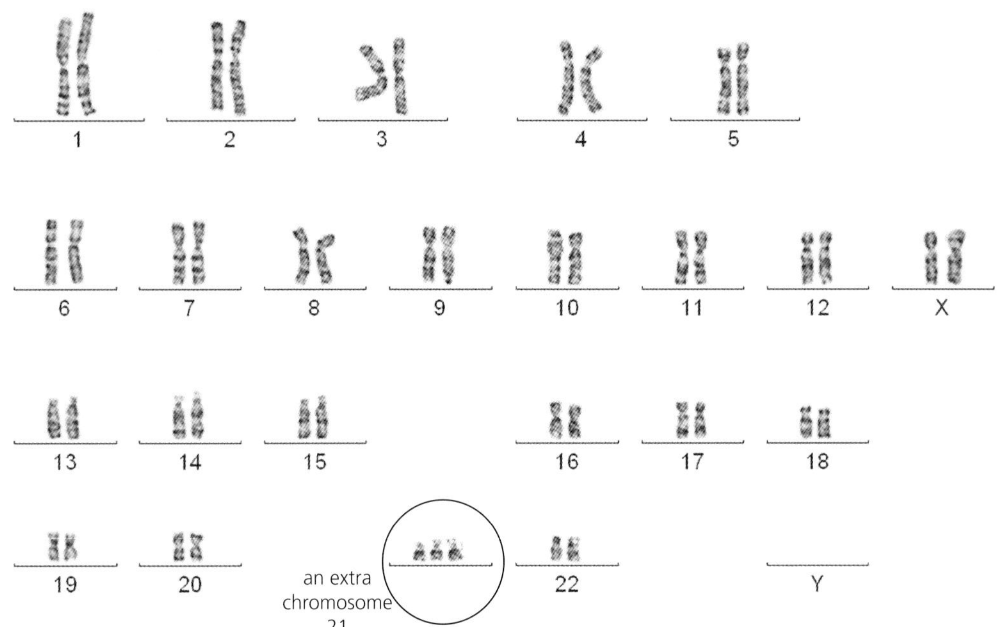

Figure 5.13 Karyogram of a person with Down's syndrome

Key terms

Turner's syndrome A condition usually caused by chromosome non-disjunction of chromosome pair 23 during gamete formation, resulting in the conception of a girl with only one X chromosome per cell. A small number of cases result from the loss of a substantial part of one X chromosome during gamete formation.

Down's syndrome A condition usually caused by the non-disjunction of chromosome pair 21, resulting in the conception of a child with three copies of this chromosome per cell. About 5 per cent of cases are caused by translocation of a large part of chromosome 21 to chromosome 14 during gamete formation.

Test yourself

16 Crossing over can occur between sister chromatids during meiosis I. Suggest what effect this would have.

17 A chromosome translocation in the gamete of a parent could, after fertilisation, result in the miscarriage of an embryo. Suggest why.

18 How many chromosomes will be present in the somatic cells of a girl with Turner's syndrome? Explain your answer.

19 Down's syndrome is often referred to as trisomy 21. Explain why.

20 Although the chances of having a baby with Down's syndrome are higher for older parents, more babies with Down's syndrome are born to younger mothers.

a) Suggest why the chances of having an affected baby increase with the age of the parents.

b) Explain why, despite the lower risk, more affected babies are born to younger mothers.

Chapter summary

Eukaryotic chromosomes

- Each eukaryotic chromosome is a double helix of DNA, several million base pairs long.
- Each chromosome is normally in a condensed state, with the DNA wrapped around histone 'beads'.
- In any species, the number and shape of their chromosomes is fixed.
- Cells with only one copy of each chromosome are termed haploid. Cells with two copies of each chromosome are termed diploid.

Eukaryotic cell cycle

- Within a multicellular organism, only some cells are able to divide. The frequency with which they divide differs from tissue to tissue.
- The cell cycle involves three stages: interphase, nuclear division (mitosis) and cytoplasmic division (cytokinesis).
- Interphase is the non-dividing stage of a cell. In addition to metabolising, a cell in interphase will grow, produce new organelles and replicate each of its chromosomes.

Mitosis

- One mitotic division produces two daughter cells that contain exactly the same number and type of chromosomes as the parent eukaryotic cell. These identical cells are clones.
- In diploid organisms, mitosis contributes to growth, repair and asexual reproduction. In haploid organisms it contributes to gamete formation.
- The microscopic examination of cells undergoing mitosis reveals four stages: prophase, metaphase, anaphase and telophase.
- In prophase, the chromosomes shorten and thicken. Each appears as two thicker strands, called chromatids, held together by a centromere at one point along their length. The two chromatids are copies of a single chromosome, produced during interphase. As the chromosomes thicken, the nuclear membrane disperses and a network of protein fibres is formed – the spindle. In animal cells, the centrioles are responsible for spindle formation.
- In metaphase, each chromosome is pulled to the middle of the spindle. It is pulled by the contraction of spindle fibres attached to its centromere.
- In anaphase, each centromere divides, releasing the two chromatids. The two chromatids are pulled by spindle fibres, one to each pole of the spindle.
- In telophase, new nuclear membranes form around the two groups of chromatids, forming new nuclei.

Cytokinesis

- During cytokinesis, the cytoplasm divides, producing two cells each with an identical nucleus.
- In animal cells, division is by pinching inwards of the cell surface membrane.
- In plant cells, division occurs from the middle of the cell as a new middle lamella and cell walls are formed.

Meiosis

- A diploid cell has two copies of each chromosome – a homologous pair.
- In meiosis, nuclear division results in daughter cells with only one chromosome from each homologous pair.
- Meiosis involves two nuclear divisions.
- In the first division (meiosis I), homologous chromosomes pair together and are pulled by spindle fibres, one to each pole of the spindle.
- In the second division (meiosis II), the sister chromatids of each chromosome are separated.
- Random segregation of chromosomes and crossing over during meiosis I result in genetic variation among the daughter cells.
- Chromosome translocation and chromosome non-disjunction can lead to further genetic variation.

Practice questions

1 In mitosis, sister chromatids are separated during:

A anaphase
B metaphase
C prophase
D telophase *(1)*

2 The cultivated potatoes that humans eat are tetraploid, i.e., they contain four copies of each chromosome (4*n*). A daughter cell produced by meiosis in a potato cell will be:

A haploid (*n*)
B diploid (2*n*)
C tetraploid (4*n*)
D octoploid (8*n*) *(1)*

3 Copy and complete the table comparing and contrasting features of meiosis and mitosis. *(6)*

Feature	Meiosis	Mitosis
Number of nuclear divisions		
Homologous chromosomes pair together		
Sister chromatids are separated		
Number of chromosomes in daughter cells is the same as in parent cell		
Is a major source of genetic variation		
Involves formation of a spindle of fibres		

4 The graph represents changes in the relative mass of DNA in a cell during a single cell cycle. The curve has been labelled at six points, A to F.

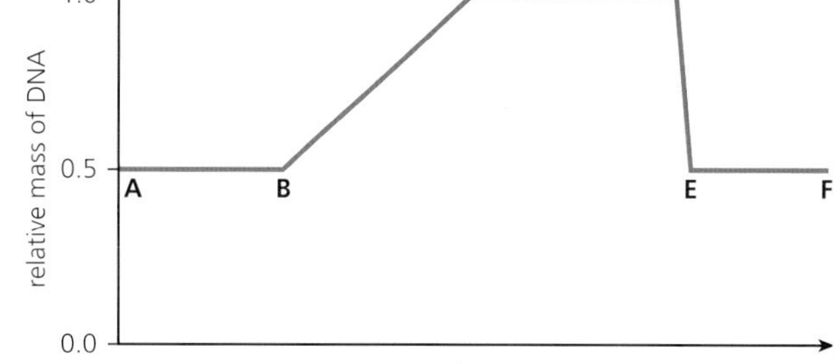

a) Explain the shape of the curve between points **B** and **C**. *(2)*

b) Give the two letters, **A** to **F**, between which each of the following occurs:

i) anaphase

ii) S phase

iii) cell increases in mass. *(3)*

c) Does the curve show that cytokinesis occurred? Explain your answer. *(2)*

5 The following statements relate to meiosis.

i Genetic variation is caused by random segregation of homologous chromosomes.

ii Genetic variation is caused by crossing over.

iii Genetic variation is caused by gene mutation.

Which statements best describe the sources of genetic variation in meiosis?

A i and ii **C** ii and iii

B i and iii **D** i, ii and iii *(1)*

6 The diagram shows a cell with two pairs of homologous chromosomes. Each diagram shows this cell in one stage of division.

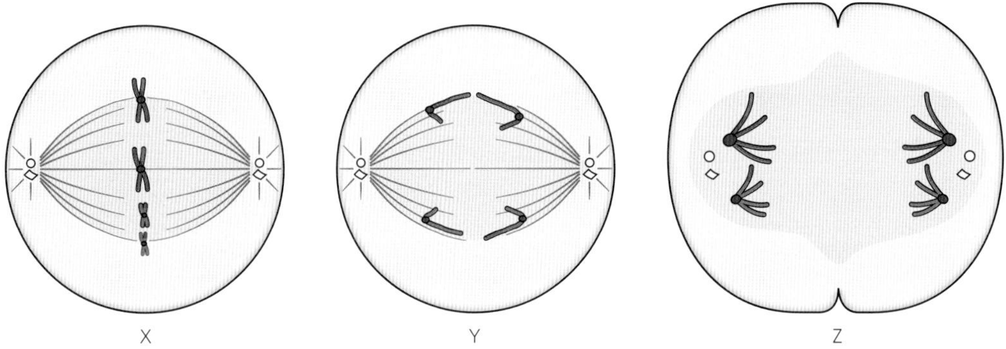

a) Is the cell in the diagram an animal cell or a plant cell? Justify your answer. *(1)*

b) Other than size and shape, how does a chromosome of one homologous pair differ from a chromosome of the other homologous pair? *(1)*

c) Identify the type and stage of cell division in cells X, Y and Z. *(3)*

d) Explain the reason for your answer for cell Z. *(2)*

7 The diagram shows the life cycle of three organisms: yeast (a single-celled fungus); human (a multicellular animal); *Ulva* (a multicellular protoctist). The diagram shows whether each stage is haploid (n) or diploid ($2n$).

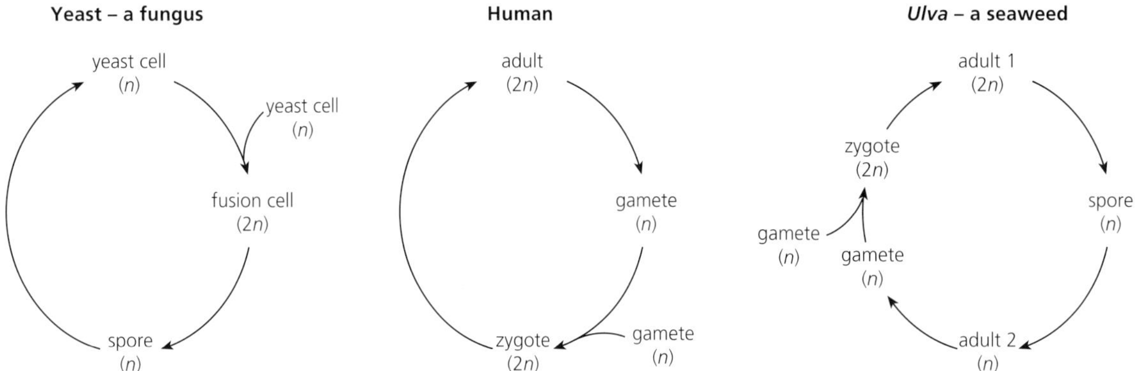

a) On a copy of the diagram write the letter **M** by each arrow on the three life cycles that represents meiosis. Write the letter **T** by each arrow on the three life cycles that represents mitosis. *(3)*

b) Is it true to say that gametes are produced by meiosis? Use evidence from the diagram to justify your answer. *(2)*

c) The two adults in the life cycle of *Ulva* look identical. Outline how you could tell which is which? Details of any procedure(s) are **not** required. *(2)*

8 The photo shows a pair of homologous chromosomes during meiosis.

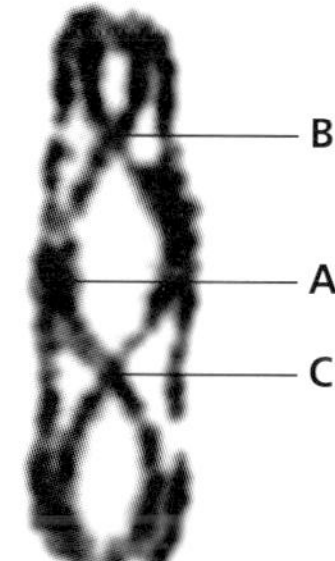

a) Explain what is meant by the term 'homologous chromosomes'. *(1)*

b) Name the structure labelled A. *(1)*

c) Explain the appearance of the chromosomes in the diagram. *(4)*

d) The same event has occurred at the points labelled B and C in the diagram. This event is more likely to occur at point B than at point C. Suggest why. *(2)*

Stretch and challenge

9 A group of scientists investigated mitosis in one species of flowering plant.

- They planted seeds in pots of sawdust. After 2 weeks, they collected healthy root tips from the germinated seeds at 2-hourly intervals throughout a 24-hour period.
- They left each sample of root tips for 24 hours in 2 cm^3 of a 3:1 mixture of ethanol:ethanoic acid.
- After this time, they transferred the root tips into warm, dilute hydrochloric acid for 5 minutes.
- They then removed about 1 mm from the end of each root tip, placed each on a glass slide containing orcein and squashed it under a cover slip.
- Finally, they examined the slides under a compound light microscope and counted the cells in each stage of mitosis.

a) Suggest one reason why a group of scientists, rather than a single scientist, carried out this work.

b) In each case, explain why the scientists:

i) placed the root tips in a mixture of ethanol and ethanoic acid

ii) transferred the root tips into warm, dilute hydrochloric acid

iii) removed about 1 mm from the end of each root tip

iv) placed orcein on the glass slide

v) squashed the root tips.

The table shows the scientists' results.

Time of day/ hours	Percentage of cells in each stage of mitosis				
	Prophase	Metaphase	Anaphase	Telophase	Interphase
06:00	41.2	8.8	7.4	6.6	36.0
08:00	35.0	11.9	11.3	13.0	28.8
10:00	28.0	18.7	14.5	15.4	22.4
12:00	29.7	22.0	19.2	11.4	17.7
14:00	27.8	24.8	17.9	10.8	18.7
16:00	23.6	25.6	18.9	14.2	17.7
18:00	17.2	23.4	18.8	20.1	20.5
20:00	18.1	15.1	20.1	21.1	25.6
22:00	27.2	13.6	14.7	20.4	30.2
24:00	17.5	12.5	12.5	14.5	43.0
02:00	22.5	11.6	12.2	6.9	46.8
04:00	28.9	11.7	9.1	8.0	42.3

c) Explain why the scientists converted their raw data to the percentage values shown in the table.

d) As this investigation was carried out by professional scientists, explain how they would have ensured their data were accurate.

e) At what time of day was most DNA synthesis occurring? Explain your answer.

f) Describe how the percentage of cells in prophase changed over the period shown in the table.

g) Explain the relationship between the percentage of cells in prophase and metaphase between 06:00 and 16:00 hours.

10 At the beginning of this chapter, we saw that the cell cycle is a regulated process. A protein called p53 is one of many factors involved in this regulation. Find out what you can about p53 and its involvement in regulation of the cell cycle and in cancer.

6 Sexual reproduction in mammals and plants

Prior knowledge

In this chapter you will need to recall that:

- ➜ sexual reproduction involves fertilisation, in which haploid gametes fuse to produce a diploid zygote
- ➜ in some organisms, fertilisation is external and in others internal
- ➜ in animals, female gametes are called ova (eggs) and male gametes are called spermatozoa (sperm)
- ➜ the sperm of mammals are small and motile whereas the ova of mammals are larger and not motile
- ➜ in mammals, the development of a zygote into an embryo and fetus occurs within the uterus of the female parent
- ➜ during embryological development, the placenta acts as the major exchange surface of the developing offspring
- ➜ in flowering plants, male gametes are associated with pollen grains that pass to the female parts of a flower during the process of pollination
- ➜ the ova of a flowering plant remain within the flowers of the parent plant
- ➜ following fertilisation in a flowering plant, an embryo is contained within a seed which, in turn, is contained with a fruit.

Test yourself on prior knowledge

1 A gamete is haploid. What is meant by 'haploid'?

2 The offspring produced by sexual reproduction between the same parents show great variation. Give **three** ways in which this variation is produced.

3 In mammals and in flowering plants, the ova remain within the parent plant. Give **two** advantages of retaining the ova within the body of the parent.

4 In flowering plants, pollination is not the same as fertilisation. Explain why.

5 Which of the following plant organs is **not** a fruit: apple; cucumber; lettuce; tomato? Explain your answer.

Reproduction is the production of new individuals by an existing member or members of the same species. It is one of the fundamental characteristics of life.

As you saw in Chapter 5, reproduction can be asexual or sexual. The distinctive feature of sexual reproduction is that a genetically novel individual is formed as a result of the mixing of chromosomes from two individuals – the parents. The parental chromosomes are carried by cells called gametes. At fertilisation, the nuclei of two gametes fuse to form a new nucleus inside a cell called a zygote. At some point in the life cycle of sexually reproducing organisms, meiosis must occur so that future gametes contain only half the chromosome number again. Mammals and flowering plants can reproduce by sexual reproduction.

Key terms

Gametes Cells carrying half the normal chromosome number; two gametes fuse during sexual reproduction.

Fertilisation The fusion of the nuclei of two gametes to form the nucleus of a zygote, containing the chromosomes from both gametes.

Zygote The cell formed by the fusion of two gametes.

Sexual reproduction in mammals

Key term

Sex The sex of an organism has a genetic basis. In mammals, it depends on the absence or presence of an activated gene, *SRY*, located on the Y chromosome. The karyotype XY is male and XX is female.

The events involved in sexual reproduction are basically the same in all mammals. We will use ourselves as examples of mammals, so the following account relates to humans.

The sexes are separate in humans. In biology, the **sex** of an organism has a precise meaning and it has a genetic basis. In Figure 5.2 (page 100) you saw a karyogram of a human male. It showed a pair of sex chromosomes – a male has one X chromosome and one Y chromosome. This would be true of all mammals and it is the possession of a Y chromosome that determines the sex of a male. We can, in fact, be a little more precise than this. It is one particular gene on the Y chromosome, called *SRY*, which determines that a zygote will develop into a male.

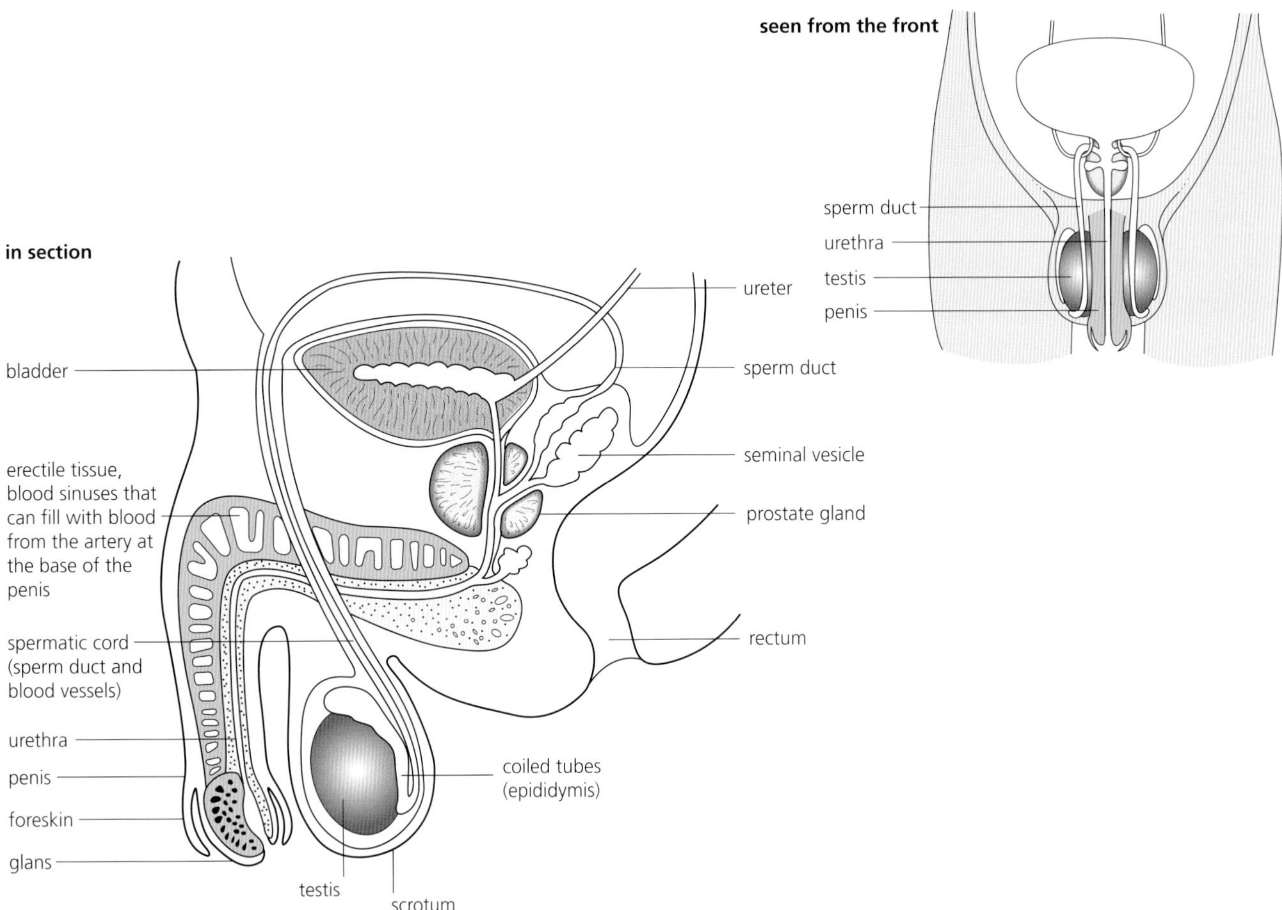

Figure 6.1 The reproductive system of a human male

A male zygote has a Y chromosome. Activation of the *SRY* gene on this chromosome causes the gonads to develop into testes. As a result, the associated reproductive structures develop into a male reproductive system, shown in Figure 6.1. In contrast, a female zygote lacks a Y chromosome. In the absence of an activated *SRY* gene, she develops ovaries and, as a consequence, the other associated structures of the female reproductive system, shown in Figure 6.2.

seen from the front

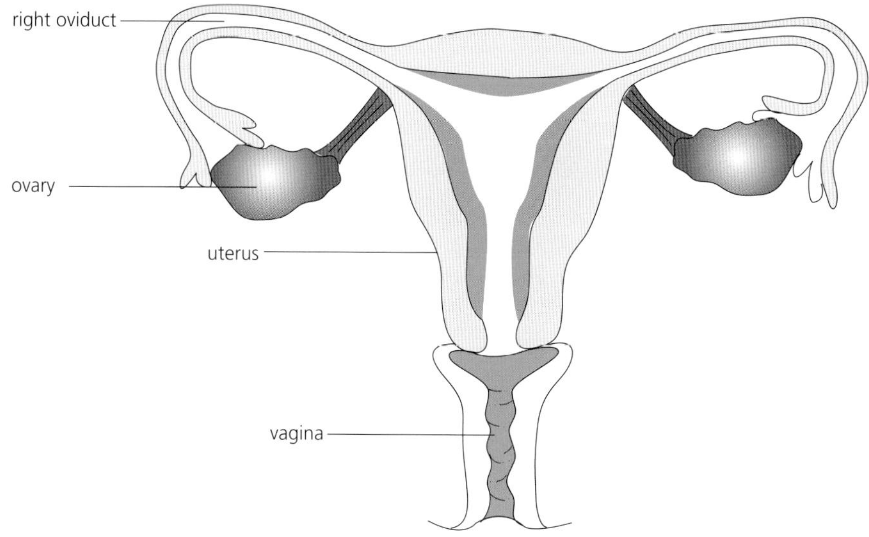

in section

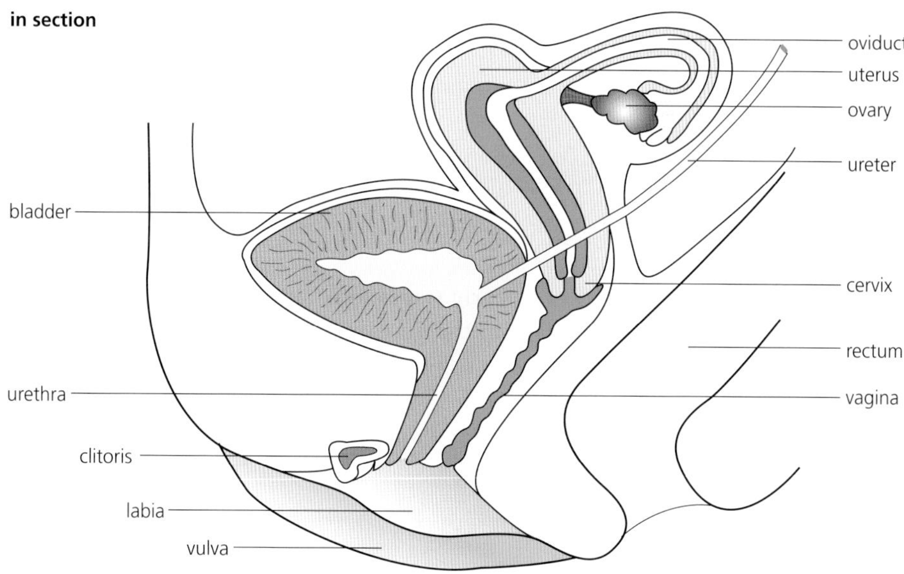

Figure 6.2 The reproductive system of a human female

Gametogenesis in humans

Gametogenesis is the process of gamete production. The female and male gametes are produced in organs called gonads. The female gonads are **ovaries** and the gametes they produce are called **ova** (singular: ovum or, simply, egg cell). The male gonads are **testes** and the gametes they produce are called **spermatozoa** (singular: spermatozoon or, simply, sperm cell).

Whilst there are several differences in outcome, the process of gametogenesis in females and males shares a common sequence of three phases:

- **multiplication** (proliferation), in which cells present in a layer called the germinal epithelium divide by mitotic cell division. This division is repeated to produce many cells capable of becoming gametes

Key terms

Gametogenesis The process by which gametes are produced. In animals, egg cells are produced by oogenesis and sperm cells are produced by spermatogenesis.

Gonad An animal organ that produces gametes.

Germinal epithelium A single layer of cells (epithelium) that undergoes regular mitosis, producing other cells.

- then each of these cells undergoes **growth**
- finally **maturation** occurs, which involves meiosis and results in the formation of haploid gametes.

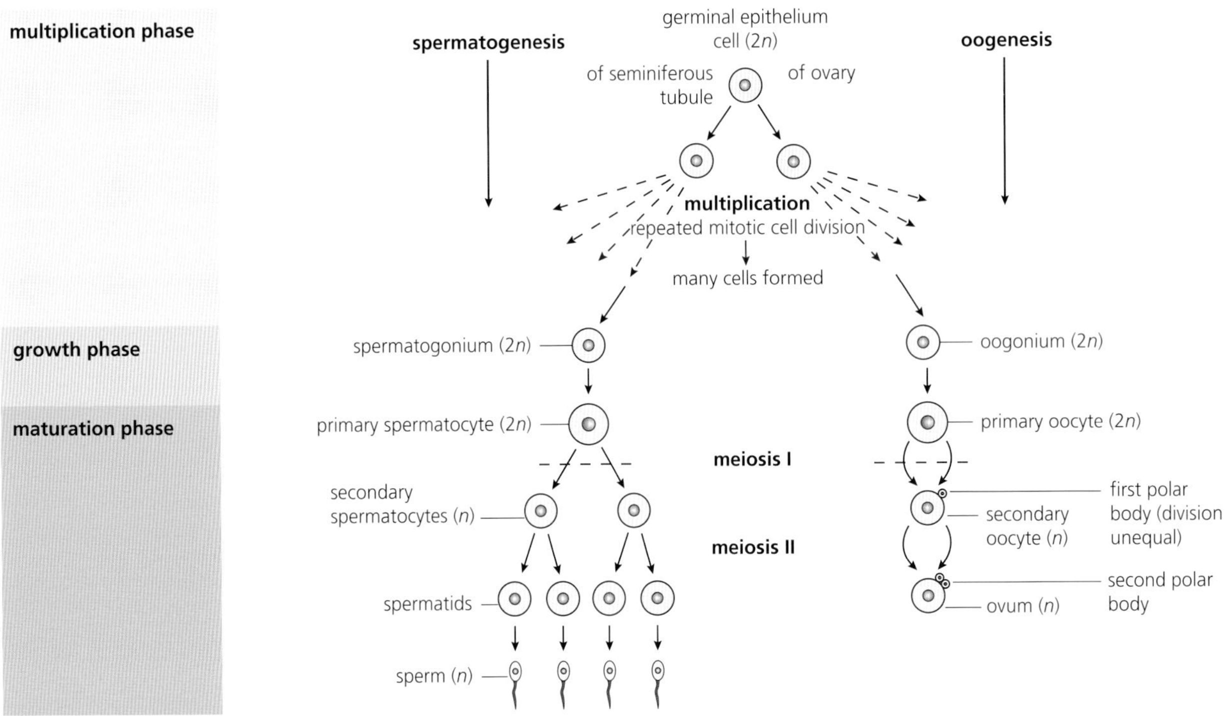

Figure 6.3 Gametogenesis in humans

You can see these phases in Figure 6.3. The early stages look similar. In the multiplication phase of both, mitosis of cells in the germinal epithelium gives rise to cells that, in turn, undergo repeated mitosis to produce large numbers of either **oogonia** or **spermatogonia**. This is followed by a growth phase in which these cells develop into either **primary oocytes** or **primary spermatocytes** that can enter the maturation phase and undergo meiosis.

If you look at what happens after the formation of primary oocytes and primary spermatocytes in Figure 6.3, you can see a difference between oogenesis and spermatogenesis.

The primary oocyte produces one haploid secondary oocyte and a smaller, haploid, polar body, which is lost. Meiosis II of the secondary oocyte has a similar outcome – a large ovum and a smaller polar body, which is lost. Only one gamete – the ovum – is produced from a primary oocyte.

In contrast, the primary spermatocyte produces haploid secondary spermatocytes that are the same size, both of which undergo meiosis II to produce four gametes.

What Figure 6.3 does not show is the timing of oogenesis and spermatogenesis, and herein lies another difference. In a human male, the entire process of spermatogenesis shown in Figure 6.3 occurs in his testes only after puberty. He then produces millions of sperm cells every day throughout his life. In a female, all the stages up to production of primary oocytes occur in her ovaries whilst she is a fetus. As a result, a girl is born with thousands of primary oocytes already formed in her ovaries. Unusually, almost all of these cells remain in the prophase of meiosis II. The stimulus needed for them to complete meiosis II is fertilisation.

Table 6.1 shows a fuller comparison of oogenesis and spermatogenesis.

Table 6.1 A comparison of oogenesis and spermatogenesis

Oogenesis	Spermatogenesis
Oogonia formed in the embryonic ovaries, long before birth.	Spermatogonia formed from the time of puberty, throughout adult life.
Oogonia become surrounded by follicle cells, forming tiny primary follicles, and remain dormant within the ovary cortex. Most fail to develop further – they degenerate.	All spermatogonia develop into sperm, nurtured by the Sertoli cells in the seminiferous tubules of the testes.
Each month from puberty until the menopause, a few primary oocytes undergo meiosis I to become secondary oocytes. Only one of these secondary oocytes forms a Graafian follicle – the others degenerate.	Millions of sperm are formed *daily*.
One ovum is formed from each oogonium (the polar bodies degenerate too).	Four sperm are formed from each spermatogonium.
The Graafian follicle releases a secondary oocyte into the oviduct at ovulation.	Sperm are released from the body by ejaculation.
Meiosis II reaches prophase and then stops until a male nucleus enters the secondary oocyte, triggering completion of meiosis II.	Meiosis I and II go to completion during sperm production.
The fertilised ovum is non-motile and becomes lodged in the endometrium of the uterus where cell divisions (cleavage) lead to embryo formation.	Sperm are small, motile gametes.

Test yourself

1 How does a gamete differ from a somatic cell from the same organism?
2 Explain why biologists refer to a person's sex rather than gender.
3 Trisomy can result in humans with the karyotype XXY. What sex will this person be? Explain your answer.
4 State the function of a germinal epithelium.
5 Give **two** ways in which the *processes* of oogenesis and spermatogenesis differ.

The ovary and secondary oocyte

Figure 6.4 puts the process of oogenesis into the context of an ovary.

You can see in Figure 6.4 that the germinal epithelium is an outer layer of the ovary. You can also see how oocytes develop inside structures called follicles. Each follicle starts as a layer of cells around the oocyte but eventually develops into a fluid-filled sac, called a **Graafian follicle**. You can also see in Figure 6.4 that ovulation involves the release from a follicle of a secondary oocyte, still surrounded by a layer of follicle cells. In a woman of reproductive age, ovulation occurs about every 28 days. The empty Graafian follicle becomes filled with hormone-secreting cells, forming a yellow body, or **corpus luteum**. If the secondary oocyte is not fertilised, the corpus luteum quickly degenerates.

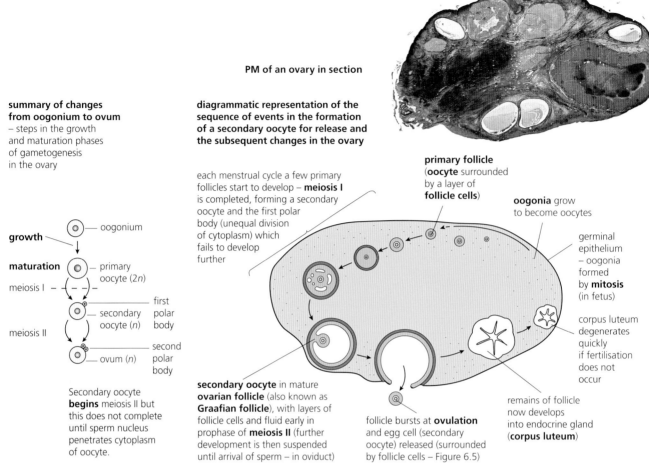

PM of an ovary in section

summary of changes from oogonium to ovum
– steps in the growth and maturation phases of gametogenesis in the ovary

growth

oogonium

maturation

primary oocyte (2*n*)

meiosis I

secondary oocyte (*n*)

first polar body

meiosis II

ovum (*n*)

second polar body

Secondary oocyte **begins** meiosis II but this does not complete until sperm nucleus penetrates cytoplasm of oocyte.

diagrammatic representation of the sequence of events in the formation of a secondary oocyte for release and the subsequent changes in the ovary

each menstrual cycle a few primary follicles start to develop – **meiosis I** is completed, forming a secondary oocyte and the first polar body (unequal division of cytoplasm) which fails to develop further

primary follicle (**oocyte** surrounded by a layer of **follicle cells**)

oogonia grow to become oocytes

germinal epithelium – oogonia formed by **mitosis** (in fetus)

corpus luteum degenerates quickly if fertilisation does not occur

secondary oocyte in mature **ovarian follicle** (also known as **Graafian follicle**), with layers of follicle cells and fluid early in prophase of **meiosis II** (further development is then suspended until arrival of sperm – in oviduct)

follicle bursts at **ovulation** and egg cell (secondary oocyte) released (surrounded by follicle cells – Figure 6.5)

remains of follicle now develops into endocrine gland (**corpus luteum**)

Figure 6.4 A human ovary and stages in oogenesis

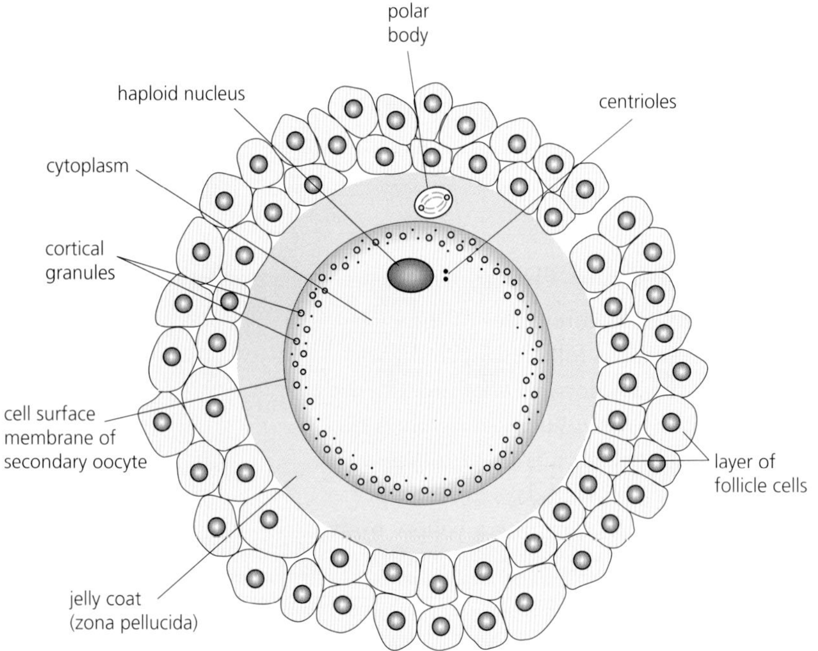

Figure 6.5 A secondary oocyte after ovulation

Figure 6.5 is an enlarged drawing of a secondary oocyte, surrounded by follicle cells. At about 150 μm in diameter, the oocyte is much larger than the follicle cells. Notice the **cortical granules** – vesicles around the outside of the cytoplasm of the oocyte. As you will see later, these vesicles play an important role in ensuring the oocyte can be fertilised by only one sperm cell. Also notice the layer of glycoprotein, called the **zona pellucida**, between the oocyte and the follicle cells. You will see the importance of this when we consider fertilisation.

The testis and spermatozoa

Figure 6.6 puts the process of spermatogenesis into the context of a testis. Unlike an ovary, a testis is filled with tiny tubules, called **seminiferous tubules**, in which sperm are made. You can see in the lower drawing of Figure 6.6 that the germinal epithelium is close to the outer edge of each seminiferous tubule. You can also see spermatocytes and mature spermatozoa. Notice how the heads of the spermatozoa are positioned against large **Sertoli cells**. These cells nourish sperm as the mature.

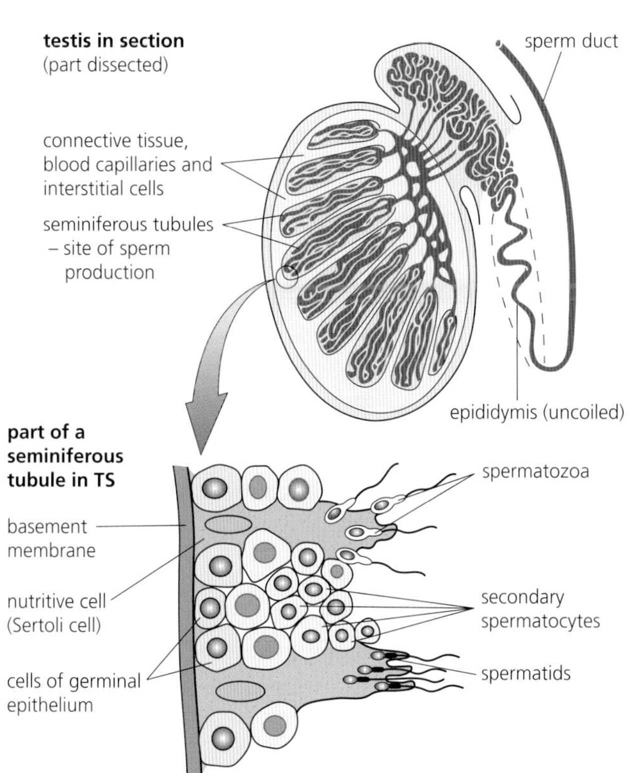

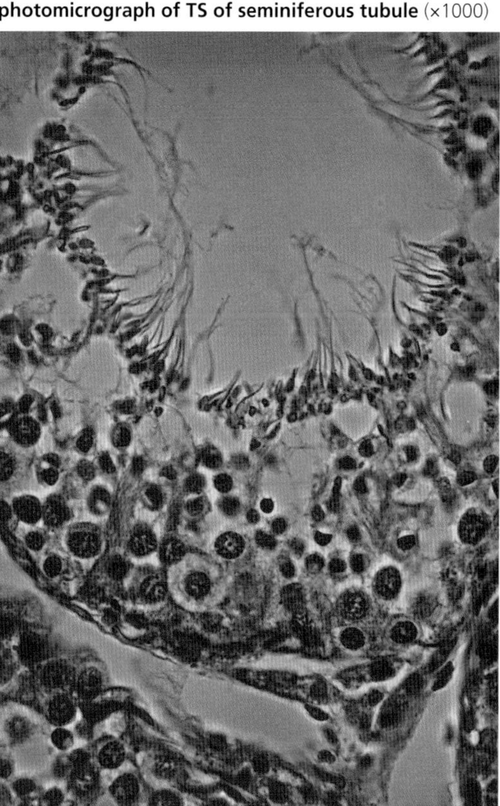

Figure 6.6 A seminiferous tubule and stages in spermatogenesis

Figure 6.7 shows the structure of an individual sperm cell. You can see it is divided into three sections:

- a **head**, containing a haploid nucleus and an acrosome
- a **middle piece**, packed with mitochondria – the organelles that produce ATP
- a **tail**, containing microtubules in an arrangement similar to that of a cilium.

The sperm is a very small cell: its 'head' is about 5 μm long and 3 μm wide and its 'tail' is about 50 μm long. Although not visible in Figure 6.7, the head of the sperm is coated with glycoproteins picked up from the epididymis. These glycoproteins must be removed to make the sperm capable of fertilisation. This occurs inside the uterus and oviduct of the female.

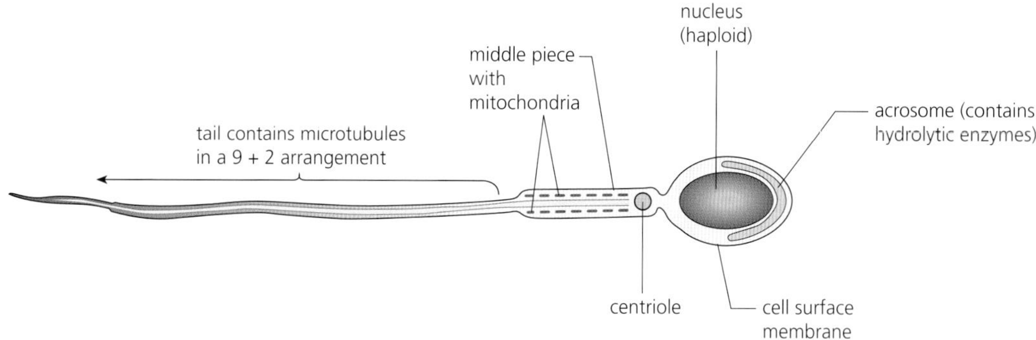

Figure 6.7 A mature spermatozoon

Test yourself

6 Use information in the text to calculate the ratio of the diameter of a human ovum to the width of the head of a human sperm cell.

7 In most animals, the sperm is much smaller than the ovum. Suggest **two** advantages of this difference in size.

8 Does ovulation involve release of the ovum from a human ovary? Explain your answer.

9 Give the role of the polar bodies produced during oogenesis.

10 What is the difference between a primary oocyte and a secondary oocyte?

Fertilisation in humans

Following ovulation, the secondary oocyte is captured by the oviduct (Figure 6.8) and is moved along it by the beating action of cilia on the cells lining the oviduct. Since the oocyte quickly becomes disorganised, successful fertilisation can only occur in the upper part of the oviduct. Of the millions of sperm deposited in the vagina, only a few hundred actually reach the upper part of the oviduct. While in the uterus and oviduct, these sperm have become capable of fertilisation by a process called **capacitation**. This process involves two events that change the head of the sperm.

- The cell surface membrane of the sperm head is stripped of the glycoproteins it acquired during its time in the epididymis.
- The **acrosome reaction** occurs. During this reaction, the acrosome swells and fuses with the cell surface membrane of the sperm, releasing its hydrolytic enzymes. Of equal importance, the exposed remains of the membrane around the acrosome acquire the potential to fuse with the cell surface membrane of the secondary oocyte.

Both events are important in enabling sperm cells to become fully capable of fertilisation.

Figure 6.8 shows the events involved in fertilisation. One or more of the few capacitated spermatozoa to reach the secondary oocyte begin to pass between the follicle cells surrounding the oocyte. Once through, these spermatozoa encounter the jelly-like layer, the zona pellucida. As a result of the acrosome reaction mentioned above, enzymes released from the acrosomes hydrolyse the glycoprotein from which the zona pellucida is made. This allows the passage of the spermatozoa to the surface membrane of the oocyte.

Key terms

Capacitation Changes to the head of a sperm cell, making it fully capable of fertilisation. This process occurs within a few hours of a sperm cell entering the uterus of a female.

Acrosome reaction One event during capacitation in which a sperm's acrosome releases its hydrolytic enzymes into the zona pellucida and its cell surface membrane becomes capable of fusing with the cell surface membrane of the secondary oocyte.

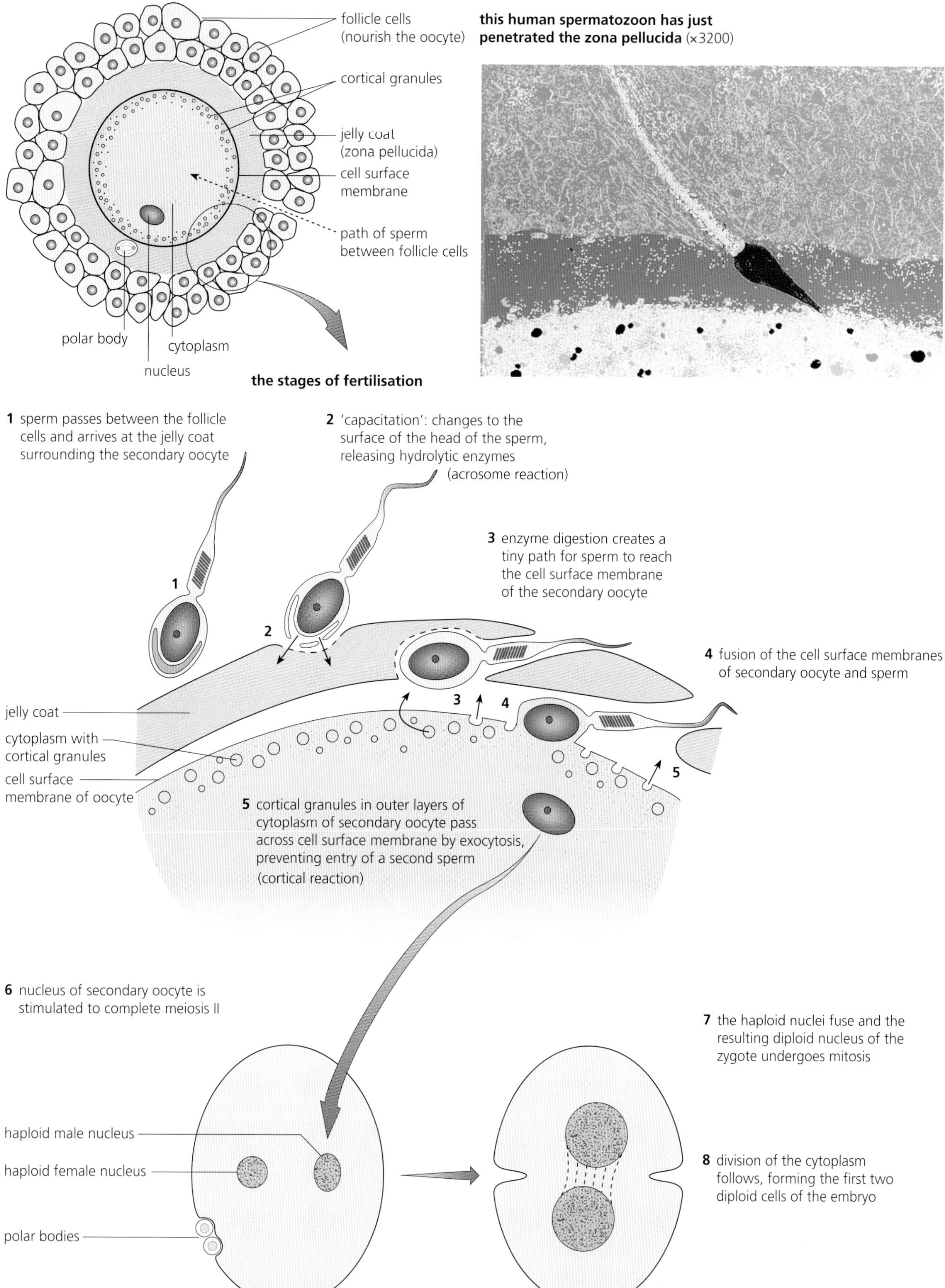
follicle cells
(nourish the oocyte)
cortical granules
jelly coat
(zona pellucida)
cell surface
membrane
path of sperm
between follicle cells
polar body
cytoplasm
nucleus
this human spermatozoon has just penetrated the zona pellucida (×3200)
the stages of fertilisation
1 sperm passes between the follicle cells and arrives at the jelly coat surrounding the secondary oocyte
2 'capacitation': changes to the surface of the head of the sperm, releasing hydrolytic enzymes (acrosome reaction)
3 enzyme digestion creates a tiny path for sperm to reach the cell surface membrane of the secondary oocyte
4 fusion of the cell surface membranes of secondary oocyte and sperm
jelly coat
cytoplasm with cortical granules
cell surface membrane of oocyte
5 cortical granules in outer layers of cytoplasm of secondary oocyte pass across cell surface membrane by exocytosis, preventing entry of a second sperm (cortical reaction)
6 nucleus of secondary oocyte is stimulated to complete meiosis II
7 the haploid nuclei fuse and the resulting diploid nucleus of the zygote undergoes mitosis
haploid male nucleus
haploid female nucleus
polar bodies
8 division of the cytoplasm follows, forming the first two diploid cells of the embryo

Figure 6.8 Fertilisation of a human secondary oocyte

The head of a spermatozoon now comes to lie tangentially in contact with the cell surface membrane of the secondary oocyte. Microvilli on the surface of the oocyte then engulf the sperm head. As soon as this happens, there is a sudden increase in the concentration of calcium ions within the cytoplasm of the oocyte. This increase in calcium ions causes:

- the **cortical reaction**, in which the cortical granules are released from the oocyte. This causes the zona pellucida to harden, the result being that no other sperm can now cross the cell surface membrane of the oocyte. This reaction prevents polyspermy – the entry of more than one sperm into the oocyte
- the secondary oocyte to complete meiosis II, producing a haploid **ovum** and another smaller, haploid polar body.

Key term

Cortical reaction
Release of cortical granules from a fertilised secondary oocyte, preventing the entry of further sperm cells.

The haploid nucleus from the sperm now fuses with that of the ovum, forming the diploid nucleus of a cell that is now called a **zygote**.

Early development and implantation

Following fertilisation, the zygote is moved down the oviduct by ciliary action. It arrives in the uterus around 3 to 4 days later. As shown in Figure 6.9, during this

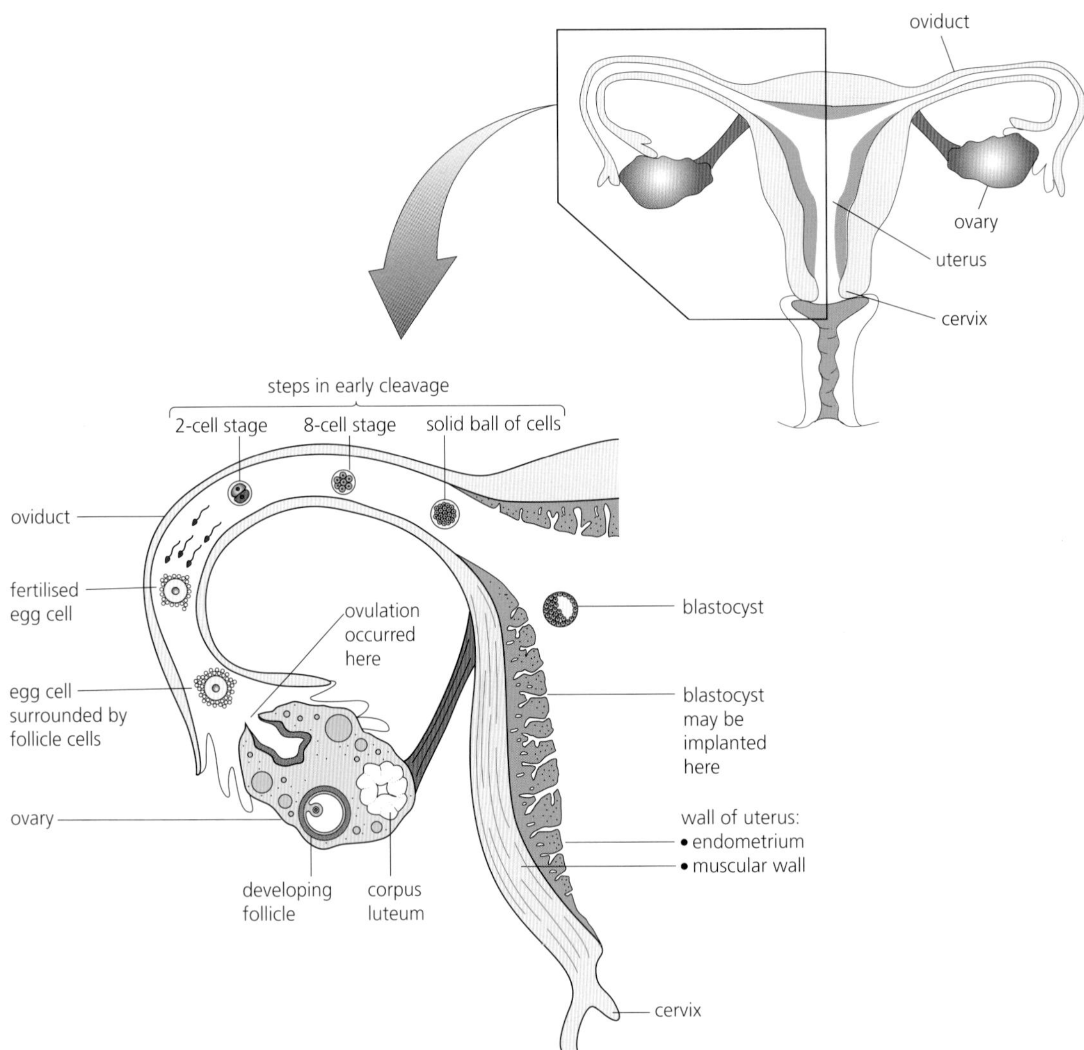

Figure 6.9 The site of fertilisation and early stages of development

time, mitosis and cell division occur. Each of these cell divisions is referred to as a **cleavage division** and results in new cells, called blastomeres. Notice in Figure 6.9 that no growth occurs at this stage. You can see that, as more cleavage divisions occur, the blastomeres become progressively smaller. After about 4 days, the zygote has become a solid ball of tiny blastomeres. Between now and the 7th day after fertilisation, a number of important changes occur. You can see some of these in the upper part of Figure 6.10. The ball of blastomeres now contains about 128 cells and it has grown. Instead of being a solid ball, it has now formed a hollow ball of cells, called a blastocyst. The hollow ball has an outer layer of cells, now called **trophoblasts**, an inner cell mass of blastomeres and a fluid-filled **blastocoel**.

What you cannot see in Figure 6.10 is that something more fundamental has occurred.

Firstly, the cells have differentiated to form different types of cell. It is the inner cell mass that is destined to become the **embryo** that will give rise exclusively to a **fetus**. The outer trophoblasts are destined to become a membrane (the amnion) that helps to nourish the embryo and fetus.

Key terms

Blastocyst A fluid-filled ball of cells (called blastomeres) formed by the repeated cell division of a zygote. In humans, a blastocyst is formed 4 to 5 days after fertilisation.

Blastomeres The cells formed by cleavage divisions of the zygote as it is moved down the oviduct.

blastocyst at about day 7

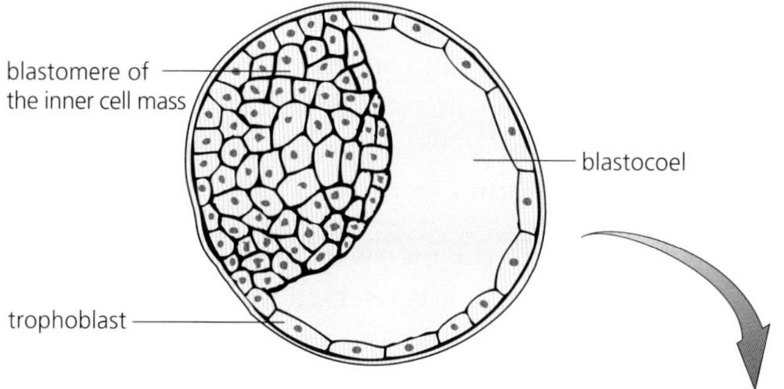

implanted (14 days after fertilisation)

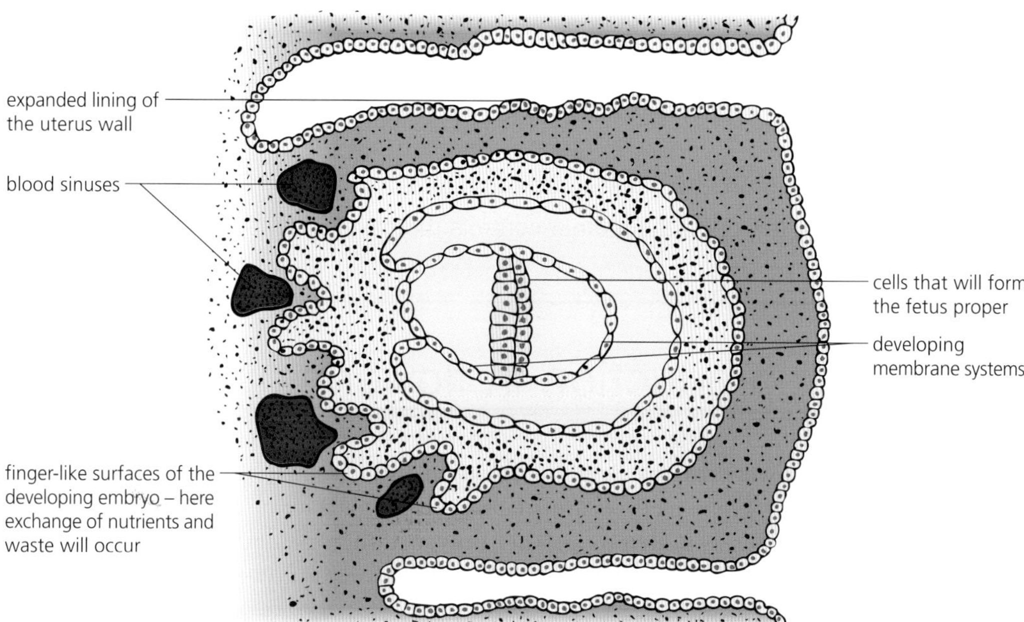

Figure 6.10 Development of the blastocyst and implantation

Key term

Endometrium The lining of the uterus. By the time of ovulation, the endometrium has become thicker and contains more blood vessels. This adaptation enables an embryo to obtain nourishment for its growth and development.

Secondly, control of development has switched from the mother to the blastocyst. During cleavage in the oviduct, the cytoplasm of the secondary oocyte, including all the cell organelles and mRNA it contained, was used by the blastocyst. Not until about the 8-cell stage does the blastocyst destroy its inherited maternal mRNA and begin to produce its own.

In Figure 6.9, we saw a blastocyst 'floating' in the uterus. From uterine secretions, this blastocyst is able to obtain oxygen and other metabolic substrates and to excrete metabolic wastes, such as carbon dioxide. As you will see in Chapter 9, however, there is a limit to the size this blastocyst could grow depending only on these secretions. It is important at this stage that the blastocyst embeds itself in the lining of the uterus, or endometrium. Look at the endometrium in Figure 6.9. You can see that it is relatively thick and has many invaginations. A developing blastocyst becomes embedded in one of these invaginations in a process called **implantation**. Once implanted, the blastocyst starts to receive nutrients directly from the endometrium. Clearly, as the blastocyst grows, the rate at which it uses nutrients will increase. This in turn is matched by an increase in uptake of nutrients facilitated by the development of a **placenta**.

The placenta contains both maternal and embryonic tissue. In the lower part of Figure 6.10, you can see the beginnings of the placenta. Blood vessels in the maternal tissue have begun to fuse to form the **blood sinuses** you can see in the drawing. The trophoblast layer of the implanted blastocyst increases its surface area by producing finger-like villi. Not only do these villi increase the surface area for exchange, they also help to anchor the blastocyst in the endometrium.

The successfully implanted blastocyst will remain in the uterus for about 270 to 290 days, a period called **gestation**. For the first 2 months, it is referred to as an **embryo**, after which it is referred to as a **fetus**.

Test yourself

11 Sponges release their gametes into the seawater in which they live; fertilisation is external. In contrast, fertilisation in mammals is internal. Suggest **two** advantages of internal fertilisation over external fertilisation.

12 Suggest **one** disadvantage of internal fertilisation.

13 Give **three** events that occur during capacitation that enable a sperm to fertilise an egg cell.

14 What is the role of the trophoblast layer in a blastocyst?

15 During the first few days, the mother controls the development of a blastocyst. Explain how.

Sexual reproduction in flowering plants

Flowering plants contain their reproductive organs in their flowers (or **inflorescences**). Many plants have flowers that are brightly coloured and conspicuous, like the buttercup shown in Figure 6.11. These features are adaptations that attract insects, on which this plant depends to transfer its pollen to another flower. Others plants, that rely on the wind to transfer their pollen, usually have dull, inconspicuous flowers, for example grasses.

Figure 6.11 shows a vertical section (VS) through the flower of a meadow buttercup (*Ranunculus acris*), a plant common in the UK. Like many plants, this buttercup is a **hermaphrodite**, in other words it carries both female and male reproductive structures.

The female structures are known as carpels. You can see in Figure 6.11 that each **carpel** consists of a **stigma** – a platform on which pollen grains may land – a **style** that supports the stigma, and an **ovary**. Inside the ovary, you can see an **ovule** that contains the female gametes. The male structures are known as **stamens**. Again, as you can see in Figure 6.11, each stamen consists of an **anther** and a **filament**. The anther produces pollen grains that contain the male gametes, and the filament supports the anther in a position that will eventually enable it to shed its pollen grains.

Key term

Hermaphrodite
A multicellular organism that possesses both male and female reproductive structures. Most flowering plants are hermaphrodites. Fewer animals are hermaphrodites, but this condition is common in organisms such as slugs, snails and is seen in some fish.

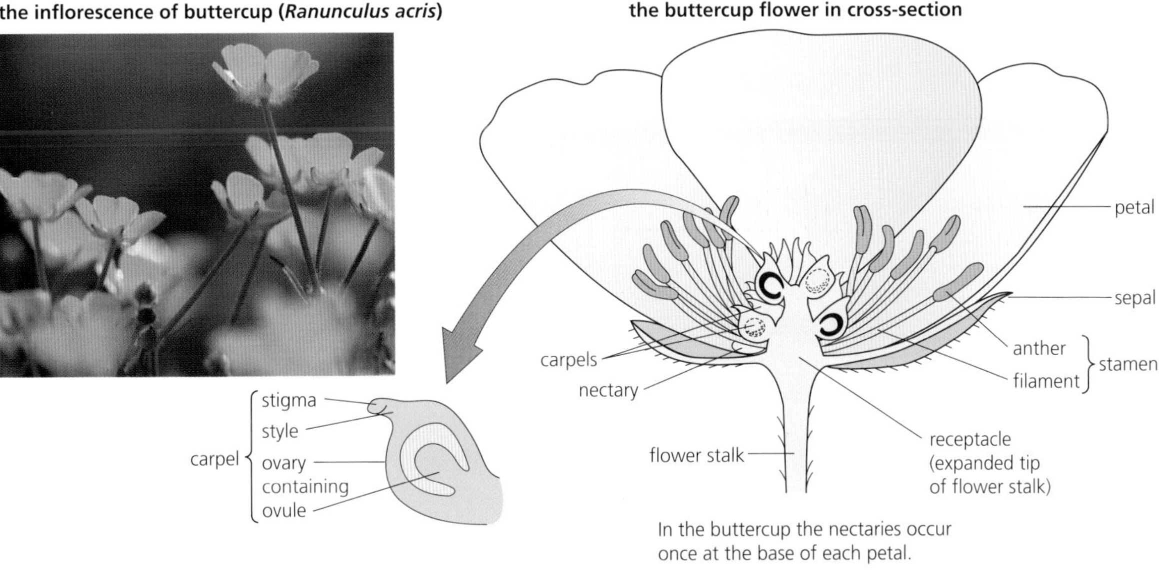

Figure 6.11 The flower of a meadow buttercup (*Ranunculus acris*)

Formation of female gametes

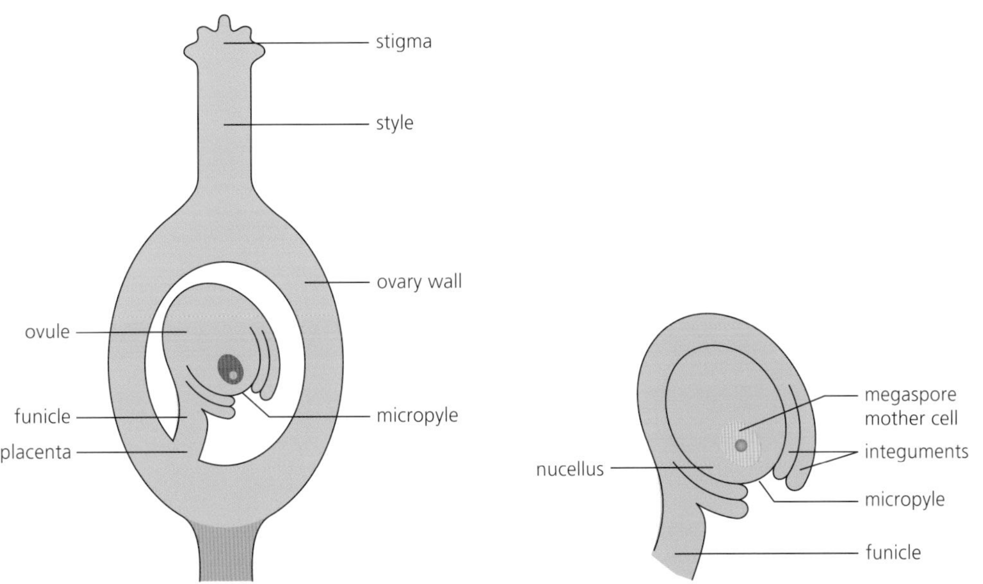

Figure 6.12 a) A vertical section (VS) through an ovary containing a single ovule; b) VS through an immature ovule

Depending on the species, one or more ovules develop inside an ovary. Figure 6.12 shows an ovary with just one ovule. Within its central mass of tissue, called the **nucellus**, is a large, diploid **megaspore mother cell** surrounded by two layers of cells, called **integuments**. As these integuments grow, they almost enclose the nucellus, leaving only a tiny hole called the **micropyle**.

Figure 6.13 shows how a megaspore mother cell divides by meiosis to produce four haploid cells, the **megaspores**. Three of them disintegrate. The one that survives grows until it almost fills the nucellus. The nucleus of this surviving megaspore divides three times by mitosis to form a cell containing eight haploid nuclei. This single cell with eight nuclei is an immature **embryo sac**. The cytoplasm of the embryo sac then divides. You might expect it to divide to form eight cells. In fact it doesn't. Instead, it divides to form seven cells. The three nearest the micropyle are the ovum and, on either side, the **synergids**. The three furthest from the micropyle are the **antipodal cells**. The two remaining nuclei remain in the centre of the embryo sac. These are the two **polar nuclei**. You can see all these in the mature embryo sac shown in Figure 6.13.

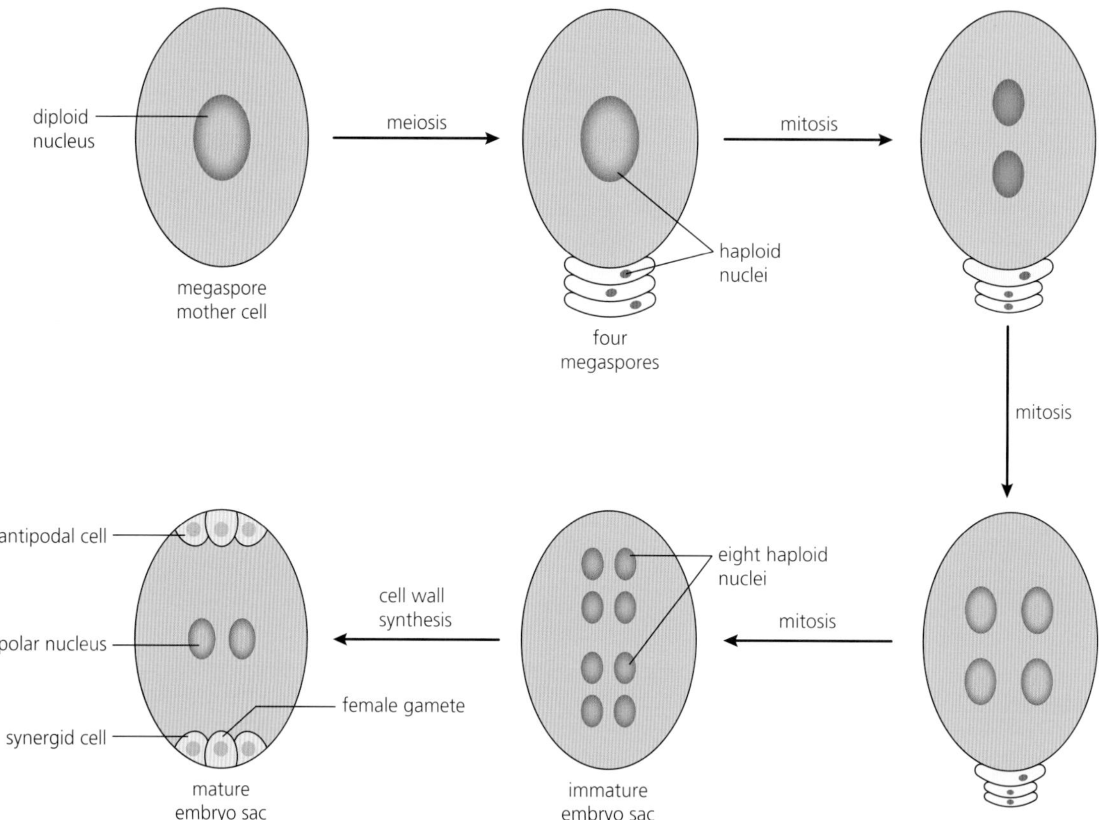

Figure 6.13 The formation of a mature embryo sac

Formation of male gametes

Depending on the species, each anther has two or four lobes. Within the tissues in each lobe are a number of diploid **microspore mother cells**. Each of these cells divides once by meiosis to produce four haploid **microspores**. Each microspore then divides once by mitosis to produce two haploid nuclei:

- the tube nucleus
- the generative nucleus, which is the male gamete.

The microspore – a single cell containing these two nuclei – is now called a **pollen grain**. You can see a large number of pollen grains in the anther of a lily flower in Figure 6.14. If you look closely, you should be able to see both nuclei in some of these pollen grains.

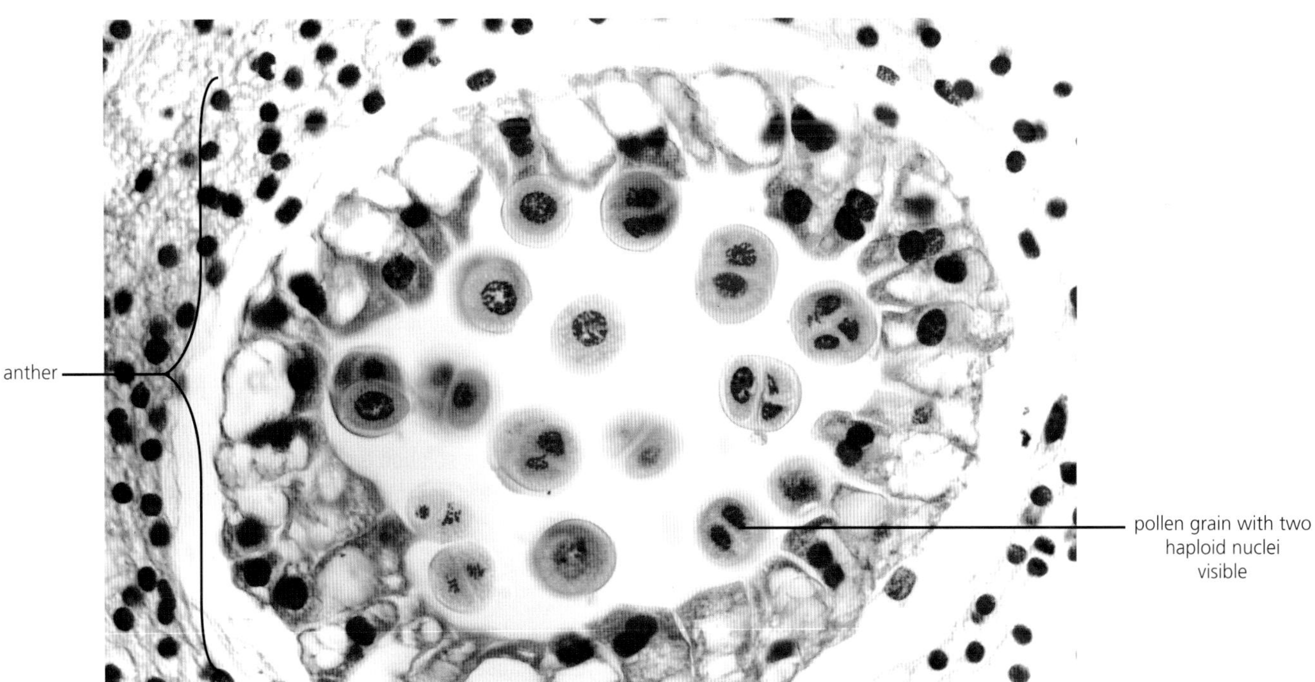

Figure 6.14 Vertical section (VS) through an anther of a lily flower

Pollination

Pollination occurs when a pollen grain lands on the stigma of a plant of the same species. **Self-pollination** occurs when pollen is transferred from anther to stigma of the same plant. **Cross-pollination** occurs when pollen is transferred from the anther of one plant to the stigma of another plant. During cross-pollination, the pollen is carried from one plant to another by insects, other animals or the wind, depending on the species of plant. Pollen grains have shapes and surface protrusions that are unique to each plant species. Only if a pollen grain lands on a stigma with complementary patterns can the pollen grain germinate to form a pollen tube.

Key term

Pollination Transfer of pollen from an anther to a stigma. Depending on the species of plant, the transfer of pollen could be by wind, water, insects, birds or mammals. The structure of flowers is closely adapted to their method of pollen transfer.

Core practical 4

Investigate the effect of sucrose concentrations on pollen tube growth or germination

Background information

When a ripe pollen grain lands on the stigma of a plant of the same species, it is dry. Under appropriate conditions, a pollen grain will absorb water and germinate, producing a pollen tube. Depending on the time you have available, you could investigate the effect of different conditions on the germination of pollen grains or on the rate of pollen tube growth. To save time, you could work in groups, each member of the group investigating a different sucrose concentration, and then pool your data.

Carrying out the investigation

Aim: To investigate the effect of sucrose concentrations on the germination of pollen grains.

Risk assessment: It is the responsibility of your centre to carry out an appropriate risk assessment. CLEAPSS *Hazcards* might be helpful. Wear eye protection when performing this experment.

1. Remove the lids from two clean Petri dishes. Place a filter paper in each of the two Petri dishes. Moisten the paper with water and replace the lids.
2. Use the pollen culture medium and 1.2 mol dm^{-3} sucrose solution to make up a range of solutions of different sucrose concentrations. You will need no more than 10 cm^3 of each sucrose solution.
3. Prepare a table in which you can record your raw data.
4. Use a clean dropper pipette to add a drop of one of your sucrose concentrations to each of two clean microscope slides.
5. Take a flower that is shedding pollen grains. Gently rub its anthers using the tip of a mounted needle so that pollen grains fall onto the drop of sucrose solution on one of your slides.
6. Repeat step 5 so that you have pollen grains in the solution on your second slide.
7. Note the time and carefully place the microscope slides into the Petri dishes, one to each dish. Replace the lids.
8. At regular intervals, examine each slide using a light microscope. Make a note of the time at which the pollen grains begin to germinate.
9. After each observation, carefully return the slides to the Petri dishes and replace the lids.
10. Repeat steps 4 to 9 using another of your sucrose solutions.

Questions

1. One student decided to make her sucrose solutions in the following way. She labelled six test tubes 1 to 6 and added 5 cm^3 of pollen culture medium to tubes 2 to 6. After this, she placed 10 cm^3 of 1.2 mol dm^{-3} sucrose solution into tube 1. She then transferred 5 cm^3 of solution from tube 1 to tube 2. She thoroughly mixed the contents of tube 2 and then transferred 5 cm^3 of this solution to tube 3. She continued this procedure until she had added 5 cm^3 of solution from tube 5 to tube 6. What was the concentration of her solution in tube 4?
2. How did you prepare your table for raw data in step 3?
3. Explain why you should record the time in seconds.
4. Did pollen grains stick to your mounted needle in step 5? If so, how did you remove them?
5. Why were you told to keep the slides in the Petri dishes between observations?
6. How could you use this method to find the sucrose solution at which germination is fastest?
7. What additional equipment would you need to investigate the effect of sucrose concentration on the rate of growth of pollen tubes?
8. How would you calculate the rate of growth of pollen tubes from your raw data?

Fertilisation

To achieve fertilisation, the male gamete within the pollen grain must fuse with the female gamete in the embryo sac. When a mature pollen grain lands on the stigma of an appropriate plant, it absorbs water, swells and splits open. Once open, it forms a pollen tube that grows through the tissues of the stigma, style and ovary towards the embryo sac. In Figure 6.15, you can see the pollen tube nucleus at the tip of the pollen tube, controlling growth of the tube. Growth of the pollen tube is made possible because it digests the recipient plant's tissues as it moves through the style. The absorbed products of digestion provide the raw materials for the growth of the pollen tube. As the generative nucleus follows the pollen tube nucleus down the pollen tube, it divides by mitosis to produce two haploid nuclei. These nuclei are the **male gametes**. You can see them in Figure 6.15.

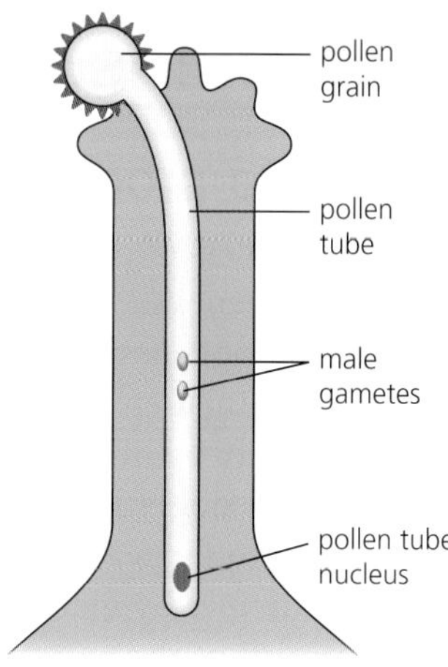

Figure 6.15 Growth of a pollen tube

When it reaches the ovule, the pollen tube grows through the micropyle and into the embryo sac. The tip of the pollen tube breaks down and the pollen tube nucleus disintegrates. Figure 6.16 shows this stage. The two male gametes, present only as nuclei, move into the embryo sac and an event unique to flowering plants then occurs – a **double fertilisation**. One male nucleus fuses with the female gamete, forming a diploid zygote. The other male nucleus fuses with the two polar nuclei to form a triploid **primary endosperm cell**. The other five nuclei within the embryo sac disintegrate. During subsequent development:

- the zygote will develop into an embryo plant, with an embryonic root (radical) and embryonic shoot (plumule)
- the primary endosperm cell forms a mass of food tissue called the endosperm
- the embryo sac develops into a seed, with its integuments forming the seed coat
- the wall of the ovary develops into a fruit.

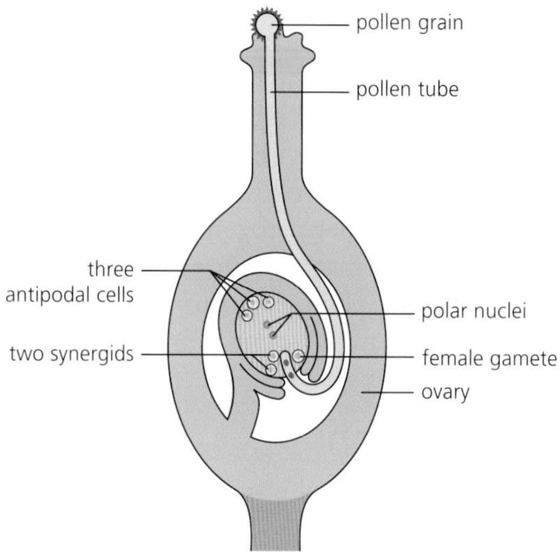

Figure 6.16 Double fertilisation in a flowering plant

Test yourself

16 What is meant by the term 'hermaphrodite'?

17 Name the cell that gives rise to the embryo sac in a flowering plant.

18 Give **one** way in which a male gamete of a flowering plant is different from a male gamete of a human.

19 Explain the difference between pollination and fertilisation in a flowering plant.

20 Double fertilisation is unique to flowering plants. What is meant by double fertilisation?

Chapter summary

Gamete production in mammals

- The process of producing gametes is called gametogenesis.
- During oogenesis in mammals, diploid cells in the germinal epithelium of ovarian follicles divide repeatedly by mitosis to form diploid oogonia (singular oogonium). Each oogonium divides by mitosis to form a diploid primary oocyte, which then divides by meiosis.
- Meiosis I of the primary oocyte results in a large, secondary oocyte and a small, redundant polar body. Both these cells are haploid.
- Meiosis II, which in humans occurs only after fertilisation, results in the formation of the female gamete – the haploid ovum – and another redundant polar body.
- Spermatogenesis within the seminiferous tubules of a male's testes follows a similar course, with each diploid spermatogonium producing a diploid primary spermatocyte that divides by meiosis to form two haploid secondary spermatocytes and then four haploid spermatids. All four spermatids develop into sperm.

Fertilisation

- A secondary oocyte and sperm meet in the oviduct of a female.
- On contact with a secondary oocyte, the head of a sperm is stripped of its surface glycoproteins (capacitation) and releases hydrolytic enzymes (the acrosome reaction).
- The secondary oocyte releases cortical granules that harden its outer layer (the cortical reaction), preventing the entry of further sperm.
- The secondary oocyte then completes meiosis II and the ovum fuses with the haploid sperm nucleus to form a zygote.

Early development of the embryo

- As the zygote is moved down the oviduct, it divides repeatedly by mitosis to form a hollow ball of cells called a blastocyst, which has an outer layer of cells (trophoblasts), an inner mass of cells (blastomeres) and a fluid-filled blastocoel.
- The inner blastomeres will become the embryo that will give rise to a fetus. The trophoblasts will become the amnion, a membrane that surrounds the developing embryo and fetus.
- During implantation, a blastocyst embeds itself into one of the folds in the endometrium – the uterus lining.

Gamete production in flowering plants

- The gametes of flowering plants are produced within their flowers.
- The female structures within a flower are the carpels, each with an ovary, a style and a stigma. The male structures are stamens, each with a filament and lobed anther.
- An ovary contains one or more ovules. Within an ovule, a diploid megaspore mother cell divides by meiosis to produce a megaspore. This megaspore divides three times by mitosis to produce a cell, called the embryo sac, with eight haploid nuclei. One is the female gamete and two are called polar nuclei.
- Within the male anthers, diploid microspore mother cells divide by meiosis to produce haploid microspores. Their nuclei divide by mitosis to produce a pollen grain – a single cell with two nuclei, the pollen tube nucleus and the generative nucleus.
- When a pollen grain lands on the stigma of a suitable flower, it germinates and, under the control of the pollen tube nucleus, produces a pollen tube that grows into the ovule.
- During this growth, the generative nucleus divides by mitosis to produce two haploid nuclei: the male gametes.
- Double fertilisation then occurs. One male nucleus fuses with the female gamete, forming a diploid zygote. The other fuses with both polar nuclei, forming a triploid primary endosperm cell.

Practice questions

1 The following mammalian cells are stages in oogenesis. Give the letter, or letters, representing any cell that is diploid.

A cell in germinal epithelium

B oogonium

C primary oocyte

D secondary oocyte *(1)*

2 In human reproduction, the cortical reaction prevents:

A capacitation of sperm cells

B disintegration of the polar bodies

C meiosis II occurring in the secondary oocyte

D polyspermy *(1)*

3 The cell from which the female gamete is produced in a flowering plant is the:

A antipodal cell

B micropyle

C megaspore

D synergid *(1)*

4 The photograph shows a false-colour transmission electronmicrograph of a human sperm cell.

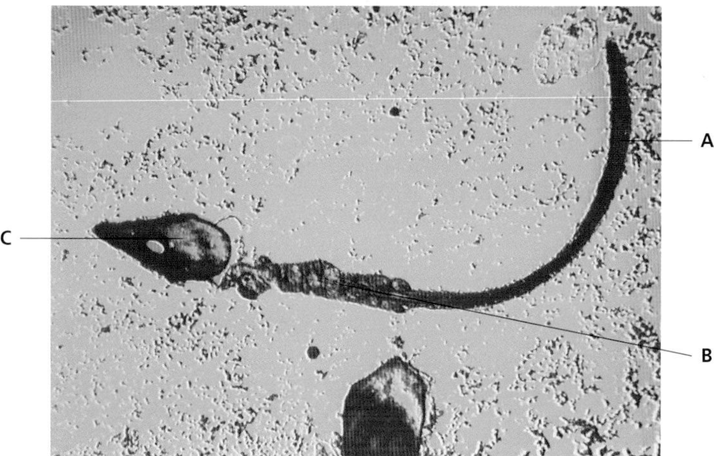

a) Copy and complete the table to shows the name and function of each of the labelled structures A, B and C. *(6)*

Structure	Name	Function
A		
B		
C		

b) The head of the sperm cell shown in the micrograph is 3 μm wide. Calculate the magnification of this electronmicrograph. *(2)*

5 A cucumber plant has a haploid chromosome number of 22.

a) Copy and complete the table to show the number of chromosomes in each of the cells identified. One row has been completed for you. *(3)*

Cell	Number of chromosomes
Petal of flower	
Male gamete	22
Zygote	
Endosperm	

b) Explain the answer you gave in the table for the cell in the endosperm. *(2)*

6 During *in vitro* fertilisation (IVF), sperm cells from a donor are mixed in a Petri dish with secondary oocytes.

a) Suggest why early attempts to achieve IVF were unsuccessful. *(4)*

b) Describe what would happen to the secondary oocyte during the 4 days following successful IVF. *(4)*

7 A group of students germinated seeds on moist filter paper. They investigated changes in the dry mass of two components of seeds during germination. Their results are shown in the table.

Time since sowing/days	Mean dry mass/mg	
	Embryo	Endosperm
0	5.1	44.6
2	5.2	43.9
4	6.9	35.8
6	12.7	17.4
8	19.6	11.3

a) Explain why the students recorded mass as dry mass. *(2)*

b) Suggest how the students could have determined the dry mass of the embryos. *(2)*

c) Describe how you would use the data in the table to calculate the rate of growth of the embryo during the first 4 days. *(2)*

d) Explain the relationship between the dry mass of the embryo and the dry mass of the endosperm. *(3)*

8 Primroses are flowering plants that are common in gardens in the UK. Within a population of primroses there are two types of plant – those with only pin-eyed flowers and those with only thrum-eyed flowers. The diagram shows the difference between these two types of flower.

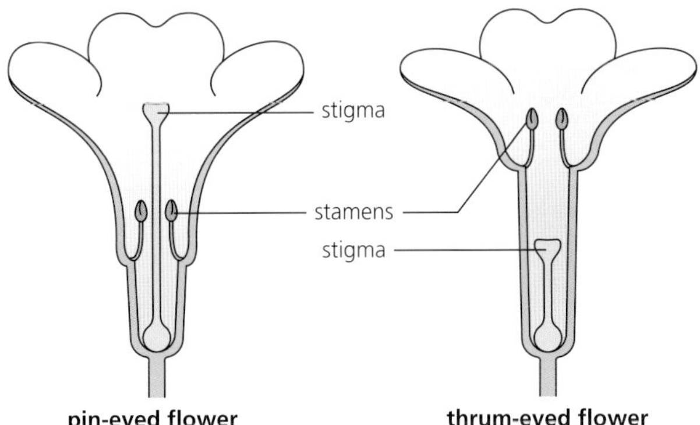

a) Describe the differences between a pin-eyed flower and a thrum-eyed flower. *(2)*

b) Primroses secrete a sugary fluid, called nectar, at the base of their flowers. Bees collect this nectar by inserting their long mouthparts into both types of flower. As they do so, pollen from the flower sticks to their mouthparts.

i) Use information from the diagram to suggest how the structure of pin-eyed and thrum-eyed primrose flowers ensures that cross-pollination occurs. *(4)*

ii) Suggest the biological advantage of cross pollination. *(3)*

Stretch and challenge

9 Release of sperm is called ejaculation and the fluid released is called the ejaculate.

a) In humans, the mean volume of a single ejaculate is $3.4\,cm^3$ and the mean concentration of sperm is 100 000 sperm mm^{-3}. Use these figures to calculate the mean number of sperm in a single ejaculate. Give your answer in standard form.

b) If a man has fewer than 20 000 sperm mm^{-3} of ejaculate, he is likely to be infertile. Suggest why this is the case.

A clinical technician can assess the fertility of a man using the nomogram shown in the diagram.

To use the nomogram, the technician:

- draws a straight line between the observed number of sperm (scale A) and the percentage of sperm that are motile after 2 hours (scale C)
- she draws a straight line from the intersection of this line with scale B, to scale E
- reads the fertility index where this second line crosses scale D.

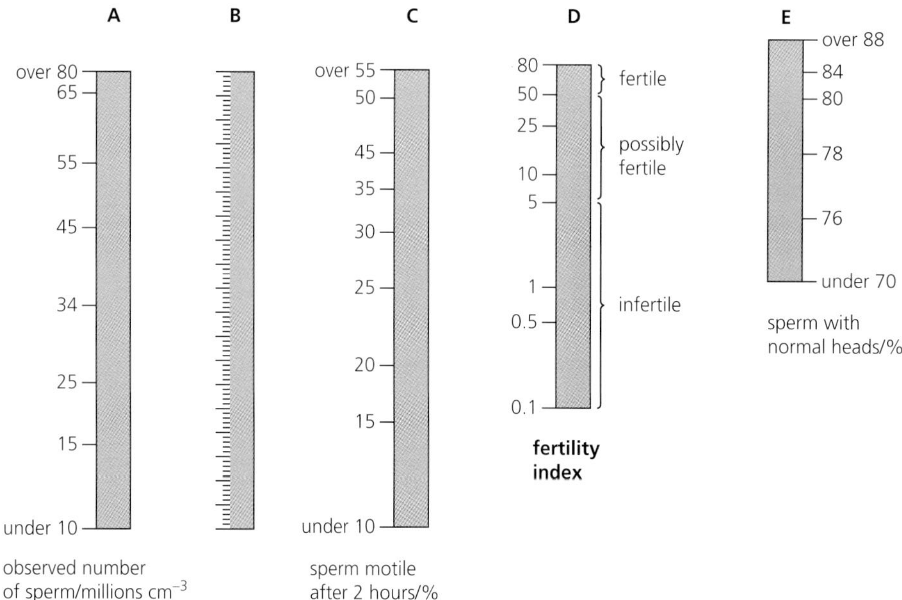

c) Use the nomogram to assess the fertility of a man whose ejaculate contained 25 million sperm per cm^3, 35% of which were motile after 2 hours and 82% of which had normal heads.

10 A technician investigated the growth of pollen tubes. She added pollen grains to a suitable growth medium. At regular intervals, she removed a sample from the culture medium and placed drops of this sample onto individual glass slides. She then examined the slides under a light microscope and measured the lengths of the pollen tubes. Her results are shown in the first graph. The bars represent one standard deviation of the mean (1 × SD).

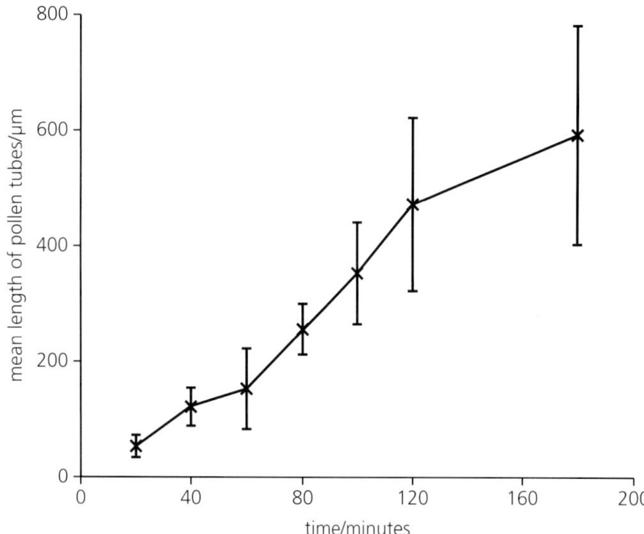

a) How would the technician modify the light microscope in order to measure the length of pollen tubes?

b) What can you conclude from the data in the graph?

The technician repeated her experiment to investigate the effect of certain inhibitors on the growth of pollen tubes. She used three growth media:

- Medium **A** – normal growth medium
- Medium **B** – normal growth medium plus actinomycin D, an inhibitor of DNA transcription
- Medium **C** – normal growth medium plus cycloheximide, an inhibitor of mRNA translation.

Her results are shown in the second graph.

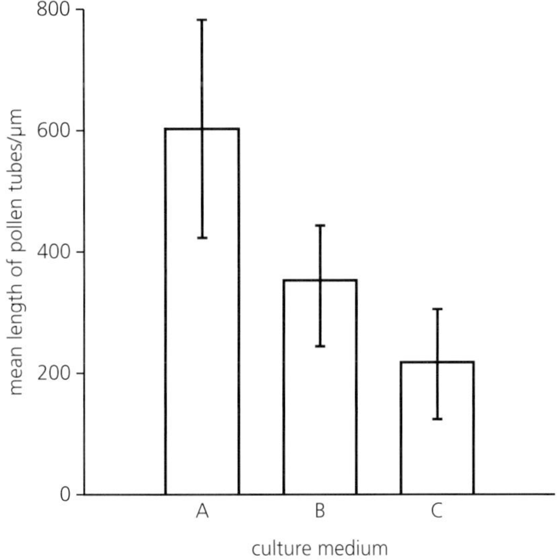

c) Use information in this question to suggest explanations for the effects of actinomycin D and cycloheximide on the growth of pollen tubes.

7 Classification

Prior knowledge

In this chapter you will need to recall that:

- living things are normally given two names: a genus name and a species name; this is known as binomial classification
- accurate classification of living organisms is extremely important to all scientists
- identifying separate species is often very difficult
- there are many undiscovered species on Earth
- the basic structure of DNA is a double helix held together by hydrogen bonding
- the genetic code is made up of four nucleotides containing the bases adenine, guanine, cytosine and thymine (for details, see Chapter 3).

Test yourself on prior knowledge

1 State the binomial names of the following organisms:
   a) lion
   b) tiger
   c) daisy
   d) dandelion
   e) common edible mushroom.
2 Lions and tigers are closely related and could interbreed. Give **two** reasons why they do not normally interbreed.
3 List the full classification of the lion from kingdom to species.
4 Name the **three** components of a DNA nucleotide.
5 Which of the bases in DNA are purines?
6 How are the two strands of DNA held together?
7 What are the main differences between DNA and RNA?
8 What are the names of the five kingdoms that have been used in one method of classification?
9 What are the differences between prokaryotes and eukaryotes?

The range of living things and their classification

There are vast numbers of living things in the world – almost unlimited diversity in fact. No other aspect of life is more characteristic than this great variety of different organisms. Up to now, about 2 million species have been described and named. Meanwhile, previously unknown species are being discovered all the time. We will return to this issue of the diversity of living things – referred to as 'biodiversity' – in the next chapter (Chapter 8).

What we mean by 'species'

The term **species** refers scientifically to a particular type of living thing. We are now confident that living things change with time, and that species have evolved, one from another (Chapter 8).

Later in this chapter we will return to the issue of defining the term 'species' because there are limitations to our definition. First of all we shall locate species in the context of an agreed scheme of classification.

> **Key term**
>
> **Species** A group of living organisms with similar characteristics that interbreed to produce fertile offspring.

Taxonomy – the classification of diversity

Classification is essential to biology because there are too many different living things to study and compare unless they are organised into manageable categories.

Biological classification schemes are the invention of biologists, based upon the best available evidence at the time. With an effective classification system in use, it is easier to organise our ideas about organisms and make generalisations.

The science of classification is called **taxonomy**. The word comes from 'taxa' (sing. = taxon), which is the general name for groups or categories within a classification system. The scheme of classification has to be flexible, allowing newly discovered living organisms to be added into the scheme where they fit best. It should also include fossils, since we believe living and extinct species are related.

> **Key term**
>
> **Taxonomy** The science of classification of living things.

The process of classification involves:

- giving every organism an agreed name
- imposing a scheme upon the diversity of living things.

The binomial system of naming

Many organisms have local names, but these often differ from locality to locality around the world, so they do not allow observers to be confident they are talking about the same thing. For example, in America the name 'robin' refers to a bird the size of the European blackbird – altogether a different bird from the European robin. Instead, scientists use an international approach called the binomial system (meaning 'a two-part name'). By this system everyone, anywhere in the world, knows exactly which organism is being referred to.

Figure 7.1 'Magpie' species of the world

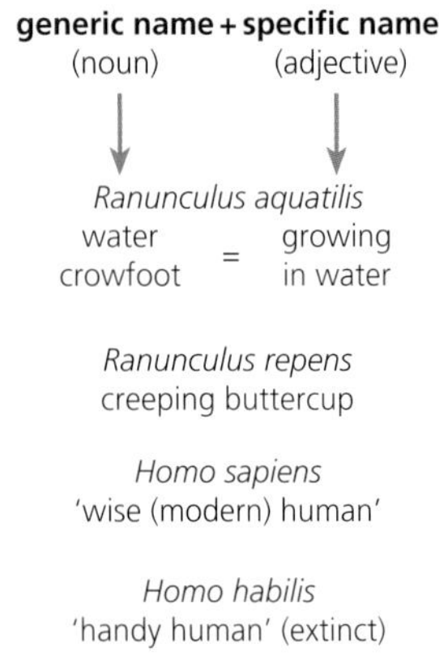

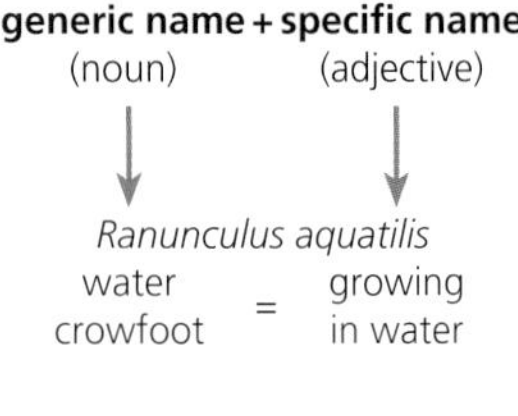

generic name + specific name
(noun)
(adjective)
Ranunculus aquatilis
water crowfoot
=
growing in water
Ranunculus repens
creeping buttercup
Homo sapiens
'wise (modern) human'
Homo habilis
'handy human' (extinct)

Figure 7.2 Naming organisms by the binomial system

So each organism is given a scientific name consisting of two words in Latin (Figure 7.1). The first (a noun) designates the **genus**, the second (an adjective) the species. The generic name begins with a capital letter, followed by the specific name. Conventionally, this name is written in *italics* (or is underlined).

As shown in Figure 7.2, closely related organisms have the same generic name; only their species names differ. You will see that when organisms are frequently referred to the full name is given initially, but thereafter the generic name is shortened to the first (capital) letter. Thus, in continuing references to humans in an article or scientific paper, *Homo sapiens* would become *H. sapiens*.

The scheme of classification

In classification, the aim is to use as many characteristics as possible in placing similar organisms together and dissimilar ones apart. Just as similar species are grouped together into the same genus (plural = genera), so, too, are similar genera grouped together into families. This approach is extended from families to orders, then classes, phyla and kingdoms. This is the hierarchical scheme of classification; each successive group containing more and more different kinds of organism. The taxa used in taxonomy are given in Figure 7.3.

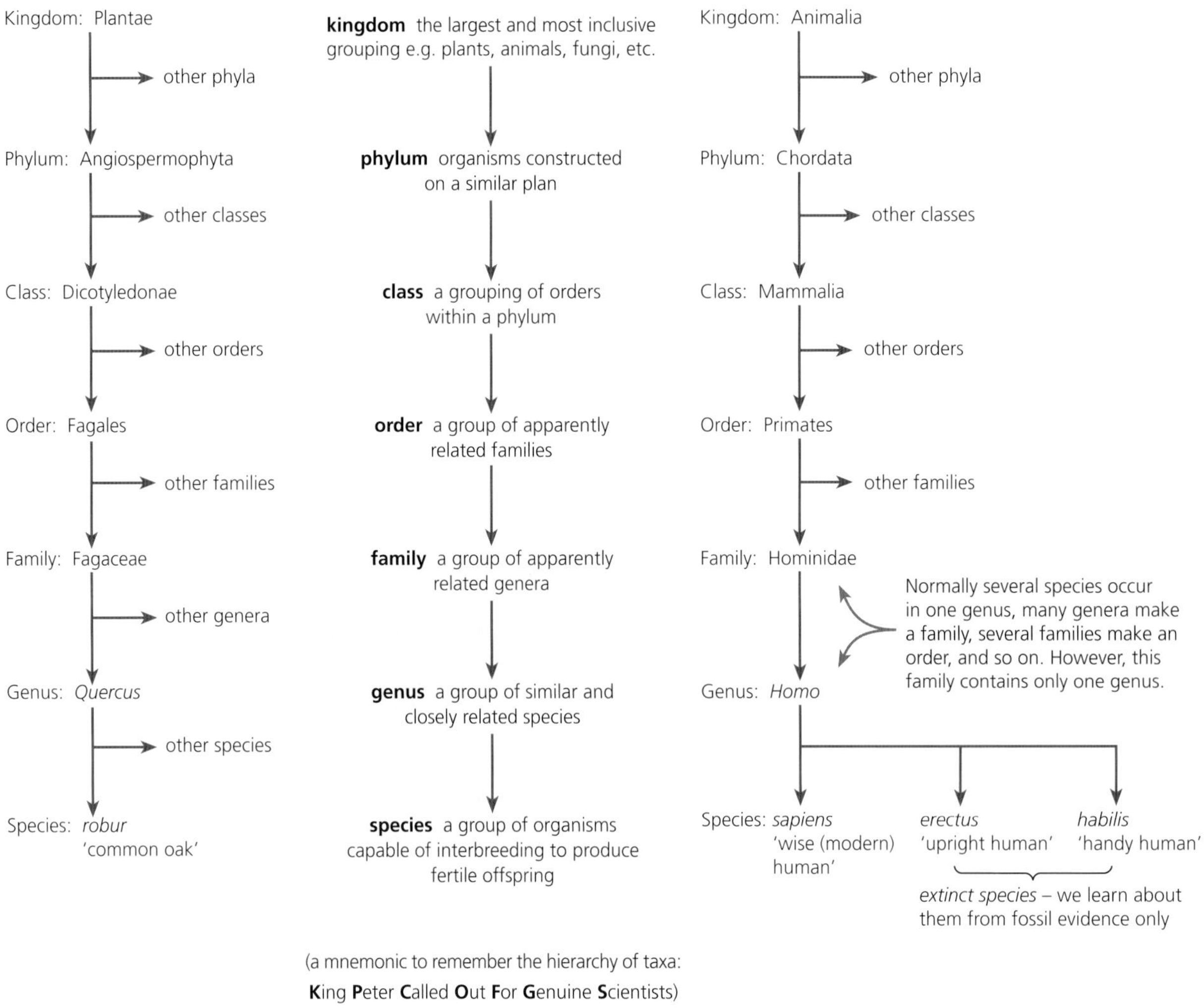

Kingdom: Plantae
other phyla
Phylum: Angiospermophyta
other classes
Class: Dicotyledonae
other orders
Order: Fagales
other families
Family: Fagaceae
other genera
Genus: Quercus
other species
Species: robur
'common oak'
kingdom the largest and most inclusive grouping e.g. plants, animals, fungi, etc.
phylum organisms constructed on a similar plan
class a grouping of orders within a phylum
order a group of apparently related families
family a group of apparently related genera
genus a group of similar and closely related species
species a group of organisms capable of interbreeding to produce fertile offspring
Kingdom: Animalia
other phyla
Phylum: Chordata
other classes
Class: Mammalia
other orders
Order: Primates
other families
Family: Hominidae
Normally several species occur in one genus, many genera make a family, several families make an order, and so on. However, this family contains only one genus.
Genus: Homo
Species: sapiens
'wise (modern) human'
erectus
'upright human'
habilis
'handy human'
extinct species – we learn about them from fossil evidence only
(a mnemonic to remember the hierarchy of taxa:
King Peter Called Out For Genuine Scientists)

Figure 7.3 The taxa used in taxonomy, applied to the genera from two different kingdoms

The features of organisms selected in classification

The *quickest* way to classify living things is on their immediate and obvious similarities and differences. For example, we might classify together animals that fly, simply because the essential organs – wings – are so easily seen. This would include almost all birds and many insects (as well as the bats and certain fossil dinosaurs). However, resemblances between the wings of the bird and the insect are superficial. Both are aerofoils (structures that generate 'lift' when moved though the air); they are built from different tissues and have different origins in the body. We say that the wings of birds and insects are **analogous structures**.

Consequently, they illustrate only superficial resemblances. A classification based on analogous structures is an artificial classification.

Alternatively, a natural classification is based on similarities and differences due to close relationships between organisms because they share common ancestors. The bone structure of the limbs of all vertebrates suggests they are modifications of a common plan we call the pentadactyl limb. So, there are many comparable bones in the human arm, the leg of a horse and the limb of a mole – in other words they are **homologous structures** (Figure 7.4)

> **Key terms**
>
> **Genus** A division of biological classification that is ranked above species but below family.
>
> **Analogous structures** These resemble each other in function but differ in their fundamental structure.
>
> **Homologous structures** These are structures built to a common plan but adapted for different purposes.

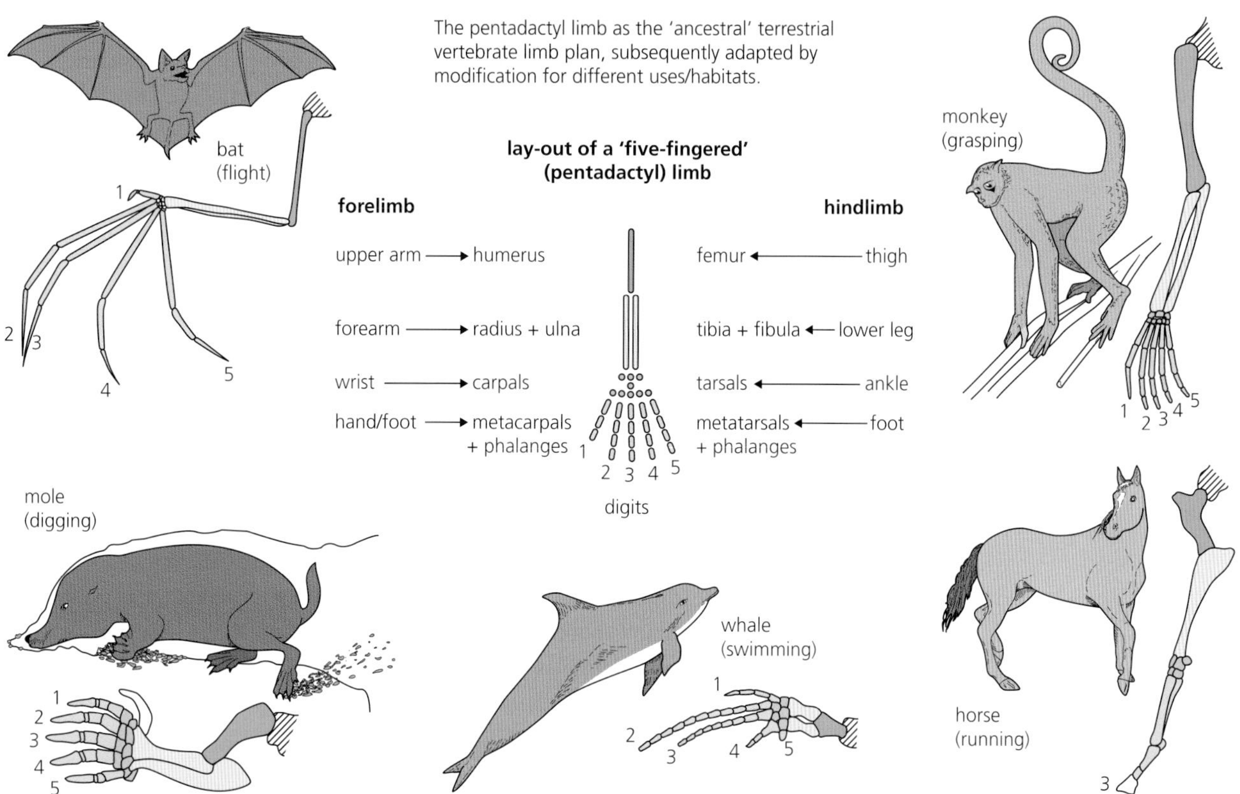

Figure 7.4 Homologous structures show adaptive radiation

The ideal solution – a classification system based on evolutionary relationships

A natural classification based on homologous structures is believed to reflect evolutionary relationships. It is what taxonomists work towards.

Today, similarities and differences in the biochemistry of organisms have become important in taxonomy in addition to structural features. For example, the composition of nucleic acids (and cell proteins) often shows relationships more accurately than structural features. Large molecules like nucleic acids are subjected to changes with time – we call these changes in nucleic acids mutations. Biochemical changes like mutations in DNA occur at a more or less constant rate, and can be used as a 'molecular clock'. It is possible to estimate the relatedness of different groups of organisms by the amount of variation in their DNA – which is a function of time since particular organisms share a common ancestor. Since the rate of change can be reliably estimated, the extent of change is a function of the time that has passed between the separations of evolutionary lines.

DNA sequencing

Key term

DNA sequencing The process of determining the exact order of the nucleotides in a DNA molecule.

DNA sequencing used to be a laborious laboratory analysis, where pieces of DNA some 50 000–100 000 bases long would take a year to analyse. Today the whole process has been refined and is now carried out automatically by very expensive machines capable of doing the same analysis in a few hours. Despite this automation the principles of the analysis are very similar:

1. The DNA molecule is cut into pieces at very specific points by enzymes.
2. The pieces of DNA are chemically modified and tagged with fluorescent dyes, which give a different colour for each base.
3. These pieces of DNA are then separated by electrophoresis and the bases recognised by the colour of their fluorescence.
4. When the sequence of these pieces of DNA are recorded they are then linked together to make up the base sequence of the whole DNA molecule.

Extracting and cutting up DNA

DNA can be extracted from tissue samples by mechanically breaking up the cells, filtering off the debris and breaking down cell membranes by treatment with detergents. The protein framework of the chromosomes is then removed by incubation with a protein-digesting enzyme (protease). The DNA, now existing as long threads, is isolated from this mixture of chemicals by precipitation with ethanol and is thus 'cleaned'. The DNA strands are then re-suspended in aqueous, pH-buffered medium. They are now ready for 'slicing' into fragments.

The DNA is sliced or chopped into fragments by addition of restriction endonucleases (restriction enzymes). These enzymes occur naturally in bacteria, where they protect against viruses that enter the bacterium by cutting the viral DNA into small pieces, thereby inactivating it. (Viral DNA might otherwise take over the host cell.) Viruses that specifically parasitise bacteria are called bacteriophages or phages. Restriction enzymes were so named because they restrict the multiplication of phage viruses.

Many different restriction enzymes have been discovered and purified, and today they are used widely in genetic engineering experiments. A distinctive and important feature of restriction enzymes is that they cut at particular base sequences (Figure 7.5) and are of two types, forming either 'blunt ends' or 'sticky ends' to the cut fragments. Sticky ends are single-stranded extensions formed in the double-stranded DNA after 'digestion' with a restriction enzyme that cuts in a staggered fashion. In DNA profiling, a selected restriction enzyme is used to cut at specific base-sequence sites.

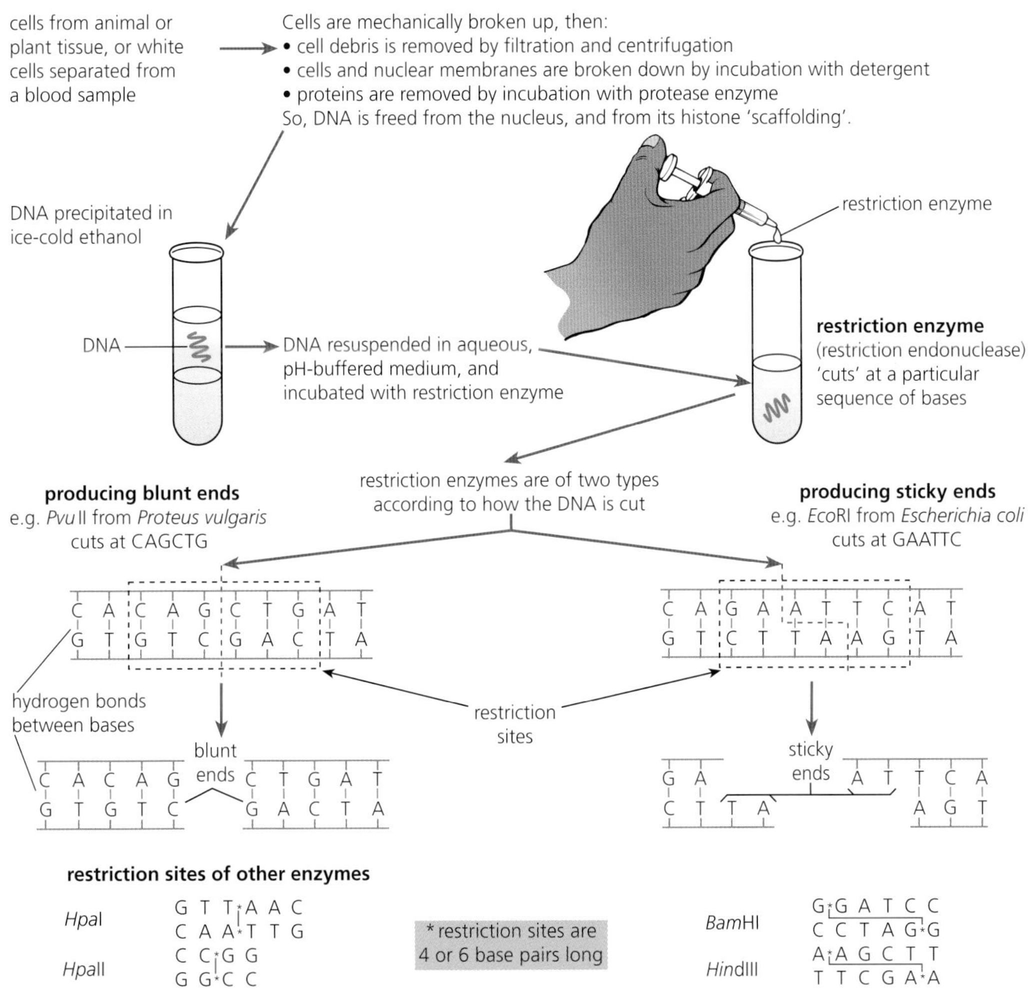

Figure 7.5 Isolating and cutting of DNA

Isolating DNA fragments – electrophoresis

Electrophoresis is a process used to separate particles, including biologically important molecules such as DNA, RNA, proteins and amino acids. It is typically carried out on an agarose gel (a very pure form of agar) or on polyacrylamide gel (PAG). Both these substances contain tiny pores, which allow them to act like a molecular sieve. Small particles can move through these gels quite quickly, whereas larger molecules move much more slowly.

> **Key term**
>
> **Electrophoresis**
> A technique of separating charged ions in a fluid by applying a potential difference.

Biological molecules separated by electrophoresis also carry an electrical charge. In the case of DNA, phosphate groups in DNA fragments give them a net negative charge. Consequently, when DNA molecules are placed in an electric field they migrate towards the positive pole.

So, in electrophoresis, separation occurs according to the size and the charge carried. This is the double principle of electrophoretic separations. Separation of DNA fragments produced by the actions of restriction enzymes is shown in Figure 7.6. Note that the bands of DNA fragments are not visible on the gel until, in this case, a DNA-binding fluorescent dye as been added.

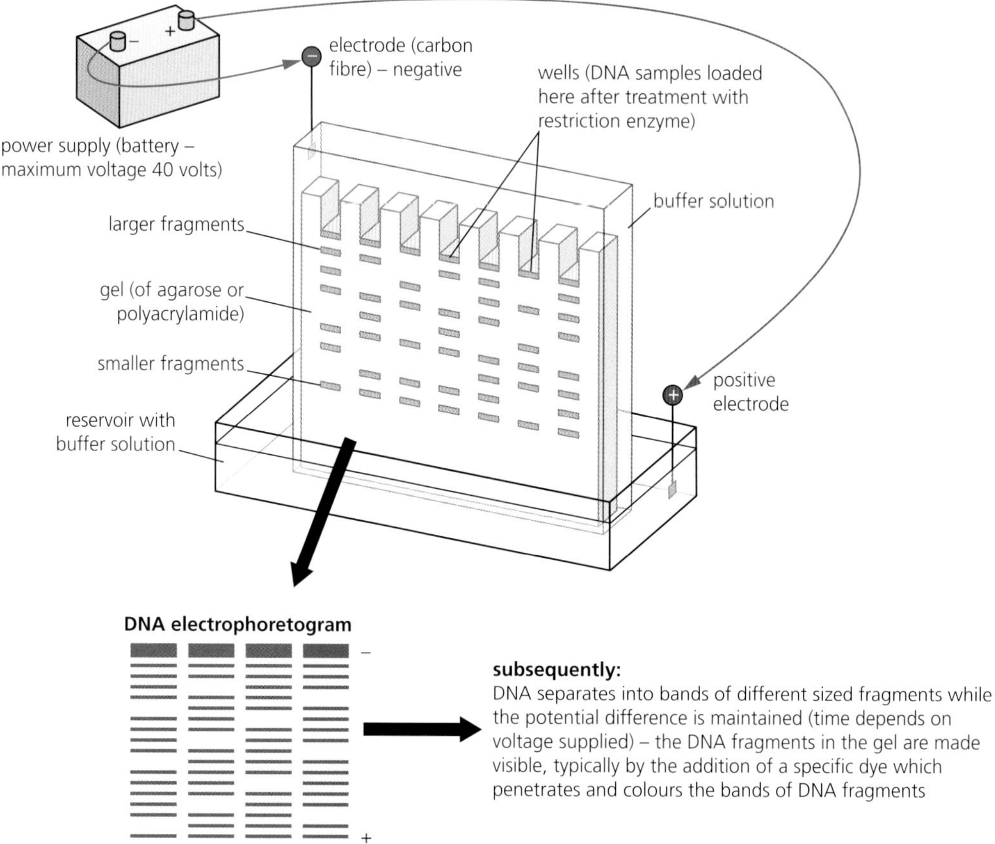

Figure 7.6 Electrophoretic separation of DNA fragments

DNA differences used to determine evolutionary relationships

The relatedness of organisms is studied experimentally by investigation of differences in DNA.

1 By DNA hybridisation

The genetic differences between the DNA of various organisms give us data on degrees of divergence in their respective evolutionary histories. By the technique of DNA hybridisation, the matching of DNA samples of different species has enabled the discovery of how closely related particular species are (Figure 7.7).

The degree of similarity of samples of DNA from two organisms is disclosed by measuring the temperature at which they separate. The more distantly related the organisms are, the fewer the bonds (due to base-pairing) that will form between the strands of DNA when mixed. A lower temperature is then required to separate them (Figure 7.7).

DNA hybridisation is a technique that involves matching the DNA of different species, to discover how closely they are related.
DNA extracted from cells and 'cut' into fragments, about 500 bases long
fragments are heated to cause them to become single strands
single strands are mixed with DNA strands from another species, prepared in exactly the same way (therefore comparable)
base pairing causes strands of DNA to align with complementary DNA
the greater the complementarity of the two strands, the more bonds link them together
high complementarity
low complementarity
The closeness of the two DNAs is measured by finding the temperature at which they separate – the fewer bonds formed, the lower the temperature required.
The degree of relatedness of the DNA of **primate species** can be correlated with the estimated number of years since they shared a common ancestor.
common chimp
pygmy chimp
human
gorilla
orang-utan
common gibbon
siamang gibbon
old world monkey
difference in DNA /%
0
1
2
3
4
5
6
7
8
mya
0
5
10
15
20
25
30
35

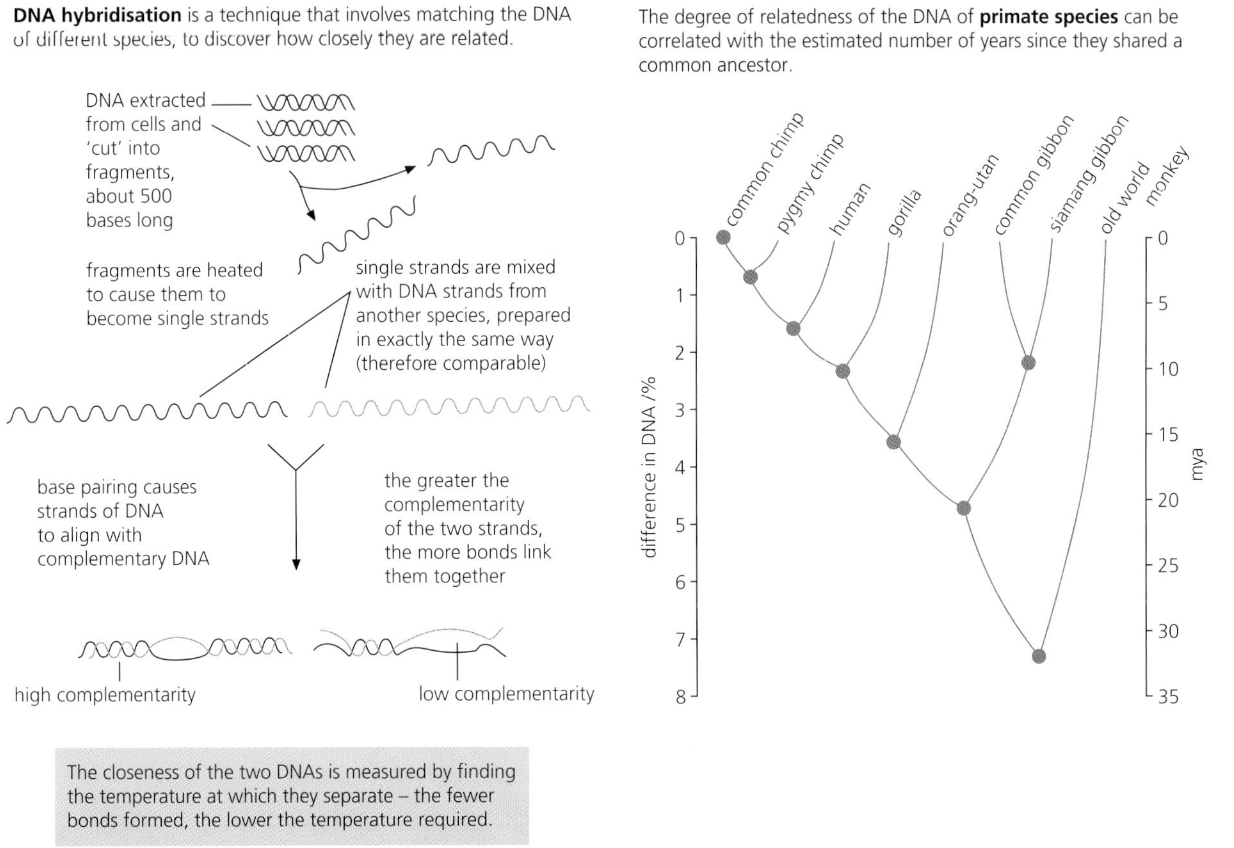

Figure 7.7 Genetic difference between DNA samples and evolutionary relatedness

2 By application of developments in the new discipline of bioinformatics

At the centre of this development is the creation and maintenance of databases concerning nucleic acid sequences (and the proteins derived from them). Already, the genomes of many prokaryotes and eukaryotes have been sequenced, as well as that of humans. This huge volume of data requires organisation, storage and indexing to enable practical use of the subsequent analyses. These tasks involve applied mathematics, informatics, statistics and computer science, and are collectively referred to as **bioinformatics**.

One possible outcome is the use of the GenBank database to determine differences in base sequence of a gene in two species. For example, it is possible to compare the nucleotide sequences of the cytochrome c oxidase gene of humans with that of the Sumatran orang-utan or other species, as shown in Figure 7.8, with a view to determining the degree of relatedness of the two species. This process involves using The National Center for Biotechnology Information web services, which provide access to biomedical and genomic information.

These approaches exploit the fact that organisms that are closely related show fewer differences in the composition of specific nucleic acids (and therefore cell proteins) that they possess. But despite these impressive additional sources of evidence, evolutionary relationships are still only partly understood, so current taxonomy is only partly an evolutionary or **phylogenetic** classification.

Key terms

Bioinformatics The storage, manipulation and analysis of biological information via computer science.

Phylogeny The evolutionary development and history of a species or other group of organisms.

Tip

Learning and understanding the detailed structure of nucleic acids is very useful in many sections of the specification for both AS and A Level.

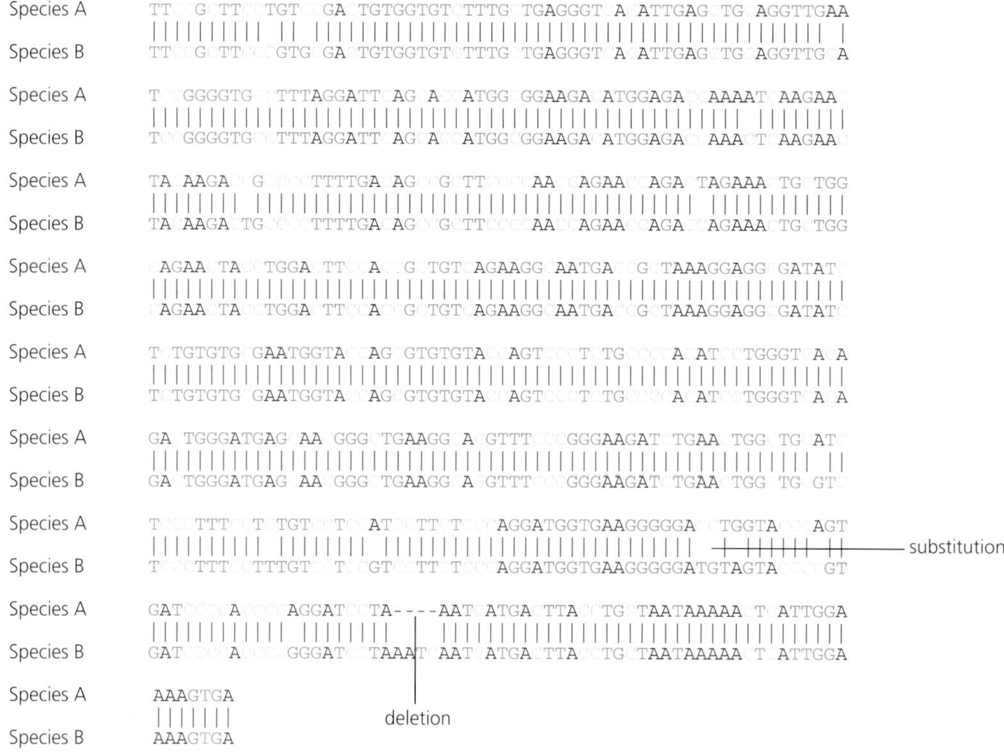

Figure 7.8 Cytochrome oxidase base sequence comparison for two species

Test yourself

1 Explain why using observable features alone may give a false classification of living organisms.

2 Use the diagrams in Figure 7.5 to explain why a restriction enzyme such as *Eco*RI would be used to produce DNA fragments that could be easily attached to other pieces of DNA

3 Which part of the DNA nucleotide gives the molecule an overall negative charge?

4 Which other property of DNA fragments allows them to be separated by the agarose gel?

5 Why will DNA formed from two strands from distantly related organisms separate at a lower temperature?

6 What is the difference between an analogous and a homologous structure?

The five kingdoms

At one time the living world seemed to divide naturally into two kingdoms (Table 7.1).

Table 7.1 Living things divided into two kingdoms

The plants	The animals
Photosynthetic (autotrophic nutrition)	Ingestion of complex food (heterotrophic nutrition)
Mostly rooted (i.e. stationary) organisms	Typically mobile organisms

These two kingdoms grew from the original disciplines of biology, namely botany, the study of plants, and zoology, the study of animals. Fungi and microorganisms were conveniently 'added' to botany! Initially there was only one problem; fungi possessed the typically animal heterotrophic nutrition but were more plant-like in structure.

Later, with the use of the electron microscope came the discovery of the two types of cell structure, namely prokaryotic and eukaryotic. As a result, the bacteria with their prokaryotic cells could no longer be 'plants' since plants have eukaryotic cells. This led to the idea that living things should be divided into five kingdoms (Table 7.2).
The evolutionary relationships of the kingdoms are suggested in Figure 7.9.

Table 7.2 The five kingdom classification

Prokaryotae (prokaryotes)	bacteria and cyanobacteria (photosynthetic bacteria), predominately unicellular organisms
Protoctista (protoctists)	eukaryotes, predominately unicellular, and seen as resembling the ancestors of the fungi, plants and animals
Fungi	eukaryotes, predominately multicellular organisms, non-motile, and with heterotrophic nutrition
Plantae (plants)	eukaryotes, multicellular organisms, non-motile, with autotrophic nutrition
Animalia (animals)	eukaryotes, multicellular organisms, motile, with heterotrophic nutrition

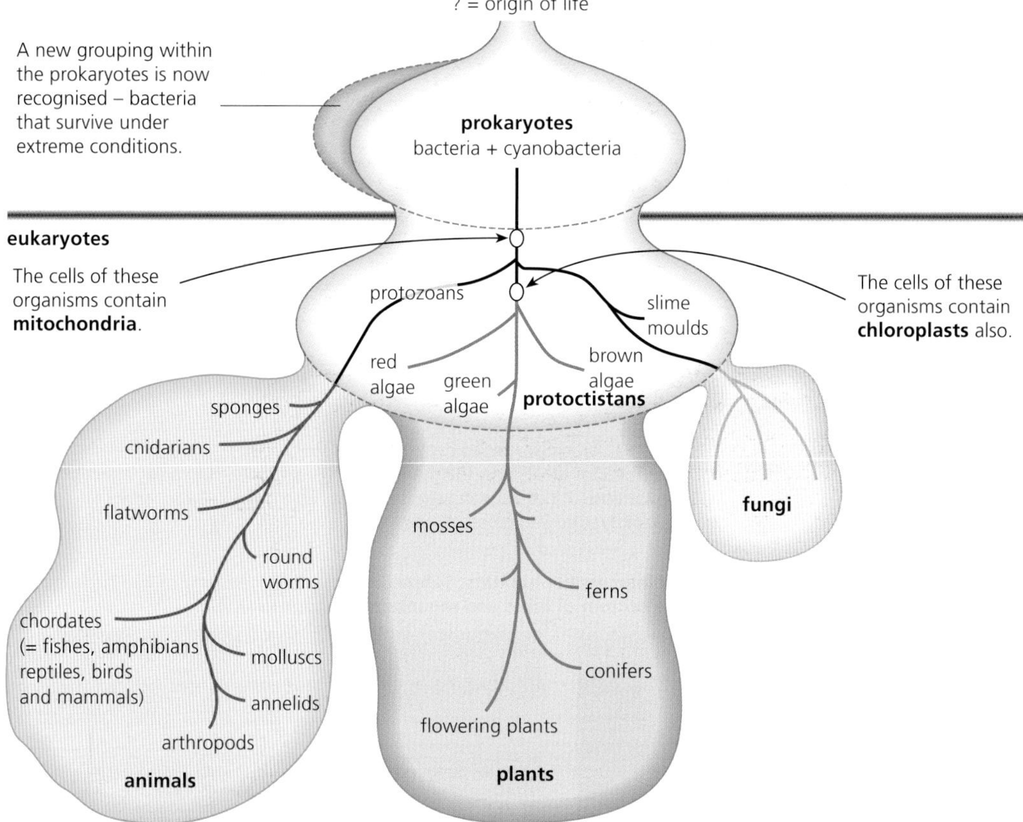

Figure 7.9 Possible evolutionary relationship of the five kingdoms

A new scheme of classification

Then came the discovery of species of bacteria that survive and prosper in extremely hostile environments (the **extremophiles**), such as the 'heat-loving' bacteria found in hot-springs at about 70 °C. Subsequently, extremophiles were found in a wider range of hostile habitats.

Table 7.3 The range of extremophile bacteria

'Salt-loving' bacteria (halophytes)	common in salt lakes and where sea water becomes trapped and concentrated by evaporation and where salt has crystallised
'Alkali-loving' bacteria (alkalinophiles)	survive at above pH 10 – conditions typical of soda lakes
Bacteria that thrive in extremely acidic conditions (acidophiles)	found in conditions of <pH2, such as some sulfur bacteria found in hot, thermal vents
'Heat-loving' bacteria (thermophiles)	occur in hot-springs at about 70 °C; some are adapted to survive at temperatures of 100–115 °C (**hyperthermophilic** prokaryotes)
Bacteria that thrive in sub-zero temperatures	common at temperatures of −10 °C, as in the ice of the poles where salt depresses the freezing point of water

The classification of living organisms into three domains on the basis of their ribosomal RNA

These evolutionary relationships have been established by comparing the sequences of bases (nucleotides) in the ribosomal RNA (rRNA) present in species of each group.

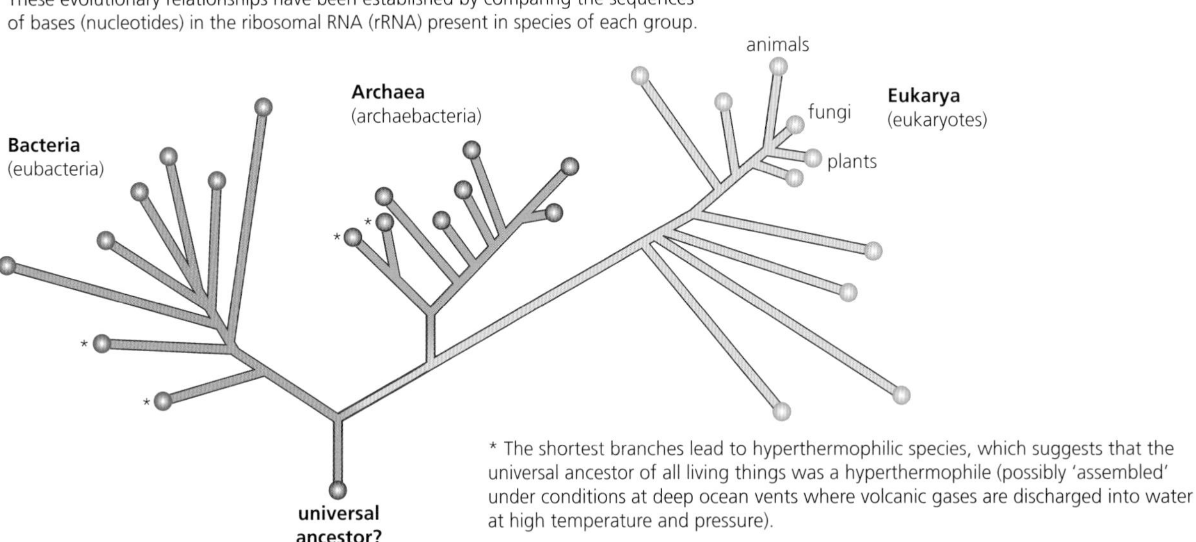

* The shortest branches lead to hyperthermophilic species, which suggests that the universal ancestor of all living things was a hyperthermophile (possibly 'assembled' under conditions at deep ocean vents where volcanic gases are discharged into water at high temperature and pressure).

Archaea were discovered among prokaryotes of extreme and inaccessible habitats. Subsequently, other members of the Archaea were found more widely – in the gut of herbivores and at the bottom of lakes and mountain bogs, for example.

Figure 7.10 Ribosomal RNA and the classification of living organisms

These microorganisms of extreme habitats all have cells that we can identify as prokaryotic. However, the larger RNA molecules present in the ribosomes of extremophiles were discovered to be different from those of previously known bacteria. Further analyses of the biochemistry of extremophiles, in comparison with that of other groups, suggested new evolutionary relationships and led on to a new scheme of classification (Figure 7.10).

Classification into three domains

As a result, we now recognise three major forms of life, called **domains**. The organisms of each domain share a distinctive, unique pattern of ribosomal RNA and there are other differences, which establish their evolutionary relationships (Table 7.4).

These domains are:

- the **Archaea** (the extremophile prokaryotes)
- the **Eubacteria** (the true bacteria)
- the **Eukaryota** (all eukaryotic cells – the protoctista, fungi, plants and animals).

Incidentally, the Archaea have now been found in an even broader range of habitats than merely extreme environments. Some occur in the oceans and some in fossil fuel deposits deep underground. Some species occur in deep ocean vents, high-temperature habitats such as geysers, in salt pans and in polar environments. Others occur only in anaerobic enclosure such as the guts of termites and of cattle, and at the bottom of ponds, among the rotting plant remains. Here they breakdown organic matter and release methane – with important environmental consequences.

Key term

Domain One of three major forms of life used in the most recent suggestion for classification of living things.

Table 7.4 Biochemical differences between the domains

Biochemical features	Domains		
	Archaea	Eubacteria	Eukaryota
DNA of chromosome(s)	Circular genome	Circular genome	Chromosomes
Bound protein (histone) present in DNA	Present	Absent	Present
Introns in genes	Typically absent	Typically absent	Frequent
Cell wall	Present – not made of peptidoglycan	Present – made of peptidoglycan	Sometimes present – never made of peptidoglycan
Lipids of cell membrane bilayer	Archaeal membranes contain lipids that differ from those of eubacteria and eukaryotes (Figure 7.11)		

Phospholipids of archaeal membranes

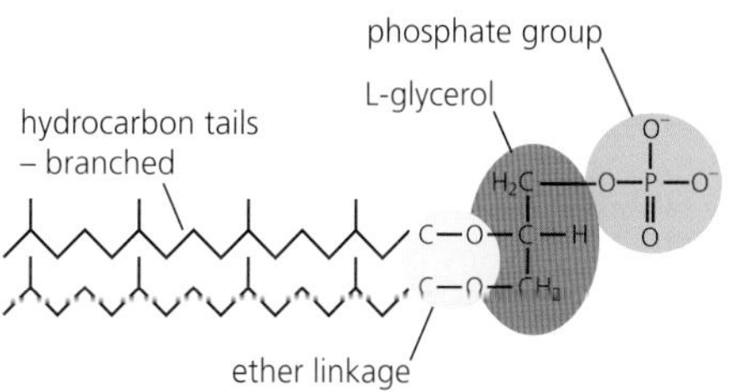

Phospholipids of eubacteria and eukaryote membranes

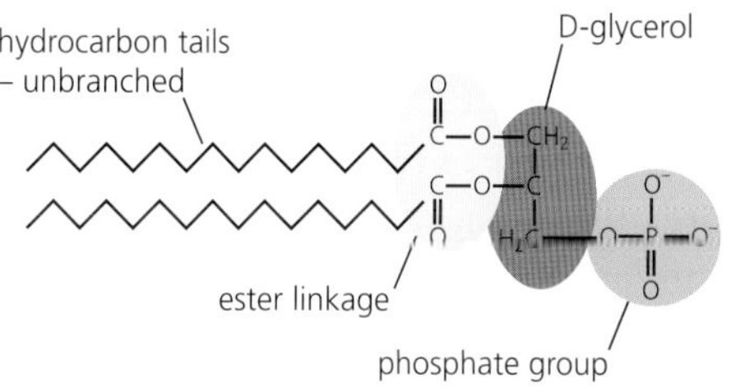

Figure 7.11 Lipid structure of cell membranes in the three domains

The issue of what is a species

On a day-by-day basis, biologists frequently use the term 'species' when they refer to an organism they are studying, within the context of a particular aspect of its biology. For example:

- **ecologists** refer to species as defined by their ecological niche and how they interact with the living and non-living parts of their environment
- **geneticists** refer to species as part of a population whose members have the potential to interbreed and produce viable fertile offspring
- **morphologists** refer to species as defined by common body shape and other structural features by which they are distinguished
- **taxonomists** refer to species as the smallest group of individuals that share a common ancestor – a single 'branch of the tree of life'.

We can see that the term is commonly used on a daily basis, in at least four different contexts, with different meanings and therefore definitions.

Origin of the term 'species'

When Linnaeus devised the binomial system of nomenclature in the eighteenth century there was no problem in defining species. It was believed that each species was derived from the original pair of animals created by God. Since species had been created in this way they were fixed and unchanging.

In fact, present-day living things have arisen by change from pre-existing forms of life. This process has been called 'descent with modification' and 'organic evolution', but perhaps '**speciation**' is better because it emphasises that species change. The fossil record provides evidence that these changes do occur in living things – human fossils alone illustrate this point. We now know that species have evolved, one from another, in the course of the history of life on Earth. The concept of species has been modified – we no longer have a simple definition of a species that is totally accurate in all cases.

Today, as many different characteristics as possible are used in order to define and identify a species. The main characteristics used are:

- morphology and anatomy (external and internal structure)
- cell structure (whether cells are eukaryotic or prokaryotic)
- physiology (blood composition, renal function) and chemical composition (comparisons of nucleic acids and proteins, and the similarities in proteins between organisms, for example).

A **species** can be defined as consisting of organisms of common ancestry that closely resemble each other structurally and biochemically, and which are members of natural populations that are actually or potentially capable of breeding with each other to produce fertile progeny, and which do not interbreed with members of other species.

The last part of this definition cannot be applied to self-fertilising populations or to organisms that reproduce only asexually. Such groups are species because they are very similar to each other morphologically and in all other features.

Having set the scene about the challenge of defining species, we can now agree that on a day-to-day basis the term 'species' is satisfactory and useful provided we think of a species as defined above.

Naming and classifying species – the scale of the task

We have noted there are vast numbers of living things in the world. Up to now, about 2 million species have been described and named. However, until very recently there has been no attempt to produce an international 'library of living things', where new discoveries are automatically checked out (see below). Consequently, some known organisms may have been 'discovered' more than once. Meanwhile, previously unknown species are being discovered all the time. In the UK alone, several hundred new species have been described in the past decade. We might have expected all the wildlife in these islands to be known, since Britain was one of the countries to pioneer the systematic study of plants and animals. Apparently this is not the case; previously unknown organisms are frequently found here, too.

Worldwide, the number of unknown species is estimated at between 3–5 million at the very least, and possibly as high as 100 million. So scientists are not certain just how many different types of organism exist.

Scientists do not agree – the debate continues

This chapter is quite different from others on the same subject. It describes several different ideas about how living things are classified but if you read carefully you will see that all the suggested schemes have drawbacks. The five-kingdom model has a group called Protoctista, whose members are really difficult to define. If you look up a definition of Protoctista you will probably find a description concentrating on features they do not possess rather than features they have in common. You might find something like this: 'The Kingdom Protoctista is defined by exclusion: its members are neither animals (which develop from a blastula), plants (which develop from an embryo), fungi (which lack undulipodia and develop from spores), nor prokaryotes.' In other words it is a collection of organisms that do not necessarily have a great deal in common. Not surprisingly, although this model was widely accepted because it had some clear reasoning, many biologists did not agree.

The discovery of more details of the structure of some bacteria led to the idea that classification should be more strictly based on possible evolutionary history, and hence the very different idea of three domains, with the Eukaryota containing almost all the living things that most people would recognise. Although many biologists accept the logic behind this, once again, many do not agree.

The whole field of classification continues to be hotly debated, as it has for at least 300 years! Even the father of modern classification Carolus Linnaeus (1735) chose to include just plants and animals, ignoring the whole group of single-celled organisms discovered by Anthony van Leeuwenhoek, using the first microscope, some 60 years earlier.

Tip

In exam questions, be prepared to show that you understand that the models of classification are still under debate and that none is perfect. The developments, such as studying DNA from different cells, mean that new evidence is being collected all the time.

Table 7.5 shows some developments of the debate following the introduction of techniques of molecular analysis in the 1970s.

Table 7.5 A recent timeline of the classification debate

Date	Author	Model
1977	Woese	Structure of extremophile RNA suggests they are a separate group. = 6 kingdoms
1990	Woese	More molecular evidence suggests ancient origin of two types of bacteria with all other living things in one other group. = 3 domains
1993	Cavalier-Smith	Other evidence used to dispute the idea that all bacteria and other single-celled protists should be grouped together = 8 kingdoms
1998	Cavalier-Smith	Groups all bacteria together and links all Protozoa = 6 kingdoms

This is a very simplified summary and there have been many other suggestions based on evidence from molecular biology advances since 1998. It is important therefore to understand that all the different models have their strong points and their drawbacks.

Test yourself

7 Give the correct binomial names of five organisms that would be classified as Prokaryotes in the five-kingdom classification.

8 Name the **two** compounds that form a peptidoglycan.

9 Which molecules were first found to be different in Archaea compared with other domains?

10 Who is often described as the father of classification?

11 What was the main problem with defining the group Protoctista?

12 Why are there likely to be many species yet to be discovered?

How do scientists investigate their ideas?

The first thing to understand is that scientific ideas and facts are constantly changing. Some basic principles have stood the test of time, but other ideas have changed dramatically or have needed modification and are still changing. Only 70 years ago biologists did not agree that DNA was the genetic material.

Unfortunately many people think of scientific progress as the story of Archimedes – odd-looking people working away in a strange laboratory and rushing out shouting 'eureka' as they reveal some perfect answer. The truth is that very big steps forward are rare and a great deal of scientific research involves painstakingly repeating investigations to provide reliable evidence for a proposed model, but without this type of research we could never build a solid, reliable body of information.

The process of research begins with an idea or theoretical model. This may be an accepted model or a new approach but it will be only a theory unless there is solid evidence to support it. At this stage it is necessary to make some prediction based on the model, which can be tested experimentally. Designing a valid investigation to test the prediction requires ingenuity, imagination and extensive background knowledge. To make real advances it is often necessary to design new methods or to use available technology in a novel way. This stage is normally a collaborative effort with a team of other scientists. In this way it is possible to collect evidence to support the model. As more and more evidence is collected and more predictions prove to be correct, then the model will be accepted by most scientists. However, it only takes one well-designed investigation to produce results that contradict the model to undermine it completely.

Tip

Validity is about the design of the investigation, controlling variables effectively and being confident that it is the independent variable that is shown to be affecting the dependent variable.

How do scientists check the validity of investigations?

This is a really important question as many scientific developments are built on the work of others over many years. It is essential that conclusions made in the past and the present are valid and that progress is made based upon reliable information. There are several ways in which evidence is carefully checked and becomes accepted by the scientific community.

1 **Scientific journals**

All scientists publish full details of their investigations in well-known scientific journals. Their reports must contain full details of their methodology, the original data and an analysis of their findings, following some strict rules. These journals are available to scientists worldwide who can read about the work of others and the latest developments in their field.

2 **Peer review**

Before a scientific journal will accept work for publication it must be verified by senior scientists in the place where it was carried out. It is then scrutinised by an independent panel of scientists who are experts in the same field. They check the details of the method, the data collected and the validity of conclusions. Peer reviewers often ask for more details or a revision of conclusions before approving its publication. The process of peer review and publication of scientific papers is quite strict and therefore ensures that the information contained in the papers is very reliable. In this way a large body of scientific knowledge and understanding has been built up over many years.

3 **Conferences (symposia)**

Most important fields of research are carried out by many scientists in several countries. Universities and other institutions often host meetings of scientists from around the world specialising in one particular area of research. At these meetings invited participants often present their latest findings before they have been published. However, the most important function of these meetings is to allow individuals to share ideas, discuss common problems and argue their case where different models are proposed.

Finally it is important to realise that scientists are also human. Debates on the merits of different models can become very heated as proponents defend their ideas.

Tip

This section on how scientists investigate and validate their findings is also relevant to many other parts of the specification so can be tested in any of the exam papers, including those questions testing practical skills.

Chapter summary

Classification

- Organisms are named using a binomial system. Each has a species and genus title.
- The exact definition of a species is still a matter of debate amongst scientists.
- Species can be defined according to their structure but this can be confusing since some structures such as wings can look similar but are very different (analogous) whilst others may not look similar but have identical origins (homologous).
- Most scientists agree that the best classification would be one based on evolutionary relationships (phylogenetic). However, tracing such relationships over millions of years is difficult.
- New techniques of DNA analysis are now used to investigate changes in base sequences in different organisms.
- DNA sequencing involves using enzymes to cut DNA into fragments, which then have a coloured marker attached to them. These fragments can then be separated by electrophoresis and recognised by their colours. Knowing the structure of the fragments allows biologists to piece them together to reveal longer base sequences, which can then be compared.
- Electrophoresis is a technique where charged particles such as DNA fragments are separated in a liquid by applying an electric current across it, causing the particles to move towards the opposite electrode. DNA is negatively charged so moves to the positive electrode.
- By carrying out electrophoresis on a gel, the movement of larger particles is slowed down more than that of smaller particles, so the fragments are separated by size.
- Using sophisticated mathematical techniques and large databases allows biologists to analyse evolutionary changes in DNA in different organisms, a process known as bioinformatics.

Modern ideas of classification

- Early attempts at classification were often unsatisfactory because finding a single kingdom for such groups as bacteria and fungi proved very difficult. During the 20th century a compromise classification of five kingdoms was developed, which simply gathered together all the awkward groups into a kingdom called Protoctista, but this did not solve the basic problem.
- The most recent suggestion proposes three domains known as Archaea, Eubacteria and Eukaryota. This is based on chromosome structure, cell wall and membrane structure and DNA differences.
- The three domain classification comes largely from the discovery of extremophilic bacteria found in deep-sea vents at very high temperatures and pressures and has led to suggestions that the earliest forms of life may have originated in such conditions.
- Not all scientists agree with these models and there is constant debate at international conferences, fuelled by new research and new data published in scientific journals.

Practice questions

1 Which of the following represents the correct hierarchy of classification?

A phylum → class → family → order → genus → species

B phylum → class → order → family → genus → species

C phylum → class → order → genus → family → species

D phylum → class → family → genus → order → species *(1)*

2 Which of the following applies to all members of the same species?

A have identical external features

B have the same DNA

C cannot interbreed with any other species

D produce fertile offspring with other members of the same species *(1)*

3 *Halobacterium salinarum* is a bacterium found in very saline environments.

a) Name two cellular features of this bacterium that could be investigated to show that it is not a eukaryote. *(2)*

b) Analysis of the genes for ribosomal RNA (rRNA) is often used to distinguish Archaea from prokaryotes and eukaryotes. Explain why this molecule is particularly useful for this purpose. *(3)*

c) Many Archaea are extremophiles, which live in harsh environmental conditions. Some live in hot springs at temperatures of 80 °C or higher.

What are the major problems faced by cells at these temperatures and how might the modifications of Archaea cell structure help to overcome them? *(4)*

4 The table shows the base sequence of the same section of DNA taken from the gene for 12S ribosomal RNA in three different animals. All are mammals but the dog and mole are modern placental mammals where the young develop inside the uterus supplied with nutrients through the placenta. Marsupial mammals are largely confined to Australia and are much more primitive, giving birth to tiny underdeveloped young, which are then kept in an external pouch to develop further.

Animal	12S rRNA DNA base sequence
Dog	G G T C C T A G C C T T C C T A T T A G T T T T T A G T A G A C T T A C
Mole	G G T C C C A G C C T T T C T A T T A G C T G T C A G T A A A A T T A C
Marsupial mole	G G T C C T A G C C T T A T T A T T A A T T A T T G C T A G T C C T A C

a) How many amino acids would be coded by these base sequences? *(1)*

b) Count the number of differences in base sequence between:

i) the mole and the dog **ii)** the mole and the marsupial mole. *(2)*

c) Which two animals are most closely related? Explain your answer. *(2)*

★**d)** Explain how the evolutionary history of these animals may account for the relationships between them. *(4)*

e) i) The strands of DNA from each animal were treated with the restriction enzyme *Hpa*II, which breaks the bond between the bases G–C. How many fragments would be formed from each of the DNA samples shown in the table? *(1)*

ii) Following this enzyme treatment each sample was separated by electrophoresis. Which sample would produce a band on the electrophoresis gel that was closest to the negative electrode? Explain your answer. *(4)*

Stretch and challenge

5 Peptic ulcer disease is a common complaint. Sections of the stomach wall become damaged and the highly acidic contents cause severe pain and can lead to perforation, with the risk of septicaemia. It is also a strong risk factor for stomach cancer.

For many years the main cause was thought to be excess stomach acid. Treatments ranged from simple antacids taken orally to more sophisticated drugs such as hydrogen ion pump inhibitors to limit acid production. Most doctors around the world treated patients in this way and the pharmaceutical industry spent many millions of pounds producing a range of ingenious ways to limit acid production.

This view was challenged by two Australian doctors, Marshall and Warren, between 1980 and 1990. Their story leads from an initial rejection of their research paper to the award of a Nobel prize in 2005. It illustrates that research is a human activity, not always as objective as it might be and subject to many influences. It is also a good example of the role played by peer review, journals and conferences in the process of validation.

You will need to read the story, which is presented as a timeline and can be found by searching for 'Marshall and Warren *Helicobacter* timeline' in a search engine.

Further research into *Helicobacter pylori* will also provide you with interesting background information.

Use this timeline and your own understanding of scientific research to answer the following questions. The abbreviation PUD is used for peptic ulcer disease.

a) What did Marshall and Warren suggest about the role of *Helicobacter pylori* in PUD?

b) Describe two pieces of evidence that suggested a bacterium might be involved in PUD well before Marshall and Warren began their work.

c) Describe the role played by meetings, conferences and congresses held in 1982, 1983, 1984 and 1990.

d) In 1984, Marshall carried out a very unusual demonstration. Why would the scientific community consider this to be of very low validity?

e) In 1994 the patents for the popular drugs used to reduce acid in the stomach ran out. Why would this make drug companies less likely to oppose the introduction of the new antibiotic treatment?

Tip

Question 4 is a very long question for an AS paper but it is a good example of how you will need to follow through several parts of a question that may require knowledge taken from different sections of the specification. These are synoptic questions and a common feature of the full A level examination.

8 Natural selection and biodiversity

Prior knowledge

In this chapter you will need to recall that:

- ➜ individuals of the same species often occur in groups called populations, living in one habitat
- ➜ single populations are linked to others in communities
- ➜ a group of communities with the non-living parts of the habitat form an ecosystem
- ➜ organisms show adaptations to their environment
- ➜ the theory of natural selection was proposed by Charles Darwin in his book *On the Origin of Species*
- ➜ the animals and plants of the Galapagos islands in the Pacific Ocean showed many features that provided Darwin with evidence for his theory
- ➜ the theory of natural selection has been developed using modern biological knowledge
- ➜ evolution by natural selection can lead to the formation of new species
- ➜ there is a worldwide threat to biodiversity
- ➜ there are basic rules for simple genetic crosses
- ➜ individuals can be homozygous or heterozygous with respect to one pair of alleles
- ➜ genes are carried on chromosomes
- ➜ meiosis halves the chromosome number in gamete production
- ➜ conservation efforts are attempting to preserve biodiversity.

Test yourself on prior knowledge

1 Name the title of the book published by Charles Darwin, which first proposed the theory of natural selection.

2 Which ship took Darwin on his famous expedition around the world?

3 Name the group of islands that provided Darwin with some of his most important evidence.

4 How did Darwin come to the conclusion that there was a 'battle for survival' in most species?

5 Explain what is meant by:
  a) continuous variation
  b) discontinuous variation.
  Give **one** example of each.

6 What is an allele?

7 Explain the terms:
  a) homozygous
  b) heterozygous.

8 State the **two** main causes of variation in living organisms.

9 List **two** adaptations that are common to vertebrates living in polar regions.

10 State the name given to a group of members of the same species living in one location.

Niche – a concept central to ecology

> **Key term**
>
> **Ecosystem** A community of organisms and their surroundings – the environment in which they live.

Ecology is the study of living things within their environment. It is an essential part of modern biology – understanding the relationships between organisms and their environment is just as important as knowing about the structure and physiology of animals and plants, for example. One of the ideas that ecologists have introduced into biology is that of the **ecosystem**. An ecosystem is defined as a community of organisms and their surroundings – the environment in which they live. An ecosystem is a basic functional unit of ecology since the organisms that make up a community cannot realistically be considered independently of their physical environment. An example of an ecosystem is woodland.

> **Key term**
>
> **Ecological niche** This describes not only where a species lives but all of its activities, such as feeding, its predators and how it interacts with the non-living environment around it.

Within an ecosystem are numerous habitats. The term *habitat* refers to the place where an organism lives. Within a woodland ecosystem, for example, some organisms have a habitat restricted to a small area. An example is a leaf-tissue parasite such as the holly leaf-miner insect, especially at the larval stage, as it is restricted to the interior of the holly leaf. Other species are abundant, for example *Pleurococcus*, a single-celled alga found on all damp surfaces such as most tree trunks and branches. So there is no particularly precise definition of a habitat – but the term is useful.

On the other hand, the term **ecological niche** is more informative. It defines just how an organism feeds, where it lives and how it behaves in relation to other organisms in its habitat. A niche identifies the precise conditions a species needs.

We can illustrate the value of the niche concept by reference to two common and rather similar sea birds, the cormorant and the shag (Figure 8.1).

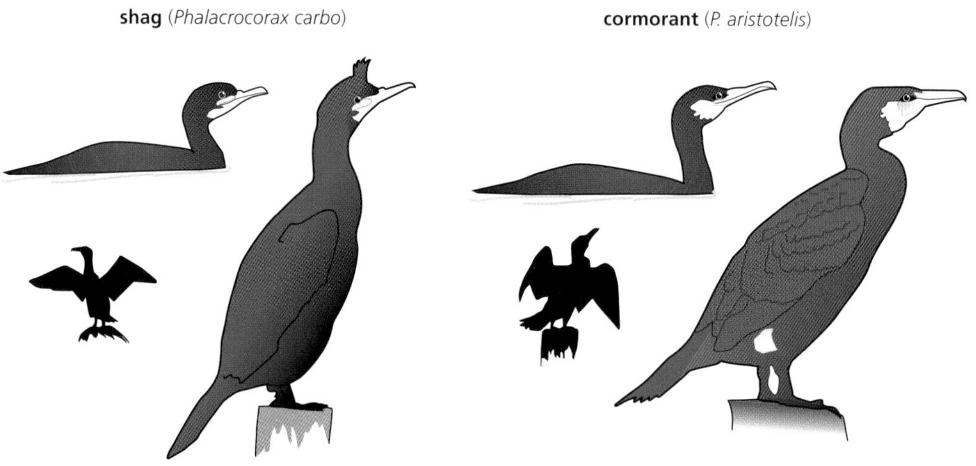

diet is a key difference in the niches of these otherwise similar birds

prey		% of prey taken by shag	% of prey taken by cormorant
surface-swimming prey	sand eels	33	0
	herring	49	1
bottom-feeding prey	flatfish	1	26
	shrimps, prawns	2	33

Figure 8.1 The sea birds cormorant and shag – their niches

Both birds live and feed along the coastline and they rear their young on similar cliffs and rock systems. We can say that they apparently share the same habitat. However, their diet and behaviour differ. The cormorant feeds close to the shore on sea-bed fish, such as flatfish. The shag builds its nest on much narrower cliff ledges. It also feeds further out to sea and captures fish such as sand eels from the upper layers of the waters. Since these birds feed differently and have different behaviour patterns, although they occur in close proximity, they avoid competition. They have different niches.

Adaptation of organisms to their environment

Adaptation is the process by which an organism becomes fitted to its environment. There are countless examples of this process to be observed in all habitats.

Adaptations can be physiological or anatomical. Physiological adaptations are those which are the results of changes to the metabolism of the organism which are advantageous to survival in their particular habitat, such as the production of different algal pigments as described in the following section. Anatomical adaptations are changes to the actual structure of organisms, such as the size of ears in hares and rabbits.

Physiological adaptation

An example of a physiological adaptation is shown in the marine algae known as 'greens', 'browns' and 'reds', which flourish at different zones of the shoreline community.

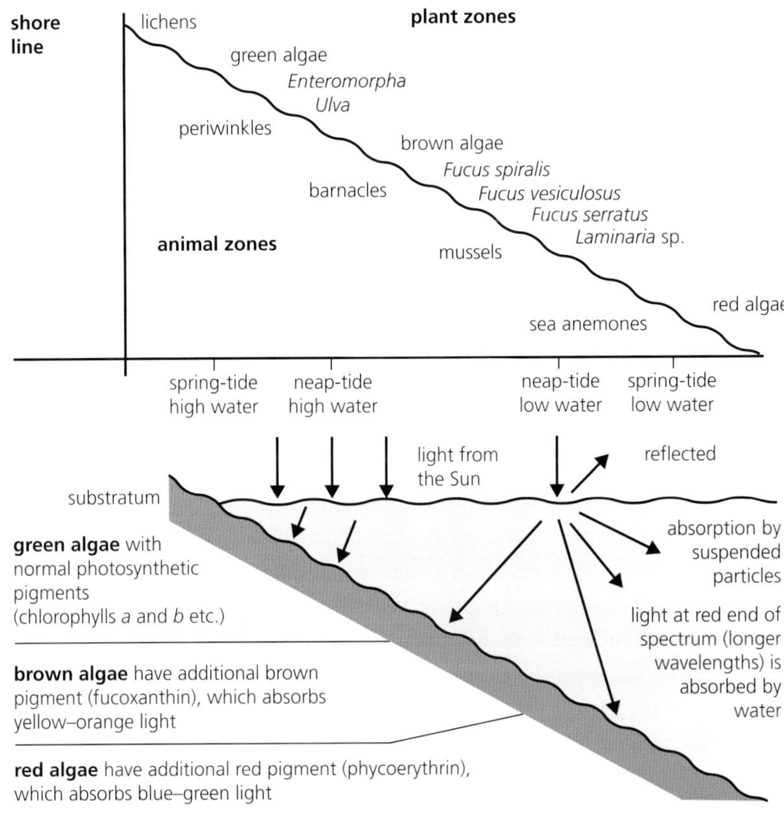

Figure 8.2 Zonation of green, brown and red seaweeds

The colour differences in these seaweeds are due to the particular photosynthetic pigments they contain. These pigments enable algae to absorb and exploit different wavelengths of light. In the marine environment, with increasing depth, progressively more of the higher wavelengths of white light are absorbed or scattered by the sea water and its suspended particles. Consequently, the red algae, equipped to absorb the blue–green light that is transmitted to greater depths, flourish there. Here, the brown and green algae cannot photosynthesise because the wavelengths of light they are adapted to absorb do not reach that depth.

Meanwhile, at lesser depths, red seaweeds are progressively crowded out in competition with the vigorous-growing brown seaweeds and green seaweeds as their particular pigments permit the efficient absorption of the incident light available closer to the surface.

Incidentally, the barnacles *Chthamalus* and *Semibalanus* exhibit differing abilities to endure exposure in the intertidal zone, and this too is an example of physiological adaptation.

Physiological adaptations of extremophiles

In recent years the discovery of unique ecosystems surrounding hydrothermal vents has provided the most remarkable examples of extreme adaptations. These vents are found in the deep ocean on the boundaries of tectonic plates, where there is volcanic activity as the plates forming the Earth's crust move against each other. The water ejected from these vents is highly acidic, contains many toxic sulfides and is at a temperature of over 350 °C and a pressure 250 times greater than that at the surface. The greatest surprise was to find any life at all under such conditions, let alone the variety of worms and crustaceans, such as the giant tube worm *Riftia pachyptila*, which is over 2 m long. There is no light at this depth and the whole ecosystem depends on bacteria using metal sulfides from the vents in **chemosynthesis** to produce organic compounds on which all the other organisms depend.

Key term

Chemosynthesis A method used by some microorganisms to release energy from inorganic molecules. Typically molecules such as ammonia or metal sulfides are oxidised and the energy released used to build organic molecules.

Many of these organisms are still being studied but it is obvious that, in addition to specialised nutrition, they must have remarkable adaptations to thrive in such a niche. Compared with other organisms they have remarkably stable enzymes, membranes and nucleic acids, which enable them to function in extreme temperatures, pressures and pH levels.

Anatomical adaptations

Examples of anatomical adaptations are body structures adapted to regulate heat loss in various mammals. Mammals are described as endotherms, since their body's heat comes from the metabolic reactions of many body organs. Body temperature is largely regulated by varying heat loss from the body. The total heat produced from internal organs largely depends upon the volume of the body, but the amount of heat loss is dependent upon the surface area. As the size of an organism increases, the volume increases more rapidly than the surface area. In other words its surface-area-to-volume ratio decreases, reducing the relative heat loss. (We shall look at the concept of surface-area-to-volume ratios in Chapter 10.) Consequently, animals in cold regions of the world tend to be large. An example is the polar bear. Smaller animals in colder regions need a high metabolic rate and consequently require a regular and substantial food supply to survive.

Meanwhile, mammals living in hot regions typically have external ears adapted as efficient radiators. These flaps of skin bear little fur (hair provides a heat insulation layer) and are richly supplied with blood capillaries. Heat brought to the external ears from the body interior by warm blood is quickly lost when capillaries here are dilated. A comparison of ear size in hares and rabbits in natural habitats at various latitudes on the North American continent appears to support this (Figure 8.3).

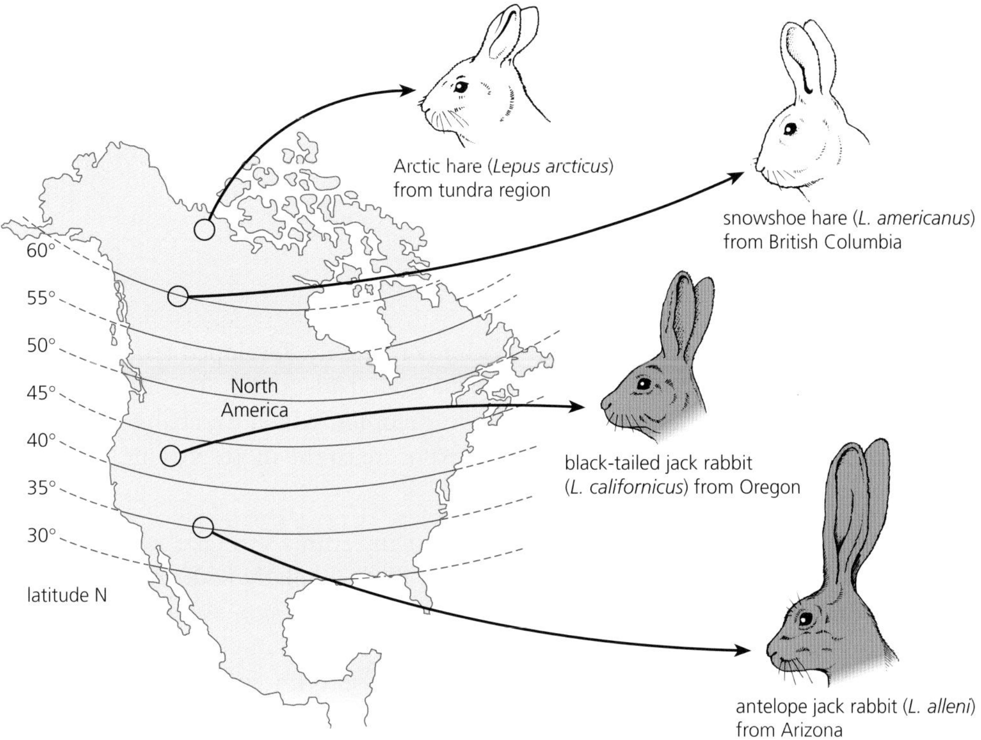

Figure 8.3 External ear sizes of hares in relation to latitude

Behavioural adaptation

Many animals are unable to regulate their body temperature effectively by internal means. They are known as ectotherms and rely on absorbing heat from their surroundings. However, this does not prevent them from occupying a wide variety of niches. Desert environments present particularly challenging problems associated with temperature control. They are extremely hot during the day and often well below freezing at night. Despite this, ectotherms such as lizards and snakes are common desert animals.

To survive in such conditions, ectotherms have adapted their behaviour to avoid large fluctuations in their body temperature (Table 8.1 and Figure 8.4).

Table 8.1 Typical behavioural adaptations of desert ectotherms

Adaptation	Function
Activities limited to morning and evening	Avoids the hottest times of day
Early morning basking on rocks	Raises body temperature quickly after cold nights
Burrowing into sand	Avoids direct sunlight and finds a cooler environment
Seeking deep crevices at night	Rocks retain heat longer during the night

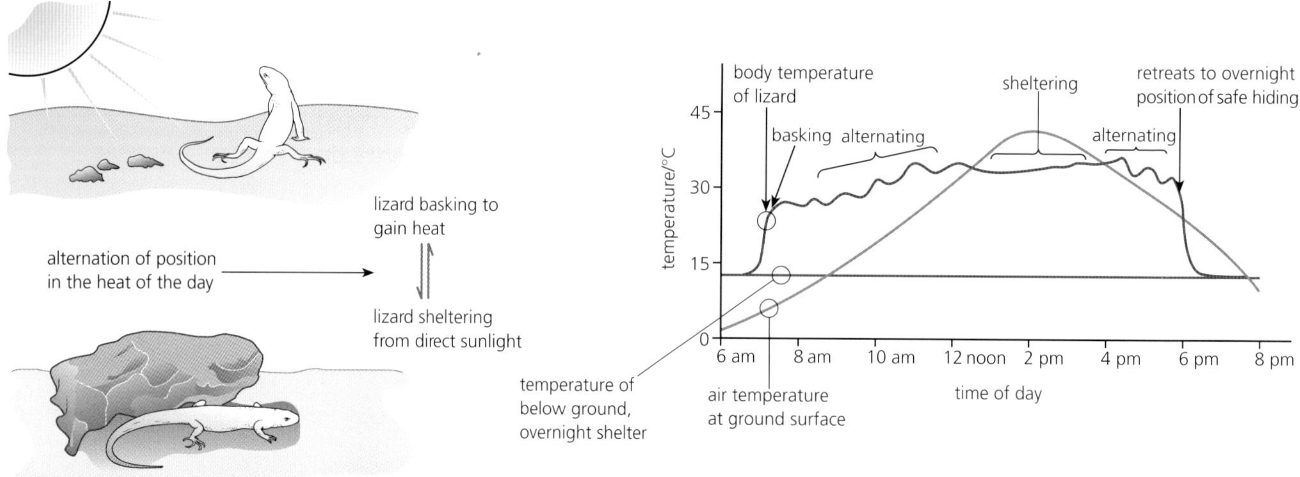

Figure 8.4 Thermoregulation in an ectotherm

Even advanced mammals, such as humans, with many highly developed temperature control mechanisms, have adopted numerous behavioural adaptations to ensure their survival. We build shelters and heat them, we wear clothes, which we change according to the environmental conditions, and we avoid exposure to the most extreme weather conditions.

Migration is a behavioural technique employed by many animals to take advantage of seasonal changes for feeding and breeding. Many birds regularly make incredible annual journeys across the world. The Arctic tern, *Sterna paradisaea*, uses the abundant insect food in northern Europe and the southern Arctic to raise its chicks during the summer. It then embarks upon one of the longest migrations known to avoid the severe winters. During the southern hemisphere summer it is found on the fringes of Antarctica, only to return to the Arctic later in the year. This remarkable feat of endurance and navigation entails a round-trip of over 45 000 miles. The Arctic tern therefore experiences two summers and probably more daylight than any other animal.

Incidentally, the differing feeding habits of the cormorant and shag are also examples of behavioural adaptation.

Test yourself

1 Apart from its exact place in a habitat, name **three** other properties of a species described by the term 'ecological niche'.

2 Why might you expect Peruvian people living in the high Andes to have high red blood cell counts?

3 Why do animals living in polar regions tend to be large?

4 Describe anatomical adaptations to desert life that are typically found in cacti.

5 State **three** ways in which the cormorant and the shag occupy different niches in order to avoid competition.

6 Research the main ways in which it is thought that birds are able to navigate over long distances.

How adaptation is brought about – natural selection

It was Charles Darwin whose careful observations over many years led him to realise what natural process brought about the adaptations of organisms in response to challenging environmental conditions. He coined the term 'natural selection' for this.

Charles Darwin put forward his ideas in 1859, in a book titled *On the Origin of Species*, published by John Murray of Albemarle Street, London. He was proposing a mechanism for the **evolution** of organisms.

Key term

Evolution The development of new types of living organism from pre-existing types by the accumulation of genetic differences over long periods of time.

By 'evolution', we mean the gradual development of life in geological time. The word evolution is used widely, but in biology it specifically means the processes by which life has been changed from its earliest beginnings to the diversity of organisms we know about today, living and extinct.

Charles Darwin (and nearly everyone else in the scientific community of his time) knew nothing of Mendel's work. Instead, biologists generally subscribed to the concept of 'blending inheritance' when mating occurred (which would only reduce the genetic variation available for natural selection, if it actually occurred). Today we are really talking about 'Neo-Darwinism', which is essentially a restatement of the concepts of evolution by natural selection in terms of Mendelian and post-Mendelian genetics.

The evidence and arguments for natural selection are as follows:

1 **Organisms produce many more offspring than survive to be mature individuals.** Darwin did not coin the phrase 'struggle for existence', but it does sum up the point that the over-production of offspring in the wild leads naturally to competition for resources. Table 8.2 lists the normal rates of production of offspring in some common species but clearly not all of these survive to pass on their genes to the next generation.

Table 8.2 Numbers of offspring produced

Organism	Number of eggs/seeds/young per brood or season
Rabbit	8–12
Great tit	10
Cod	2–20 million
Honey bee (queen)	120 000
Poppy	6000

In fact, in a stable population, a breeding pair gives rise to a single breeding pair of offspring, on average. All their other offspring are casualties of the 'struggle'; many organisms die before they can reproduce.

So, populations do not show rapidly increasing numbers in most habitats, or at least, not for long. Population size is naturally limited by restraints we call 'environmental factors'. These include space, light and the availability of food. The never-ending competition for resources results in the majority of organisms failing to survive and reproduce. In effect, the environment can only support a certain number of organisms, and the number of individuals in a population remains more or less constant over a period of time.

2 **The individuals in a species are not all identical**, but show variations in their characteristics. Today, modern genetics has shown us that there are several ways by which genetic variations arise in gamete formation during meiosis and at fertilisation. You will learn much more about the origins of variation in Chapter 20 but for AS, the important point is that variation is largely produced during meiosis and it is the essential raw material for selection. You cannot select if you have nothing to choose from!

As described on page 113, genetic variations arise via:

- **random assortment** of paternal and maternal chromosomes in meiosis – this occurs in the process of gamete formation
- **crossing over** of segments of individual maternal and paternal homologous chromosomes that results in new combinations of genes on the chromosomes of the haploid gametes produced by meiosis
- the **random fusion of male and female gametes** in sexual reproduction – this source of variation *was* understood in Darwin's time.

Additionally, variation arises due to **mutations** – either chromosome mutations (page 114) or gene mutations (page 64).

As a result of all these, the individual offspring of parents are not identical. Rather, they show variations in their characteristics.

3 **Natural selection results in offspring with favourable characteristics.** When genetic variation has arisen in organisms:

- the favourable characteristics are expressed in the phenotypes of some of the offspring
- these offspring may be better able to survive and reproduce in a particular environment; of course, other offspring will be less able to compete successfully, survive and reproduce.

Thus natural selection operates, determining the survivors and the genes that are perpetuated in future progeny. In time, this selection process leads to adaptation to the environment, later to new varieties and then to new species.

The operation of natural selection is sometimes summarised in the phrase 'survival of the fittest', although these were not words that Darwin used, at least not initially. To avoid the criticism that 'survival of the fittest' is a circular phrase (how can fitness be judged except in terms of survival?) the term 'fittest' is applied in a particular context. For example, the fittest of the wildebeest of the African savannah (hunted herbivore) may be those with the acutest senses, quickest reflexes and strongest leg muscles for efficient escape from predators. By natural selection, the health and survival of wildebeests is assured.

Test yourself

7 Explain why the rabbit produces only 8–12 offspring per season whereas the cod produces up to 20 million.

8 If a pair of rabbits produced eight offspring every year and their offspring become sexually mature after only 1 year, how many rabbits would there be after 3 years if all the rabbits survived? You may assume that there are equal numbers of males and females.

9 State **three** reasons why the majority of offspring in most populations do not survive to breed.

10 Which forms of genetic variation are simply mixing up alleles into different combinations and which actually change the alleles present?

11 Describe Darwin's role on board *H.M.S. Beagle*.

12 Darwin returned from his voyage in 1836 but his book *On the Origin of Species* was not published until 1859. Why did it take so long?

New evidence for evolution

Evidence from **fossils** (palaeontological evidence) was at one time a main source of information about life forms now extinct. Fossilisation is an extremely rare, chance event; scavengers and bacterial action normally dismember and decompose dead plant and animal structures before they can be fossilised. Of the organisms that have been fossilised, most are never found, recovered or interpreted. Nevertheless, numerous fossils have been uncovered. They include:

- petrified remains (organic matter of the dead organism is replaced by mineral ions)
- moulds (the organic matter decays but the vacated space becomes a mould)
- traces (an impression of a form, such as of a leaf or a footprint)
- preserved, intact whole organisms (trapped in amber, ice or in anaerobic, acidic peat, for example).

An example can be seen in Figure 8.5.

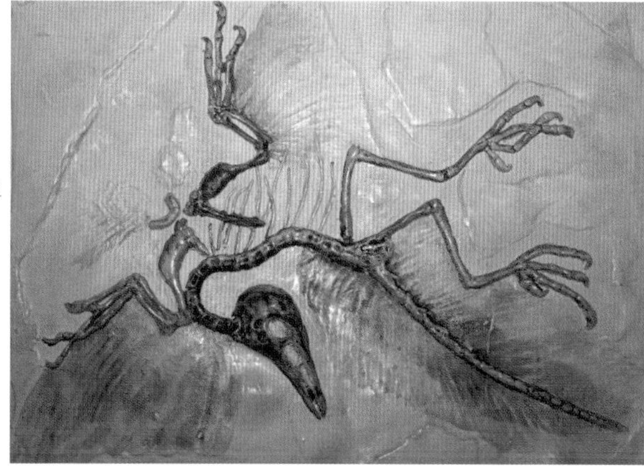

Figure 8.5 A fossil of *Archaeopteryx*, found in 1861

Additionally, it has sometimes been possible to date quite accurately the rocks surrounding fossils by exploiting the known rates of decay of certain isotopes, including carbon (^{14}C) and the ratio of potassium to argon ($^{40}K/^{40}Ar$) present in lava deposits. Using the decay rate of ^{14}C gives ages of fossils formed in the last 60 000 years. Using the ratio of $^{40}K/^{40}Ar$ gives an approximate age of sedimentary rocks (and their fossils) below and above a lava layer from geological time back to the Cambrian period (580 mya), although these are unreliable for the most recent half million years.

Exciting and illuminating fossil finds abound. Two of the most moving are, perhaps, those of the first hominid (a 'southern ape' named Lucy) at Hadar in Ethiopia in 1974, and the footsteps at Laetoli in Tanzania in 1976, found in volcanic ash and dated 3.6 mya – our first record of bipedalism.

Today, studies in comparative physiology and biochemistry are a new tool in the investigation of evolutionary change.

Most living things have DNA as their genetic material. The genetic code is virtually universal. The processes of 'reading' the code and protein synthesis, using RNA and ribosomes, are very similar in prokaryotes and eukaryotes, too. Processes such as respiration involve the same types of steps and similar or identical intermediates and biochemical reactions, similarly catalysed. ATP is the universal energy currency. Among the autotrophic organisms, the biochemistry of photosynthesis is virtually identical as well.

Key term

Proteomics The study of the proteins coded for by specific genes found in the human genome.

So, early biochemical events in the evolution of life have been 'inherited' widely, as and when forms of life diversified. However, large molecules like nucleic acids and the proteins they code for are subjected to some changes with time, so knowledge of these changes may be an aid to the study of the timings of evolutionary change. It is possible to measure the relatedness of different groups of organisms by the amount of difference between specific molecules such as DNA, proteins and enzyme systems. One aspect of these investigations is **proteomics**. This is the study (qualitative and quantitative) of the proteins coded for by specific genes of the human genome.

Immunological studies

The immune reaction provides a mechanism of detecting differences in specific proteins, and therefore (indirectly) their relatedness. Serum is the liquid produced from blood when blood cells and fibrinogen have been removed. Protein molecules present in the serum act as antigens when serum is injected into animals with an immune system that lacks these particular proteins. Typically, a rabbit is used when investigating relatedness to humans. The injected serum triggers the production of antibodies against the injected 'foreign' proteins. Then, fresh serum produced from the treated rabbit's blood (it now contains antibodies against human proteins) is tested against serum from a range of animals. The more closely related the animal is to humans, the greater the precipitation observed. This is illustrated in Figure 8.6.

The precipitation produced by reaction with human serum is taken as 100 percent. For each species, the greater the precipitation, the more recently the species shared a common ancestor with humans. This technique, called comparative serology, has been used by taxonomists to establish phylogenetic links in a number of cases, in both mammals and non-vertebrates.

Immunological studies are a means of detecting differences in specific proteins of species, and therefore (indirectly) their **relatedness**.

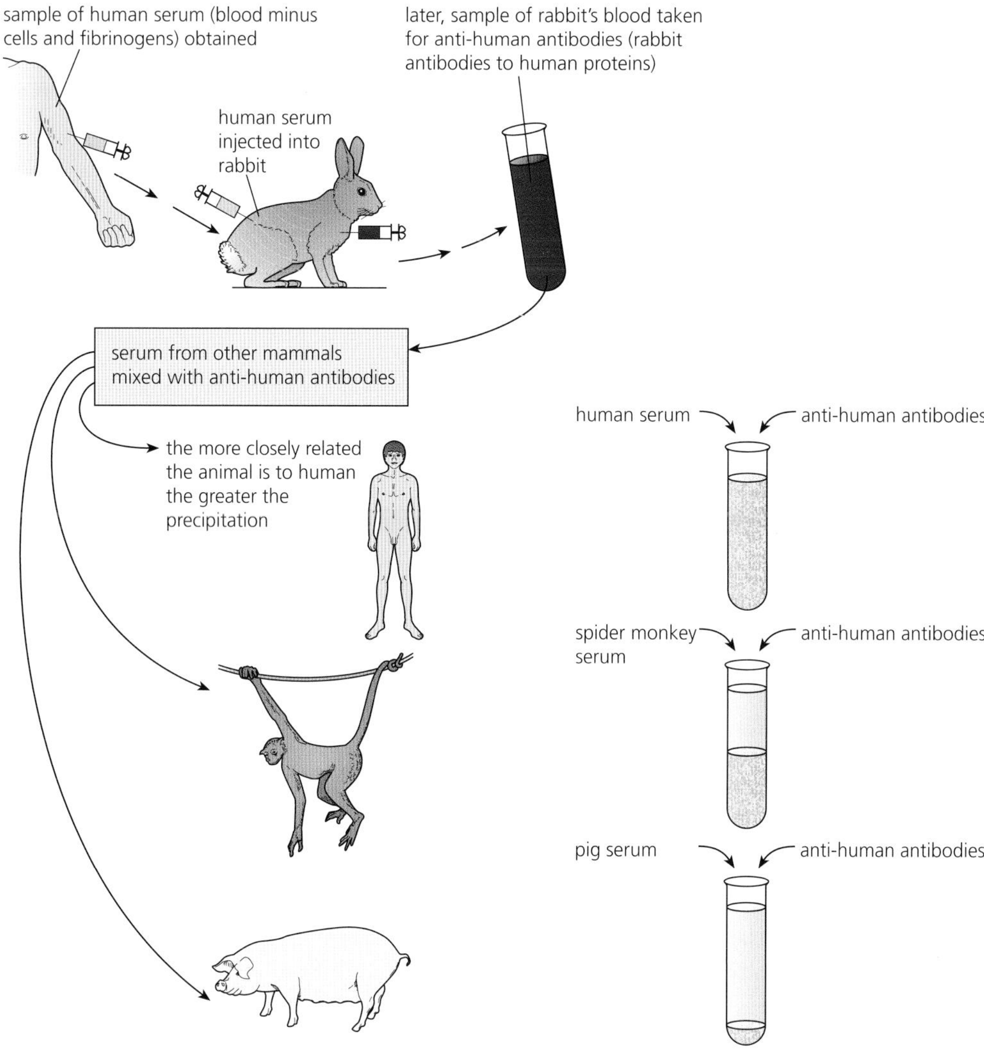

Figure 8.6 The immune reaction and evolutionary relationships

Genetic differences in nucleic acids

The technique of DNA hybridisation involves matching DNA from different species to test the degree of base pairing that occurs (Figure 8.7). This tells us the approximate degree of divergence between closely related groups, such as families within the primates. This data can then be correlated with data on the estimated number of years since they shared a common ancestor.

DNA as a molecular clock

Measurement of changes in DNA from selected species has potential as a molecular clock. DNA in eukaryotic cells occurs in both the chromosomes of the nucleus (99 per cent) and also in the mitochondria. Mitochondrial DNA (mtDNA) is a circular molecule, very short in comparison with nuclear DNA. Cells contain any number of mitochondria, typically between 100 and 1000.

DNA hybridisation is a technique that involves matching the DNA of different species, to discover how closely they are related.

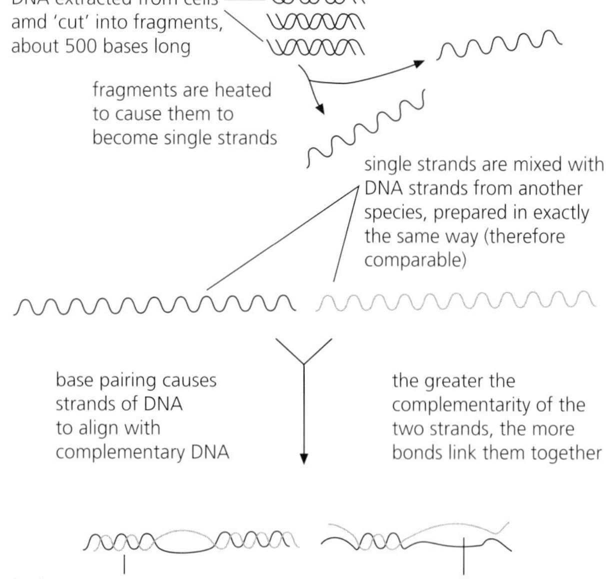

DNA extracted from cells amd 'cut' into fragments, about 500 bases long
fragments are heated to cause them to become single strands
single strands are mixed with DNA strands from another species, prepared in exactly the same way (therefore comparable)
base pairing causes strands of DNA to align with complementary DNA
the greater the complementarity of the two strands, the more bonds link them together
high complementarity
low complementarity

The closeness of the two DNAs is measured by finding the temperature at which they separate – the fewer bonds formed, the lower the temperature required.

Figure 8.7 DNA hybridisation

Mitochondrial DNA has approximately 16 500 base pairs. Mutations occur at a very slow, steady rate in all DNA, but chromosomal DNA has with it enzymes that may repair the changes in some cases. These enzymes are absent from mtDNA.

Thus mtDNA changes 5–10 times faster than chromosomal DNA – involving about 1–2 base changes in every 100 nucleotides per million years. Consequently, the length of time since organisms (belonging to different but related species) have diverged can be estimated by extracting and comparing samples of their mtDNA.

Furthermore, at fertilisation, the sperm contributes a nucleus only (no cytoplasm and therefore no mitochondria). So, all the mitochondria of the zygote come from the egg cell, and there is no mixing of mtDNA genes at fertilisation. All the evidence about relationships from studying differences between samples of mtDNA is easier to interpret in the search for early evidence of evolution.

Ribosomal RNA studies

We have seen in Chapter 7 how ribosomal RNA sequencing has led to new debates as to the main kingdoms and their evolutionary relationship, and a new three-domain model with the Archaea as a separate evolutionary line.

Natural selection and speciation

You will remember that in Chapter 7 we discussed how difficult it can be to define exactly what we mean by a species. The key ideas were a group of organisms that (a) normally interbreed and (b) produce fertile offspring. It is obvious that organisms undergoing natural selection will begin to change, but at what point do they change enough to be recognised as a separate species?

We refer to all of the possible genes and alleles in a population as the **gene pool**.

Key term

Gene pool The total variety of genes and alleles present in a sexually reproducing population.

Natural selection operates on this gene pool and can lead to changes in the proportions of genes and alleles present in the population. Mutation can also introduce new forms of genes. The details of exactly how these changes can be measured and monitored are discussed further in Chapter 20.

How changing gene pools may lead to speciation

Species exist almost exclusively as local populations, even though the boundaries to these populations are often rather open and ill-defined. Individuals of local populations tend to resemble each other more closely than they resemble members of other populations. Local populations are very important as they are potential starting points for **speciation**.

> **Key term**
>
> **Speciation** The name given to the process by which one species may evolve from another.

Speciation is much more likely if part of the population is isolated in some way so that the gene pool of each part begins to change in different ways. Even then, many generations may elapse before the composition of the gene pool has changed sufficiently to allow us to call the new individuals a different species. Isolation therefore is very important in this process and can be brought about in different ways.

Allopatric speciation

If a population is suddenly divided by the appearance of a barrier, resulting in two populations isolated from each other, **allopatric speciation** occurs. Before separation, individuals shared a common gene pool but after isolation, 'disturbing processes' like natural selection, mutation and random genetic drift may occur independently in both populations, causing them to diverge in their features and characteristics.

> **Key term**
>
> **Allopatric speciation** This occurs when two populations are totally separated from each other by a barrier. This prevents interbreeding and mixing of their gene pools.

Geographic isolation between populations occurs when natural, or human-imposed, barriers arise and sharply restrict movement of individuals (and their spores and gametes, in the case of plants) between the divided populations (Figure 8.8).

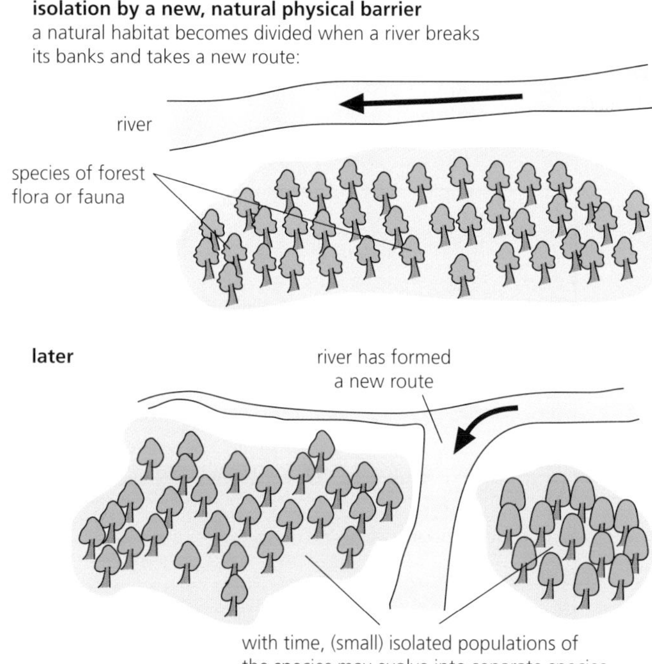

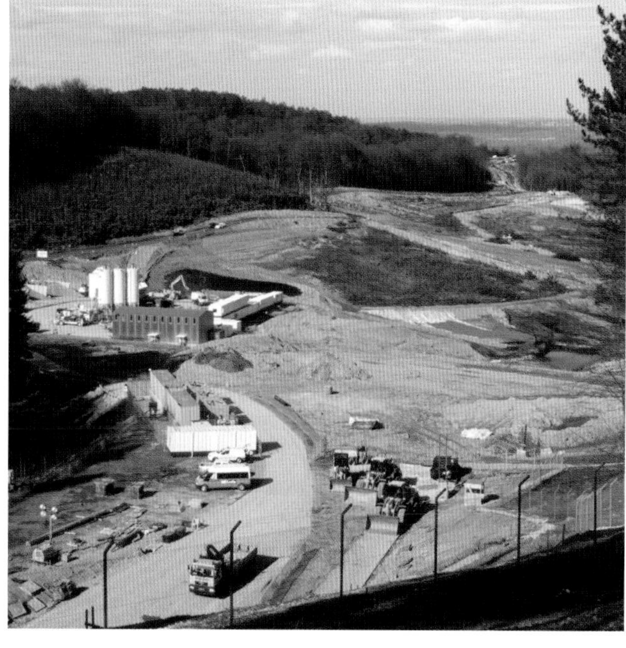

Figure 8.8 Geographical barriers

Geographic isolation also arises when motile or mobile species are dispersed to isolated habitats – as, for example, when organisms are accidentally rafted from mainland territories to distant islands. The 2004 tsunami generated examples of this in South East Asia. Violent events of this type have punctuated world geological history with surprising frequency.

Charles Darwin visited the isolated islands of Galapagos, off the coast of South America, during his voyage with *The Beagle* in 1831–36. The islands are 600 miles (970 km) from the South American mainland. Their origin is volcanic – they appeared out of the sea about 16 million years ago, at which point they were of course uninhabited. Today, they have a flora and fauna that relate to mainland species.

Darwin encountered examples of population divergence on the Galapagos islands. For example, the tortoises found on these islands had distinctive shells. With experience, an observer could tell which individual island an animal came from by its appearance, so markedly had the local, isolated populations diverged since their arrival from the mainland. These giant tortoises are certainly unlike any in other parts of the world and their differences could lead to the formation of separate species. In any case they are unlikely to interbreed with those on the other islands.

Key term

Sympatric speciation
This occurs when two populations are still able to mix freely in the same area but some individuals accumulate changes in their gene pools, which are sufficient to prevent interbreeding.

Sympatric speciation

Once again, the unique habitats of the Galapagos islands provide examples of **sympatric speciation** in action (Figure 8.9). The iguana lizard had no mammal competition when it arrived on the Galapagos islands. It became the dominant form of vertebrate life and was extremely abundant when Darwin visited. By then, two species were present, one terrestrial and the other fully adapted to marine life. The latter is assumed to have evolved locally as a result of pressure from overcrowding and competition for food on the islands (both species are vegetarian), which drove some members of the population out of the terrestrial habitat.

Many organisms (e.g. insects and birds) may have flown or been carried on wind currents to the Galapagos from the mainland. Mammals are most unlikely to have survived drifting there on a natural raft over this distance, but many large reptiles can survive long periods without food or water.

immigrant travel to the Galapagos

The **giant iguana lizards** on the Galapagos Islands became dominant vertebrates, and today are two distinct species, one still terrestrial, the other marine, with webbed feet and a laterally flattened tail (like the caudal fin of a fish).

The Galapagos islands

Today the tortoise population of each island is distinctive and identifiable.

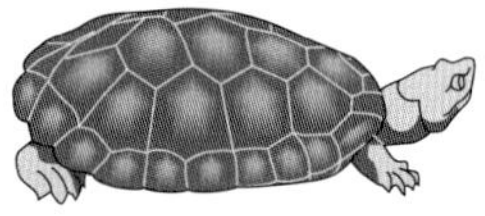

Figure 8.9 The Galapagos islands and species divergence

Where populations co-exist in the same area, speciation can occur where changes brought about by natural selection result in reproductive isolation.

Reproductive isolation mechanisms occasionally develop that are strong enough to prevent interbreeding between members of small, isolated populations that have diverged genetically, if only slightly, as a result of their isolation. Cases of reproductive isolation are likely to be less consistently effective than geographic separation in bringing about complete isolation in the early stages. Examples can be seen in Table 8.3.

Test yourself

13 Give **two** reasons why fossils are very rare.

14 Which **three** cellular molecules are found in almost all living things?

Table 8.3 Types of reproductive isolation

Mismatch of genitalia	This can make successful copulation impossible.
Barriers to fertilisation	Changes in the uterus of animals or the stigma of plants can prevent gametes from meeting (Figure 8.10).
Formation of sterile hybrids	Horses can successfully mate with asses (donkeys) but their offspring (mules) will be sterile. This is because the horse and ass have different chromosome numbers of 60 and 66 respectively, but the hybrid mule has 63. This makes it impossible for the mule's chromosomes to form pairs in meiosis and therefore produce viable gametes.
Behavioural changes	Many animals have elaborate courtship displays where even small changes will result in rejection by a potential mate. Many birds will only choose mates with the correct song; the Galapagos finches are known to select partners with the correct beak size and shape.
Temporal changes	Where such factors as available food supply cause changes in the timing of gamete production, fertilisation will be prevented.
Ecological changes	Where two populations occupy different parts of the habitat, they are unlikely to meet. The separation of marine and terrestrial iguanas, explained above, is a good example.

Incompatibility in flowering plants refers to physiological mechanisms that may make fertilisation impossible by preventing the growth of pollen tubes on the stigma or through the style.

Pollen that lodges on a stigma 'germinates' and attempts to send out a pollen tube that may eventually reach the embryo sac. Growth of pollen tubes that are opposed or unsupported by the stigma tissue fails.

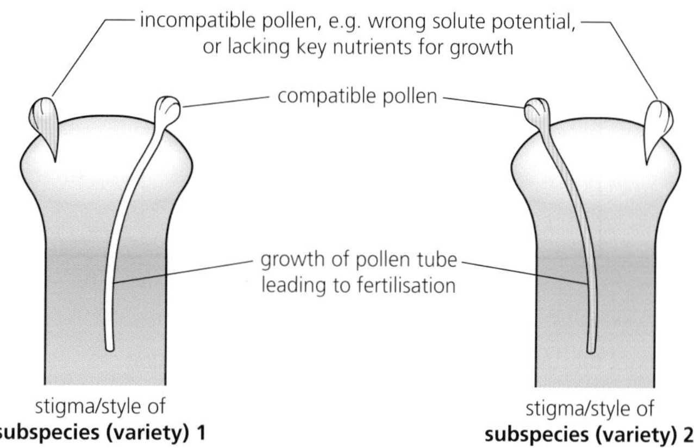

Figure 8.10 An example of reproductive isolation in a flowering plant

Tip

When answering questions, make sure you make it clear that selection affects the gene pool of a population in future generations. It does not change individuals – they have to live with the genome they inherited, so for them it is simply whether they survive to breed or not.

> **Key term**
>
> **Stabilising selection** This occurs where conditions are favourable and not changing, so pressures to change in one way are less than the advantage in remaining the same.

Types of selection

Natural selection operates on individuals, or rather on their phenotypes. Phenotypes are the product of a particular combination of alleles, interacting with the effects of the environment of the organism.

Consequently, natural selection causes changes to the composition of gene pools. However, the effects of these changes vary. We can recognise different types of selection.

- **Stabilising selection** occurs where environmental conditions are stable and largely unchanging. It does not lead to evolution, but rather it maintains favourable characteristics that enable a species to be successful, and the alleles responsible for them, and eliminates variants and abnormalities that are useless or harmful. Probably most populations undergo stabilising selections. The example in Figure 8.11 comes from human birth records on babies born between 1935 and 1946 in London. It shows there is an optimum birth weight for babies, and those with birth weights heavier or lighter are at a selective disadvantage.

The birth weight of humans is influenced by **environmental factors** (e.g. maternal nutrition, smoking habits, etc.) and by **inheritance** (about 50%).

When more babies than average die at very low and very high birth weights, this obviously affects the gene pool because it tends to eliminate genes for low and high birth weights.

> **Key term**
>
> **Directional selection** This occurs when environments are changing and there is a clear advantage in the population changing in one particular direction.

The data are an example of continuous variation. The 'middleness' or central tendency of this type of data is expressed in three ways:

1. **mode** (modal value) – the most frequent value in a set of values
2. **median** – the middle value of a set of values where these are arranged in ascending order
3. **mean** (average) – the sum of the individual values, divided by the number of values

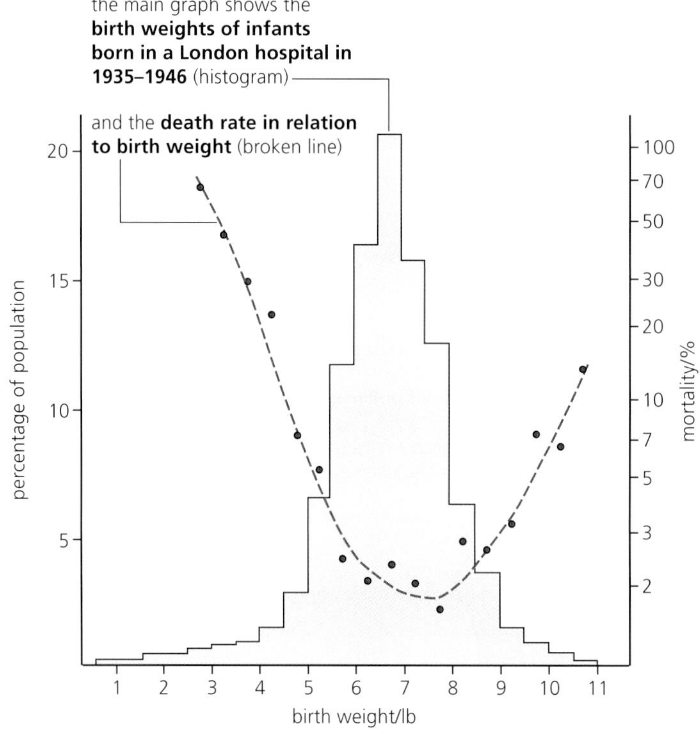

This is an example of **stabilising selection** in that the values (weights) at the extremes of a continuous variation are at a selective disadvantage. This means that infants of these birth weights are more likely to die in infancy.

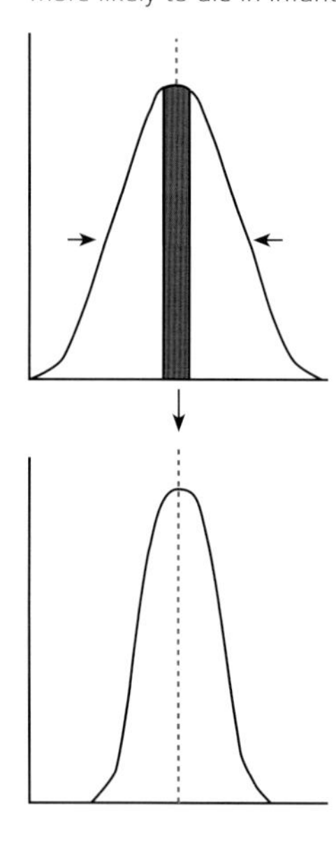

Figure 8.11 Birth weight and infant mortality, a case study in stabilising selection

- **Directional selection** is associated with changing environmental conditions. In these situations, the majority of an existing form of an organism may no longer be best suited to the environment. Some unusual or abnormal forms of the population may have a selective advantage.
  An example of directional selection is the development of resistance to an antibiotic by bacteria. Certain bacteria cause disease, and patients with bacterial infections are frequently treated with an antibiotic to help them overcome the infection.

Antibiotics are very widely used. In a large population of a species of bacteria, some may carry a gene for resistance to the antibiotic in question. Sometimes such a gene arises by spontaneous mutation. Alternatively the gene is acquired in a form of sexual reproduction between bacteria of different populations.

A 'resistant' bacterium has no selective advantage in the absence of the antibiotic and must compete for resources with non-resistant bacteria. But when the antibiotic is present, most bacteria of the population are killed off. Resistant bacteria remain and create the future population, all of which now carry the gene for resistance to the antibiotic (Figure 8.12). The gene pool has been changed abruptly.

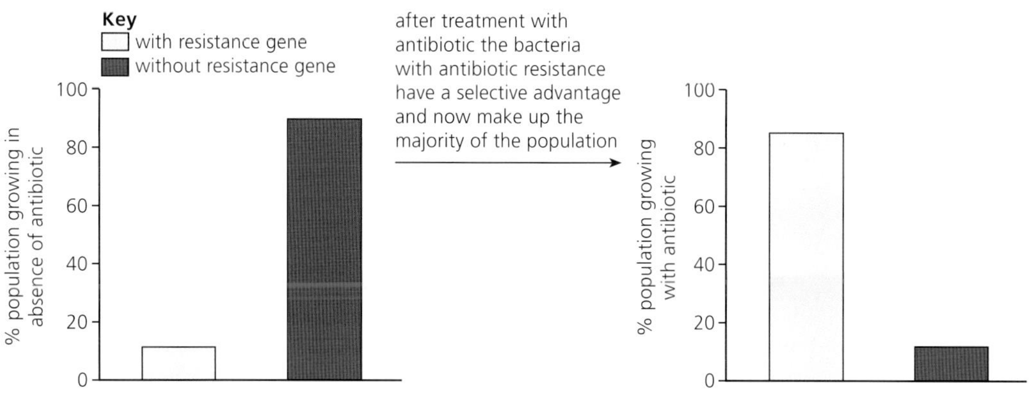

Figure 8.12 Directional selection

An evolutionary race

The discovery of antibiotics in the 1940s and 1950s was hailed as the end of many diseases caused by bacteria. For a time this seemed to be a reasonable assumption as new types of antibiotics were discovered and were very effective. Unfortunately this ignored the effect of evolution and how widespread use of antibiotics would mean that selection pressures were increased and along with it the rate of evolutionary change. First, increased doses of antibiotics were needed to bring about the same effect, and then strains of bacteria that were entirely resistant to their effect began to appear, until today there is a major problem with bacteria that are resistant to most of the common families of antibiotics.

Methicillin resistant *Staphylococcus aureus* (**MRSA**) is today well known as a 'superbug' causing serious problems in all hospitals.

No biologist would be entirely surprised by these developments as similar examples can be found throughout the natural world. It is generally referred to as an '**evolutionary race**' between the host or medical science and the pathogens.

As in any prolonged race, the lead can change many times. It would be true to say that in the past 50 years the introduction of antibiotics means that medical science has gained a large advantage. But that lead is now under serious threat as it becomes much more difficult to find new antibiotics while the majority of pathogens are rapidly developing multiple resistance to those in use.

Test yourself

15 Why should the hybrid DNA of more closely related organisms need a higher temperature to separate the strands than the hybrid DNA of less closely related species?

16 Give **two** reasons why analysis of mitochondrial DNA (mtDNA) will yield more information about evolutionary history than chromosomal DNA.

17 State the main difference between sympatric and allopatric speciation.

Key term

Pathogen An infectious agent that causes an illness or disease in its host. The term is generally applied to microorganisms but includes such things as viruses.

Biodiversity

Species richness and biodiversity

Key term

Species richness The total number of different species within a given area or community.

Species richness is defined as the total number of different species within a given area or community. To produce this information, a precise listing of all the different types of organism is required. However, the abundance of each species present is not required. As such, species richness is not a complete measure of biodiversity of a habitat. The diversity of species present in a habitat can be measured by applying the formula known as the Simpson Diversity Index:

$$\text{diversity} = \frac{N\,(N - 1)}{\Sigma n(n - 1)}$$

where N = total number of organisms of all species found
and n = number of individuals of each species.

Measuring genetic variability

In a population – a group of individuals of a species living close together and able to interbreed – the alleles of the genes located in the reproductive cells of those individuals make up a **gene pool**. A sample of the alleles of the gene pool will contribute to the genomes (gene sets of individuals) of the next generation, and so on, from generation to generation.

The size of an interbreeding population has a direct impact on the genetic diversity of the individuals. A very small population can be described as an **inbreeding** group – the individuals are closely related. In fact, the smaller the population, the more closely related the offspring will be. The important genetic consequence of inbreeding is that it leads to **homozygosity** – at more and more of the loci there will be identical alleles. There is progressively less variation in the population. While the individuals of that population may initially be well adapted, in the face of environmental changes the population is less able to adapt. The genetic fitness of a population is compromised.

It is in these latter cases of small, isolated populations that genetic variability is most critical. In the cases of populations of endangered species, the question is whether there is sufficient genetic diversity to allow the population to adapt to future changes in the environment and so survive.

This is a practical problem faced by modern zoos, which have taken on the role of attempting to conserve genetic variation within endangered species via captive breeding programmes. It is also an issue for endangered organisms in the wild, where population numbers have been reduced to small, isolated groups in former strongholds. This problem can be illustrated by examining current conservation research being undertaken in the tropical rainforests of Sabah in Malaysia, Borneo.

A conservation case study based on genetic diversity analyses

Orang-utans (*Pongo pygmaeus*), together with gorillas and chimpanzees, are great apes. Most of their features (including their large cranium and well-developed brains, elongated arms and highly developed muscles) are common to humans too, although they are not our direct ancestors. Orang-utans are the largest ape species after the gorilla – females typically weigh in excess of 35 kg and males up to 80 kg. A standing male may be up to 150 cm high. They are arboreal and active by day, with a diet largely consisting of fruits and shoots. They may be solitary, or live in pairs or very small family groups, sleeping in tree 'nests' and moving on from day to day. The young (birth weight about 1.5 kg) remain with their mother for up to 5 years of parental care. They reach maturity at about 10 years, and their total life expectancy is 30 years or more. Humans are their only predator, either directly (through poaching) or indirectly (through logging and forest clearing for agriculture).

Sabah, situated on the north-eastern part of the island of Borneo, has an orang-utan population that has been in decline for the past 100 years (Table 8.4). This collapse was triggered by massive deforestation that began in the 1890s and accelerated in the 1950s and 1970s.

Currently, the orang-utans of Sabah are threatened with extinction in the near future due to the continuing logging of the forest trees, clearing of whole forests for oil palm plantations and illegal killings. Today's population estimates are based on ground surveys and are confirmed by aerial surveys (nest counts) made by helicopter. While Sabah is the main stronghold of these primates in North Borneo, the present estimated population is of only 11 000 individuals, distributed in the remaining pockets of rainforest, as shown in Figure 8.13. More than half live outside protected areas, in forests still frequently disturbed by selective logging activities.

Table 8.4 Estimated orang-utan numbers in Sabah, Borneo, over the past 100 years or so

Year	Number of orang-utans
1900	310 000
1980	25 000
2003	13 000

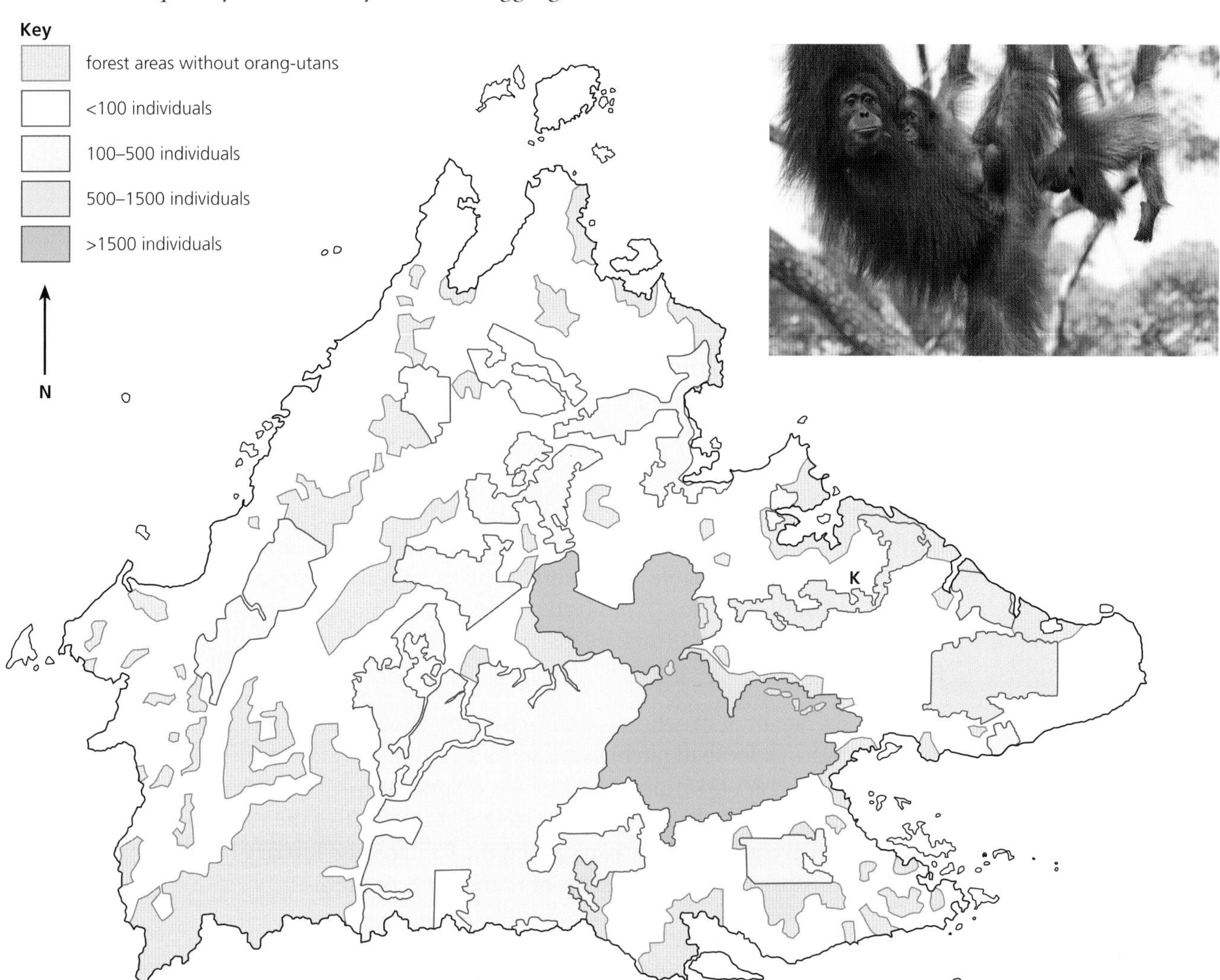

Figure 8.13 Map of Sabah in Malaysia showing the positions of the remaining rainforest, colour coded to show the densities of orang-utans in each; the Kinabatangan Wildlife Sanctuary is marked **K**

A team of conservation biologists, led by Professor Mike Bruford and Dr Benoit Goossens of the Biodiversity and Ecological Processes Group, School of Biosciences, Cardiff University, is investigating the genetic diversity of these populations in an attempt to devise sustainable schemes that will effectively support remaining orang-utan populations. Their data are being collected from animals living in Kinabatangan Wildlife Sanctuary (Figure 8.11).

By collecting hair and faeces found at fresh nest sites, they are able to extract DNA to create genetic profiles. Genetic markers called microsatellites are applied to the DNA samples, which distinguish, among other things, heterozygous genes from homozygous genes. They serve as tools to evaluate inbreeding levels, the genetic structure and past history of populations, and to assess both gene flow between populations and effective population size.

The results establish that, in Kinabatangan Sanctuary, the orang-utans do not cross the rivers but do move freely through the forest areas on either side. Studies indicate that, if nothing is done about the existing sanctuary provision here, then this situation will almost certainly lead to extinction. If an elaborate series of wildlife corridors is set up between remaining areas of forest, survival can hopefully be assured.

Since these measures are probably more expensive than local economies can sustain, the team has devised a programme of transfers of individuals between sites (referred to as translocations), together with a modest programme of corridor establishment. This proposal, known as the Kinabatangan Management Plan, is being prepared for presentation to the agencies and authorities who must find the necessary funding for whichever measures they choose to support.

The case of the vanishing rainforests

Rainforests cover almost 2 per cent of the Earth's land surface, but they provide habitats for almost 50 per cent of all living species. It has been predicted that if all non-vertebrates occurring in a single cubic metre of tropical rainforest soil were collected for identification, there would be present at least one completely previously unknown species. Tropical rainforests contain the greatest diversity of life of any of the world's **biomes**.

> **Key term**
>
> **Biome** A very large area of interconnected ecosystems of the Earth with similar climatic and geographic conditions.

Sadly, tropical rainforests are being rapidly destroyed. Satellite imaging of the Earth's surface provides the evidence that this is so – where no other reliable sources of information are available. The world's three remaining tropical forests of real size are in South America (around the Amazon Basin), in West Africa (around the Congo Basin) and in the Far East (particularly, but not exclusively, on the islands of Indonesia).

The current rate of destruction is estimated to be about one hectare (100 m × 100 m – a little larger than a football pitch) every second. This means that each year an area larger than the British Isles (31 million hectares) is cleared. While extinction is a natural process, this current rate is on a scale equivalent to that at the time of the extinction of the dinosaurs (an event 65 million years ago at the Cretaceous–Tertiary boundary). Table 8.5 states several reasons for conservation of rainforest ecosystems.

New species evolve, but other species (less suited to their environment, perhaps) become extinct, as much of the fossil record throughout geological time indicates. One example of a well-documented extinction is that of the dodo bird.

Table 8.5 Why conserve rainforest ecosystems?

Ecological reasons	Most species of living things are not distributed widely, but instead are restricted to a narrow range of the Earth's surface. In fact, the majority of species living today occur in the tropics. So when tropical rainforests are destroyed, the only habitat of a huge range of plants is lost, and with them very many of the vertebrates and non-vertebrates dependent upon them. In effect, the rainforests are critically important 'outdoor laboratories' where we learn about the range of life that has evolved, the majority of which consists of organisms as yet unknown. The soils under rainforests are mostly poor soils that cannot support an alternative ecosystem for very long. To destroy rainforest is to remove the most productive biome on the Earth's surface – in terms of converting the Sun's energy to biomass. If destroyed but later left to regenerate, only species that have not become extinct may return. Re-grown rainforest will be deprived of its variety of life.
Economic reasons	The whole range of living things is functionally a gene pool resource, and when a species becomes extinct its genes are permanently lost. The destruction of rainforests decreases our genetic heritage more dramatically than the destruction of any other biome. As a consequence future genetic engineers and plant and animal breeders are deprived of a potential source of genes. Many new drugs and other natural products, in some form or another, are manufactured by plants. The discovery of new, useful substances often starts with rare, exotic or recently discovered species. 7 million km^2 of humid tropical forests have so far been cleared – about half of the original forest present before clearance programmes started. Much is 'cleared' to make way for the production of crops for food (as illustrated in the article in Figure 8.14). Yet only 2 million km^2 have remained in agricultural production. Mostly, the soil does not sustain continued cropping. Rainforest is a continuing resource of hardwood timber, which if selectively logged can be productive, but when cleared as forest, is lost as a source of timber in the future. Trees help stabilise land and prevent disastrous flooding downriver. Huge areas of productive land are washed away once mountain rainforest has been removed. Trees in general are carbon dioxide 'sinks' that help reduce global warming. Without these trees, other ways of reducing atmospheric CO_2 must be found.
Aesthetic reasons	These habitats are beautiful, exhilarating and inspirational places to visit. They are part of the inheritance of future generations, which should be secured for future people's enjoyment, too.
Ethical reasons	This biome is home to many forest peoples who have a right to traditional ways of life. Similarly, many higher mammals, including relatively close 'relatives' of *Homo*, live exclusively in these habitats. The needs of all primates must be respected.

The IUCN Red List of Threatened Species

Currently, the rate of extinctions is exceptionally high. Environmentalists seek the survival of endangered species by initiating and maintaining local, national and international action. For example, the **International Union for the Conservation of Nature (IUCN)**, working with appropriate local organisations, publishes a series of Regional Red Lists. These assess the risk of extinction to species within countries and regions. The lists are based upon criteria relevant to all species and all regions of the world. They convey the urgency of conservation issues to the international community and to policy makers. The aim is to stimulate action to combat loss of endangered species and of the habitats that support them.

Practical conservation – what does it entail?

Conservation involves applying the principles of ecology to manage the environment so that, despite human activities, a balance is maintained. The aims of conservation are to preserve and promote habitats and wildlife, and to ensure natural resources are used in a way that provides a sustainable yield. Conservation is an active process, not simply a case of preservation, and there are many different approaches to it. Practical conservation involves:

- the designation and maintenance of representative habitats as nature reserves
- preservation of endangered species and their genetic diversity through the maintenance of botanical and zoological gardens (with their captive breeding programmes) and the establishment of viable seed banks.

Table 8.6 What active management of nature reserves involves

Continuous monitoring of the reserve so that causes of change are understood, change may be anticipated, and measures taken early enough to adjust conditions without disruption, should this be necessary.
Maintenance of effective boundaries and the limiting of unhelpful human interference. The enthusiastic involvement of the local human community sends out messages about the purposes of conservation (a local 'education' programme, in effect) and that everyone has a part to play.
Measures to facilitate the successful completion of life cycles of any endangered species for which the reserve is 'home', together with supportive conditions for vulnerable and rare species.
Restocking and re-introductions of once-common species from stocks produced by captive breeding programmes of zoological and botanical gardens.

Conservation by promotion of nature reserves

Nature reserves comprise carefully selected land set aside for restricted access and controlled use, to allow the local maintenance of biodiversity. This is not a new idea; the New Forest in southern Britain was set aside for hunting by royalty over 900 years ago. An incidental effect was to produce a sanctuary for wildlife.

Today, this solution to extinction pressures on wildlife includes the setting up and maintenance of areas of special scientific interest as nature reserves, of our National Parks (the first National Park was Yellowstone, set up in North America in 1872) and of the African game parks, which have been more recently established. In total, these sites represent habitats of many different descriptions, in many countries around the world. Some of the conservation work they achieve may be carried out by volunteers.

In a nature reserve, the area enclosed is important – a tiny area may be too small to be effective. However, the actual dimensions of an effective reserve vary with species size and life style of the majority of the threatened species it is designed to protect. Also, for a given reserve there is an 'edge effect'. A compact reserve with minimal perimeter is less effective than one with an extensive perimeter interface with its surroundings.

The use to which the surrounding area is put is important, too; if it is managed sympathetically, it may indirectly support the reserve's wildlife. Another feature is geographical isolation – reserves positioned at great distances from other protected areas are less effective than reserves in closer proximity. Also, it has been found that connecting corridors of land are advantageous (Figure 8.14). In agricultural areas these may simply take the form of hedgerows protected from contact with pesticide treatments that nearby crops receive.

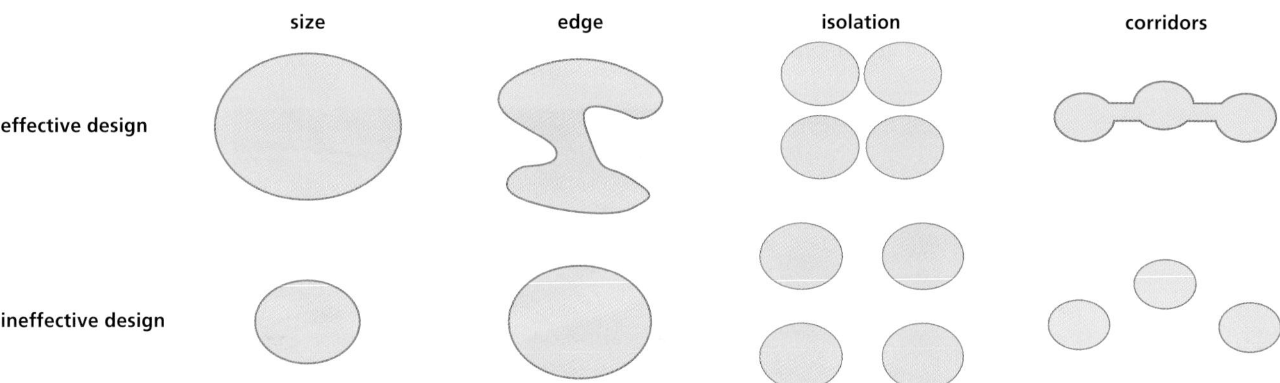

Figure 8.14 Features of effective nature reserves

Ex-situ conservation – an appraisal

Zoological (and botanical) gardens and their captive breeding programmes

Endangered species typically have very low population numbers and are in serious danger of becoming extinct. For some species whose numbers have dwindled drastically, captive breeding may be their last hope of survival.

Today, many zoos cooperate to manage individuals of the same species, held in different zoos, as a single population. A 'stud book' – a computerised database of genetic and demographic data – has been compiled for many of these species. This provides the basis for the recommendation and conduct of crosses designed to preserve the gene pool and avoid the problems of inbreeding.

Animals are shipped between zoos, or the technique of artificial insemination is employed. Some species can be very hard to breed in captivity, while with others there has been a high success rate.

Other successes include individuals bred in captivity that have been released and have survived in the wild. Examples include red wolves, Andean condors, bald eagles and golden lion tamarins.

Critics of the process fear that genetic diversity may have dwindled so much already that a species cannot be regenerated, and suggest that the work concentrates on a few, highly attractive species, and that at great cost (with funds diverted from more effective habitat conservation) it gives a false sense that extinction problems are being solved.

The building up of seed banks

Storing seeds in seed banks is an inexpensive and space-efficient method of *ex-situ* conservation (Figure 8.15). The natural dormancy of seeds allows for their suspended preservation for long periods, typically in conditions of low humidity and low temperature. The steps, following collection and preparation are:

- seed drying (to below 7 per cent water)
- packaging (in moisture-proof containers)
- storage (at a temperature of −188 °C)
- periodic germination tests
- re-storage or replacement.

Figure 8.15 Wellcome Trust Millenium Building, Wakehurst Place – home of the Millenium Seed Bank (an initiative of the Royal Botanical Gardens, Kew)

The advantages of all these approaches are reviewed in Table 8.7.

Table 8.7 Pros and cons of *in-situ* and *ex-situ* conservation

In-situ **conservation – terrestrial and aquatic nature reserves**	***Ex-situ*** **conservation – captive breeding programmes of zoological and botanical gardens, and seed banks**
Habitats that are already rare are especially vulnerable to natural disaster – rare habitats themselves are easily lost if a range of examples are not preserved as nature reserves.	Originally, zoos were collections of largely unfamiliar animals kept for curiosity, with little concern for any stress caused, but now captive breeding programmes make good use of these resources.
When a habitat disappears the whole community is lost, threatening to increase total numbers of endangered species.	Captive breeding maintains the genetic stock of rare and endangered species.
A refuge for endangered wildlife allows these species to lead natural lives in a familiar environment for which they are adapted, and be a part of their normal food chains.	The genetic problems arising from individual zoos having very limited numbers to act as parents is overcome by inter-zoo cooperation (and artificial insemination in some cases).
The biota of a reserve may be monitored for early warning of any further deterioration in numbers of a threatened species, so that remedial steps can be taken.	Animals in zoos tend to have significantly longer life-expectancies, and are available to participate in breeding programmes for much longer than wild animals.
The offspring of endangered species are nurtured in their natural environment and gain all the experiences this normally brings, including the acquisition of skills from parents and peers around them.	Captive breeding programmes, for most species they are applied to, have been highly successful, although the young do not grow up in the 'wild', so there is less opportunity to observe and learn from parents and peers.
There is an established tradition of maintaining reserves and protected areas in various parts of the world, so there is much experience to share on how to manage them successfully.	Captive breeding programmes generate healthy individuals in good numbers for attempts at re-introduction of endangered species to natural habitats – a particularly challenging process, given that natural predators abound in these locations.
Nature reserves are popular sites for the public to visit (in approved ways), thereby maintaining public awareness of the environmental crisis due to extinctions, and individual responsibilities that arise from it.	Zoos and botanical gardens are accessible sites for the public to visit (often sited in urban settings where many may have access), contributing effectively to public education on the environmental crisis.
Reserves are ideal venues to which to return endangered individuals that are the product of captive breeding programmes – providing realistic conditions for re-adaptation to their habitat, where progress can be monitored.	Seed banks are a convenient and efficient way of maintaining genetic material of endangered plants, which make use of the ways in which seeds survive long periods in nature.

Test yourself

18 Explain why homozygosity will prevent natural selection.

19 State the difference between *in-situ* and *ex-situ* conservation.

20 Describe the purpose of stud books in captive breeding programmes.

Chapter summary

Natural selection

- Natural selection brings about genetic changes in populations when genetic variation results in differential reproductive success within a population.
- Natural selection can be directional or stabilising.
- Natural selection has resulted in the development of bacterial populations that are resistant to one or more antibiotics.
- If two or more groups from a population become reproductively isolated, natural selection can bring about speciation.
- Reproductive isolation may occur through geographical separation of groups, leading to allopatric speciation, or without geographical separation of groups, leading to sympatric speciation.

Biodiversity

- Biodiversity can be assessed at different levels: within a habitat at the species level and within a species at the genetic level.
- Within a community, an index of diversity (D) can be calculated from sampling data using the formula:

  $$D = \frac{N(N-1)}{\sum n(n-1)}$$

  where N is the number of organisms of all species and n is the number of organisms of each species.
- The process of conservation is used to maintain biodiversity and the sustainable use of natural resources.
- The maintenance of biodiversity can be justified using economic and ethical reasons.
- *Ex-situ* conservation involves establishing seed banks, botanical gardens and zoological gardens to maintain biodiversity. *In-situ* conservation involves designating and protecting areas of natural habitat.

Practice questions

1 A population is best described as:

A a group of organisms occupying the same habitat

B a group of organisms of the same species occupying the same habitat

C a group of organisms of the same species occupying the same ecosystem

D a group of organisms of the same genus occupying the same ecosystem *(1)*

2 Which of the following would promote the development of antibiotic-resistant strains of bacteria?

A Failing to complete a course of antibiotic treatment

B Taking very high doses of antibiotics

C Treatment with more than one antibiotic

D Treatment with other drugs but not antibiotics *(1)*

3 **a)** Describe how seeds are prepared and stored by seed banks. *(3)*

b) Explain the importance of seed banks in maintaining biodiversity. *(3)*

4 Three weed species appeared in a vegetable plot left as bare soil for 1 year. Individual plants were counted and the results are shown in the table.

Species	Number of individual plants
Groundsel	45
Shepherd's purse	40
Dandelion	10
Total	95

a) Calculate the Simpson Diversity Index for this habitat. *(3)*

b) Explain why using a measure such as a diversity index would be more useful than using species richness to compare the diversity of this habitat with others. *(3)*

Tip

You will find the formula you require in the diversity section of this chapter. In an exam you may be required to select the right formula from a data sheet or you may be given it in the question).

5 **a)** Use the information in this chapter and Figure 8.11 to explain why the current organisation of the Kinabatangan Sanctuary will almost certainly lead to the extinction of orang-utans even though this is a protected reserve. *(4)*

***b)** Changing the organisation of the Kinabatangan Sanctuary and conserving the orang-utan population in the future is an expensive process. Evaluate the ethical and economic arguments that could be made to justify this investment. *(6)*

6 The kakapo (*Stripops habroptila*) is the world's largest parrot, weighing up to 2 kg. It cannot fly but can climb trees well and walk long distances. It feeds on a variety of fruits, seeds and roots and is nocturnal. If in danger, it

will stand perfectly still for long periods. When breeding every 2–4 years it builds its nest on the ground and the males compete for 'calling posts' from where they emit a loud booming sound at night to attract females. Prior to the nineteenth century, kakapos were a very successful species, colonising all the islands of New Zealand, where it is thought their main predator was the (now extinct) giant eagle.

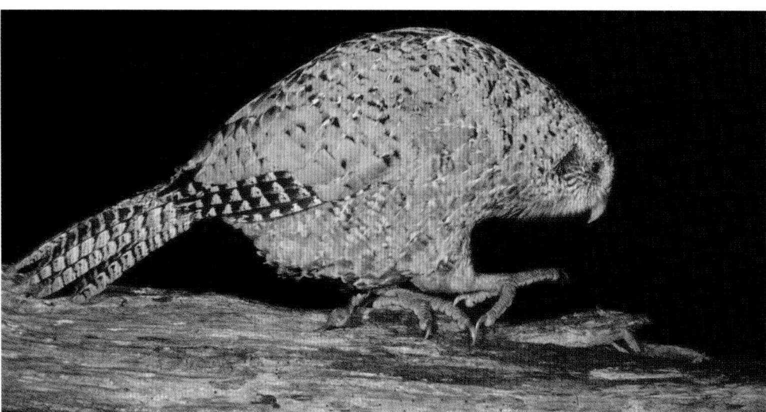

a) Use the information provided to explain how the unique adaptations shown by the kakapo made it a successful bird species in its niche before 1800. *(4)*

b) After the end of the nineteenth century, the giant eagle was extinct and New Zealand was rapidly colonised by European settlers. They brought with them domesticated cats as well as rats, and began to farm large areas of the land and hunt kakapos as an easily available source of meat. In 2012 there were only 125 birds remaining on a few isolated islands.

Explain why the changes after the nineteenth century have resulted in the near-extinction of the kakapo. *(3)*

c) At the present time conservationists are making an effort to save the kakapo from extinction. All the known kakapos have been collected and released onto a small, isolated island free from predators.

What are the advantages and disadvantages of this strategy to prevent extinction? *(4)*

Tips

Parts (a) and (b) of this question are aimed at AO2, which is designed to test your ability to apply knowledge and understanding to a new situation.

The command word 'explain' is important here. You cannot gain credit for merely repeating information from the stem of the question. You must explain clearly how the changes named would have their effect on the population.

Part (c) is designed to test AO3, which assesses your ability to use your knowledge to consider evidence or argument and come to a reasoned conclusion.

Stretch and challenge

7 Humans have taken such control of their environment that they have eliminated natural selection pressures and therefore will cease evolving.

To what extent would you agree or disagree with this statement?

8 Areas designated National Parks in the UK are subject to strict controls but they also provide exceptional recreational opportunities in a small, highly populated island.

To what extent are the roles of National Parks in conservation of habitats and biodiversity in conflict with pressures for recreational spaces and industrial development? Does this mean that we must choose one or the other?

Tip

It would be best to approach Question 8 with some research-specific examples of projects being undertaken in one or more National Parks with a view to managing this conflict. Use your research evidence to come to some conclusion.

9 Cell transport mechanisms

Prior knowledge

In this chapter you will need to recall that:

- ➜ cell surface membranes are found on the surface of plant and animal cells and around cell organelles
- ➜ plant and animal cells have cytoplasm bound by a membrane; in addition, plant cells are covered with a cell wall
- ➜ cell surface membranes have a common structure formed mainly from a lipoprotein bilayer
- ➜ diffusion is the movement of molecules from a region of high concentration to a region of lower concentration
- ➜ osmosis is the movement of water molecules from a dilute to a more concentrated solution across a partially permeable membrane
- ➜ both osmosis and diffusion will continue until there is no longer a concentration difference
- ➜ both diffusion and osmosis are driven by the kinetic energy of the molecules concerned; there is no external energy input needed
- ➜ where substances need to be moved against a concentration gradient then energy will be needed in the form of ATP
- ➜ ATP is the universal form of chemical energy used in all cells.

Test yourself on prior knowledge

1 What type of lipids are found in cell surface membranes?

2 What are the **two** main types of protein present in the membrane?

3 What is the most common chemical constituent of a plant cell wall?

4 What name is given to the difference in concentrations across a membrane?

5 Which has a greater concentration of water molecules, a dilute solution or a concentrated solution?

6 Which molecule is formed when energy is released from ATP?

7 Why will diffusion 'stop' when the two concentrations are equal, even though there is still a great deal of random movement of the particles?

8 What is the only molecule that moves during osmosis?

The structure of the cell surface membrane

The cell surface membrane is the structure that maintains the integrity of the cell (it holds the cell's contents together). It is also the barrier across which all substances entering and leaving the cell must pass. So the membrane's properties, based on its chemical composition and structure, are all important in the operation of the cell.

The cell surface membrane is made almost entirely of protein and lipid, together with a small and variable amount of carbohydrate. In Figure 9.1, a model of the molecular structure of the cell surface membrane, known as the **fluid mosaic model**, is illustrated. The cell surface membrane is described as a *mosaic* because the proteins are clearly scattered about in this pattern, and *fluid* because the components (lipids and proteins) are able to move past each other in a linear plane.

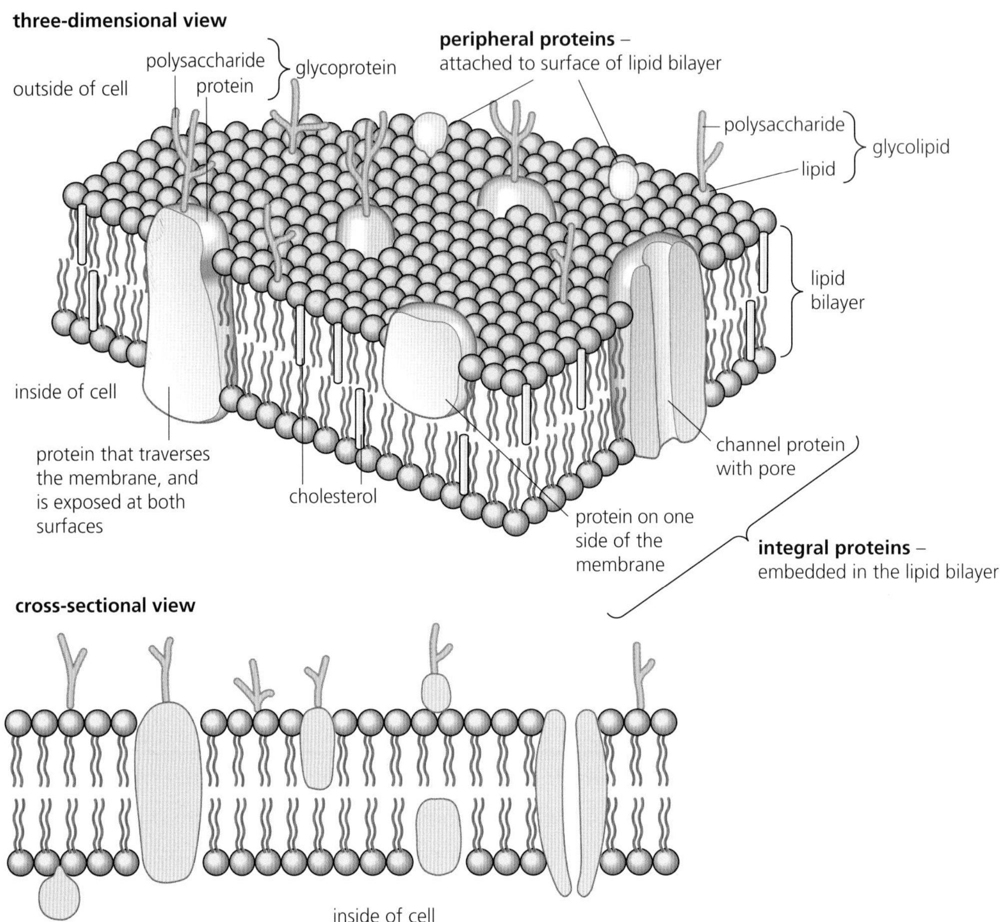

Figure 9.1 The fluid mosaic model of the cell surface membrane

Evidence for the fluid mosaic model

It was in 1972 that two cytologists, S. J. Singer and G. L. Nicolson, proposed the fluid mosaic model of membrane structure. The model was built up from a body of evidence that had accumulated over a period of time, from studies of cell structure (cytology), cell biochemistry and cell behaviour (cell physiology). This is another good example of the way in which important advances are made in science, which was discussed in Chapter 7. This evidence was in the form of ten important observations.

1 Cell contents are observed to flow out when the cell surface is ruptured, as illustrated in Figure 9.2 in a damaged red blood cell. This confirms the presence of a physical barrier around the cytoplasm that is, under normal circumstances, well able to contain and protect the cell contents.

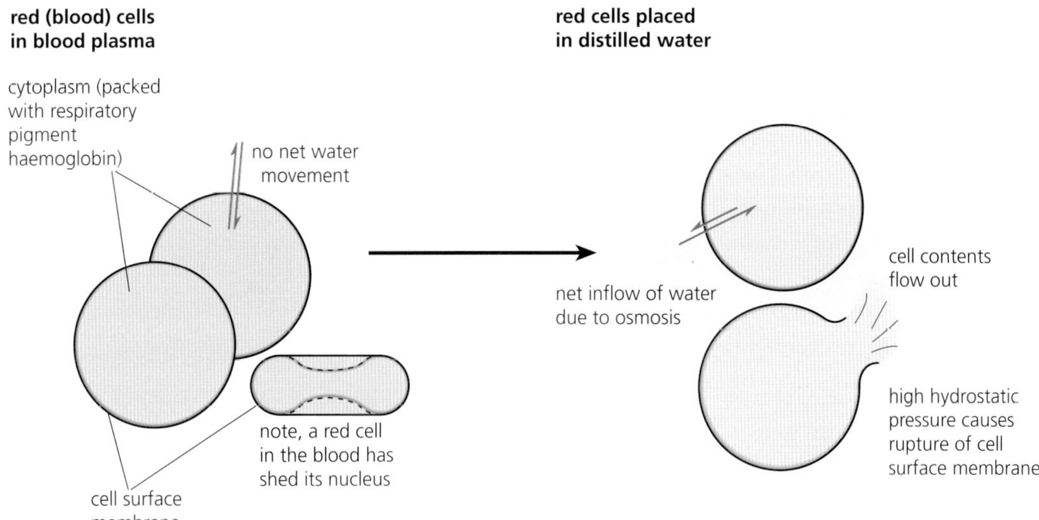

Figure 9.2 A red cell with a damaged cell surface membrane

2 Water-soluble compounds enter cells less readily than compounds that dissolve in lipids (these will be non-polar compounds and hydrophobic substances). This implies that lipids are a major component of the cell surface membrane.

3 Lipids obtained from cell membranes consist of a type of compound known as a **phospholipid**. The chemical structure of a phospholipid is shown in Figure 1.19 in Chapter 1.

A phospholipid has a 'head' composed of a glycerol group, to which is attached one ionised phosphate group. This latter part of the molecule has **hydrophilic** (water-loving) properties. For example, **hydrogen bonds** readily form between the phosphate head and water molecules.

The remainder of the phospholipid comprises two long, fatty acid residues consisting of hydrocarbon chains. These 'tails' have **hydrophobic** (water-hating) properties. So phospholipids are unusual in being partly hydrophilic and partly hydrophobic.

4 The behaviour of phospholipids when added to water was predicted from this structure – and is demonstrated in practice. With a small quantity of phospholipid in contact with water, these molecules form a monolayer that floats with the hydrocarbon tails exposed above the water (see Figure 1.20 in Chapter 1). When more phospholipid is available, the molecules arrange themselves as a bilayer, with the hydrocarbon tails facing together. This latter is the situation in the cell surface membrane model. Furthermore, in the lipid bilayer, attractions between the hydrophobic hydrocarbon tails on the inside, and between the hydrophilic glycerol/phosphate heads and the surrounding water molecules on the outside, result in a stable, strong barrier.

5 Chemical analysis of cell surface membranes has also shown that, although a significant proportion of lipid is present, there is insufficient in total to cover the whole of the cell surface in a bilayer. Furthermore, protein is also present as a major component. The proteins of cell surface membranes are globular proteins (see Chapter 2).

Key terms

Integral proteins Proteins present in the cell surface membrane that are partially or totally buried within the lipid bilayer.

Peripheral proteins Proteins present in the cell surface membrane that are superficially attached to the lipid bilayer.

6 Work on the extraction of protein from cell surface membranes indicated that, while some occur on the external surfaces and are easily extracted, other proteins occur buried within or across the lipid bilayer. These are difficult to extract.

7 Electron micrographs (EMs) of cell surface membrane fragments, which had by chance split down the midline, showed that some proteins occur buried within or across the lipid bilayer (Figure 9.3). Proteins that occur partially or fully buried in the lipid bilayer are described as **integral proteins**. Those that are superficially attached on either surface of the lipid bilayer are known as **peripheral proteins**. The roles of membrane proteins have also been investigated, and these are diverse. Membrane proteins may be channels for transport of metabolites, or enzymes or carriers; others may be receptors or antigens.

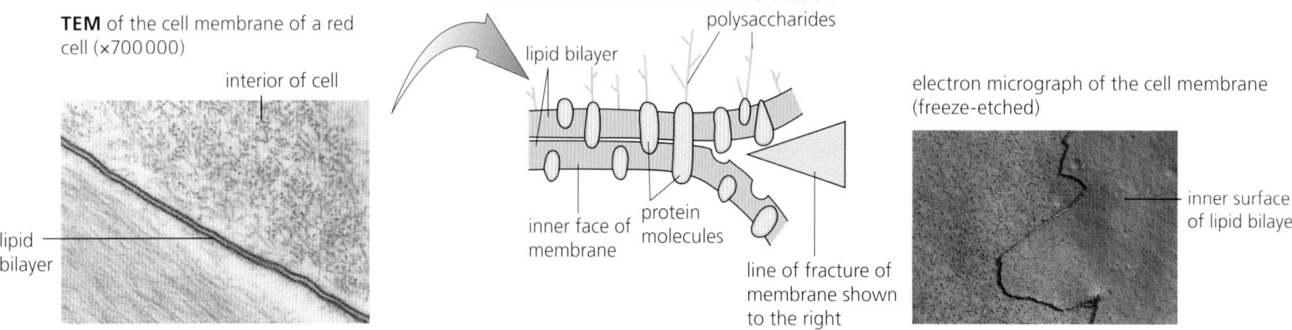

Figure 9.3 Cell surface membrane structure; evidence from the electron microscope

8 Experiments in which specific components of membranes are 'tagged' by reaction with marker chemicals (typically fluorescent dyes) show that the component molecules within membranes are continually on the move. The membrane's structure can truly be described as 'fluid'.

9 Lipid bilayers have been found to contain molecules of a rather unusual lipid, in addition to phospholipids. This lipid is known as **cholesterol**. Cholesterol has the effect of disturbing the close-packing of the phospholipids, thereby increasing the flexibility of the membrane.

10 On the outer surface of the cell, antenna-like carbohydrate molecules form complexes with certain of the membrane proteins (forming **glycoproteins**) and lipids (**glycolipids**). The functions of these complexes have since been shown to be cell–cell recognition, or as receptor sites for chemical signals. Others are involved in the binding of cells into tissues.

Energy transfers in cells

In this chapter and several others you will meet ideas about how cells use and transfer energy. At this level it is really important to describe these processes in a scientifically accurate way. To do this we must keep to one of the most important rules in science. It may sound daunting but it is the first law of thermodynamics and is very straightforward. Put simply, it says that **we cannot create or destroy energy**. Energy can only be transferred from one form to another and the amount of energy you start with is always the same as the amount of energy at the end.

The role of ATP

Energy made available within the cytoplasm may be transferred to a molecule called **adenosine triphosphate** (**ATP**). This substance occurs in all cells at a concentration of 0.5–2.5 $mg\,cm^{-3}$. It is a relatively small, soluble organic molecule – **a nucleotide** – with an unusual feature. It carries three phosphate groups linked together in a linear sequence.

> **Tip**
>
> At AS and A level, you must watch your language very carefully. In examinations, phrases such as 'energy is made in respiration' or 'energy is used up in muscles' are simply wrong and will gain you no credit.

adenosine triphosphate

adenine

ribose

phosphate

phosphate

phosphate

OH OH

adenosine diphosphate

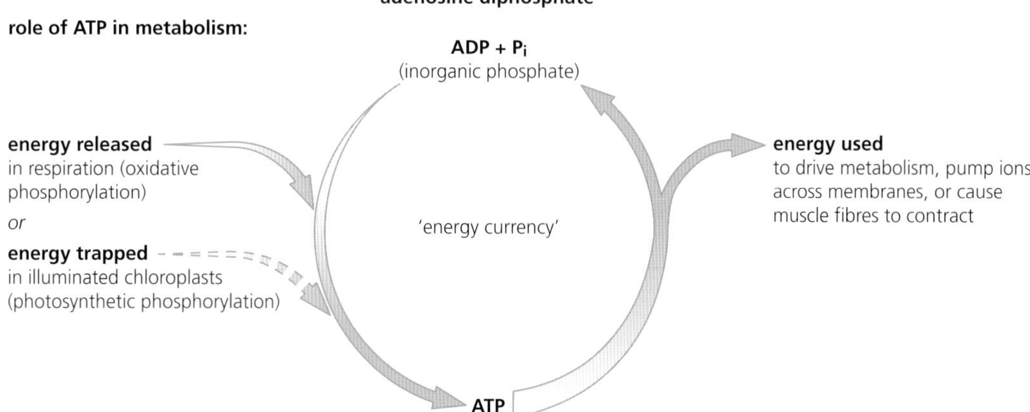

Figure 9.4 The structure and role of ATP

ATP is formed from adenosine diphosphate (ADP) and a phosphate ion (P_i) by transfer of energy from other reactions. ATP is referred to as 'energy currency' because, like money, it can be used for different purposes, and it is constantly recycled. ATP contains a considerable amount of chemical energy locked up in its structure. What makes ATP special as a reservoir of **stored chemical energy** is its role as a common intermediate between energy-yielding reactions and energy-requiring reactions and processes.

Energy-requiring reactions include the synthesis of cellulose from glucose, the synthesis of proteins from amino acids and the contraction of muscle fibres.

The free energy available in ATP is approximately 30–34 $kJ\,mol^{-1}$, made available in the presence of a specific enzyme. Some of this energy is lost as heat in a reaction, but much free energy is made available to do useful work – more than sufficient to drive a typical energy-requiring reaction of metabolism.

Sometimes ATP reacts with water (a hydrolysis reaction) and is converted back to ADP and P_i. Direct hydrolysis of the terminal phosphate groups like this happens in muscle contraction, for example. Therefore ADP is exactly the same molecule as ATP in Figure 9.4 but with one less phosphate group attached to it.

Mostly, ATP reacts with other metabolites and forms **phosphorylated** intermediates, making them more reactive in the process. The phosphate groups are released later, so both ADP and P_i become available for re-use as metabolism continues. These are very good examples of energy transfers not 'making' or 'using up' energy.

In summary, ATP is a molecule universal to all living things; it is the source of energy for chemical change in cells, tissues and organisms. The important features of ATP are that it can:

- move easily within cells, by facilitated diffusion
- take part in many steps in cellular respiration and in very many reactions of metabolism
- transfer energy in relatively small amounts, sufficient to drive individual reactions.

Test yourself

1 State which part of a phospholipid is:
   a) hydrophobic
   b) hydrophilic.
2 State what type of protein is found in the cell surface membrane structure.
3 Give the name for proteins buried within the phospholipid bilayer.
4 What other lipid is found in the cell surface membrane structure?
5 State the function of glycoproteins found on the surface of the cell surface membrane.
6 What type of chemical molecule is ATP?
7 What does the first law of thermodynamics state about the nature of energy?
8 Name the type of reaction involved in converting ATP to ADP + P_i.

Movement across the cell surface membrane

There is continuous and rapid movement of many substances across the cell surface membrane of living cells. Water, respiratory gases (O_2 and CO_2), nutrients such as glucose, essential ions and excretory products are always moving across these membranes, either entering or leaving the cell. Cells may secrete substances such as hormones and enzymes, and they may receive growth substances and certain hormones.

Plant cells secrete the chemicals that make up their walls through their cell membranes, and assemble and maintain the wall outside the membrane. Certain mammalian cells secrete structural proteins such as collagen, in a form that can be assembled outside the cells in the production of connective tissues, for example.

In addition, the cell surface membrane is where the cell is identified by surrounding cells and organisms. For example, protein receptor sites are recognised by hormones, neurotransmitter substances from nerve cells and other chemicals sent from other cells. Figure 9.5 is a summary of this movement, and also identifies the possible mechanisms of transport across membranes.

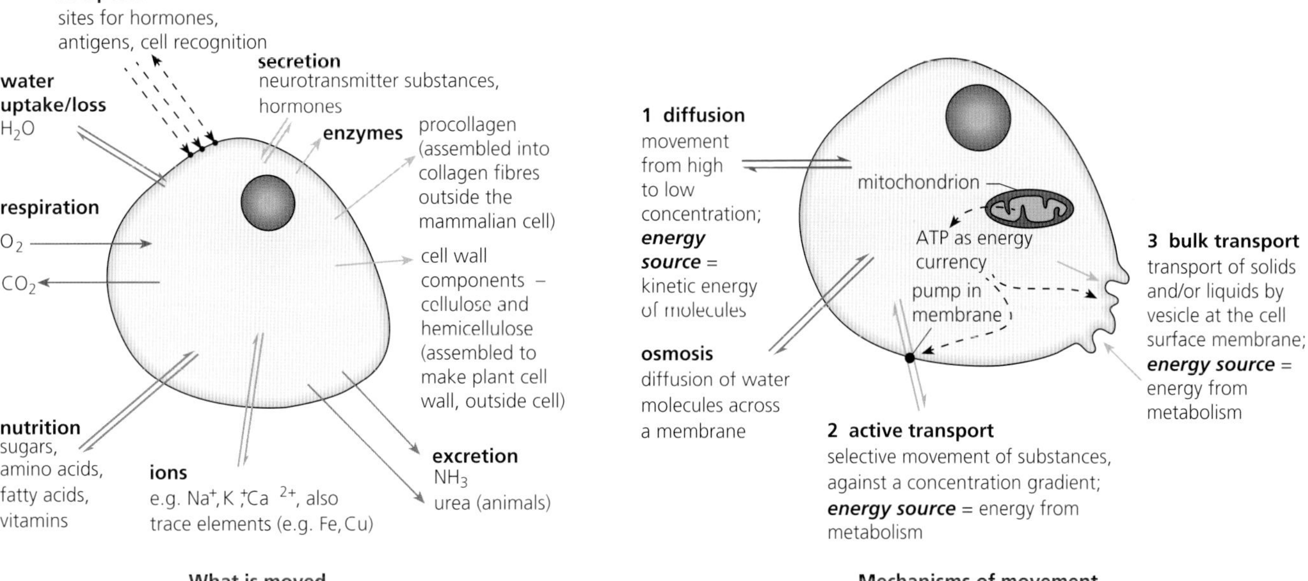

Figure 9.5 Movements across the cell surface membrane

1 Movement by diffusion

The atoms, molecules and ions of fluids (liquids and gases) undergo continuous random movements. Given time, these movements result in the complete mixing and even distribution of the components of a gas mixture, and of the atoms, molecules and ions in a solution. So, for example, from a solution we are able to take a tiny random sample and analyse it to find the concentration of dissolved substances in the whole solution – because any sample has the same composition as the whole. Similarly, every breath we take has the same amount of oxygen, nitrogen and carbon dioxide as the atmosphere has as a whole. This process is called **diffusion**.

Where a difference in concentration has arisen between areas in a gas or liquid, random movements carry molecules from a region of high concentration to a region of low concentration. As a result, the particles become evenly dispersed. The energy for diffusion comes from the **kinetic energy** of molecules.

> **Key terms**
>
> **Diffusion** The free passage of molecules (and atoms and ions) from a region of their high concentration to a region of low concentration until they are evenly distributed.
>
> **Kinetic energy** The energy possessed by a particle because it is in continuous motion.

Diffusion in cells

Diffusion across cell surface membranes (Figure 9.6) occurs where:

- the cell surface membrane is fully permeable to the solute – the lipid bilayer of the cell surface membrane is permeable to non-polar substances, including steroids and glycerol, and also oxygen and carbon dioxide in solution, all of which diffuse quickly via this route
- the pores in the membrane are large enough for a solute to pass through. Water diffuses across the cell surface membrane via the protein-lined pores of the membrane (**channel proteins**), and via tiny spaces between the phospholipid molecules. This latter movement occurs easily where the fluid-mosaic membrane contains phospholipids with unsaturated hydrocarbon tails, for here the hydrocarbon tails are spaced more widely. The membrane is consequently especially 'leaky' to water, for example.

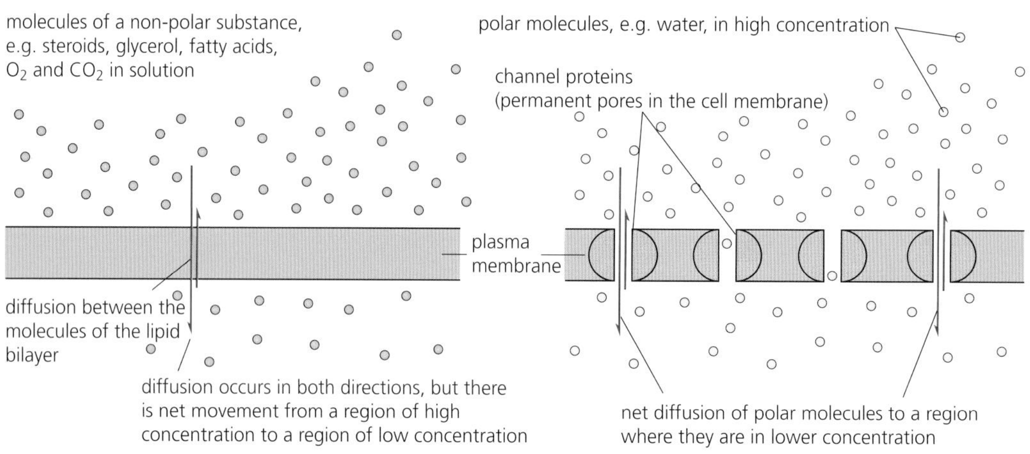

Figure 9.6 Diffusion across the cell surface membrane

Key term

Betalains A group of plant pigments found in certain plants such as beetroot.

Core practical 5

Investigate the effect of temperature on beetroot membrane permeability

Background information

The cells of beetroot contain an intensely red, water-soluble pigment called betalain in their interior – it is found in the large central vacuole of each cell. The pigment may escape in sufficient quantities to be detected in the aqueous medium around the tissue. This occurs if harmful external conditions are applied to beetroot tissue. For example, let us consider the effect of externally applied heat energy. One effect of heat is to denature proteins, and this applies to the proteins of membranes as well as those elsewhere in cells. Once membrane proteins have been denatured, the integrity of the lipid bilayer of the cell surface membranes may also be compromised. Escape of the vacuole contents will indicate this has happened. So, in effect, we can experimentally investigate the approximate temperature at which membrane proteins are seriously denatured.

It is also possible to adapt this technique to investigate the effect of chemical substances (for example, strong solutions of ions, or organic solvents such as alcohol) on the permeability of membranes.

Carrying out the investigation

Aim: To determine the temperature at which the beetroot cell surface membrane is denatured by heat.

Risk assessment: Good laboratory practice is sufficient to avoid a hazard. Wear eye protection when performing this experiment.

1 The first step is to prepare washed beetroot tissue cylinders, about 3 cm long and 0.5 cm in diameter (Figure 9.7). You should carefully cut ten cylinders.
2 Submerge one cylinder in a water bath at 70 °C for 1 minute. Then withdraw it and place it in 15 cm^3 of distilled water in a test tube (labelled 'treatment at 70 °C') at room temperature for 15 minutes. After this, you should remove the tissue cylinder and discard it.
3 Cool the water bath to 65 °C and repeat the process with a second cylinder – heat-treat it, allow it to stand in a tube of fresh distilled water (labelled 'treatment at 65 °C') for 15 minutes, and then discard it.
4 Repeat, using heat treatments with water that is 5 °C cooler each time. Make 25 °C the lowest temperature treatment.
5 The distilled water in the test tubes becomes coloured by any pigment that has escaped from the tissue cylinders as a result of heat treatment. You can measure the pigment loss from the tissue into the test tube solutions using a colorimeter containing a complementary colour filter (so, for a red solution, a blue filter is required). Set the scale to zero using the solvent (distilled water) only.

Questions

Read through the method carefully.

1 If the pigment betalain leaks from the central vacuole of a plant cell, how many membranes must it cross to reach the surrounding water? What are the names of these membranes?
2 Why is it necessary to wash the cylinders in water before heat treating them?

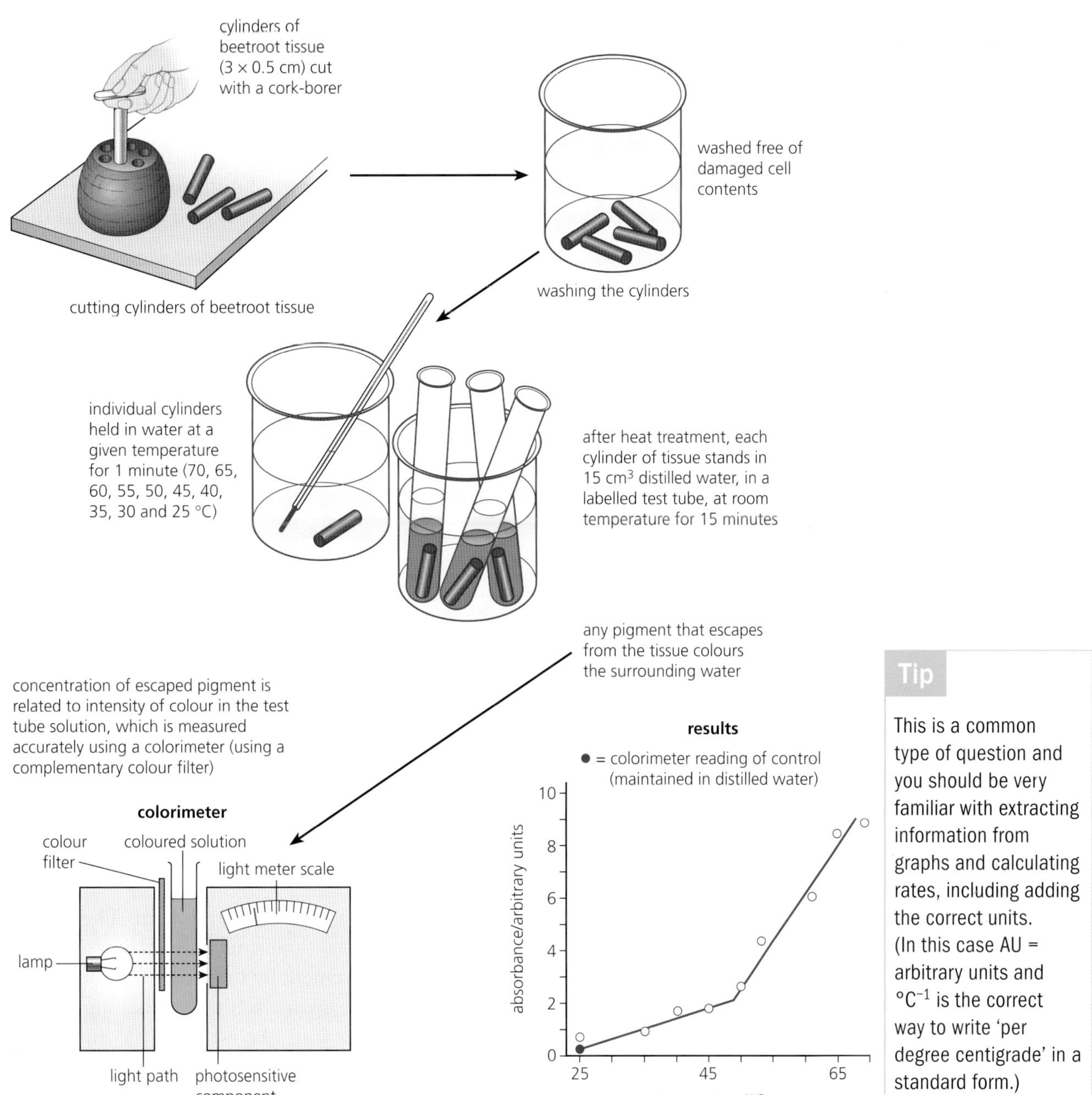

cylinders of beetroot tissue (3 × 0.5 cm) cut with a cork-borer
cutting cylinders of beetroot tissue
washed free of damaged cell contents
washing the cylinders
individual cylinders held in water at a given temperature for 1 minute (70, 65, 60, 55, 50, 45, 40, 35, 30 and 25 °C)
after heat treatment, each cylinder of tissue stands in 15 cm3 distilled water, in a labelled test tube, at room temperature for 15 minutes
any pigment that escapes from the tissue colours the surrounding water
concentration of escaped pigment is related to intensity of colour in the test tube solution, which is measured accurately using a colorimeter (using a complementary colour filter)
colorimeter
colour filter
coloured solution
light meter scale
lamp
light path
photosensitive component
results
● = colorimeter reading of control (maintained in distilled water)
absorbance/arbitrary units
temperature/°C
0
2
4
6
8
10
25
45
65

Figure 9.7 Investigating membrane permeability

Tip

This is a common type of question and you should be very familiar with extracting information from graphs and calculating rates, including adding the correct units. (In this case AU = arbitrary units and °C^{-1} is the correct way to write 'per degree centigrade' in a standard form.)

3 The method also suggests that the cylinders are kept in distilled water at room temperature for exactly 15 minutes. Would this be regarded as a good description of variable control?

4 Look at the graph in Figure 9.7. Is this showing absorption or transmission measured by the colorimeter? Explain your answer.

5 If the membrane proteins do not denature before 40 °C, why should the graph rise between 25 °C and 40 °C as shown in Figure 9.7?

6 Use the graph in Figure 9.7 to compare the rate of increase of absorption with temperature between 25–45 °C and 50–65 °C.

Facilitated diffusion

In facilitated diffusion, a substance that otherwise is unable to diffuse across the cell surface membrane does so as a result of its effect on particular molecules present in the membrane. These latter molecules, made of globular protein, form into pores or channels large enough for diffusion – and close up again when that substance is no longer present (Figure 9.8). In facilitated diffusion, the energy comes from the kinetic energy of the molecules involved, as is the case in all forms of diffusion. Energy from metabolism is not required. An important example of facilitated diffusion is the movement of ADP into and out of mitochondria.

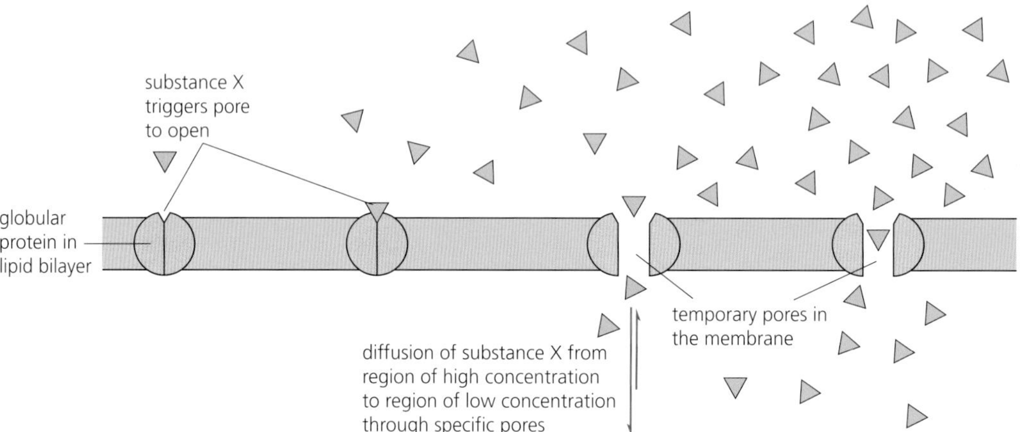

Figure 9.8 Facilitated diffusion

> **Key term**
>
> **Osmosis** The net movement of water molecules (solvent), from a region of high concentration of water molecules to a region of lower concentration of water molecules, across a partially permeable membrane.

Osmosis – a special case of diffusion

Osmosis is a special case of diffusion. It is the diffusion of water molecules across a membrane that is permeable to water. Since water makes up 70–90 per cent of living cells and cell membranes are **partially permeable** membranes, osmosis is very important in biology.

Dissolved substances attract a group of polar water molecules around them. The forces holding water molecules in this way are weak chemical bonds, including **hydrogen bonds**. Consequently, the tendency for random movement by these dissolved substances and their surrounding water molecules is restricted. Organic substances like sugars, amino acids, polypeptides and proteins, and inorganic ions like Na^+, K^+, Cl^- and NO_3^-, have this effect on the water molecules around them.

The stronger the solution (that is, the more solute dissolved per volume of water), the larger the number of water molecules that are slowed down and held almost stationary. So, in a very concentrated solution, many more of the water molecules have restricted movement than in a dilute solution. On the other hand, in pure water, all of the water molecules are free to move about randomly, and do so.

When a solution is separated from water (or a more dilute solution) by a membrane permeable to water molecules (such as the cell surface membrane), water molecules that are free to move tend to diffuse across the membrane, while dissolved molecules and their groups of water molecules move very much less, if at all. So there is a net flow of water into a concentrated solution, from water or a weaker solution, across the membrane. The membrane is described as partially permeable.

Test yourself

9 What is the driving force that causes movements by diffusion?

10 Name **two** substances that can pass freely through the lipid bilayer of cell surface membranes.

11 By what route do substances pass through the cell surface membrane by facilitated diffusion?

12 Which important cellular compounds pass across mitochondrial membranes by facilitated diffusion?

Osmosis and plant cells

Figure 9.2 shows what happens when water enters an animal cell by osmosis. As the cell expands the membrane is stretched until it bursts. Whilst this demonstrates just how important it is for animal body fluid concentrations to be strictly controlled, the situation in plant cells is very different. This is caused by the differences between animal and plant cell structure. Plant cells have similar membranes but they are covered with a strong cell wall, often made of cellulose, which only expands a little.

The best way to understand the principles involved is to think of the plant cell as a bicycle tyre containing an inner tube. If you remove the tyre and pump up the inner tube it is quite easy to get it to expand like a balloon and eventually burst. However, with the tyre replaced, pumping up the inner tube becomes progressively harder and harder as the pressure inside builds, until you can no longer force more air inside. The tyre is acting exactly like the plant cell wall. As water enters the plant cell the turgor pressure (P) inside the cell builds up, because the plant cell wall exerts an equal and opposite pressure, until it equals the pressure of the water entering by osmosis. At this point, water neither enters nor leaves and the cell is said to be fully turgid. A fully turgid cell is quite hard and solid and is a vital means of support to the plant. In young plants this is often the only means of support but is also very important to adult plants.

The opposite happens when water leaves the plant cell by osmosis. The pressure inside the cell drops and eventually the outer membrane (plasmalemma) shrinks away from the cell wall (just as if you take all the air out of an inner tube). This process of breaking away from the cell wall is called plasmolysis. At this point the cell loses all its firmness and becomes soft, and is said to be flaccid. The effect of this can be seen in Figure 9.9. As the plant is starved of water the turgor pressure in the cells falls and the plant loses support and wilts.

Water potential

So far we have used a general description of water movements into and out of plant cells, but we need to express what is happening in more scientific terms. This is done by use of the term water potential (given the Greek letter **psi** – ψ).

The units of water potential are those of pressure, pascals (Pa), or more usually **kilopascals** (**kPa**).

(1 pascal = 1 newton per square metre)

This is where we need to think logically and it leads us to using negative numbers, which can be confusing.

Key terms

Turgor pressure (P) The pressure inside plant cells caused by water entering the cell.

Fully turgid Plant cells are said to be fully turgid when the turgor pressure inside is so high that it prevents further entry of water by osmosis.

Plasmalemma The name given to the cell surface membrane surrounding the outside of the cytoplasm in plant and animal cells.

Plasmolysis This occurs as water leaves a plant cell by osmosis, causing the cytoplasm to shrink away from contact with the cell wall.

Flaccid Plant cells are said to be flaccid when water is withdrawn by osmosis and they lose their firmness.

Water potential A measure of the tendency for water to pass from one place to another. In biology this often means the tendency of water to move into or out of a cell.

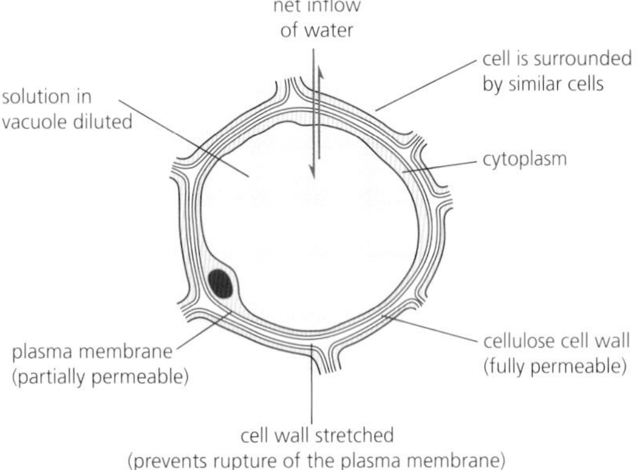

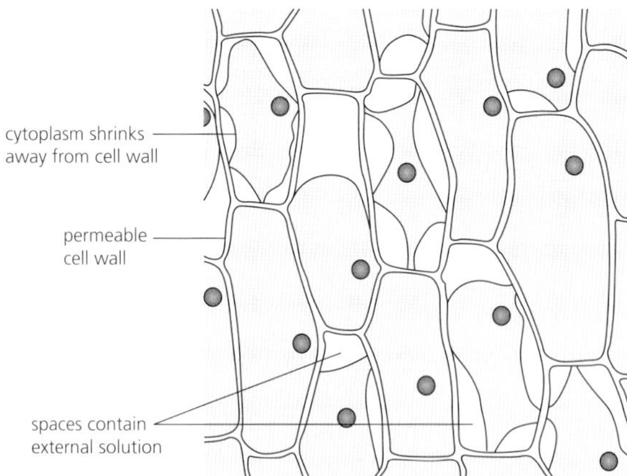

b wilting
In the cells of the epidermis of the leaf stalk of rhubarb (Rheum rhaponticum) the solutions in the vacuoles are coloured. They can be seen under the microscope without staining.
When they are placed in a solution of water potential greater than that of the cell solution, plasmolysis of the cells can be observed by microscopy.
cytoplasm shrinks away from cell wall
permeable cell wall
spaces contain external solution

Figure 9.9 Turgidity supports plant tissue

Start by looking again at the explanation of osmosis as a special case of diffusion, at the beginning of this section.

- Water will always move from a region where there is more water (dilute solution) to a region where there is less water (concentrated solution).
- Making a solution more concentrated (adding solutes) means the water molecules are less free to move.
- So when there are no dissolved solutes (pure water) then the water molecules have their greatest potential to move.
- This means that pure water has the highest possible water potential.
- In other words, any solution must have a *lower* water potential than pure water.
- However, if every other solution is more negative then we are left with only one conclusion. **The water potential of pure water is zero.**

Negative values of water potential in increasingly concentrated solutions:

$$\underset{\text{(pure water)}}{0} \longrightarrow -10\,\text{kPa} \longrightarrow -20\,\text{kPa} \longrightarrow -30\,\text{kPa}$$

more concentrated solutions = more negative water potential

The greater negative water potential of a solution is caused by the solutes dissolved in it and is called its **osmotic potential** (π), which, because it is a solution, will always be negative.

There can be a positive pressure if some force is causing water to leave the solution or cell.

For example, the turgor pressure exerted by the plant cell wall as the cell takes in water tends to push water out of the cell and therefore would be labelled positive (+) Remember, we have already stated that the osmotic potential of the cell contents would tend to draw water into the cell and this is negative, therefore it is a logical step to assume that the turgor pressure tending to force water out will be positive.

Overall, therefore, we have the following relationship, which you will be expected to learn:

water potential = turgor pressure + osmotic potential

$$\psi = P + \pi$$

Key term

Osmotic potential (π)
The increased water potential of a solution caused by the solutes dissolved in it. Sometimes referred to as solute potential, it will always have a negative value.

Example

1 Plant tissue has been immersed in pure water overnight. Cells in the tissue are found to have an osmotic potential of –600 kPa. What will be their turgor pressure?

$\psi = P + \pi$

2 Two adjacent animal cells, M and N, are part of a compact tissue. They have the following values:

	Cell M	Cell N
Osmotic potential (π)	–580 kPa	–640 kPa
Turgor pressure (P)	+410 kPa	+420 kPa

In which direction will water flow between these cells?

$\psi = P + \pi$

Answers

1 If the plant cell is fully turgid, water will not enter or leave so WP = 0 (there is no tendency for water to enter).

Hence 0 = P – 600

and P = +600 kPa

Not surprisingly, our answer shows that turgor pressure will be equal and opposite to the osmotic potential, which explains why there is no net water movement.

2 Water potential of cell M = +410 – 580 = –170 kPa

Water potential of cell N = +420 – 640 = –220 kPa

Water will flow from a less negative to a more negative water potential. So water flows from cell M to cell N.

Test yourself

13 Explain why water molecules will be attracted to ions in a solution.

14 Name the membrane that surrounds the vacuole in a plant cell.

15 Which structure in a plant cell will cause the build up of turgor pressure as water enters by osmosis?

16 State the units of water potential.

17 Name the compound that has the highest possible water potential.

Core practical 6

Determining the water potential of a plant tissue

Background information

In order to determine the water potential of the cells in a plant tissue you will be expected to understand the terms 'water potential', 'osmotic potential' and 'turgor pressure'.

The principle of this investigation is to place plant tissue in a range of concentrations of an external solution and to measure changes caused by osmosis. The most accurate way to measure the changes caused by osmosis is to measure the change in mass of the tissue as it gains or loses water.

The theory behind water potentials tells us that when the water potential of the cell contents and the osmotic potential of the external solution are the same, then the overall water potential will be zero and at this point there will be no gain or loss in mass of the tissue left in the solution. This is what we are attempting to find in this investigation.

Carrying out the investigation

Risk Assessment: There are no significant risks in this procedure provided normal laboratory rules are observed.

1 Take one large potato and cut six cylinders, 4 cm long, using the same cork borer (at least 0.5 cm in diameter). Check that none of the cylinders has any peel attached. Blot each cylinder carefully to remove any excess liquid and weigh it. You will need to be as accurate as possible and it is advisable to use a balance capable of measurements to at least 0.01 g.

2 Label five large boiling tubes, one for each of the following: distilled water, 0.25 mol dm^{-3}, 0.5 mol dm^{-3}, 0.75 mol dm^{-3} and 1.0 mol dm^{-3}. It is useful to add more concentrations within this range if time or apparatus permit.

3 Make up 30 cm^3 of 0.25 mol dm^{-3}, 0.5 mol dm^{-3}, 0.75 mol dm^{-3} and 1.0 mol dm^{-3} of sucrose solution. Place one cylinder of potato in each boiling tube and add 30 cm^3 of the correct appropriate solution to each tube. (The actual volume may vary according to the boiling tube you are using but it is important that the volume is the same for each and as much as you can fit into your chosen container.)

4 Leave all the boiling tubes and their contents in a cool place for at least 2 hours (but not longer than 24 hours). After this time, carefully pour out the liquid and blot the cylinders very carefully as some may be quite soft. Reweigh the dried cylinders and record the new mass, again taking care to match each one with their initial mass.

5 Calculate the percentage change in mass for each cylinder and plot a graph of percentage change on the vertical axis and osmotic potential of the solution along the horizontal axis, using Table 9.1.

Table 9.1 Osmotic potential of different concentrations of sucrose solution

Concentration of sucrose/mol dm^{-3}	Osmotic potential of the solution/kPa
0	0
0.25	−680
0.5	−1450
0.75	−2370
1.0	−3510

Use your graph to identify the osmotic potential of the sucrose solution at which the potato tissue neither gains nor loses mass. This will be equal to the water potential of the potato tissue.

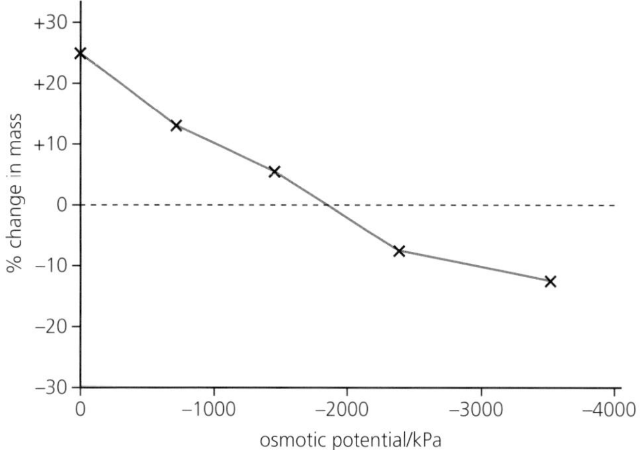

Figure 9.10 Graph of typical results from this investigation

Questions

1 You could take the opportunity here to use a 1 mol dm^{-3} sucrose solution to make your own dilutions to match the values required. Exactly 15 cm^3 of 1 mol dm^{-3} solution made up to 30 cm^3 with distilled water would give you a 0.5 mol dm^{-3} solution. How could you make up the other concentrations?

2 Why is it essential to use the same potato?

3 Why should you use as large a volume as possible of the sucrose solution?

4 Why should you leave the cylinders in solution for at least 2 hours?

5 How do you calculate percentage change?

6 Why is change in mass measured as a percentage?

7 Should the graph be drawn as a line of 'best fit'?

Tip

Using the final value and not the initial value is a very common error in calculating percentage change. If you wish to know the change then you must compare it with what you started with.

2 Movement by active transport

You have seen that diffusion is due to random movements of molecules and occurs spontaneously, from a high to a low concentration. However, many of the substances required by cells have to be absorbed from a weak external concentration and taken up into cells that contain a higher concentration. Uptake against a concentration gradient cannot occur by simple diffusion as it requires a source of energy to drive it. This type of uptake is known as **active transport**.

Key term

Active transport The movement of substances across a cell surface membrane against a concentration gradient, using energy in the form of ATP.

- **Active transport can occur against a concentration gradient** – that is, from a region of low concentration to a region of higher concentration. The cytoplasm of a cell normally holds some reserves of substances valuable in metabolism, like nitrate ions in plant cells or calcium ions in muscle fibres. The reserves of useful molecules and ions do not escape; the cell membrane retains them inside the cell. Yet when more of these or other useful molecules or ions become available for uptake, they are actively absorbed into the cells. This happens even though the concentration outside is lower than inside.
- **Active uptake is highly selective**. For example, in a situation where potassium ions (K^{+}) and chloride ions (Cl^-) are available to an animal cell, K^+ ions are more likely to be absorbed. Similarly, where sodium ions (Na^+) and nitrate ions (NO_3^-) are available to plant cells, NO_3^- ions will be absorbed more rapidly. This is often important in ensuring that the needs of the cell are met and that unwanted ions are excluded.

- **Active transport involves special molecules of the membrane**. These molecules pick up particular ions and molecules and transport them to the other side of the membrane, where they are then released. These **carrier proteins** are globular proteins that span the lipid bilayer (Figure 9.1). Movements by these carrier proteins require reaction with ATP; this reaction supplies metabolic energy to the process. Most of these proteins are specific to particular ions and molecules and this is the way selective transport is brought about. If the carrier for a particular substance is not present, the substance will not be transported.

Active transport is a feature of most living cells. You meet examples of active transport in the active uptake of ions by plant roots, in the mammalian gut where absorption occurs, in the kidney tubules where urine is formed, and in nerve fibres where an impulse is propagated.

The carrier proteins of cell surface membranes are of different types. Some transport a particular molecule or ion in one direction (Figure 9.11) while others transport two substances (like Na^+ and K^+) in opposite directions (Figure 9.12). Occasionally, two substances are transported in the same direction, for example Na^+ and glucose during the absorption of glucose in the small intestine.

Many ion channels in the carrier proteins have controlled opening and closing. These are called **gated ion channels**. Those which are controlled by small potential differences are called **voltage-gated ion channels**, while those that are sensitive to chemical signals are called **ligand-gated ion channels**.

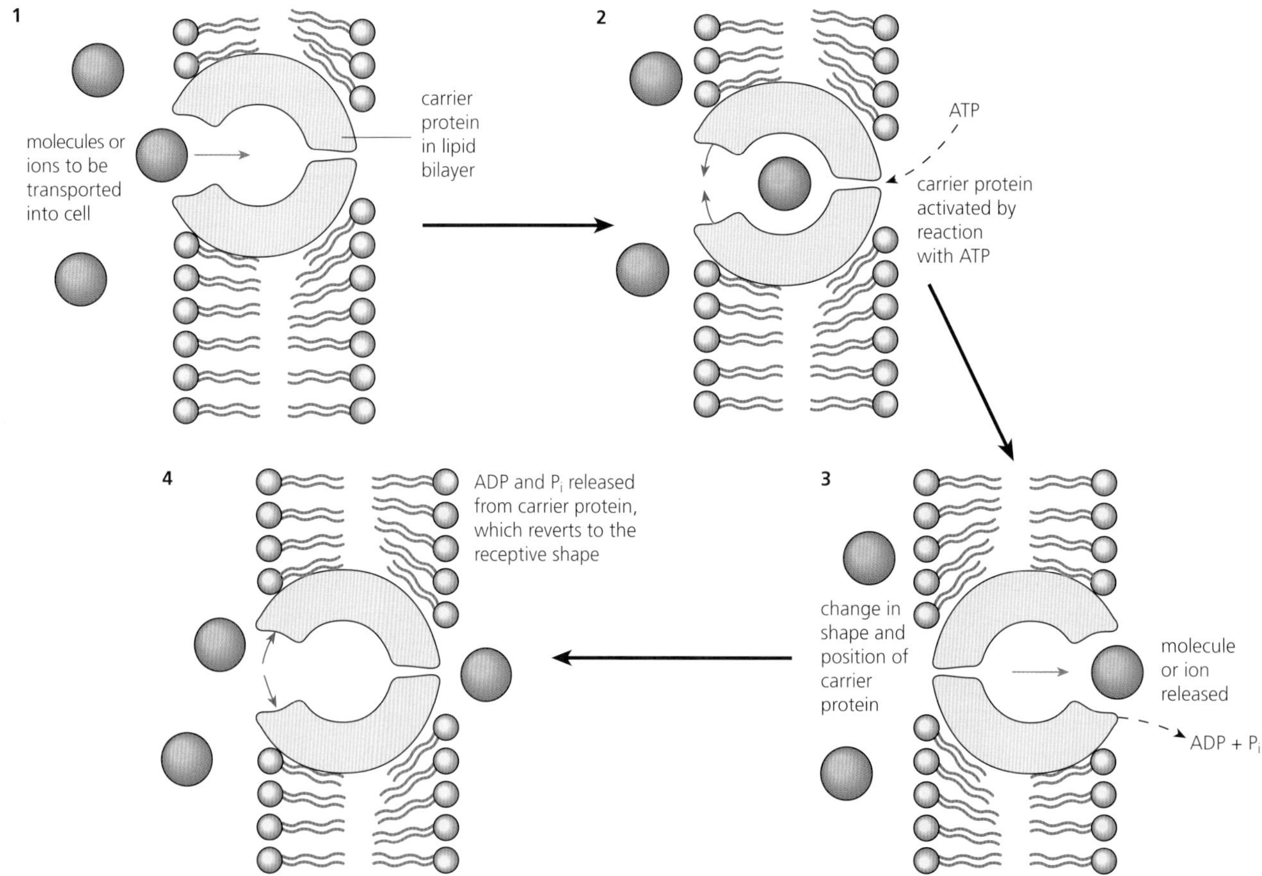

Figure 9.11 Active transport of a single substance

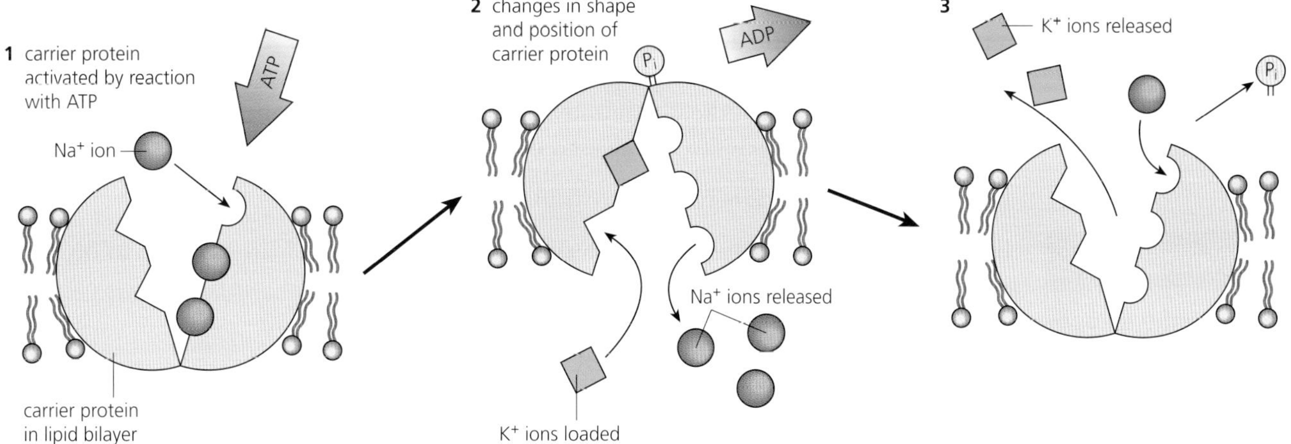

Figure 9.12 The sodium–potassium ion pump

3 Movement by bulk transport

Another mechanism of transport across the cell surface membrane is known as **bulk transport**. It occurs through the movement of **vesicles** of matter (solids or liquids) across the membrane, by processes known generally as **cytosis**. Uptake is called **endocytosis** and export is **exocytosis** (Figure 9.13).

The strength and flexibility of the fluid mosaic membrane makes this activity possible. Energy from metabolism (ATP) is also required to bring it about. For example, when solid matter is being taken in (**phagocytosis**), part of the cell surface membrane at the point where the vesicle forms is pulled inwards and the surrounding cell surface membrane and cytoplasm bulge out. The matter thus becomes enclosed in a small vesicle.

In the human body, there are a huge number of phagocytic cells, called the **macrophages**. They engulf the debris of damaged or dying cells and dispose of it (phagocytosis means 'cell eating'). For example, we break down about 2×10^{11} red blood cells each day, which are ingested and disposed of by macrophages.

Key terms

Vesicles Membrane-bound cell organelles containing liquid or solid particles.

Cytosis The bulk transport of materials across cell membranes contained in vesicles.

Endocytosis Movement of materials into cells.

Exocytosis Movement of materials out of cells.

Phagocytosis This occurs when cells (phagocytes) use their membranes to surround external particles to form vesicles within their own cytoplasm.

Macrophages Large white blood cells that are able to engulf cell debris and foreign particles by the process of phagocytosis.

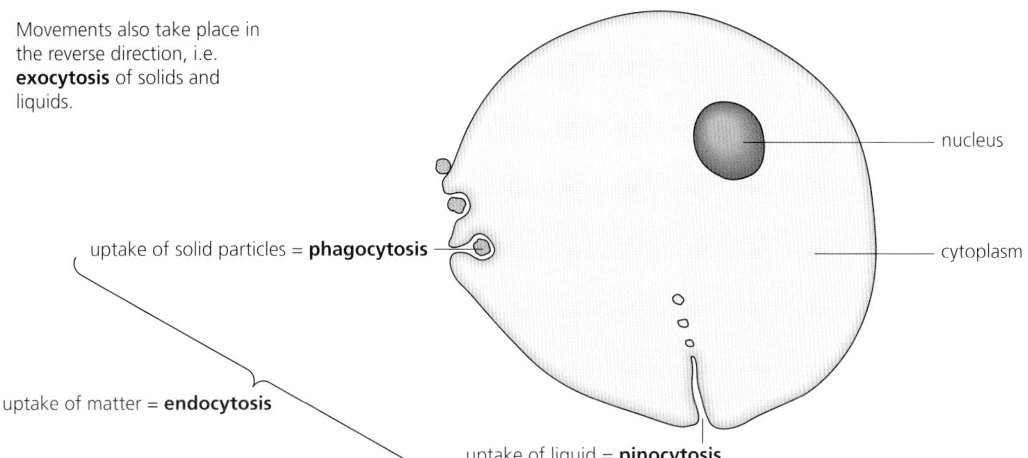

Figure 9.13 Transport by cytosis

Cells produce many highly active substances such as enzymes and hormones. Simply releasing these into the cytoplasm would obviously cause major disruption. To overcome this problem many compounds are only assembled into their active form inside the membranes of the Golgi body. From there they are transported in bulk inside membrane-bound vesicles to be released outside the cell by exocytosis.

Bulk transport of fluids is referred to as **pinocytosis**.

Bulk transport is one way in which very large molecules, which are not able to be moved in other ways, can be transported into the cell.

Key term

Pinocytosis Movement of materials in liquid form into and out of cells.

Test yourself

18 Name the source of energy needed to transport substances against a concentration gradient.

19 State which structural part of the cell surface membrane is required for active transport.

20 NO_3^- ions are often transported into plant roots by active transport. State why these ions are so important to a plant.

21 Very large molecules and solid particles cannot be transported through the cell surface membrane. Name the process that allows them to be taken up by a cell.

22 State the name of the process by which macrophages engulf red blood cells.

Properties of transported materials

You have seen that substances can be transported across membranes in different ways. The method by which they are transported will vary according to the nature of the substance itself.

The most important features of the molecules, atoms or ions to be transported are:

- the size of the particle – obviously very large molecules such as some proteins will be simply too big to pass through carrier channels or between the molecules of the membrane itself, so bulk transport will be the only pathway. In general, smaller particles are transported more quickly than larger particles
- the solubility of the particle – almost all transport takes place in solution, so particles with limited solubility will only be transported slowly. When substances dissolve they dissociate into charged ions. Not only does this make them smaller but the ions are also much more mobile. Substances that dissolve easily in lipids will obviously pass through the phospholipid layer very easily
- the charge present – the structure of the cell surface membrane makes it difficult for charged particles to pass through. Electrostatic attraction or repulsion will prevent free movements. All ions are charged atoms and polar molecules have weak charges on their structure (see Chapter 1 for the structure of a water molecule). For this reason most ions and some other charged particles pass through the membrane using specialised protein channels.

Some common substances transported into and out of cells and their properties are listed in Table 9.2.

Table 9.2 Properties and membrane transport of some common cellular substances

Substances	Properties	Mode of membrane transport
O_2, CO_2, N_2	Small non-polar molecules	Direct diffusion
H_2O	Small polar molecule	Facilitated diffusion through special protein channels (aquaporins) and sometimes directly through the phospholipid bilayer by osmosis
Glucose	Large polar molecule	Facilitated diffusion using specialised carrier proteins
Glycerol, fatty acids, steroids; vitamins A, D and E	Lipid–soluble molecules	Direct diffusion
Ions, e.g. Na^+, Cl^-, NO_3^-	Small charged atoms	Active transport using carrier proteins; passive movements can occur through protein channels when the concentration gradient is favourable
ATP, ADP	Larger polar molecules	Move in and out of mitochondria by facilitated diffusion

Chapter summary

Cell surface membrane structure

- The fluid mosaic model of the cell surface membrane explains how substances can move into and out of cells.
- Evidence has shown that a typical membrane is a bilayer of phospholipid molecules with hydrophobic 'tails' orientated inwards and hydrophilic 'heads' on the surface.
- Integral protein molecules embedded in this phospholipid layer form important transport channels.

Transport across membranes

- Small, non-polar molecules can cross cell surface membranes passively by diffusion.
- Water moves across membranes by osmosis, which is a special form of diffusion.
- Ions and charged molecules can cross cell surface membranes by facilitated diffusion or by active transport.
- Active transport requires energy, which is released by the molecule ATP when it is hydrolysed to ADP.
- Diffusion is a purely passive process of free movement of particles determined by their random movement from higher to lower concentrations. Facilitated diffusion is also a passive process but involves protein channels in the membrane opening to allow the unrestricted flow of some particles.
- Larger particles or vesicles containing highly active substances are transported across membranes by mass transport known as cytosis.

Osmosis in plant cells

- Water entering or leaving plant cells causes different effects as they are surrounded by cellulose cell walls, which have only limited elasticity.
- Water tends to enter plant cells by osmosis because of the concentration of solutes in the cytoplasm (osmotic potential).
- As water enters the plant cell, turgor pressure builds up inside until the net tendency for more water to enter (water potential) becomes zero.
- The relationship between these pressures is shown by the equation:
  water potential = turgor pressure + osmotic potential
  where all pressures are measured in kilopascals (kPa).

Practice questions

1 Cholesterol molecules in the phospholipid bilayer increase the flexibility of the cell surface membrane. The main reason for this is because:

A cholesterol molecules carry a negative charge

B cholesterol molecules disturb the tightly packed phospholipids

C cholesterol molecules penetrate all the way through the membrane

D cholesterol molecules form additional pores in the membrane *(1)*

2 The formation of ATP from ADP + P_i is:

A a condensation reaction

B an oxidation reaction

C a reduction reaction

D a hydrolysis reaction

3 Explain how very large molecules such as proteins in solution can be taken across the cell surface membrane into a cell. *(4)*

Tip

Question 3 is a very straightforward question asking you to recall accurately some basic specification content (AO1). However, it is a good exercise in writing an accurate description to gain all the marks available – something that will be vital if you are to achieve higher grades.

Tip

Questions 1 and 2 are simple recall questions (AO1). There will be several of these in a question paper. Do think carefully before selecting your answer. If you are not sure, at least try to eliminate the possible answers that you know are wrong before selecting an answer. There will be clear instructions on how to correct your choice if you change your mind but, above all, do not select two possible answers, as this is always marked wrong.

4 The diagram shows a typical plant cell that has been immersed in a concentrated glucose solution for several hours.

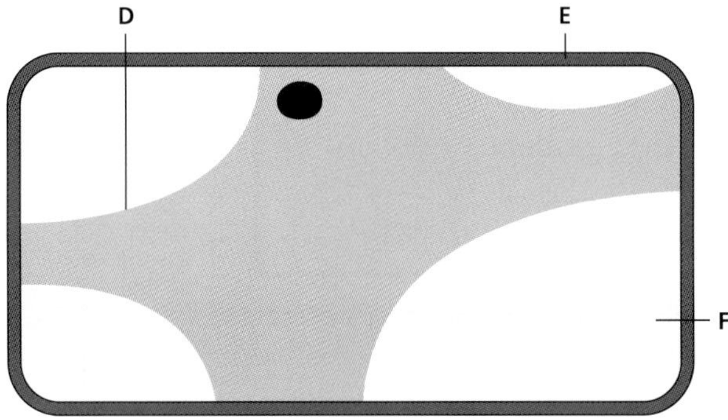

a) Name the parts of the cell labelled D and E. *(2)*

b) Name the substance present in the space labelled F. *(1)*

c) Explain why a plant with many cells in the condition shown in the diagram will begin to wilt. *(4)*

Tip

Question 4 is another example of AO1 but with the need to show you understand the principles involved. Part (b) often catches students out.

5 Use your knowledge of the fluid mosaic model of cell surface membrane structure to explain the following observations.

a) When extracting proteins from a cell membrane, one group of proteins was shown to be easily extracted but a second group was much more difficult to extract. *(3)*

b) Analysis of the total phospholipid content of a single cell membrane showed that there was much more than required for a single layer surrounding the cell but less than that required to form a complete double layer. *(3)*

Tip

Question 5 is a typical question that asks you to apply your knowledge (AO2). Although the answers are covered in this book it would be an application question, as the specification only refers to the actual structure, so this is actually asking you to apply your knowledge of the structure to these observations.

Tip

Question 6 is an application question (AO2) where you are asked to use your knowledge of the water potential equation to perform the calculation. It is important to check for simple arithmetical errors and to set out your calculations clearly. If you simply write down an answer without clear working, one slip will lose you all of the marks.

6 A small cylinder of plant tissue is placed in a sodium chloride solution.

a) If the plant cells have a turgor pressure of +250 kPa and an osmotic potential of −650 kPa, calculate their water potential if placed in a sodium chloride solution of osmotic potential −1245 kPa. *(4)*

b) Explain why a phospholipid bilayer will inhibit the passage of water molecules, yet they are able to move freely across the cell surface membrane. *(3)*

Tip

Question 7 is a more difficult question as it asks you to do several things. Calculating rates from a graph is a common type of question, which you should be comfortable with, but remember to take the values from the graph as accurately as the printed illustration will allow. Linking ATP production to active transport is an obvious AO2 application question, which can rely on information from several parts of the specification (synoptic).

7 The uptake of K^+ ions by barley roots was investigated by placing fresh root sections in a solution containing radioactively labelled K^+ ions. Samples of roots were then taken out of the solution over a period of 12 hours. The concentration of K^+ ions in each sample was then determined by measuring the amount of radioactivity they contained. This investigation was then repeated with potassium cyanide added to the K^+ ion solution. Cyanide ions inhibit an enzyme in mitochondria called cytochrome c oxidase, which prevents them from carrying out their main function. The results of this investigation are shown in the graph.

a) Calculate the rate of uptake of K^+ ions in both solutions between 3 and 12 hours. *(3)*

b) Explain the difference in the rate of K^+ ion uptake by the roots in the different solutions. *(3)*

c) Explain the difference between the K^+ ion concentration found in the roots placed in the cyanide-containing solution, after 3 hours and 12 hours. *(2)*

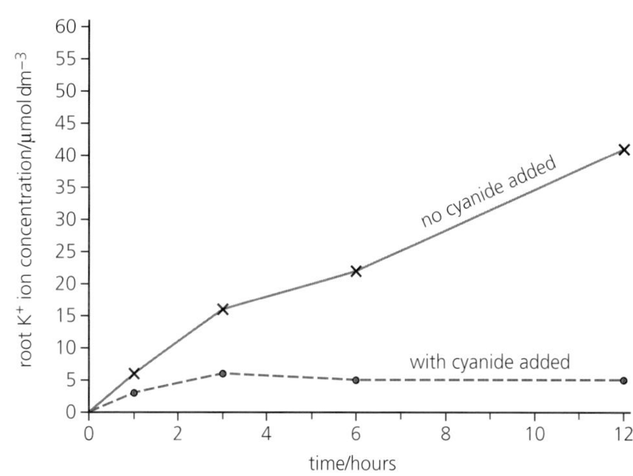

8 A student investigated the effect of temperature on beetroot cell membranes. She cut a cylinder of beetroot, washed it in distilled water and blotted it carefully. She then placed the cylinder in a water bath at 70 °C for 1 minute. Then she took the cylinder out of the water bath and placed it in 15 cm^3 of distilled water in a test tube at 25 °C for 15 minutes. After this, she removed the cylinder.

She then measured the amount of red coloured pigment in the distilled water using a colorimeter. The colorimeter was set to read absorbance using a blue filter.

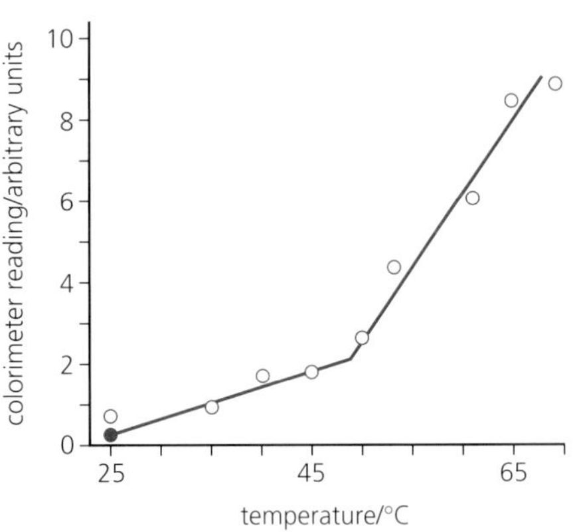

She then repeated the procedure nine times, using identical cylinders from the same beetroot with the temperature of treatment being reduced by 5 °C each time. The results of this investigation are shown in the graph.

a) Explain why a blue coloured filter would be used in the colorimeter to measure the absorbance in this investigation. *(2)*

b) Explain how the temperature treatment of each cylinder could be changed to give more reliable data. *(2)*

★**c)** The student concluded that the results of this investigation 'showed that the proteins in the beetroot membranes denatured above 50 °C'. Discuss the validity of this conclusion. *(4)*

Tip

Question 8 illustrates two important principles. You must understand the science behind the core practicals, not just regard them as a recipe. Secondly this question is a part of AO3, which asks you to be able to suggest amendments to experimental design and make judgements about exactly what conclusions can (and cannot) be drawn from experimental data.

Stretch and challenge

9 Fish are aquatic animals that can be found living in a wide range of habitats, from freshwater streams containing almost no ions to seawater containing high concentrations of ions, especially Na^+ and Cl^-. Many fish have impermeable skins with scales but all have gills, which means that a very large surface area is in contact with the water and separated from it by thin cell surface membranes.

a) Use your knowledge of membranes and transport to explain the problems faced by fish living:

i) in freshwater

ii) in seawater.

b) Consider ways in which these fish might overcome the problems they face. Begin by thinking of possible ideas yourself and then research the actual physiology of some fish. You may come across remarkable examples such as salmon or eels, which spend much of their lives in the open ocean but return to freshwater rivers to breed.

10 Gas exchange and transport

Prior knowledge

In this chapter you will need to recall that:

- → living organisms exist in a wide range of sizes from minute unicellular forms to very large mammals
- → gas exchange occurs mainly by diffusion
- → plants have much lower metabolic rates and therefore lower rates of gas exchange
- → living organisms show adaptations for gas exchange depending upon their size and environment
- → gas exchange surfaces need to have a large surface area and thin membranes
- → larger organisms need to couple their gas exchange surfaces to a transport system
- → mammals use haemoglobin in their bloodstream to transport oxygen
- → haemoglobin is contained within red blood cells
- → the gas exchange surfaces in fish are called gills, and in mammals, lungs
- → most gas exchange in plants takes place through stomata in leaves.

Test yourself on prior knowledge

1 Explain why gas exchange surfaces need to have thin membranes.

2 Why do some animals have pigments such as haemoglobin in their blood?

3 State the correct name for a red blood cell.

4 Explain why plants have lower metabolic rates than animals.

5 Most plants close many of their stomata at night. Explain why.

6 State which gas is likely to diffuse out of leaves at night.

7 Explain why most stomata are usually found on the under-surfaces of leaves.

8 Describe where, in an active mammal, oxygen is most likely to pass from the blood into the tissues.

9 State which of the following contains most oxygen per cm^3 at the same temperature and pressure:

A water

B air

Size and surface area

The size and shape of an organism influence its method of gas exchange. The amount of gas an organism needs to exchange is largely proportional to its volume (the bulk of respiring cells), but the amount of exchange that can occur is proportional to its surface area over which diffusion takes place. This relationship is very important as it determines important features of living things.

Consider what happens as a cell increases in size. If we take the simple example of a cell being cube-shaped, as shown in Figure 10.1, with a side of length, l, then its volume is l^3 and its surface area is $6 \times l^2$. This is really important mathematically because as l increases, the volume increases as l^3 and the surface area increases as l^2. In terms of gas exchange, the volume (demand) increases a lot more than the surface area (supply). As a result it does not take much of an increase in size before this fact becomes a limiting factor (it limits further increases in size).

In an organism that consists of a single small cell, the surface area is large in relation to the amount of cytoplasm it contains. Here, the surface of the cell is sufficient for efficient gas exchange because the sites where respiration occurs in the cytoplasm are never very far from the surface of the cell. The **surface-area-to-volume ratio** is very high for single-celled organisms, and this makes for efficient gas exchange.

The geometric 'organisms' in Figure 10.1 illustrate how the surface-area-to-volume ratio changes as the size of an organism increases. Increasing size lowers the surface area per unit of volume of the whole structure – that is, the larger the object, the smaller its surface-area-to-volume ratio.

This is another example of how ratios can be very useful when comparing different organisms. For example, a blue whale is about 30 m long and weighs about 140 tonnes, so it would be rather pointless to say that it is bigger than a dormouse, which is about 70 mm long without its tail and weighs about 17 g. However, a dormouse has a surface-area-to-volume ratio over 4 times greater than that of the blue whale. This tells us many things about the different problems faced by these animals.

It is obviously advantageous for single cells to remain small, but if organisms are to exploit different habitats then they need to increase in size and show cell specialisation to increase efficiency. Therefore multicellular organisms need special adaptations to overcome the limitations of larger size and so we see a wide range of respiratory surfaces.

One way of increasing surface area is to change shape. A thin and flat shape – such as that of the leaves of a plant, the fronds of seaweed and the body of a flatworm – has a larger surface-area-to-volume ratio and therefore gas exchange is extremely efficient (Figure 10.2).

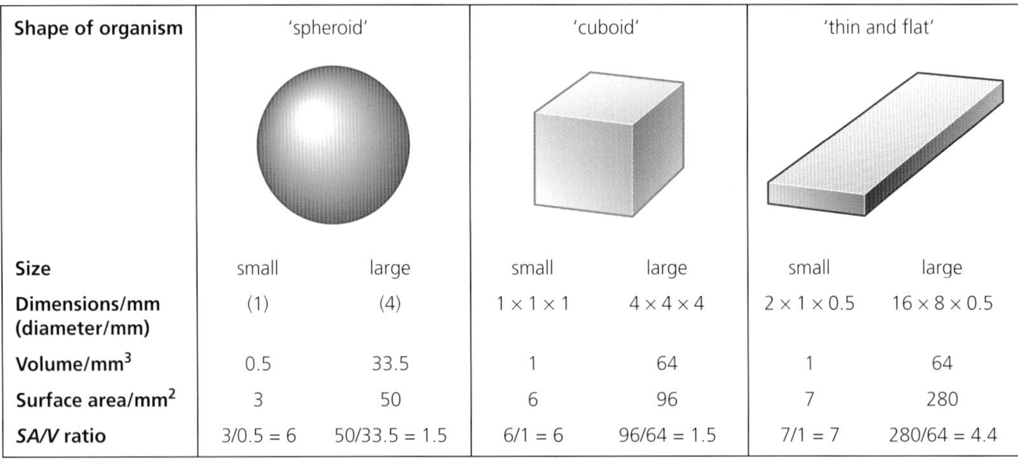

Shape of organism	'spheroid'		'cuboid'		'thin and flat'	
Size	small	large	small	large	small	large
Dimensions/mm (diameter/mm)	(1)	(4)	1 × 1 × 1	4 × 4 × 4	2 × 1 × 0.5	16 × 8 × 0.5
Volume/mm^3	0.5	33.5	1	64	1	64
Surface area/mm^2	3	50	6	96	7	280
***SA/V* ratio**	3/0.5 = 6	50/33.5 = 1.5	6/1 = 6	96/64 = 1.5	7/1 = 7	280/64 = 4.4

Figure 10.1 Size, shape and surface-area-to-volume ratios

Amoeba, a large, single-celled protoctist living in pond water and feeding on the tiny protoctists around it. Food is taken into food vacuoles. Gases are exchanged over the whole body surface.

Size = about 400 μm

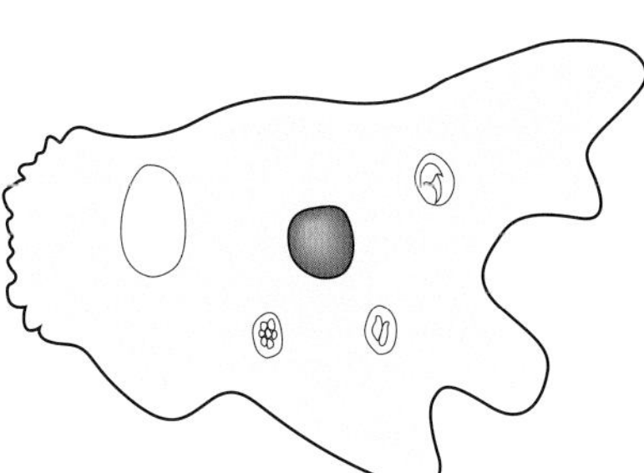

Ulva, the sea lettuce, an anchored or free-floating seaweed. It floats near the surface of water and photosynthesises in the light. Gases are exchanged over the whole body surface.

Size = about 5–15 cm long, about 30–35 μm thick

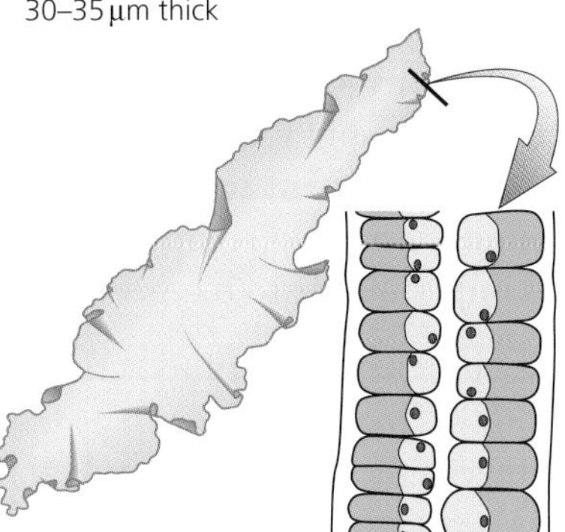

Dugesia tigrina, a free-living flatworm found in ponds under stones or leaves or gliding over the mud. It feeds on smaller animals and fish eggs. It is a very thin animal that exchanges gases over the whole body surface.

Size = about 20 mm

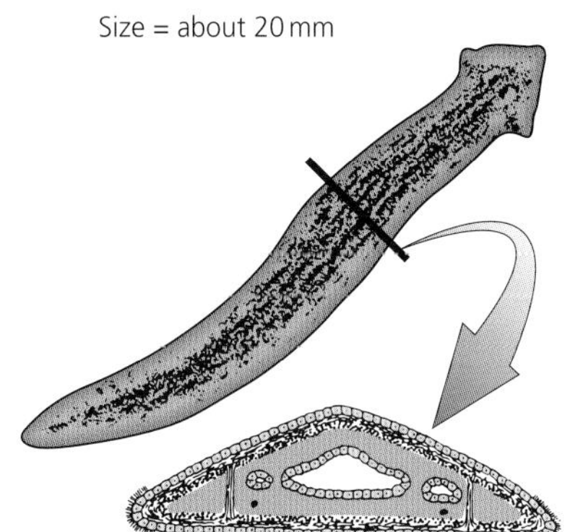

Figure 10.2 Organisms in which gas exchange takes place through their external surface

There are many different ways of adapting respiratory surfaces to provide sufficient diffusion to meet the needs of the organism, but all follow the same pattern:

- The surfaces have a large area.
- The surfaces have thin membranes.
- There must be some means of maintaining a diffusion gradient across the membranes.
- Where demands are high then the surfaces must be linked to a transport system.

Test yourself

1 Name **two** ways in which organisms can increase their surface area.

2 Copy and complete the following table for cells that are perfect spheres. (Volume (V) = (4/3) πr^3; surface area (SA) = $4\pi r^2$)

Radius/mm	Surface area/mm^2	Volume/mm^3	*SA:V* ratio
1	12.57	4.19	3
2			
3			
4			

3 State the mathematical reason for the trend in *SA:V* ratio shown in the table in Question 2.

4 Explain why thin membranes and a high diffusion gradient are essential features of a respiratory surface.

Gas exchange

Gaseous exchange in insects

Insects are an amazing group of animals. There are more species of insect, and they are more numerous, than any other specialised multicellular group. There are many reasons for their success, but one major factor is that they possess a tough external **exoskeleton**. This has been adapted for rapid flight as well as agile movement on land. The insect exoskeleton is made up of **chitin**, which is a specialised polysaccharide usually combined with other compounds to make a composite material of great strength and flexibility. However, chitin is impermeable to oxygen, and so forms a barrier to gas exchange.

Key term

Tracheae A series of fine tubes that carry gases to and from active organs in the body of an insect.

In order to provide sufficient oxygen to active tissues such as flight muscles, insects have a branching network of fine tubes known as **tracheae**. Tracheae are supported by rings of chitin, which prevent them collapsing when the pressure changes yet still allow them to be flexible. This is exactly the same function as rings of cartilage in the mammalian trachea (and the strengthening rings in a vacuum cleaner hose).

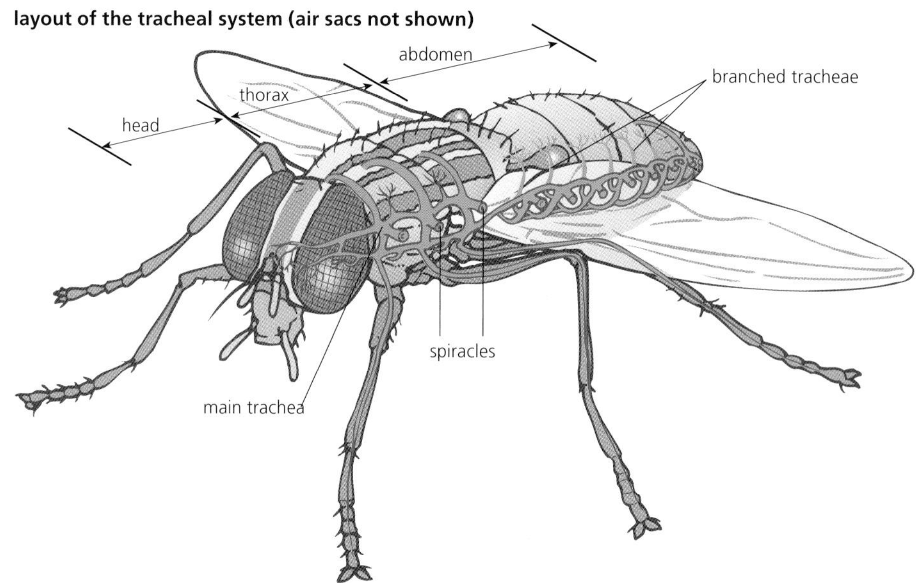

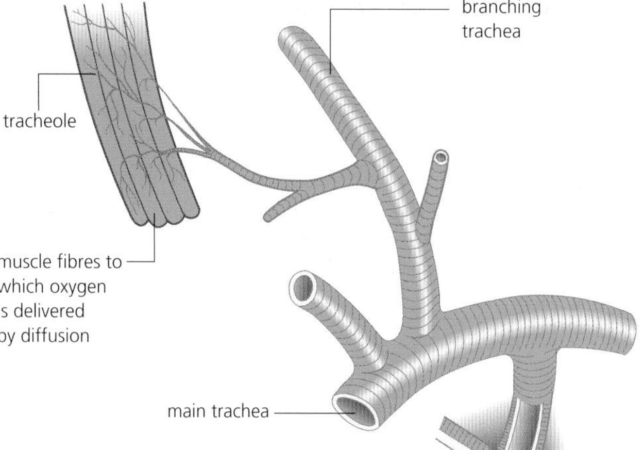

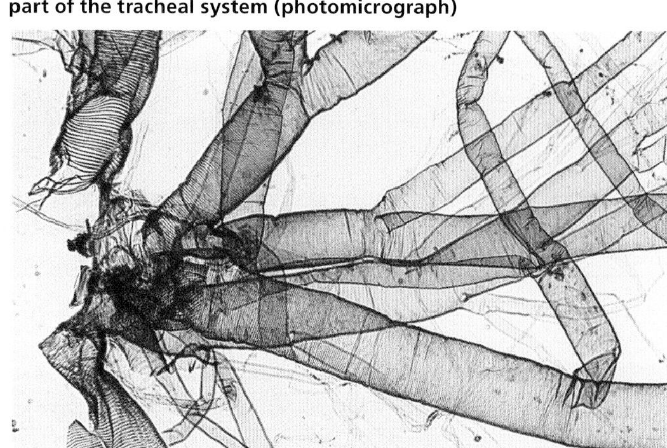

Figure 10.3 The tracheal system of a typical insect

Larger tracheae form the main pathway along the length of the insect body with much smaller branches called **tracheoles** leading directly into the tissues. Tracheae are connected to the outside atmosphere by valves called **spiracles**, which can often be seen as a series of eight small holes on each side of the abdominal segments and two more pairs on the thorax. Spiracles can be opened and closed by means of small muscles. They often have fine hairs, which prevent the entry of small particles that could block the tracheoles.

Key term

Spiracles Valves found on the thorax and abdomen of insects through which gaseous exchange takes place.

Gas exchange along the tracheae is largely brought about by **diffusion**. Tracheoles, ending in the tissues, have very thin walls to allow diffusion into and out of the cells. Remember that diffusion relies on concentration gradients so each gas must be considered separately. Hence, high levels of carbon dioxide produced by active tissues mean that there will be a large gradient between the tracheoles and the very low levels of carbon dioxide in the external atmosphere. Exactly the opposite applies for oxygen, so the two gases will move in different directions down their respective concentration gradients.

Simple diffusion along the tubes can be insufficient to supply all the needs of the insect tissues and it is thought that movements of the abdomen, especially during flight, compress and expand the tubes, flushing air through them much faster. Opening and closing of certain spiracles also helps to ensure a flow of fresh air through the main tracheae. Many insects are highly adapted to life in very dry environments. The presence of many fine tubes leading to the atmosphere will obviously be a potential source of water loss. Closing spiracles at times when gas exchange is slow helps to conserve water.

Core practical 7

Dissect an insect to show the structure of the gas exchange system

Ethical issues

All dissections raise ethical issues. At the very least it would be expected that any biologist would ensure that any animal was treated with due care and respect.

The law places very strict guidelines on the use of higher animals in any investigation but this does not apply to invertebrates. There is considerable debate on why this should be the case and you need to research the different sides of the debate.

Most of all you will be expected to understand what is meant by an ethical issue. The main point to grasp here is that, although at the centre of the debate might be the question of what is the right thing to do, different people will hold perfectly valid but opposing ethical viewpoints.

To take two extremes, you might wish to argue that killing any living thing is wrong. On the other hand you might wish to argue that killing any other living thing can be justified as long as it is not a human.

Obviously both opinions can have a reasoned argument but both are full of complications. Does not killing any living thing include all plants or harmful insects? Does killing any other living thing apart from humans mean we are free to slaughter anything we choose, including threatened species, and who decides where we draw the line? So many ethical issues are very difficult to resolve.

So, you are free to take your own ethical stand but you will be expected to show that you have reasoned arguments for doing so and that you understand the reasoning of others who may take a different view.

Carrying out the investigation

Risk assessment: In all dissections, hygiene is important to minimise any risk of infection. Animal materials must be obtained from a biological supplier or premises licenced with the local authority. Gloves are not necessary, but hands should be washed thoroughly after the activity. Note: some people may be allergic to insect cuticle. Safe use of dissection instruments will be demonstrated by your teacher. Any remains from the dissection should be disposed of according to the instructions you are given by your teacher.

Equipment: The dissection can be carried out successfully with a minimum of equipment, but is easier with some simple options:

- a pair of the smallest, sharpest dissection scissors available
- a pair of fine forceps (tweezers)
- a dissection dish
- microscope slides and cover slips
- light microscope + a binocular microscope (useful but not essential)
- a hand lens or magnifying glass
- preserved locust or similar insect (the larger the better)

It is important for this dissection to secure the insect carefully. A classic dissection dish has a thick layer of heavy wax in the bottom to facilitate this. A simple economical alternative is to use a large ice-cream container. The walls of this need to be trimmed to about 7–8 cm high. In the bottom of this use waterproof glue to stick a piece of polystyrene or the flower arranging material 'oasis', about 1 cm thick. This will form a platform for the dissection and allow the insect to be covered with water. You may need to trim the sides of the container further to ensure that, when covered with water, the dissection is easy to access.

Dead houseflies or blowflies can be used but their scale makes the dissection more difficult.

1. Hold the insect with the forceps and examine it carefully using a hand lens. Identify the following:
   a) the three main body sections – head, thorax and abdomen
   b) spiracles – these vary slightly in different insects but are often small ovals on the rear of most abdominal segments. Thoracic spiracles are more difficult to identify; in the locust they are found close to where the legs join the abdomen

   Whilst not part of the respiratory system, other features such as compound eyes and the mouthparts are often well worth a close examination.
2. Secure the insect to the bottom of the dissecting dish using plain straight pins with a row of visible spiracles pointing upwards. Use pins to fix the wings upwards so that the side of the abdomen is not covered (Figure 10.4). Then add just enough water to cover it.

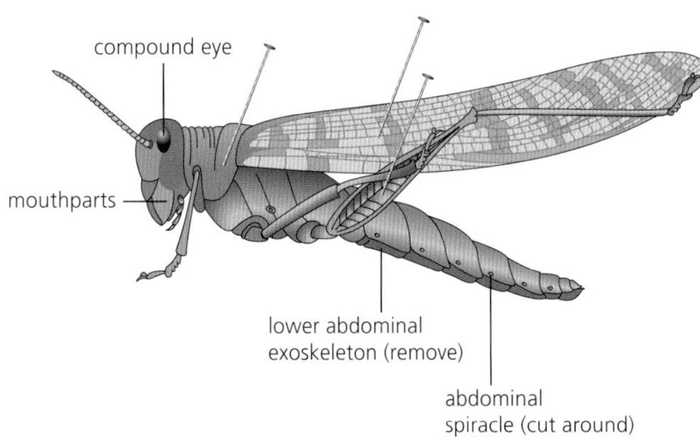

Figure 10.4 Locust dissection

3. Hold the insect firmly with the forceps and cut through the exoskeleton around one spiracle.
4. Use the forceps to take hold of the spiracle and the small piece of exoskeleton and pull gently to remove it from the abdomen. TAKE CARE not to pull too hard. If the spiracle and a small piece of underlying tissue do not come away easily then use the scissors to cut around it to free it.
5. Mount the spiracle and the tissue on a microscope slide with a drop of water and add a cover slip. Take care to hold the cover slip with one edge against the water drop and lower slowly to avoid trapping air bubbles.
6. Examine the slide carefully under medium power of the microscope and look for tracheae with rings of chitin and any visible features of the spiracle to add to your previous observations. The photomicrograph in Figure 10.3 will help you to identify tracheae.
7. Select a suitable part of your slide and draw a simple illustration of what you see. Use single clear, sharp, pencil lines without shading. Try to ensure that the proportions of your drawing are correct and show important features rather than attempting to draw an artistic 'picture'. Add a scale to your drawing to show the approximate size of the tubes.
8. Finally, turn the insect over on its back and relocate it with pins. You may need to cut off the wings to do this. Insert the scissors under one side of the last abdominal segment. Keep the points of the scissors pointing upwards towards you to avoid cutting into the tissues beneath. Cut the exoskeleton in a line down one side toward the head. Repeat this on the other side of the abdomen so that you can carefully remove a whole strip of the exoskeleton under the abdomen.
9. You will now see lots of white fat surrounding the gut along with other organs. Do not disturb this too much but use a magnifying glass to try to identify the tracheal network. It is a double line of fine empty tubes which, unlike other organs, look shiny because they contain air. Compare the pattern of these tubes with the photomicrograph in Figure 10.3.

Test yourself

5. Name the valves linking the tracheae to the atmosphere.
6. Name the structures that prevent tracheae collapsing when the pressure inside is reduced.
7. State **two** ways in which insects can increase the rate of gas exchange through tracheae.
8. The largest insects in the world are only about 10 cm long. What features of their gas exchange system may limit their overall size?

Gaseous exchange in a bony fish

Fish and other aquatic organisms face different problems of gas exchange from those using air. First of all, water contains about 25 times less oxygen by volume than air and this gets less the warmer the water becomes. Secondly water is almost 800 times denser than air, so is much more difficult to move around. Despite this, highly mobile fish such as trout and salmon have adaptations that enable them to extract enough oxygen from water in order to sustain a high metabolic rate.

Fish obtain oxygen from water by means of **internal gills**. The structure of the gills of a bony fish such as a herring is shown in Figures 10.5 and 10.6. You can see that bony fish have four pairs of gills, supported by a bony arch. Each gill has two rows of **gill filaments** arranged in a V-shape. Filaments are very thin structures carrying rows of thin-walled **gill plates** on both surfaces. A tough muscular flap of skin, the operculum, protects the gills and is partly responsible for maintaining a continuous flow of water over them. The space inside the mouth containing the gills is called the buccal cavity.

Key terms

Operculum A tough muscular flap covering the gills of bony fish.

Buccal cavity The space inside the mouth of fish and other animals.

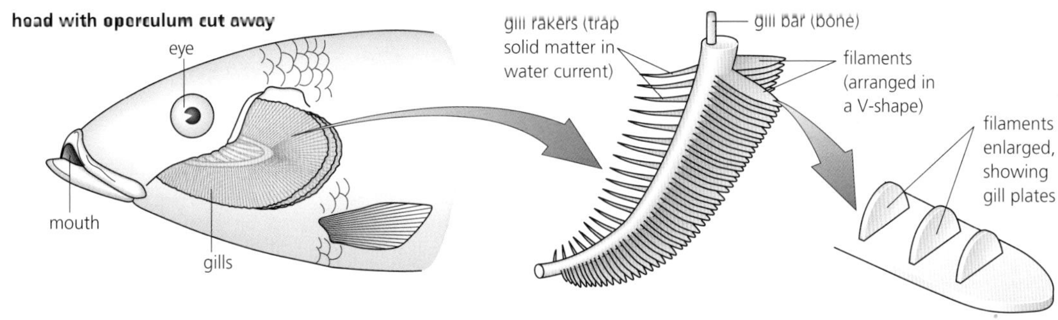

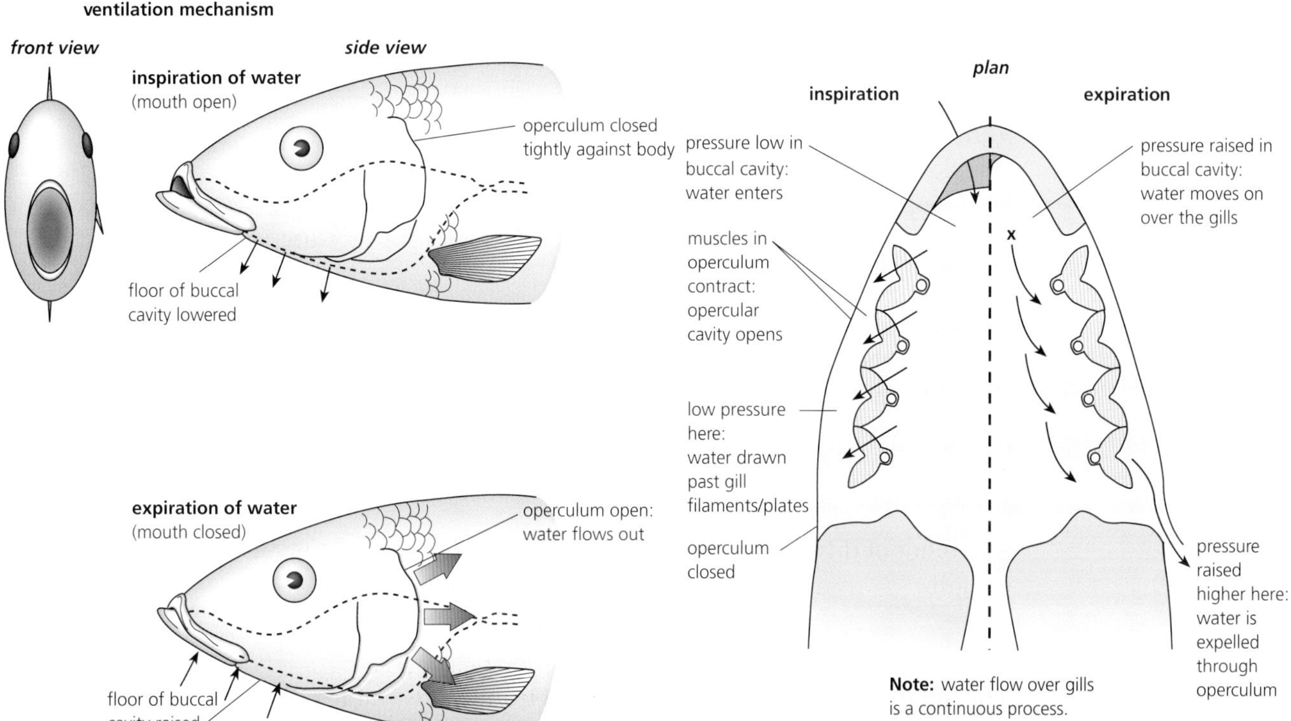

Figure 10.5 The structure of the mouth, pharynx and gill region of a bony fish and its ventilation mechanism

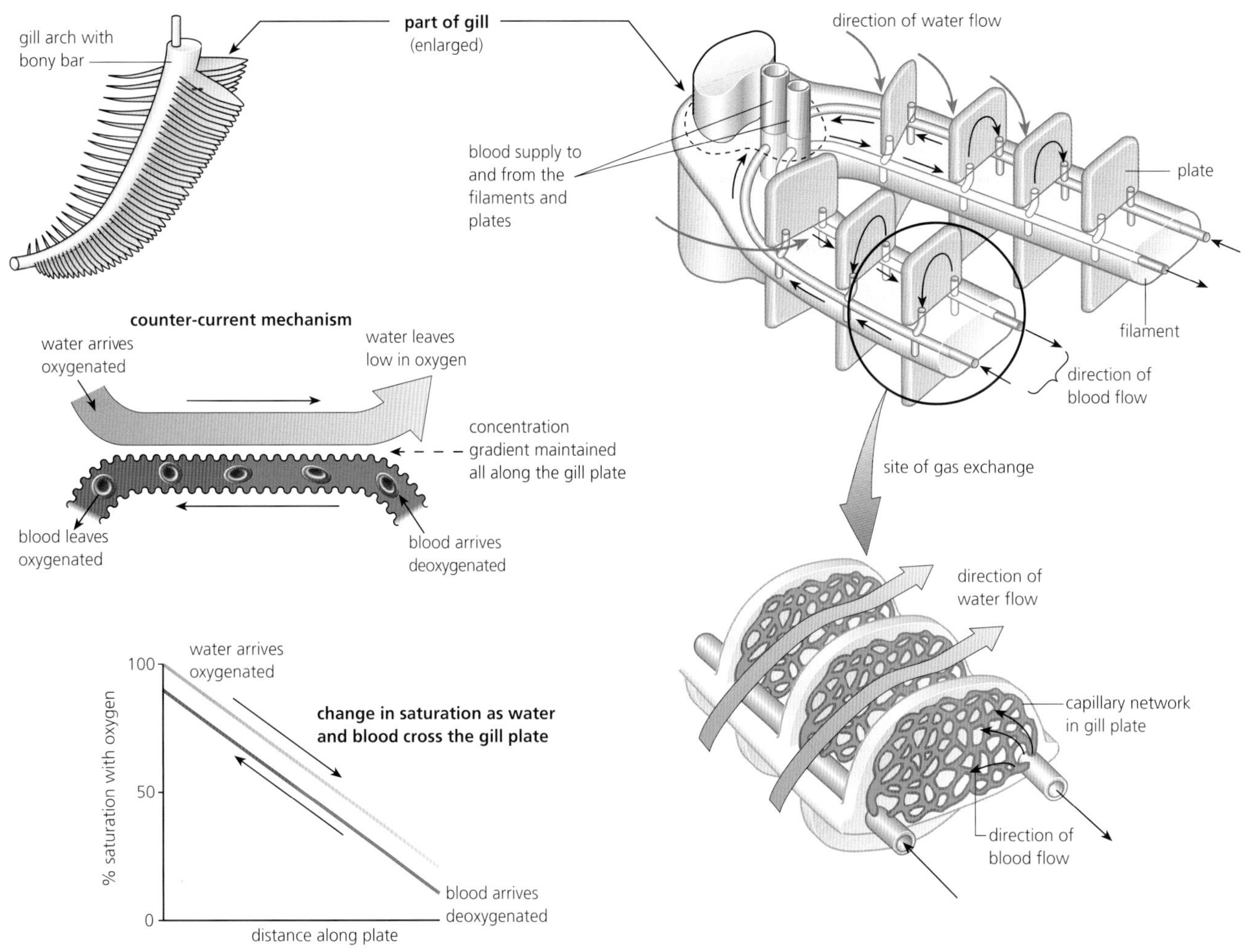

Figure 10.6 Gill structure of a bony fish and gas exchange by counter-current mechanism

Ventilation of the gills

The flow of water across the gills is maintained by changes of water pressure. As the mouth opens, the floor of the buccal cavity is lowered and the operculum is closed tight against the body. This increase in volume decreases the pressure, compared with the outside, so water flows in.

The contracting muscles in the operculum cause it to bulge outwards, increasing the volume of the opercular cavity. This decreases the pressure in this area and water flows across the gills. To keep up this flow, the mouth closes and the floor of the buccal cavity is raised, forcing more water across the gills. Finally this increases the pressure behind the operculum until it exceeds that of the water outside, forcing the operculum to open and allowing water to flow out.

The result of this opening and closing of the mouth is a continuous flow of water across the gills.

> **Key term**
>
> **Haemoglobin** A red iron-containing protein found in red blood cells, which combines with oxygen.

Gaseous exchange in the gills

The gill filaments and gill plates have very thin walls and together they form a very large surface area. The capillaries themselves have walls that are only one-cell thick and carry blood with large numbers of red cells. These cells contain **haemoglobin**, which enables the blood to carry oxygen very efficiently. Further details of this process are discussed later in this chapter.

As water passes over the gills, it flows in the opposite direction to the blood. This is an example of a **counter-current mechanism**, which allows the fish to remove 80–90 per cent of the dissolved oxygen from the water. The principle of the counter-current mechanism is that it maintains a concentration gradient along the whole length of the blood–water boundary. If blood and water flowed in the same direction they would quickly reach the same concentration and therefore only 50 percent of the available oxygen would be transferred. (We will meet this idea again later in the book when we consider kidney function.)

> **Key term**
>
> **Counter-current mechanism** An arrangement where fluids are caused to flow close to each other in opposite directions to maximise exchange between them.

Test yourself

9 Describe the features of the gills that give them a large surface area.

10 Explain how the pressure of water in the buccal cavity is increased to force it across the gills.

11 State how much oxygen by volume would be contained in 1 cm^3 of pure water under standard conditions.

12 State the advantage of the counter-current flow of water and blood in the gills.

> **Tip**
>
> It is useful to bear in mind different applications of the same principle, such as the counter-current mechanism, as they can form the basis of synoptic questions.

Gaseous exchange in mammals

Almost all mammals are extremely active animals with a very high demand for oxygen. They maintain a constant body temperature, which is also a high energy-demand activity. The organs of gaseous exchange in mammals are the **lungs**. Lungs are extremely efficient. The structure of the human thorax, which houses the lungs, is shown in Figure 10.7.

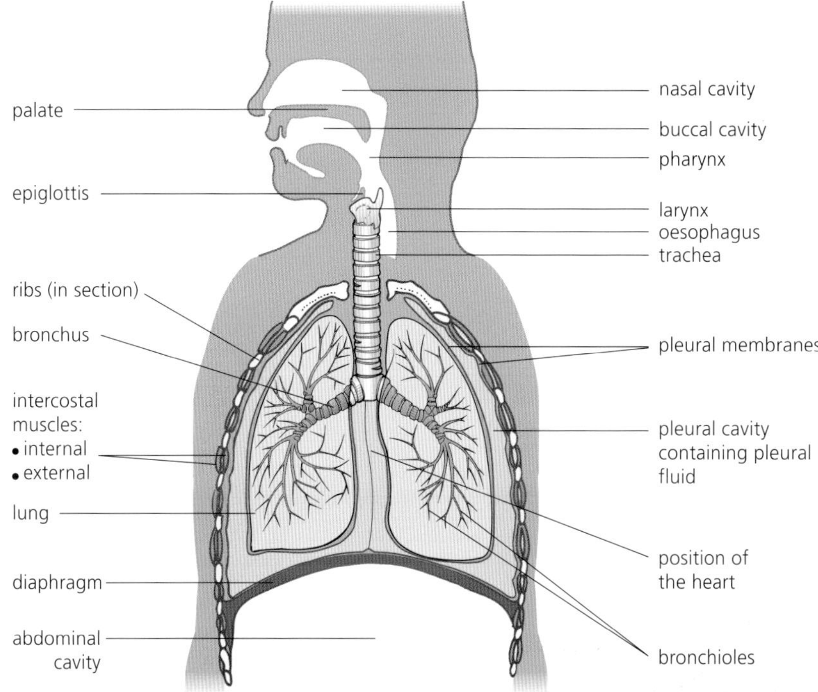

Figure 10.7 The structure of the human thorax

Key terms

Diaphragm A muscular sheet at the bottom of the thorax.

Pleural membranes Double membranes surrounding the lungs, which are lubricated with pleural fluid to prevent friction during breathing.

Alveoli Tiny air sacs within the lungs where gas exchange takes place.

Tip

Be careful to use accurate language when describing ventilation. It is the active movement of muscles that causes a change in lung volume, then the pressure changes and finally air flows in or out from high to low pressure. Be careful to keep to this sequence.

Lungs are housed in the **thorax**, an air-tight chamber formed by the rib-cage and its muscles (**intercostal muscles**), with a domed floor, which is the **diaphragm**. The diaphragm is a sheet of muscle attached to the body wall at the base of the rib-cage, separating thorax from abdomen. The internal surfaces of the thorax are lined by the **pleural membranes**, which secrete and maintain the pleural fluid. Pleural fluid is a lubricating liquid derived from blood plasma that protects the lungs from friction during breathing movements.

The lungs connect with the pharynx at the rear of the mouth by the **trachea**. Air reaches the trachea from the mouth and nostrils, passing through the larynx ('voice box'). Entry into the larynx is via a slit-like opening, the glottis. Directly above this is a cartilaginous flap, the **epiglottis**. Glottis and epiglottis work to prevent the entry of food into the trachea. The trachea initially runs beside the oesophagus (food pipe). Incomplete rings of cartilage in the trachea wall prevent collapse under pressure from a large bolus (ball of food) passing down the oesophagus.

The trachea then divides into two **bronchi**, one to each lung. Within the lungs the bronchi divide into smaller **bronchioles**. The finest bronchioles end in air sacs (**alveoli**). The walls of bronchi and larger bronchioles contain smooth muscle, and are also supported by rings or tiny plates of cartilage, preventing collapse that might be triggered by the sudden reduction in pressure that occurs with powerful inspirations of air.

Ventilation of the lungs

Air is drawn into the alveoli when the air pressure in the lungs is lower than atmospheric pressure, and it is forced out when pressure is higher than atmospheric pressure. Since the thorax is an air-tight chamber, pressure changes in the lungs occur when the volume of the thorax changes. The ventilation mechanism of the lungs is shown in Figure 10.8.

inspiration:
- external intercostal muscles contract – ribs move upwards and outwards, and the diaphragm down
- diaphragm muscles contract

air in

expiration:
- external intercostal muscles relax – ribs move downwards and inwards, and the diaphragm up
- diaphragm muscles relax

air out

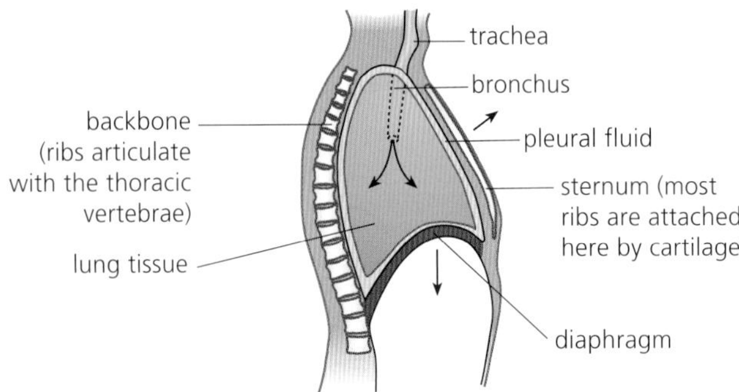

volume of the thorax (and therefore of the lungs) increases; pressure is reduced below atmospheric pressure and air flows in

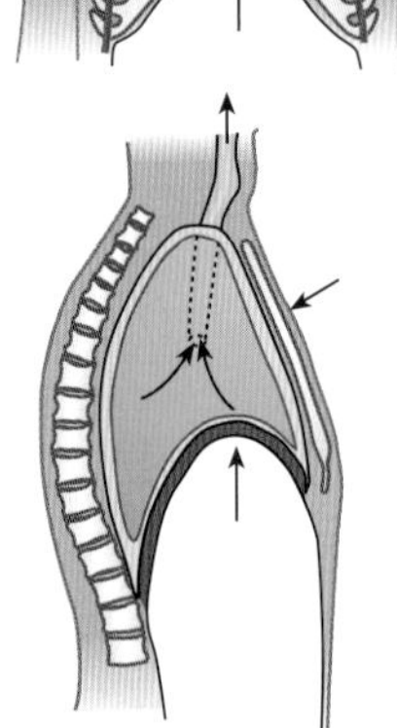

volume of the thorax (and therefore of the lungs) decreases; pressure is increased above atmospheric pressure and air flows out

Figure 10.8 The ventilation mechanism of human lungs

Alveolar structure and gas exchange

There are some 700 million alveoli present in a pair of human lungs, providing a surface area of about 70 m^2. This is an area 30–40 times greater than that of the body's external skin. The wall of an alveolus is made up of **squamous epithelium**, which has a single layer of cells about 0.1 μm thick. Lying very close is a network of capillaries whose walls are made up of a single layer of thin **endothelial** cells. This means the total thickness of the walls separating air and blood is only 4–5 μm. The capillaries are extremely narrow – just wide enough for red blood cells to squeeze through (Figure 10.9).

> **Key terms**
>
> **Squamous epithelium** A single layer of flattened cells forming an outer covering.
>
> **Endothelium** A single layer of cells forming an inner lining.

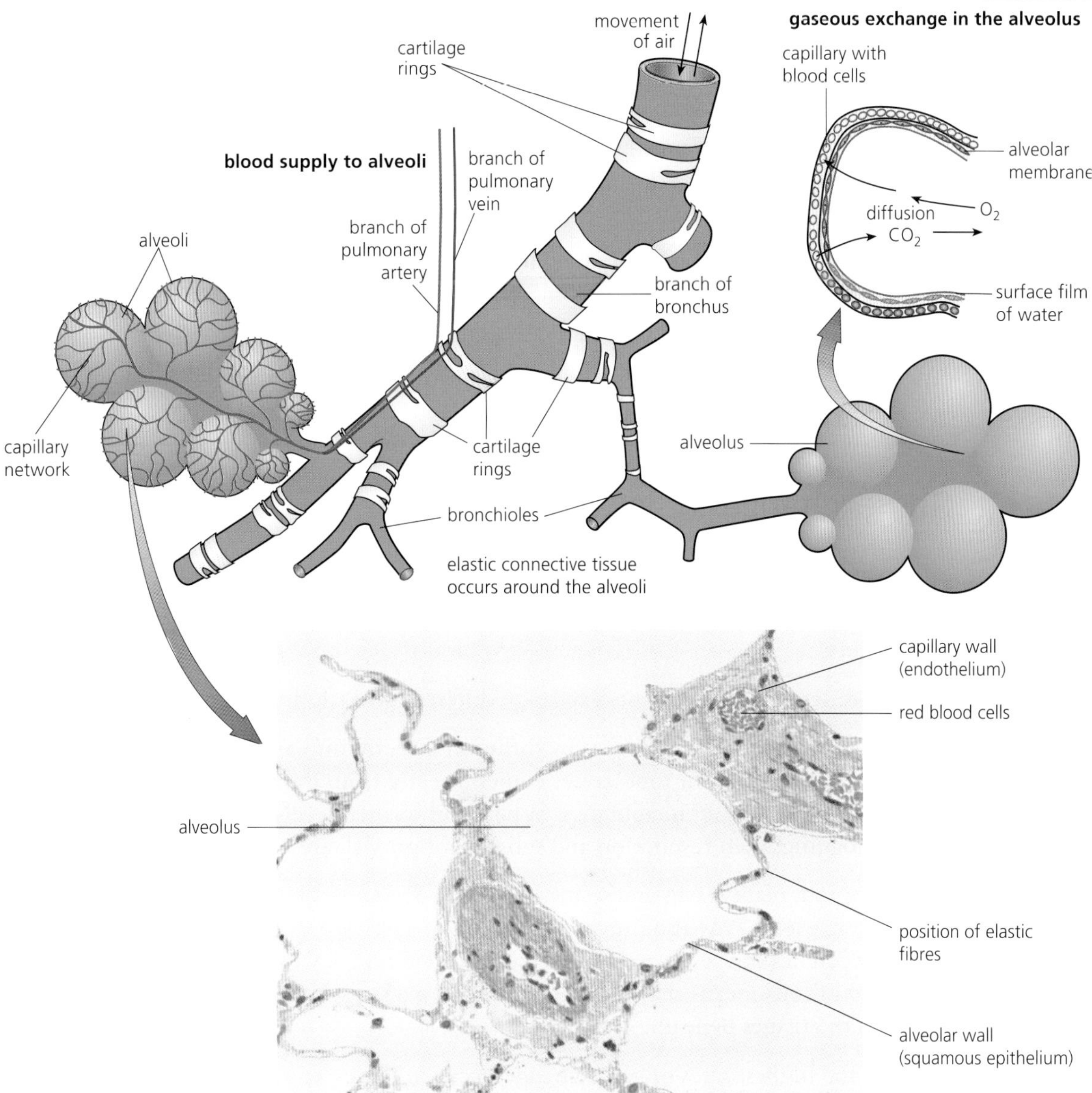

Figure 10.9 Blood supply and gaseous exchange in the alveolus

Blood arriving in the lungs is low in oxygen (it has a lower *partial pressure* of oxygen than the alveolar air, see Table 10.1) but high in carbon dioxide (it has a higher *partial pressure* of carbon dioxide than alveolar air). As blood flows past the alveoli, gaseous exchange occurs by diffusion. Oxygen dissolves in the surface film of water then diffuses across into the blood plasma and finally into the red blood cells. Here, it combines with haemoglobin to form oxyhaemoglobin. (We shall discuss the details of this process later in this chapter.) At the same time carbon dioxide diffuses from the blood into the alveolus.

Tip

It is important to remember that plants, like animals, need oxygen to carry out cellular respiration in order to form ATP at all times. Only when light is present do they photosynthesise. At this time the volume of oxygen given off by photosynthesis quickly exceeds that taken up by respiration and so there is a net diffusion of oxygen into the atmosphere. So gaseous exchange varies with the light available in any 24 hour period.

Table 10.1 The composition of air in the lungs

	Approximate percentage of each gas present/%		
	Inspired air	**Alveolar air**	**Expired air**
Oxygen	20	14	16
Carbon dioxide	0.04	5	4.0
Nitrogen	79	81	79
Water vapour	variable	saturated	saturated

Test yourself

13 Explain how food is prevented from entering the trachea.

14 Name the **two** sets of muscles that are used to increase the volume of the thorax during inspiration.

15 Suggest why a wound penetrating the rib cage would cause the lungs to collapse.

16 If atmospheric pressure at sea level is 102 kPa and 19% of the air is oxygen, what will be the partial pressure of oxygen at sea level?

17 Name the **two** tissues that a molecule of oxygen must cross to pass from an alveolus to the inside of a capillary.

Gas exchange in flowering plants

In contrast to most animals, plants have low metabolic rates and much lower rates of gaseous exchange. In consequence they do not show such advanced adaptations. The main reasons for this are that plants do not move and do not maintain a high body temperature.

Another difference is that plants exchange different gases at different times of day.

Figure 10.10 Lenticels in a woody stem

Most gaseous exchange in plants is by diffusion directly into and out of the tissues. Oxygen for respiration in root tissues comes directly from the soil through the permeable cell walls and membranes. Where soil oxygen levels are limited, for example by waterlogging, then respiration and subsequent growth are severely restricted.

Above ground, plant leaves and stems are often covered with cuticle or a bark to prevent water loss. This also prevents diffusion of gases. To overcome this, stems often have tiny patches of very loosely packed cells called **lenticels** (Figure 10.10). The loose packaging of cells means that there are many air spaces, which allow direct diffusion to and from the tissues beneath.

In plants the highest rates of gas exchange occur in leaves, to supply carbon dioxide for photosynthesis. The supply of water is also essential for this process, so leaves are adapted to prevent excessive water-loss and to allow rapid diffusion. Layers of waterproof cuticle cover the leaf but the epidermis of the underside of leaves usually contains many thousands of pores called **stomata** (singular stoma – Figure 10.11).

Key terms

Lenticels Areas of loosely packed cells forming pores on the surface of plant stems.

Stomata Pores on the leaf surface allowing diffusion of gases into and out of the leaf.

These pores are surrounded by a pair of bean-shaped **guard cells**, which can alter the size of the stoma by changes in their turgor pressure. When turgid, their curved shape means the stoma opens, and when they lose turgor (become flaccid) and straighten, the pore closes. This allows the leaf to maximise gas exchange in the light when photosynthesising, and to limit water loss when less gas exchange is needed in the dark.

Key term

Spongy mesophyll Loosely packed inner leaf tissue.

Carbon dioxide diffusing through open stomata enters the air spaces of the spongy mesophyll inside the leaf. From here it dissolves in the **water films** surrounding the spongy mesophyll cells and can then freely diffuse through the cell surface membrane into the photosynthesising tissues. Oxygen will diffuse outwards by the same route.

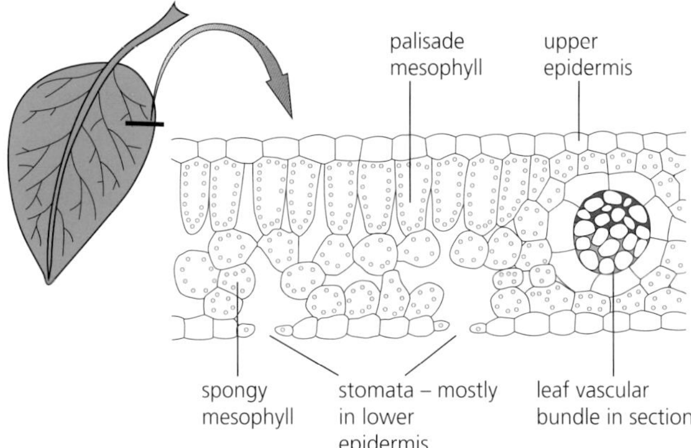

photomicrograph of lower surface of leaf – showing distribution of stomata among the epidermal cells (×100)

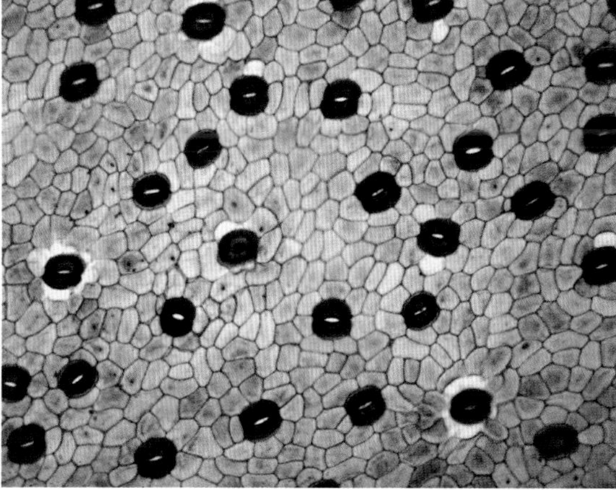

Figure 10.11 Distribution of stomata in a typical leaf

Test yourself

18 Suggest why gas exchange organs in plants are less specialised than in animals.

19 Name the actual gas exchange surface in a leaf.

20 State which gases will be exchanged in plant roots during daylight hours.

Transport of gases in the blood

You have seen that active animals need specialised organs to ensure that gas exchange is increased to meet their demands. However, once gas exchange has taken place it is vital that the oxygen is delivered and carbon dioxide removed from all of the tissues of the body in an equally efficient manner. This requires a specialised system of loading and unloading the gases in the blood and rapidly transporting the blood to all parts of the body. This section deals with gas transport by the blood. We shall look at the design of the circulatory system and other functions of the blood cells in the next chapter.

Key terms

Conjugated protein A protein that contains non-polypeptide chemical groups in its structure.

Erythrocytes Mammalian red blood cells.

Haemoglobin

Oxygen and carbon dioxide have only limited solubility in the liquid blood plasma, so a much more efficient mechanism is required for their transport. In many animals, including mammals and bony fish, the red pigment **haemoglobin** is used to increase the volume of oxygen carried by the blood. Haemoglobin is a **conjugated protein** made up of four interlocking sub-units. Each of these is composed of a large globular protein with an iron-containing **haem group** attached (Figure 10.12).

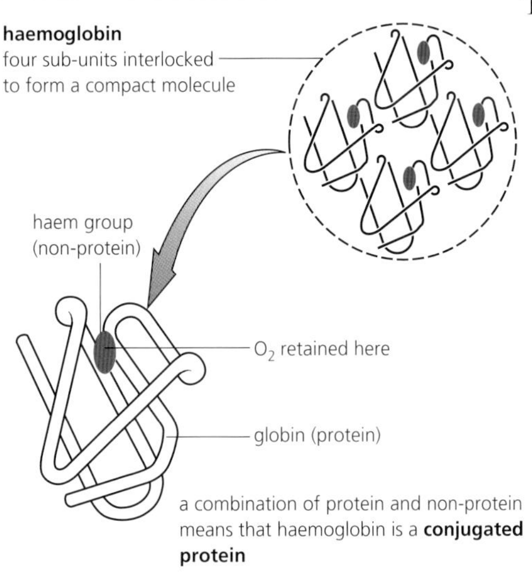

Figure 10.12 The structure of haemoglobin

The oxygen molecules are carried by haemoglobin attached to the haem groups. Therefore one haemoglobin molecule can carry four oxygen molecules to form **oxyhaemoglobin**.

$$\underset{\text{haemoglobin}}{Hb} + \underset{\text{oxygen}}{4O_2} \rightleftharpoons \underset{\text{oxyhaemoglobin}}{Hb(O_2)_4} + \underset{\text{hydrogen ions}}{H^+}$$

Haemoglobin is contained inside the red blood cells (**erythrocytes**), not in the blood plasma. Erythrocytes are very strange cells. They are constantly manufactured in the red bone marrow. Mammalian erythrocytes have no nucleus but their cytoplasm is rich in haemoglobin. They are biconcave disc-shaped and have typical cell surface membranes, which gives them a large, thin surface area ideal for transfer of gases by diffusion and the maximum volume of haemoglobin. (see Figure 11.2, Chapter 11). Blood gains its thick, red appearance because the erythrocytes are so numerous (about 5×10^6 per mm^3), which means that about one quarter of all the cells in our bodies are erythrocytes.

Partial pressures

Key term

Partial pressure (p) The pressure due to one gas in a mixture of gases. The total pressure of a mixture of gases is made of the sum of partial pressures due to each gas.

Air is a mixture of several different gases. The total pressure of the air is made up of the sum of the pressures of the individual gases. So, if atmospheric pressure is, say 100 kPa, this does not mean that all the gases within it are at a pressure of 100 kPa. To calculate the individual pressures of the gases in the mixture we simply use their relative abundance in the mixture. Therefore if air is 20 per cent oxygen its partial pressure would be 20 per cent of 100 = pO_2 = 20 kPa. To show this is part of a mixture we use the term **partial pressure (p)**. So in this case the partial pressure of the oxygen is 20 kPa. We will often refer to partial pressures in gas exchange because there is almost always a mixture of gases involved and we wish to consider each one individually.

The law of partial pressures states that in a mixture of ideal gases, each gas has a partial pressure that is the pressure that the gas would have if it alone occupied the volume. The total pressure of a gas mixture is the sum of the partial pressures of the individual gases in the mixture.

Oxygen dissociation curves

As oxygen molecules combine with haemoglobin they become attached one by one to the four haem groups. The more oxygen that is available, the more haem groups are filled. If we draw a graph of the amount of oxygen taken up by the haemoglobin compared with the concentration of oxygen around it (expressed as its partial pressure in kPa), we might expect it to be a straight line (directly proportional). This is not the case because as an oxygen molecule becomes attached it makes it easier for the next two to be taken in, but the final oxygen is more difficult to add, so the graph shows a distinctive elongated S-shape (Figure 10.13). This type of graph is known as an **oxygen dissociation curve**.

The graph shows that this results in the ideal situation. Where external oxygen concentrations are low, oxyhaemoglobin will become less saturated and oxygen will be released; and vice-versa where oxygen concentrations are high.

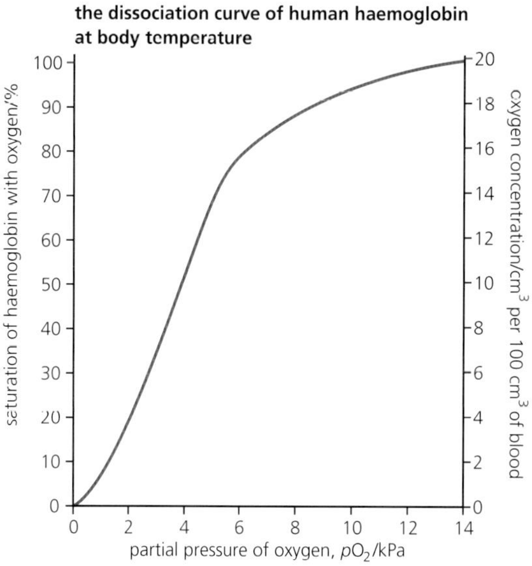

the dissociation curve of human haemoglobin at body temperature

saturation of haemoglobin with oxygen/%

oxygen concentration/cm^3 per 100 cm^3 of blood

partial pressure of oxygen, pO_2/kPa

Figure 10.13 Oxygen dissociation curve for human haemoglobin at body temperature

Bohr effect

Most oxygen is required by the most active cells. These cells will also produce higher concentrations of carbon dioxide. High levels of carbon dioxide cause oxyhaemoglobin to release more oxygen. This is known as the **Bohr effect**. The oxygen dissociation curve is shifted to the left (Figure 10.14), which gives a boost to the oxygen available at just the point where it is needed most.

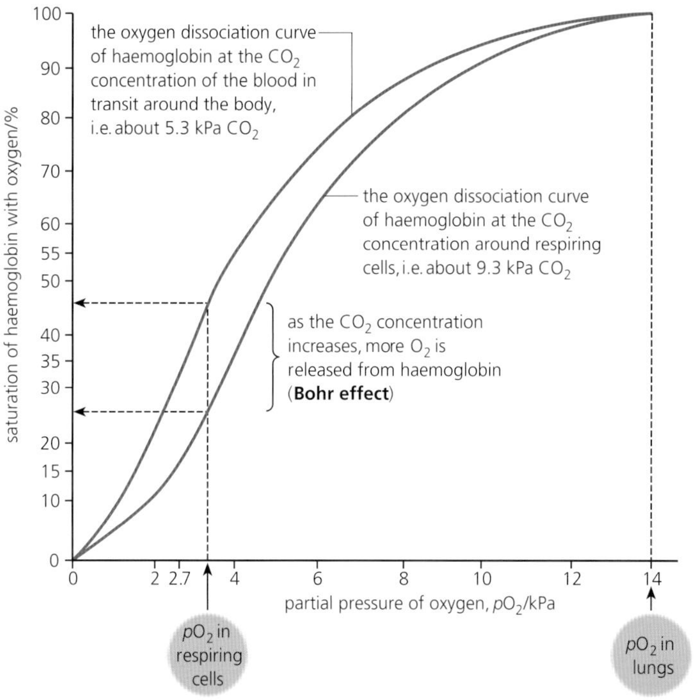

Figure 10.14 Bohr effect – how carbon dioxide affects oxyhaemoglobin

Key terms

Oxygen dissociation curve A graph showing the percentage saturation of haemoglobin at different external concentrations of oxygen.

Bohr effect The reduction of the oxygen-carrying capacity of haemoglobin caused by increasing concentrations of carbon dioxide.

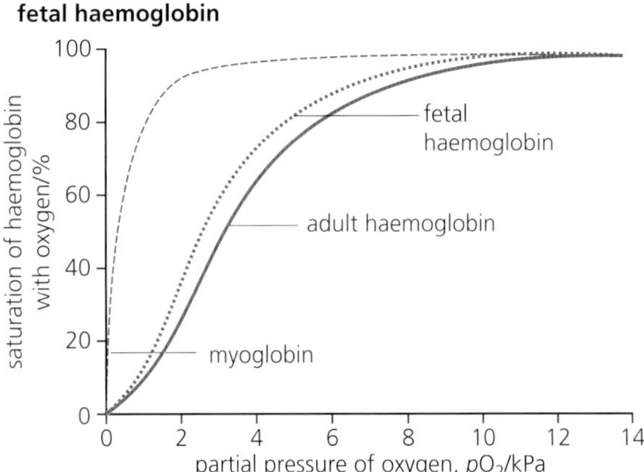

Figure 10.15 Oxygen dissociation curve for adult haemoglobin, myoglobin and fetal haemoglobin

Myoglobin

Whilst it is vital to have pigments such as haemoglobin in the blood because they have a strong affinity for oxygen, it also creates a problem. How do we get haemoglobin to give up all of its oxygen to other tissues? The obvious answer is to ensure that other pigments are present in the tissues that have a higher affinity for oxygen than haemoglobin. In mammals, working muscles have a high oxygen demand and to ensure that this is met they contain a pigment called **myoglobin**. The higher affinity for oxygen will be shown by an oxygen dissociation curve for myoglobin being further to the left than that of haemoglobin (Figure 10.15).

To achieve this higher affinity, myoglobin molecules have a modified structure. Like haemoglobin, myoglobin is a conjugated globular protein and carries oxygen attached to a haem group. Unlike haemoglobin it has only one haem group attached to a complex globular protein, just like the single sub-unit shown in Figure 10.12. As a result myoglobin becomes fully saturated at about pO_2 40 kPa whilst haemoglobin requires about pO_2 80 kPa.

Not only does myoglobin assist in the transfer of oxygen from haemoglobin to muscles but its stronger affinity for oxygen means that it is normally fully saturated so forms a useful reservoir of oxygen within the muscles, enabling them to keep working longer when oxygen demand exceeds supply.

Tip

Many questions use different dissociation curves so it is very useful to remember that, in general, a curve further to the left means that at any given oxygen concentration it will have a higher saturation and therefore a better affinity for oxygen. A curve further to the right means a lower affinity for oxygen.

Fetal haemoglobin

A very similar problem arises in the placenta of pregnant mammals. How can oxygen be transferred across the placenta from the maternal blood to the fetal circulation? In this case the use of pigments such as myoglobin would be unsuitable as their very strong affinity for oxygen would not allow sufficient exchange between fetal blood and the growing tissues.

The answer is provided by the presence of **fetal haemoglobin**. During the development of the embryo the genes coding for haemoglobin are expressed in varying ways. The result of this is that the haemoglobin proteins undergo subtle changes during development that affect their properties. Fetal haemoglobin has a slightly greater affinity for oxygen than adult haemoglobin (again its dissociation curve is slightly to the left) but the change is just enough to transfer oxygen from maternal haemoglobin but not enough to affect its normal working within the fetal circulation (Figure 10.15).

Haemoglobin and carbon dioxide transport

Most carbon dioxide is transported in the plasma and red blood cells as hydrogen carbonate ions:

$$CO_2 + H_2O \xrightarrow{\text{carbonic anhydrase}} HCO_3^- + H^+$$

The presence of the enzyme carbonic anhydrase inside red blood cells means that greater volumes of carbon dioxide can be transported than simply relying upon limited solubility in the plasma. The exchange of carbon dioxide is therefore much more efficient.

A much smaller amount of carbon dioxide (around 10 per cent) is combined directly with the amino groups of the polypeptide chains of haemoglobin inside red blood cells to form carbaminohaemoglobin.

carbon dioxide + haemoglobin → carbaminohaemoglobin + H^+

Both of these reactions release H^+ ions. Haemoglobin can also take up some of these to buffer the blood and prevent it becoming too acidic.

Test yourself

21 Name **two** differences between haemoglobin and myoglobin.

22 State exactly where haemoglobin is found in the blood.

23 Suggest the effect an increase in carbon dioxide concentration would have on the ability of haemoglobin to carry oxygen.

24 Explain why myoglobin in muscles is normally fully saturated with oxygen.

25 State the difference in oxygen affinity between fetal haemoglobin and adult haemoglobin.

Chapter summary

Size and surface area

- As cells and organisms increase in size their surface area : volume ratio decreases.
- Specialised gas exchange surfaces have thin membranes and a large surface area.
- Active animals with high gas exchange demand have mechanisms to maintain diffusion gradients across membranes coupled with a transport system.

Gas exchange in insects

- Insects have tough impermeable exoskeletons made up of chitin.
- Small tubes called tracheae ending in finer branches called tracheoles carry gases directly to active tissues.
- Tracheae are open to the atmosphere through valves in abdominal segments called spiracles.
- Gases move along tracheae by diffusion assisted by opening and closing of spiracles and compression of the tubes by abdominal movements.

Gas exchange in bony fish

- Bony fish use gills made up of filaments and plates that increase surface area.
- A constant flow of water across the gills is maintained by changes in water pressure controlled by muscles of the buccal cavity.
- Flow of blood in gills and flow of water across them are arranged as a counter-current that maximises diffusion gradients.

Gas exchange in mammals

- Lungs are contained in an airtight thorax.
- The volume of the thorax and hence the pressure in the lungs is controlled by muscles in the diaphragm and by intercostal muscles moving the ribcage.
- Muscle movements cause pressure changes, forcing gases in or out of the lungs.
- The trachea, bronchi and bronchioles connect the lungs to the atmosphere via the nose and mouth.
- The trachea and bronchi have rings of cartilage that prevent collapse during pressure changes.
- Gas exchange takes place in alveoli, which have thin endothelial walls and a surrounding capillary network.

Gas exchange in flowering plants

- Gases are exchanged through pores known as lenticels in stems and stomata in leaves by passive diffusion.
- Stomata have guard cells that open and close the pore by changes in turgor pressure.
- In leaves gases diffuse through stomata and dissolve in water films surrounding the spongy mesophyll cells.

Transport of gases in the blood

- Haemoglobin is a conjugated protein with four haem groups, each containing an iron atom. It is found inside the red blood cells.
- Haemoglobin readily combines with oxygen and with carbon dioxide.
- An oxygen dissociation curve shows how much oxygen is taken up by haemoglobin as the pressure of oxygen is increased. The curve is an elongated S-shape.
- An increase in carbon dioxide concentration in the blood causes less oxygen to be carried by haemoglobin (the Bohr effect).
- Different pigments such as myoglobin (muscle) and fetal haemoglobin have different affinities ensuring that oxygen can be transferred to muscles or across the placenta.
- Carbon dioxide is transported as hydrogen carbonate ions in plasma and in red blood cells as carbaminohaemoglobin.

Practice questions

1 The reason why the surface-area-to-volume ratio of organisms decreases as they become larger is:

A Surface area increases with the cube of the dimension but volume increases with the square of the dimension.

B Surface area increases logarithmically but volume increases linearly.

C Surface area increases with the square of the dimension but volume increases with the cube of the dimension.

D Surface area increases linearly but volume increases logarithmically. *(1)*

2 Structures that allow gas exchange to take place in plant stems are called:

A stomata

B spiracles

C lenticels

D micropyles *(1)*

★3 Explain how a continuous flow of water is maintained across the gills of a bony fish. *(5)*

Tip

Question 3 is a very simple recall question but it is useful practice in writing concisely and accurately to achieve full marks.

4 The graph below shows the oxygen dissociation curves of fetal and adult haemoglobin.

a) The curves for fetal haemoglobin and adult haemoglobin show a similar shape as the partial pressure of the oxygen increases. Explain how the structure of a haemoglobin molecule can account for the pattern of oxygen uptake shown by these curves. *(3)*

b) Explain what is meant by the term partial pressure. *(2)*

c) i) What is the difference between the oxygen saturation of fetal haemoglobin and adult haemoglobin when the partial pressure of oxygen is 4 kPa? *(1)*

ii) Explain the importance of this difference to the development of the fetus in a mammal. *(3)*

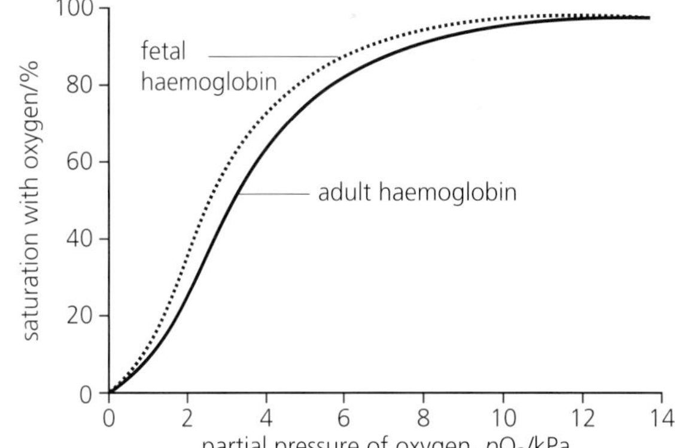

Tip

Dissociation curves are very common in examination questions. They may be directly linked to the specification, as in Question 4, or they may show curves from different animals you have not met before. In this case there is some straight recall (AO1) but also an element of applying your knowledge for AO2 in part a) and in part c) ii).

Tip

Question 4 asks you to apply your knowledge of gaseous exchange in the blood and expects you to have some other scientific knowledge necessary to understand this topic. In both AS and A level examinations you will meet synoptic questions that test your knowledge of two or more parts of the specification or your practical skills. This question begins to test your ability to draw together different scientific concepts.

5 The diagram shows two of the chemical reactions that take place inside red blood cells within a capillary close to actively respiring tissues.

H^+ = hydrogen ions; HbO_2 = oxyhaemoglobin; HHb = haemoglobin; HCO_3^- = hydrogen carbonate ions

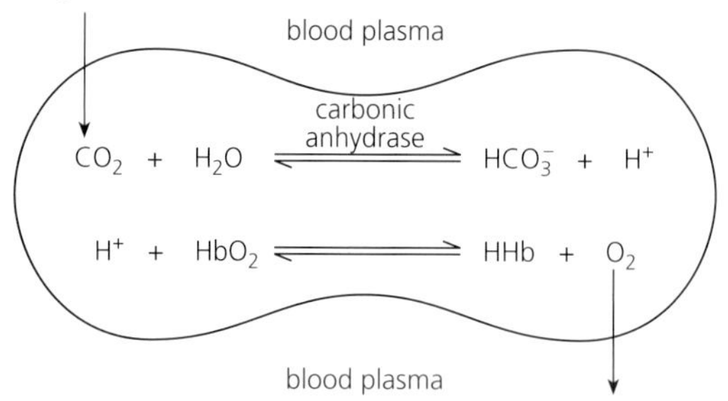

a) Describe two ways in which a human red blood cell is adapted for gas exchange. *(2)*

b) i) Haemoglobin acts as a chemical buffer in the blood. What is meant by a chemical buffer? *(2)*

ii) Use the information in the diagram to explain how haemoglobin can act as a buffer in blood. *(3)*

c) The binding of hydrogen ions to oxyhaemoglobin causes small changes in the shape of the oxygen binding sites. Explain how this may bring about the Bohr effect as carbon dioxide concentration increases. *(3)*

Stretch and challenge

6 Haemoglobin is a very common respiratory pigment used for the transport of oxygen. It can be found in a wide range of animals including vertebrates, but it is not the only pigment found in living organisms, as shown in the table below.

Respiratory pigment	Occurrence	Colour change (deoxygenated → oxygenated)
Haemoglobin	Most vertebrates	purple red → bright red
Haemocyanin	Crustaceans (crabs and lobsters)	colourless → blue
Chlorocruorins	Marine annelid worms	green → red

The chemical structure of the sub units making up these pigments is shown here. (Note that most carbon atoms have been omitted to make them clearer.)

Haemocyanin

Haemoglobin

Chlorocruorin

a) Use your knowledge of the structure of haemoglobin to describe the similarities and differences between these pigments.

b) i) What might the structure of these molecules indicate about their origins in evolution?

ii) The diagram on the right shows the chemical structure of chlorophyll a. What are the similarities and differences between chlorophyll a and haemoglobin? Is this further evidence for evolutionary ancestry?

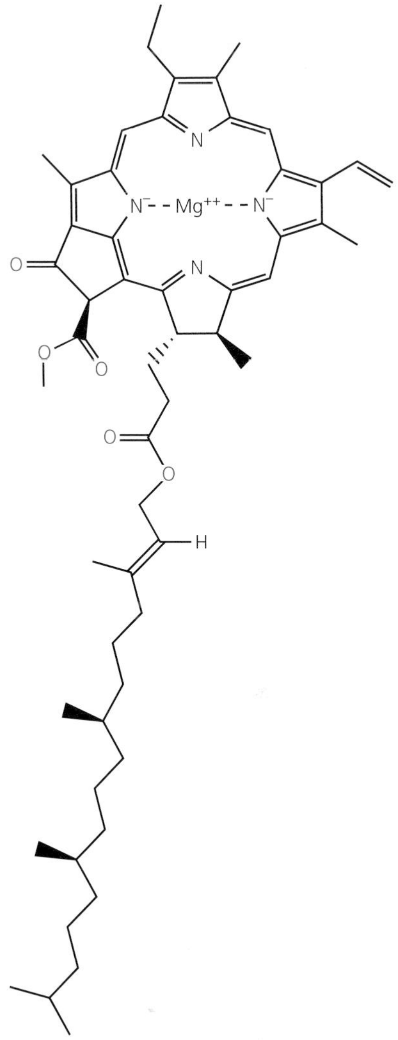

c) Haemoglobin in humans is always found inside red blood cells. Other pigments are normally found dissolved in the plasma. How does this arrangement make the functioning of haemoglobin more efficient?

N

N^{-} - - Mg^{++} - - N^{-}

N

O

O

O

O

O

H

11 Mammalian circulation

Prior knowledge

In this chapter you will need to recall that:

- the human heart has four chambers and is divided into two by the septum
- the left side of the heart carries oxygenated blood and the right side deoxygenated blood
- the heart is made up of a specialised tissue called cardiac muscle
- ventricles have thick muscular walls to pump blood to the lungs from the right ventricle and around the body from the left ventricle
- atria have much thinner walls and pump blood to the ventricles
- valves between atria and ventricles and at the base of main arteries ensure a one-way flow of blood through the heart
- arteries have thicker elastic walls and carry high-pressure blood away from the heart
- veins have thinner walls and contain valves; they carry low-pressure blood back to the heart
- capillaries have very thin walls, only one-cell thick, and form a network linking arteries and veins
- blood transports nutrients around the body and defends the body against pathogens by clotting and by destroying foreign bodies using the immune system
- blood is made up of several types of white cell, red cells and platelets suspended in a fluid called plasma.

Test yourself on prior knowledge

1. Name the main artery carrying blood from the left ventricle.
2. State the type of valves found at the base of main arteries in the heart.
3. The muscular wall of the left ventricle is much thicker than that of the right ventricle. Explain why.
4. Name the only artery that carries deoxygenated blood.
5. Explain why veins need valves but arteries don't.
6. Explain why the walls of capillaries are only one cell thick.
7. Why do arteries need elastic walls?
8. State which component of the blood is concerned with blood clotting.
9. What is the general name for all white blood cells?
10. State the name given to the arteries supplying cardiac muscle with nutrients.

Circulatory systems

Living cells require a supply of water and nutrients such as glucose and amino acids, and most need oxygen. The waste products of cellular metabolism have to be removed, too. In single-celled organisms and very small organisms, internal distances are small, so here movements of nutrients can occur efficiently by diffusion, as discussed in Chapter 10.

In more active organisms, cells need to be supplied with nutrients at a much faster rate, so there is a greater need for an efficient internal transport system. Larger animals have a **blood circulatory system** that links the parts of the body and makes resources available where they are required.

Internal transport systems at work are examples of mass flow. In mass flow, fluid moves in response to a pressure gradient, flowing from a region of high pressure to regions of lower pressure. Any suspended and dissolved substances present in the fluid are carried along in the same direction.

> **Key term**
>
> **Mass flow** A system of transport that uses a fluid, which is moved by a pressure gradient. Substances to be transported are suspended or dissolved in the fluid and all move in one direction.

Advantages of a double circulation

Mammals have a **closed circulation** in which blood is pumped by a powerful, muscular heart and circulated in a continuous system of tubes – the **arteries**, **veins** and **capillaries** – under pressure. The heart has four chambers and is divided into right and left sides by the **septum**. Blood flows from the right side of the heart to the lungs, where it is oxygenated, and then back to the left side of the heart. From here it is pumped around the rest of the body and back to the right side of the heart. As the blood passes twice through the heart in every single circulation of the body, this is called a **double circulation**.

The circulatory system of mammals is shown in Figure 11.1, alongside an alternative system found in fish. Fish also have a closed circulation, where blood flows only once through the heart in every circulation of the body, a condition known as a **single circulation**. This means that blood emerging from the gills (see Chapter 10) has only a low pressure and therefore flows around the body much more slowly.

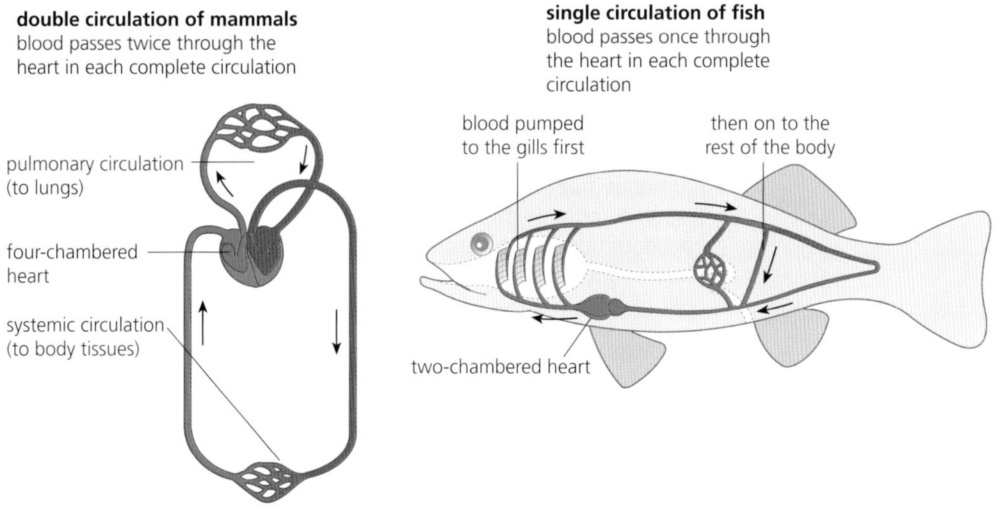

double circulation of mammals
blood passes twice through the heart in each complete circulation
pulmonary circulation (to lungs)
four-chambered heart
systemic circulation (to body tissues)

single circulation of fish
blood passes once through the heart in each complete circulation
blood pumped to the gills first
then on to the rest of the body
two-chambered heart

Figure 11.1 Single and double circulation

Figure 11.1 shows oxygenated blood as red and deoxygenated blood as blue. To overcome the problem of low pressure, a double circulatory system returns blood to the heart. This poses the danger that oxygenated and deoxygenated blood will mix, so blood pumped around the body will contain far less oxygen. The division of the heart into two separate halves prevents this happening so only fully saturated blood from the lungs enters the systemic circulation.

It becomes clear that the major advantages of the mammalian circulation are that:

- oxygenated blood is delivered at high pressure to all body tissues
- oxygenated blood reaches the respiring tissues undiluted by deoxygenated blood.

In discussing the mammalian blood circulation, we will take the human circulation as the example.

Test yourself

1 Why would a fish heart not be divided into two complete halves?

2 Suggest why fish survive and flourish, even though they have a less-efficient single circulation.

3 Give **two** features of a mass-flow transport system.

The transport medium – the blood

Blood is a special tissue consisting of a liquid medium called **plasma**, in which are suspended red cells (**erythrocytes**), white cells (**leucocytes**) and **platelets** (Figure 11.2). The plasma is the medium for exchange of substances between cells and tissues; the red cells are involved in transport of respiratory gases; and the white cells are adapted to combat infection. The roles of the components of blood are summarised in Table 11.1. In addition to transport, the blood functions as an important defence mechanism and the source of tissue fluid and lymph, which we will consider in more detail later in this chapter.

Table 11.1 The components of the blood and their roles

Component	Role
Plasma (Note: 'serum' is plasma from which all cells and the soluble protein fibrinogen have been removed.)	Transport of: • nutrients from gut or liver to all cells • excretory products, e.g. urea from the liver to the kidneys • hormones from the endocrine glands to all tissues and organs • dissolved proteins that have roles including regulating the osmotic concentration (water potential) of the blood • dissolved proteins that are antibodies • heat to all tissues.
Red cells	Transport of: • oxygen from the lungs to respiring cells • carbon dioxide from respiring cells to the lungs (also carried in the plasma).
White cells	**Lymphocytes** have major roles in the immune system, including forming antibodies. **Phagocytes** such as **monocytes** and **neutrophils** ingest bacteria or cell fragments. **Eosinophils** are identified by taking up the red stain eosin and stimulate allergic responses and histamine production.
Platelets	Involved in the blood clotting mechanism.

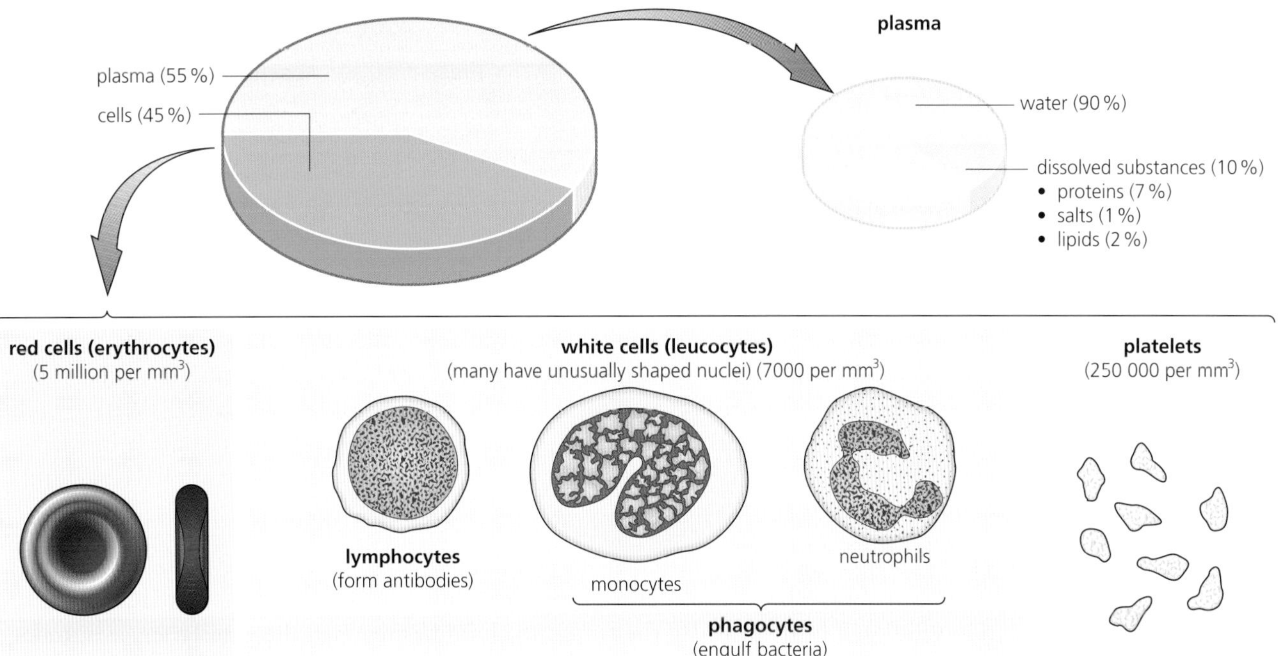

Figure 11.2 The composition of the blood

The plumbing of the circulatory system – arteries, veins and capillaries

There are three types of vessel in the circulatory system:

- **arteries**, which carry blood away from the heart
- **veins**, which carry blood back to the heart
- **capillaries**, which are fine networks of tiny tubes linking arteries and veins.

Figure 11.3 shows an artery, vein and capillary vessel in section, and details of the wall structure of these three vessels.

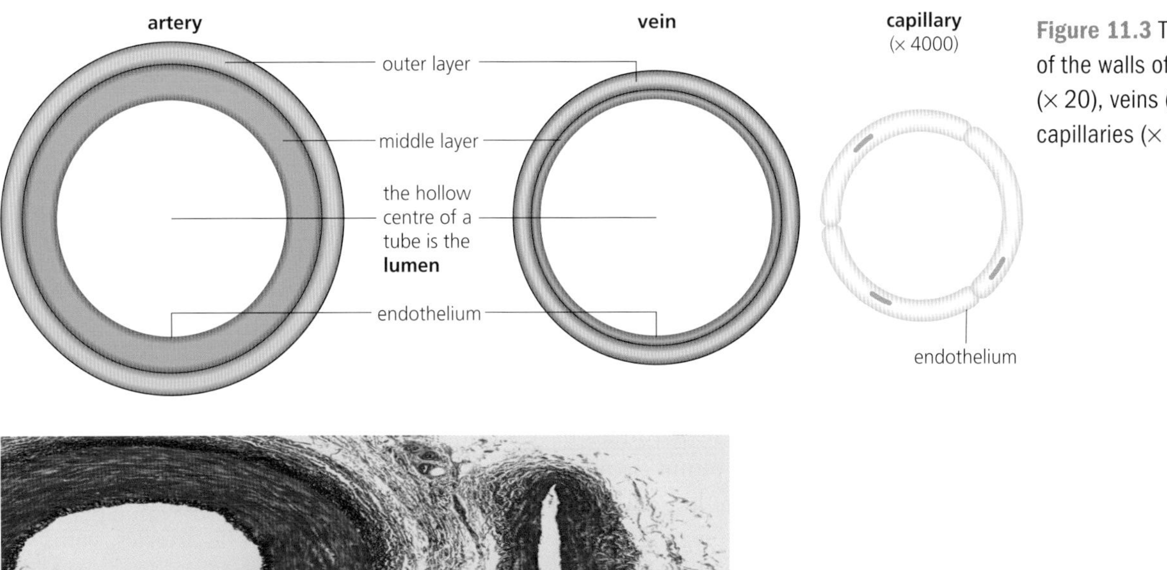

Figure 11.3 The structure of the walls of arteries (× 20), veins (× 20) and capillaries (× 4000)

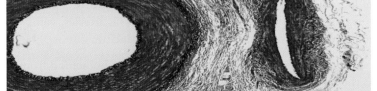

Table 11.2 Differences between arteries, veins and capillaries

	Artery	Capillary	Vein
Outer layer (tunica externa) collagen fibres	Present	Absent	Present
Middle layer (tunica media) elastic fibres and smooth (involuntary muscle)	Thick layer	Absent	Thin layer
Endothelium (tunica intima) pavement epithelium	Present	Present	Present
Valves	Absent	Absent	Present

Tip

The elastic recoil of arteries shows another example of the need to write accurately about energy that we met in Chapter 10. Notice that, once again, we avoid talking about energy being 'used up' or 'lost' and concentrate on how it is transferred from one form to another.

Both arteries and veins have strong, elastic walls, but the walls of the arteries are very much thicker and much more elastic than those of the veins. The strength of the walls comes from the collagen fibres present, and the elasticity is due to the elastic fibres and involuntary (smooth) muscle fibres. The walls of the capillaries, on the other hand, consist of endothelium only (endothelium is the innermost lining layer of arteries and veins). Capillaries branch profusely and bring the blood circulation close to cells – no cell is far from a capillary.

Blood leaving the heart is under high pressure, and travels in waves or **pulses**, following each heart beat. By the time the blood has reached the capillaries, it is under very much lower pressure, without a pulse. This difference in blood pressure accounts for the differences in the walls of arteries and veins.

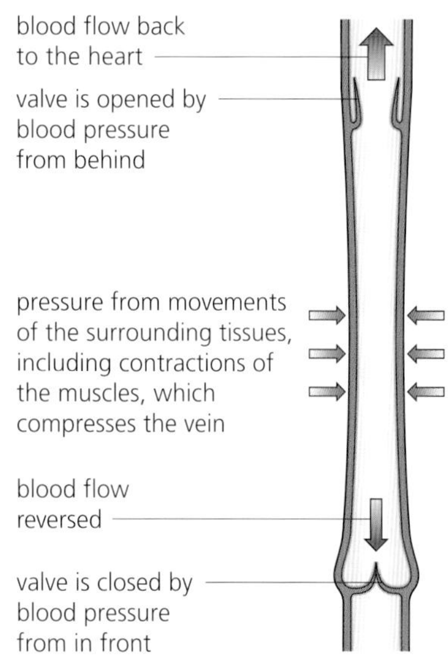
blood flow back to the heart
valve is opened by blood pressure from behind
pressure from movements of the surrounding tissues, including contractions of the muscles, which compresses the vein
blood flow reversed
valve is closed by blood pressure from in front
Figure 11.4 The valves in veins

The importance of elastic arteries

As the ventricles of the heart contract, blood is forced into arteries at very high pressure but the ventricles must then relax to refill with blood. The result of this could be that the blood would flow in a stop–start fashion. Obviously, this would be very inefficient. However, elastic fibres and smooth muscle in the walls of arteries are stretched when the blood is at high pressure. Therefore some of the energy in the blood is stored as potential energy in the elastic walls of the arteries. When the pressure of the blood falls this stored energy is used to maintain the flow until the ventricles contract again. In this way the pressure fluctuations of the blood are smoothed out to give a more continuous flow. This is known as **elastic recoil of arteries**.

The importance of valves in veins

Having squeezed through the capillary network, blood in veins is at a low pressure, yet still needs to be returned to the heart. For example, low-pressure blood in veins in your feet has to be pumped a vertical height of about a metre to reach the heart. Veins have **valves** at intervals, which prevent the backflow of blood (Figure 11.4). These valves also mean that as surrounding muscles contract and press against the veins, they force the blood from one valve to the next, so helping the return flow.

Key terms

Pulmonary circulation The pathways of arteries, veins and capillaries carrying blood from the heart to the lungs and back to the heart.

Systemic circulation The pathways of arteries, veins and capillaries carrying blood from the heart to all body tissues and back to the heart.

The arrangement of arteries and veins

You have already seen that mammals have a double circulation. It is the role of the right side of the heart to pump deoxygenated blood to the lungs. The arteries, veins and capillaries serving the lungs are known as the **pulmonary circulation**. The left side of the heart pumps oxygenated blood to the rest of the body. The arteries, veins and capillaries serving the body are known as the **systemic circulation**.

In the systemic circulation, organs are supplied with blood by arteries branching from the main artery known as the **aorta**. Within individual organs, the arteries branch into numerous arterioles (smaller arteries) and the smallest arterioles supply the capillary networks. Capillaries drain into venules (smaller veins), and venules join to form veins. The veins join the main vein (**vena cava**) carrying blood back to the heart. The branching sequence in the circulation is, therefore:

aorta → artery → arteriole → capillary → venule → vein → vena cava

For the pulmonary circulation this becomes:

pulmonary artery → arteriole → capillary → venule → vein → pulmonary vein

Arteries and veins are often named after the organs they serve (Figure 11.5). The blood supply to the liver is via the hepatic artery, but the liver also receives blood directly from the small intestine, via a vein called the **hepatic portal vein**. This brings much of the products of digestion, after they have been absorbed into the blood circulation in the gut.

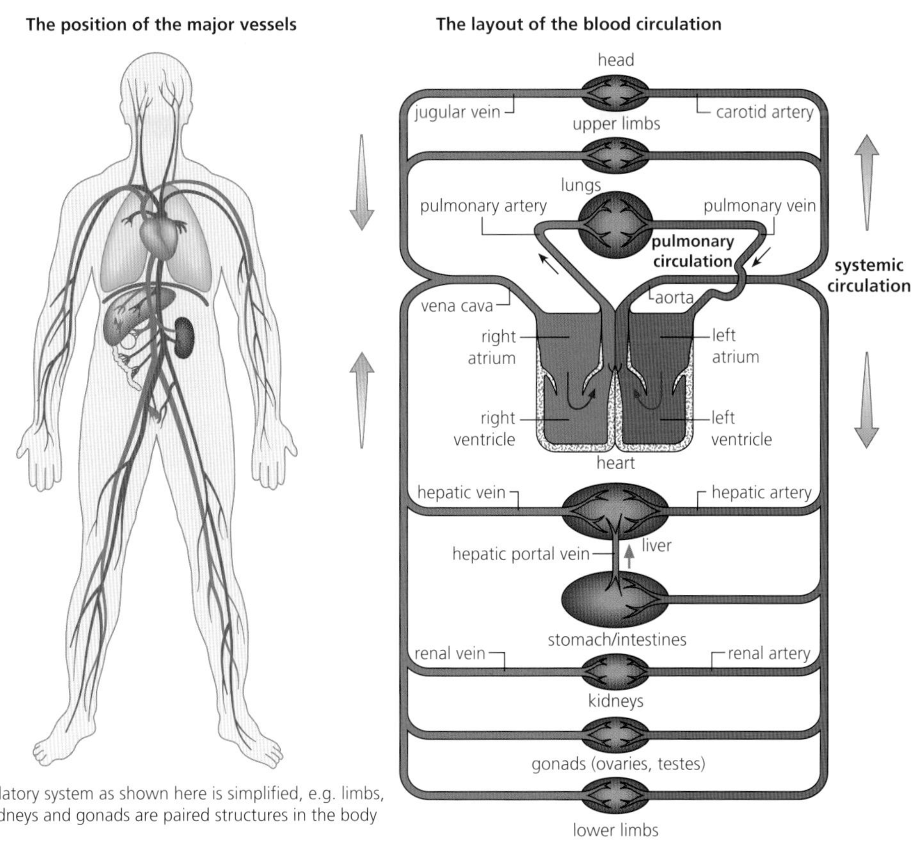

Figure 11.5 The layout of human circulation

Test yourself

4 Name the white cell that is involved in the allergic response.
5 Explain what is meant by a phagocyte.
6 Name the protein that is found in the outer layers of arteries and veins.
7 Explain why veins have much thinner walls than arteries.
8 Suggest how the flow of blood in the circulation would be different if artery walls were rigid.

heart viewed from the front of the body with pericardium removed

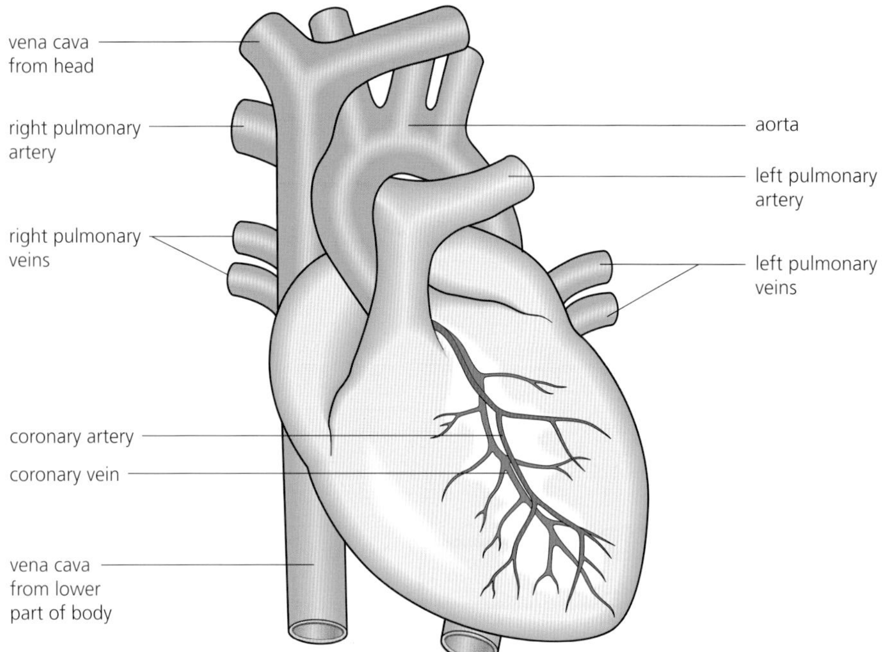

heart in LS

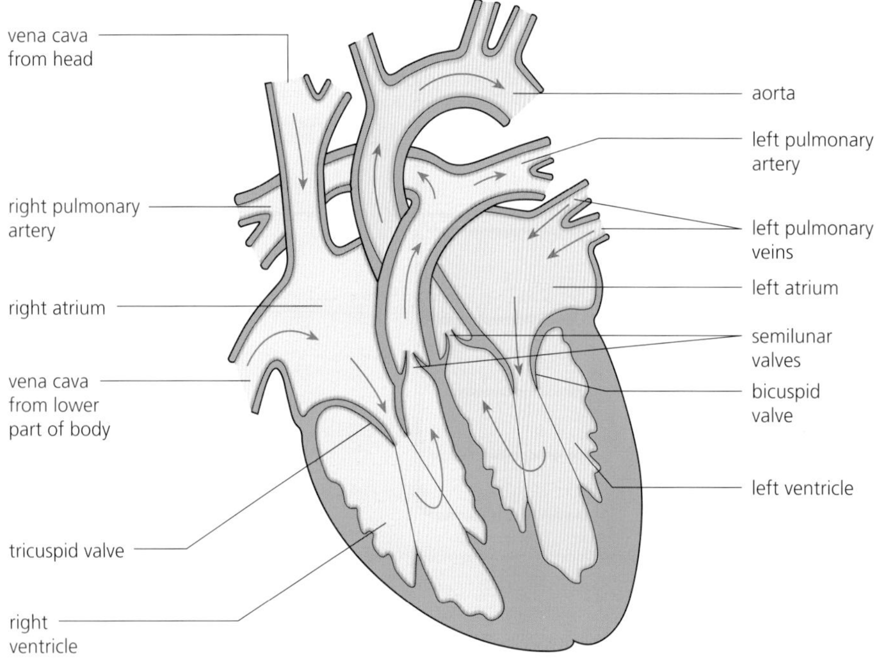

Figure 11.6 The structure of the heart

The heart as a pump

The human heart is the size of a clenched fist. It is found in the thorax between the lungs and beneath the breastbone (sternum). The heart is a hollow organ with a muscular wall, and is contained in a tightly fitting membrane, the pericardium – a strong, non-elastic sac that anchors the heart within the thorax.

The cavity of the heart is divided into four chambers, with those on the right side of the heart completely separate from the left side. The two upper chambers are thin-walled **atria** (singular: atrium). These receive blood into the heart. The two lower chambers are thick-walled **ventricles**. The ventricles pump blood out of the heart, with the muscular wall of the left ventricle being much thicker than that of the right ventricle. However, the volumes of the right and left sides (the quantities of blood they contain) are identical.

Note that the walls of the heart (the heart muscle) are supplied with oxygenated blood via **coronary arteries**. These arteries, and the capillaries they serve, deliver to the cardiac muscle fibres the **oxygen** and **nutrients** essential for the maintenance of the pumping action.

The **valves** of the heart prevent backflow of the blood, thereby maintaining the direction of flow through the heart. The **atrio-ventricular valves** are large valves, positioned to prevent backflow from ventricles to atria. The edges of these valves are supported by tendons anchored to the muscle walls of the ventricles below. These tendons do not move the valves. The opening and closing of these valves is caused by pressure differences between atria and ventricles. However, the tendons are vital, as the pressure from the ventricle is so great the flaps would simply be pushed upwards into the atrium. The tension in the tendons is equal and opposite to this pressure and so the valve flaps simply close tightly against each other.

The valves on the right and left sides of the heart are individually named: on the right side, the **tricuspid valve**; on the left, the **bicuspid** or mitral valve.

A different type of valve separates the ventricles from pulmonary artery (right side) and aorta (left side). These are pocket-like structures called **semilunar valves**, rather similar to the valves seen in veins. Once again these valves are opened and closed by pressure differences, this time between ventricles and the main arteries leaving the heart. As the ventricle relaxes the pressure drops below that in the artery and the semilunar valve 'cups' fill with blood to completely close off the artery, preventing backflow.

The action of the heart – the cardiac cycle

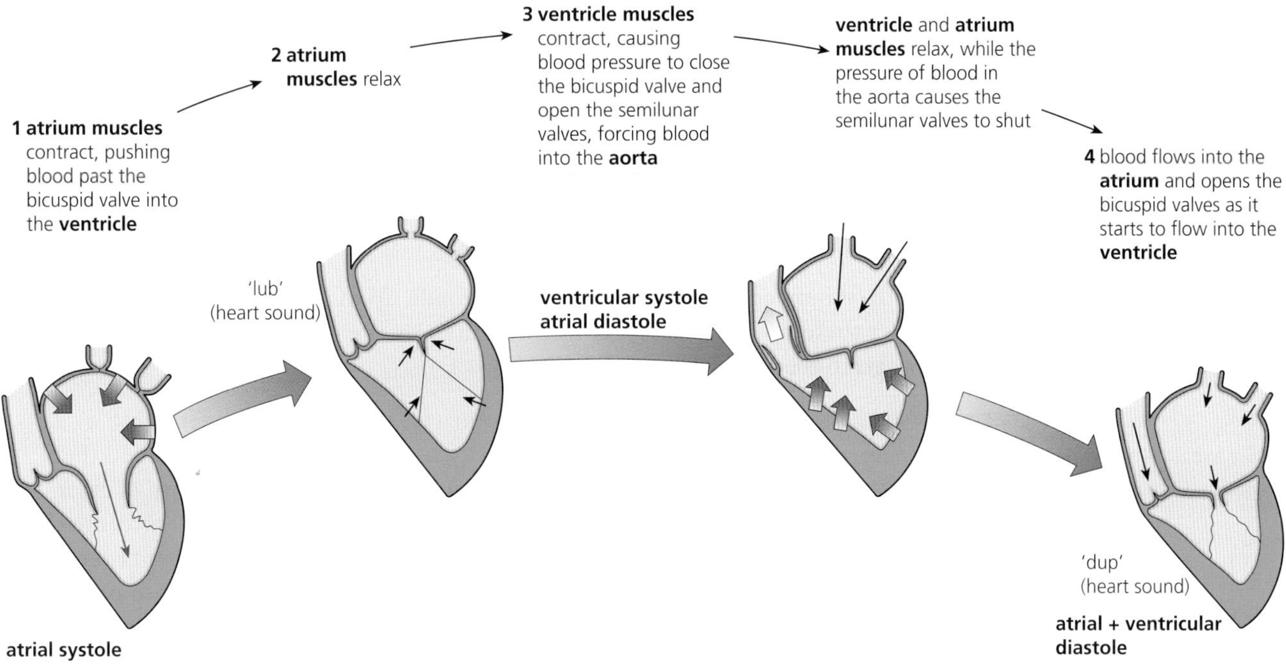

Figure 11.7 The cardiac cycle

The heart normally beats about 75 times per minute – approximately 0.8 seconds per beat. In each beat, the heart muscle contracts strongly, and this is followed by a period of relaxation. As the muscular walls of a chamber of the heart contract, the volume of that chamber decreases. This increases the pressure on the blood contained there, forcing the blood to a region where pressure is lower. Since the valves prevent blood flowing backwards, blood consistently flows on through the heart.

Look at the steps involved in contraction and relaxation, illustrated in the left side of the heart in Figure 11.7. (Both sides function together, with simultaneous contraction of the chambers.)

1 We start at the point where the atrium contracts. Blood is pushed into the ventricles (where the contents are under low pressure) by contraction of the walls of the atrium. This contraction also prevents backflow by blocking off the veins that brought the blood to the heart. This contraction step is known as **atrial systole**.

2 The atrium now relaxes. The relaxation step is called **atrial diastole**.

3 Next the ventricle contracts, and contraction of the ventricle is very forceful indeed. This step is known as **ventricular systole**. The high pressure this generates slams shut the atrio-ventricular valve and opens the semilunar valves, forcing blood into the aorta. A **pulse**, detectable in arteries all over the body, is generated.

4 This is followed by relaxation of the ventricles. Each contraction of cardiac muscle is followed by relaxation and elastic recoil. This stage is referred to as **ventricular diastole**.

Control of the cardiac cycle

If the heart is completely separated from all other connections it will continue to beat with a frequency of about 50 b.p.m. Because this rhythm originates from the heart muscle itself it is called **myogenic**.

> **Key term**
>
> **Myogenic** Myogenic activity originates within muscles rather than through the nervous system.

The myogenic stimulation of the heart provides a perfectly coordinated sequence of activity to ensure maximum efficiency from the cardiac cycle.

The cycle begins in a specially modified structure in the wall of the right atrium called the **sino-atrial node** (SAN). The cells of the SAN depolarise to a point where a wave of excitation similar to a nerve impulse spreads rapidly across the atria, causing them to contract simultaneously (atrial systole).

The boundary between atria and ventricles is made up of connective tissue that does not conduct these impulses. To pass to the ventricles the impulses stimulate another node, the **atrio-ventricular node (AVN)**.

P-wave	Atrial depolarisation (atrial systole)
QRS wave	Ventricular depolarisation (ventricular systole)
T wave	Ventricular repolarisation (ventricular diastole)

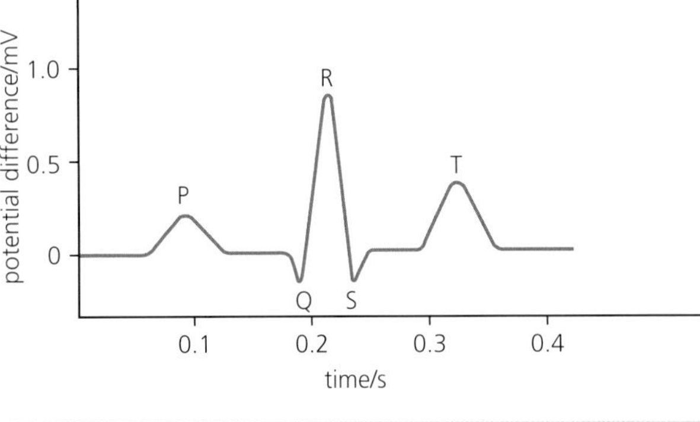

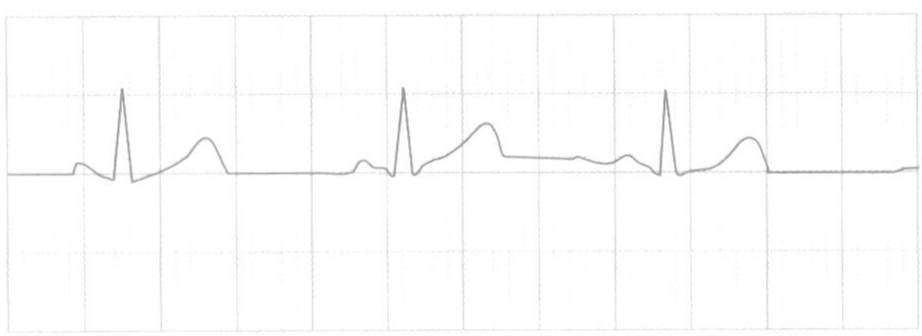

A complete ECG trace from a healthy patient

Figure 11.8 An electrocardiogram

To reach the ventricles the AVN is connected to a bundle of specially modified muscle fibres called the **Bundle of His** and then through a network of finer branching **Purkyne tissue** to the base of the ventricles. Purkyne tissue carries the impulses five times faster than the surrounding muscle to ensure that the base of the ventricles contracts first in ventricular systole, forcing blood in the right direction.

After every contraction, cardiac muscle has a period of insensitivity to stimulation known as the **refractory period**. In the heart, this is longer than most other muscles and means that the heart muscles relax to allow refilling and are less likely to suffer from fatigue.

Measuring electrical activity in the heart

Electrical activity in the heart can be measured by attaching electrodes to the thorax and recording the changing patterns of potential differences. These are displayed as an electrocardiogram (ECG) by means of a chart recorder. The patterns can be matched to the events described above and provide detailed diagnostic information about heart function (Figure 11.8).

The sequence of pressure changes during systole and diastole coupled with the electrical activity of the heart are shown in Figure 11.9.

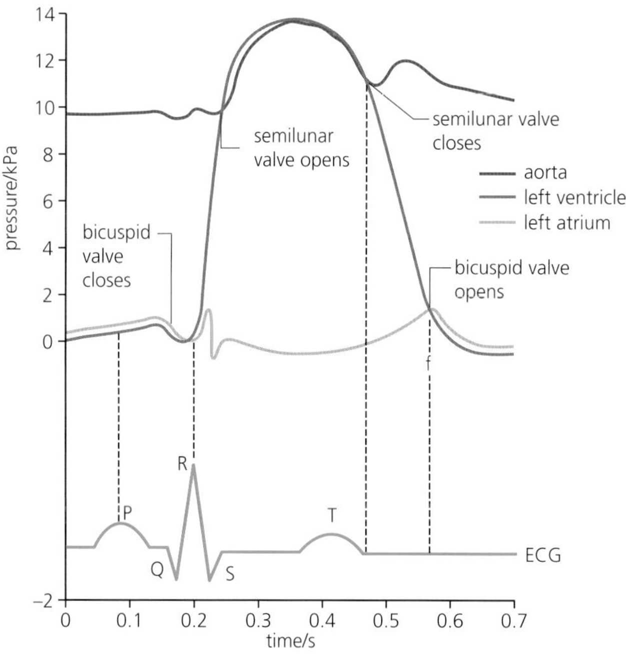

Figure 11.9 Pressure changes and electrical activity in the heart during one cardiac cycle

Test yourself

9 If a heart beats, on average, about 75 times per minute, calculate how many heartbeats will have been completed in a 70-year-old person.

10 It is essential that the total volume of the right and left ventricles is identical. Explain why.

11 Suggest a reason why the bicuspid valve of the left ventricle has only two flaps but the mitral valve has three.

12 The valve tendons are attached to small outgrowths of the ventricular muscle wall called papillary muscles. These contract at the same time as the rest of the ventricle. How might this help the valves to function?

13 State the forces that cause the opening and closing of cardiac valves.

14 Explain the reasons for the following:

a) It is essential for the heart to have specialised tissues such as Purkyne fibres in the Bundle of His.

b) It is essential that the Purkyne fibres reach to the base of the ventricles.

15 The electrocardiogram sequence in Figure 11.8 shows a trace taken over 4 seconds. What will be the heart rate of this patient in beats per minute?

Exchange in the tissues – tissue fluid and lymph

The formation of **tissue fluid** assists in the delivery of nutrients to cells and the removal of waste products. Tissue fluid is formed from the plasma, components of which escape from the blood and pass between the cells in most of the tissues of the body. Red cells and most of the blood proteins are retained in the capillaries.

The walls of the capillaries are selectively permeable to many components of the blood plasma, including glucose and mineral ions. Nutrients like these, in low concentration in the tissues, diffuse from the plasma into the tissue fluid (Figure 11.10). There are also tiny gaps in the capillary walls, found to vary in size in different parts of the body, which facilitate formation of tissue fluid. It is the pressure of the blood that drives fluid out (that is, the **hydrostatic pressure** generated as the heart beats). Meanwhile, the proteins and some other components are retained in the blood. These soluble substances maintain an **osmotic gradient**. The water potential of the tissue fluid is less negative than the blood, so some of the water forced out by hydrostatic pressure returns to the blood by osmosis all along the capillary. However, initially there is a net outflow because the hydrostatic pressure is greater than fluid movement due to the osmotic gradient.

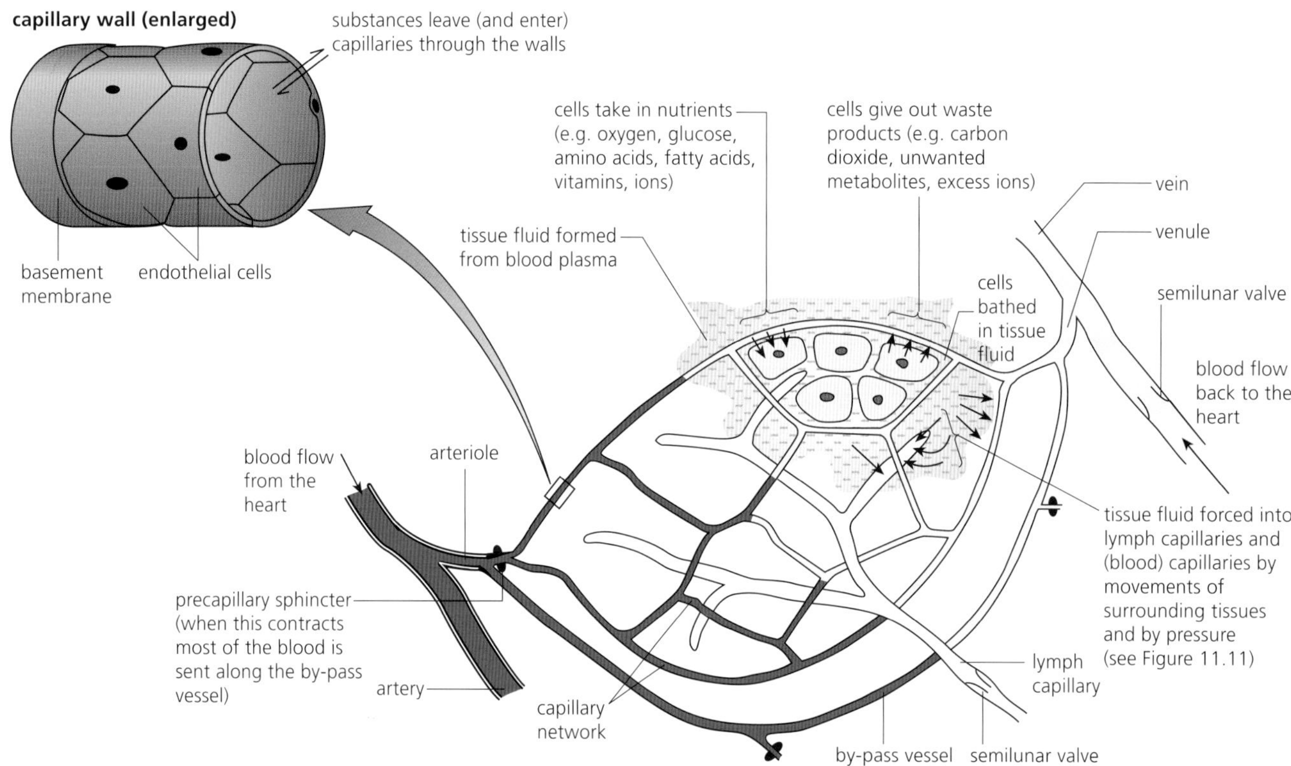

Figure 11.10 Exchange between blood and cells via tissue fluid

Return of tissue fluid to the circulation

Further along the capillary, there is a net inflow of tissue fluid to the capillary (Figure 11.11). Hydrostatic pressure has now fallen as fluid is lost from the capillaries. Water returns by osmosis, and a diffusion gradient carries unused metabolites and excretory material back into the blood.

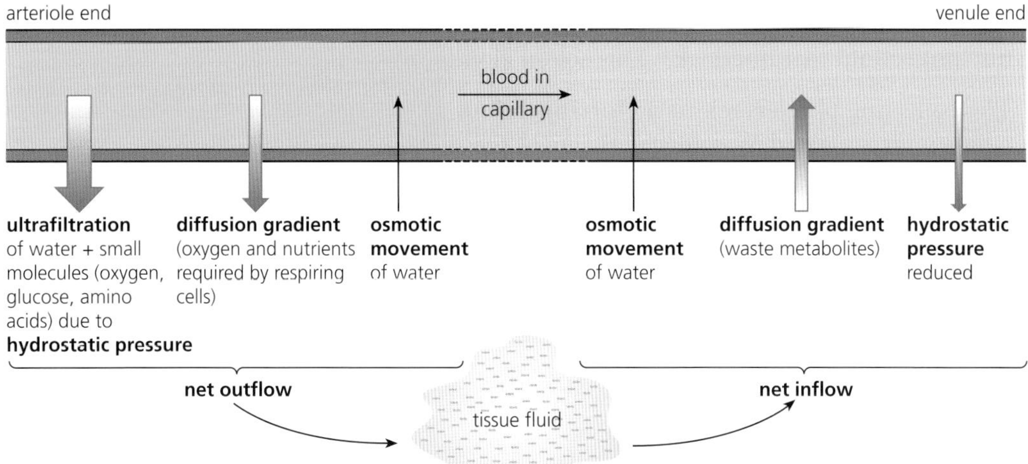

Figure 11.11 Forces for exchange in capillaries

Formation of lymph

Not all tissue fluid returns to the blood capillaries – some enters the **lymph capillaries**. Molecules too large to enter blood capillaries can pass into the lymph system at tiny valves in the vessel walls. Liquid is moved along these and larger lymph vessels by compression due to body movements; backflow is prevented by valves. Lymph finally drains back into the blood circulation in veins close to the heart.

Lymph nodes are also the site of production of lymphocytes, which makes the lymph system an important part of the immune system. We shall return to this in more detail later in the book. The lymph system is also a pathway for lipids to be transported from intestines to the bloodstream following digestion.

Test yourself

16 State which has a higher water potential at the arterial end of a capillary network – plasma or tissue fluid.

17 Water enters and leaves capillaries by osmosis. What other force causes water to leave capillaries?

18 Name the white cells that are most abundant in the lymph system.

Blood clotting as a defence mechanism

In the event of a break in our closed blood circulation, the dangers of a loss of blood and the possibility of a fall in blood pressure arise. It is by the clotting of blood that escapes are prevented, either at small internal haemorrhages, or at cuts and other wounds. In these circumstances, a clot both stops the outflow of blood and reduces invasion opportunities for disease-causing organisms (pathogens). Subsequently, repair of the damaged tissues can get underway. Initial conditions at the wound trigger a **cascade of events** by which a blood clot is formed.

Firstly, **platelets** collect at the site. These are components of the blood that are formed in the bone marrow along with the red and white cells. They are circulated throughout the body, suspended in the plasma, with the blood cells. Platelets are actually cell fragments, disc-shaped and very small (only 2 μm in diameter) – too small to contain a

Key term

Cascade of events
When one signal event sets off a whole sequence of reactions, leading to an important outcome. In the case of blood clotting, damage to blood vessels leads to protein fibres trapping red blood cells to form a clot, through numerous intermediate events.

nucleus. Each platelet consists of a sac of cytoplasm rich in vesicles containing enzymes, and is surrounded by a cell surface membrane. Platelets stick to the damaged tissues and clump together there. (At this point they change shape from sacs to flattened discs with tiny projections that interlock.) This action alone seals off the smallest breaks.

The collecting platelets release a **clotting factor** (a protein called thromboplastin), which is also released by damaged tissues at the site. This clotting factor, along with vitamin K and calcium ions, always present in the plasma, causes a soluble plasma protein called **prothrombin** to be converted to the active, proteolytic enzyme **thrombin**. The action of this enzyme is to convert another soluble blood protein, **fibrinogen**, to insoluble **fibrin** fibres at the site of the cut. Red cells are trapped within this mass of fibres and the blood clot is formed.

SEM of blood clot
showing meshwork of fibrin fibres and trapped blood cells

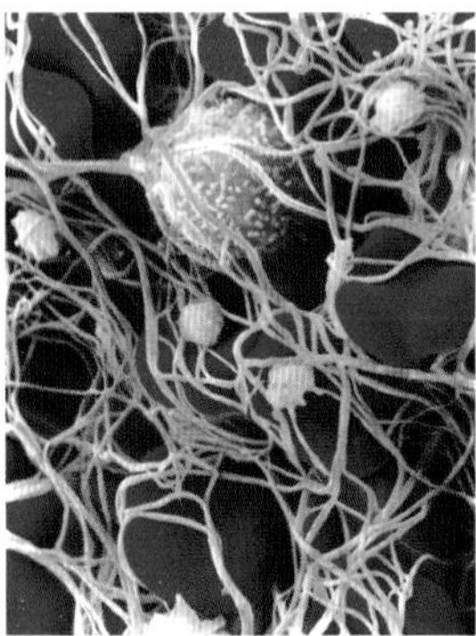

damaged blood vessel

exposed collagen fibres and damaged endothelium

platelets collect, adhere and release

platelet plug formed – sufficient to block minor breaks

release clotting factor (thromboplastin) from damaged tissue

local acting hormones (prostaglandins)

clotting factor (thromboplastin)

Ca^{2+} and vitamin K from plasma

prothrombin (soluble protein in plasma) → thrombin (proteolytic enzyme)

fibrinogen (plasma protein) → insoluble fibrin fibres

fibrin fibres

trapped blood cells

blood clot

constriction of damaged vessel

stabilised plug
- prevents further blood loss
- prevents entry of bacteria

Figure 11.12 The blood clotting mechanism

Test yourself

19 Name the ions in the blood that are essential for blood clotting.

20 Name the insoluble protein used to form a network, trapping red blood cells in clotting.

21 Name one enzyme in the blood clotting cascade.

It is most fortunate that clot formation is not normally activated in the intact circulation; clotting is triggered by the abnormal conditions at the break. The complex sequence of steps involved in clotting may be seen as an essential **fail-safe mechanism**. This is necessary because a casual formation of a blood clot within the intact circulatory system immediately generates the risk of a dangerous and possibly fatal blockage in the lungs, heart muscle or brain.

Atherosclerosis – a disease of the human circulatory system

Diseases of the heart and blood vessels are known as **cardiovascular diseases** (**CVD**). These are responsible for more premature deaths in the developed world than any other single cause. By premature death, we mean a death that occurs before the age of 75 years. Most of these are due to **atherosclerosis**. The structures of a healthy artery wall and one affected by atherosclerosis are shown in Figure 11.13.

Key term

Atherosclerosis The progressive degeneration of artery walls.

The steps in the development of an atherosclerosis condition are as follows:

1 **Endothelial damage**. Healthy arteries have pale, smooth linings, and the walls are elastic and flexible. However, in arteries that have become unhealthy, the walls have strands of yellow fat deposited under the endothelium. This fat builds up from certain lipoproteins and from cholesterol that may be circulating in the blood. This damage causes white blood cells (macrophages) to invade the fatty streaks where they begin to take up cholesterol from low density lipoproteins and develop fibrous connective tissue forming an **atheroma** (Figure 11.13).

2 **Raised blood pressure**. These deposits start to impede blood flow and contribute to raised blood pressure. Thickening of the artery wall leads to loss of elasticity and this, too, contributes to raised blood pressure. In the special case of the arteries serving the heart muscle – the coronary arteries – progressive reduction of the blood flow impairs oxygenation of the cardiac muscle fibres, leading to chest pains. These are known as **angina**, and are usually brought on by physical exertions.

3 **Lesion formation and an inflammatory response**. Where the smooth lining actually breaks down, the circulating blood is exposed to the fatty, fibrous deposits. These lesions are known as atheromatous **plaques**. Further deposition occurs as cholesterol and triglycerides accumulate, and smooth muscle fibres and collagen fibres proliferate in the plaque. Blood platelets tend to collect at the exposed, roughened surface, and these platelets release factors that trigger a defensive response called inflammation, which includes blood clotting (see Figure 11.12). A blood clot may form within the vessel. This clot is known as a **thrombus** (Figure 11.13), at least until it breaks free and is circulated in the bloodstream, whereupon it is called an **embolus**.

healthy

endothelium

flow of blood

diseased

blood clot = thrombus formed where atheroma has broken through the endothelium

lipid + fibre deposit = atheroma

photomicrograph of diseased human artery in TS (×20)

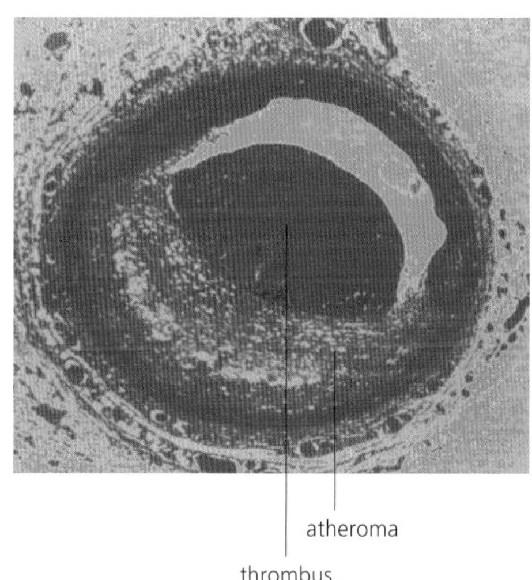

Figure 11.13 Atherosclerosis, leading to a thrombus

Myocardial infarctions, strokes and aneurysms

An embolus may be swept into a small artery or arteriole that is narrower than the diameter of the clot, causing a blockage. Immediately, the blood supply to the tissue downstream of the block is deprived of oxygen. Without oxygen, the tissue dies.

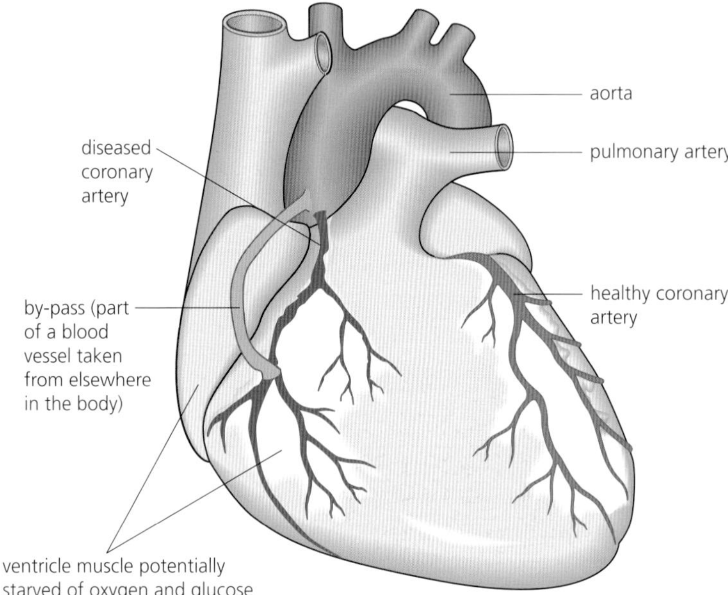

Figure 11.14 A heart by-pass

The arteries supplying the heart are the coronary arteries. These arteries are especially vulnerable, particularly those to the left ventricle. When heart muscle dies in this way, the heart may cease to be an effective pump. We say a heart attack has occurred (known as a **myocardial infarction**). Coronary arteries that have been damaged can be surgically by-passed (Figure 11.14).

When an embolus blocks an artery in the brain, a **stroke** occurs. Neurones of the brain depend on a continuous supply of blood for oxygen and glucose. Within a few minutes of the blood supply being lost, the neurones affected will die. Neurones cannot be replaced, so the result of the blockage is a loss of some body functions controlled by that region of the brain.

In arteries where the wall has been weakened by atherosclerosis, the remaining layers may be stretched and bulge under the pressure of the blood pulses. Ballooning of the wall like this is called an **aneurysm**. An aneurysm may burst at any time.

Factors affecting the incidence of coronary heart disease (CHD)

In the developed world, cardiovascular diseases remain high on the list of most serious health problems, despite recent improvements. For example, in the UK, CHD is responsible for the highest percentage of deaths before the age of 75 years in both males and females (Figure 11.15). Another feature of CHD is that the condition may go largely unnoticed for many years – often until it is too late.

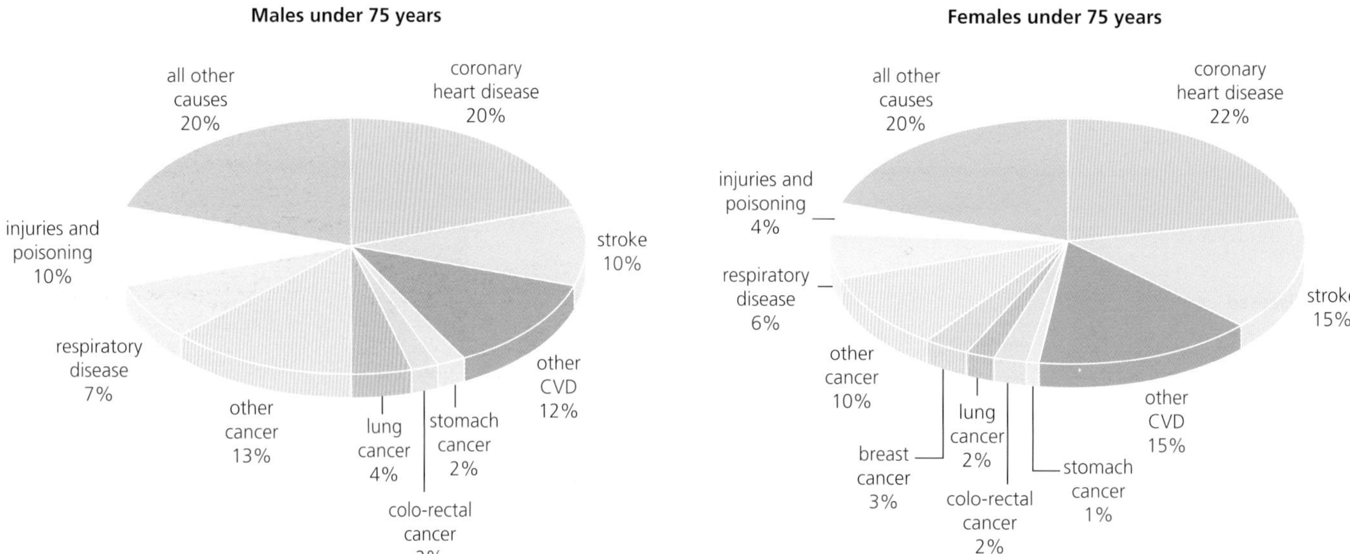

Figure 11.15 Premature death by causes in Europe, published in 2012

Major risk factors that cannot be controlled

- **Increasing age**. The risk of coronary atherosclerosis increases with age. Over 80 per cent of people who die from CHD are aged 65 years or more. However, a word of caution is required here, for the evidence is that the genesis of this condition may lie much earlier in life. Post-mortem studies of soldiers killed in action have disclosed early but well-developed 'fatty plaques' in the arteries of young males of average age 22 years, suggesting that these commenced development in their bodies during their adolescence. This suggests why, for individuals brought up in the developed world, after the ages of 35 in men and 45 in women, the chance of dying from CHD increases dramatically.
- **Genetic factors** (including ethnicity). The occurrence of heart attacks at a relatively early age frequently runs in families, suggesting that there are genes that may confer vulnerability to CHD. Children of parents with heart diseases are distinctly more likely to develop the condition. This aspect will become clearer as knowledge of the human genome is developed to identify the roles of individual genes and their effects on metabolism.

Additionally, some races are more prone to CHD and strokes. This is the case with Afro-Caribbean people, for example. Another genetic factor beyond dispute is gender, for the possession of a Y chromosome (being a male) predisposes to greater risk of CHD than that carried by females. It has been suggested that the production of the hormone oestrogen by females inhibits the formation of atheroma and reduces their risk of CHD.

Major risk factors that we can control or reduce

- **Hypertension**. Persistently high blood pressure is defined as systolic pressure greater than 140 mm Hg (18.7 kPa) and diastolic pressure greater than 90 mm Hg (12 kPa). A blood pressure of 120/80 mm Hg (16/10.7 kPa) is regarded as normal.
  Hypertension is known as a 'silent killer' because of the damage it does to the heart by increasing its workload, causing the heart to enlarge and weaken with time. It also causes damage to blood vessels, accelerating the onset of atherosclerosis. The brain and kidneys are also damaged, although without causing noticeable discomfort. Hypertension increases the risk of strokes, too, and it makes a brain haemorrhage more likely.
  The following factors in this list all make the condition of hypertension more likely. However, hypertension is a condition that, once detected and regularly monitored, can be successfully treated with drugs (see below).
- **Smoking**. The habit of cigarette smoking generates the greatest risk of fatal ill-health, especially from cardiovascular diseases. It is principally the nicotine and carbon monoxide in tobacco smoke that damage the cardiovascular system. Carbon monoxide combines irreversibly with the pigment haemoglobin in red cells, reducing the ability of the blood to transport oxygen to all respiring cells, including to cardiac muscle fibres. The effects of nicotine are via its stimulation of adrenaline production. This hormone triggers an increase in heart rate and causes arteries to contract (**vasoconstriction**). The result is raised blood pressure.
  There have been huge investments in the tobacco industry for a long time, via the growth of the crop and the manufacturing of tobacco products. The enthusiastic endorsement of cigarette smoking in the developed world (manifested by the free availability of cigarettes to the troops in two World Wars, for example) has now spread to developing countries as fresh markets for tobacco products have opened up. Consequently, the dangers of smoking have not had the attention they deserve, and some people have even suggested the evidence against tobacco is equivocal.
  Yet from the earliest statistical studies there has been no room for doubt. The late Dr Richard Doll and colleagues, working at St Thomas' Hospital, London from 1947, investigated the cause of death of a sample of 3500 people admitted to hospital

for treatment. Whatever the symptoms these people had, the vast majority of those who were smokers later died from a cardiovascular disease.

This study was followed up by one of a group of 40 000 healthy, working doctors (among whom the habit of smoking was widespread at that time), which was more conclusive still. Some of Richard Doll's data from his studies with doctors are shown in Table 11.3. Today, few doctors smoke.

Table 11.3 Mortality from cardiovascular disease caused by cigarette smoking

Cause of death	Non-smokers	Continuing cigarette smokers
CHD	606	2067
stroke	245	802
aneurysm	14	136
atherosclerosis	23	111
Total	**888**	**3116**

- **High levels of cholesterol in the blood**. Lipids are a more diverse group of biochemicals than just the triglycerides we met earlier in Chaper 1, for they include steroids. Steroids occur widely in nature, and one very important steroid is **cholesterol** (Figure 11.16). The 'skeleton' of a steroid is a set of complex rings of carbon atoms. The bulk of the molecule is hydrophobic but the polar chemical –OH group is hydrophilic.

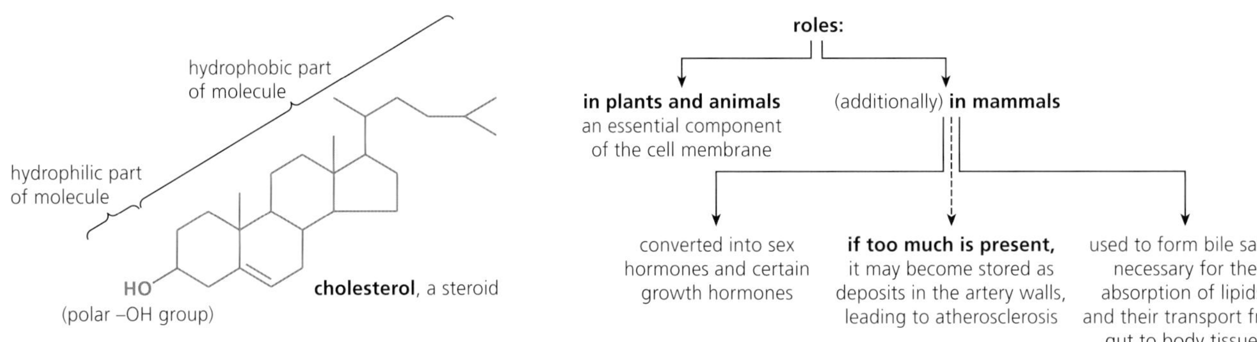

Figure 11.16 The steroid cholesterol

Lipids are absorbed into the body in the gut, and are stored as body fat. They have to be transported around the body, both in their role as respiratory substrates for the transfer of energy, and as cholesterol for use in the production of steroid hormones and the maintenance and repair of cell membranes. Since they are insoluble in water, they are carried in association with proteins, as either **low-** or **high-density lipoproteins** (LDLs or HDLs) according to the relative proportions of protein and lipid. Triglycerides combine with them. These components are introduced in Table 11.4.

Table 11.4 Low- and high-density lipoproteins

	Protein (raises density)/%	Lipid (reduces density)/%	Particle size/nm*	Known as:
Low-density lipoprotein (LDL)	10–27	5–61	20–90	'Bad cholesterol' – when combined with saturated fats.
High-density lipoprotein (HDL)	50	3	7–10	'Good cholesterol' – when combined with insaturated fats.

**A nanometre is an SI-derived unit of length, and is 10^{-9} metres. So, a metre is divided into 1000 millimetres, a millimetre is divided into 1000 micrometres (µm or microns) and a micrometre is divided into 1000 nanometres (nm) – a really small unit of length!*

Most cholesterol is transported as LDLs, but an excess of these in the bloodstream has been shown to block up the many receptor points in the cell membranes of cells that metabolise or store lipid, leaving even higher quantities of LDLs circulating in the blood plasma. The excess is then deposited under the endothelium of artery walls, initiating or enhancing plaque formations. However, monounsaturated fats help remove the circulating LDLs, and polyunsaturated fats are even more beneficial for they further increase the efficiency of the receptor sites at removing 'bad cholesterol' from the blood.

A note of caution is needed here. While you can (and should) avoid a diet that is excessively rich in saturated fats and cholesterol, this lipid is an essential body metabolite that is manufactured in the liver in the absence of absorbed dietary cholesterol. To some extent, your blood cholesterol levels are genetically controlled. A causal relationship is suggested by statistical studies of deaths from CHD per 1000 of the population each year, plotted against the levels of cholesterol and LDLs measured in blood (serum) (Figure 11.17). The establishment of the actual role of LDLs in triggering CHD is provided by experimental laboratory and clinical evidence that destructive plaques are created as a result of raised levels of blood serum LDLs, as described above.

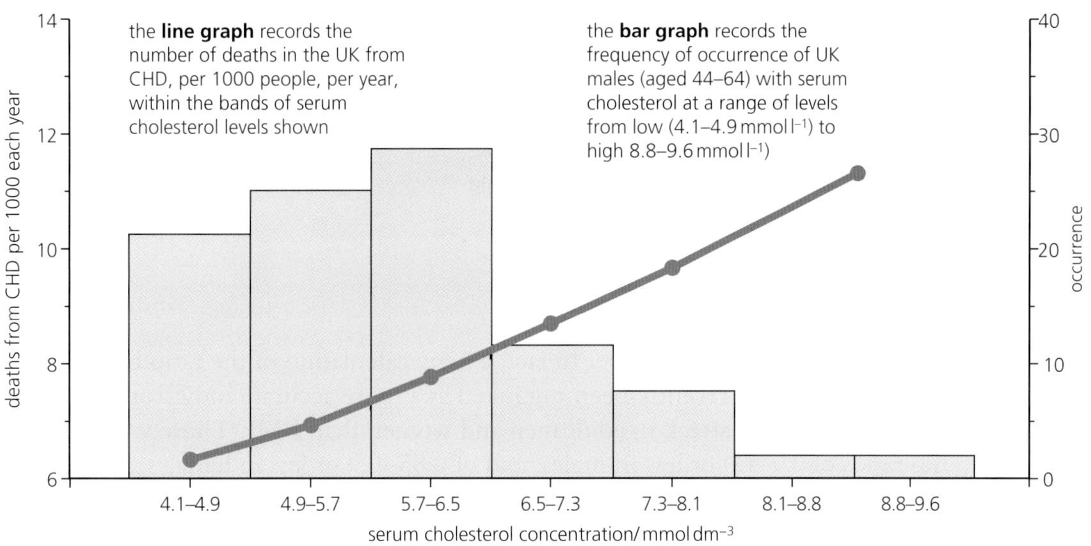

Figure 11.17 The relationship between deaths from CHD and blood serum cholesterol levels

Tip

Cause and effect – correlation isn't causation

Look carefully at Figure 11.17. It is possible to state that the straight line graph shows there is a **positive linear correlation** between deaths from CHD and blood cholesterol levels. You will see later in the book how this link can also be tested statistically. But does this mean you can also state that cholesterol *causes* CHD? This would be a very dangerous conclusion to make as the history of science is littered with perfectly good correlations leading to false conclusions. In this case you can see from Table 11.4 that 'cholesterol' does not tell the whole story. In addition, this chapter lists other strong risk factors for CHD so how do you know it wasn't one of these? For example, egg yolk, liver and butter contain high levels of cholesterol. If some other ingredient, only found in egg yolk, caused CHD then people eating lots of eggs would have high levels of this ingredient but also, coincidentally, high levels of cholesterol. This is exactly what we mean by a false correlation. So the best we could say objectively is that this finding 'supports the idea that...' In other words much more evidence needs to be found before we can confidently identify the cause. There is now plenty of research to show how cholesterol has its effect but it is not the whole story.

- **Alcohol**. An excessive intake of alcohol leads to raised blood pressure, damaged heart muscle and irregular heartbeats. It also causes raised LDL levels in the blood, and is associated with certain cancers, too. This harm may arise when more than one unit of alcohol a day is imbibed by women and more than two units per day by men. In those who consistently stick to the recommended limits, the risks of CHD may be lower than in non-drinkers. But 'binge' drinking is especially dangerous. This risk factor is of growing importance.
- **Physical inactivity, obesity and generally being overweight**. A sedentary lifestyle increases the risk of CHD, but physical activity, even only moderate activity, helps prevent heart and blood-vessel disorders. Regular, vigorous physical activity is especially beneficial, not least because it helps prevent obesity.

  We need to be able to quantify the conditions of the body we believe are 'underweight', 'normal', 'overweight' and 'obese' for different people, if individuals are to be able to satisfactorily regulate their body weight.

  To accurately and consistently quantify body weight in relation to health, the **body mass index (BMI)** has been devised. We calculate our BMI according to the following formula:

  $$\frac{\text{body mass in kg}}{(\text{height in m})^2}$$

  Using our calculated BMI and Table 11.5 below, we can determine our 'weight status'.

  Table 11.5 The 'boundaries' between being underweight, normal and overweight

BMI	Status
Below 18.5	Underweight
18.5–24.9	Normal
25.0–29.8	Overweight
30.0 and over	Obese

  Another factor here is body shape. In fact, a basic calculation of the ratio between waist and hip size has recently been suggested as a more accurate indicator of the risk of having a heart attack in adult men and women than BMI. Those with waist to hip ratios of 0.9–1.0 or less in males, and of 0.85–0.9 or less in females, have a significantly lower risk of a cardiac infarction (heart attack). This correlation is attributed to abdominal fat cells being a major source of LDLs, and a source of metabolites that damage the insulin production system in the body.

  Note that the condition of clinical obesity is defined as having a BMI of 30 and over. The incidence of obesity has substantially increased over the past 20 years. Studies by the World Health Organization, published in 2003, estimate that 300 million people are clinically obese worldwide. In the population of a developed country like the UK, 13–17 percent of men and 16–19 percent of women are clinically obese.
- **Diabetes**. This is a disease that carries a significantly raised risk of the patient developing CVD, and people with this condition require especially close monitoring of their blood pressure and blood glucose to ensure they are continuously controlled within safe parameters.

- **Other dietary issues**. These include the question of salt consumption. Sodium chloride is a widely used food preservative, traditionally popular in many cultures and used in diverse prepared food products. Today it plays a major part in the prevention of food poisoning when used as a preservative in packaged convenience foods and 'ready meals'. While it has this and other advantages, it does cause raised blood pressure after it has been absorbed into the bloodstream and prior to its excretion by the kidneys. The Food Standards Agency recommends a salt intake of no more than 6 g per day, but it is common for an individual's intake to be twice that.

Test yourself

22 Explain how atherosclerosis leads to a stroke.

23 Name the blood vessels that become blocked to cause myocardial infarction.

24 Which compound is present in higher proportion in high-density lipoproteins?

25 What is known as 'bad' cholesterol?

26 BMI is a better measure of body proportion than simply measuring mass. Explain why.

27 Define what is meant by 'hypertension'.

Chapter summary

Blood

- Blood is made up of liquid plasma, red cells, white cells and platelets.
- Plasma is used to transport hormones, nutrients, excretory products and dissolved proteins. It also transfers heat around the body.
- Red cells (erythrocytes) transport oxygen and carbon dioxide.
- The major types of white cells are: lymphocytes – have major roles in the immune response, including antibody production; phagocytes (monocytes and neutrophils) – ingest bacteria and cell fragments; eosinophils – stimulate allergic responses and histamine production.
- Platelets have an important role in blood clotting.

Vessels and circulation

- Arteries and veins have a tough collagen coat and a lining of endothelium.
- The middle layer of arteries is much thicker than that of veins. It contains smooth muscle and elastic fibres.
- Elastic fibres in arteries allow them to stretch and the elastic recoil smooths out blood flow when the heart relaxes.
- Capillaries have a single epithelial layer allowing transfer of materials to and from tissues.
- Mammals have a double circulation where blood returns to the heart after passing through the lungs. Hence high pressure oxygenated blood can be pumped into the main arteries.

Heart

- The heart has four chambers, two thin-walled atria and two thicker-walled ventricles.
- Semilunar valves prevent backflow of blood from the main arteries into the ventricles. Atrio-ventricular valves (mitral and tricuspid) prevent blood passing from ventricles back into the atria.
- Contraction of the atria (atrial systole) forces blood into the ventricles. This is followed by contraction of the ventricles (ventricular systole) forcing blood into the main arteries.
- Relaxation of atria or ventricles is called diastole.
- The cardiac cycle is controlled by a myogenic rhythm. The sino-atrial node depolarises to spread a wave across the atria. This reaches the atrio-ventricular node, which triggers an impulse in the Bundle of His and Purkyne fibres to the base of the ventricles. The pattern of activity in the heart can be shown in an electrocardiogram.

Tissue fluid and lymph

- Hydrostatic pressure forces tissue fluid, containing dissolved solutes, out of the capillaries to bathe surrounding tissues. Other nutrients will also diffuse into the cells.
- Remaining proteins in the plasma create an osmotic gradient that draws water back into the capillaries as the hydrostatic pressure falls.
- Some fluid and molecules that are unable to pass back through capillary endothelia are collected by lymph vessels. Body movements, aided by valves in the vessels, help to return lymph to the main circulation.

Blood clotting

- Clotting is triggered by the release of thromboplastin from platelets and damaged tissue.
- Ca^{2+} ions and vitamin K then activate thrombin, which causes the soluble fibrinogen in plasma to form insoluble fibrin. A network of fibrin threads traps blood cells to form a clot.

Atherosclerosis

- Excess lipoproteins and cholesterol cause fatty streaks to appear in the endothelial lining of arteries.
- White blood cells invade the damaged area, taking up more cholesterol and causing fibrous tissue to develop. This area swells to form an atheroma.
- The atheroma narrows the artery and means it is less elastic, decreasing blood flow and increasing pressure.
- Epithelial damage attracts platelets, which can cause tiny blood clots. If a clot is released it can block small coronary arteries to cause a heart attack or arteries in the brain to cause a stroke.
- Hypertension, smoking, alcohol, obesity and diabetes have all been shown to be important risk factors for cardiovascular disease.

Practice questions

1 Which of the following would be found in blood plasma but not in tissue fluid?

A a lymphocyte **C** a calcium ion

B a glucose molecule **D** an erythrocyte *(1)*

2 In the first stage of blood clotting, platelets collect at the site of damage and release which substance?

A prothrombin **C** thrombin

B thromboplastin **D** thrombus *(1)*

★3 Explain how the myogenic stimulation of cardiac muscle brings about the sequence of events in the cardiac cycle. *(6)*

Tip

Question 3 is basically an AO1 question, testing your ability to show you understand a part of the specification. But take care to read it carefully and make sure that you link the electrical changes with what happens in the cardiac cycle rather than just regurgitate some facts. This could easily be a stand-alone question or attached to a longer question with some data.

4 **a)** Describe two ways, other than causing lung cancer, in which it is thought that smoking can damage the cardiovascular system. *(4)*

b) In a study of the link between smoking and coronary heart disease, the medical histories of 187 000 American men were examined. The data on smoking habits was collected from their files as recorded by their doctors following consultation.

The data are shown in the graph.

i) Why were the data plotted as a percentage of non-smokers? *(2)*

ii) Describe two pieces of evidence from these data that support the hypothesis that smoking causes coronary heart disease. *(2)*

c) Describe three ways in which the data collection could be modified to improve the reliability of any conclusions made. *(3)*

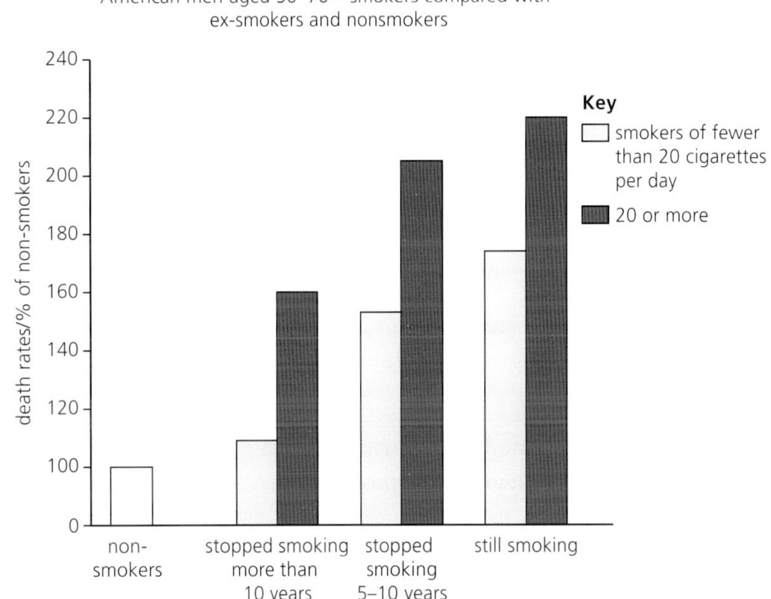

Tip

Question 4 is a typical question that combines knowledge of basic specification material (part a)) for AO1 with testing your practical skills of data interpretation and experimental design (parts b) and c)) for AO3.

5 The diagram shows the values of hydrostatic pressure and water potential in two parts of a capillary surrounded by tissue fluid. One part of the capillary (A) was close to the arteriole supplying the capillary and the other (B) close to the venule carrying blood away.

Key
H = hydrostatic pressure (kPa)
W = water potential of solution (kPa)

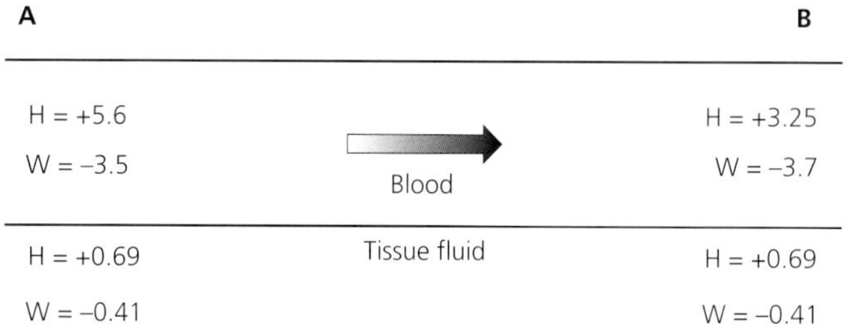

	A		B
Blood	H = +5.6 W = −3.5	→	H = +3.25 W = −3.7
Tissue fluid	H = +0.69 W = −0.41		H = +0.69 W = −0.41

a) i) In which direction will water flow in part A? *(1)*

ii) Calculate the overall (net) pressure tending to cause water to flow in this direction. *(3)*

b) i) Calculate the percentage change in water potential of the blood between part A and part B. *(2)*

ii) Explain why there is a change in water potential of the blood between part A and part B. *(2)*

Stretch and challenge

6 Statins are compounds that have been shown to reduce the level of cholesterol in the blood. In recent years medical guidelines have consistently reduced the levels of blood LDLs (low-density lipoproteins) at which statins should be prescribed and some have gone as far as recommending statins be taken by everyone over the age of 50.

a) What are statins and how do they reduce levels of LDLs in the blood?

b) Many doctors and patients are opposed to prescribing in this way. Discuss the advantages and disadvantages of mass-medication with statins as a means of reducing the incidence of CVD.

c) Several plant foods, including nuts, contain natural cholesterol-reducing compounds called sterols and stanols. These are widely advertised and added to various products.

i) How are these thought to bring about their effect?

ii) Why are they not recommended by doctors and the government advisory body NICE?

7 a) Describe the structure of lymph nodes and explain why they are important.

b) i) People sitting on an aircraft for long periods can experience swelling of the ankles and feet (oedema). Explain why this might happen.

ii) Describe how wearing elasticated stockings ('flight socks') can help alleviate this problem.

Tip

In Question 5 you are asked to show you understand some basic concepts, including water potential from Chapter 9. This is quite common – there are synoptic questions such as this in AS papers and in A level papers. Part a) ii) asks you to apply your understanding of the formation of tissue fluid; part b) i) is a very typical percentage calculation that can appear in a wide range of questions.

Tip

In Question 6(b) you are asked to 'discuss'. This type of question could appear in an A level exam paper. The important point is to show that you understand the arguments for and against; if the command word was 'evaluate' then you would be required, in addition, to come to a conclusion. Whichever is the case, this extension work will provide an opportunity to practise this approach.

12 Transport in plants

Prior knowledge

In this chapter you will need to recall that:

- → xylem tissue carries water and mineral ions in plants
- → xylem tissue plays an important part in supporting plant stems
- → phloem tissue carries the products of photosynthesis around the plant
- → transpiration is the loss of water vapour from the leaves of a plant
- → transpiration is responsible for drawing water up the xylem tissues of a plant
- → water vapour is lost from leaves though open stomata
- → light and temperature can affect the rate of transpiration
- → water enters plants through root hair cells
- → mineral ions enter plant root cells by active transport
- → plant cells have cellulose cell walls, which are freely permeable to water.

Test yourself on prior knowledge

1. State whether xylem vessels are living or dead.
2. State whether phloem sieve tubes are living or dead.
3. What is the chemical nature of the products of photosynthesis carried in phloem tissues?
4. Describe the effect that increasing temperature has on the rate of transpiration.
5. Explain why it is an advantage to the plant to close stomata at night.
6. Suggest why the cellulose structure of a plant cell wall is so permeable to water.
7. The root hair cell needs active transport to take up many important ions from soil water. Why is this necessary?

Transport tissues of a flowering plant

Key term

Vascular bundles Groups of phloem, xylem and support tissues found in the stems and roots of plants.

Internal transport in plants requires specialised tissues just as it does in animals. There are two separate tissues. Water and mineral ions are transported in **xylem tissue**. Sugars, produced by photosynthesis, and some amino acids are transported in **phloem tissue**. Like mammals, the main transport mechanism is by mass-flow but unlike mammals there is no central pump. Xylem and phloem are collectively known as vascular tissue and they are usually found together in the **vascular bundles** in the stem, and in the central stele in the root. You can see the arrangement of vascular tissue in a plant in Figures 12.1 and 12.2.

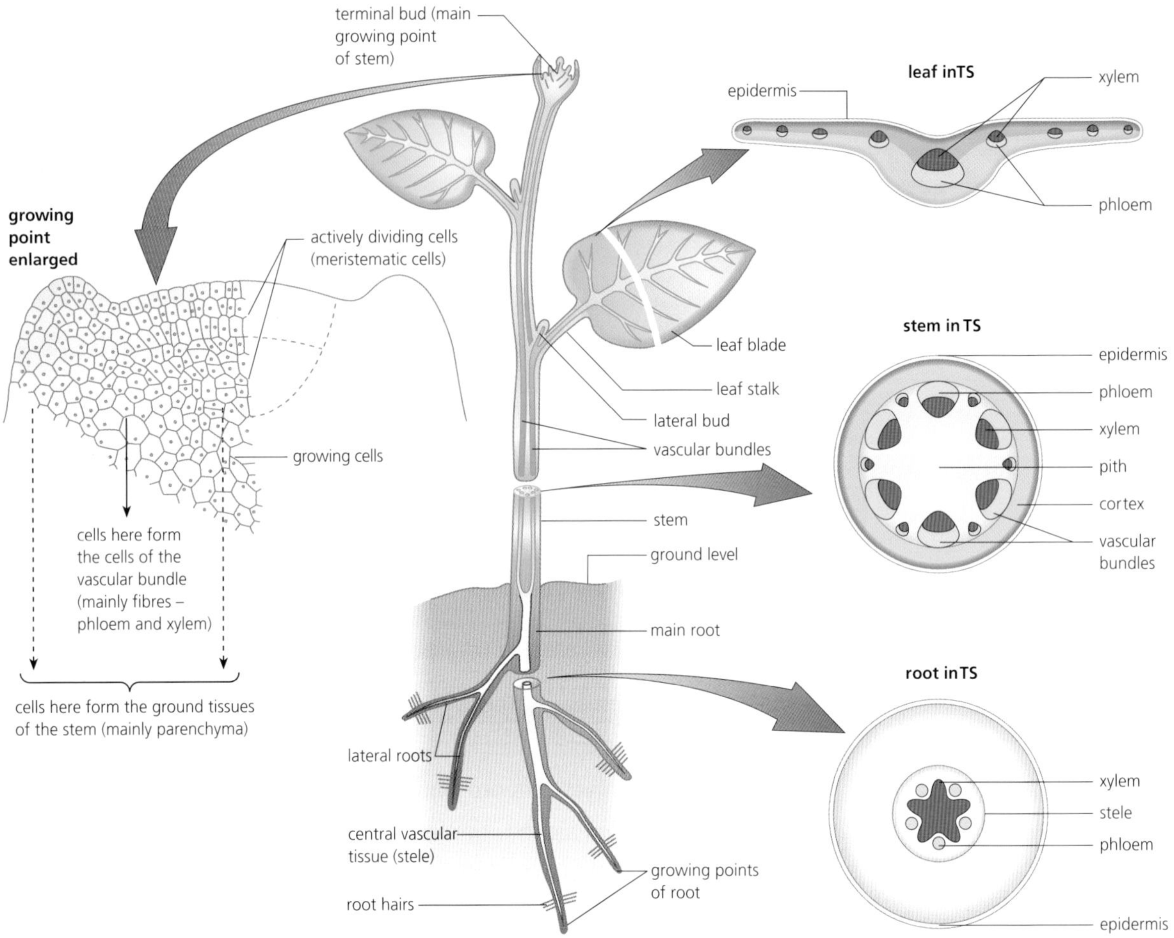

terminal bud (main growing point of stem)
growing point enlarged
actively dividing cells (meristematic cells)
growing cells
cells here form the cells of the vascular bundle (mainly fibres – phloem and xylem)
cells here form the ground tissues of the stem (mainly parenchyma)
leaf blade
leaf stalk
lateral bud
vascular bundles
stem
ground level
main root
lateral roots
central vascular tissue (stele)
root hairs
growing points of root
leaf in TS
epidermis
xylem
phloem
stem in TS
epidermis
phloem
xylem
pith
cortex
vascular bundles
root in TS
xylem
stele
phloem
epidermis

Figure 12.1 The distribution of xylem and phloem tissue in the flowering plant

TS vascular bundle, HP
TS mature stem
epidermis
vascular bundle
cortex
pith cavity
leaf trace
fibres
phloem
xylem
ground tissue of cortex (parenchyma)
ground tissue of pith (parenchyma)

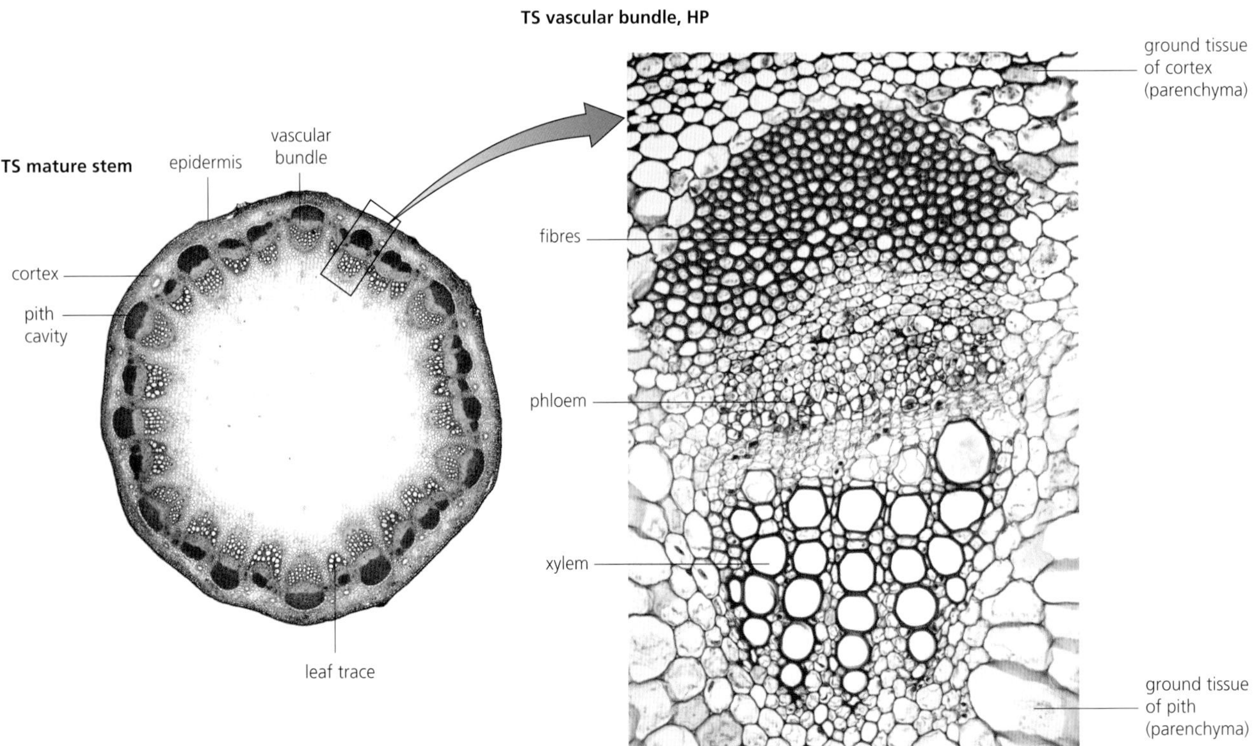

Figure 12.2 (a) The vascular tissue in the stem of *Ranunculus* (buttercup)

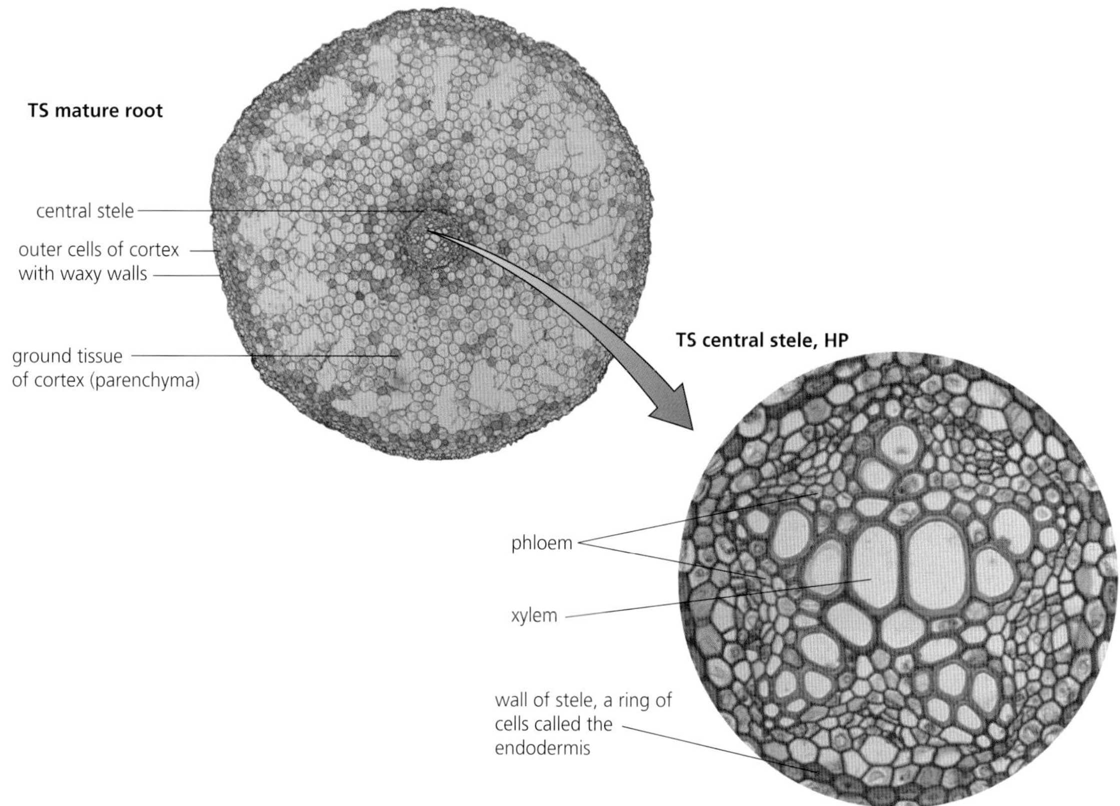

Figure 12.2 (b) The vascular tissue in the root of *Ranunculus* (buttercup)

Xylem tissues

Xylem vessels

The main water transport tissue in xylem is made up of **xylem vessels**. These cells begin life as typical elongated plant cells. As the vessels grow, a complex carbohydrate polymer called **lignin** is laid down in the spaces between the cellulose fibres of the cell wall. This makes them much stronger but also impermeable, so the cytoplasm dies. The end walls of each of the cells break down to form long continuous tubes, ideal for water transport. Table 12.1 summarises these adaptations. Although you may be unfamiliar with the name 'lignin', you are almost certainly very familiar with lignified xylem vessels. If you are sitting on a wooden chair or at a wooden desk, look at it carefully, as wood is nothing more than dead vessels coated with lignin. In most plants the lignification process tends to stop after vessel formation but in woody plants it continues until the vessels are blocked. Whilst this is of no use for water transport it forms an ever thicker stem for support in larger plants. New large vessels formed every Spring to restore water transport give the woody stem its characteristic **annual rings**.

Key term

Lignin A complex polymer of phenols used to thicken plant cell walls.

Table 12.1 Structural adaptations of xylem tissues for water transport

Structure	Adaptation
Dead empty xylem vessels	Creates a wide lumen for unrestricted water flow
End walls of vessels break down	Creates a long continuous tube for water transport
Cell walls of vessels lignified	Prevents vessels collapsing when contents are under tension
Cell walls lignified with rings, spirals and in a reticulate manner	Allows vessels to be flexible, preventing breakage as the stem moves

Key term

Pits Areas of the cell wall that lack lignin and so allow lateral transport.

Figures 12.3 and 12.4 show other adaptations of xylem vessels. In order to allow water and ions to be transferred to all parts of the plant, vessels have **pits**. These are areas of the cell wall where there is no lignin and water can move laterally as well as up the stem. In addition to pits, vessels have different types of lignin thickening. The transport of water inside vessels causes a slight reduction in pressure, threatening to cause them to collapse. The lignin thickening helps to overcome this problem but stems still need to be flexible if they are not to break. Therefore the pattern of thickening is often in the form of rings, spirals or networks.

photomicrograph of xylem tissue in LS

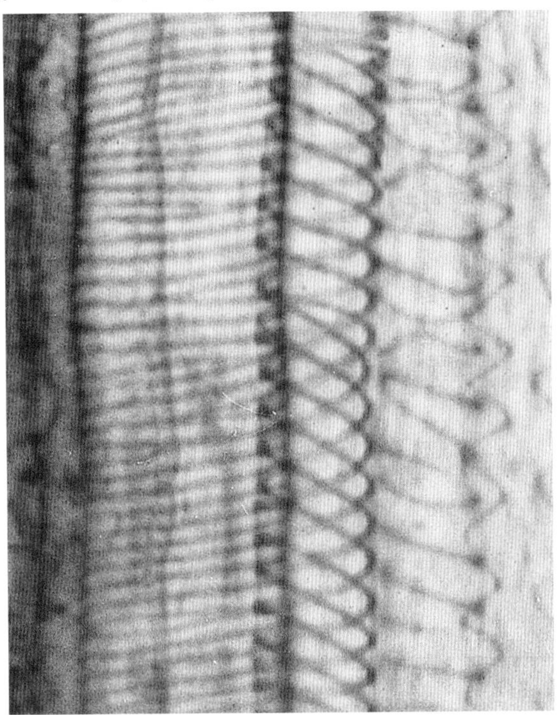

drawing of xylem vessels in TS and LS

TS

all vessels have lignin-free 'pit' areas in their walls

fibre

xylem parenchyma (the only living cells of xylem tissue)

LS

lignin thickening as spirals, rings, network or solid blocks – deposited on inside of vessel, strengthening the cellulose layers

Figure 12.3 The structure of xylem tissue

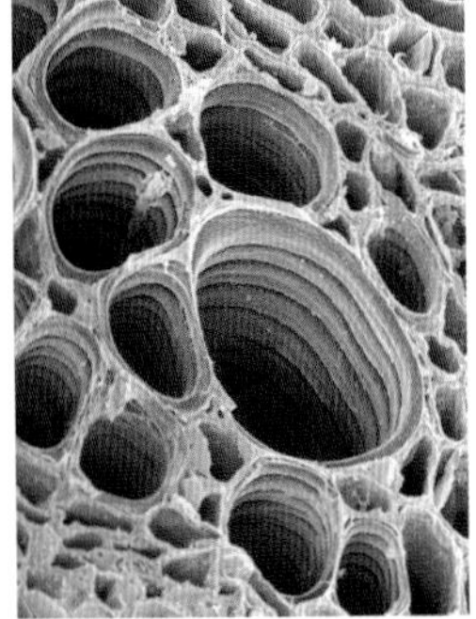

Figure 12.4 SEM of xylem vessels

Other xylem tissues

Not all the xylem is made up of vessels. Other types of tissue can be found in different plants.

- **Xylem tracheids** are similar to vessels but are narrower and shorter with tapering ends. They are found in less-advanced species such as conifers, where they are the main water-carrying tissue. Like vessels, their sloping end walls break down to form continuous tubes as they become lignified.
- **Xylem parenchyma cells** are typical plant cells with no thickening. They are found among the vessels or tracheids and remain as living tissue.
- **Xylem fibres** are narrow, highly thickened dead cells with only a small gap (lumen) in the centre. They are very similar to the fibres found in many other parts of plants. Their structure means they cannot transport water but are used for support.

Test yourself

1 Name the complex carbohydrate laid down in plant cell walls that forms wood.

2 Xylem vessels die when their walls become thickened. Explain why.

3 Explain why many xylem vessels have rings or spirals of thickening and not a solid coating.

Phloem tissues

Sieve tubes

Sieve tubes are elongated living cells with a very specialised structure. As they develop they lose their nuclei and their cytoplasm is restricted to a very thin peripheral layer with few organelles, but they still remain alive. Their end walls have many holes called **sieve pores**, which form a sieve plate between each cell. Running through the large lumen and the sieve pores between each tube element are strands of **phloem protein**. Sieve tubes are connected to their companion cells through channels in the cell walls called plasmodesmata (singular: plasmodesma).

Companion cells

Running alongside the sieve tubes are **companion cells**. These are typical plant cells but with dense cytoplasm and many organelles. Their cytoplasm is connected to the sieve tube through the plasmodesmata and it is thought that they carry out many cellular functions, enabling the sieve tubes to stay alive and transport materials, even though they have no nucleus and very little cytoplasm. You can see sieve tubes and companion cells in Figure 12.5.

Other phloem tissues

Phloem contains very similar additional tissues to xylem, including **phloem parenchyma** and **phloem fibres**. Once again these are not concerned with sugar transport. Table 12.2 summarises the main adaptations of phloem tissue to its role in solute transport.

Table 12.2 Structural adaptations of phloem tissues for solute transport

Structure	Adaptation
Sieve tubes have limited peripheral cytoplasm and organelles	Creates space for sugar transport through the cell
End walls form sieve plates with sieve pores	Form direct connections for transport from one sieve tube element to the next
Companion cells and sieve tubes are connected by plasmodesmata	Enables the sieve tube to stay alive without a nucleus and with very limited cytoplasm
Companion cells have dense cytoplasm and many organelles	Thought to be needed to support sieve tubes

Key terms

Sieve plates Perforated end walls of phloem sieve tubes.

Companion cells Plant cells with dense cytoplasm connected to sieve tubes in phloem tissue.

Plasmodesmata Channels in adjacent cell walls of plant cells that form cytoplasmic bridges for communication and transport.

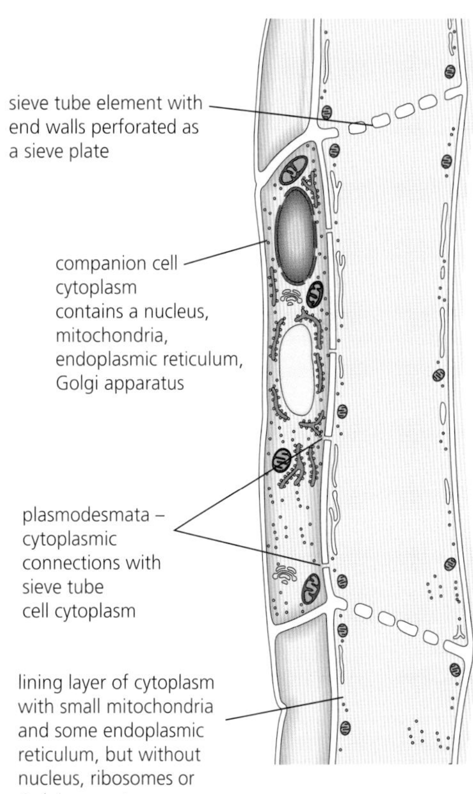

Figure 12.5 Phloem tissue

Test yourself

4 State **two** ways in which sieve tubes differ from xylem vessels.
5 Explain why sieve tubes have reduced peripheral cytoplasm.
6 How are sieve tubes connected to companion cells?

Key terms

Apoplast pathway The route of water transport across plant cells that passes through the fibrous cell walls.

Symplast pathway The route of water transport across plant cells that passes from cell to cell through plasmodesmata.

Movement of water through the plant

The three routes of water movement through plant cells and tissues are shown in Figure 12.6. They are as follows:

- **Mass flow** through the interconnected 'free' spaces between the cellulose fibres of the plant cell walls. This pathway does not pass through membranes or the living contents of the cell and is known as the **apoplast pathway**. The apoplast includes water-filled spaces of dead cells such as xylem vessels and is the major route of water transport.
- **Diffusion** through the cytoplasm of the cells using the channels through cell walls called plasmodesmata. This is called the **symplast pathway**. The cytoplasm of cells is packed with organelles and other molecules that slow diffusion, so this is a much more restricted pathway.
- **Osmosis** from vacuole to vacuole of plant cells using their partially permeable membranes (sometimes known as the **vacuolar pathway**). This is driven by a gradient of water potential. Although this is also a limited pathway for movement of large quantities of water, it is the way in which individual cells take in water. Root hair cells take up water from the soil in this way as their contents have a much more negative water potential than the very dilute solution of ions found in soil water.

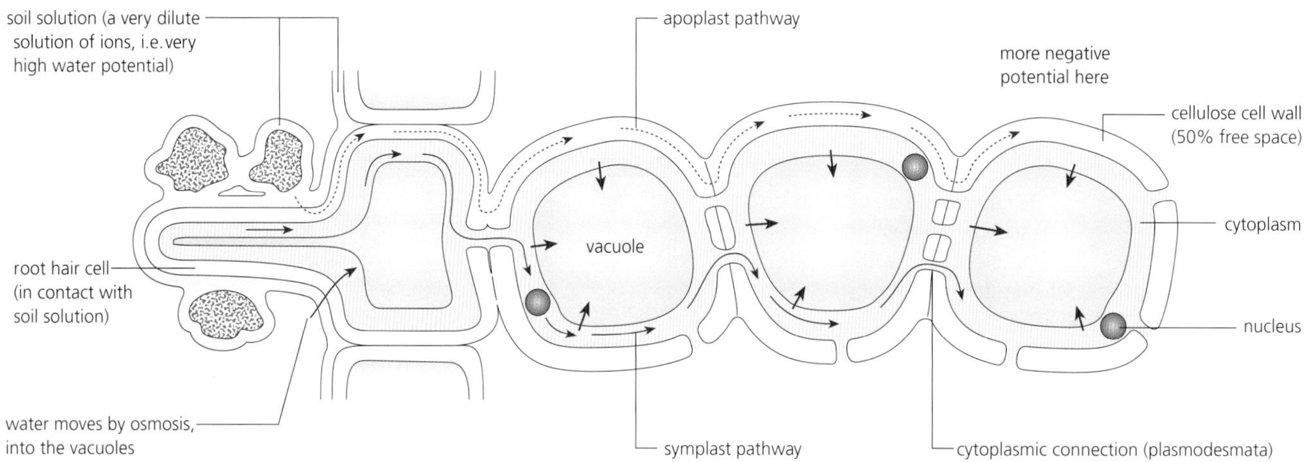

Figure 12.6 How water moves across plant cells

Movement of water up xylem vessels

Figure 12.7 shows how water entering root hair cells by osmosis can be transported across the root to the xylem vessels, which have pits, allowing the water to enter freely. At this point water must be drawn up the xylem vessels to reach the leaves. In many plants this means a long ascent. Giant redwood trees, *Sequoia sempervirens,* grow to over 100 m tall. The **cohesion–tension model** suggests the way in which this might be achieved.

The evaporation of water from the aerial parts of the plant (**transpiration**) means that a tension is applied to the water column in the xylem vessels. This tension is sufficient to draw up the continuous column of water from the root. However, this would not be possible if it were not for the remarkable properties of water molecules. We saw in Chapter 1 that water molecules are attracted to each other by weak **hydrogen bonds**, a property known as **cohesion**. Although weak, there are many billions of such bonds, giving the column of water great **tensile strength**. In simple terms this means the column of water can be drawn upwards to a great height without breaking. Water molecules are also attracted to other molecules, a property known as **adhesion**. This means they are attracted to molecules in the vessel walls, which also assists in their upward movement without the column breaking.

Key terms

Transpiration The loss of water vapour from the aerial parts of plants.

Cohesion A property of water molecules by which hydrogen bonds give columns of water great tensile strength.

Evidence for the cohesion–tension model

- When xylem vessels are punctured air enters, demonstrating water under tension not under pressure.
- Xylem vessels have thickened lignin walls to prevent them collapsing under tension.
- Rates of water uptake are strongly linked to factors affecting transpiration from leaves.
- Fine columns of water placed under tension show sufficient tensile strength to account for transport up the highest trees.

Tip

Remember to use the correct terminology. 'Water vapour' is the accurate description here. Water molecules will constantly escape from liquid water at a wide range of temperatures (steam is very different). 'Water' alone can imply the liquid.

Factors affecting the rate of water movement

The faster the rate of transpiration, the faster will be the movement of water up the xylem as this is the main driving force. The following factors affect transpiration:

- **Temperature**. Figure 12.7 shows that, in leaves, water vapour evaporates from the apoplast of the spongy mesophyll cells into the air spaces. From here it diffuses into the atmosphere through the stomata. An increase in temperature means the water molecules will have more kinetic energy. With more energy, more water molecules will evaporate into the air spaces and they will diffuse out faster, increasing the overall rate of transpiration.
- **Light**. To escape into the atmosphere, water molecules must pass through the stomatal pores. As light intensity decreases, the guard cells of the stomata begin to lose their turgidity, causing them to flatten against each other, closing the stomatal pores. As the pores close diffusion of water vapour is severely restricted.
- **Humidity**. Humidity is simply a measure of the amount of water vapour in the surrounding atmosphere. As the number of water molecules in the air increases, the diffusion gradient compared with the inside of the leaf is reduced, slowing diffusion.
- **Air movements**. In still air, water vapour diffusing out of the stomata tends to build up close to the surface of the leaf. Again, this reduces the diffusion gradient and slows transpiration. As the movement of air increases, more of the water vapour surrounding the leaf is removed, increasing the diffusion gradient and speeding up transpiration.

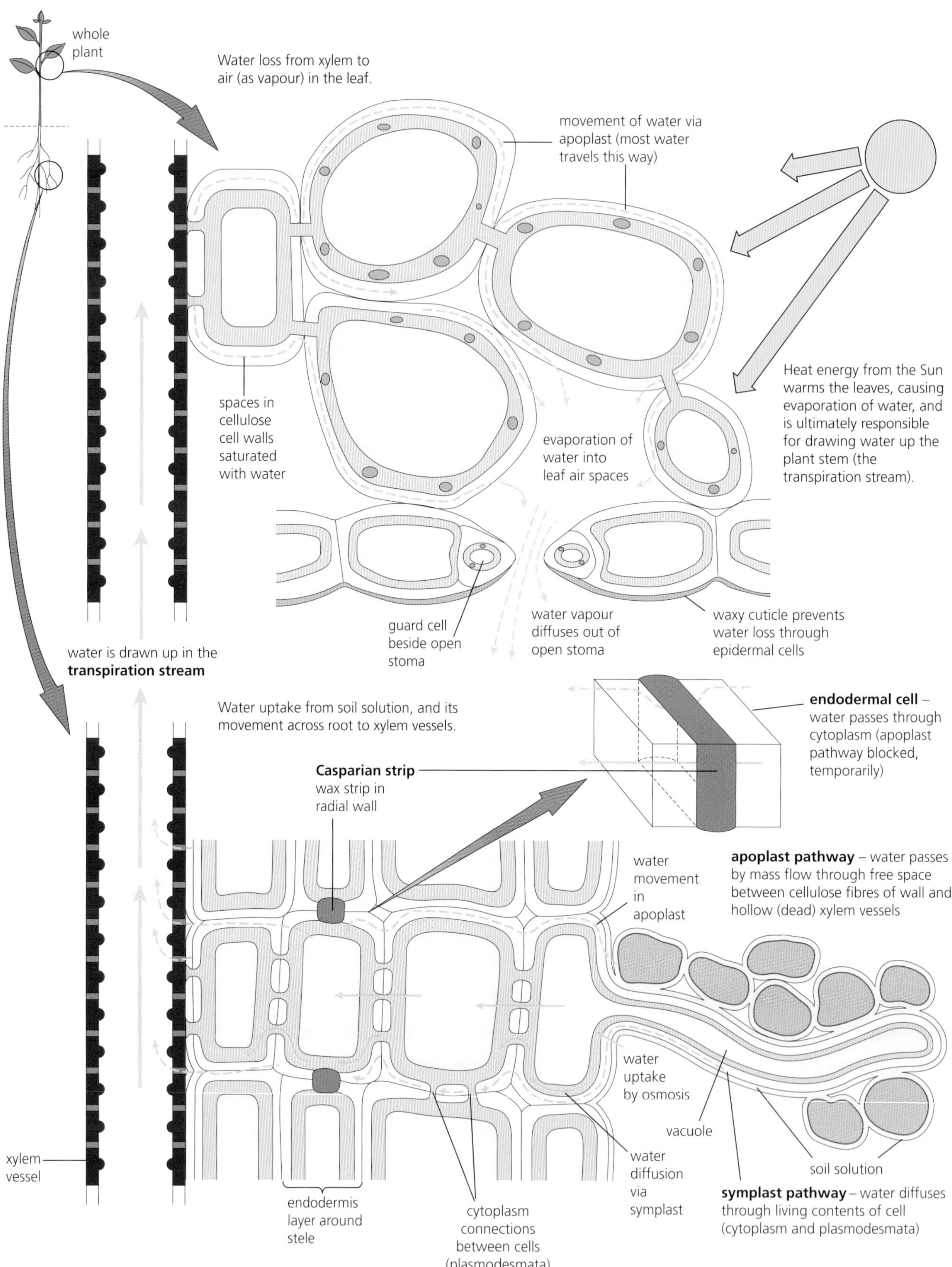
whole
plant
Water loss from xylem to
air (as vapour) in the leaf.
movement of water via
apoplast (most water
travels this way)
spaces in
cellulose
cell walls
saturated
with water
evaporation of
water into
leaf air spaces
Heat energy from the Sun
warms the leaves, causing
evaporation of water, and
is ultimately responsible
for drawing water up the
plant stem (the
transpiration stream).
guard cell
beside open
stoma
water vapour
diffuses out of
open stoma
waxy cuticle prevents
water loss through
epidermal cells
water is drawn up in the
transpiration stream
endodermal cell –
water passes through
cytoplasm (apoplast
pathway blocked,
temporarily)
Water uptake from soil solution, and its
movement across root to xylem vessels.
Casparian strip
wax strip in
radial wall
water
movement
in
apoplast
apoplast pathway – water passes
by mass flow through free space
between cellulose fibres of wall and
hollow (dead) xylem vessels
water
uptake
by osmosis
vacuole
xylem
vessel
water
diffusion
via
symplast
soil solution
symplast pathway – water diffuses
through living contents of cell
(cytoplasm and plasmodesmata)
endodermis
layer around
stele
cytoplasm
connections
between cells
(plasmodesmata)

Figure 12.7 The pathway of water movement from soil to leaf

Test yourself

7 Explain why cellulose cell walls have so much 'free' space for water molecules to pass through.

8 Name the pathway for water movement that involves passage through plasmodesmata.

9 Describe the feature of water molecules that gives the liquid a high tensile strength.

10 If the lumen of a xylem vessel has a diameter of 25 μm, what will be the mass of water contained in a continuous xylem vessel of a redwood tree 100 m tall?

11 Explain why an increase in humidity will slow transpiration.

Core practical 8

Investigate factors affecting water uptake by plant shoots using a potometer

Background information

The principle of this investigation is very simple in theory but controlling variables poses interesting challenges. A **potometer** is simply a tube filled with water attached to a plant shoot. As the shoot draws water up the xylem vessels then the meniscus of the water in the tube will be drawn along a scale. The rate of water uptake can be measured by calculating the volume of the water in the tube drawn up in a fixed time. When the meniscus reaches the end of the tube it needs to be reset by refilling the tube. In the apparatus shown in Figure 12.8 this is done by using a reservoir of water. This allows the tube to be refilled simply by opening the tap and pressing the syringe, so the shoot is not disturbed. Whilst it is very convenient, this type of potometer is expensive. It is possible to collect very reliable data by using a simple capillary tube about 30 cm long attached to a shoot by a piece of rubber tubing. This can be refilled by injecting water through the rubber tubing using a syringe with a fine needle.

Carrying out the investigation

Aim: to investigate the rate of water uptake by a plant shoot

Risk assessment: There are no significant risks associated with this investigation unless the shoot is cut with a sharp knife, when care must be taken to cut downwards onto a hard surface.

1 First of all you will need to select a suitable plant shoot. To do this, check the internal diameter of the rubber tubing, which is used to attach the shoot to the potometer. To achieve a good seal the diameter of the shoot you choose needs to be slightly larger than the rubber tubing. It is also helpful to choose shoots from a woody plant with a strong stem. It is important that any shoots you use are placed in water as soon as they are removed from the parent plant as water continues to be drawn up the xylem, introducing air locks. Cutting off 1–2 cm of the shoot under water just before use helps to ensure any air locks are removed.

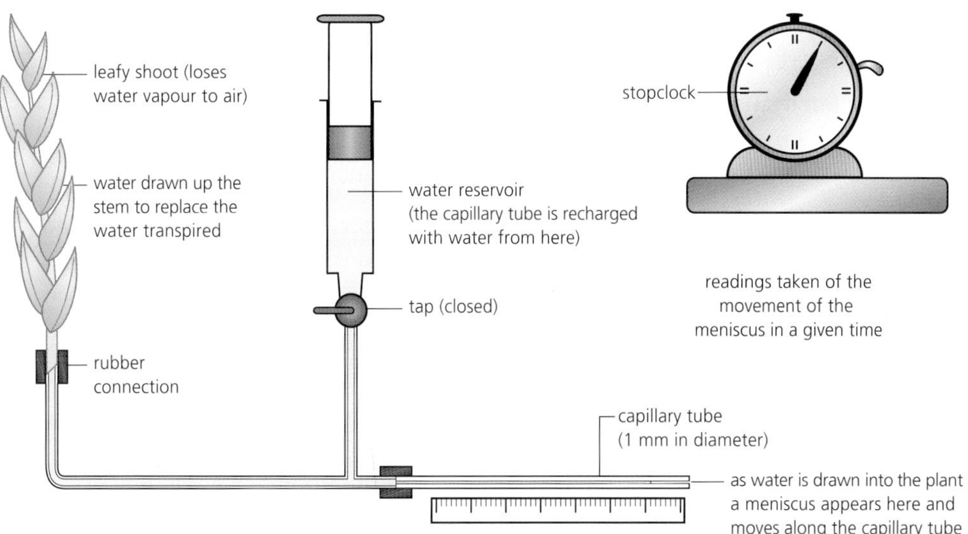

Figure 12.8 A potometer used to investigate water uptake by a plant shoot. There are various designs of potometer, all operating in a similar way

2 When you are ready with a suitable shoot in water close at hand, fill the capillary tube and the rubber tubing to the very brim by opening the tap and pushing down on the syringe. Close the tap and insert the shoot in the rubber tubing. Make sure the whole shoot is secured with a stand and clamps as movements may squeeze the rubber tubing, giving erratic readings.
3 The water meniscus should begin to move along the capillary. If the water leaks from the open end of the capillary then there is a poor seal and you must repeat the process above. Smearing grease around the seal can help, but make sure this does not cover the cut surface. Once the potometer is working smoothly, check how quickly it moves along the scale and decide on a suitable time interval to record the movement.
4 Now you will need to consider very carefully how to vary conditions to investigate factors affecting transpiration. Light intensity and air movements are the factors that you can manipulate more easily. For light, you will need to darken the laboratory and use a bench lamp at different distances but remember that the light intensity needs to be measured using a simple light meter. If you have a suitable 'app' on your mobile phone you can use the camera setting to give intensity readings. You will need to carry out some simple trials to decide upon suitable distances and times of recording.

Air movements can also be investigated if you have a fan with variable speed settings.

Questions

1 Why does a potometer measure rate of water uptake and not the rate of transpiration?
2 How can the volume of water taken up be measured?
3 Will it make a difference to your graph if you use just the distance moved against time rather than the volume taken up against time?
4 Why would simply covering the shoot with a black polythene bag not give you valid data about the effect of lack of light on water uptake?
5 A bench lamp placed 20 cm from the potometer gives a light meter reading of 100 AU. If the lamp is moved to 40 cm from the photometer, what will be the light intensity?

The movement of organic solutes through the plant

Scientists and models

In Chapter 7 you looked at ideas of classification, where there is scientific disagreement. Most scientific advances begin with the development of a model to try to explain something. This is not some idle speculation but is usually based upon the available evidence at the time. This model stimulates debate and allows scientists to make predictions about what might happen if the model is correct. This is the stage at which collaboration, ingenuity and the ability to think objectively need to be applied in designing reliable investigations to test the model. Very rarely can any one investigation be decisive, but as more and more predictions based on the model are shown to be correct then the model becomes widely accepted. That is, of course, until one single investigation of an important prediction proves to be incorrect!

You have seen that the cohesion–tension model of water transport has many sound features and offers a wide range of scientific explanations. It is therefore widely accepted. The story of the transport of solutes in phloem is much less clear and the mass-flow model considered here has many unanswered questions, which means that it is, at best, an incomplete explanation or there may even be much better explanations.

As a scientist, it is really important that you keep asking questions such as 'How do we know that?' or 'What other explanation might there be?' rather than expecting to look into textbooks and find the perfect answer or regard the knowledge you have as 'fact'. At A level your ability to consider or evaluate evidence will be tested in the written papers.

The movement of solutes through phloem tissue

The transport of sugars, especially sucrose, through sieve tubes can easily be demonstrated using radioactively labelled carbon dioxide and collecting their contents using aphids (greenfly), which pierce stems with their fine mouthparts to feed off phloem contents. If the feeding insects are anaesthetised and the mouthparts cut off, the contents of the sieve tubes flow out and can be analysed. Similarly, radioactively labelled sugars can be traced throughout the plant to follow their movements. Unlike water, the paths of solute movements can be in different directions, not just down from the leaves. Many plants use storage organs such as bulbs of daffodils or stem tubers of potatoes. In spring the compounds they contain must be transported to the shoots to enable them to grow and begin photosynthesis.

The sugars in sieve tubes come from photosynthesis in leaves and are transported around the plant in a process called translocation.

Key terms

Translocation The name given to the transport of manufactured solutes, such as sucrose and amino acids, in the phloem.

Mass flow A method of transport in which pressure differences are used to move a fluid to carry substances in one direction.

The mass-flow hypothesis of phloem transport

One model of transport in the phloem is called the mass-flow **hypothesis**. You saw in Chapter 11 that a mass-flow system uses a fluid to carry substances in one direction using pressure differences to move it along. This same idea has been suggested as the mechanism for movement in phloem.

This model suggests that pressure differences to drive the fluid movement are generated in different parts of the plant, as shown in Figure 12.9.

In cells of the leaf, sugars are manufactured by photosynthesis. These sugars dissolve in the cytoplasm, causing a lowered (more negative) water potential. This causes water to enter the cells by osmosis and build up a high hydrostatic pressure. This is called the **source area**.

In other parts of the plant, sugars are used up rapidly in respiration or converted into starch. Starch is insoluble and forms starch grains, which have no osmotic effect. This removal of dissolved sugars raises the water potential (less negative) and therefore water tends to flow out of the cell, forming a region of lower hydrostatic pressure. This is called the **sink area**.

The model suggests that this pressure difference forces sugars into the sieve tubes at the source and induces mass-flow through the phloem towards the sink. The remaining fluid in the sink is then returned to the source through the xylem vessels.

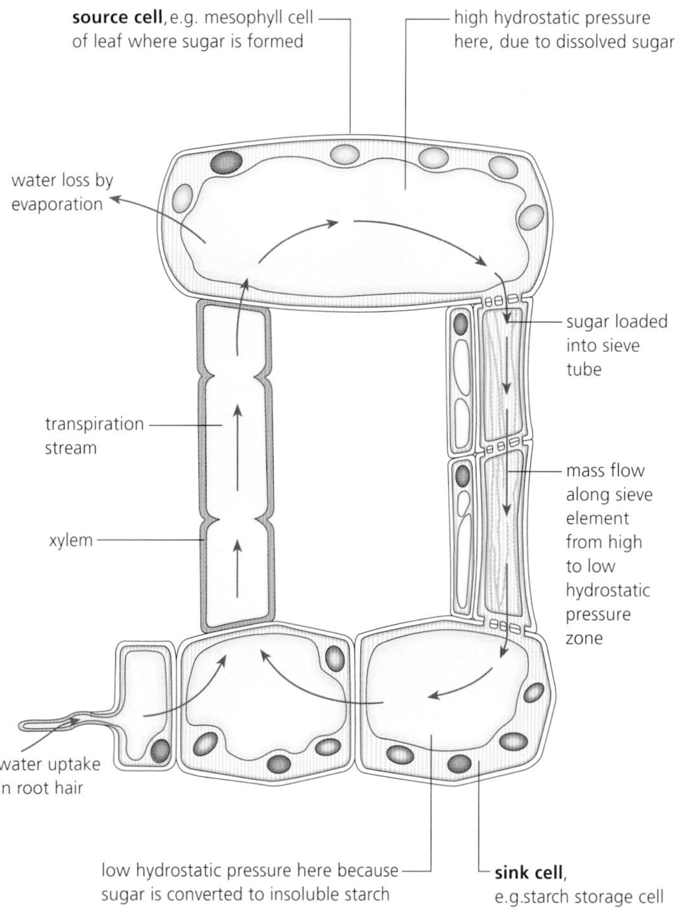

Figure 12.9 The mass-flow hypothesis

Strengths and weaknesses of the mass-flow hypothesis

Strengths of the model:

- It is possible to measure the gradients suggested and show they are present.
- When pierced by insect mouthparts, the contents of sieve tubes flows out, showing them to be under pressure as the model predicts.
- The model links the phloem and xylem systems in a plausible way.

Weaknesses of the model:

- Organic solutes move around the plant in different directions, not just to the lowest pressure sinks.
- Sieve tubes and companion cells are living tissue and do not work if killed off. The model does not really explain why.
- Starch grains are found in many plant cells, not just sinks.
- The basic model suggests an entirely passive process but phloem has a higher metabolic rate than most other plant tissues.

Other features the model does not yet explain:

- Sugar needs to be 'loaded' into sieve tubes at the source; this is not yet fully explained.
- Why do almost all sieve tubes contain phloem protein strands?
- What is the purpose of sieve plates? They appear to be a hindrance to mass flow, not an adaptation to facilitate it.

It will be obvious that the model is far from accepted by the scientific community and much more research needs to be done to find more evidence to support it or to develop other models.

Test yourself

12 Name the process of transporting sugars and amino acids around plants.

13 Explain **two** ways in which it can be shown that phloem sieve tubes are involved in the transport of solutes.

14 Name the main sugar transported by sieve tubes.

15 Suggest where, in plants, you would expect to find the main 'source areas'.

16 Why is the presence of sieve plates a problem for the mass-flow hypothesis?

17 Describe how the fluid is moved in all mass-flow systems.

Chapter summary

Transport tissues in plants

- Water and mineral ions are transported in xylem tissue.
- Xylem vessels are elongated cells with walls that become thickened with lignin. This causes the cells to die and their end walls break down to form long tubes. To retain some flexibility lignin is often laid down as rings or helices.
- Xylem vessels also have unthickened pits that allow water and ions to move laterally across the stem and root.
- Xylem tissue can also contain more primitive vessels called tracheids, fibres for support and unspecialised parenchyma.
- Organic solutes are transported by phloem tissue.
- Phloem sieve tubes have a thin layer of peripheral cytoplasm and perforated end walls forming sieve plates. Strands of phloem protein run through the sieve tubes and sieve plates.
- Companion cells with dense cytoplasm surround sieve tubes and are connected to them through pores called plasmodesmata.
- Phloem tissue also has parenchyma and fibres like xylem.

Movement of water in plants

- Movement of water by mass flow through the free spaces between cellulose fibres of cell walls is known as the apoplast pathway.
- Movement of water by diffusion through the cytoplasm is known as the symplast pathway.
- Movement of water by osmosis from vacuole to vacuole is known as the vacuolar pathway.
- The cohesion-tension model suggests water is drawn up xylem vessels as evaporation from leaves exerts sufficient force to move the column of water from the roots.
- Special properties of water, such as hydrogen bonding, create great tensile strength to make this possible.

Movement of organic solutes

- The mass-flow hypothesis may account for the transport of organic solutes but is not generally accepted.
- It suggests that pressure differences drive movements of fluid carrying solutes.
- High pressure is generated at the source as leaves produce sugars, which dissolve to create a more negative water potential. Water is then drawn into cells by osmosis creating a high hydrostatic pressure.
- Lower hydrostatic pressure is formed in sink areas as sugars are converted to starch, thus creating a less negative water potential, which causes water to leave by osmosis.
- Pressure forces sugar solutions into the phloem whilst fluid removed in the sink areas is returned to leaves via the xylem.
- At present this model gives only a partial explanation and leaves many questions unanswered.

Practice questions

1 One feature of a mass flow system is:

A it transports only soluble substances

B all substances are transported in one direction

C it involves a pump

D it involves active transport *(1)*

2 Which of the following is an adaptation to transport in **both** xylem vessels and phloem sieve tubes?

A presence of simple pits

B presence of plasmodesmata

C presence of a large lumen

D no cytoplasm present *(1)*

3 Which of the following is an essential feature of water transport via the apoplast pathway in plants?

A high osmotic potential in cell vacuoles

B high proportion of free space in cellulose cell walls

C cell membranes permeable to water molecules

D presence of a large number of mitochondria *(1)*

4 **a)** Explain how the differences between the apoplast and symplast pathways in plants result in much faster water transport through the apoplast pathway. *(4)*

b) In plant roots water is taken up by osmosis through root hair cell membranes. To enter the xylem the water must cross the endodermis surrounding the central stele. The cells of the endodermis have cell walls containing a Casparian strip of cork-like material, which is impermeable. Describe the effect that this structure will have on the flow of water into xylem vessels. *(3)*

5 A student carried out an investigation into the effect of air speed on the rate of transpiration of a woody shoot. The selected shoot was carefully attached to a potometer 1 metre in front of a slow-moving fan and the air speed measured using a flow meter. The student then measured the volume of water taken up by the shoot in 5 minutes.

The water level of the potometer was then reset and the fan speed was increased. A flow meter was again used to measure the air speed and the volume of water taken up in 5 minutes measured.

This was repeated four times with increased air flow each time. A graph of the results is shown below.

Tip

Question 4 is a very typical AO2 question, where you are expected to apply your knowledge of the structure to show you understand how it functions. Many questions you will meet might look a bit unfamiliar but can easily be answered by using your knowledge of the specification content.

Tip

Many questions based on the core practicals will ask you to show that you understand the principles behind them. You will also find, as in Question 5, that you will need your wider practical skills to answer them well.

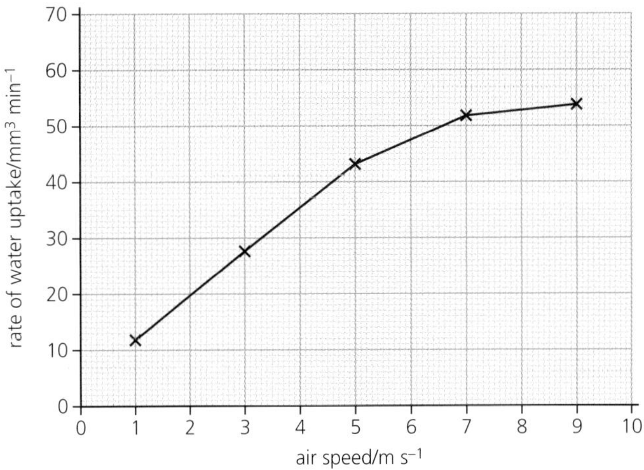

a) What is the relationship between air speed and rate of water uptake in the range of air speed from 1–5 $m s^{-1}$? *(1)*

b) Analyse the data and calculate the average increase in water uptake between 1 and 5 $m s^{-1}$. *(3)*

c) Explain the difference in the effect on the rate of water uptake of increasing air speed from 1–5 $m s^{-1}$ and from 5–9 $m s^{-1}$. *(3)*

d) Describe two other variables that would need to be controlled to ensure that valid conclusions could be drawn from this investigation. *(2)*

e) Explain why the line graph of the results is not drawn through the origin point (0, 0). *(2)*

6 a) Explain how the structure of xylem vessels is adapted for their role in water transport. *(4)*

b) Explain how the unique properties of water molecules are essential for the transport of water and ions from the roots to the shoots in flowering plants. *(4)*

Stretch and challenge

7 Plants and animals have fundamental differences. In particular, plants do not move around or maintain a high body temperature. This means plants have a much lower metabolic rate. In addition, plants manufacture their own respiratory substrates from simple molecules such as carbon dioxide and water. These differences are reflected in their internal transport systems.

a) What are the similarities and differences between transport of water from root to shoots in plants and the vascular system of a mammal?

b) How are these reflected in their structures?

8 A key element of the mass-flow model of phloem transport is that the sucrose must be 'loaded' into sieve tubes at the source area. What theories have been proposed for this mechanism?

Tip

The graph in Question 5 needs you to check exactly what information is being displayed. It is really important in questions containing graphs that you pause to check exactly what the axis labels tell you – especially the units. There is more on graphs in Chapter 27.

Tip

Both parts of Question 6 are concerned with adaptations of structure to function. Take care that your answer clearly links the two together. In part a) you will find that each adaptation is given only 1 mark but requires both in the explanation.

Tip

Question 7 begins with recall of information but as this is from two different parts of the specification it is synoptic. Having decided on some relevant information, write your answer in extended prose to practise assembling information and writing in an accurate, concise way.

13 Cellular respiration

Prior knowledge

In this chapter you will need to recall that:

- chemical reduction involves the gain of electrons
- chemical oxidation involves the loss of electrons
- hydrogen atoms have one proton and one electron
- hydrogen ions have just one proton and hence are positively charged
- ATP and ADP molecules are used to transfer energy within cells
- mitochondria are the sites of ATP formation
- glucose is the most common respiratory substrate
- energy is neither created nor destroyed but simply transformed from one form into another
- aerobic respiration yields more ATP than anaerobic respiration
- the end products of aerobic respiration are carbon dioxide, water and ATP.

Test yourself on prior knowledge

1 State why reactions are referred to as REDOX reactions rather than simply oxidation or reduction.

2 We very rarely find hydrogen atoms moving around freely. Why is this?

3 Explain why ATP is described as the 'energy currency' of the cell.

4 Galactose is a 6-carbon monosaccharide with the formula $C_6H_{12}O_6$. Whilst this is the same as glucose, many organisms cannot use galactose as a respiratory substrate. Explain why this is the case.

5 State the most common form of energy, apart from chemical energy, found in an actively respiring cell.

6 State what other compounds form respiratory substrates in animals apart from glucose.

Aerobic respiration

Key term

Aerobic respiration The chemical breakdown of substrate molecules in cells to release energy in the form of ATP when oxygen is present.

Organisms require energy to maintain all their living cells and to carry out their activities and functions. Respiration is the process by which that energy is transferred in usable form. Cellular respiration that involves oxygen is described as **aerobic respiration**. Most animals and plants and very many microorganisms respire aerobically most, if not all of the time.

In **aerobic respiration**, sugar is oxidised to carbon dioxide and water and much energy is made available. The steps involved in aerobic respiration can be summarised by a single equation. Note that this equation is equivalent to a balance sheet of inputs (the raw materials) and outputs (the products), but it tells us nothing about the steps.

glucose + oxygen → carbon dioxide + water + energy

$$C_6H_{12}O_6 + 6O_2 \rightarrow 6CO_2 + 6H_2O + \text{energy}$$

Sometimes aerobic respiration is compared to combustion – for example, people may talk about 'burning up food' in respiration. In fact this comparison is unhelpful. In combustion, the energy in fuel is released in a one-step reaction, as heat. Such a violent change would be disastrous for body tissues. In cellular respiration, a very large number of small steps occur, each catalysed by a specific enzyme (Figure 13.1). Because energy in respiration is transferred in small quantities, much of the energy is made available and may be trapped in the energy currency molecule, ATP. However, some energy is still lost as heat in each step.

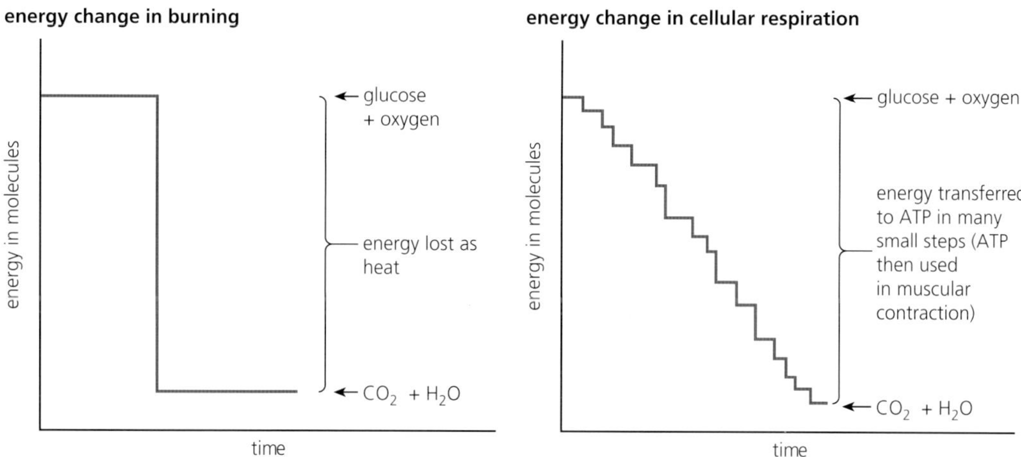

Figure 13.1 Combustion and respiration compared

ATP – the universal energy currency

Energy made available within the cytoplasm is transferred to a molecule called adenosine triphosphate (ATP). (Remember, the cytoplasm comprises both the fluid part – the cytosol – and the organelles.) ATP is referred to as 'energy currency', because like money it is constantly recycled (see Figure 9.4 on page 195). ATP as the universal energy currency was discussed in Chapter 9. Refresh your memory of the structure, roles and importance of this nucleotide now.

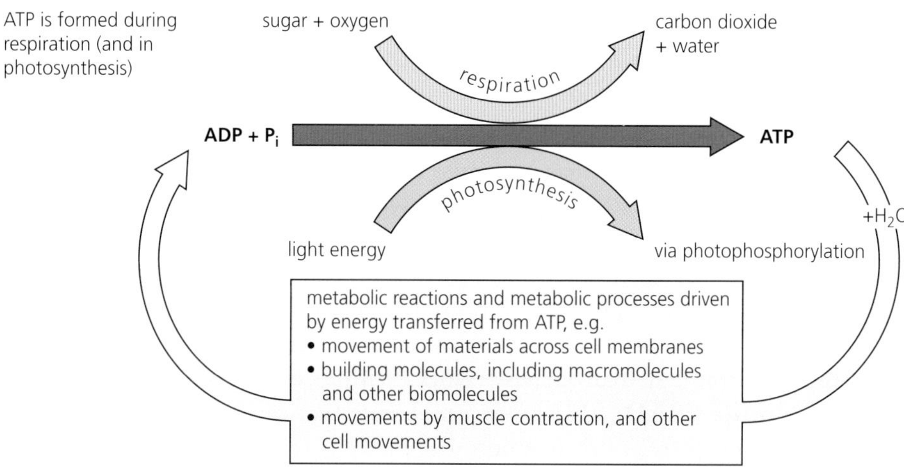

Figure 13.2 The ATP $\rightarrow$ ADP + P_i cycle

Key terms

Glycolysis The first stage in respiration in which glucose is broken down to pyruvic acid.

Krebs cycle An intermediate stage in aerobic respiration during which the products of glycolysis are decarboxylated to form carbon dioxide and reduced coenzymes.

Oxidative phosphorylation The stage of aerobic respiration where protons and electrons are passed through a series of carriers to produce ATP.

The steps involved in aerobic cell respiration

The overall outcome of aerobic respiration is that the respiratory substrate, glucose, is broken down to release carbon dioxide, and the hydrogen of glucose is combined with atmospheric oxygen, with the transfer of a large amount of energy. Much of the energy transferred is lost in the form of heat energy, but cells are able to retain significant amounts of chemical energy in ATP.

During aerobic cellular respiration, glucose undergoes a series of enzyme-catalysed oxidation reactions. These reactions are grouped into three major phases:

1. Glycolysis, in which glucose is converted to pyruvate.
2. The **link reaction** and the Krebs cycle, in which pyruvate is converted to carbon dioxide.
3. Oxidative phosphorylation (the electron-transport system), in which hydrogen removed in the oxidation reactions of glycolysis and the Krebs cycle, is converted to water, and the bulk of the ATP is synthesised.

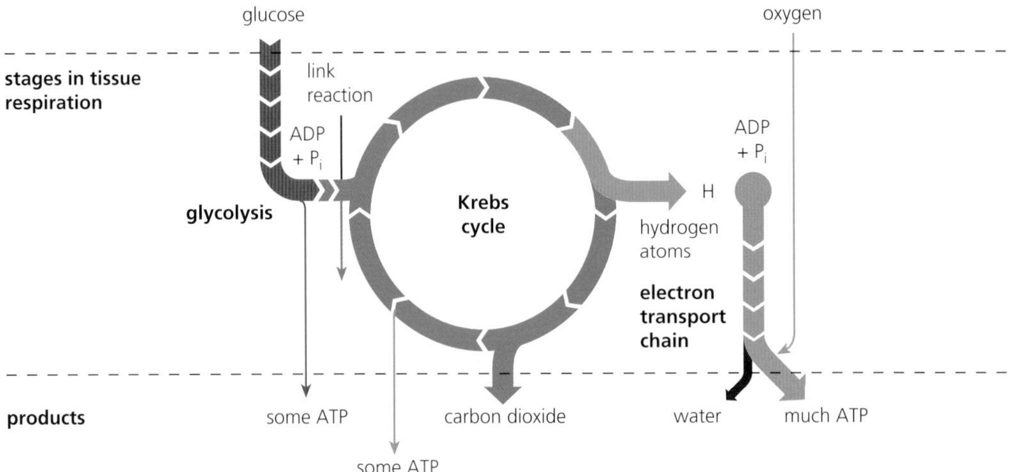

Figure 13.3 The three phases of aerobic cell respiration

1 Glycolysis

Glycolysis is a linear series of reactions in which a six-carbon sugar is broken down to two molecules of the three-carbon pyruvate ion. The enzymes of glycolysis are located in the cytosol (that is, the cytoplasm outside the organelles) rather than in the mitochondria. Glycolysis occurs in four stages.

- **Phosphorylation** by reactions with ATP is the way glucose is first activated, eventually forming a six-carbon sugar with two phosphate groups attached (called fructose bisphosphate). At this stage of glycolysis two molecules of ATP are consumed per molecule of glucose.
- **Lysis** (splitting) of the fructose bisphosphate now takes place, forming two molecules of a three-carbon sugar (called glycerate 3-phosphate (GP)).
- Oxidation of the three-carbon sugar molecules occurs by removal of hydrogen. The enzyme for this reaction (a dehydrogenase) works with a coenzyme, **nicotinamide adenine dinucleotide** (**NAD^+**). NAD^+ is a molecule that can accept hydrogen ions (H^+) and electrons (e^-). In this reaction, the NAD is reduced to NADH and H^+ (known as reduced NAD):

  $NAD^+ + 2H^+ + 2e^- \longrightarrow NADH + H^+$ (sometimes represented as $NADH_2$)

  (Reduced NAD can pass hydrogen ions and electrons on to other acceptor molecules, as described below, and when it does it becomes oxidised back to NAD.)

- **ATP formation** occurs twice in the reactions, by which each triose phosphate molecule is converted to pyruvate. This form of ATP synthesis is referred to as being 'at substrate level' in order to differentiate it from the bulk of ATP synthesis that occurs later in cell respiration, during operation of the electron transport chain (see below). At this stage of glycolysis as two molecules of glycerate 3-phosphate (GP) are converted to pyruvate, four molecules of ATP are synthesised. So, in total, there is a net gain of two ATPs in glycolysis.

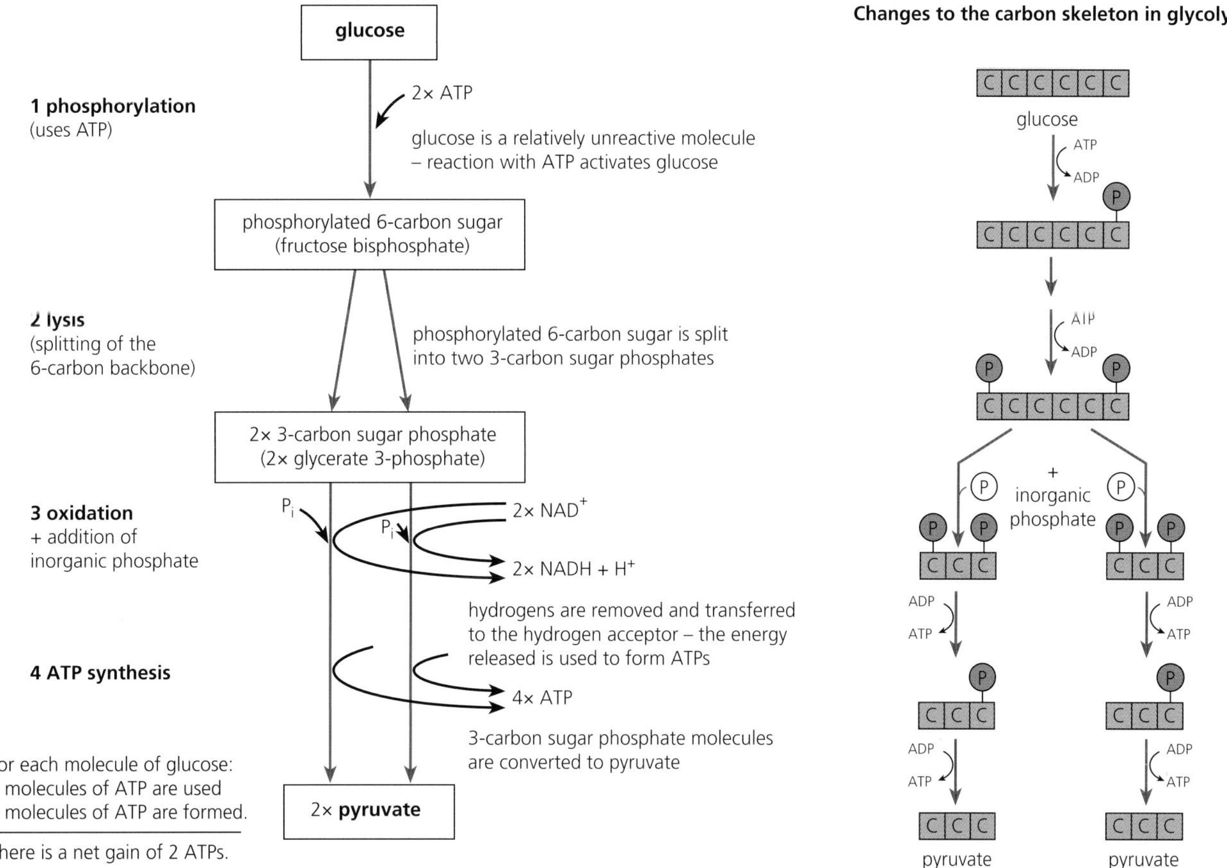

Figure 13.4 A summary of glycolysis

Test yourself

1 Explain why two molecules of ATP are used to phosphorylate glucose at the start of glycolysis.

2 State the name of the three-carbon sugar formed by the splitting of fructose bisphosphate.

3 State the end products of glycolysis.

4 Describe where in the cell the reactions of glycolysis take place.

2 The link reaction and Krebs cycle

The subsequent steps in aerobic respiration occur in the organelles known as mitochondria.

Key term

Coenzyme An organic non-protein molecule that binds to an enzyme to allow it to carry out its function.

In the link reaction, pyruvate diffuses into the matrix of the mitochondrion as it forms, and is metabolised there. First, the three-carbon pyruvate is decarboxylated by removal of carbon dioxide and, at the same time, oxidised by removal of hydrogen. Reduced NAD is formed. The product of this oxidative decarboxylation reaction is an acetyl group – a two-carbon fragment. This acetyl group is then combined with a **coenzyme** called coenzyme A, forming acetyl coenzyme A.

The production of acetyl coenzyme A from pyruvate is known as the link reaction because it connects glycolysis to reactions of the Krebs cycle, details of which now follow.

In the Krebs cycle, acetyl coenzyme A reacts with a four-carbon organic acid (oxaloacetate, OAA). The products of this reaction are a six-carbon acid (citrate) and, of course, coenzyme A. This latter, on release, is re-used in the link reaction.

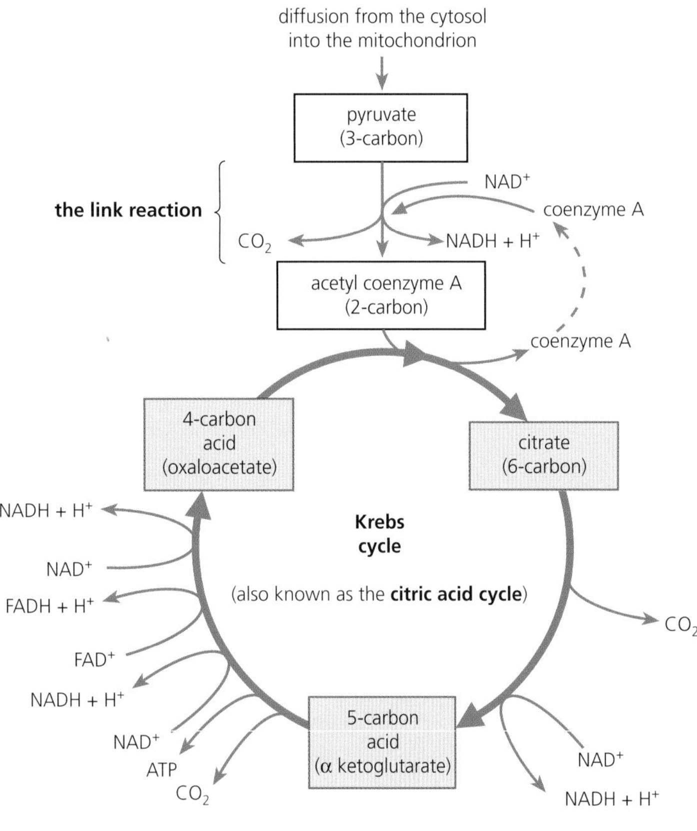

Figure 13.5 A summary of the Krebs cycle

The Krebs cycle is named after Hans Krebs who discovered it, but it is also sometimes referred to as the citric acid cycle, after the first intermediate acid formed.

Then the citrate is converted back to the four-carbon acid (an acceptor molecule, in effect) by the reactions of the Krebs cycle. These involve the following changes:

- Two molecules of carbon dioxide are given off in separate decarboxylation reactions.
- A molecule of ATP is formed as part 1 of the reactions of the cycle – as with glycolysis, this ATP synthesis is 'at substrate level' too.
- Three molecules of reduced NAD are formed.
- One molecule of another hydrogen accepter – FAD (flavin adenine dinucleotide) is reduced. (NAD is the chief hydrogen-carrying coenzyme of respiration but FAD is another coenzyme with this role in the Krebs cycle).

Because glucose is converted to two molecules of pyruvate in glycolysis, the whole Krebs cycle sequence of reactions 'turns' twice for every molecule of glucose that is metabolised by aerobic cellular respiration.

This gives us the products shown in Table 13.1.

Table 13.1 Net products of aerobic respiration of glucose at the end of the Krebs cycle

	Product			
Step	**CO_2**	**ATP**	**Reduced NAD**	**Reduced FAD**
Glycolysis	0	2	2	0
Link reaction (pyruvate → acetyl CoA)	2	0	2	0
Krebs cycle	4	2	6	2
Totals	6	4	10	2

As you can see, this table shows a very small yield of ATP but a large yield of reduced NAD and some reduced FAD. The final stage of aerobic respiration explains how these reduced coenzymes can be converted into ATP and exactly how the remaining product, water, is formed.

Test yourself

5 State which final product of respiration is generated in the link reaction and Krebs cycle.
6 Describe where exactly in the cell the reactions of the link reaction and the Krebs cycle take place.
7 Describe how reduced NAD is formed in the link reaction.
8 State which product of the link reaction enters the Krebs cycle.
9 Explain why NAD and FAD are known as coenzymes.
10 The Krebs cycle completes the breakdown of glucose molecules. Explain why the ATP yield is so low.

3 Oxidative phosphorylation and terminal oxidation

This section depends on your knowledge of mitochondrial structure, which you met in Chapter 4, Figure 4.16. It is important that you look back at your notes before continuing.

The removal of pairs of hydrogen atoms from various intermediates of the respiratory pathway is a feature of several of the steps in glycolysis and the Krebs cycle. On most occasions, oxidised NAD is converted to reduced NAD, but in the Krebs cycle it is an alternative hydrogen-acceptor coenzyme known as FAD that is reduced.

In this final stage of aerobic respiration, the hydrogen atoms (or their electrons) are transported along a series of carriers, from the reduced NAD (or FAD), to be combined with oxygen to form water. Hence the role of oxygen in this process is that of the **final hydrogen acceptor**. Note that this final reaction to form water only occurs after the energy level has been lowered by a series of transfers between carriers, bringing about the gradual transfer of energy shown in Figure 13.1.

As electrons are passed between the carriers in the series, energy is transferred. Transfer of energy in this manner is controlled and can be used by the cell. The energy is

Tip

Before attempting to understand this section, make sure you are very clear about hydrogen ions and atoms. Hydrogen atoms lose their only electron so a hydrogen ion is left as a proton. This is why you will see H^+ and proton as alternatives in the diagram. The electrons move down a chain of carriers.

transferred to ADP and P_i, forming ATP. Normally, for every molecule of reduced NAD that is oxidised (that is, for every pair of hydrogens) approximately three molecules of ATP are produced.

The process is summarised in Figure 13.6. The total yield from aerobic respiration is **about 38 ATPs per molecule of glucose** respired. This is obviously much more than from glycolysis. There are other pathways associated with this process, which means the overall yield is given as 'about' 38 ATPs.

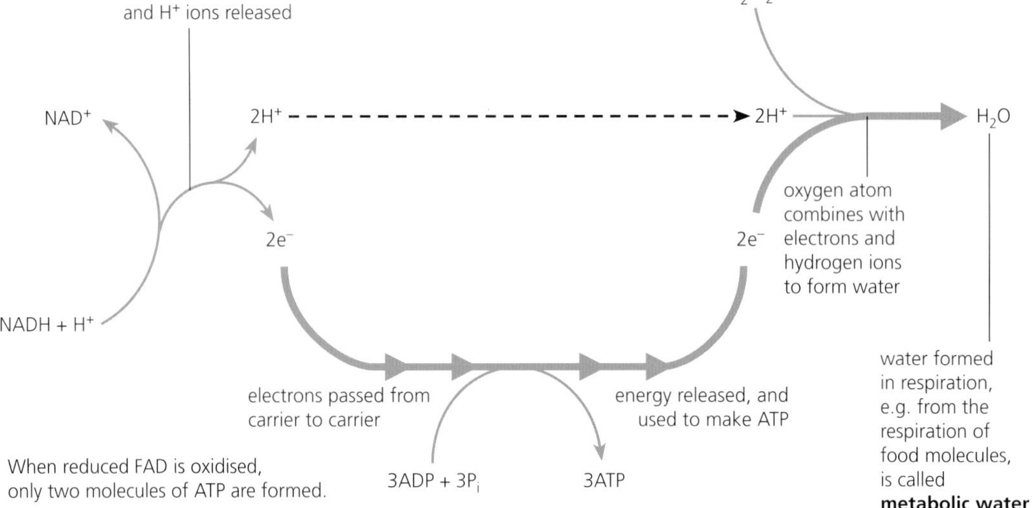

Figure 13.6 Terminal oxidation and formation of ATP

ATP formation by chemiosmosis

In Chapter 7 we discussed how scientists suggested new ideas or models that formed the basis of predictions that could be tested experimentally. Only when sufficient experimental data accumulate does the model gradually become accepted.

The 'chemiosmotic model' grew out of studies of bacterial metabolism carried out by biochemist Peter Mitchell in 1961. Gradually, over the next decade and more, scientists were able to confirm the presence of the correct gradients of H^+ ions and the necessary protein pumps in the mitochondrial membranes. The model stood up well to these investigations and in 1975 Mitchell was awarded the Nobel Prize for his work, confirming that this had indeed become the accepted model.

Key term

Chemiosmosis The process by which the movement of protons across the inner mitochondrial membrane is coupled to the synthesis of ATP.

Chemiosmosis is a process by which the synthesis of ATP is coupled to electron transport via the movement of protons as shown in Figure 13.7. **Electron-carrier proteins** are arranged in the inner mitochondrial membrane in a highly ordered way. These carrier proteins oxidise the reduced coenzymes, and energy from this process is used to pump hydrogen ions (protons) from the matrix of the mitochondrion into the space between inner and outer mitochondrial membranes.

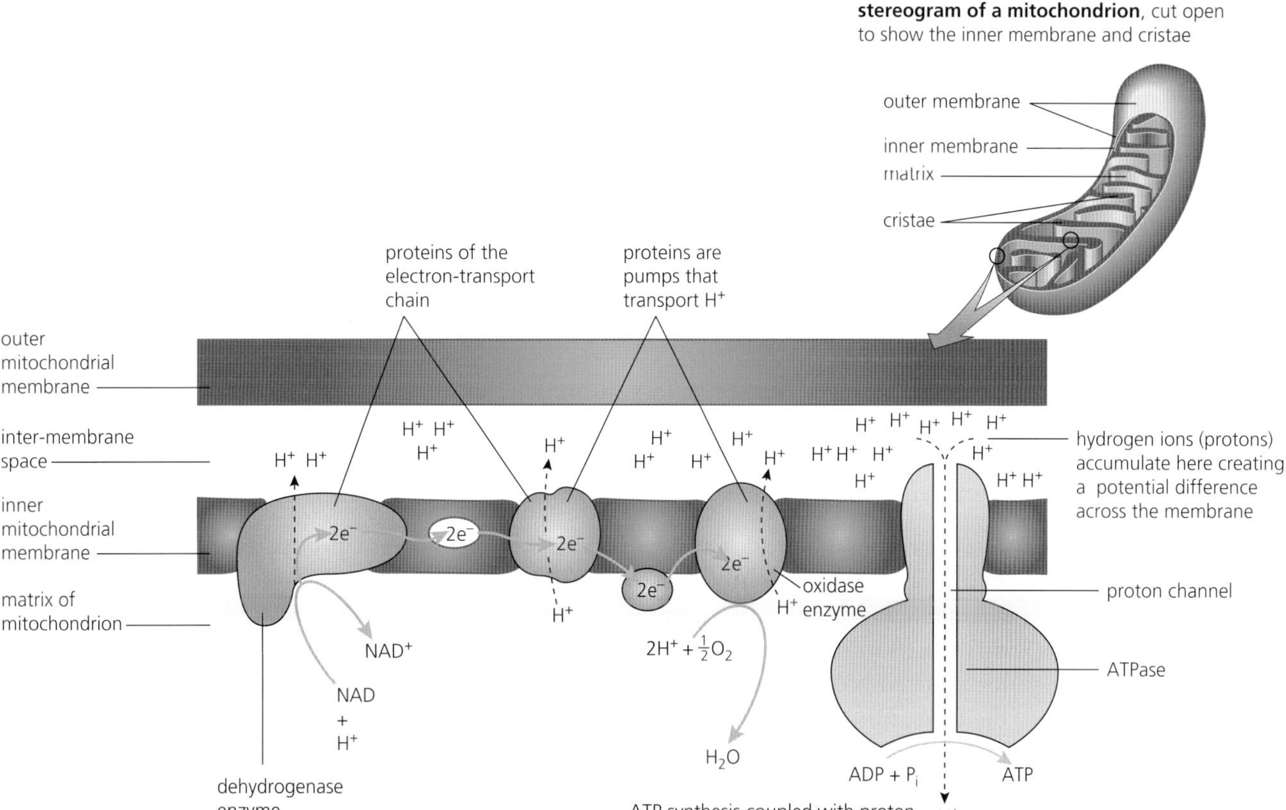

Figure 13.7 Mitchell's chemiosmotic theory

Here the H^+ ions accumulate – incidentally, causing the pH to drop. Because the inner membrane is largely impermeable to ions, a significant difference in hydrogen ion concentration builds up, generating an electrochemical gradient across the inner membrane – a store of potential energy.

Eventually, the protons do flow back into the matrix, via channels in **ATP synthetase** enzymes, also found in the inner mitochondrial membrane. As the protons flow down their concentration gradient through the enzyme, the energy is transferred and ATP synthesis occurs.

Key term

ATP synthetase An enzyme found in the inner mitochondrial membrane, which channels hydrogen ions through the membrane during ATP synthesis by chemiosmosis.

Test yourself

11 During oxidative phosphorylation electrons are passed from one carrier to another. Explain why they do this.

12 Explain why hydrogen is combined with oxygen to form water only at the end of the chain of carriers.

13 a) State where in the mitochondria there is a high concentration of H^+ ions.

b) Describe how a high concentration of H^+ ions is built up in this region.

14 Explain why a high H^+ ion concentration means a drop in pH.

15 In what ways is ATP synthetase unlike a normal enzyme?

Key term

Anaerobic respiration The process by which substrate molecules are broken down in cells to release energy in the form of ATP in the absence of oxygen.

Anaerobic respiration or fermentation

In the absence of oxygen, many organisms (and sometimes certain tissues in organisms when deprived of sufficient oxygen) will continue to respire by a process known as fermentation or **anaerobic respiration**, at least for a short time.

A knowledge of aerobic respiration shows us the effect that a lack of oxygen will have. If oxygen is the final hydrogen acceptor, then without it the carriers of oxidative phosphorylation will all become reduced and the flow of electrons and protons will cease. This will also mean that the supply of NAD^+ will be halted and the Krebs cycle will also come to a stop.

With only glycolysis operating, you can see that there is a net gain of only 2ATPs per glucose molecule compared with about 38ATPs from complete aerobic respiration. Therefore, whilst anaerobic respiration can continue without oxygen it is a very inefficient process.

A second consequence of a lack of oxygen is that the end-product of glycolysis, pyruvic acid, will begin to accumulate. As the concentration of pyruvic acid increases it is channelled into other biochemical pathways, as shown in Figure 13.8. In animal cells this results in the formation of **lactate** (lactic acid) as the pyruvate acts as the acceptor for reduced NAD, whilst in plant cells **ethanal** acts as this acceptor and this results in the formation of **ethanol**. In effect these compounds are replacing oxygen as the final hydrogen acceptor to allow glycolysis to continue.

Both lactate and ethanol contain large quantities of chemical energy, indicating that the glucose has only been partially broken down and explaining the low ATP yield.

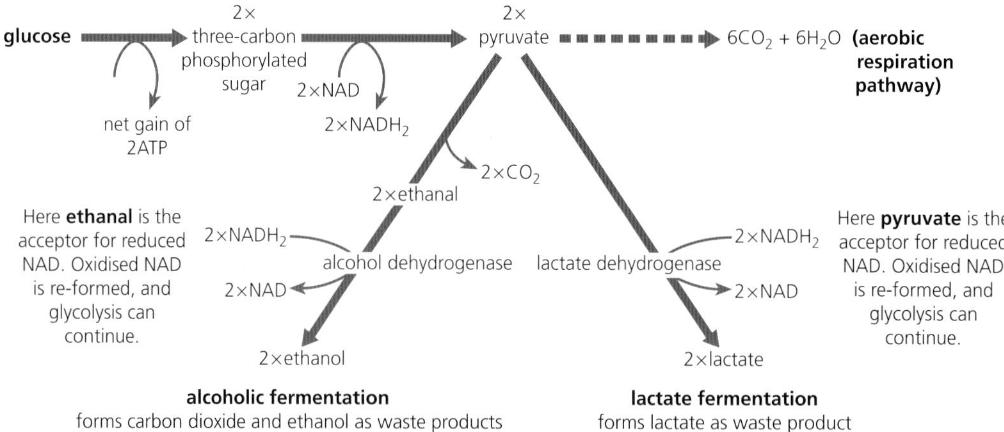

Figure 13.8 The respiratory pathways of anaerobic respiration

Anaerobic respiration in vertebrate muscle

Active vertebrate muscles have a high oxygen demand. If they continue to work at a high rate their demand for oxygen quickly exceeds the maximum rate of supply. In order to continue working, the muscles need to respire anaerobically. This means that the concentration of lactate will begin to rise. The effect of this lactate is to gradually inhibit the muscle contractions.

You are probably familiar with this effect. If you begin to sprint, you will quickly begin to experience lactate build up in your muscles and the effect we know as fatigue. No matter how much you try to run faster, your muscles will not respond, and then begin to feel painful.

If you then rest, your muscles can begin to feel quite stiff, another symptom of lactate presence. However, the lactate is slowly transported to the liver where it is converted back to sugars and used in glycolysis.

Anaerobic fermentation in plants and yeast

The ability of plant cells and particularly the fungus, yeast, to produce ethanol by anaerobic fermentation is the basis of a very large international alcohol industry. As ethanal is formed from pyruvate it is quickly reduced to ethanol. Most plant cells cannot metabolise ethanol and as its concentration rises they are often killed by its toxic effects.

In addition to the drinks industry, ethanol is an important raw material for the chemical industry as well as being an excellent fuel.

Test yourself

16 State which intermediate accepts hydrogen in alcoholic fermentation in plant cells.

17 Suggest in what way a build up of lactate in muscles could cause them to function less efficiently.

18 Suggest why further gentle exercise would help to reduce the effects of lactate in muscles.

19 State the percentage difference in the yield of ATP between aerobic respiration and anaerobic respiration.

Core practical 9

Investigate the factors affecting the rate of aerobic or anaerobic respiration using a respirometer

Background information

The rate of respiration of an organism is normally measured as the volume of oxygen taken up in a given time. A respirometer is a form of manometer, which will measure changes in pressure or volume. Enclosing a living organism in a chamber attached to a manometer will show any changes in volume. Unfortunately the volume of carbon dioxide given off in respiration will be the same as the volume of oxygen taken in, so no change would be seen. To overcome this, a carbon dioxide absorber is placed in the chamber. The volume/pressure inside will therefore decrease and the liquid in the manometer will move according to the volume of oxygen taken up. The apparatus shown in Figure 13.9 is a simple respirometer where the manometer is a straight piece of capillary tubing with a small drop of coloured liquid moving along it.

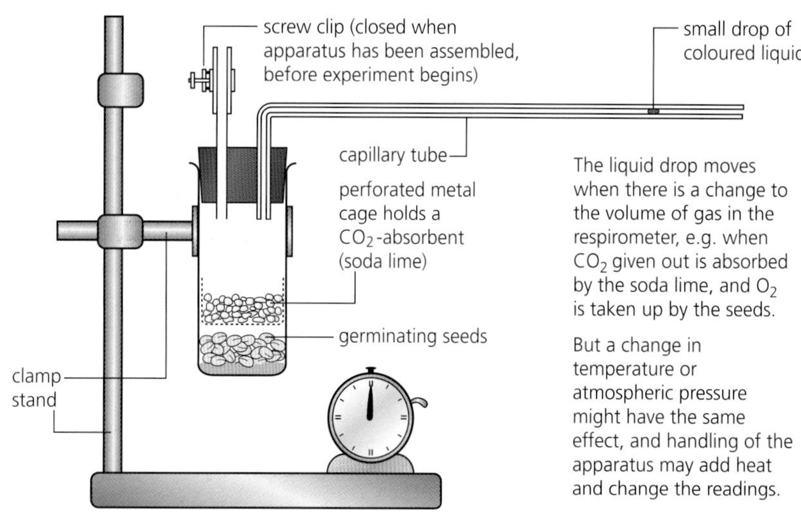

Figure 13.9 A simple respirometer

Carrying out the investigation

Aim: to measure the rate of respiration of a living organism.

Risk assessment: Common carbon dioxide absorbers contain calcium, sodium and potassium hydroxides. Soda lime is a mixture of all three, but fresh, concentrated sodium or potassium hydroxide solution is an excellent carbon dioxide absorber. All are extremely corrosive and eye protection should be worn at all times. If you are handling the chemicals yourself, you must wear chemically resistant (nitrile) gloves and goggles. Your teacher will show you the safe procedure and supervise closely.

Your teacher may decide to provide place the alkaline solutions/solids in the respirometer before the lesson, in which case you will not need to handle the chemicals directly.

Any living animals used in the investigation must be treated with respect. Care must be taken to wash hands thoroughly after handling organisms such as blowfly larvae. Higher-order animals should not be used in this investigation.

1 Your first step will be to select some suitable respiring tissue. The most common are germinating seeds that have been soaked in water for at least 24 hours or blowfly larvae (maggots), which are easily available from your local angling shop. Check the size of the tube or chamber of the respirometer and estimate a suitable mass of tissue to use.
2 Weigh out the respiring tissue and add it to the empty tube.
3 Taking note of the risk assessment above, half-fill the metal cage with a carbon dioxide absorber. Slide the metal cage into the chamber above the respiring tissue but remember, the absorber is corrosive so make sure the cage fits tightly into the tube and does not touch the tissue below.
4 Make sure that the screw clip shown in the diagram is open and push the rubber bung firmly into the top of the chamber to form an airtight seal. Leave the apparatus to equilibrate for 5 minutes.
5 Close the screw clip and after a few moments hold a small drop of coloured liquid on the end of a glass rod against the open end of the capillary tube for a short time.
6 If all is well then a small amount of liquid should be drawn slowly into the capillary. As soon as there is a small visible amount of liquid in the tube, take away the glass rod.
7 You will now need to decide on a suitable time interval for recording the movement. Place a ruler alongside the capillary tube and measure how much movement the liquid drop makes in 1 minute. Choose your timing period so that the liquid moves at least 1 centimetre along the scale in each period. The actual volume of gas consumed can be calculated from the radius of the capillary (r) and the distance moved by the coloured liquid (l) as $\pi r^2 l$. When the coloured liquid reaches the end of the capillary tube you can introduce another drop of liquid at the end of the capillary. Some simple respirometers have a syringe attached to the screw clip tube, which will enable you to gently push the coloured fluid back to the end of the capillary after each series of measurements.
8 Repeated measurements will provide you with a mean respiration rate and, if time permits, you might consider investigating the effect of some variables such as temperature on the overall rate.

Questions

1 What is the main variable that can cause large errors in respirometry?
2 Figure 13.10 shows a modified respirometer. How will the design of this apparatus compensate for temperature changes?
3 Why is it important to use germinating seeds that do not show any evidence of green leaves?
4 Why is it important to record the mass of tissue used?
5 How could the respirometer shown in Figure 13.9 be used to measure the rate of respiration of a culture solution of a green photosynthetic alga?
6 Why does using active animals such as blowfly larvae introduce extra variables that are difficult to control?

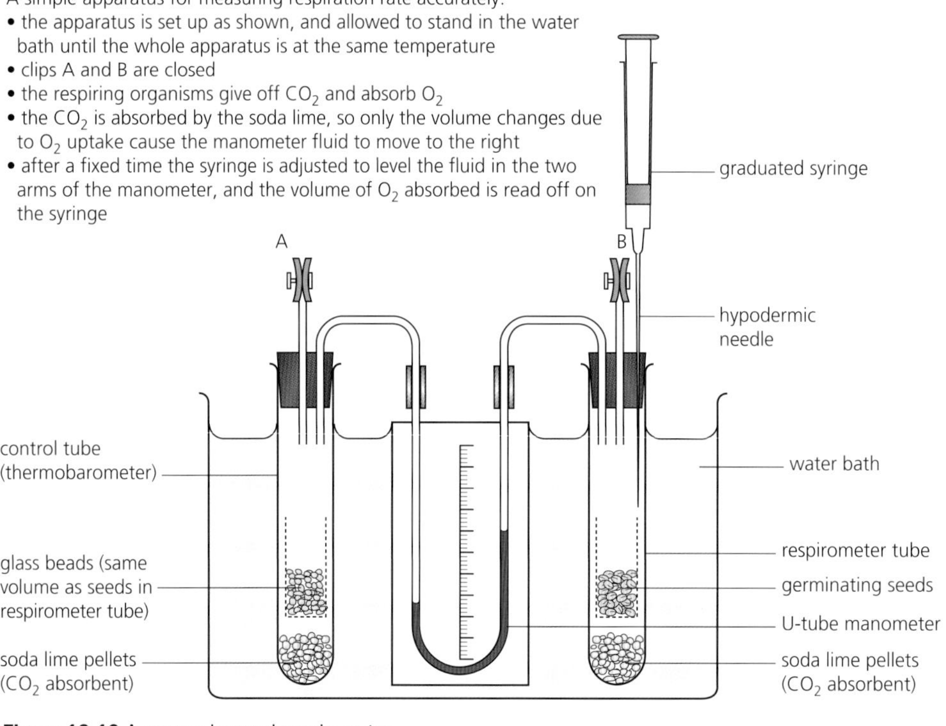
A simple apparatus for measuring respiration rate accurately:
• the apparatus is set up as shown, and allowed to stand in the water bath until the whole apparatus is at the same temperature
• clips A and B are closed
• the respiring organisms give off CO_2 and absorb O_2
• the CO_2 is absorbed by the soda lime, so only the volume changes due to O_2 uptake cause the manometer fluid to move to the right
• after a fixed time the syringe is adjusted to level the fluid in the two arms of the manometer, and the volume of O_2 absorbed is read off on the syringe
A
B
graduated syringe
hypodermic needle
control tube (thermobarometer)
water bath
glass beads (same volume as seeds in respirometer tube)
respirometer tube
germinating seeds
U-tube manometer
soda lime pellets (CO_2 absorbent)
soda lime pellets (CO_2 absorbent)

Figure 13.10 A more advanced respirometer

Chapter summary

Aerobic respiration

- Aerobic respiration breaks down substrates such as glucose in the presence of oxygen to release carbon dioxide, water and energy.
- Adenosine triphosphate (ATP) is the common carrier of chemical energy in cells.
- There are three main phases of aerobic respiration: glycolysis, Krebs cycle and oxidative phosphorylation.
- In glycolysis glucose molecules are phosphorylated then broken down to form pyruvate. The release of hydrogen carried by NADH is used to form a limited amount of ATP.
- In the Krebs cycle pyruvate is completely broken down to form carbon dioxide. The hydrogen released is used to form reduced hydrogen carriers NADH and FADH.
- Oxidative phosphorylation is the process by which hydrogen atoms and electrons are passed along a chain of carriers at gradually reducing energy levels. At each transfer the energy released is used to form ATP. This is by far the largest source of ATP in the process.
- At the end of the chain, oxygen combines with hydrogen ions and electrons to form water.
- The formation of ATP from carriers depends upon electron transport proteins embedded in mitochondrial membranes transporting protons to form high concentrations in the inter-membrane space.
- These protons are then channelled through ATPase molecules to form ATP from ADP. The formation of ATP in this way is called chemiosmosis.

Anaerobic respiration

- This is the partial breakdown of glucose in the absence of oxygen.
- As oxygen is the final hydrogen acceptor in aerobic respiration, without it oxidative phosphorylation and the Krebs cycle become blocked.
- As intermediate compounds build up, pyruvate molecules are forced to take alternative pathways, which result in the formation of ethanol in plants and lactate in animals.
- Without oxidative phosphorylation, anaerobic respiration can only yield 2 ATP molecules per glucose molecule compared with 38 ATP molecules for complete aerobic breakdown.

Practice questions

1 A coenzyme can be described as:

A a protein catalyst

B a non-protein catalyst

C a protein essential for some enzyme activity

D a non-protein essential for some enzyme activity *(1)*

2 During chemiosmosis in mitochondria, energy is used to pump hydrogen ions:

A across the outer membrane into the cytoplasm

B across the outer membrane into the space between membranes

C across the inner membrane into the matrix

D across the inner membrane into the space between membranes *(1)*

Question 2 is a straightforward recall question but it does illustrate the level of detail you must aim at learning in your revision.

3 The end product of the link reaction in aerobic respiration is:

A acetyl coenzyme A

B pyruvic acid

C citric acid

D glycerate-3-phosphate *(1)*

4 The diagram shows an outline of part of the biochemical pathways of anaerobic respiration in plant and animal cells.

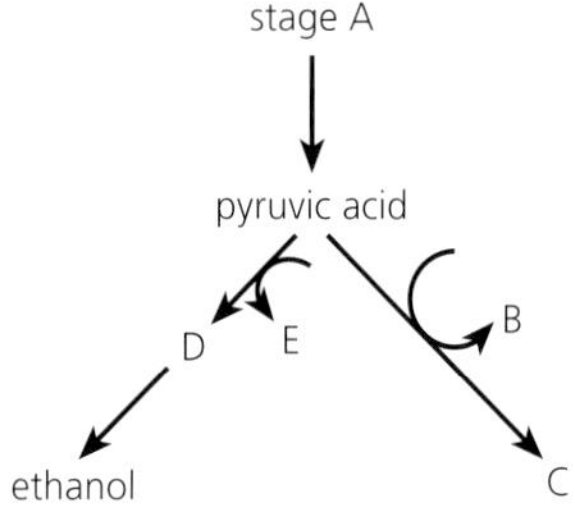

Name the following parts of this diagram:

a) the stage of respiration labelled A *(1)*

b) the coenzyme formed at B *(1)*

c) the compound labelled C *(1)*

d) the compound labelled D *(1)*

e) the 1C molecule labelled E *(1)*

5 A student investigated the rate of respiration of germinating seeds at two different temperatures using the apparatus shown in the diagram.

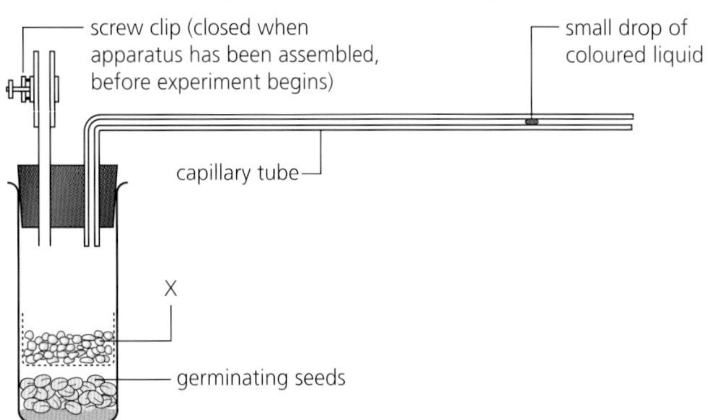

Tip

Question 5 contains typical elements of a core practical-based question. Some parts are designed to test your understanding of the experimental procedure itself and others test your application of Level 2 maths or interpretation of data.

a) Name **one** compound that would be added to the wire cage X and explain its purpose. *(2)*

b) The student assembled the apparatus as shown in the diagram by adding 8 g of germinating wheat seeds to the tube, which was then immersed in a water bath at 20 °C for 10 minutes. The screw clip was then closed and readings taken of the movement of the coloured liquid each minute for 10 minutes. This was then repeated using a water bath maintained at 30 °C.

Explain why the screw clip was left open for 10 minutes before the investigation was started. *(2)*

c) The graph shows the results of this investigation.

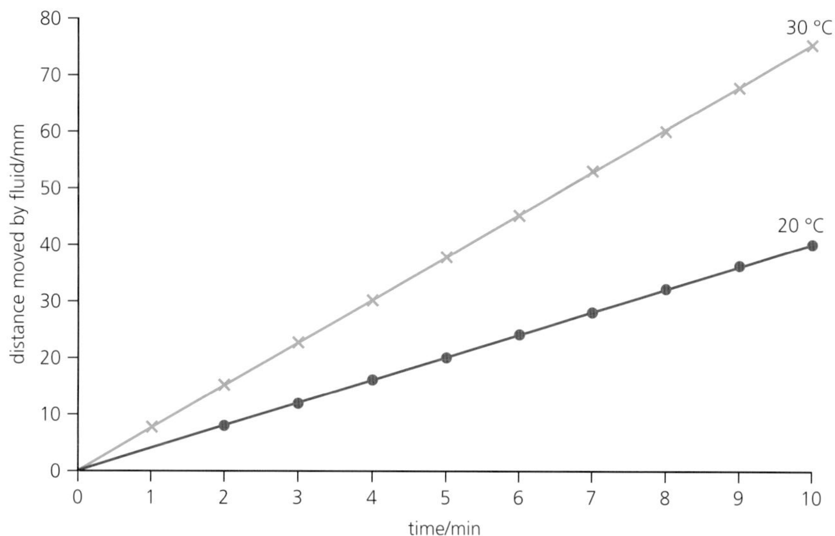

i) Temperature or pressure fluctuations often cause problems when using respirometers. Explain what the graph shows about the effectiveness of variable control in this investigation. *(2)*

ii) The diameter of the capillary tube was 3 mm. Calculate the rate of oxygen uptake of the germinating seeds at each temperature during the course of this investigation. *(4)*

iii) Calculate the percentage increase in respiration rate caused by raising the temperature from 20 °C to 30 °C. *(2)*

★**6** Explain how the structure and properties of cell membranes are essential for the production of ATP in aerobic respiration. *(7)*

Stretch and challenge

7 Most organisms use other respiratory substrates in addition to glucose. Both lipids and proteins can be channelled into respiration by various biochemical pathways.

a) What is meant by a 'biochemical pathway'?

b) Many plants and animals use lipids as energy storage molecules. Suggest what the advantages of this would be to a groundnut seed and a mammal such as a fox.

Tip

Question 6 is a typical synoptic question that you will find in A level papers. It asks you to show knowledge and understanding of membrane structure and the biochemistry of aerobic respiration, and then to apply your knowledge to explain some selected detail of the process (AO2). As this is a slightly extended prose question, take care to keep to the rubric without straying into lots of details of respiration or mitochondria, which are not relevant.

c) If germinating seeds with a very high lipid content are used in a respirometer, the results show that a much greater volume of oxygen is required for the respiration of the fatty acids they contain compared to respiration of glucose.

The summary equation for the respiration of fatty acids is shown below.

$$\underset{\text{fatty acid}}{C_{18}H_{36}O_2} + 26O_2 \rightarrow 18CO_2 + 18H_2O$$

i) Explain how this equation shows that more oxygen will be needed to oxidise one molecule of fatty acid compared to one molecule of glucose.

ii) How do the proportions of hydrogen and oxygen in glucose and fatty acid help to explain this difference?

8 Training programmes for endurance sports such as long-distance running and cycling involve careful monitoring of lactate levels in the blood by taking blood samples.

The graph below shows the blood lactate levels (blood [la]) of an athlete at increasing workloads, measured in Watts (w) achieved by increasing speeds on a treadmill. LT indicates the lactate threshold.

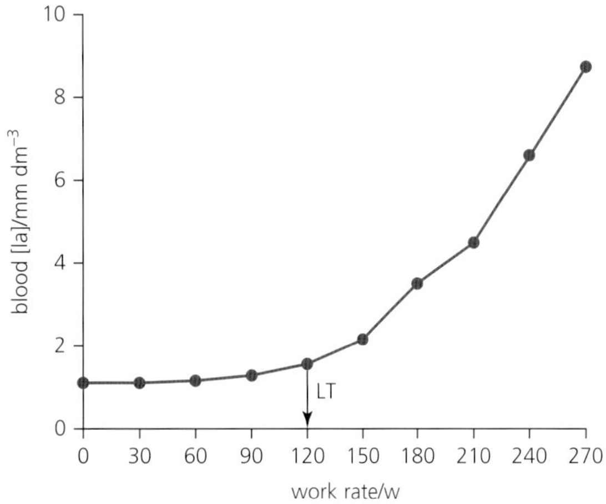

a) Explain the changes in lactate levels at work rates below the threshold and the changes at work rates above the threshold.

b) Suggest how the results of such monitoring might be used to design individual training programmes for endurance athletes.

14 Photosynthesis

Prior knowledge

In this chapter you will need to recall that:

- green plants are able to manufacture sugars using light energy, carbon dioxide and water
- oxygen is a waste product of photosynthesis
- several stages of photosynthesis take place in cell organelles called chloroplasts
- light is absorbed by plant cells using pigments such as chlorophyll
- colours of light are determined by different wavelengths
- photosynthesis using sunlight energy is the starting point for the large majority of food chains
- plants need to respire to produce ATP for cellular processes; photosynthesis produces the respiratory substrates required.

Test yourself on prior knowledge

1 State where chlorophyll molecules are attached in chloroplasts.

2 Explain why a solution of ink will appear blue when white light is shone through it.

3 If photosynthesis produces sugars that are respired to produce ATP, suggest why many plants accumulate large food stores.

4 Explain why many plant cells have food stores consisting of starch rather than sugars.

5 Name the organisms that cause the Earth's oceans to be a major contributor to atmospheric oxygen.

Photosynthetic pigments

The purpose of photosynthetic pigments is to absorb light energy and convert it into chemical energy. Higher plants have two types of pigments – chlorophylls and carotenoids. The most important pigments are the chlorophylls, which play a direct role in the first stages of photosynthesis. Carotenoids absorb light energy, which is passed on to chlorophyll, so they are called **accessory pigments**. Other plants such as marine algae (seaweeds) have other accessory pigments. Some common photosynthetic pigments are listed in Table 14.1.

Key term

Accessory pigments Light-absorbing molecules that pass on the energy they absorb to chlorophyll molecules at the start of photosynthesis.

Table 14.1 Common photosynthetic pigments

Chlorophylls	Carotenes	Others
Chlorophyll *a* (green)	β-carotene (orange)	Phycoerithrin (red)
Chlorophyll *b* (green)	Xanthophyll (yellow)	Fucoxanthin (brown)

the structure of chlorophyll *a*

chlorophyll *b* has an aldehyde group (—CHO) in place of this —CH_3 group

conjugated protein head containing magnesium (hydrophilic and associated with the proteins in the membranes of the grana)

hydrocarbon tail (hydrophobic and occurs folded, associated with the lipid of the membranes)

Figure 14.1 The structure of chlorophyll

The structure of chlorophyll

The chlorophyll molecule has two parts. The head of the molecule is a **hydrophilic** ring structure with a magnesium atom at its centre. Attached to this is a long **hydrophobic** hydrocarbon tail. This arrangement means that chlorophyll molecules are attached to the membranes of the chloroplast by their long tails whilst the heads lie flat on the membrane surface to absorb the maximum amount of light. The structure of chlorophyll can be seen in Figure 14.1. You will see how this is linked to the first stage of photosynthesis later in this chapter.

> **Key terms**
>
> **Hydrophilic** Having an affinity for water and soluble in water.
>
> **Hydrophobic** Substances that repel water. They are mainly insoluble in water but can be soluble in lipids.

Absorption and action spectra

To investigate the roles of photosynthetic pigments it is important to know more about their absorption of light. You can do this by simply shining light of different wavelengths through a solution of the pigment and measuring how much is absorbed. The graph of the amount of light absorbed at each wavelength, as shown in Figure 14.2, is known as an **absorption spectrum**.

To provide evidence that these pigments do play an important part in the process of photosynthesis, you can produce an **action spectrum** by plotting a graph of the rate of photosynthesis of a green plant (measured as explained in Core practical 10) at different wavelengths. As you can see in Figure 14.2, the action spectrum for photosynthesis shows a very similar pattern to that of the absorption spectrum for the pigments. This provides good evidence to support the model of light being trapped by these pigments and used in photosynthesis.

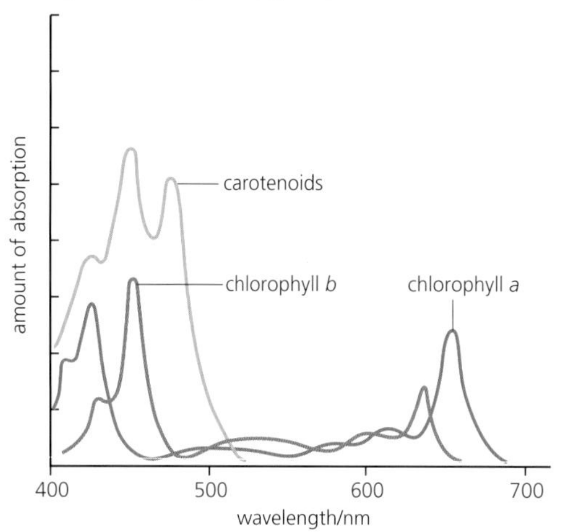

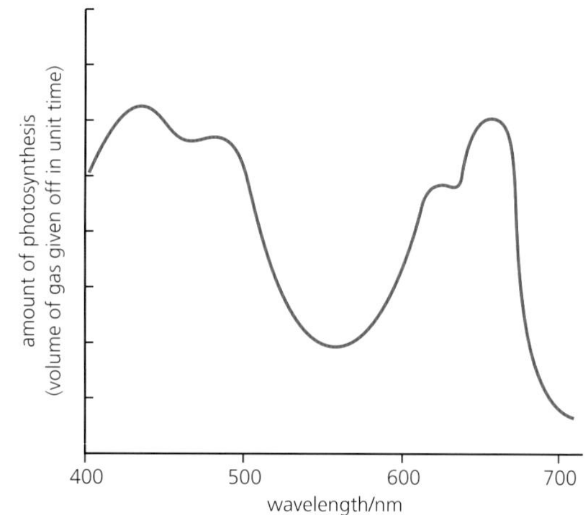

Figure 14.2 Absorption and action spectra

Why do plants need more than one photosynthetic pigment?

If you look carefully at the absorption spectra in Figure 14.2 you can see that the absorption of chlorophyll *a* and *b* is not quite the same. Both chlorophyll *a* and *b* absorb strongly in the blue and red ends of the spectrum but in the blue end of the spectrum chlorophyll *a* absorbs most strongly at about 430 nm, whilst chlorophyll *b* absorbs most strongly at 470 nm. In this way a combination of two or more pigments means that a greater range of wavelengths can be absorbed efficiently. You can see a very similar pattern at the red end of the spectrum. Almost all plants use chlorophylls as their primary pigments at the start of photosynthesis but the range of accessory pigments can vary considerably depending upon their habitat.

Key terms

Absorption spectrum A graph of the amount of light absorbed at different wavelengths by a pigment.

Action spectrum A graph of the rate of photosynthesis of a plant at different wavelengths of light.

Test yourself

1. Suggest why the hydrocarbon chains of a chlorophyll molecule will attach themselves easily to chloroplast membranes.
2. Describe how the 'heads' of chlorophyll molecules are adapted to capture the maximum number of photons.
3. State which colour of light in the visible spectrum has the longest wavelength.
4. Describe what happens to the energy trapped by accessory pigments.

Core practical 11

Investigate the presence of different chloroplast pigments using chromatography

Background information

Chromatography is a very common technique used in biochemistry to separate and identify small quantities of different compounds. There are many different variations but all work on similar principles.

The process involves a stationary phase – the chromatogram, which can be absorptive paper in paper chromatography, a powdered solid in column chromatography or a thin film of dried solid on a glass or plastic sheet in thin-layer chromatography. In each case the mixture to be separated is loaded on to the stationary phase as a small spot and allowed to dry. The edge of the paper or other medium is then dipped in a solvent, which will be drawn up through the spot by capillarity. The different compounds in the mixture will have different solubilities in the solvent and will interact with the stationary phase in different ways, so will move up the paper at different rates. As part of this interaction it is usually necessary to ensure the chromatogram is surrounded by solvent vapour by sealing it in a container.

If the compounds are coloured then it is easy to find the bands or spots formed on the complete chromatogram; if they are not then some other treatment will be necessary such as staining or viewing them under UV light.

Carrying out the investigation

Aim: To identify the pigments present in an extract of plant leaves.

Risk assessment: The solvents used in this investigation, propanone and petroleum ether, produce highly flammable heavy vapours. These can spread unseen along benches so there should be no other naked flames in the laboratory during their use. Both solvents produce potentially harmful vapours, which should not be inhaled. Filling of chromatography vessels should be carried out in a fume cupboard. In general, you should wear eye protection. Gloves may be advisable if you have sensitive skin.

1. To prepare the extract for chromatography you will need to collect leaves of a plant that have a dark green colour. Soft leaves such as spinach, which are easier to crush, are ideal.
2. Cut the leaves into small pieces with scissors and place them into a small mortar with a sprinkling of fine sand.
3. Use a pestle to grind the leaves into a fine paste. Add a small amount of propanone to the paste as you grind. Keep the volume of propanone as low as you can to make sure your extract is as concentrated as possible.
4. Allow the mixture to settle and then draw off the dark green chlorophyll solution with a small pipette. Place this in a small, sealed tube and allow any solids to settle. The mixture can be filtered but you will need to add even more propanone as some is absorbed by the filter paper.
5. To prepare the chromatogram for loading, cut a piece of chromatography paper to fit the container you are to use. Use a pencil to draw a line about 1 cm from the bottom of your paper as shown in Figure 14.3, on the next page.
6. Assemble your chromatogram inside the container and make a mark on the outside to indicate the level of solvent you will need to add. This should be sufficient to cover the end of the paper but it must not touch the spot of extract you are about to load onto it.

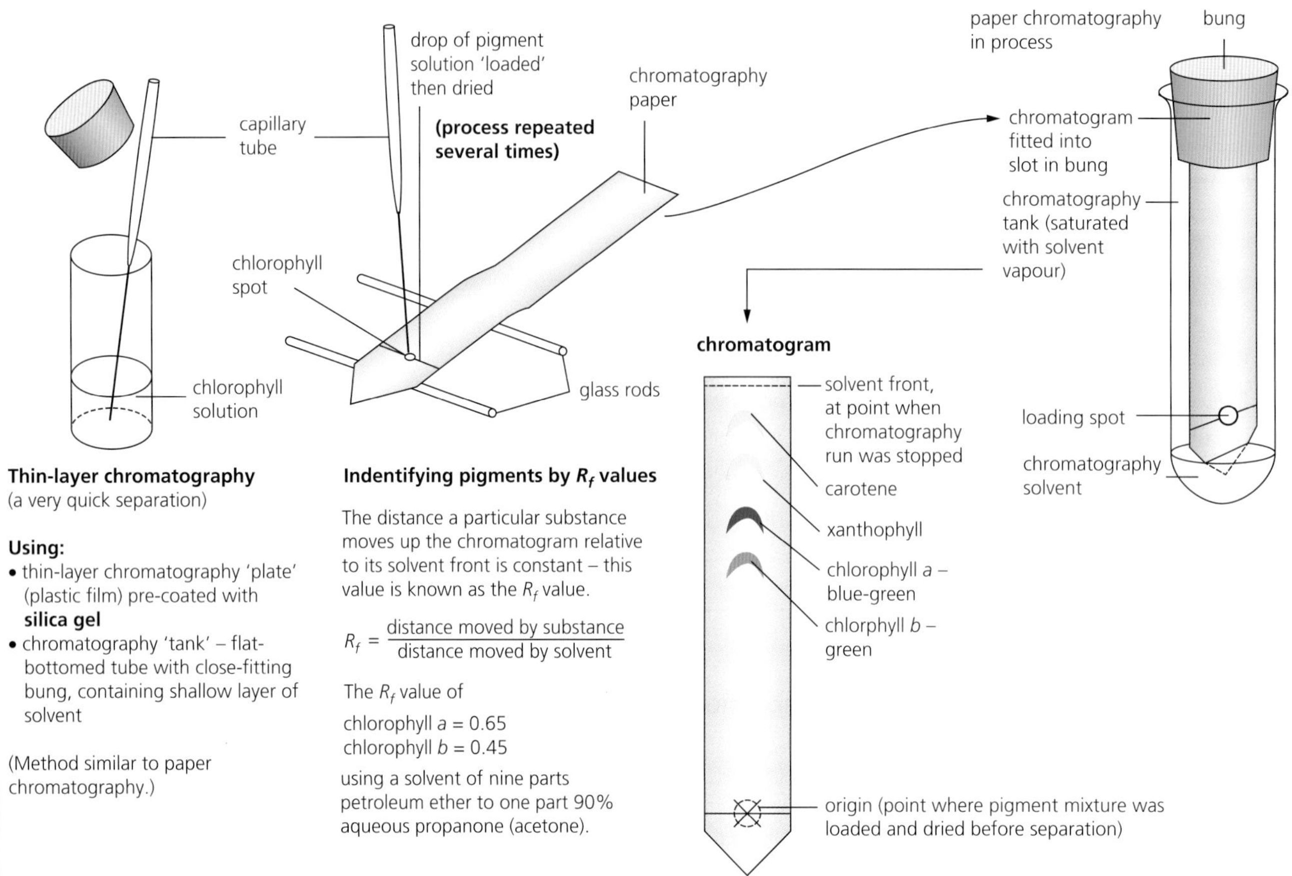

capillary tube
chlorophyll solution
drop of pigment solution 'loaded' then dried
(process repeated several times)
chlorophyll spot
chromatography paper
glass rods
paper chromatography in process
bung
chromatogram fitted into slot in bung
chromatography tank (saturated with solvent vapour)
loading spot
chromatography solvent
chromatogram
solvent front, at point when chromatography run was stopped
carotene
xanthophyll
chlorophyll a – blue-green
chlorphyll b – green
origin (point where pigment mixture was loaded and dried before separation)
Thin-layer chromatography
(a very quick separation)
Using:
• thin-layer chromatography 'plate' (plastic film) pre-coated with silica gel
• chromatography 'tank' – flat-bottomed tube with close-fitting bung, containing shallow layer of solvent
(Method similar to paper chromatography.)
Indentifying pigments by R_f values
The distance a particular substance moves up the chromatogram relative to its solvent front is constant – this value is known as the R_f value.
$R_f = \frac{\text{distance moved by substance}}{\text{distance moved by solvent}}$
The R_f value of
chlorophyll a = 0.65
chlorophyll b = 0.45
using a solvent of nine parts petroleum ether to one part 90% aqueous propanone (acetone).

Figure 14.3 Chromatographic separation of chlorophyll pigments

7 To load the extract on the paper (the stationary phase), you will need to support the paper so that the origin does not touch any surface. Then use a very fine paintbrush or a short length of fine capillary tubing. Dip this into the extract and just touch a tiny spot onto the origin line you have marked on the paper. At this stage it is crucial to use a little patience. Your spot must be as small and as concentrated as you can make it, so you need to make several additions to it, but you must allow each addition to dry before adding the next. The final spot should not be more than about 2 mm in diameter.
The solvent you will use is made up of nine parts petroleum ether to one part propanone. (CAUTION! see Risk assessment.)

8 Add the solvent to your container until it reaches the mark you made. Attach your loaded paper to the bung and lower it carefully into the solvent so that the bung fits tightly and the bottom of the paper touches the solvent. The paper must hang freely and not touch the sides of the container. Keep the tube in a shaded position, or a dark cupboard, as several of the coloured pigments fade quickly.

9 Allow the solvent to rise almost to the top of the paper but do not allow it to continue any longer. When removing the completed chromatogram you will need to act quickly. Make sure you have a sharp pencil; quickly mark the final level of the solvent and draw around any coloured spots you see, noting their colour. Avoid inhaling the solvent vapour.

10 To help identify the pigments, measure the distances shown in Figure 14.3 and calculate their R_f values.

Questions

1 Why is it necessary to use powerful organic solvents in this investigation?

2 Why do you need to act quickly to mark the solvent front and the pigments?

3 How can the pigments be identified from their R_f values?

4 Why is it important not to allow the solvent to touch the origin spot at the start of the investigation?

5 Why must the loading spot be as small as possible?

6 Why is it important to remove the chromatogram before the solvent front reaches the top of the paper?

Photosynthesis

Green plants use the energy from sunlight to produce sugars from the inorganic raw materials, carbon dioxide and water, by a process called photosynthesis. The waste product is oxygen. Photosynthesis occurs in plant cells containing chloroplasts – typically, these are found mainly in the leaves of green plants. Here, light energy is trapped by the green pigment chlorophyll, and becomes the chemical energy in molecules such as glucose and ATP. (Note that we say light energy is transferred to organic compounds in photosynthesis, rather than talking of the 'conversion' of energy, although the latter term was used widely at one time.) This mode of nutrition is known as **autotrophic** as large organic molecules are built up from simple inorganic ingredients such as carbon dioxide and water.

Key term

Autotrophic nutrition The synthesis of larger organic molecules from simpler inorganic compounds as carried out by plants during photosynthesis.

Sugar formed in photosynthesis may temporarily be stored as starch, but sooner or later most is used in metabolism. For example, plants manufacture other carbohydrates, together with lipids, proteins, growth factors, and all the other metabolites they require. For this they need, in addition, certain mineral ions, which are absorbed from the soil solution. Figure 14.4 is a summary of photosynthesis and its place in plant metabolism.

photosynthesis: a summary

The process in the chloroplast can be summarised by the equation:

carbon dioxide + water + LIGHT ENERGY $\xrightarrow[\text{in chloroplast}]{\text{chlorophyll}}$ organic compounds, e.g. sugars + oxygen

raw materials	*energy source*	*products*	*waste product*

$6CO_2 + 6H_2O + \text{light} \xrightarrow[\text{in chloroplast}]{\text{chlorophyll}} C_6H_{12}O_6 + 6O_2$

plant nutrition: a summary

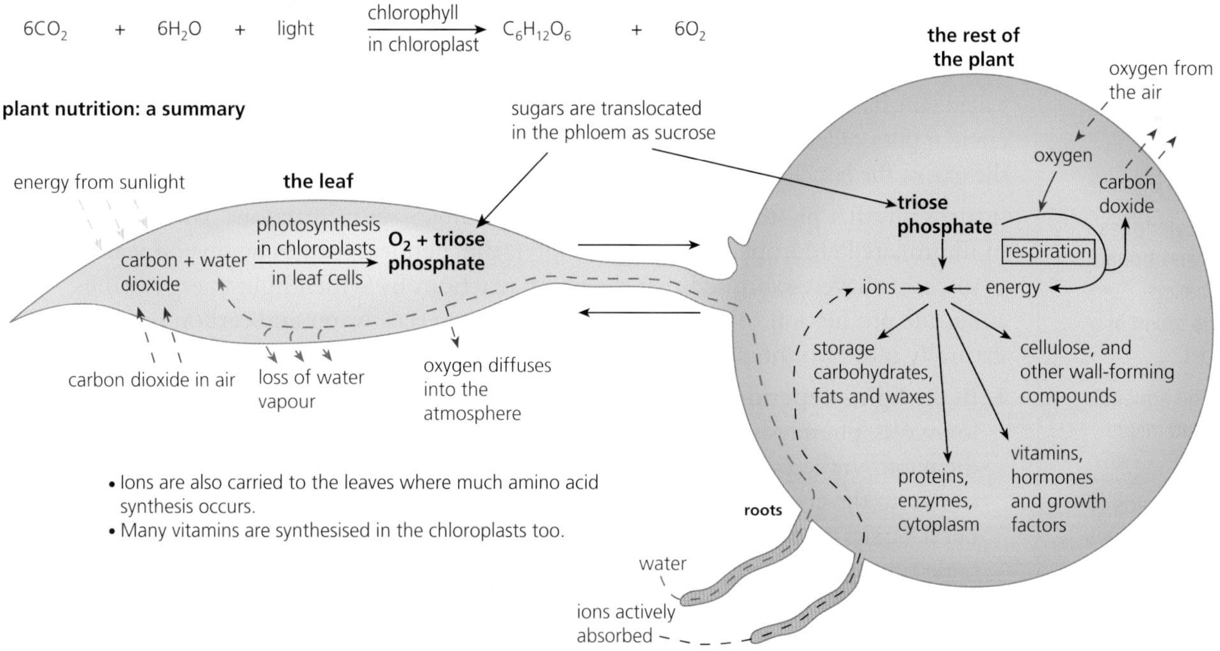

- Ions are also carried to the leaves where much amino acid synthesis occurs.
- Many vitamins are synthesised in the chloroplasts too.

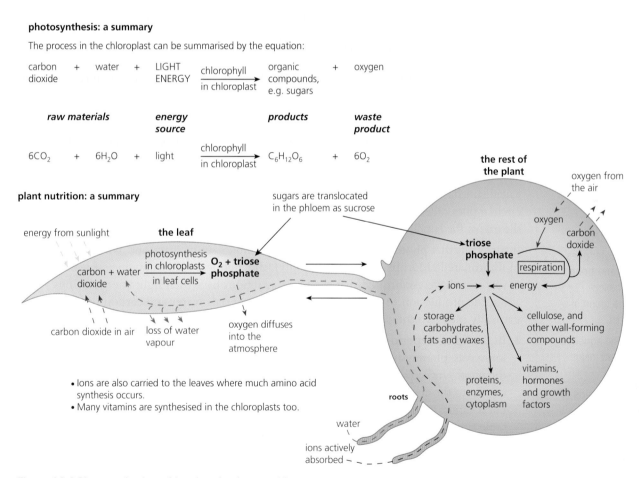

Figure 14.4 Photosynthesis and its place in plant nutrition

the process

fresh leaf tissue

↓

into **'fixing'** solution to kill cells and harden cytoplasm in life-like position and **stained** using solutions of salts of (electron-dense) heavy metal atoms e.g. osmium

↓

tissue **dehydrated** and **embedded** in plastic resin

↓

sectioned on ultramicrotome with glass or diamond knife

↓

sections **mounted** on a copper grid for placing in the electron microscope

Figure 14.5 The production of a TEM of chloroplasts

Chloroplasts – site of photosynthesis

Just as the mitochondria are the site of many of the reactions of respiration, as we explained in Chapter 13, so the chloroplasts are the organelles where the reactions of photosynthesis occur. Remember, chloroplasts are members of a group of organelles called plastids. (Amyloplasts, where starch is stored, are also plastids.)

TEM of thin section of chloroplasts (×22 000)

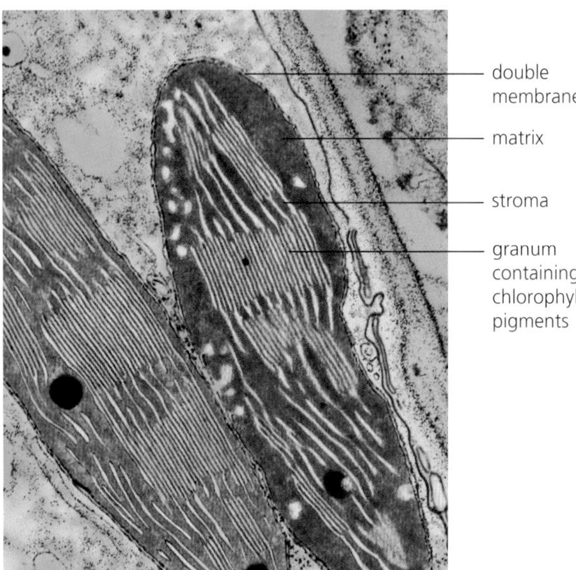

The chloroplast is one of the larger organelles found in plant cells, yet typically measures only 4–10 μm long and 2–3 μm wide. (A micrometre or micron, μm, is one-millionth of a millimetre.) Consequently, while chloroplasts can be seen in outline by light microscopy, for detail of fine structure (ultrastructure) electron microscopy is used.

A transmission electron micrograph (TEM) showing chloroplasts can be produced from thin sections of mesophyll cells, specially prepared (Figure 14.5).

Ultrastructure of chloroplasts and the reactions of photosynthesis

Examine the TEM of the chloroplasts in Figure 14.5, and the diagram in Figure 14.6. You will see that the chloroplast is contained by a double membrane. The outer membrane is a continuous boundary, but the inner membrane 'infolds' to form branching membranes called lamellae or **thylakoids** within the organelle. Some of the thylakoids are arranged in circular piles called **grana**. Here, the photosynthetic pigment, chlorophyll, is held. Between the grana, the lamellae are loosely arranged in an aqueous matrix, forming the **stroma**.

It turns out that photosynthesis consists of a complex set of reactions, which take place in illuminated chloroplasts (unsurprisingly). Biochemical studies by several teams of scientists have established that the many reactions by which light energy brings about the production of sugars, using the raw materials water and carbon dioxide, fall naturally into two interconnected stages (Figure 14.7).

- In the **light-dependent reactions**, light energy is used directly to split water (a process known as 'photolysis', for obvious reasons). Hydrogen is then removed and retained by the photosynthetic-specific hydrogen acceptor, known as $NADP^+$. ($NADP^+$ is very similar to the coenzyme NAD^+ involved in respiration, which you met in Chapter 13, but it carries an additional phosphate group, hence the abbreviation NADP). At the same time, ATP is generated from ADP and phosphate, also using energy from light. This is known as **photophosphorylation**. Oxygen is given off as a waste product of the light-dependent reactions. This stage occurs in the grana of the chloroplasts.
- In the **light-independent reactions**, sugars are built up using carbon dioxide. This stage occurs in the stroma of the chloroplast. Of course, the light-independent reactions require a continuous supply of the products of the light-dependent reactions (ATP and reduced hydrogen acceptor $NADPH + H^+$), but do not directly involve light energy (hence the name). Names can be misleading, however, because sugar production is an integral part of photosynthesis, and photosynthesis is a process that is powered by transfer of light energy.

Key terms

Grana Circular piles of membrane-bound vesicles called thylakoids found in a chloroplast.

Stroma The aqueous matrix found inside chloroplasts.

Thylakoids Infolds of the inner membranes of chloroplasts that carry photosynthetic pigments.

Photophosphorylation The production of ATP from ADP using energy from light during photosynthesis.

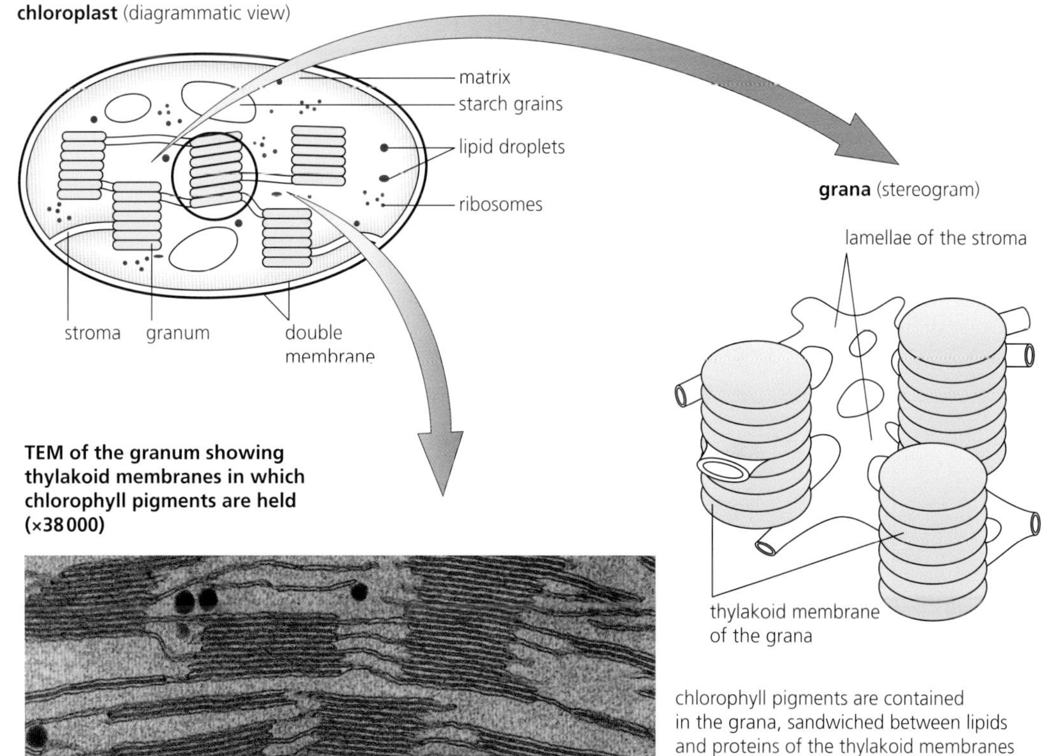

Figure 14.6 The ultrastructure of a chloroplast

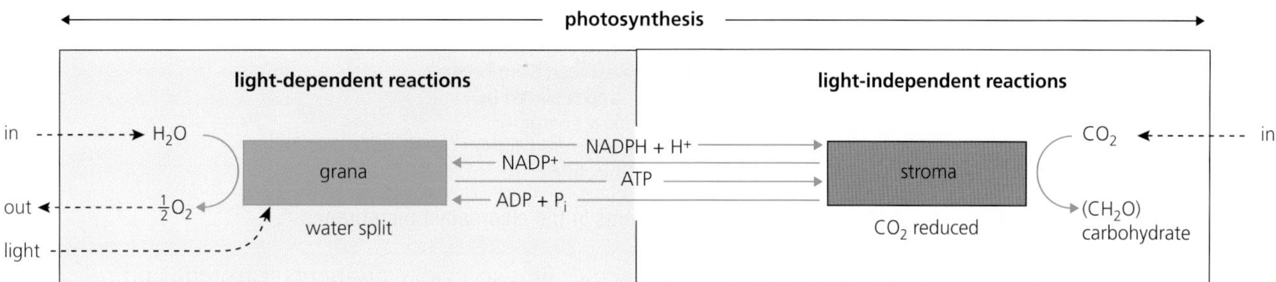

Figure 14.7 The two reactions of photosynthesis

In the next section we shall consider each stage in turn, in order to understand more about how these complex changes are brought about.

Test yourself

5 Explain what is meant by *transmission electron microscopy.*

6 Give the general term used to describe compounds such as the hydrogen acceptor $NADP^+$.

7 State in what form carbon dioxide enters the cytoplasm and chloroplasts of a plant cell.

8 Name the stage of photosynthesis during which oxygen is given off.

9 Describe the difference between the main hydrogen acceptors in photosynthesis and respiration.

The light-dependent reactions

In the light-dependent stage, light energy is trapped by the photosynthetic pigment, chlorophyll. Chlorophyll molecules do not occur haphazardly in the grana. Rather, they are grouped together in structures called photosystems, held in the thylakoid membranes of the grana (Figure 14.8).

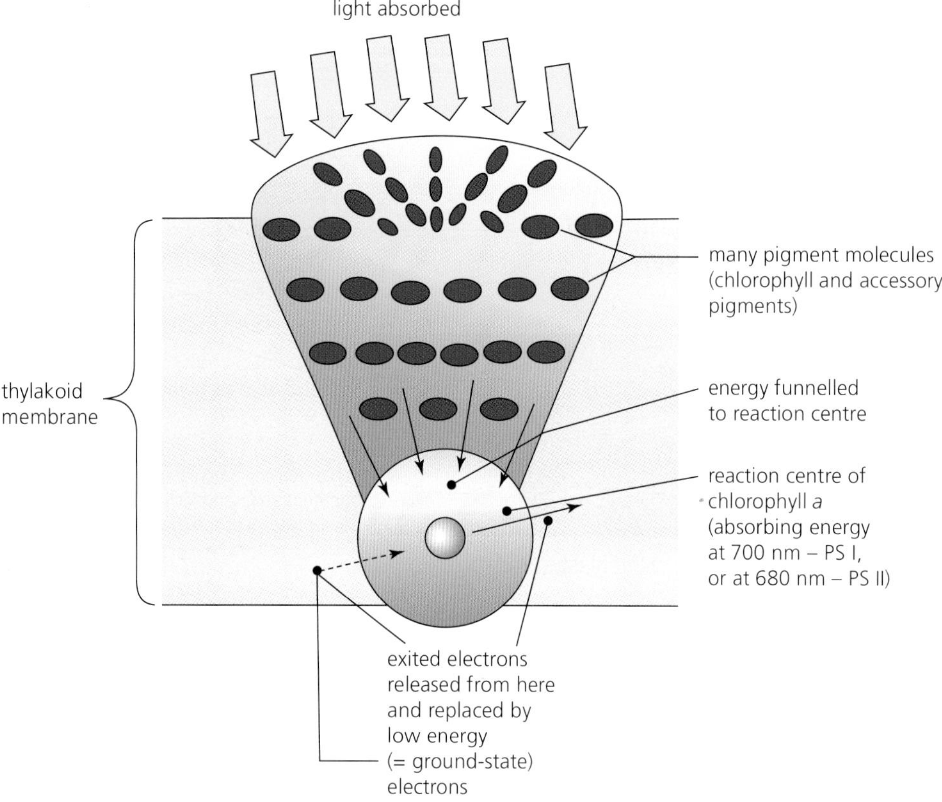

Figure 14.8 The structure of photosystems in the chloroplast membranes

Several hundred chlorophyll molecules plus accessory pigments (carotene and xanthophylls) are arranged in each photosystem. All these pigment molecules harvest light energy, and they funnel the energy to a single chlorophyll molecule in the photosystem, known as the reaction centre. The different pigments around the reaction centres absorb light energy of slightly different wavelengths.

There are two types of photosystem present in the thylakoid membranes of the grana, identified by the wavelength of light that the chlorophyll of the reaction centre absorbs.

- **Photosystem I** has a reaction centre activated by light of wavelength 700 nm. This reaction centre is also referred to as P700.
- **Photosystem II** has a reaction centre activated by light of wavelength 680 nm. This reaction centre is also referred to as P680.

> **Key term**
>
> **Photosystems I and II** Two chains of electron carriers responsible for the capture of light energy in the first stages of photosynthesis.

Photosystems I and II have differing roles, as you shall see shortly. However, they occur grouped together in the thylakoid membranes of the grana, along with certain proteins that function quite specifically in one of the following roles:

1. Enzymes catalysing the splitting of water into hydrogen ions, electrons and oxygen atoms.
2. Enzymes catalysing the formation of ATP from ADP and phosphate (P_i).

3 Enzymes catalysing the conversion of oxidised H-carrier ($NADP^+$) to reduced carrier ($NADPH + H^+$).

4 Electron-carrier molecules (these are large proteins).

When light energy reaches a reaction centre, 'ground-state' electrons in the key chlorophyll molecule are raised to an 'excited' state by the light energy received. As a result, high-energy electrons are released from this chlorophyll molecule, and these electrons bring about the biochemical changes of the light-dependent reactions (Figure 14.9). The spaces vacated by the high-energy (excited) electrons are continuously refilled by non-excited or 'ground-state' electrons.

We will examine this sequence of reactions in the two photosystems next.

- Firstly, the excited electrons from photosystem II are picked up by, and passed along, a chain of electron-carriers. As these excited electrons pass, some of the energy causes the pumping of hydrogen ions (protons) from the chloroplast's matrix into the thylakoid spaces. Here they accumulate – incidentally, causing the pH to drop. The result is a proton gradient that is created across the thylakoid membrane, and which sustains the synthesis of ATP. This is an example of chemiosmosis, which is described in detail in Chapter 13.

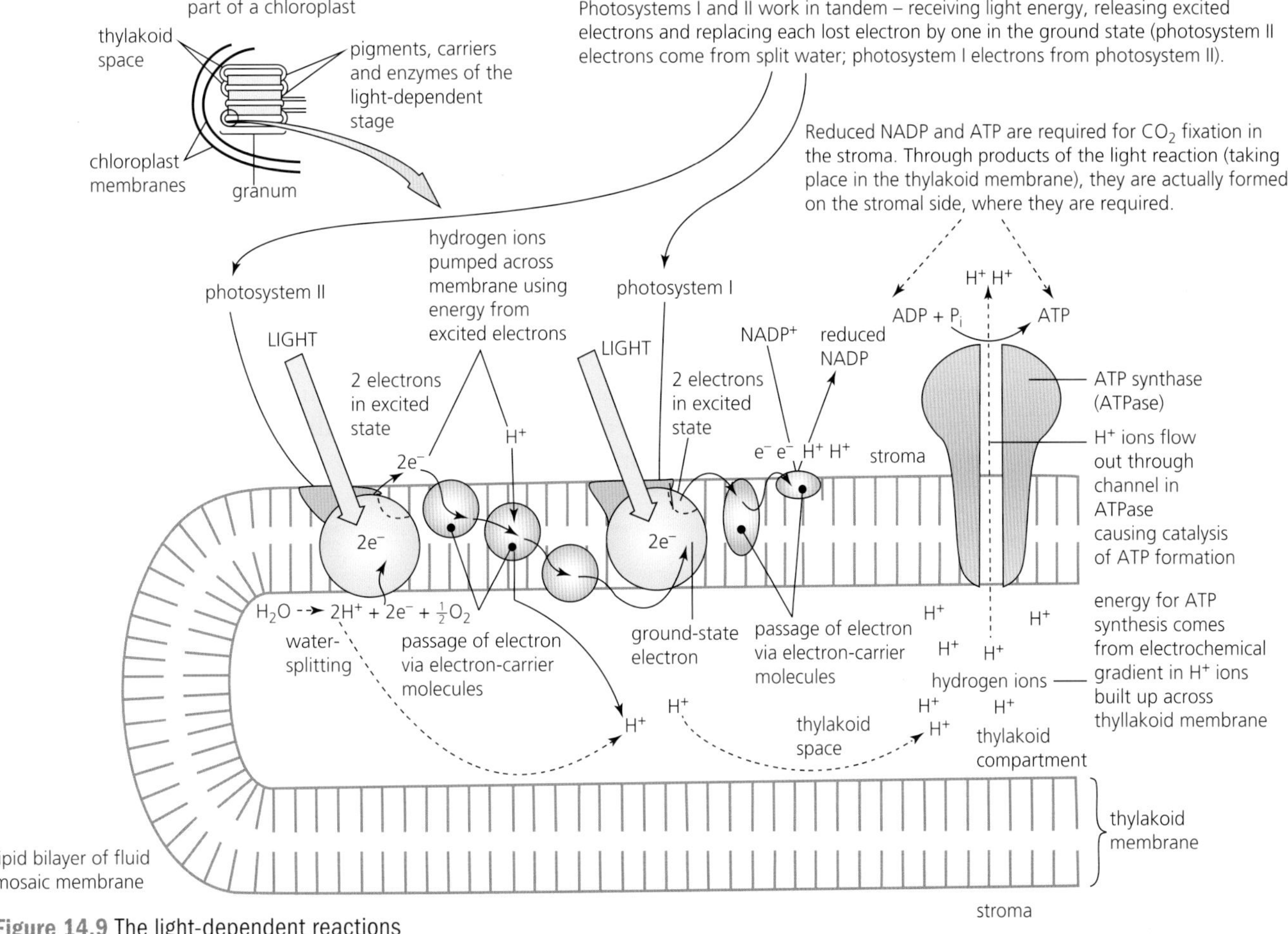

Figure 14.9 The light-dependent reactions

As a result of these energy transfers, the excitation level of the electrons falls back to 'ground state' and they come to fill the vacancies in the reaction centre of photosystem I. Thus, electrons have been transferred from photosystem II to photosystem I.

Meanwhile the 'holes' in the reaction centre of photosystem II are filled by electrons (in their 'ground state') from water molecules. In fact, the positively charged 'vacancies' in photosystem II are powerful enough to cause the splitting of water (photolysis) in the presence of a specific enzyme. The reaction this enzyme catalyses then triggers the release of hydrogen ions and oxygen atoms, as well as 'ground-state' electrons.

The oxygen atoms combine to form molecular oxygen, the waste product of photosynthesis. The hydrogen ions are used in the reduction of $NADP^+$ (see below).

In the grana of the chloroplasts, the synthesis of ATP is coupled to electron transport via the movement of protons by chemiosmosis. Here, the hydrogen ions trapped within the thylakoid space flow out via ATP synthetase enzymes, down their electrochemical gradient. At the same time, ATP is synthesised from ADP and P_i. This is called photophosphorylation.

Key term

Non-cyclic photophosphorylation The production of ATP from ADP using light energy in a linear series of reactions.

You have seen that the 'excited' electrons that eventually provide the energy for ATP synthesis, originate from water. They fill the vacancies in the reaction centre of photosystem II and are subsequently moved on to the reaction centre in photosystem I. Finally, they are used to reduce $NADP^+$. The photophosphorylation reaction in which they are involved is described as **non-cyclic photophosphorylation**, because the pathway of electrons is linear.

- Secondly, the excited electrons from photosystem I are picked up by a different electron acceptor. Two at a time, they are passed to $NADP^+$, which – with the addition of hydrogen ions from photolysis – is reduced to form $NADPH + H^+$.

By this sequence of reactions, repeated again and again at very great speed throughout every second of daylight, the products of the light-dependent reactions (ATP and $NADPH + H^+$) are formed.

ATP and reduced NADP do not normally accumulate, however, as they are immediately used in the fixation of carbon dioxide in the surrounding stroma (in the light-independent reactions). Then the ADP and $NADP^+$ diffuse back into the grana for re-use in the light-dependent reactions.

Test yourself

10 Explain what happens to the energy from photons immediately after they are 'captured' by a chlorophyll molecule.

11 Describe what happens to the H^+ ions released from the splitting of water in photosystem II.

12 State the similarities between ATP production in oxidative phosphorylation in respiration and here in the light-dependent stage.

13 Suggest why the ATP produced in the light-dependent stage is not available for general metabolic purposes in the cytoplasm.

The light-independent reactions

In the light-independent reactions, carbon dioxide is converted to carbohydrate. These reactions occur in the stroma of the chloroplasts, surrounding the grana. Carbon dioxide readily diffuses into the chloroplast where it is built up into sugars in a cyclic process called the Calvin cycle.

In the Calvin cycle, carbon dioxide is combined with an acceptor molecule in the presence of a special enzyme, **ribulose bisphosphate carboxylase** (rubisco for short). The stroma is packed full of rubisco, which easily makes up the bulk of all the protein in a green plant. In fact, it is the most abundant enzyme present in the living world.

The acceptor molecule is a five-carbon sugar, ribulose bisphosphate (referred to as RuBP) and carbon dioxide is added in a process known as fixation (Figure 14.11). The product is not a six-carbon sugar, but rather two molecules of a three-carbon compound, **glycerate-3-phosphate (GP)**. GP is then reduced to form another three-carbon compound called **glyceraldehyde 3-phosphate (GALP)**. Some of the GALP is converted into the products of photosynthesis, such as glucose, or amino acids and fatty acids. The glucose may be immediately respired, or stored as starch until required. But the bulk of GALP is converted to more acceptor molecule, enabling fixation of carbon dioxide to continue.

Key terms

Calvin cycle A sequence of reactions in the light-independent stage of photosynthesis where carbon dioxide is taken in and sugars are produced.

Rubisco The abbreviation for the enzyme ribulose bisphosphate carboxylase, which is important in fixing atmospheric carbon dioxide during photosynthesis.

Ribulose bisphosphate Important 5-carbon sugar in the light-independent stage of photosynthesis, which is used to fix carbon dioxide from the atmosphere.

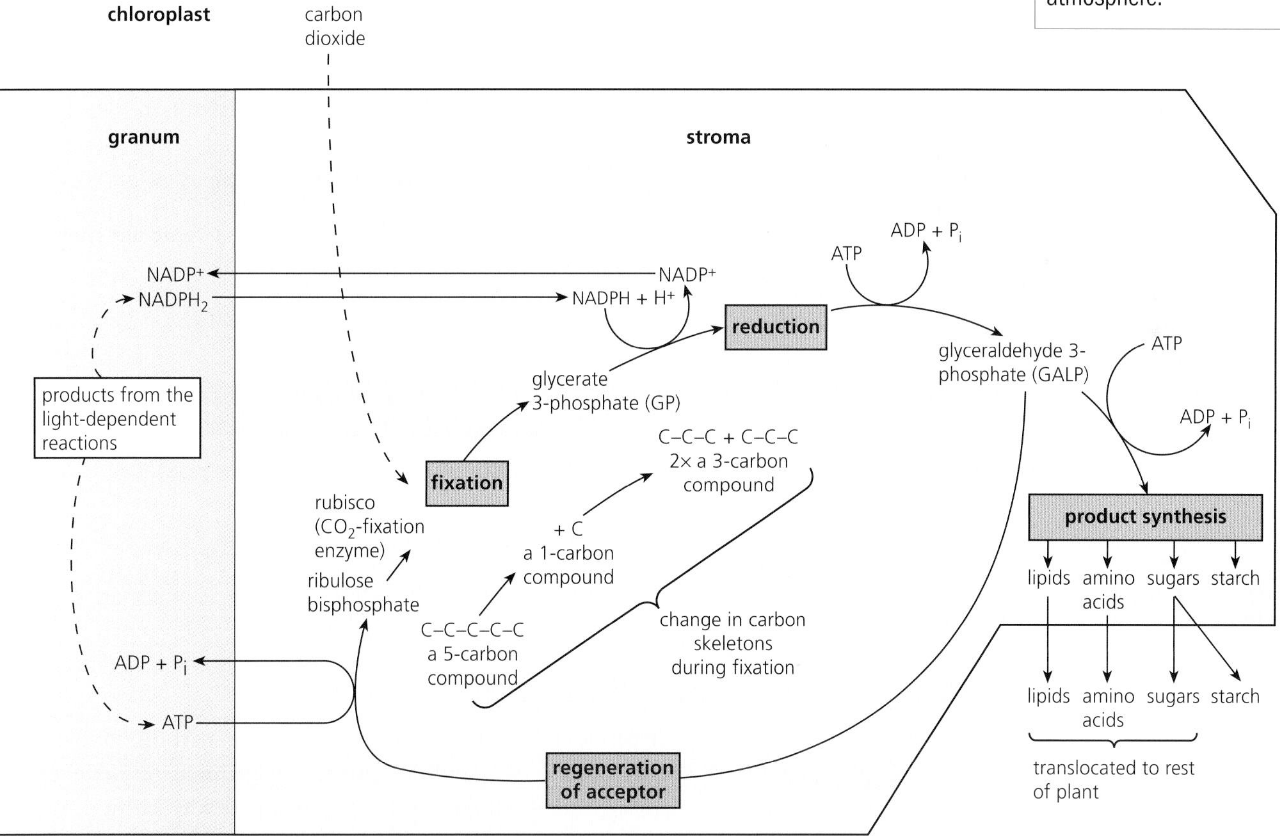

Figure 14.10 The light-independent reactions *in situ*

Figure 14.11 The path of carbon in photosynthesis – a summary

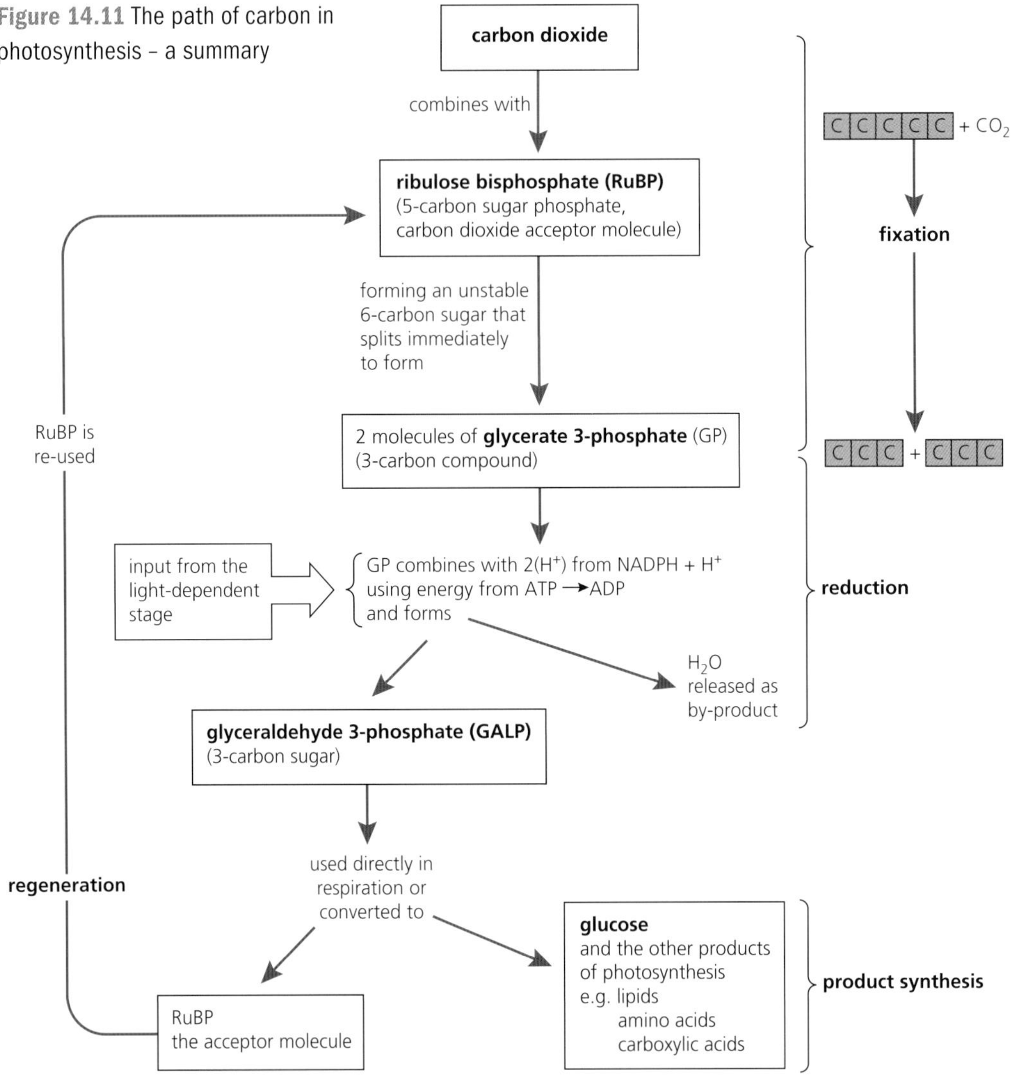

Test yourself

14 Suggest why the enzyme rubisco has justifiable claims to be the most important enzyme on Earth.

15 Name the compound that is the initial product of the reaction catalysed by rubisco.

16 State the two main uses of glyceraldehyde 3-phosphate (GALP).

Photosynthesis and plant metabolism

As you have seen, the first sugar produced in photosynthesis is a three-carbon compound, glycerate 3-phosphate (GP) (Figure 14.11). Some of this product is immediately converted into the acceptor molecule for more carbon dioxide fixation, by a pathway known as the Calvin cycle. The remainder is converted into the carbohydrate products of photosynthesis, mainly glucose and starch, or serves as intermediates that are the starting points for all the other metabolites the plant requires. By *intermediates*, we mean all the substances of a metabolic pathway from which the end product is assembled.

Glucose is also the substrate for respiration. By *substrate*, we mean a molecule that is the starting point for a biochemical pathway, and a substance that forms a complex with an enzyme (thereby getting the pathway 'up and running'). The intermediates of respiration are also starting points for the synthesis of other metabolites. In other words, the biochemical pathways of both photosynthesis and respiration interact to supply metabolism with the intermediates required. These include:

- specialist carbohydrates, such as sucrose for transport and cellulose for cell walls
- lipids, including those in membranes
- amino acids and proteins, including those in membranes and those that function as enzymes
- nucleic acids, growth factors, vitamins, hormones and pigments.

The fates of the products of photosynthesis are summarised in Figure 14.12.

Test yourself

17 Name the ion required for the manufacture of all amino acids from the Calvin cycle intermediates.

18 Name the ion required for the synthesis of nucleic acids.

19 Describe exactly where ions enter the plant and how they reach organs such as the leaf.

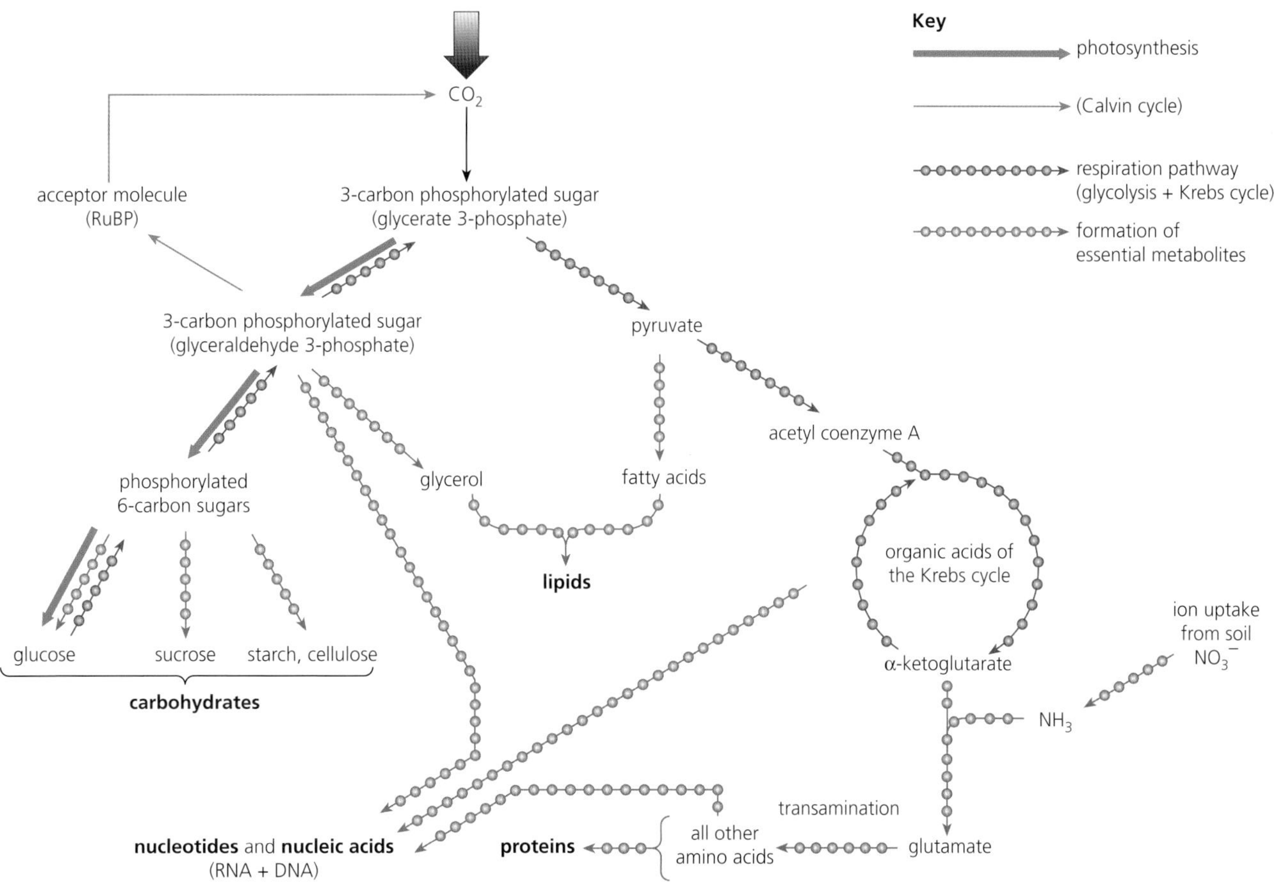

Figure 14.12 How the products of photosynthesis are linked with other plant cell metabolism

Core practical 10

Investigating the effect of different wavelengths of light on the rate of photosynthesis

Background information

You can follow the rate of photosynthesis in several ways but the most common way is to measure the rate of oxygen evolution by aquatic plants. Using aquatic plants means that it is much easier to collect the gas given off with simple apparatus. As you have seen in Chapter 13, this is not always straightforward as plants also respire and therefore use up some of the oxygen before you can collect it. Fortunately, most plants give off far more oxygen than they consume and provided you can assume that the rate of respiration is constant then the rate of oxygen evolution will be directly proportional to the rate of photosynthesis.

The most common plant to use for this investigation is the Canadian pondweed *Elodea canadensis*. This can easily be obtained from ponds and streams in the wild, as well as many aquarium suppliers as it is often used to oxygenate fish tanks. Unfortunately, very few aquatic plants give off oxygen in a controlled way that will allow you to collect it. *Elodea* can be rather unreliable in this respect and the tropical pondweed *Cabomba* sp. is often recommended as a more reliable alternative.

You can collect the gas given off in a given time and draw it into a capillary tube, where its volume can be calculated in a similar manner to the respirometer described in Core practical 9 (Chapter 13).

Lamps to produce different wavelengths of light are very expensive. Coloured filters are normally used to produce a range of wavelengths within the visible spectrum but it is important that the light source is of high intensity. It is useful to have filters of known wavelengths to produce more accurate data.

Carrying out the investigation

Aim: To investigate the effect of different wavelengths of light on the rate of photosynthesis.

Risk assessment: There are no significant risks associated with this investigation. Reasonable care and attention will be needed when manipulating light sources which may be hot. Care should be taken when using large volumes of water close to electricity.

Care should also be taken when using low energy light bulbs (compact fluorescent tubes) in bench lamps to light the pond weed. The bulbs contain small amounts of mercury and are coated in a chemical which fluoresces. If breakages occur, the fragments should be swept up carefully, and the light disposed of in the same way as fluorescent tubes. The room should be well ventilated.

1. Before setting up the apparatus as shown in Figure 14.13, it is important to check that you have a section of pondweed that will produce a good stream of oxygen bubbles consistently. Measure out a length of pondweed (*Cabomba* is recommended) that will fit comfortably into a large boiling tube.
2. Cut off about 1 cm from the end of the stem to ensure that there is a free passage for any gas given off.
3. Cover this with a dilute solution of sodium hydrogencarbonate to provide an excess supply of carbon dioxide (hydrogencarbonate ions) in the water.
4. Place a bench lamp 15 cm from the edge of the boiling tube and observe the end of the stem for a few minutes. It is useful to include a beaker of clean water between the lamp and the tube to act as a heat shield, helping to keep the temperature of the tube constant.
5. Set up the apparatus shown in Figure 14.13, making sure that the whole of the capillary tube is full of water by using the syringe. Move the pondweed until the stream of bubbles is directly under the end of the capillary tube as shown in the diagram and no bubbles are escaping. Check that the lamp is exactly 15 cm from the tube.
6. Start the stopclock and collect the gas given off for at least 5 minutes. You will need to adjust the time so there is sufficient volume of gas to measure, as all plant samples will vary.
7. At the end of your chosen period, use the syringe to draw up the bubble into the capillary tube so that its length can be measured on the scale. Repeat this at least three times with the lamp having no filter.
8. Cover the tube with the first coloured filter, without moving the lamp. Leave the apparatus for at least 5 minutes to settle down to a constant rate with the new filter.
9. Remove any gas bubble formed during this time by drawing it to the far side of the scale using the syringe, then take three more measurements.
10. Repeat the whole process with different coloured filters using the same piece of pondweed.

Questions

1. What effect will an increase in temperature have on the volume of oxygen given off?
2. Will changing the colour of the filter change other light variables?
3. Why do only some aquatic plants give off a predictable stream of bubbles?
4. Some protocols suggest counting bubbles as an alternative to measuring the volume of oxygen. Why would this be very inaccurate?

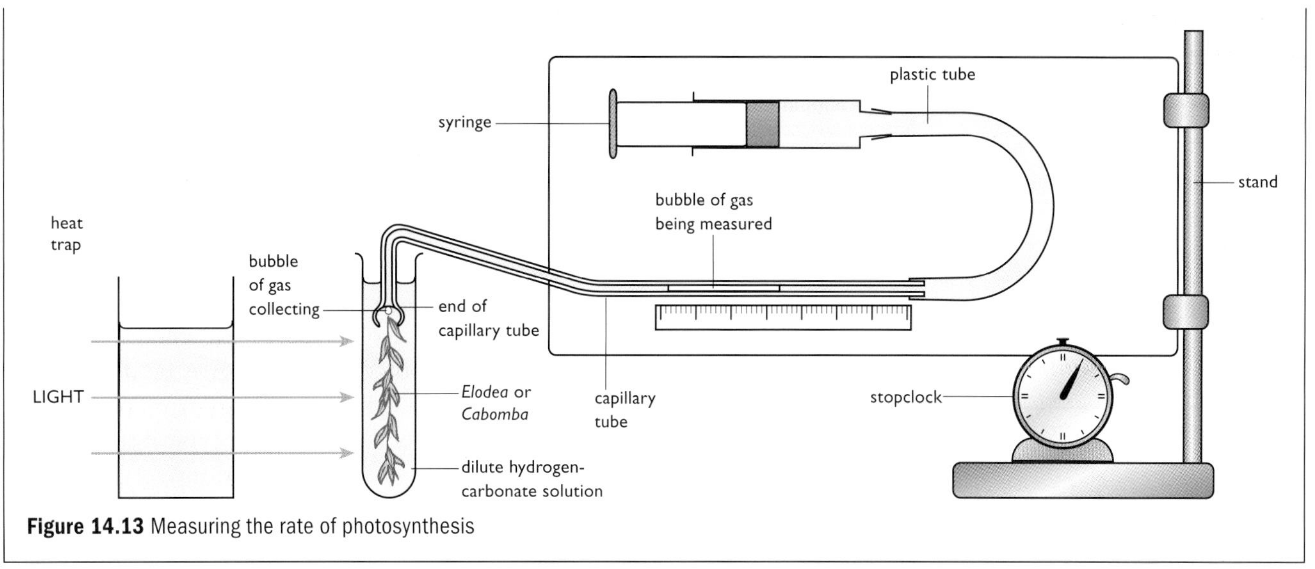

Figure 14.13 Measuring the rate of photosynthesis

Factors affecting the rate of photosynthesis

The rate of photosynthesis is affected by a number of different factors. The main factors are light, carbon dioxide concentration and temperature. In the plant's normal habitat these factors are constantly changing throughout each day, therefore it is not possible to name one overall factor that is most important. What we can say at any one time is that the factor that will have the greatest influence will always be the one that is least favourable. This is known as the **Law of limiting factors**. For example, in open grassland on a sunny day at noon there will be lots of light available and the temperature will be fine, so the availability of carbon dioxide might be the **limiting factor** for photosynthesis. However, later in the day, as the sun goes down, then it is most likely that light intensity will become the limiting factor. Some of these effects are summarised in Figure 14.14.

> **Key term**
>
> **Limiting factor** In any process controlled by more than one factor then the rate of the overall process will be determined by the availability of the least favourable factor.

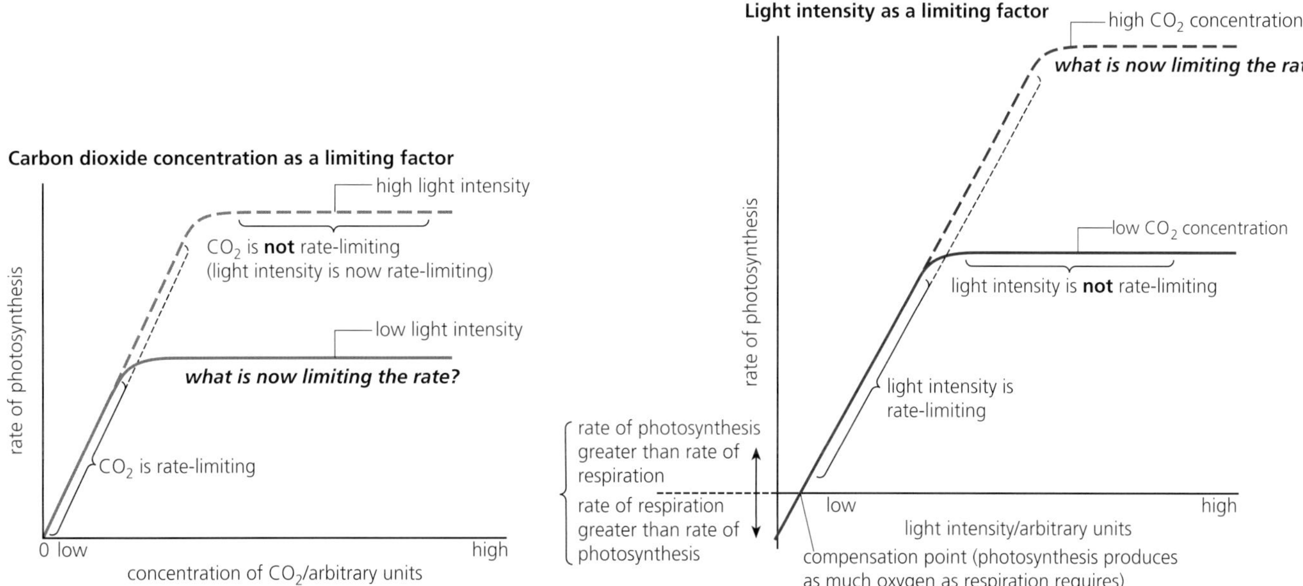

Figure 14.14 Carbon dioxide concentration and light intensity as limiting factors

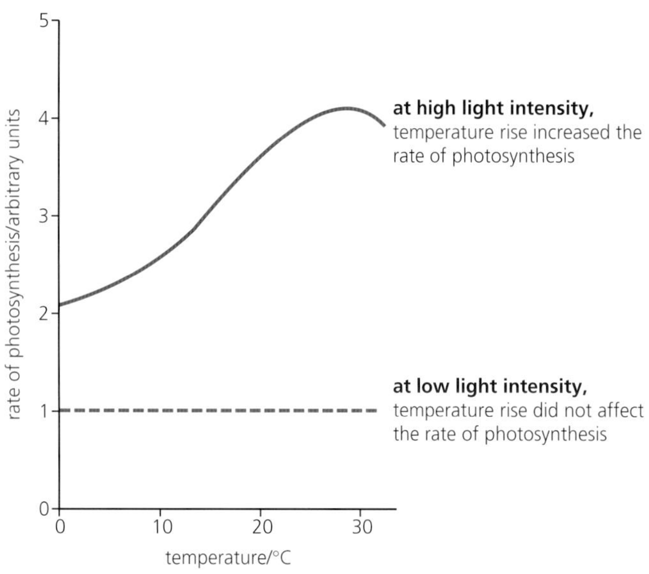

Figure 14.15 The effect of temperature on the rate of photosynthesis

The effect of temperature on the rate of photosynthesis

Unlike a normal series of enzyme-controlled reactions, photosynthesis shows a different response to temperature according to the level of light intensity. In general, temperature has no effect on the rate at low light intensities but shows a familiar response to increased temperature at high light intensities as shown in Figure 14.15. One reason for this is that photosynthesis is a two-stage process where the light-dependent photochemical stage is unaffected by temperature (as it is driven by energy from photons) but the light-independent stage is a typical series of temperature-sensitive enzyme reactions.

Chapter summary

Photosynthetic pigments

- The main photosynthetic pigments absorb light energy and convert it to chemical energy. Chlorophyll a and b are an integral part of photosynthesis.
- Accessory pigments such as carotenes, phycoerythrin and fucoxanthin have the same function but pass on the absorbed energy to chlorophylls at the start of photosynthesis.
- Chlorophyll molecules have magnesium atoms with a conjugated protein 'head' and long hydrocarbon 'tails' with which they attach to membranes.
- A graph of the amount of light absorbed by a pigment at different wavelengths is called an absorption spectrum.
- A graph of the rate of photosynthesis of a plant illuminated at different wavelengths is called an action spectrum.

Chloroplasts

- Chloroplasts are organelles surrounded by a double membrane.
- The inner membrane is folded to form thylakoids. Some thylakoids are arranged in stacks called grana, which contain chlorophyll 'sandwiched' between their membranes.
- The stroma is the watery matrix inside the chloroplast, which can often contain starch grains, ribosomes and lipid droplets.

Light-dependent reactions of photosynthesis

- Light-dependent reactions take place on the thylakoid membranes in the grana.
- Chlorophyll molecules are arranged on the grana in groups of several hundred called photosystems. In each group the energy absorbed is all passed to one molecule called the reaction centre.
- There are two types of photosystem, which each absorb different wavelengths of light.
- The reaction centres of both photosystems use the energy passed to them to release high-energy electrons.
- Electrons from photosystem II are passed along carriers to release energy that is used to pump H^+ ions into the intergranal space.
- The electrons from photosystem II are replaced by splitting water molecules, releasing oxygen (photolysis).
- Photosystem I takes up the electrons from photosystem II and raises their energy level so that, with H^+ ions from photolysis, they can produce NADPH + H^+.
- ATP is produced by chemiosmosis using the gradient of H^+ ions built up across the granal membranes.

Light-independent reactions of photosynthesis

- Carbon dioxide gas is fixed by reaction with ribulose bisphosphate (RuBP) in the stroma of the chloroplast to form glycerate phosphate (GP).
- NADPH + H^+ and ATP from the light-dependent reactions are then used to first reduce and then phosphorylate GP to form glyceraldehyde-3-phosphate (GALP), which is the starting point for biochemical synthesis of sugars, proteins and fats.
- Some GALP is used to regenerate RuBP to continue the cyclical process.
- Factors such as light, carbon dioxide concentration and temperature will all affect the rate of photosynthesis. At any time the least favourable of these will control the whole rate. This is known as the Law of Limiting Factors.

Practice questions

1 Carotenoid pigments that pass on their electrons to chlorophylls are known as:

A auxiliary pigments **C** accessory pigments

B augmenting pigments **D** additional pigments *(1)*

> **Tip**
>
> Not all multiple-choice questions will be simple recall like Question 1. Some, such as Question 2, will need understanding of a principle and some careful thought, so this would be AO2.

2 A mixture of substances, M, contains a compound, X. Chromatography was used to separate compound X from the mixture but two different solvents were needed. The mixture was first separated in solvent A and then the paper was turned through 90 degrees (as shown in the diagram) to be separated again with a different solvent, B. In each case the solvent front was allowed to reach the top of the paper before the paper was removed.

The R_f value of compound X in solvent A was 0.5 and its R_f value in solvent B was 0.75.

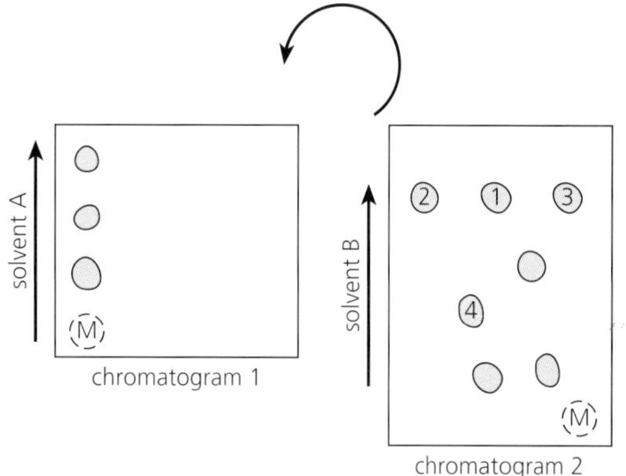

Compound X will be found in chromatogram 2 at the spot labelled:

A 1 **C** 3

B 2 **D** 4 *(1)*

3 a) The graph shows the absorption spectrum of chlorophyll *a* and chlorophyll *b* taken from a marine alga (seaweed).

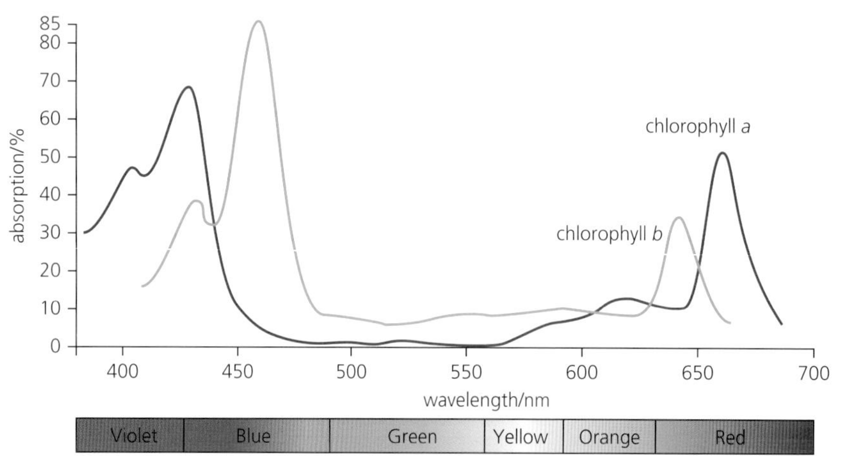

> **Tip**
>
> Question 3 is a typical mixture of AO1 – asking you to show you understand basic specification material and AO2 – asking you to apply that understanding to data in a new context.

i) Analyse the data and explain how it illustrates the need for more than one pigment in photosynthesis. *(3)*

ii) Explain how chlorophyll molecules are able to trap light energy in the first stage of the light-dependent reaction of photosynthesis. *(3)*

b) Photosynthetic marine algae (seaweeds) are often found growing in oceans at depths of 10 m or more.

The table below shows how the different wavelengths of light are absorbed by clear seawater.

Wavelength of light/nm	Depth of seawater at which 90% of the light is absorbed/m
450	40
525	24
575	9
610	5
680	2

i) Describe the trend shown by the data in this table. *(2)*

ii) In addition to chlorophyll *a* and *b*, many marine algae found at this depth also contain the pigment fucoxanthyn. The absorption spectrum of fucoxanthyn shows a strong peak between 510–525 nm. Explain how the presence of this pigment will assist the growth of marine algae at depths below 15 m. *(3)*

4 The diagram represents a simplified scheme for the reactions of photosynthesis.

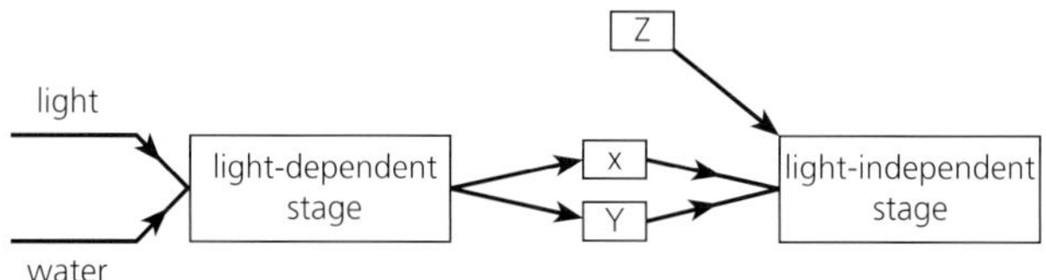

a) Name the intermediates labelled X, Y and Z. *(3)*

b) Explain how oxygen molecules are formed during the light-dependent stage. *(3)*

c) During the early stages of research into the biochemistry of photosynthesis, Otto Warburg used flashes of light to investigate the nature of the whole process. He used a culture of algae and a high concentration of carbon dioxide with a high-intensity lamp. The algal cultures were illuminated by spinning a disc in front of the lamp. The disc had segments cut out so that the speed of rotation would change the frequency of the flashes. The rate of photosynthesis during the period of illumination was measured at different frequency of flashes. Some of his results are summarised in the table on the next page.

Tip

Question 4 is also a mixture of AO1 and AO2 but is a more difficult question as you need to think carefully about the overall process of photosynthesis and only part (a) is simple recall. You are unlikely to have met the data in this form so the question requires you to understand the links between the two stages in some depth.

Frequency of flashes/min^{-1}	Relative rate of photosynthesis
continuous illumination	100
4	110
8000	200

i) Why did Warburg use a high concentration of carbon dioxide? *(1)*

ii) We now believe that the reactions of the light-dependent stage occur very rapidly and that there are two stages in the overall process of photosynthesis. Explain how the results of this experiment support this model of photosynthesis. *(3)*

★**5** It has been suggested that because of the similarities between mitochondria and chloroplasts, they might have had some common origin in evolutionary time. Use your knowledge of the structure and function of mitochondria and chloroplasts to assess the validity of this suggestion. *(9)*

Stretch and challenge

6 All plants fix carbon dioxide using the enzyme rubisco and the compound RuBP, and are known as C3 plants because they form the 3-C molecule GP. However, some plants such as maize and sugar cane use an additional pathway, called the C4 pathway, to fix carbon dioxide. These plants are able to photosynthesise more rapidly and grow more quickly than C3 plants. You might think that C4 plants would out-compete C3 plants and be the dominant form of photosynthesis, but this is not the case.

a) What C4 compounds are used to fix carbon dioxide in C4 plants?

b) What is the function of bundle sheath cells in the C4 process?

c) Maize and sugar cane are C4 plants and dominate food crops in tropical countries. In temperate zones C3 plants, such as wheat, are the major crops. Why are C4 plants at an advantage in tropical regions but not in cooler climates?

Tip

Question 5 is first of all a synoptic question where you will need to use your knowledge of the functions of organelles from the first parts of the course in addition to respiration and photosynthesis. It also requires that you compose your answer carefully in continuous prose and make sure that you make comparisons (similarities and differences) as this is marked using a 'levels' making scheme (see further details in the 'Preparing for the exams' chapter at the end of this book). Simply describing mitochondria and chloroplasts separately will gain you few marks. You will be expected to come to some form of conclusion, for example do you think that the similarities indicate that they may have a common ancestor or are the differences too great?

15 Microbial techniques

Prior knowledge

In this chapter you will need to recall that:

→ microorganisms include bacteria, fungi and single-celled protoctists
→ many microorganisms are pathogenic
→ aseptic techniques allow microorganisms to be studied safely
→ bacteria have prokaryotic cells, whereas fungi and protoctists have eukaryotic cells.

Test yourself on prior knowledge

1 What is a pathogen?
2 Name two differences between a prokaryotic cell and a eukaryotic cell.
3 Give **two** features that a bacterial cell and a fungal cell have in common.
4 Figure 15.1 shows a student pouring a growth medium into a dish.
 a) Name the type of dish into which she is pouring the growth medium.
 b) Explain **one** aseptic technique you can see she is using in the drawing.

Types of media used to culture microorganisms

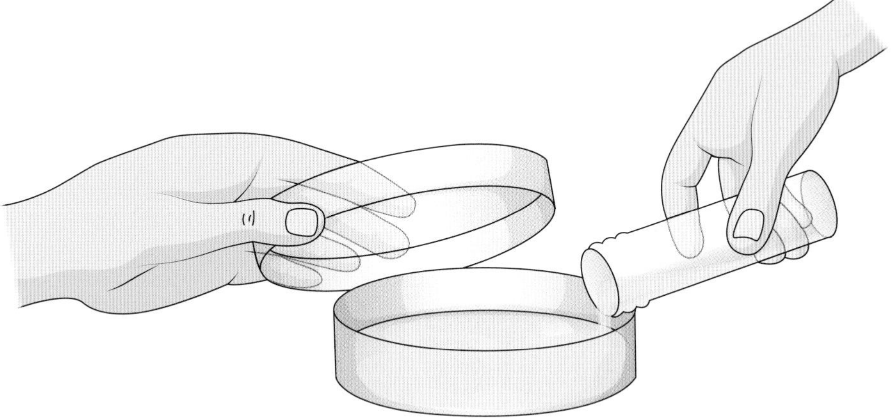

Figure 15.1 A student pouring a liquid growth medium into a dish

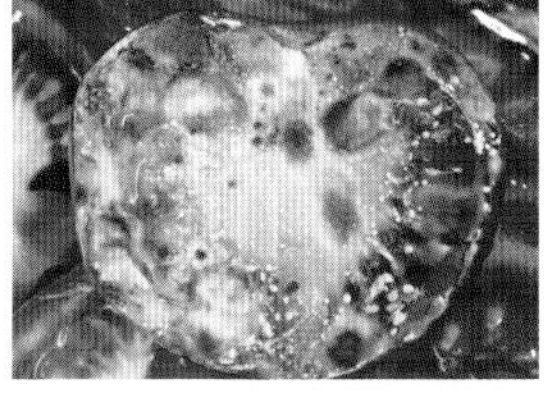

Figure 15.2 This cut tomato has been colonised by microorganisms. They grow by secreting hydrolytic enzymes onto the food and absorbing the products of digestion

It is remarkably easy to grow microorganisms. All you need do is leave food uncovered, especially if the environment is warm. You will soon notice microorganisms growing on the food. Look at the tomato in Figure 15.2. After a few days' exposure in a warm room it had been colonised by many microorganisms. The blue-grey patches are colonies of *Penicillium* and the tiny white spots are colonies of yeast. This room was not an unusual environment; bacterial and fungal spores are ever present in the air around us, including the air in your college or school laboratory.

A culture medium provides the essential nutrients that a population of microorganisms needs for its growth. All microorganisms share basic nutritional needs – a source of the elements carbon and nitrogen, for example. Consequently, all synthetic culture media are based on a buffered solution of inorganic ions. To such a solution, growth factors specific to the needs of a particular microorganism are added, for example an energy source or vitamins.

Broth and solidified culture media

Culture media can be either liquid or solidified. Table 15.1 outlines the relative advantages of these two types of media.

Key terms

Agar An extract from seaweed that is used as a gelling agent to solidify culture media. Since few microorganisms can hydrolyse agar, the medium stays solid as the microorganisms grow.

Petri dish A shallow glass or plastic dish with a slightly larger dish that fits over it as a lid. Invented in 1887 by a German scientist, and used correctly, it enables scientists to transfer cultures to and from a solidified culture medium with minimal exposure to air.

Inoculum The small sample of a microbial culture that, using aseptic techniques, is transferred to a new medium.

Table 15.1 A comparison of liquid and solidified culture media

Type of culture medium	Usual method of cultivation in a laboratory	Advantage of this method
Liquid (broth culture)	In a partially filled conical flask, or similar flask that enables maintenance of a large surface area in contact with the air. The broth is usually agitated or stirred and, when culturing aerobic microorganisms, provided with sterile air.	Ensures that the culture does not die, so active cells are always available. Allows harvesting of any useful metabolic products from the microorganisms.
Solidified	The addition of a gelling agent, such as agar (an extract from seaweed), to a liquid medium makes it solidify.	Being solid, there is little risk of spillage, so these cultures are useful for storing microorganisms.
	In a Petri dish	Provides a large surface area for growth and for gas exchange with the air in the dish. Individual cells inoculated onto the surface of the agar develop into a visible colony, allowing isolation and identification of the microorganisms from a mixed inoculum.
	In a glass flat-sided bottle (often called a 'medical flat') or test tube.	Provides a greater depth of agar than a Petri dish, reducing the risk of dehydration and salt crystallisation.

In addition to the advantages shown in Table 15.1, a liquid culture allows us to carry out two types of culture:

- **Batch culture** – **inoculation** of microorganisms into a sterile container with a fixed volume of growth medium.
- **Continuous culture** – inoculation of microorganisms into a sterile container containing liquid growth medium. From time to time, some of the culture is removed and replaced by fresh sterile medium. Figure 15.3 shows a typical set up of equipment for continuous culture.

Only batch culture is possible using solidified culture media since it contains a limited mass of agar.

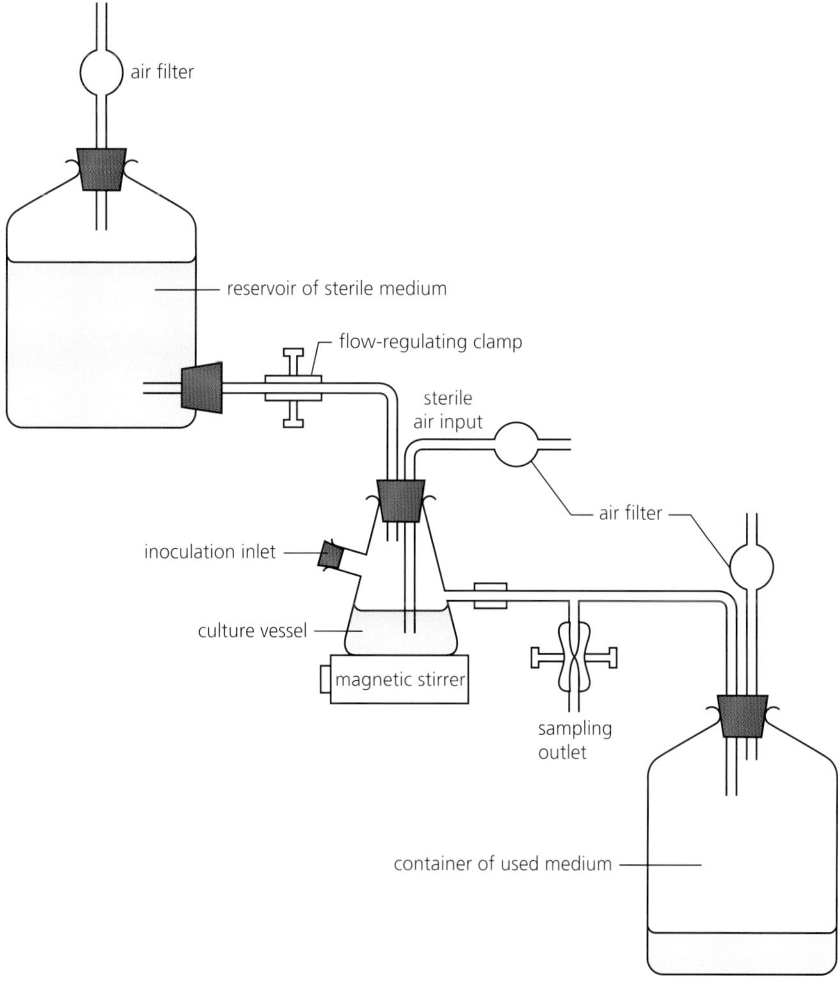

Figure 15.3 A typical arrangement of laboratory equipment needed to maintain a continuous culture of microorganisms

Broad spectrum and narrow spectrum culture media

Many culture media, such as nutrient agar, contain the basic nutrients that most microorganisms need for growth. Consequently, they can be used to grow a wide variety of microorganisms. They are known as general purpose or **broad spectrum media**. They often contain yeast extracts – a mixture of soluble amino acids, peptides, sugars, vitamins, bases and inorganic ions; or peptones – partly hydrolysed protein.

A broad spectrum culture medium is the type you are most likely to use in your college or school laboratory. In addition to being general purpose, you would also use them if you did not know the nutritional requirements of a particular microorganism.

Some media, however, will allow the growth of only a few, or even one, species of microorganism. These are called narrow spectrum media, or **selective media**. If you were to inoculate a mixed culture onto a selective medium, only the specific organism, for which the medium had been designed, will grow. The growth of any others will be suppressed.

You might wonder why selective media are used. Their main role is in diagnostic work in pathology laboratories and veterinary laboratories. MacConkey agar is a selective medium, allowing only the growth of Gram negative bacteria (see Chapter 4, page 90). If a medical laboratory technician inoculated a sample of human faeces onto MacConkey agar containing bile salts, any bacteria that grew would belong to the genus *Salmonella*. The technician would then be able to alert surgeons that this patient was harbouring a pathogenic bacterium, so that a suitable drug could be prescribed. Later in this chapter (Figure 15.9), you will see bacteria growing on agar containing bovine blood. This selective medium allows the identification of bacteria belonging to the genera *Staphylococcus* and *Streptococcus*.

In a different context, the bacterium *Acidithiobacillus thiooxidans* is used in a process called bioleaching – the removal of metals from their ores by bacterial action. This bacterium uses sulfates as an energy source. The selective broth medium for *Acidithiobacillus thiooxidans* contains $10\,g\,dm^{-3}$ of powdered sulfur. This discourages the growth of other bacteria so, if inoculated as part of a mixed culture, the growth of any bacteria allows identification of *Acidithiobacillus thiooxidans* in the mixed culture.

Incubation

Following inoculation, a culture medium is incubated. This means that it is placed in a temperature-controlled cabinet for a suitable period of time.

Environmental temperature is a variable that is important in determining the ecological niche of each species of microorganism. You must, therefore, incubate media at a temperature that is appropriate for the microorganism being cultured. Although pathogenic bacteria grow best at your own body temperature, some bacteria grow well in the cold of the Antarctic and others in hot-water springs and deep thermal vents. On the basis of the temperature at which they grow best, bacteria are commonly classified into three groups.

- **Psychrophiles** grow best at low temperatures, in the range −10 °C to 20 °C.
- **Mesophiles** grow best at ambient temperatures, in the range 20 °C to 45 °C.
- **Thermophiles** grow best at high temperatures, in the range 55 °C to 85 °C.

In your college or school laboratory, you will probably incubate at a temperature at, or just above, room temperature. You will certainly not incubate cultures at 37 °C, in other words, your body temperature.

Can you think why this is an important safety rule?

Aseptic techniques

When you grow microorganisms in a laboratory, you need to be aware that all surfaces are contaminated by microorganisms. This applies to the surface of your skin, of the laboratory bench and of every item of laboratory equipment. Normally this does not matter, but when you grow microorganisms, it does. You need to avoid:

- contamination of your **microbial culture**. You normally grow a pure culture, in other words a culture containing only one type of microorganism. Since the air, the laboratory equipment and your skin and clothing are contaminated by microorganisms, they could easily enter your culture
- contamination of yourselves or other laboratory workers. You will be working with microorganisms that are considered safe, that is they will not cause disease. Remember, though, that:
  - you might accidentally grow a harmful microorganism that has contaminated your culture
  - microorganisms can change their nature by, for example, mutation or by passing nucleic acid from one cell to another (Figure 15.4)
  - some people are more susceptible to infection than others.

Test yourself

1 Explain why media for growing bacteria must contain a source of nitrogen.

2 'Since few microorganisms can hydrolyse agar, the medium stays solid as the microorganisms grow.' Explain why few microorganisms can hydrolyse agar.

3 Give **one** advantage of using a broth culture over a solid culture.

4 Distinguish between a broad spectrum medium and a selective medium.

5 'You will certainly not incubate cultures at 37 °C, in other words your body temperature.' Explain why.

Key term

Microbial culture
A population of microorganisms growing in a liquid growth medium or on a solid growth medium.

When culturing microorganisms, you must always work as though the microorganisms in your culture are potentially harmful. The microbial techniques you will learn are the same as those that technicians working with potentially lethal microorganisms would use. They are called **aseptic techniques**.

Sterilisation methods

The only way you can be sure that bench surfaces and items of laboratory equipment are free of microorganisms is to kill them or remove them. In other words, you need to *sterilise* any equipment you will use. There are several **sterilisation methods** you can use. Which one you use depends on the nature of the object you wish to sterilise. Table 15.2 summarises commonly used sterilisation methods and shows when you use them.

Table 15.2 A summary of sterilisation methods commonly used when working with microorganisms

Method	Description	Use in aseptic techniques
Chemical agents	Disinfectants are chemicals that stop, or slow, the growth of bacteria. They are ineffective against bacterial spores, though.	Clean laboratory bench before and after working with microorganisms. Dispose of wet laboratory equipment immediately after use, e.g. glass pipettes. Treat any spillages that occur. (Note that disinfectants take time to become effective, so any spillages should be covered with disinfectant and left for at least 15 minutes before being mopped up.)
Heat treatment	Naked flame – hold an object in, or pass an object through, a Bunsen flame. This method is simple and effective as no microorganism can survive exposure to a naked flame.	An inoculating loop is 'flamed' by holding it in the hottest part of a Bunsen flame until it glows red (Figure 15.5, next page). Needles and forceps can also be flamed during manipulation of cultures. Flame sterilisation is often used on glass rods and glass spreaders after they have been dipped in 70% alcohol. The neck of a glass bottle, flask or tube containing a culture of microorganisms is sterilised by passing it through a Bunsen flame without allowing it to become red hot (Figure 15.6, page 313).
	Dry heat – place an object in a hot-air oven at 160 °C for at least 1 hour.	A routine method for the sterilisation of laboratory glassware prior to its use.
	Moist heat – place objects in an **autoclave** at 121 °C for at least 15 minutes.	This is the preferred method for many items of laboratory equipment and for culture media that are not heat-sensitive. It is also used to sterilise old cultures and spent media before disposing of them.
Filtration	Pass a liquid culture through a filtration device that has itself been sterilised by, e.g., dry heat. Using a filter of pore size 0.2 µm will remove bacteria (but not viruses).	The sheer size of the pores involved (typically 0.20 to 0.45 µm) makes this unsuitable for all but the smallest volumes of liquid.
Radiation	Expose items to UV or ionising radiation.	UV radiation with a wavelength less than 330 nm is most effective but, as this can damage the retina, is not used in college or school laboratories. Ionising radiation, such as γ-rays, cannot be used in a college or school laboratory since industrial facilities are needed. Many sterile plastic items, however, are supplied in packages that have been treated using UV or γ-radiation.

Key terms

Aseptic technique
A way of working with microorganisms that ensures that only one type of microorganism, that is one population, grows in each culture and that no microorganisms escape the culture.

Sterilisation methods
Steps you can take to remove, or destroy, any microorganisms that might contaminate your cultures.

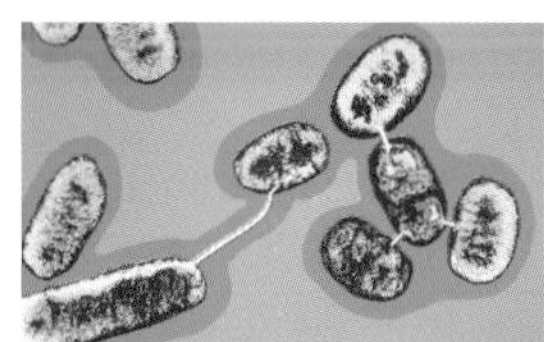

Figure 15.4 A false-colour transmission electron micrograph showing cells of *Escherichia coli* conjugating. The white links between cells are conjugation tubes that allow DNA (coloured orange) to pass from one cell to another (×13 000)

Key term

Autoclave A machine that works in the same way as a domestic pressure cooker. The latent heat of condensation of pressurised steam rapidly kills microorganisms, including spores.

Safety

- It is important to read this safety information before performing any microbial techniques in the classroom.
- **Sterilisation:** It is important to use steam at 121 °C for 15 minutes in an autoclave/sterilising pressure cooker.
- Wash hands thoroughly with bactericidal handwash before and after microbiological work.
- Always work on a surface that has been disinfected properly (for example, with 1% VirKon for 10 minutes), and the surface should be re-disinfected after the microbiology. BIOCIDES such as VirKon are used commercially to keep any work with microbes safe and have guarantees of effectiveness that household disinfectants do not.
- CLEAPSS and SSERC advise that all microbiology work takes place close (within 10 cm) to a roaring Bunsen flame, as this measure controls air movement.

Test yourself

6 How would you sterilise a nutrient broth for use in the laboratory in your school or college? Explain your answer.

7 The apparatus in Figure 15.3 contains three air filters. Give **two** functions of these air filters.

8 When working with microorganisms, a scientist works with a Bunsen burner permanently burning. Other than for flame-sterilising equipment, give **one** advantage of having a lit Bunsen on the bench where microorganisms are being transferred.

9 Some laboratories contain a chamber, rather like a fume cupboard, in which scientists perform transfer of microorganisms. Explain why a UV lamp would be useful in such a cabinet.

10 Figure 15.5 shows an inoculating loop being sterilised in a Bunsen flame. Suggest **one** advantage of using a loop for inoculating bacteria rather than a simple wire.

Individual steps used in aseptic techniques

You will perform at least two experiments during your A level course that involve cultures of microorganisms. Once you have started, you cannot contaminate any sterile item or put down any item of equipment until you have sterilised it. Whilst not difficult, some of the steps involved in doing this are fiddly. It is worth looking at them individually and, if you have time, practising each without using any media or microorganisms.

Flame sterilising an inoculating loop

An inoculating loop is a wire, often made of tungsten, embedded in a handle. The end of the wire is made into a loop with a diameter of about 5 mm. Rather like the loop you might have used to blow bubbles as a child, this loop picks up a relatively constant volume of fluid as a film across the loop, in this case a liquid culture of microorganisms. The heated loop can also be used to remove a sample from a bacterial colony on a solid culture medium.

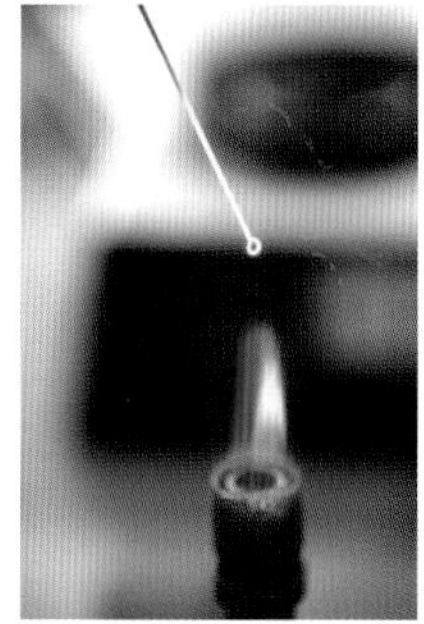

Figure 15.5 An inoculating loop being sterilised in the hottest part of a Bunsen flame

Figure 15.5 shows the end of a wire loop being sterilised. As you can see from the flame, the air inlet of the Bunsen burner is fully open and the loop is held at an angle in the hottest part of the Bunsen flame – above the blue region of unburnt gas. The loop in Figure 15.5 is white hot: no bacteria can survive this.

Flame sterilising the top of a container of microorganisms

You will be given a liquid culture of bacteria from which to take a sample. It will be in a glass container – a bottle or tube – with a 'lid'. The lid might be non-absorbent cotton wool or it might be a screw-cap. When you remove the lid from the container, you must ensure that no contaminating microorganisms get into the container and none escape from it into the air. Remember that once you have started you cannot put down the container or the lid. Figure 15.6 shows you how you should do this. The diagram shows how someone who is more comfortable using their right hand would do this; if you are more comfortable using your left hand, you should do so. Notice in Figure 15.6 that the person has removed the lid from the glass tube but is holding it in the crook of their little finger; they have not put it down. When removing a cotton wool bung, this is easy. When removing the screw cap from a bottle it is a little more difficult.

Removing a screw top from a container is something you are likely to do often, in daily life, for example when opening a bottle of cola or mineral water. You would normally use one hand to hold the bottle still and the other hand to unscrew the cap. When using aseptic techniques, you do this the other way around – you use the crook of the little finger on one hand to hold the cap still and use the other hand to unscrew the bottle.

Having removed the lid, the person in Figure 15.6 can pass the top of the container through a hot Bunsen flame.

Figure 15.6 The neck of a glass container of a microbial culture is sterilised by passing it through the flame of a Bunsen burner without letting it get red hot. Notice that the scientist has the cap of the container in the crook of her little finger. This is a skill you must practise

Using a wire loop to inoculate a culture onto a solid growth medium

As described in Table 15.1, solid growth media are usually contained within a Petri dish. This dish enables a small volume of growth medium to have a relatively large surface area.

You would use a sterile inoculating loop to transfer microorganisms to the surface of a sterile growth medium in a Petri dish. The transferred sample is referred to as an inoculum and the process of spreading the sample on an agar surface is called **plating**. Remember, your aseptic techniques prevent unwanted contamination of this sterile medium. If you fully removed the lid from the Petri dish, you would expose the entire agar surface to the air. This would enable airborne bacteria or fungi to contaminate the growth medium. The way you avoid this is simple but, again, is a technique you need to practise. Rather than fully remove the lid, you open the lid of the Petri dish at an angle with just enough room to be able to manipulate the inoculating loop inside. Figure 15.7 shows how to do this; again, showing someone who is more comfortable using their right hand.

Key term

Plating The transfer of an inoculum to the surface of a sterile agar medium.

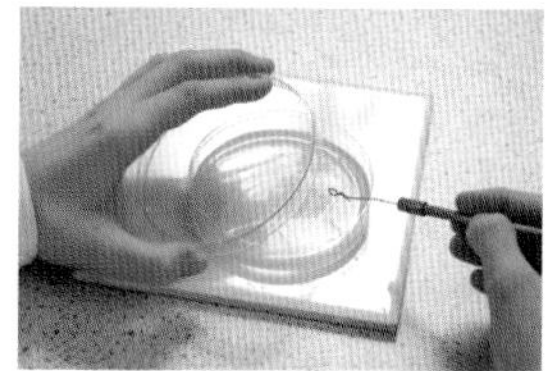

Figure 15.7 During inoculation, contamination of a sterile solid growth medium is avoided by lifting the lid of a Petri dish at an angle and as little as possible

Activity

Transferring an inoculum from a broth culture to an agar plate

Before starting one of the core practicals in this chapter, it is a good idea to practise the three skills described above as a single process. At this stage, you can safely do this with a glass container part-filled with tap water and an empty Petri dish.

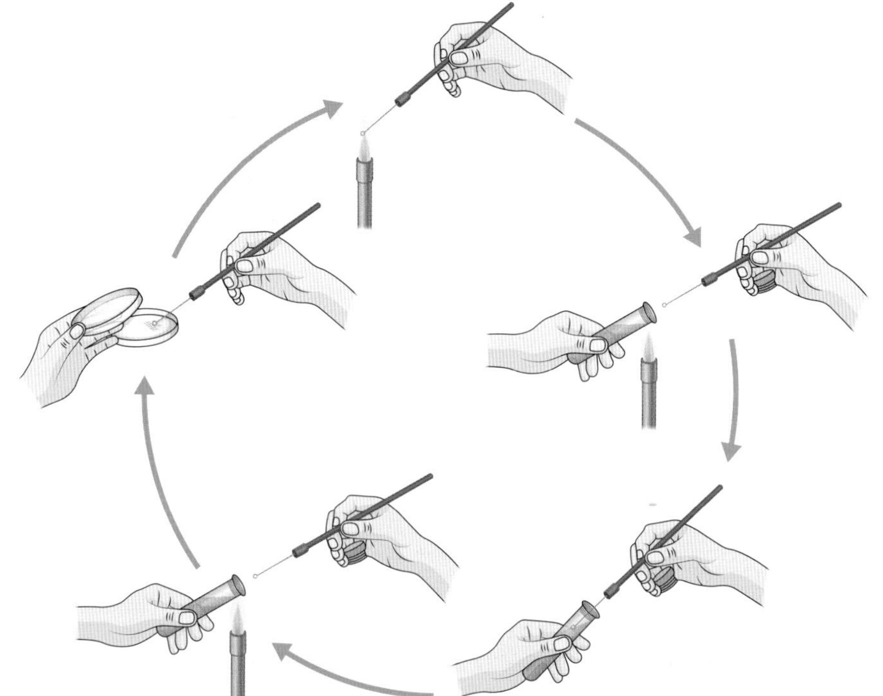

Figure 15.8 Practising the skills involved in transferring an inoculum from a broth culture to a Petri dish

Use Figure 15.8 to help you to practise the following steps.

1 Hold an inoculating loop in the hottest part of a Bunsen flame until it glows red-hot, or white-hot. Do **not** put down this inoculating loop until you have completed step 10.
2 Still holding the inoculating loop, allow it to cool.
3 Using the little finger of the hand in which you are holding the inoculating loop, remove the lid from the top of the glass container.
4 Still holding the lid in the crook of your little finger, pass the top of the glass container through the Bunsen flame. This should be a brief passage, otherwise you will risk the glass becoming so hot that you drop the container.
5 Insert the cooled inoculating loop into the glass container and remove a sample of water.
6 Still holding the lid in the crook of your little finger, pass the top of the glass container through the Bunsen flame.
7 Replace the lid on the glass container and put the container on the bench or into a test-tube rack.
8 Use your free hand to slightly raise the lid of a Petri dish. Put the tip of the inoculating loop into the Petri dish and gently slide it across the dish.
9 Replace the lid of the Petri dish.
10 Hold the inoculating loop in the hottest part of a Bunsen flame until it glows red, or white-hot. Allow it to cool and put down the inoculating loop.

You can repeat the above procedure as often as time and the availability of equipment allow, until you feel fully confident performing it.

Test yourself

11 How can you tell that the air inlet of the Bunsen burner in Figure 15.5 is fully open?
12 Suggest why you should hold an inoculating loop at an angle rather than horizontally when flame sterilising it.
13 Explain why the cotton wool used to close a tube of broth agar would be non-absorbent.
14 Explain why a microbiologist must hold the lid of a container in the crook of their little finger.
15 Other than to avoid dropping a tube that has become too hot to hold, explain why you should only briefly pass the top of a tube through a Bunsen flame when transferring an inoculum from a broth culture.

Streak plating

If you leave an agar plate open to the air, a number of microorganisms will land and start to grow and you end up with a mixed culture. You might want to isolate one type of microorganism from this mixed culture. You can do this using a technique called steak plating.

Using aseptic techniques, you use an inoculating loop to remove a sample from the mixed culture and transfer it to an agar plate. Having made the transfer, you then dilute the inoculum by spreading it time and again. Table 15.3 shows how this is done.

Table 15.3 Steps in the technique of streak plating

Description	Appearance of plate, viewed from above
Add your initials and the date to the base of the Petri dish into which you will transfer the inoculum. Use aseptic techniques to remove a sample from the mixed culture, using a sterile wire loop.	
Opening the lid of the Petri dish as little as possible, hold the loop parallel with the surface of the agar. Smear the inoculum backwards and forwards across a small area of the medium (region A in the diagram), taking care not to cut into the agar surface. Replace the lid of the Petri dish.	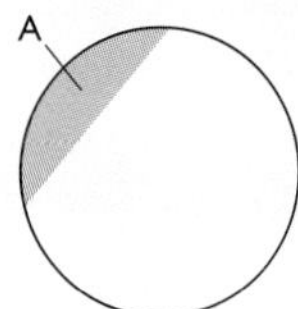
Flame the loop and allow it to cool.	
Turn the Petri dish through about 90°. Again, opening the lid of the Petri dish as little as possible, use the loop to streak the inoculum from A across the surface of the agar in three parallel lines (B). As before, take care not to cut into the agar surface. Replace the lid of the Petri dish.	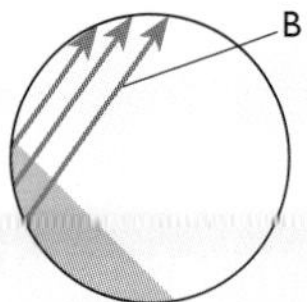
Flame the loop and allow it to cool.	
Turn the Petri dish through another 90°. Again, opening the lid of the Petri dish as little as possible, use the loop to streak the inoculum from B across the surface of the agar in three parallel lines (C), taking care not to cut into the agar. Replace the lid of the Petri dish.	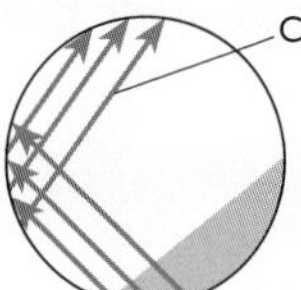
Flame the loop and allow it to cool.	
Turn the Petri dish through a final 90°. Again, opening the lid of the Petri dish as little as possible, use the loop to streak the inoculum from C across the surface of the agar as shown (D). Be careful not to cut into the agar and not to touch area A. Replace the lid of the Petri dish. 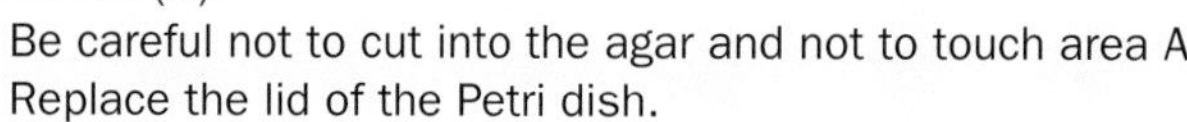	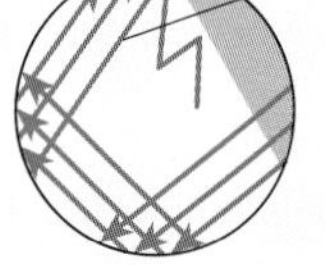
Flame the loop and allow it to cool.	

After a suitable period of incubation, colonies of microorganisms will have grown on the agar. In the areas A, B and C in Table 15.3, they will probably form a continuous mat. In area D, however, you should find small colonies formed by the division of a single microbial cell. Figure 15.9 shows the result of streak plating after incubation of the agar plate.

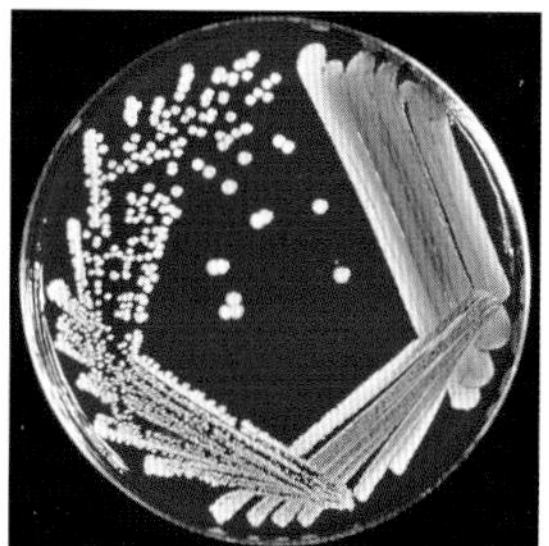

Figure 15.9 The result of streak plating. Here, the technique has been used on a culture of the skin bacterium *Staphylococcus aureus* on an agar plate containing bovine blood. This combination of agar and pathogen has been used to produce a particularly vivid photograph - it should not replicated in school laboratories

Safety note

You are now going to cover one of the core practicals in the Pearson Edexcel specification. Before you carry out this practical, or the one later in this chapter, you need a reminder of the safety issues involved in manipulating microorganisms in the laboratory. They include the following general rules.

- Wipe down the bench with disinfectant both before and after working with microorganisms.
- Have a container of disinfectant readily accessible. You might need it for a sudden emergency.
- Organise your bench, making sure you have everything you need to use within easy reach. Once you have started, you cannot put things down without first sterilising them.

- Work in a controlled way. On a crowded bench, any sudden movements could put one of your fellow students in peril.
- Do not make any hand-to-mouth movements. Putting anything to your mouth, including food, the end of your pen or even your finger, could be dangerous to you as it might result in infection.
- Cover any cuts or abrasions with a plaster or wear disposable plastic gloves. This prevents infection via your broken skin surface.
- Take care when using sharp instruments, such as mounted needles or glass pipettes.
- Do not put any waste culture medium down the sink. It must be autoclaved before being disposed of.
- Put contaminated items into disinfectant immediately after use. This applies to items such as pipettes, slides and glass spreaders.
- Keep flammable objects well away from the Bunsen flame. You will be working with a Bunsen burner constantly burning with its hottest flame. You must not let anything catch fire.

Core practical 13

Isolate individual species from a mixed culture of bacteria using streak plating

Before starting this investigation, make sure you thoroughly understand the steps shown in Figure 15.8, Table 15.3 and the text accompanying both. If possible, you should practise the skills described before carrying out this practical with microorganisms.

This investigation involves two practical sessions. In the first, you will use the streak plate method to inoculate sterile agar plates with a broth culture with which you have been provided. These agar plates will then be incubated for you.

In the second session, you will remove bacteria from one colony and inoculate them onto sterile agar plates. These will then be incubated for you.

Session 1

1. Ensure the bench is clear of anything you will not need to use.
2. Clean the bench using a disinfectant solution. Ensure that all the equipment you need is arranged on the bench so that it is easily accessible.
3. Light a Bunsen burner and turn the air inlet valve to produce the hottest flame.
4. Use a Chinagraph pencil or permanent marker to label the **base** of two Petri dishes containing sterile nutrient agar. Label with your initials and the date.
5. Sterilise the inoculating loop in the Bunsen flame.
6. Remove the lid from the tube of broth culture by grasping it in the crook of the little finger of the hand in which you are holding the inoculating loop.
7. Pass the neck of the tube through the Bunsen flame.
8. Remove a loopful of broth culture.
9. Pass the neck of the tube through the Bunsen flame and replace its lid.
10. Lift the lid from one of the Petri dishes just high enough to be able to insert the loop.
11. Using free arm movement from your elbow, smear the loop across part of the surface of the agar (see Table 15.3, area A).
12. Replace the lid of the Petri dish and sterilise the loop in the Bunsen flame.

13 As described in Table 15.3, turn the Petri dish through about 90°. Using free arm movement from your elbow, streak the inoculum across the agar in three parallel lines.
14 Repeat steps 12 and 13 until you have replicated the process described in Table 15.3.
15 Repeat steps 5 to 14 using the second Petri dish of sterile agar.
16 Sterilise the inoculating loop by passing it through the Bunsen flame.
17 Seal the lids of both Petri dishes to their bases using strips of sticky tape.
18 Hand your inoculated plates to your teacher to be incubated.
19 Clean the bench with disinfectant.
20 Wash your hands.

Session 2

1 Ensure the bench is clear of anything you will not need to use.
2 Clean the bench using a disinfectant solution. Ensure that all the equipment you need is arranged on the bench so that it is easily accessible.
3 Light a Bunsen burner and turn the air inlet valve to produce the hottest flame.
4 Use a Chinagraph pencil or permanent marker to label the **base** of two Petri dishes containing sterile nutrient agar. Label with your initials and the date.
5 **Without removing their lids**, examine your agar plates from session 1. Choose whichever has produced single colonies of bacteria in the most diluted of the streaks you made. Remove the strips of sticky tape from this Petri dish.
6 Sterilise the inoculating loop in the Bunsen flame.
7 Lift the lid from the chosen Petri dish just high enough to be able to insert the loop.
8 Carefully remove a small sample from a single colony that has grown on this plate. Replace the lid.
9 Take a Petri dish containing sterile agar and inoculate this plate with the sample you have just taken. Smear the inoculum across the surface of the agar plate.
10 Repeat steps 5 to 8 using a second Petri dish containing sterile agar.
11 Sterilise the inoculating loop by passing it through the Bunsen flame.
12 Re-seal the lid of the Petri dish you have used from session 1. Hand both Petri dishes from session 1 to your teacher for safe destruction.
13 For the Petri dishes you have just inoculated, seal the lids to their bases using strips of sticky tape.
14 Hand your newly inoculated plates to your teacher to be incubated.
15 Clean the bench with disinfectant.
16 Wash your hands.
17 After incubation, check your plates from session 2 and record the appearance of the colonies that are growing. Can you conclude that you have successfully isolated a pure culture?

Questions

1 Suggest why you were told to arrange the equipment you needed so that it was easily accessible.
2 Why should you label the base of the Petri dish, rather than its lid?
3 Suggest why you were instructed to use an arm movement from your elbow when smearing the loop across the agar.
4 Why did you seal your Petri dishes with sticky tape?
5 In session 2, you were told not to remove the sticky tape from the Petri dishes. How could you see which Petri dish had produced single colonies of bacteria?

Measuring the growth of bacterial cultures

To measure the growth of a bacterial population, you need to find out how many bacterial cells are in your culture medium at repeated time intervals. You can do this by making a:

- **total count** – count all the cells in the culture
- **viable count** – count only the living cells in the culture.

Although you can easily count the number of large organisms in a population, you cannot easily do so with a bacterial population. Even with the best light microscopes, bacteria are difficult to see and you can't distinguish between a dead bacterium and a living one just by looking at it.

Serial dilutions

Another problem you encounter is the sheer number of bacteria in a single population. For example, a single inoculum into a liquid growth medium, incubated overnight under optimal conditions, is likely to contain in the order of 10^8 bacteria per cm^3 of medium. This is far too many to count! You can overcome this problem by repeatedly diluting a sample from the population until you find a number of cells that you can count accurately and are confident will give you a reliable estimate of the population size. Then, knowing your dilution factor, you can multiply your count by this dilution factor to obtain an estimate of the number of cells in the undiluted culture.

Key term

Serial dilution A repeated dilution, by a constant dilution factor, of an original solution or microbial culture.

You might ask, "But how do I know how many times to dilute the culture before I can count individual cells?" The simple answer is that you don't. Instead, you make a succession of dilutions, called a **serial dilution**, from which you hope to find one that will enable you to count cells. Figure 15.10 shows how you make a serial dilution; in this case, each dilution factor is 1 in 10.

Safety tip

It is extremely dangerous to use hand-to-mouth movements when dealing with microorganisms. When making serial dilutions, you should never pipette by mouth.

Activity

Making a serial dilution

You need a microbial culture in a liquid medium in order to make a serial dilution. If you follow the steps in Figure 15.10 you will see how you would do this.

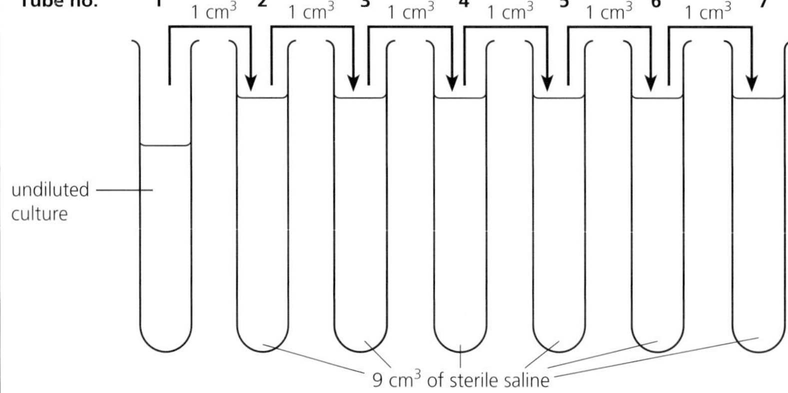

Figure 15.10 The steps involved in making a serial dilution of a broth culture of bacteria

Firstly, using aseptic techniques, you transfer 1 cm^3 of your culture solution in tube **1** into 9 cm^3 of sterile diluent in tube **2**. Then stir or agitate tube **2** to ensure complete mixing before the next 1 cm^3 sample is withdrawn and added to tube **3**. Repeat this procedure to follow the serial dilution steps in Figure 15.10.

1 Describe how you would use aseptic techniques to begin this transfer.
2 How would you sterilise a dry glass pipette?
3 How would you draw 1 cm^3 of liquid medium into the pipette?
4 If your dilution series is to give you an estimate of the population size that is close to its true value (in other words, is accurate), what size of pipette would you use to measure a 1 cm^3 sample?
5 What is the dilution factor in tube **2**?
6 You flame-sterilised the pipette before you used it to transfer the bacterial culture. Why can't you flame-sterilise it after you have used it?
7 Why must you use a new pipette for each transfer of medium?
8 Suggest why you would use a 0.9% saline solution as the diluent, rather than water.

Making total counts

The total count estimates the number of cells in a culture, regardless of whether they are alive or dead. We can make these estimates in one of three ways:

- A direct count, using a counting chamber and a light microscope.
- An indirect count, measuring the dry mass of a filtered culture.
- An indirect count, using a colorimeter to measure the turbidity of a culture.

Direct count using a haemocytometer

A haemocytometer is a special microscope slide. As its name suggests, it was originally designed for counting red blood cells. You can see in Figure 15.11(a) that a haemocytometer is thicker than a normal microscope slide. Its central platform, between the two grooves, has a grid etched into it and is slightly lower than the main glass slide. When a cover slip is placed over this central part, it produces a film of known depth over the grid.

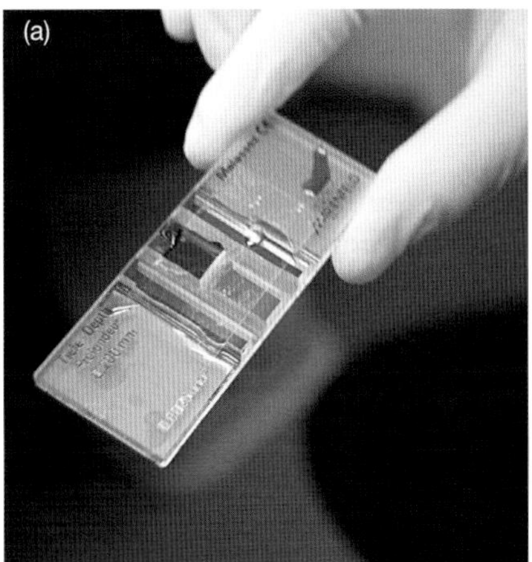

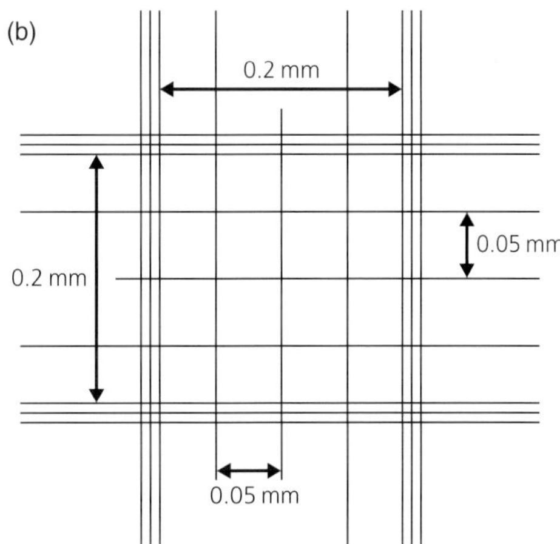

Figure 15.11 (a) A haemocytometer slide and (b) part of the grid etched onto a haemocytometer slide

Figure 15.11(b) shows part of a grid etched onto the platform of a haemocytometer. You can see that the grid is formed of squares of known dimensions. This grid is very accurate, which is why this slide is very expensive. Since you know the depth of the film of fluid and the size of an individual square, you know the volume of liquid covering each square that you view using a light microscope. So, by viewing a sample from each tube in your serial dilution, you quickly find one

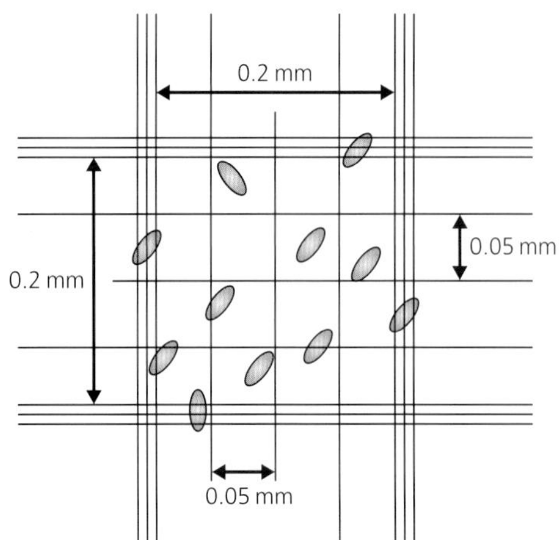

Figure 15.12 How to count cells using a haemocytometer

with a number of cells that enables you to count bacterial cells accurately, yet contains sufficient cells for you to be confident that it is a representative sample. There is, however, a further complication you need to deal with.

Look at Figure 15.12. It shows a number of cells within a 0.2 mm × 0.2 mm section of the haemocytometer grid. How many do you count? In this field of view, there are 11 cells. Some, however, are overlapping the lines delineating the 0.2 mm × 0.2 mm square. How do you deal with those?

One important aspect of scientific research is repeatability, that is other scientists must be able to replicate your method and obtain similar results. You cannot, therefore, tolerate an *ad hoc* approach to counting cells that overlap the grid lines of a haemocytometer. For example:

- **do** include in your count any cell that touches or overlaps the middle of the three lines at the top and right-hand side of a 0.2 mm × 0.2 mm square
- do **not** include any cell that touches or overlaps the middle of the three lines at the bottom and left-hand side of a 0.2 mm × 0.2 mm square.

Thus, in Figure 15.12, your cell count would be eight cells.

Indirect count measuring dry mass of cells

You are unlikely to use this technique since it is slow and involves the use of expensive filtration equipment that must be sterilised before use.

Safety

Cuvettes should be sterilised immediately after using them for microbial work.

Since the technique involves filtering a culture to remove the bacterial cells, it is only useful with small volumes of liquid media. After finding the dry mass of the sterile filtration membrane, you would filter a known volume of liquid culture. You would then heat the filter membrane, with the bacteria on its surface, in an oven at 100 °C until its mass remained constant. By subtracting the mass of the sterile filter membrane from the final mass, you find the dry mass of the bacteria. Finally, knowing the volume of medium you filtered, you can calculate the mass of cells per unit volume of culture.

Indirect count measuring turbidity

As a population of cells increases, it will make the culture medium in which it is growing, cloudier. You can measure the degree of this 'cloudiness', or **turbidity**, using a colorimeter.

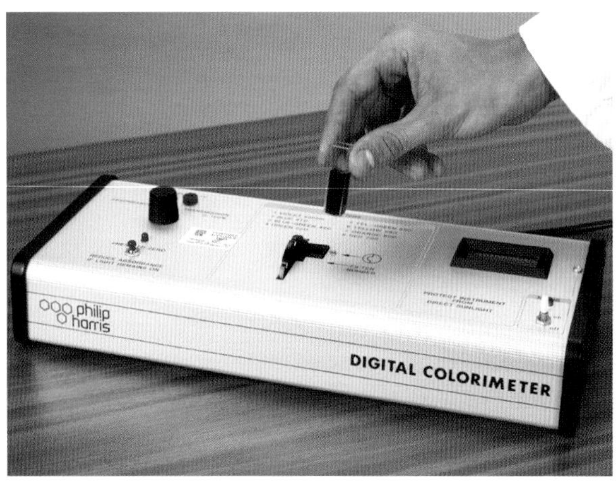

Figure 15.13 A cuvette being placed in a colorimeter

Using aseptic techniques, you would place a sample from one of the tubes in your serial dilution (Figure 15.10) in a special flat-sided tube, called a **cuvette**. You then place this cuvette into a colorimeter (Figure 15.13) and pass light through it. You can set the colorimeter to measure the amount of light absorbed by the contents of the cuvette (the **absorbance**) or the amount of light that passes through the contents of the cuvette (the **transmission**). The more bacteria present, the greater the absorbance or the less the transmission. You use these measures as an indicator of the size of the microbial population in your sample.

This technique has its drawbacks. You can only use it with liquid cultures and you cannot distinguish between living and dead cells. Additionally, you need to calibrate your measurements so that you can relate your readings of absorbance or transmission to the actual density of cells. This means that you must first produce a calibration curve, plotting the density of cells found, for example using a haemocytometer, against the measured turbidity found using a colorimeter.

Extension

Use of a Coulter counter to measure changes in electrical resistance

A method similar to measuring the turbidity of a bacterial mixture involves the use of a Coulter counter. Like the haemocytometer, the Coulter counter was originally designed for use with red blood cells. It has a probe, with two electrodes, that is put into the liquid culture. As you can see in Figure 15.14, one of its electrodes is inside a glass tube that has a tiny hole in it. As bacteria pass through this hole, the electrodes detect the changes the bacteria cause in the electrical resistance of the medium. These measurements can be relayed to a computer for data processing.

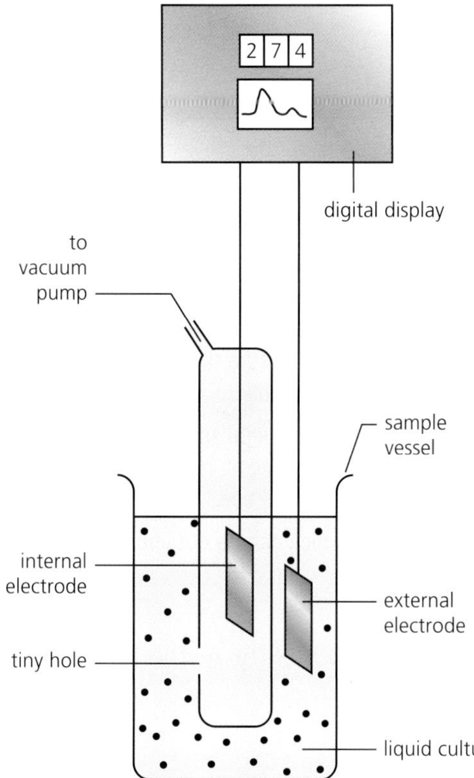

Figure 15.14 The electrodes of a Coulter counter detect changes in the electrical resistance of the culture medium caused by bacterial cells

Making viable counts using spread plates

When making a viable count, you are only interested in those bacterial cells that are capable of growing. Once plated onto a solid culture medium, the growth of each viable cell will produce a visible colony. If you look back to the streak plate in Figure 15.9, you can remind yourself of the different appearance of a single colony and the mat formed by the merger of many colonies.

As with the total count, you need to use a serial dilution so that you can obtain a growth of bacteria in which you can count a reliable number of individual colonies. You would, therefore, produce a serial dilution, as shown in Figure 15.10. You would then use aseptic techniques to pipette a small, known volume (usually $\leq 0.5\,cm^3$) of each dilution onto the surface of sterile, solidified medium in a separate Petri dish. You can see this being done in Figure 15.15(a). Having done this, you would use an L-shaped glass rod as a spreader to gently spread the pipetted suspension of bacterial cells over the whole surface of the culture medium. This is shown in Figure 15.15(b).

Of course, the glass spreader must be sterilised before (and after) use. You would traditionally do this by dipping the end of the spreader into a beaker of 70 per cent alcohol for at least five minutes, allowing the excess alcohol to drain off the spreader and then igniting the remainder in a Bunsen flame. After cooling, you can then use the spreader, as shown in Figure 15.15(b) to distribute the cell suspension over the culture medium. Following incubation, each viable cell in the dilution will produce a colony on the agar plate, as you can see in Figure 15.15(d).

Figure 15.15 Preparing a spread plate

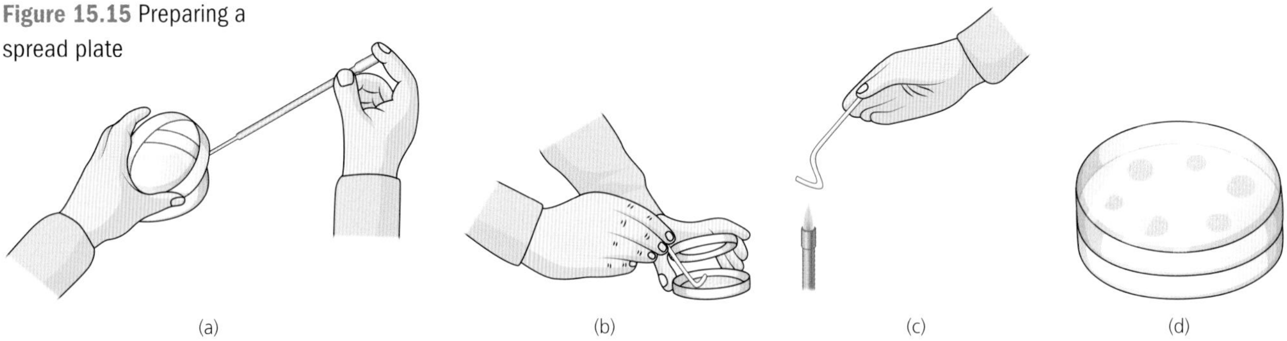

(a) (b) (c) (d)

Safety

Sterilising the L-shaped spreader involves a significant fire risk. It is important to drain excess alcohol from the spreader before igniting, to prevent the formation of flaming droplets of alcohol. It is also important to keep the Bunsen burner well away from the alcohol and to ensure the spreader is no longer flaming and has cooled before putting it back into the beaker of alcohol.

Alternatively, for sterilising spreaders, schools can choose to wrap glass/metal spreaders in greaseproof paper/aluminium foil, and then sterilise the spreader by heating at 160 °C for two hours in an oven. The spreaders will stay sterile until unwrapped just before point of use.

Alternatively, schools may choose to use sterile plastic spreaders, which can be obtained from many suppliers.

Table 15.4 provides a summary of the relative merits of each of the methods of estimating cell numbers you have examined in this chapter.

Table 15.4 A summary of the methods for estimating cell numbers

Method of estimating cell number	Relative advantage/disadvantage
Direct microscopic count	• Can only be used for total counts, since you cannot distinguish between living and dead cells • A relatively slow method • Kills the cells examined • Useful for obtaining data to produce a calibration curve for turbidity measurements
Measuring dry mass of cells	• Can only be used for total counts • A slow method, so can be used only with small volumes of culture, making results unreliable • Kills cells being weighed
Turbidity measurement	• Can only be used for total counts • A fast method • Does not kill cells examined • Unreliable for cell densities less than 10^7 cells cm^{-3}
Spread plate (colony count)	• Can be used for viable counts • A two-step process, so speed restricted by incubation time • Does not kill cells being examined

Test yourself

16 Distinguish between a total count and a viable count.

17 A student used aseptic techniques to pipette 0.1 cm^3 of broth culture into a tube containing 9.9 cm^3 of sterile saline. Calculate the dilution factor that she was using.

18 State restricts your ability to use the dry mass method to measure the growth of a bacterial culture.

19 Using a haemocytometer, you find a cell touches the bottom line of the square you are viewing. Should you include this cell in your count? Explain why.

20 Some bacteria clump together as they grow in a liquid growth medium.

a) Explain how this might affect a cell count made using a colorimeter.

b) Suggest how could you avoid this.

Core practical 12

Investigate the growth of bacteria in liquid culture

Before starting this investigation, make sure you understand the steps involved in making a serial dilution (Figure 15.10 and the accompanying text).

To enable this core practical to be completed in a single practical session, it is assumed that:

- it will be carried out as a class exercise
- the class has been provided with samples of a broth culture taken at known times after its inoculation
- a few drops of 40% methanal have been added to each sample. Methanal (also known as formaldehyde) will kill the bacteria in each sample, preventing any further growth. It also means that you no longer need to use aseptic techniques
- each person, or pair, will count the cells in one of the samples.

The investigation involves two stages. In the first, you will be given one sample and use it to produce a serial dilution. You will then use a light microscope and haemocytometer slide to find a suitable dilution with which to estimate the density of cells in your sample.

Preparing the serial dilution of broth culture

1 Label six test tubes **−1** to **−6** and place them in a test tube rack.

2 Pipette 9 cm^3 of water into each test tube.

3 Pipette 1 cm^3 of the broth culture you have been given into the tube labelled **−1**. Thoroughly mix the contents of this tube.

4 Use a clean pipette to transfer 1 cm^3 of cell suspension from the tube labelled **−1** to the tube labelled **−2**. Thoroughly mix the contents of this tube.

5 Repeat step 4, transferring cell suspension from tube **−2** to **−3**, then from tube **−3** to **−4** and so on until you add 1 cm^3 of suspension to tube **−6**.

Counting the cells in the diluted broth cultures

6 Set up a light microscope.

7 Place the special cover slip over the platform of the haemocytometer and **very gently** press it down to ensure it has made contact with the slide. When positioned correctly, you should be able to see interference rings (Newton's rings) at the edge of the cover slip.

8 Using a dropper pipette from the side of the slide, add a small amount of broth culture from tube **−1** to fill the central space above the grid (Figure 15.16). Allow it to settle for a couple of minutes.

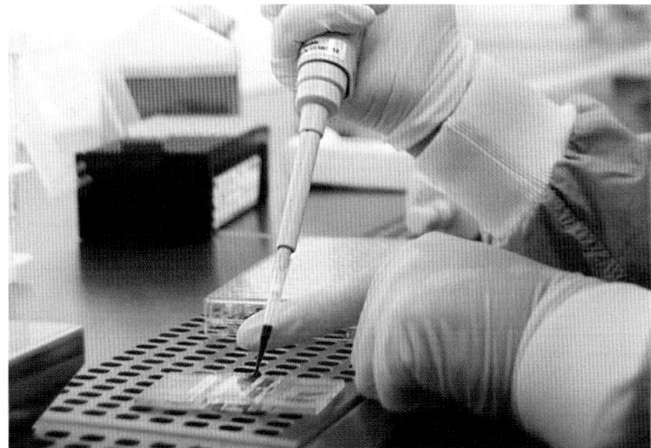

Figure 15.16 Loading a sample onto the haemocytometer slide using a pipette

9 Put the haemocytometer on the stage of the microscope and use the ×10 objective lens to examine the grid.
10 Examine the slide to see whether you can use it for a cell count. You need to find a dilution in which there are sufficiently few cells for you to be able to count them accurately but not so few that the sample will be a poor representation of the broth culture.
11 If you cannot see any cells, you might need to stain them. If so, wash the haemocytometer slide and repeat steps 7 to 9 with a fresh sample to which you have added a drop of 0.1% methylene blue stain.
12 If the dilution is not suitable because it contains too many cells, wash the haemocytometer slide.
13 Repeat steps 7 to 11 until you find a dilution that is suitable for counting cells.
14 Once you have found a dilution that is suitable for counting, switch from the ×10 objective lens to the ×40 objective lens. In doing so, take care not to scratch the objective lens on the cover slip, which is much thicker than a normal cover slip.
15 Count and record the number of cells in this dilution.
   a) Select which 0.2 mm squares to count in a pre-arranged way, for example every 4th square from left to right.
   b) Use the fine focusing screw to focus the microscope at different levels so that you include all the cells in each square.
   c) Include in your count any cell that touches or overlaps the middle of the three lines at the top and right-hand sides of each 0.2 mm square.
   d) Keep counting squares until you have included several hundred cells.
   e) Use a hand-held tally counter, if one is available.
16 Divide the total number of cells by the number of 0.2 mm squares counted to find the mean number of cells in each square.
17 Use this mean value to calculate the number of cells in the original broth culture. Your teacher will tell you the depth of the platform in the haemocytometer you used.
18 If you have time, repeat the entire process and find the mean value of your repeated results.
19 Hand in your results to your teacher so that the whole class results can be collated.
20 Use the collated class results to plot a growth curve of the broth culture. Use your graph to determine the growth rate of the bacteria.

The bacterial growth curve

Under continuous culture, using equipment such as that shown in Figure 15.3, a bacterial population could continue to grow indefinitely. If you plotted the number of bacteria against time, it would result in a curve showing exponential growth.

In a batch culture, however, a bacterial population cannot grow indefinitely. As the bacteria in a batch culture grow, they use the nutrients in the culture medium. They also excrete the waste products of their own metabolism into the culture medium. As a result, the culture medium provides an increasingly less favourable environment for the bacteria. For this reason, the growth curve of bacteria in batch culture is not exponential. Instead, it shows the four stages shown in Figure 15.17.

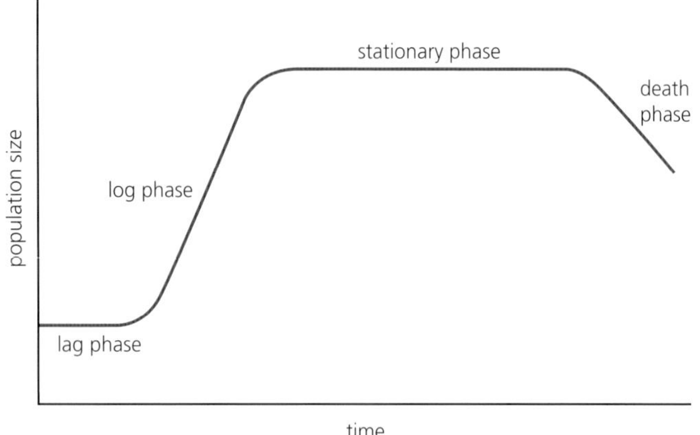

Figure 15.17 A typical growth curve of bacteria grown in batch culture

The lag phase

This part of Figure 15.17 shows a period after inoculation to a new culture medium during which there is no increase in the number of bacteria. The bacteria *are* active, however. They are absorbing water from the medium, synthesising ribosomes and, often under the stimulation of substances in the medium, switching on genes and beginning to make new mRNA. The length of this phase depends on the culture medium used and the activity of the bacteria before they were inoculated to the new medium.

The log phase

Sometimes called the exponential phase, during this part of Figure 15.17 bacterial cells are dividing by binary fission at their maximum rate. The generation time differs from species to species, but is usually very short. Table 15.5 shows the generation time of some common bacteria, grown under optimum conditions in the laboratory.

Table 15.5 The generation time of some common bacteria grown under optimal conditions

Species of bacterium	Growth medium	Generation time/minutes
Escherichia coli	Glucose and salts	17
Staphylococcus aureus	Heart infusion broth	27–30
Lactobacillus acidophilus	Milk	66–87
Mycobacterium tuberculosis	Selective medium	792–932

The stationary phase

The growth of bacteria during the log phase changes the nature of the culture medium. For example, it removes nutrients from it, adds waste products to it and changes its pH. As a result, the conditions become no longer optimal for bacterial growth and cells begin to die. During the stationary phase, the rate at which new cells are formed by binary fission is the same as the rate of cell death, in other words:

'birth rate' = 'death rate'

The death phase

As the conditions in the culture medium become less and less suitable for growth, an increasing number of cells die. The viable count will obviously fall. As many of the dead cells undergo autolysis, the total cell count might also fall.

Calculations involving the log phase of the growth curve

You can analyse the log phase quantitatively in three different ways.

Finding the number of cells uses your knowledge that bacteria divide by binary fission:

- 1 cell becomes 2; 2 cells become $2 \times 2 = 4$; 4 cells become $2 \times 2 \times 2 = 8$, and so on.

Instead of writing 2×2, you could write 2^2 and instead of writing $2 \times 2 \times 2$, you could write 2^3. This is the basis of exponential (or logarithmic) growth. At each generation, the number of cells in the starting inoculum is increasing by a factor of two, in other words:

- 1 cell becomes 2, 2 cells become 2^2, 2^2 cells become 2^3, and so on.

You could, therefore, calculate that after n generations, the original number of cells in the inoculum (N_0) will have grown to a number (N) given by:

$$N = N_0 \times 2^n$$ **Equation 1**

The exponential growth rate constant (μ) is the rate at which bacteria grow during the log phase of the growth curve. If the number of cells at time t_0 is N_0 and the number of cells at the later time t_x is N_x, you can find the exponential growth rate constant using the following formula.

$$\mu = \frac{2.303\ (\log N_x - \log N_0)}{(t_x - t_0)}$$ **Equation 2**

Tip

Calculations in your A level examination will be at GCSE higher tier level (Level 2). You need to own a good scientific calculator, know how to use it and remember to take it to your examination. You will be able to find one in national chain stores for less than £10.

Example

At 10:00 hours you begin a practical class and count 2×10^3 cells in a sample of a bacterial culture. At 12:00 hours you take another sample and count 5.7×10^4 cells in this sample. You would use equation 2 above to calculate the exponential growth rate constant of this culture as follows.

$N_0 = 2 \times 10^3$ so $\log N_0 = 3.30$

$N_x = 5.7 \times 10^4$ so $\log N_x = 4.76$

$t_x - t_0 = 2$ hours

$$\text{so } \mu = \frac{2.303\,(4.76 - 3.30)}{2}$$

$$= \frac{2.303 \times 1.46}{2}$$

$$= 1.681 \text{ hour}^{-1}$$

The generation time (**g**) is the time between two consecutive divisions. Since each division produces two new cells, this is also referred to as the **doubling time**. It can be calculated using the same symbols as Equation 2 above.

$$g = \frac{0.301\,(t_x - t_0)}{\log N_x - \log N_0}$$ **Equation 3**

Test yourself

21 What can you conclude about generation time from the data in Table 15.5?

22 Explain why the growth curve for bacteria grown in batch culture is different from that for bacteria grown in continuous culture.

23 An inoculum contains 2×10^3 bacterial cells. If grown in liquid growth medium under optimal conditions, calculate how many cells will be present after six generations.

24 Figure 15.15(d) was the result after incubating 1 cm^3 of a 10^{-5} sample from a serial dilution. Calculate how many cells were present in the undiluted culture.

25 At 10:00 hours you begin a practical class and count 2×10^3 cells in a sample of a bacterial culture. At 12:00 hours you take another sample and count 5.7×10^4 cells in this sample. Use Equation 3 to find the doubling time of the population.

Chapter summary

Aseptic techniques

- Aseptic techniques are safety precautions that reduce the risk of:
  - contamination of microbial cultures by airborne organisms
  - microorganisms in microbial cultures contaminating the air.
- A lit Bunsen burner will create an upward air current, preventing airborne microorganisms settling on the work surfaces.
- Contaminated apparatus should not be placed on the work surface.
- Containers of microbial culture should not be fully opened.
- Solutions of chemical agents that stop or slow the growth of microorganisms can be used to clean benches, dispose of contaminated laboratory glassware or clean spillages.
- Heat, filtration and radiation can be used to sterilise laboratory material before and after use.
- Hand-held apparatus, such as inoculating loops, can be flame sterilised before and after use.
- A hot air oven at 160 °C for 1 hour or autoclaving at 121 °C for 15 minutes will sterilise heat-resistant apparatus.
- Bacteria can be removed from small volumes of liquid culture by filtration through a pore size ≤ 0.2 μm.
- Exposure to UV or ionising radiation can be used to sterilise heat-susceptible plastic apparatus.

Culturing microorganisms

- Microorganisms can be grown in solid (agar) or liquid (broth) media.
- Culture media contain all the nutrients needed to enable the cultured microorganisms to flourish.
- A broad-spectrum medium can be used to grow a wide range of microorganisms.
- A narrow-spectrum medium allows the growth of few, or only one, species of microorganism. It is often used as a selective medium, to isolate one species from a microbial community.
- In batch culture, microorganisms are inoculated into a fixed volume of growth medium. In continuous culture, the spent medium is regularly replaced by fresh medium.

Estimating bacterial growth

- The growth of a bacterial population can be estimated as:
  - the viable count, i.e., only the live bacteria
  - the total count, i.e., all the bacteria whether living or dead.
- A viable count can be made using dilution plating.
- Three methods for measuring the total count of a bacterial culture are: direct count using a counting chamber and an optical microscope; indirect count by measuring the dry mass of a filtered culture; or indirect count by measuring the turbidity of a liquid culture.
- In batch culture, the growth curve of a bacterial population shows four phases:
  - the lag phase
  - the log phase
  - the stationary phase
  - the death phase
- The increase in cell number during the log phase is known as the exponential growth rate constant (μ) and can be calculated as:

$$\mu = \frac{2.303\,(\log N_x - \log N_0)}{t_x - t_0}$$

where N_x is the number of cells at time t_x and N_0 is the number at time t_0.

Practice questions

1 Which of the following describes the order of stages of growth of a bacterial batch culture?

A lag phase, log phase, stationary phase, decline phase

B lag phase, stationary phase, log phase, decline phase

C stationary phase, log phase, decline phase, lag phase

D stationary phase, log phase, lag phase, decline phase *(1)*

2 The table shows information about the stability of proteins from three different bacteria.

Species of bacterium	Percentage of proteins denatured at 60 °C
Escherichia coli	55
Bacillus subtilis	57
Unknown *Bacillus*	4

To which group of bacteria does the unknown *Bacillus* belong?

A hydrophiles **C** psychrophiles

B mesophiles **D** thermophiles *(1)*

3 Which method of sterilisation would be most appropriate for a heat-sensitive liquid growth medium?

A disinfectant **C** filtration

B dry air oven **D** flaming *(1)*

4 **a)** Give one way in which the use of aseptic techniques can be described as *ethical*. *(1)*

b) A student was given seven tubes containing a serial dilution of a bacterial culture.

i) Describe how he would transfer 1 cm^3 of the culture from the 10^{-3} dilution to an agar plate. Include descriptions of the aseptic techniques he would use. *(6)*

ii) The diagram shows some of the student's agar plates after incubation. Which should he use to estimate the number of cells in the undiluted culture? Give the reasons for your choice. *(3)*

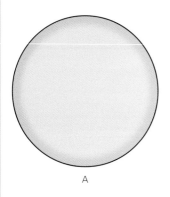

A

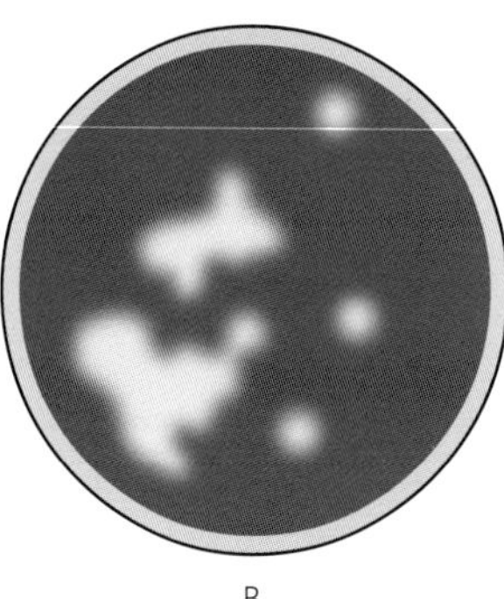
B

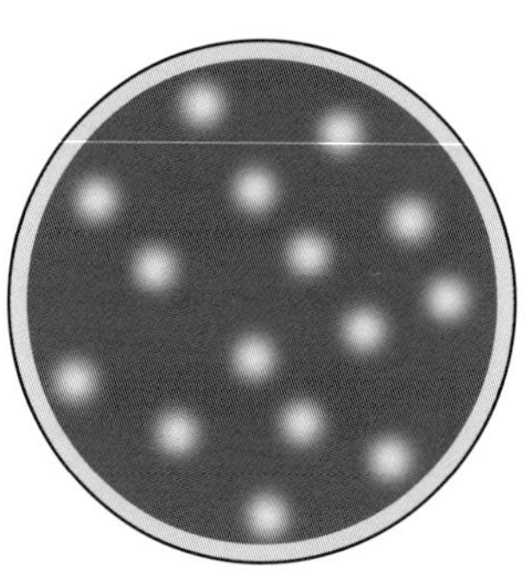
C

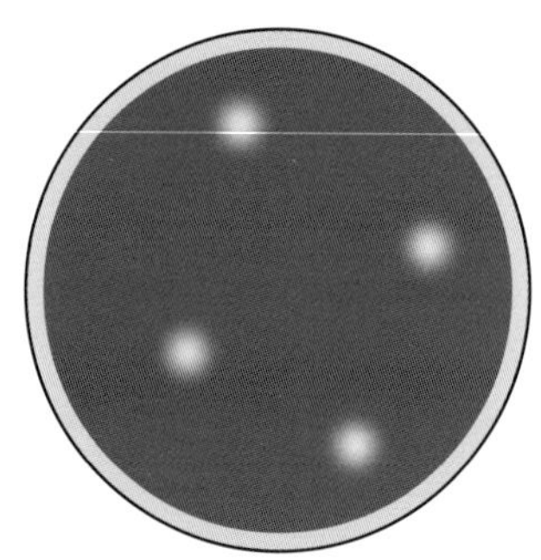
D

5 A student counted yeast cells using a light microscope and haemocytometer. The diagram on the right shows part of one of her fields of view using a dilution of the pure culture of 10^5.

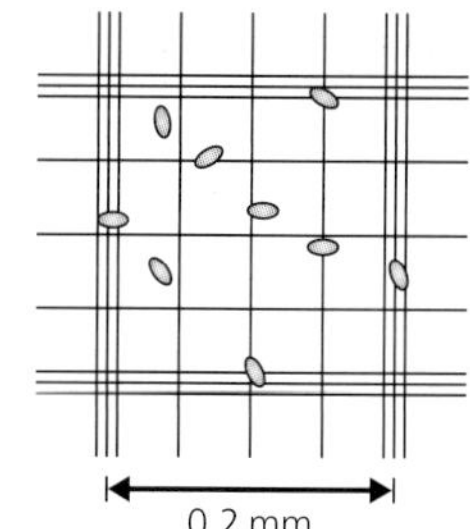

a) How many cells should she count in the square shown? Explain your answer. *(2)*

b) The mean number of cells she counted was 9.3 cells per 0.2 mm × 0.2 mm square. With the haemocytometer she used, the depth of liquid between the cover slip and the haemocytometer platform was 0.1 mm.

Use the information in this question to estimate the density of cells in the pure culture. Give your answer as cells cm^{-3}. Show your working. *(3)*

6 The graph shows a typical growth curve of a bacterial culture.

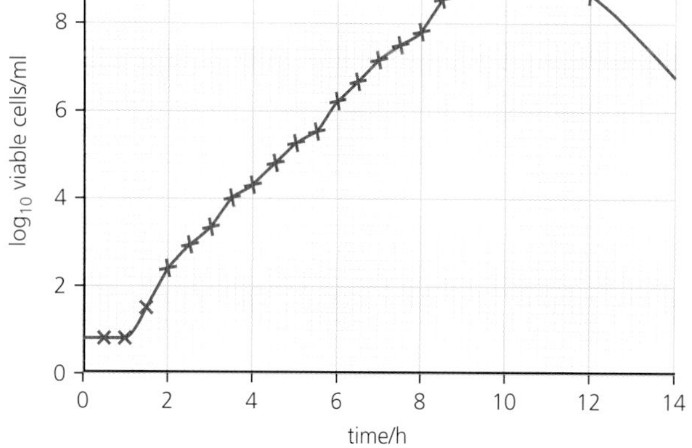

a) Explain why the number of bacterial cells is shown as a logarithm. *(1)*

b) Explain the shape of the curve during the first hour. *(2)*

c) Between 1 and $1\frac{1}{2}$ hours after inoculation, the bacteria were growing exponentially. Explain the shallow rise in the curve. *(1)*

d) Use data from the graph to calculate the growth rate constant (μ) between 90 minutes and 510 minutes. Use the formula:

$$\mu = \frac{2.303\ (\log N_x - \log N_0)}{(t_x - t_0)}$$ *(3)*

7 The total count and viable count of a bacterial culture can be investigated.

a) What is the advantage of performing a viable count over a total count? *(2)*

★b) A student wishes to investigate the viable count of a broth culture of bacteria.

Devise and outline a method by which she could do this.

Assume she has the equipment and materials she needs in her school laboratory.

Do not include any details of aseptic technique in your outline of the method. *(6)*

Stretch and challenge

8 Use a search engine and/or the resource centre in your college or school to learn more about culture media. What features of selective media can you relate to other topics in your biology studies?

9 The European Union (EU) regulations relating to mineral water for human consumption, specify a maximum plate count of 100 colony-forming units per cm^3 ($CFU\,cm^{-3}$) after incubation at 22 °C.

A serial dilution was produced from a sample taken from a freshly opened bottle of mineral water. A pour-plating technique was used to add 500 mm^3 samples of each dilution to agar plates. After incubation at 22 °C, the colony count of three plates of the 10^{-1} dilution were 28, 32 and 39. What can you conclude about this mineral water? Use the following formula to explain your answer.

$$\text{viable count per cm}^3 = \frac{c}{v} \times D$$

Where c = mean colony count at each dilution

v = volume of liquid transferred to each plate

D = reciprocal of the dilution

16 Pathogens and antibiotics

Prior knowledge

In this chapter you will need to recall that:

→ communicable diseases can be caused by viruses, bacteria, protoctists and fungi
→ animals and plants are susceptible to communicable diseases
→ viruses are non-living particles that depend on their host cell's metabolism to produce more virus particles
→ some viruses undergo a lytic cycle, at the end of which the cell they infect lyses
→ bacteria are prokaryotic organisms; their metabolism differs from that of eukaryotic organisms in many respects
→ protoctists and fungi are eukaryotic organisms
→ the spread of communicable diseases can be reduced or prevented in animals and plants using a variety of techniques.

Test yourself on prior knowledge

1 Name **two** components common to all viruses.
2 List the stages of the lytic cycle of a virus.
3 Give **two** ways in which the structure of a prokaryotic cell differs from that of a eukaryotic cell.
4 Explain **one** way in which the spread of HIV/AIDS can be slowed.
5 How do bacteria and fungi feed?

Bacteria as pathogens

Figure 16.1 on the next page shows a false colour scanning electron micrograph of the intestinal bacterium *Escherichia coli*, together with a drawing to interpret its structure. You should remember from Chapter 4 that bacteria are prokaryotic cells that lack a nucleus or membrane-bound organelles and have 70S ribosomes. This means that their metabolism is different from that of eukaryotic cells, which we will return to later in this chapter.

Like most species of bacteria, *Escherichia coli* is normally harmless. In fact, it is a very common **commensal** in the guts of mammals, including humans, and is a major component of their faeces. Some species of bacteria, however, are **pathogens**. This means that they invade the tissues of another organism, their host, and cause harm to it. The damage results from either:

- release of toxins – substances produced by the pathogen
- invasion and destruction of the host's tissues.

Key terms

Commensal A partner in an association between two organisms of different species where one (*E.coli* in our example) benefits and the other (a mammal) neither benefits nor is harmed.

Pathogen An agent of infection that invades another organism, the host, causing harm to it.

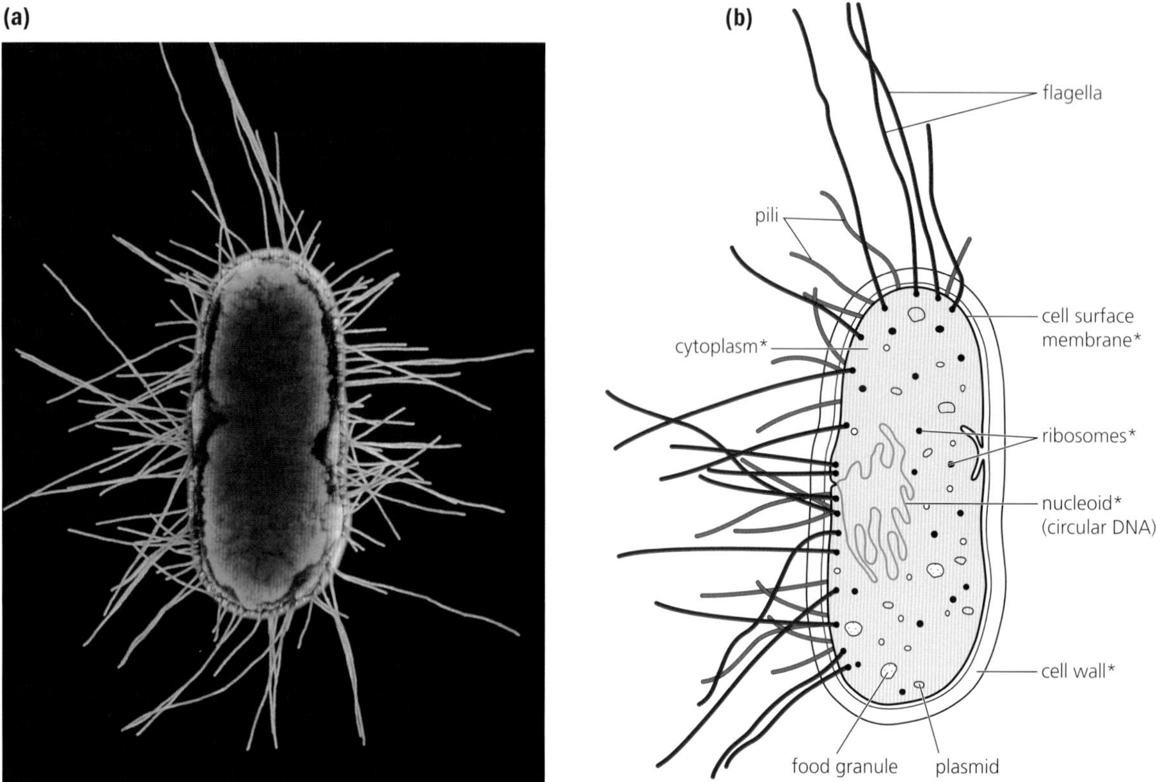

Figure 16.1 The structure of *Escherichia coli*. (a) A false colour scanning electron micrograph; (b) an interpretative drawing of the micrograph in which the asterisks show those structures that occur in all bacteria

Pathogenic effects produced by toxins

A toxin is a poison produced by an organism. Many animals and plants produce toxins, but here we will restrict ourselves to bacterial toxins. Pathogenic bacteria produce toxins that you can classify into two types: **endotoxins** and **exotoxins**. Table 16.1 summarises some of the important properties of these two types of bacterial toxin.

Table 16.1 A comparison of endotoxins and exotoxins

Property	Endotoxin	Exotoxin
Type of bacterium able to produce toxin	Gram negative only	Gram positive and Gram negative
Chemical nature of molecule	Lipopolysaccharide	Polypeptide or protein
Size of molecule/kDa	≈ 10	≈ 1000
Relationship with cell	Part of cell surface membrane	Secreted by cell
Potency/μg needed to cause symptoms	≈ 100	≈ 1
Can be denatured by boiling	No	Yes

Salmonella and endotoxins

Endotoxins are produced by bacteria with Gram-negative cell walls (see Chapter 4, page 90). Each endotoxin is a lipopolysaccharide that is embedded in the cell surface membrane of the bacterium. Figure 16.2 shows the general structure of a lipopolysaccharide.

The lipid-A component is the part that is embedded in the outer phospholipid layer of the cell surface membrane. It is this part of the lipopolysaccharide that is toxic.

The O-specific component lies outside the cell surface membrane. This part of the lipopolysaccharide is important in enabling the bacterium to invade its host. It is also this part of the lipopolysaccharide that has antigenic properties, that is, it can cause the production of antibodies against it.

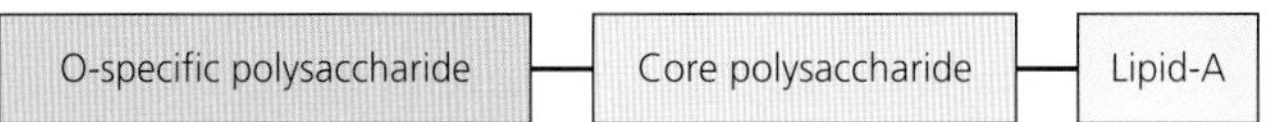

Figure 16.2 Endotoxins are lipopolysaccharide molecules

Figure 16.3 shows a scanning electron micrograph of one species of *Salmonella*, a Gram negative bacillus. Non-typhoidal *Salmonella enterica* produces a localised infection in the human intestines. The bacterium usually invades the body in contaminated food and results in food poisoning. A large number of bacteria must be ingested to cause symptoms in healthy adults. Once in the small intestine, *S. enterica* cells can invade cells lining the intestinal wall and disrupt the junctions between them. On death and lysis, the endotoxins are released from *S. enterica* cells. This causes inflammation and reduces the ability of the cells lining the intestinal wall to stop the movement of water and ions into the lumen of the intestine, resulting in diarrhoea.

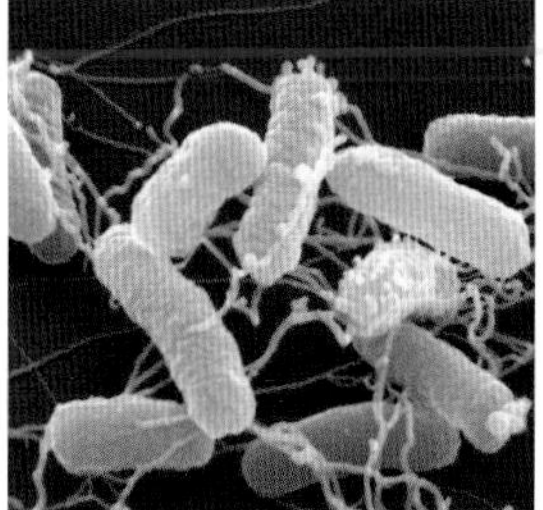

Figure 16.3 Scanning electron micrograph of *Salmonella enterica*

In contrast, typhoidal *Salmonella typhi* causes widespread symptoms. Once ingested in contaminated food, this bacterium invades the body via the lymphatic system, usually via lymph nodes in the tonsils or small intestine. Distributed via the lymph to all parts of the body, *S. typhi* invades body cells and multiplies inside them. Its endotoxins are released when the bacteria die and are lysed. Their release brings about the symptoms of typhoid fever, which include temperatures of up to 40 °C, ulcerations of the gut and, in extreme cases, death.

Staphylococcus and exotoxins

Figure 16.4 shows a scanning electron micrograph of *Staphylococcus aureus*. There are many species of *Staphylococcus* but they all show the same appearance, like bunches of grapes. In fact, that is how they get their generic name, from the Greek words for bunch of grapes (*staphyle*) and granules (*kokkos*).

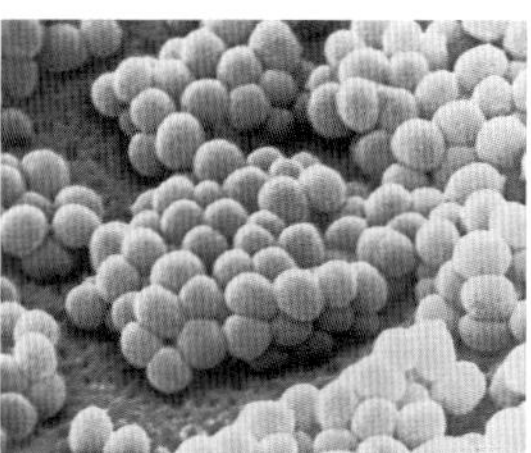

Figure 16.4 A scanning electron micrograph of *Staphylococcus aureus*, a very common bacterium on human skin. This bacterium is the causative agent of a number of human infections, including food poisoning, styes and septicaemia

Cells of *Staphylococcus* secrete a large number of enzymes, including collagenases, lipases, nucleases and proteases, which digest the tissues of their host. The products of this digestion are used by the bacteria as nutrients. *Staphylococcus* cells are also able to secrete two types of exotoxins:

- **Haemolysins** – polypeptides that become integrated in the cell surface membranes of the host's cells, creating pores. These pores cause the host's cells to lose water and ions.
- **Superantigens** – polypeptides that stimulate large numbers of cells of the immune system, resulting in a massive release of cytokines (see Chapter 17, page 362) into the blood. Toxic shock syndrome is one effect of a massive release of cytokines. In toxic shock an otherwise healthy individual develops a high fever and low blood pressure. This may progress to a coma and multiple organ failure.

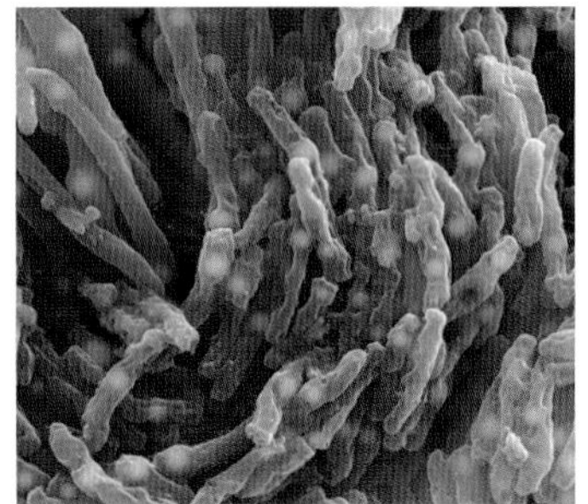

Figure 16.5 A colony of the Gram positive bacillus *Mycobacterium tuberculosis*

Pathogenic effects produced by invasion of host's tissue

Tuberculosis is a disease of the lungs caused by the bacterium *Mycobacterium tuberculosis*. Figure 16.5 shows a scanning electron micrograph of a colony of this bacterium. Infection occurs when it is inhaled, usually by droplets in coughs and sneezes. However, since its walls are rich in lipid, it can survive for many months on dry surfaces and so can be inhaled in dry dust.

Once inside the lungs, the bacteria are engulfed by macrophages (see Chapter 17, page 356) in the alveoli and bronchioles. If the recipient is in good health, the growth of bacteria is restricted in the lungs. Figure 16.6 shows how this is done. The macrophages that have engulfed the bacteria become surrounded by other cells of the immune system in a structure known as a **granuloma**. The macrophages normally kill the bacteria but a few often survive as a latent infection that could result in infection years later. In fact, between 60–80 per cent of people in the UK are thought to carry these bacteria in a dormant form like this.

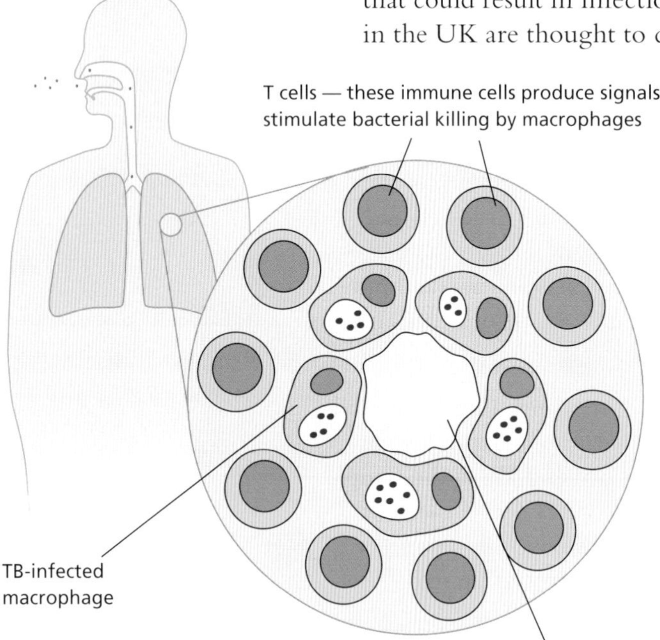
T cells — these immune cells produce signals that stimulate bacterial killing by macrophages
TB-infected macrophage
Characteristic crumbly core material containing dead cells. This is termed 'caseous necrosis': 'necrosis' meaning death and 'caseous' meaning cheese-like

Figure 16.6 A granuloma containing macrophages that have engulfed *M. tuberculosis*

If the recipient has an immune system already weakened by malnourishment or poor health, however, a chronic infection might develop within the lungs. *M. tuberculosis* secretes hydrolytic enzymes into the host's cells and digests them. Unusually, its energy source is cholesterol, which is a component of the surface membranes of mammal cells. As the bacterium digests cells, cavities appear in the lung tissues, blood vessels are broken down and fluid collects. The patient coughs blood in the sputum. The chest X-ray in Figure 16.7 shows the lung damage caused by tuberculosis.

Although initially a lung infection, macrophages can carry *M. tuberculosis* to almost any part of the body, including the central nervous system, the membranes surrounding the brain (the meninges), bone tissue, lymph glands, liver, kidneys and genital organs. Once there, the pathogen can cause cell destruction in its new location.

Test yourself

1. Distinguish between a parasite and a commensal.
2. What is a pathogen?
3. Explain how the properties of an endotoxin enable it to be embedded in the cell surface membrane of a bacterium.
4. Is the toxin produced by *Salmonella* denatured by cooking? Explain your answer.
5. It is estimated that 60 to 80% of the population carry *Mycobacterium tuberculosis*. Explain why the bacterium does not cause disease in these people.

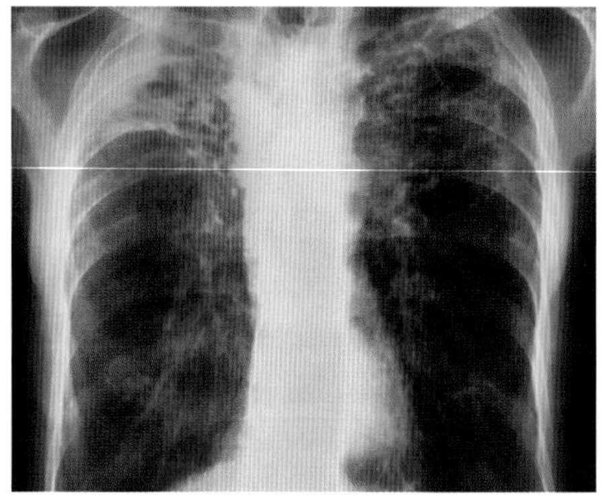

Figure 16.7 A chest X-ray showing the tissue damage caused by tuberculosis

Antibiotics

An **antibiotic** is a chemical substance that, in low concentrations, kills or inhibits the growth of microorganisms. Most are derived from fungi and bacteria commonly found in the soil, where they provide a competitive advantage to the producers.

Figure 16.8 shows an agar plate that has been inoculated with bacteria, using the spread plate technique (pages 321–322). A mast ring, with each arm impregnated with a different antibiotic, was placed on this plate before it was incubated. As each antibiotic diffused into the agar, it prevented the growth of the bacteria on the plate, leaving an area of clear agar. You can see from the diameter of the clear areas that some antibiotics were more effective against this bacterium than others.

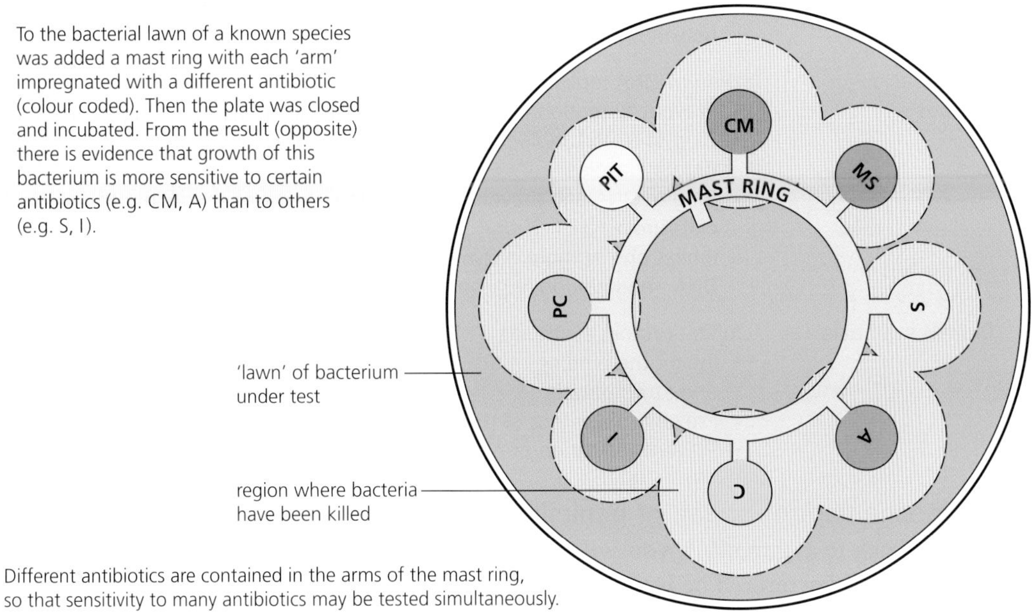

Key term

Antibiotic A substance that, in low concentrations, kills or inhibits the growth of microorganisms.

To the bacterial lawn of a known species was added a mast ring with each 'arm' impregnated with a different antibiotic (colour coded). Then the plate was closed and incubated. From the result (opposite) there is evidence that growth of this bacterium is more sensitive to certain antibiotics (e.g. CM, A) than to others (e.g. S, I).
CM
PIT
MS
MAST RING
PC
S
'lawn' of bacterium under test
I
A
C
region where bacteria have been killed
Different antibiotics are contained in the arms of the mast ring, so that sensitivity to many antibiotics may be tested simultaneously.

Figure 16.8 Investigating sensitivity to antibiotics. The mast ring shown here is available from suppliers

Some antibiotics are effective against a wide range of pathogenic bacteria; they are called **broad-spectrum antibiotics**. Tetracycline is an example of a broad-spectrum antibiotic. Others, including penicillin, are effective over a limited range of bacteria; they are called **narrow-spectrum antibiotics**. Although these terms remain useful, the development of antibiotic resistance, discussed below, results in what were once broad-spectrum antibiotics becoming restated in the range of pathogens against which they are effective.

The action of antibiotics

There are several ways in which antibiotics work. In general, though:

- **bacteriostatic antibiotics** prevent the multiplication of, but do not kill, bacteria. As a result, they prevent an infection spreading, but it is the host's immune system that finally overcomes the pathogen
- **bactericidal antibiotics** do kill bacteria.

Table 16.2 summarises the three major biochemical mechanisms that are targeted by antibiotics. Ideally, antibiotics should affect the metabolism of bacterial cells without interfering with that of the host. In some cases, however, the particular bacterial components, metabolites or enzymes targeted by the antibiotic are also components of the eukaryotic cells of the mammalian host. The extent to which this occurs influences just how toxic the drug is to the mammalian host tissues. This, in turn, determines whether, and to whom, the antibiotic might be prescribed.

Table 16.2 The biochemical mechanisms of antibiotics

Bacterial mechanism targeted	Effects of antibiotics, with specific examples
Cell wall synthesis	Disrupt the synthesis of bacterial cell walls • Inhibit the enzyme that catalyses the formation of cross-linkages between the peptidoglycan molecules in the cell wall, e.g. penicillin
Nucleic acid synthesis	Disrupt DNA replication or DNA transcription • Prevent formation of precursors of nucleic acids, e.g. sulfonamides • Bind to a DNA molecule and break down its double helix, e.g. nitroimidazoles • Bind to DNA and prevent its replication and transcription, e.g. clofazimine • Inhibit one or more enzymes that catalyse either DNA replication or DNA transcription, e.g. quinolones
Protein synthesis	Inhibit protein synthesis • Inhibit the binding of tRNA to bacterial ribosomes, e.g. tetracycline and streptomycin • Prevent movement of tRNA-peptide complex, e.g. erythromycin • Prevent formation of peptide bonds, e.g. chloramphenicol

The mechanism of action of penicillin – a narrow-spectrum antibiotic

Looking back to Figure 16.1, you will see that possession of a cell wall is a feature common to all bacteria. The wall contains layers of peptidoglycan linked together by cross-linkages. Whilst Gram negative bacteria have only a single layer of peptidoglycan in their walls, Gram positive bacteria might have as many as 40 layers.

As it grows, an individual bacterium constantly remodels its cell wall, breaking parts down and re-building them. Penicillin is an irreversible inhibitor of transpeptidase – the enzyme that catalyses the formation of the cross-linkages between the layers of peptidoglycan. It does not, however, affect the hydrolase enzymes that break the wall down. Consequently, the cell wall of a bacterium becomes thinner and thinner.

Under the influence of penicillin, Gram positive bacteria lose their cell walls entirely and are left as naked **protoplasts**. These cells are much more vulnerable than their counterparts with intact walls and are rapidly killed. Gram negative bacteria are affected in a similar way but do not completely lose their cell walls.

The mechanism of action of tetracycline – a broad-spectrum antibiotic

Bacteria possess 70S ribosomes. Each has two sub-units – a 30S and a 50S sub-unit – made of RNA and proteins. During the translation of mRNA, tRNA molecules, each carrying its appropriate amino acid, bind to the 30S sub-unit of the bacterial ribosome. Tetracycline prevents this binding, so that the affected ribosome is no longer able to manufacture a polypeptide chain. Interestingly, tetracycline does not affect eukaryotic cells because, unlike prokaryotic cells, they do not actively transport tetracycline into their cytoplasm.

Test yourself

6 Antibiotics are derived from soil bacteria and fungi. Suggest how these bacteria and fungi benefit from the antimicrobial substances they secrete.

7 Which of the antibiotics in Figure 16.8 is the most effective against the bacteria? Explain your answer.

8 Explain why the administration of bacteriostatic antibiotics usually lasts longer than that of bactericidal antibiotics.

9 Tetracycline slows bacterial protein synthesis by combining with bacterial ribosomes. It does not stop it, however. Suggest how bacteria are able to continue to produce some protein.

10 Rapidly acting bactericidal antibiotics against non-typhoidal *Salmonella enterica* can sometimes lead to symptoms. Suggest why.

Antibiotic resistance in bacteria

As you have seen, antibiotics can be classed as broad-spectrum or narrow-spectrum. Since narrow-spectrum antibiotics affect only a few groups of bacteria, it follows that others are naturally resistant to these antibiotics. This is called **primary resistance**. In recent years, groups of bacteria that were once susceptible to an antibiotic have become resistant to it. This is called **secondary resistance** and is becoming a major problem in treating disease.

Bacteria might acquire secondary resistance to antibiotics by one of three biochemical mechanisms:

- A decrease in the uptake, or increase in the expulsion, of the antibiotic by the bacterial cell.
- Production by the bacterial cell of enzymes that can modify or inactivate the antibiotic.
- Development by the bacterial cell of a biochemical pathway that bypasses the reaction affected by the antibiotic.

You might wonder how a bacterium can suddenly become resistant to an antibiotic to which it has previously been susceptible. The following facts might lead you to understand how this can happen.

- In many cases, resistance is known to be the result of a single gene. For example, resistance to the sulfonamide antibiotics is controlled by a single gene, encoding a synthase enzyme.
- During DNA replication, errors occur at an estimated rate of 1 in 10^6 base pairs. These errors are **gene mutations** that produce different alleles of a gene.
- Under optimal conditions, some bacteria replicate their DNA and divide by binary fission every 30 minutes or so.

Taking these observations together, it is easy to see how a gene mutation in a single bacterial cell might produce a new allele of a gene that confers resistance to an antibiotic. If this happened 100 years ago, before the development of antibiotics, this cell would not have been at an advantage over cells that did not possess this new allele. In fact, it might have been at a disadvantage. If this happened today, in a mammal being treated with the antibiotic, this cell would be at an advantage. Figure 16.9 shows what would then happen. The antibiotic would kill, or stop the growth of, the susceptible cells but the cell carrying the mutant allele would be unaffected. In time, it would give rise to millions of daughter cells by binary fission. As a result of DNA replication prior to binary fission, each of these daughter cells would carry the new allele, conferring resistance against the antibiotic in question. The entire population of bacteria would be antibiotic resistant.

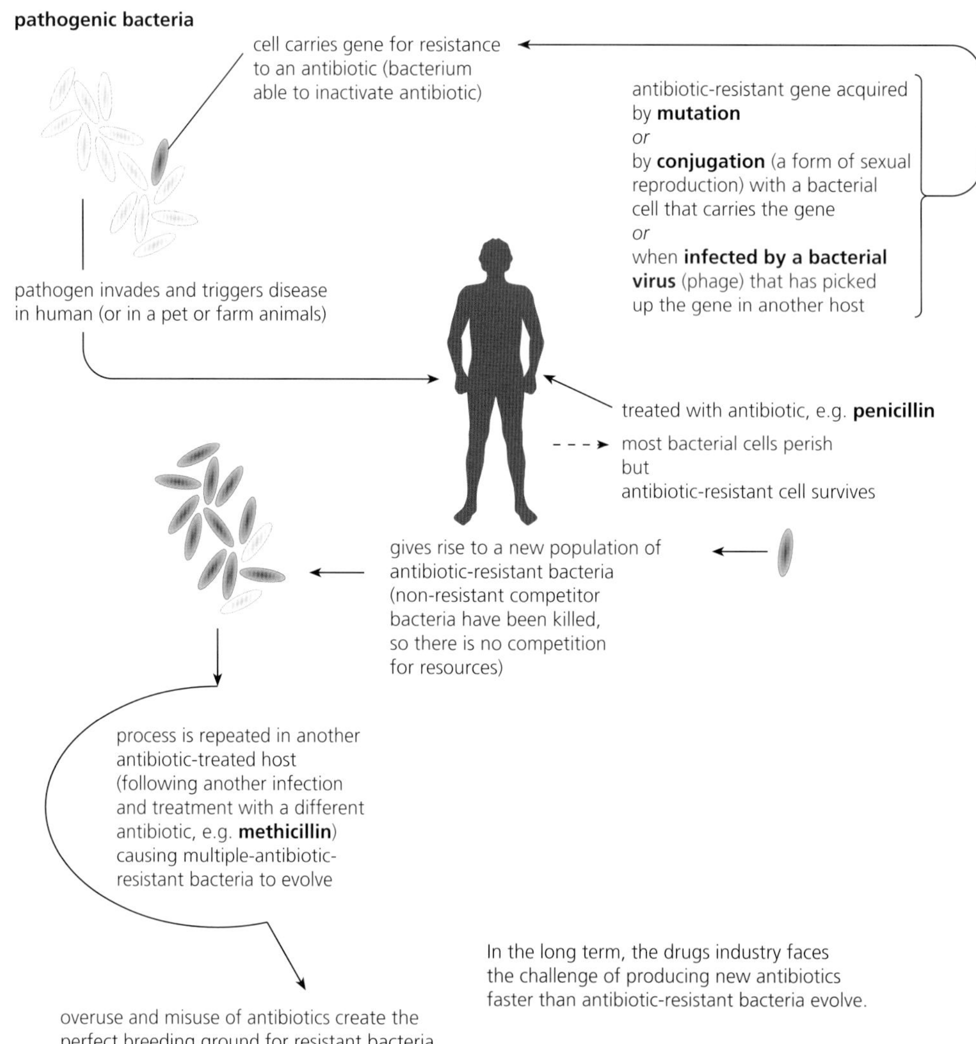

pathogenic bacteria
cell carries gene for resistance to an antibiotic (bacterium able to inactivate antibiotic)
antibiotic-resistant gene acquired by mutation or by conjugation (a form of sexual reproduction) with a bacterial cell that carries the gene or when infected by a bacterial virus (phage) that has picked up the gene in another host
pathogen invades and triggers disease in human (or in a pet or farm animals)
treated with antibiotic, e.g. penicillin
most bacterial cells perish but antibiotic-resistant cell survives
gives rise to a new population of antibiotic-resistant bacteria (non-resistant competitor bacteria have been killed, so there is no competition for resources)
process is repeated in another antibiotic-treated host (following another infection and treatment with a different antibiotic, e.g. methicillin) causing multiple-antibiotic-resistant bacteria to evolve
In the long term, the drugs industry faces the challenge of producing new antibiotics faster than antibiotic-resistant bacteria evolve.
overuse and misuse of antibiotics create the perfect breeding ground for resistant bacteria

Figure 16.9 The evolution of a multiple-antibiotic-resistant population of bacteria

Above, we have considered a bacterium that replicates its own DNA, including a mutant gene, and passes a copy to each of the daughter cells it produces by binary fission. This is known as **vertical gene transfer**. It is not the only way that bacteria can acquire new genes, however. Figure 16.10 shows a transmission electron micrograph of bacterial cells that are passing genetic material between each other. You see slender white connections between cells. These are called **conjugation tubes**. The diagrams in Figure 16.10 show that the bacteria involved can pass DNA, either one of their plasmids or a part of their own nucleoid, through the tube to a different cell. This is called **horizontal gene transfer**. If, by chance, the DNA that is passed from one cell to another contains a gene conferring antibiotic resistance, the recipient cell immediately becomes resistant to the antibiotic. This exchange can occur between bacteria of the same species, as shown in Figure 16.10, or between bacteria of different species. In the latter case, the gene conferring antibiotic resistance has 'jumped the species barrier'. Medical scientists believe that horizontal gene transfer accounts for the increasing number of bacteria that show resistance to many antibiotics – **multiple-antibiotic-resistant bacteria**.

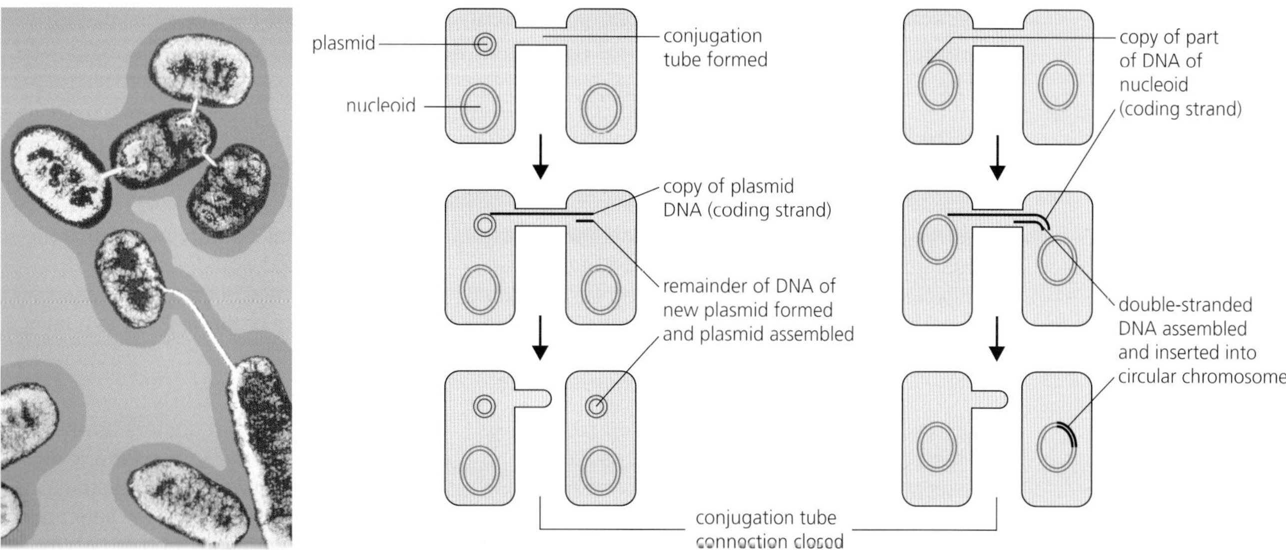

Figure 16.10 Horizontal gene transfer occurs when DNA is passed from one bacterial cell to another via a conjugation tube

Controlling the spread of antibiotic resistance in bacteria

When they were introduced in the 1940s, most bacteria were susceptible to antibiotics. As the bar chart in Figure 16.11 shows, however, even then some were not. The bar chart clearly shows that *Staphylococcus aureus* in about 3% of samples obtained worldwide were resistant to penicillin. It also shows how that percentage increased to the end of the last century. This occurred in many other species of bacteria and with many other antibiotics.

Given their rapid rate of growth, the evolution of bacterial resistance to antibiotics was almost inevitable. What has alarmed people is the rapidity of this evolution. To understand why, you need to look at ways in which antibiotics have been misused. They include the following practices.

- Sub-clinical doses of antibiotics are routinely used in agriculture as growth promoters.
- Doctors, even in the UK, prescribe antibiotics for patients with viral infections, despite the fact that viruses are unaffected by antibiotics.
- In many countries antibiotics are sold over the counter without prescription and, therefore, are often an inappropriate antibiotic.

In all three instances above, animals or humans often take sub-clinical concentrations of antibiotics. Since they are sub-clinical, they do not destroy bacteria but the presence of antibiotics does create a selective pressure for resistance. You might wonder how a doctor prescribing antibiotic for a viral infection results in people taking sub-clinical concentrations of antibiotic. Whilst taking the antibiotic, these people often begin to feel better as their own immune systems overcome the infection and so they do not complete the full treatment of antibiotic.

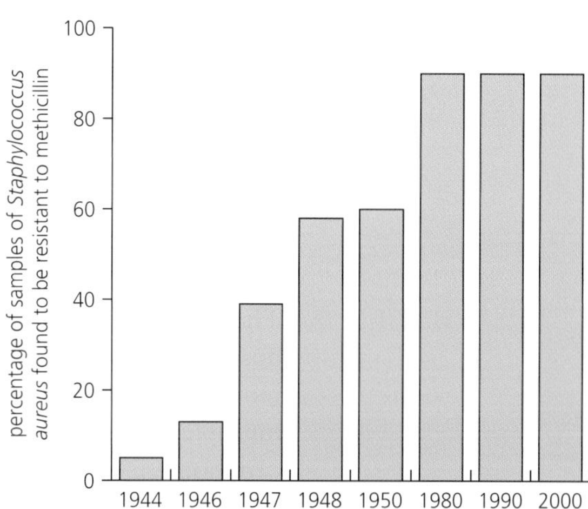

Figure 16.11 The percentage of samples of *Staphylococcus aureus* found to be resistant to penicillin from a large number of studies worldwide

The UK and the European Union parliaments have issued guidelines about the use of antibiotics. Some of the measures proposed are shown in Table 16.3. They are, however, voluntary guidelines. The parliaments feel they cannot legislate because, for example, it is not considered ethical to prevent doctors acting in what they consider to be the best interest of their patients.

Table 16.3 Measures that can reduce the use of antibiotics

Measure	Explanation	Problems that might be encountered
Restrict addition of antibiotics to animal feeds	Animal feeds account for about half all sales of antibiotics. Used at sub-clinical concentrations, they do not destroy bacteria but create a selection pressure that favours bacteria that acquire resistance.	The agricultural industry forms a strong lobby group and would resist any restriction on practices that increase the profitability of farming or the quality of their products.
Doctors to restrict prescriptions for antibiotics	If family doctors stop prescribing antibiotics as a precautionary measure and prescribe them only in cases of established need, the selective pressure favouring bacteria that acquire resistance will become less.	This might mean that doctors advise patients to go home to bed for a few days until their own immune systems overcome the infection. Many patients are unwilling to take this advice or to leave their doctor's surgery without an antibiotic, putting their doctors under severe pressure.
Patients must complete their full course of antibiotics	Many patients begin to feel better as their own immune system overcomes the bacterial infection and so stop taking the antibiotic. Again, the bacteria are not destroyed by the antibiotic but a selection pressure favouring bacteria that acquire resistance is created.	We rely on people acting in the best interests of the community at large. In general, we do what we feel like doing.
Create new antibiotics	This is the obvious solution – make new antibiotics faster than bacteria can acquire immunity against them.	The development of a new antibiotic takes years and the success rate is very low. This makes the development of new antibiotics not only a slow process but a very expensive one. If pharmaceutical companies fund this research, they must recoup their costs by making the drug expensive, thus restricting its availability. If governments fund the research, they must use taxpayers' money, possibly leading to unpopular tax rises.

The samples from which Figure 16.11 was produced were taken from patients in hospitals. This provides a clue about the origin of most infections by bacteria with multiple antibiotic resistance. In the UK, infections resulting from bacteria with multiple antibiotic resistance are mainly acquired in hospitals or in community-based care homes. The reasons for this are not hard to identify.

- Patients in hospitals or nursing homes are either elderly or ill, or both. They have weakened immune systems and so are more susceptible to disease.
- Many people are admitted to hospital because they are suffering from a bacterial infection. Consequently, hospitals are likely to have richer populations of pathogenic bacteria than the rest of the community.

In hospitals, bacteria can be transmitted from person to person by airborne or droplet transmission, by direct skin contact, or by contact with clothing, instruments and equipment. The medical councils of most European countries have issued advice about the steps that hospital staff should take to reduce the risk of transmission of bacteria. Some are listed in Table 16.4.

Table 16.4 Measures taken to reduce the spread of hospital-acquired infections and some problems that might arise in meeting these guidelines

Measure	Explanation	Problems that might be encountered
Isolation of infected patients	Reduces risk of transmission between infected patient and other vulnerable patients.	Given bed shortages in many hospitals, isolation rooms are not always available.
Hand washing by staff and visitors	Effective hand washing removes bacteria from the skin and so reduces transmission by direct skin contact. This is a cheap and readily available method of reducing transmission.	It is a voluntary act that might not be followed by the thousands of people visiting patients in hospital each day.
Staff to wear disposable gloves and aprons whilst handling patients	Provided they are disposed of after handling each patient, e.g. washing or turning patient over in bed, the aprons and gloves provide a protective barrier for patients and staff.	The time spent removing and disposing of aprons and gloves when passing from bed to bed might restrict the time that hospital staff are able to spend with each patient. There might not be enough time to put on the disposable wear if an emergency occurs with one patient. Though individually cheap, the large number of aprons and gloves would lead to a considerable additional annual cost.
Screening patients on arrival for 'superbug' infections	Screening allows the isolation of infected patients, so reducing the risk of transmission to other vulnerable patients.	Screening is costly and time-consuming and isolation rooms might not be available.

Test yourself

11 Give **three** ways in which resistance to antibiotics can arise.

12 Bacteria that are thousands of years old, found in cores of ice from the Antarctic, have been shown to be resistant to antibiotics. How can this be explained?

13 Suggest how the inclusion of sub-clinical doses of antibiotic in animal feed might increase yield.

14 Antibiotics do not cause mutations that result in antibiotic resistance. Why, then, might failing to complete a course of antibiotics result in bacteria developing resistance to the antibiotic?

15 Methicillin-resistant *Staphylococcus aureus* became a problem in hospitals during the 1990s. Explain why the problem was largely restricted to hospitals.

Other pathogenic agents

Bacteria are not the only pathogenic organisms that can cause human infections. Here, we will consider one example of each of: a fungal infection; a viral infection; and an infection caused by a protoctist.

Stem rust fungus (Puccinia graminis)

Figure 16.12 Crop plant infected by stem rust fungus

Figure 16.12 shows wheat plants infected by stem rust fungus. You can see how this parasite gets its name – it infects the plant's stem (including leaves) producing a covering that is the colour of rust. The variety of stem rust fungus shown (*Ug99*) is a new variety that first appeared in Uganda in 1999. The *Ug99* strain has since spread and is currently devastating crops of wheat in countries in East Africa, the Middle East and Asia and computer models predict it will reach India, one of the world's largest producers of wheat. Since it has been estimated that 85 per cent of the world's population depend on wheat as one of their only sources of energy and 60 per cent as their main source of dietary protein, *Ug99* has the potential to cause worldwide food scarcity.

Like most fungi, the stem rust fungus produces dormant spores. These spores are carried in the air to new plants. On landing on a new plant, the spores germinate and produce threadlike structures, called **hyphae**. A mass of fungal hyphae, such as those you can see in Figure 16.12, is called a **mycelium**. Like all fungi, the stem rust fungus secretes digestive enzymes from its hyphae onto the material on which it is growing - in this case the stem of a cereal plant. The enzymes digest chemicals in the stem and the fungus absorbs the products of this digestion.

In addition to digesting its tissues, infection by stem rust fungus damages the host plant in a number of ways:

- It weakens the stem, often causing the plant to fall over. This makes mechanical harvesting impossible.
- It uses nutrients that would otherwise be stored in the plant's seeds. This reduces the harvest.
- It breaks the outer epidermis of the plant's stem. This increases the rate of water loss from the plant as well as making the stem more susceptible to infection by other plant pathogens.

Controlling the spread of stem rust fungi

Fungicides can be used to kill the stem rust fungus. These are usually expensive, reducing their availability to poor farmers in Africa and Asia. As associations between plant roots and fungi are vital to the roots' efficient absorption of inorganic ions from soil, spraying fungicides can damage delicate ecosystems.

Since, after harvesting the seeds, cereal plants are destroyed, you might think that stem rust fungus would be a problem for only one growing season. One reason that this is not the case lies in the complex life cycle of the fungus. Although the primary host of the stem rust fungus is a cereal crop, it depends on another type of plant to complete its life cycle – the barberry. Knowing this, North America began a barberry eradication programme in 1918, which continues to this day. Although getting rid of barberry plants has reduced infection rates, it has not eliminated stem rust because new spores are carried to North America by winds from the southern states of America and Mexico, in the so-called 'Puccina pathway'. In fact, spore dispersal occurs over vary large distances. In 2002, one group of scientists reported that stem rust fungus spores had dispersed up to 8000 km from the south of Africa to Australia.

The most promising way of eradicating stem rust fungus is by gene manipulation. Scientists have identified a number of genes that confer resistance to stem rust fungus and, using genetic engineering techniques that we will discuss in Chapter 19, have produced varieties of cereals resistant to some strains of stem rust fungus. Some of the most effective have only been used in Australia, so their effectiveness in other parts of the world is, as yet, unknown.

Influenza

Influenza, or flu, is caused by a virus. Figure 16.13 shows the structure of the influenza virus. It contains eight short strands of RNA (referred to as a segmented genome), surrounded by a protein capsid. Outside the capsid is an envelope with an outer lipid layer and an inner protein layer. Glycoprotein 'spikes' project through this envelope and cover the surface of the virus. The H glycoproteins (haemagglutinin) help the virus particle enter a cell of the host. The N glycoproteins (neuramidase) allow newly formed virus particles to escape from a cell of the host.

Figure 16.14 summarises the way in which the influenza virus causes infection. The events follow the lytic cycle, which you came across in Chapter 4, page 93. The influenza virus enters the human host's lungs via droplets inhaled through the nose or mouth. The virus then enters the epithelial cells lining the bronchus and bronchioles by endocytosis.

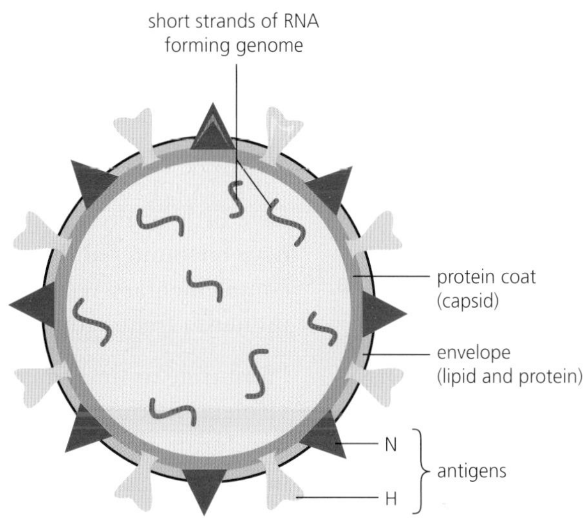

Figure 16.13 An influenza virus particle

virus particles taken into lungs in droplets

virus particles discharged into the atmosphere in droplets of mucus

antigen is an enzyme hydrolysing mucus, allowing contact between virus and membrane of epithelial cell

viral antigens attach to receptors on epithelium cell membranes and trigger endocytosis

goblet cell secretes mucus which protects epithelium

site of endocytosis

RNA segments enter nucleus – transcription and replication of nucleic acid occurs here

copies of RNA segments to cytoplasm

viruses cause new infections

viral proteins replicated here

new virus particles assembled here

infected host cells undergoes lysis

viruses exit host cell, picking up the lipid coat in the process

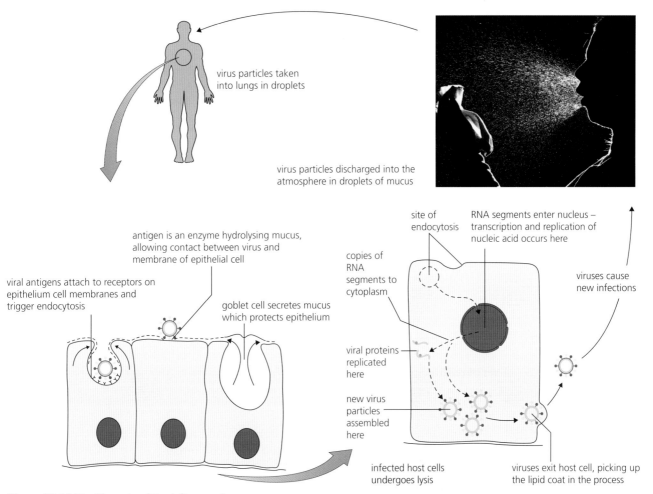

Figure 16.14 The life cycle of the influenza virus

Key terms

Antigenic variability Variation in the chemical nature of the same type of antigen resulting from frequent gene mutations and, in eukaryotes, different splicing of pre-mRNA molecules transcribed from the same gene.

Epidemic An outbreak of disease in which the number of new infections is much greater than would be expected from recent experience. The outbreak is widespread within one community at a particular time.

Pandemic A human disease that has spread worldwide.

Replication of the virus then occurs; new RNA segments are produced in the nucleus and the capsid proteins are produced in the cytoplasm of the host cell. New viral particles are assembled and the outer envelope is added as the new virus particles leave the dying host cells. As the host cells break down (lyse), toxins are released, which bring about many of the symptoms of influenza. The breakdown of epithelial cells also opens the way for secondary infections of the host's lung tissue.

Influenza viruses are classified into antigenic groups according to the H and N glycoproteins of their capsids, e.g. H5N1. When in human tissues, these glycoproteins act as antigens. The influenza virus shows great **antigenic variability**, meaning that mutations of the viral genome frequently occur that result in new forms of these antigens appearing on the outer surface of the virus. Often humans (or other hosts) have little or no resistance to these new antigens. Their immune systems will not have encountered them before, so no memory cells (see Chapter 17, page 361) with complementary receptors will be present in their lymph nodes. Because of this, influenza frequently causes a major **epidemic**.

From time to time, mutations lead to a strain of the influenza virus that is extremely virulent. A strain with just the right mix of virulence and transmissibility leads to a **pandemic** in which millions of humans die. During the last century, there were three such pandemics. These are listed and described in Table 16.5.

Table 16.5 The three flu pandemics of the 20th century

Pandemic	Profile
Spanish flu 1918–19	• Killed about 40 million people (compare this with the 10 million people killed in the First World War of 1914–18) • Nations struggled to cope; the end of the war was a time when resources were exceptionally stretched, and viruses were not understood • Vaccines were incorrectly targeted at bacteria • Civilians were put into quarantine (but troop movements continued between continents) • High levels of personal hygiene were advocated
Asian flu 1957–8	• Killed about 1 million people • Medical knowledge was more advanced than in 1918 but, also, the strain of virus was substantially less virulent • The strain of virus was identified and vaccines were produced but it was not possible to produce enough • Quarantine measures were used, again to little effect
Hong Kong flu 1968–9	• Killed about 1 million people • By this date the WHO existed and its global flu surveillance network gave early warning of an imminent pandemic as the disease spread from its origins in East Asia • Vaccines were developed quickly but not enough could be produced in time to meet the full demand

There are three pre-requisites for a flu pandemic:

- A novel virus strain, unfamiliar to human immune systems, must reach human hosts from its point of origin.
- The virus must be able to replicate in humans and cause disease.
- The virus must be efficiently transmitted between humans.

You might remember the public discussions and anxiety about the bird flu epidemic that threatened us in 2005–06. That strain was identified as H5N1. The interlocking flight paths of wild birds, migrating between seasonal feeding grounds in different parts of the globe, transmitted the infection among wild populations of birds and, occasionally, to stocks of farmed birds. Some unfortunate people, in countries as widely apart as the Far East and Eastern Europe, who had direct contact with infected birds contracted the disease. For some, this exposure proved fatal.

The H5N1 strain of 2005, although extremely virulent, failed the third of the pre-requisites listed above. It was not a strain that was quickly and easily transmitted between individual humans, and so no pandemic ensued (at that time).

The malarial parasite (*Plasmodium* spp.)

As Figure 16.15 shows, malaria is **endemic** in tropical and sub-tropical regions of the world. The WHO estimates that about 400 million people are infected with malaria, of whom 1.5 million (mostly children under 5 years old) die each year. About 80 per cent of these cases of malaria occur in sub-Saharan Africa.

Key term

Endemic A disease that occurs frequently, or is constantly present at a low level of infection, in particular areas or among people of a particular population.

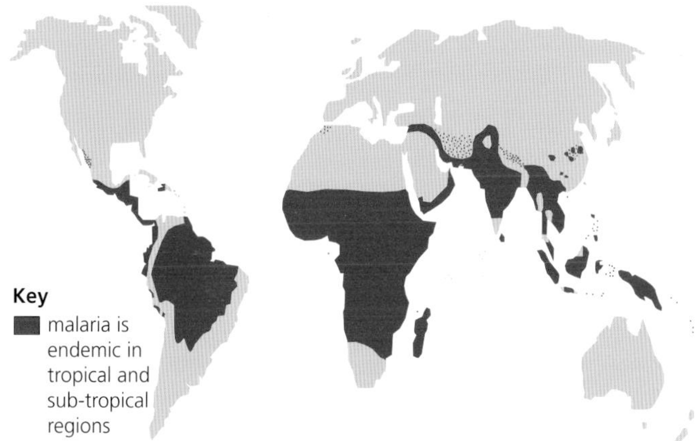

Figure 16.15 World distribution of malaria

Figure 16.16 A female *Anopheles* mosquito taking a blood meal

Malaria is caused by four species of *Plasmodium*, a single-celled protoctist. About 90 per cent of malaria cases are caused by *Plasmodium falciparum*. Transmission of *Plasmodium* from an infected person to another person is by the *Anopheles* mosquito. Although the male feeds on plant juices, the female mosquito takes a blood meal from an unsuspecting human. She does this by inserting her piercing mouthparts. Using her mouthparts rather like a mini-hypodermic needle, the female inserts them through the skin into a blood vessel and injects saliva (Figure 16.16). The saliva contains anticoagulants that enable the mosquito to draw blood through its mouthparts without the blood clotting. The saliva causes inflammation and itching of the mosquito bite. If the female mosquito is infected, the saliva also contains the infective stage, called sporozoites, of *Plasmodium*.

Within a few minutes, the injected sporozoites enter cells in the liver of their new human host. As Figure 16.17 on the next page shows, each sporozoite rapidly divides to form thousands of daughter cells, called merozoites. Eventually, the infected liver cells burst, releasing their merozoites into the blood.

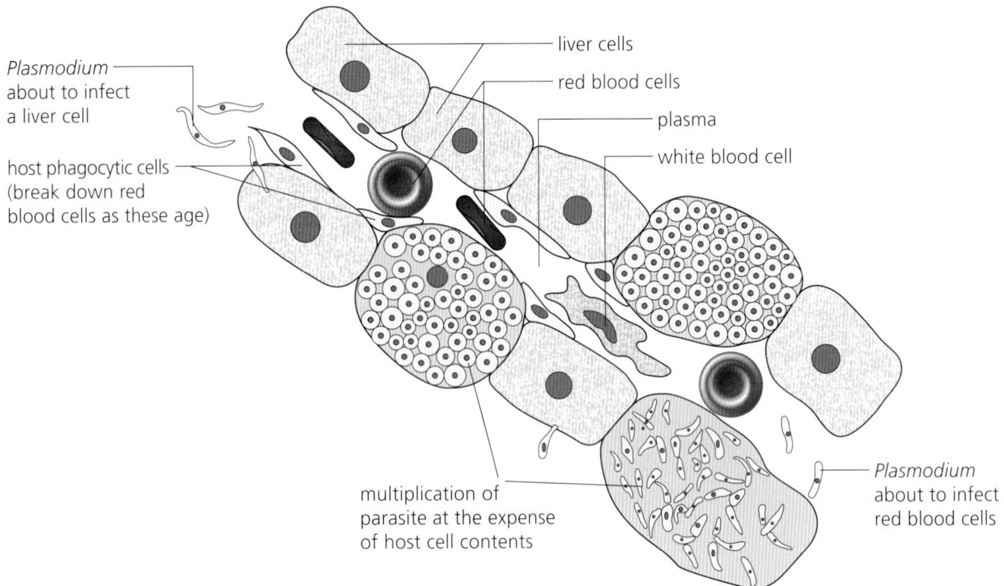

Figure 16.17 Following injection by the bite of an infected female *Anopheles* mosquito, *Plasmodium* cells enter liver cells where they divide

The released merozoites enter red blood cells, where they digest the haemoglobin as a food source. Each merozoite undergoes several cell cycles to produce between 8 and 32 new merozoites. The red blood cells burst, releasing these new merozoites into the blood, where each infects another red blood cell.

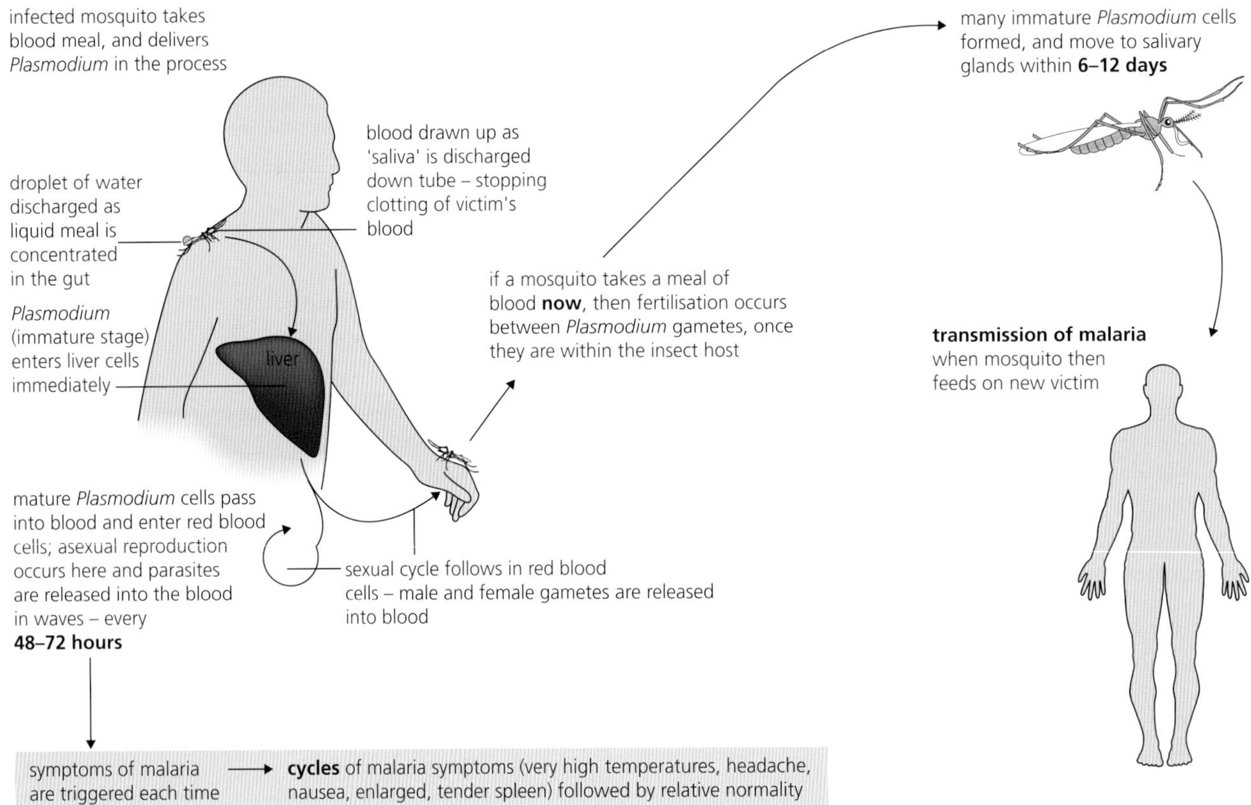

Figure 16.18 The transmission of malaria from person to person by a female *Anopheles* mosquito

A cycle of infection of red blood cells and merozoite release then follows (Figure 16.18). Every 3 to 4 days, increasing numbers of red blood cells burst, releasing merozoites that infect new red blood cells. Each red blood cell that bursts releases toxins produced during the breakdown of its contents by merozoites. These toxins cause the symptoms of malaria, including a body temperature of 40–45 °C, intense fever symptoms and a swollen spleen.

Prevention of infection includes a number of methods. Each has its drawbacks, however, as shown in Table 16.5.

Table 16.5 Some methods of preventing malaria

Method to reduce incidence of malaria	Issues
Drain wetland areas where mosquitoes breed	Not possible to drain large lakes, which are also breeding grounds for mosquitoes. Some people earn their living, or derive their main food source, from wetlands. Successful drainage might involve inter-governmental co-operation, which is not always possible.
Spray areas where malaria is endemic with insecticide to kill mosquitoes	The areas are vast, much larger than areas treated in Europe and would often involve co-operation between different governments or areas occupied by warring groups. Insecticide would damage other wildlife, including beneficial insects.
Cover beds with fine-mesh nets, coated with insecticide	This is cheap and effective, since most mosquitoes bite at night when their victims are asleep. Mosquitoes that bite during the day are, however, emerging in many areas where malaria is endemic.
Release sterilised male mosquitoes that would mate with the females but not result in viable eggs being laid	Since releasing more insects in order to reduce the number of insects is counter intuitive, local groups of people are reluctant to accept its use. Large-scale, and effective, education programmes are needed to convince people to accept such programmes.
Vaccination	A vaccine would have to be suitable for use with babies and young children, since malaria is most severe during the first years of life. Pharmaceutical companies need to charge for their products. Countries in which malaria is endemic are often poor and could not afford country-wide vaccination programmes. Plasmodium shows great antigenic variability (involving interactions between 59 different genes in the first strain of *P. falciparum* to have its genome characterised). This makes production of an effective vaccine difficult.

Test yourself

16 Suggest what data were needed to make the computer model that predicted the *Ug99* strain of stem rust fungus would spread to India.

17 Explain why the flu virus is said to have a fragmented genome.

18 Distinguish between endemic, epidemic and pandemic diseases.

19 The majority of new cases of malaria occur among children under the age of 5 years. Suggest why.

20 Malaria used to be common in southern England. The spread of malaria in England was greatly reduced when glass was introduced in windows. Suggest why glass windows had this unforeseen effect.

Chapter summary

Bacteria as pathogens

- Some bacteria are pathogens, i.e., agents of infection.
- Bacteria harm their hosts by either:
  - invading and destroying host tissues
  - releasing toxins.
- Gram-negative bacteria, e.g., *Salmonella*, have endotoxins – lipopolysaccharides – in their cell walls. These act as antigens and are often released when the bacteria die and are lysed.
- Gram-positive bacteria, e.g., *Staphylococcus*, and some Gram-negative bacteria secrete exotoxins. Exotoxins either destroy or disrupt the metabolism of the host's cells.
- *Mycobacterium tuberculosis* is a bacterium that can destroy the cells of its host. It usually destroys cells in the host's lungs but, in severe cases, can invade other organs in the host's body.

Antibiotics

- An antibiotic is a substance that, in low concentrations, affects the growth of bacteria.
- A bacteriostatic antibiotic slows the growth of bacteria.
- Tetracycline is a bacteriostatic antibiotic. It stops the translation of bacterial mRNA by preventing the binding of tRNA to bacterial ribosomes.
- A bactericidal antibiotic kills bacteria.
- Penicillin is a bactericidal antibiotic. It inhibits the formation of cross-linkages between the peptidoglycans in the cell walls of bacteria. This leads to the osmotic lysis of bacterial cells.
- Many species of bacteria have developed antibiotic resistance.
- Resistance arises as a single gene mutation resulting in an allele conferring resistance.
- Resistance is spread through a bacterial population by:
  - vertical gene transfer – the favourable allele is passed from parent cell to daughter cells following binary fission
  - horizontal gene transfer, when two bacterial cells exchange plasmids via a conjugation tube.
- When antibiotics are used, natural selection favours the allele conferring resistance.
- Among the factors that have increased the spread of antibiotic resistance are:
  - adding sub-clinical doses of antibiotics as growth promoters in animal feeds
  - inappropriate prescription of antibiotics, e.g. for viral infections
  - patients failing to complete a prescribed course of antibiotics.
- Methods to prevent the spread of antibiotic resistance include restricting the addition of antibiotics to animal feed and encouraging patients not to demand antibiotics from their doctors.

Other pathogenic agents

- When spores of the rust fungus (*Puccinia graminis*) land on a wheat plant, they germinate to form a mycelium. Fungal enzymes hydrolyse chemicals in the stem, weakening it and making it open to further infection.
- The influenza virus is spread by droplet infection and causes lysis of epithelial cells lining the host's bronchi and bronchioles.
- Sporozoites of the malarial parasite (*Plasmodium* sp.) are injected into a host's bloodstream when a female *Anopheles* mosquito takes a blood meal. Within the host's liver cells, the sporozoites rapidly multiply to form merozoites that invade the host's red blood cells. Every 3–4 days, red blood cells burst releasing more merozoites, which infect further red blood cell, and toxins that cause fever.
- The spread of malaria can be reduced by using mosquito nets and insecticides, draining wet land, and releasing sterilised male mosquitoes.

Practice questions

1 An organism that benefits by living in, or on, another organism to which it causes no harm is known as a:

A commensal | **C** pathogen

B parasite | **D** pest *(1)*

2 A substance derived from microorganisms that in low concentration kills or stops the growth of other microorganisms is called an:

A antibiotic | **C** antigen

B antibody | **D** antiseptic *(1)*

3 Influenza is caused by a:

A bacterium | **C** protozoan

B fungus | **D** virus *(1)*

4 *Staphylococcus aureus* is a species of bacterium commonly found on the skin. This bacterium can cause harm if it penetrates the skin, via a cut or graze or during surgery, and enters the bloodstream.

The charts show *Staphylococcus aureus* infection rates by females and males of different ages.

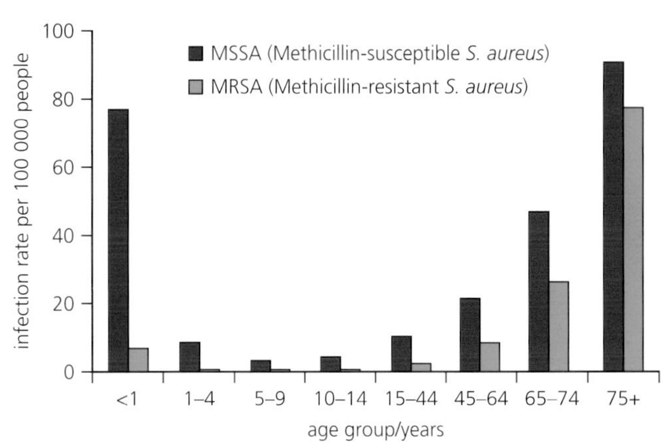

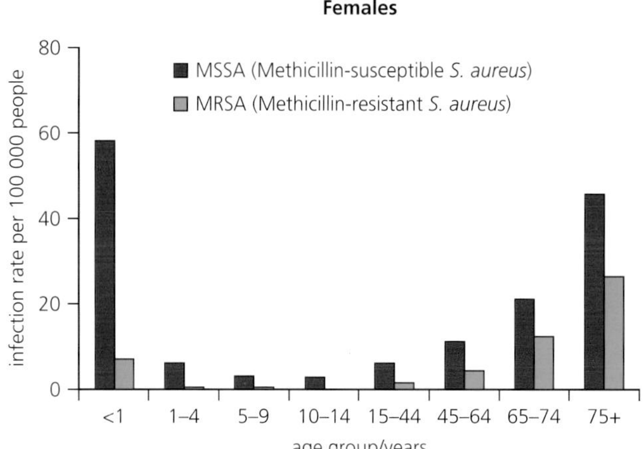

a) What can you conclude from the charts? *(3)*

b) Suggest reasons for the differences in infection rates. *(2)*

5 A hospital pathologist took samples of *Mycobacterium tuberculosis* from two patients and grew them in separate broth cultures.

He poured samples of one culture onto a number of agar plates. He then placed discs of filter paper that were impregnated with different antibiotics onto each plate.

He repeated the same procedure with samples of the second culture of bacteria and then incubated the agar plates for two days.

The diagram shows the appearance of two of his agar plates before and after incubation.

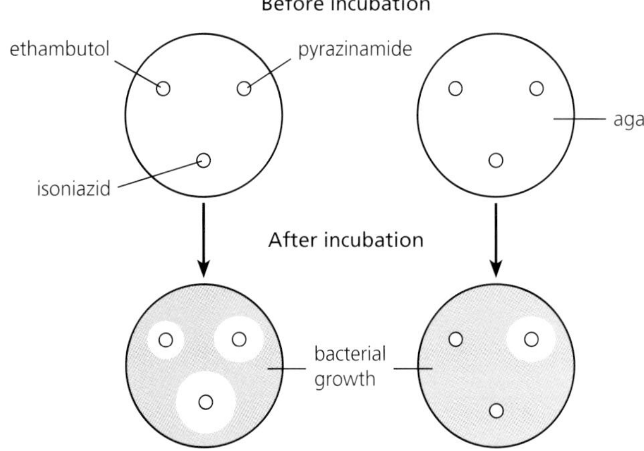

a) Explain the results of the microbiologist's investigation. *(4)*

b) When treating patients with pulmonary tuberculosis, UK doctors commonly prescribe two antibiotics to be taken every day for 6 months and a further two antibiotics to be taken every day for the first 2 months.

Explain the reasons for this treatment. *(2)*

6 Bacteraemia is a term used to describe the presence of bacteria in the blood.

The table shows data about the cases of *Staphylococcus aureus* bacteraemia reported by hospital medical laboratories in a voluntary reporting scheme in England, Wales and Northern Ireland.

Year	Number of cases of *Staphylococcus aureus* bacteraemia	
	Methicillin-sensitive (MSSA)	Methicillin-resistant (MRSA)
1993	4490	213
1994	4895	460
1995	5190	858
1996	5605	1620
1997	5609	2437
1998	5545	2858
1999	5584	3331
2000	5862	4283
2001	7168	5209
2002	7437	5529
2003	8527	6060
2004	8687	5737
2005	8622	5692
2006	8825	5393
2007	9292	4233

a) Use the data in the table to plot a graph to show the percentage of *Staphylococcus aureus* bacteraemia caused by methicillin-resistant *Staphylococcus aureus*. *(4)*

***b)** There has been great public concern about hospital-acquired MRSA. Can you conclude from the information in this question and from your graph that this concern is justified? Explain your answer. *(4)*

7 Mosquitoes carry a number of pathogens that infect humans. Scientists around the world have carried out numerous investigations of mosquito populations.

a) In one investigation, a group of scientists investigated the behaviour of one species of malaria-carrying mosquito, *Anopheles funestus*, in two villages in Benin. They found that 3 years after the introduction of long-lasting insecticide-treated mosquito nets that completely covered sleeping areas, these mosquitoes had changed their biting behaviour.

- The proportion of bites that occurred outdoors increased from 45% to 68% ($p < 0.0001$)
- The median time for catching insects switched from 02:00 hours to 05:00 hours ($p < 0.0001$)

Explain how natural selection produced this change in behaviour of the populations of *A. funestus*. *(4)*

b) In a second investigation, a group of scientists in the Cayman Islands investigated a method of controlling a species of mosquito, *Aedes aegyti*, that transmits the virus that causes dengue fever.

They produced male mosquitoes that had been genetically modified to carry a gene that caused the death of the mosquitoes' developing larvae. They compared the size of the mosquito populations in two areas. In one, they released the genetically modified males. The other was used as a control.

They estimated the population sizes by counting the number of mosquito eggs laid in traps.

Their results are shown in the graph. The rainy season in this area lasts from April to June.

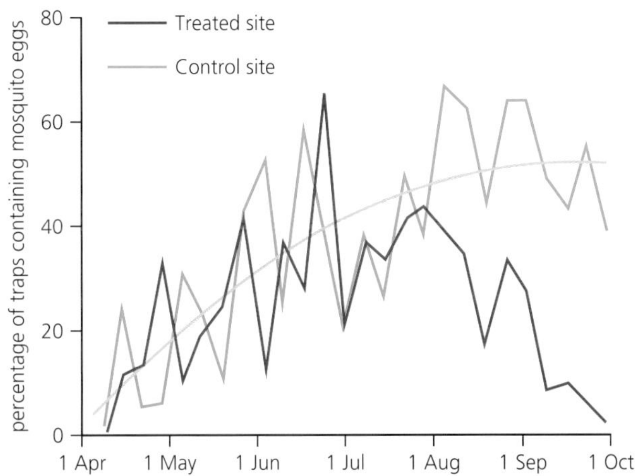

Tip

In an A level examination paper, you will commonly find questions that are synoptic. In other words, they require you to bring together your knowledge and understanding from different areas of the specification. Question 7 includes some synopsis.

i) Do the results suggest that releasing genetically modified males could be an effective method of controlling *Aedes aegypti* populations? Explain your answer. *(3)*

ii) Consider the social and ethical issues that might arise in using the release of genetically modified males to control *Aedes aegypti* populations in areas where dengue fever is common. *(4)*

Stretch and challenge

8 The sale of counterfeit antimalarial drugs is a spreading criminal activity in some parts of the world. Consider the problems this activity could bring. You might find the following factfile a useful resource to begin your research: *Malaria – a global challenge* www.microbiologyonline.org.uk.

9 How is the UK government helping to restrict the development of bacterial resistance to antibiotics? You might find it helpful to start your research with *UK Five Year Antimicrobial Resistance Strategy 2013–2018*, available from www.gov.uk.

17 Response to infection

Prior knowledge

In this chapter you will need to recall that:

- ➜ communicable diseases can be passed from person to person either directly, via a vector or by airborne and waterborne pathogens. Non-communicable diseases cannot be passed from person to person
- ➜ the non-specific defence systems of the body against pathogens include: impenetrability of the skin; entrapment of pathogens by mucus in the lungs; lysosomes in tears, saliva and urine; acidic conditions in the stomach and in the vagina
- ➜ the immune system protects the human body against disease by inflammation and by the destruction of pathogens by white blood cells, including phagocytes and antibody-releasing cells
- ➜ vaccines are used to reduce, or prevent, the spread of certain diseases

Test yourself on prior knowledge

1. Give the four main types of non-communicable disease.
2. Explain how lysozymes protect the body from pathogens.
3. Contrast the ways in which acidic conditions are produced in the stomach and in the vagina.
4. What is the role of a phagocyte?
5. Explain the difference between an antibody and an antibiotic.

You saw in the last chapter that an infectious disease is caused when another organism or virus invades the body and lives there parasitically. The invader is known as a **pathogen** and the infected organism – a human in this case – is the **host**. In this chapter you will see how your bodies respond to an infection.

First lines of defence against infectious disease

Before they can infect us, pathogens must be able to penetrate the tissues or organs of our bodies. Only then will the responses we are about to study come into play. There are three ways that pathogens can enter our tissues – via our skin, via our lungs and via our intestine. Each of these body-environment interfaces, however, has evolved mechanisms that protect us from infection. These first lines of defence are summarised in Table 17.1.

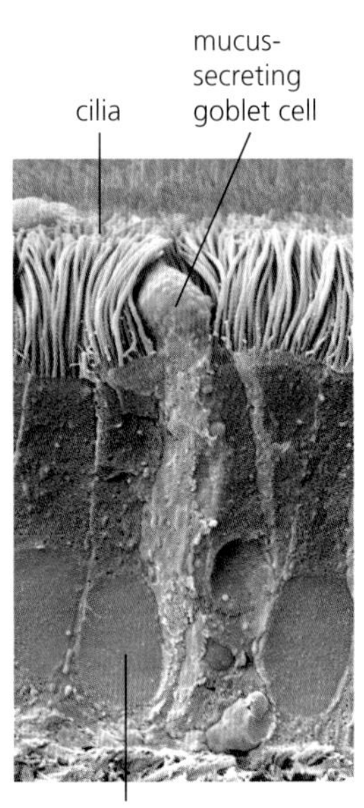

Figure 17.1 Scanning electron micrograph of cells lining the trachea. You can see a mucus-secreting cell in the middle of this SEM and the cilia that move mucus out of the lungs are clearly visible

Table 17.1 The body's first lines of defence against infection

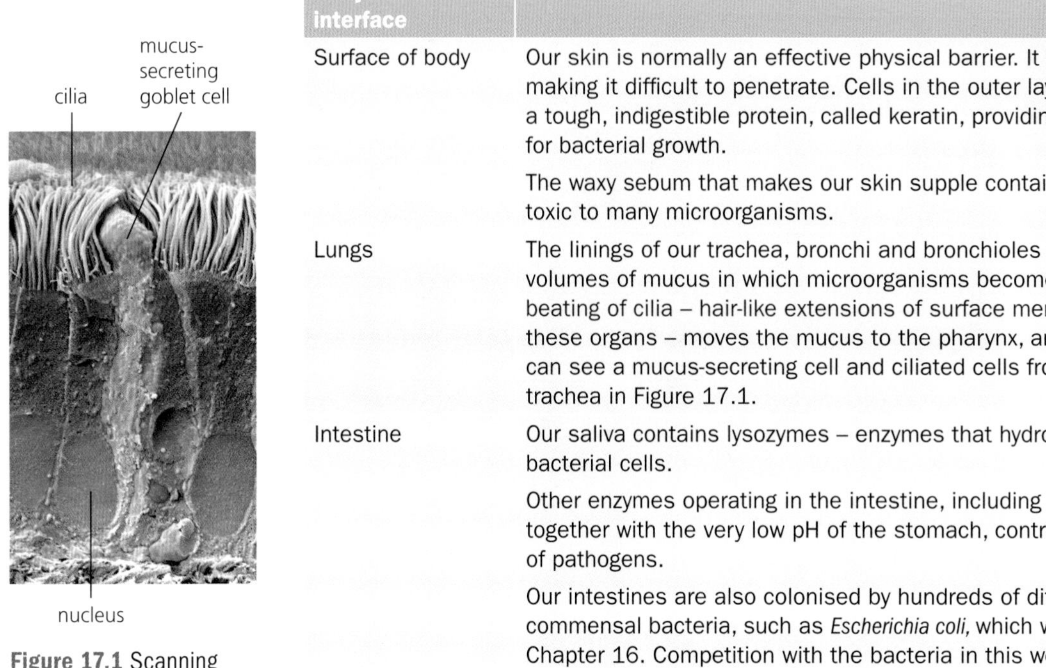

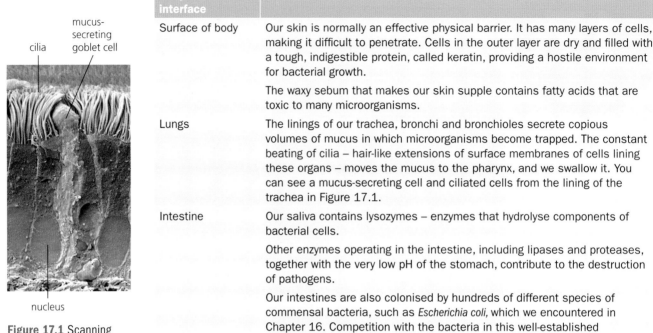

Body-environment interface	Protective mechanisms
Surface of body	Our skin is normally an effective physical barrier. It has many layers of cells, making it difficult to penetrate. Cells in the outer layer are dry and filled with a tough, indigestible protein, called keratin, providing a hostile environment for bacterial growth. The waxy sebum that makes our skin supple contains fatty acids that are toxic to many microorganisms.
Lungs	The linings of our trachea, bronchi and bronchioles secrete copious volumes of mucus in which microorganisms become trapped. The constant beating of cilia – hair-like extensions of surface membranes of cells lining these organs – moves the mucus to the pharynx, and we swallow it. You can see a mucus-secreting cell and ciliated cells from the lining of the trachea in Figure 17.1.
Intestine	Our saliva contains lysozymes – enzymes that hydrolyse components of bacterial cells. Other enzymes operating in the intestine, including lipases and proteases, together with the very low pH of the stomach, contribute to the destruction of pathogens. Our intestines are also colonised by hundreds of different species of commensal bacteria, such as *Escherichia coli,* which we encountered in Chapter 16. Competition with the bacteria in this well-established community further reduces the ability of pathogenic bacteria to become established in our intestines.

Despite these and other defences, many pathogens do enter your body. Once inside, these pathogens are much more difficult to eradicate. Not only must your body distinguish them from your own cells, it must then destroy them without causing damage to your own tissues.

Non-specific inflammatory response

If a pathogen gets into your body, an **inflammatory response** is our second line of defence. This type of response is non-specific, meaning that it is the same for all pathogens. If you look at Figure 17.2, you can follow the several processes involved in this inflammatory response.

Inflammation is the rapid, localised response of our tissues to damage. It is triggered when damaged cells release 'alarm' chemicals, including histamine and prostaglandins. These chemicals have the following immediate effects in the wounded area:

- The smooth muscle of arterioles relaxes, increasing blood flow to that area.
- Cells in the walls of capillaries draw away from one another (**diapedesis**), so that the capillaries become 'leaky', forming more tissue fluid than usual. This extra tissue fluid causes local swelling of the infected area.
- Sensory neurones become more sensitive.

The initial outcome is that the volume of blood in the damaged area is increased and we suffer local **oedema**.

Key term

Diapedesis A localised response to damage in which cells lining capillaries move apart creating gaps, through which plasma can leave the capillaries. This leads to the local production of increased volumes of tissue fluid (oedema). It also allows phagocytes to leave the capillaries.

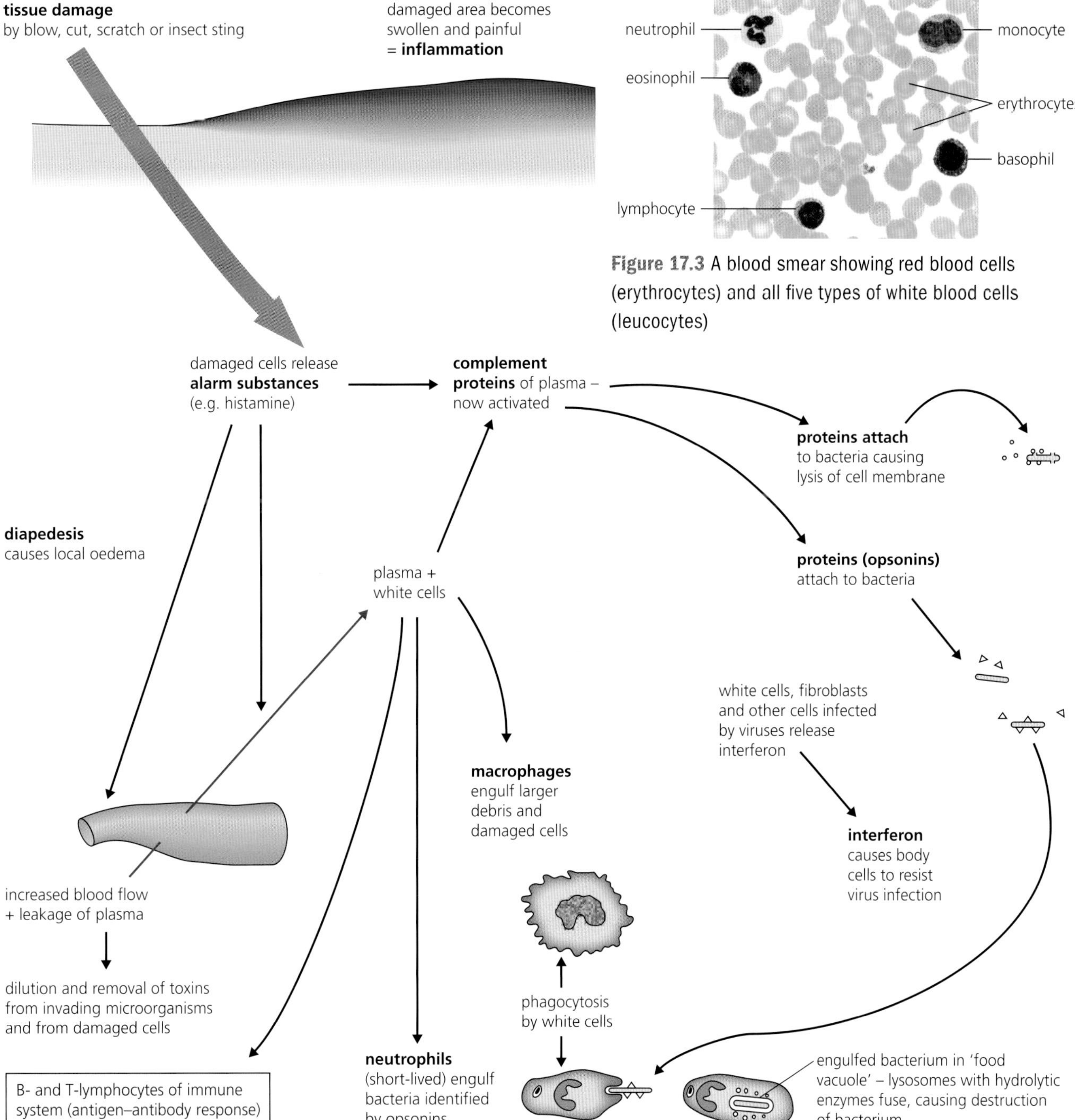

Figure 17.3 A blood smear showing red blood cells (erythrocytes) and all five types of white blood cells (leucocytes)

Figure 17.2 The processes involved in the non-specific inflammatory response to infection

The increased blood flow also results in more **leucocytes** being brought to the infected area. Figure 17.3 shows a blood smear containing red blood cells (erythrocytes) and different types of white blood cell (leucocytes). Macrophages and neutrophils are phagocytic leucocytes. Figure 17.4 shows how one of these phagocytes engulfs and destroys a foreign cell. In doing so, it must be able to distinguish foreign cells from

> **Key term**
>
> **Leucocytes** The generic term for all types of white blood cell.

the body's own cells. Phagocytes are aided in this by a group of proteins, called **complement proteins**. These have several effects including:

- attracting more phagocytes to the site of infection
- binding to, and forming pores in, the surface membranes of foreign cells, leading to the lysis of these cells
- binding to surface membranes of foreign cells, thus aiding the attachment of the surface membrane of a phagocyte to a foreign cell. These proteins are called **opsinins** and the process they invoke is opsonisation.

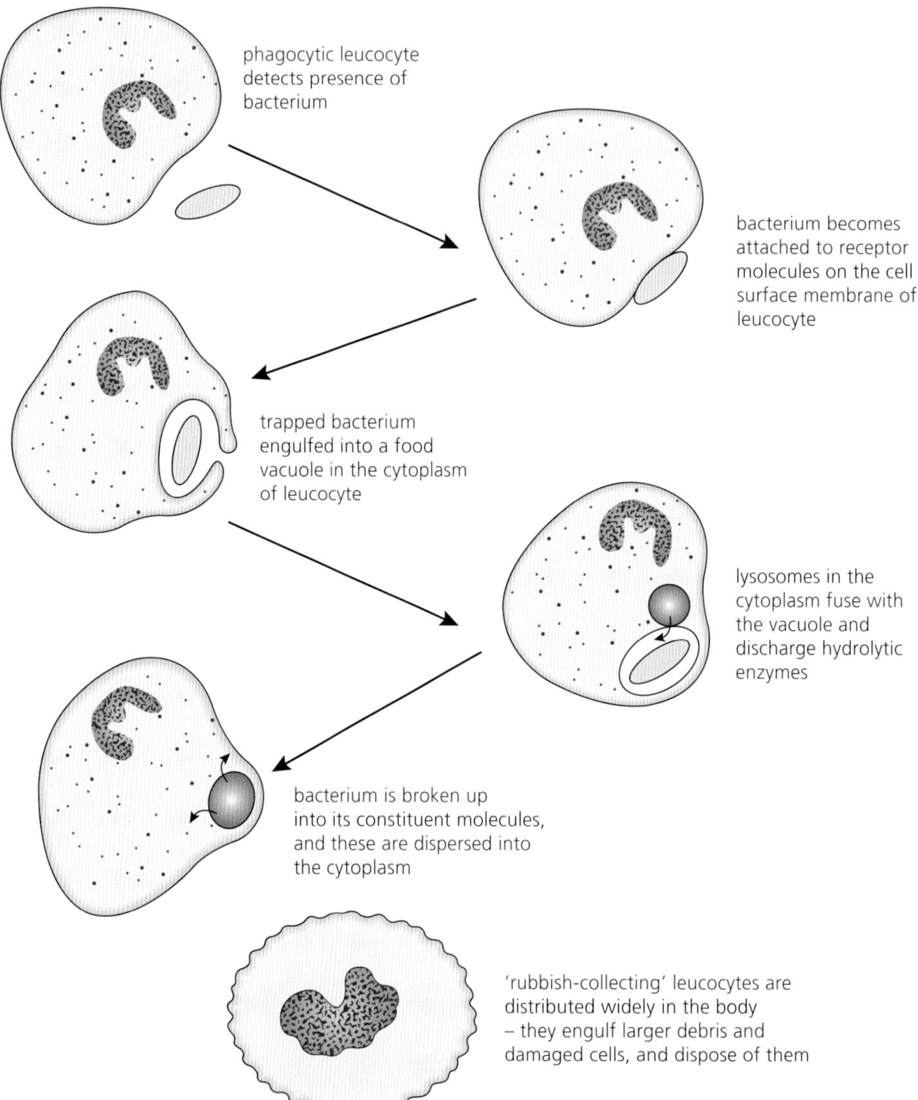
phagocytic leucocyte detects presence of bacterium
bacterium becomes attached to receptor molecules on the cell surface membrane of leucocyte
trapped bacterium engulfed into a food vacuole in the cytoplasm of leucocyte
lysosomes in the cytoplasm fuse with the vacuole and discharge hydrolytic enzymes
bacterium is broken up into its constituent molecules, and these are dispersed into the cytoplasm
'rubbish-collecting' leucocytes are distributed widely in the body – they engulf larger debris and damaged cells, and dispose of them

Figure 17.4 Phagocytosis of a bacterium

Key term

Cytokines A group of small proteins released by one type of cell that affect the behaviour of other cells.

A group of cytokines, called **interferons**, are released by cells infected by viruses. These interferons bind to neighbouring, healthy cells and trigger synthesis of antiviral proteins. As a result, viral replication is slowed or halted.

As previously stated, all the above responses to infection are referred to as non-specific responses because they help to destroy any invading pathogen. In contrast, the immune responses discussed next are triggered by, and directed towards, specific pathogens.

Test yourself

1 The frequent smoking of tobacco destroys the cilia lining the trachea and bronchi. What is the disadvantage of this?

2 Suggest why some people suffer diarrhoea after they have taken a course of antibiotics.

3 Explain each of the following effects that you might feel following a cut in your skin.

a) The affected area of your skin becomes hot.

b) The affected area of your skin swells.

c) The affected area of your skin feels painful.

4 Explain why the action of macrophages is said to be 'non-specific'.

5 State the role of interferons.

6 Neutrophils are short-lived. Suggest **one** advantage of this.

The specific immune response

You have seen above that two types of leucocyte, the macrophages and the neutrophils, react in a non-specific way to any foreign cell that enters your body. In contrast, the next group of leucocytes you will study, the **lymphocytes**, are specific. Lymphocytes make up 20 per cent of the leucocytes in your bodies.

Lymphocytes – the B cells and T cells

You have two distinct types of lymphocyte, based on the ways they function.

- B lymphocytes (**B cells**) secrete antibodies (producing the **humoral immune response**).
- T lymphocytes (**T cells**) attack infected cells (producing the **cell-mediated immune response**) and, as you shall see shortly, assist B cells.

B cells and T cells are both produced by **multipotent stem cells** in the marrow of certain bones. As Figure 17.5 (on the next page) shows, the lymphocytes then migrate to different locations where they undergo separate maturation processes.

T cells leave the bone marrow and complete their maturation in the **t**hymus gland. **B** cells do not leave, but complete their maturation within the **b**one marrow where they were formed. In both cases, during their maturation, any lymphocytes that would react against the body's own cells are selectively destroyed. Mature B cells and T cells eventually rejoin the blood system. Many are stored in lymph nodes throughout the body.

How B cells and T cells recognise 'non-self' antigens

In Chapter 9, page 192, you learnt about the fluid-mosaic model of cell surface membranes. Lodged within this structure are molecules of glycoproteins. The glycoproteins are highly variable and help to identify cells – so are called cell 'markers'. Cells in each tissue of your body have markers that are different from those in other tissues; cells from other organisms, including other people, have markers that are different from yours.

The glycoproteins that identify cells are known as the **major histocompatability complex (MHC) proteins** (in humans, these proteins are often called human leucocyte antigens – HLA). These MHC proteins are encoded by genes on the short arm of your chromosome 6. So, each individual's MHC proteins are genetically determined, and are features you inherit. For reasons that are too complex for

Key terms

Multipotent stem cells Cells that retain the ability to divide by mitosis and give rise to more than one type of daughter cell, in this case blood cells.

Major histocompatability complex (MHC) proteins Glycoproteins found on the cell surface membrane of a cell that are unique to that individual. In humans, these are often called human leucocyte associated antigens, or HLA.

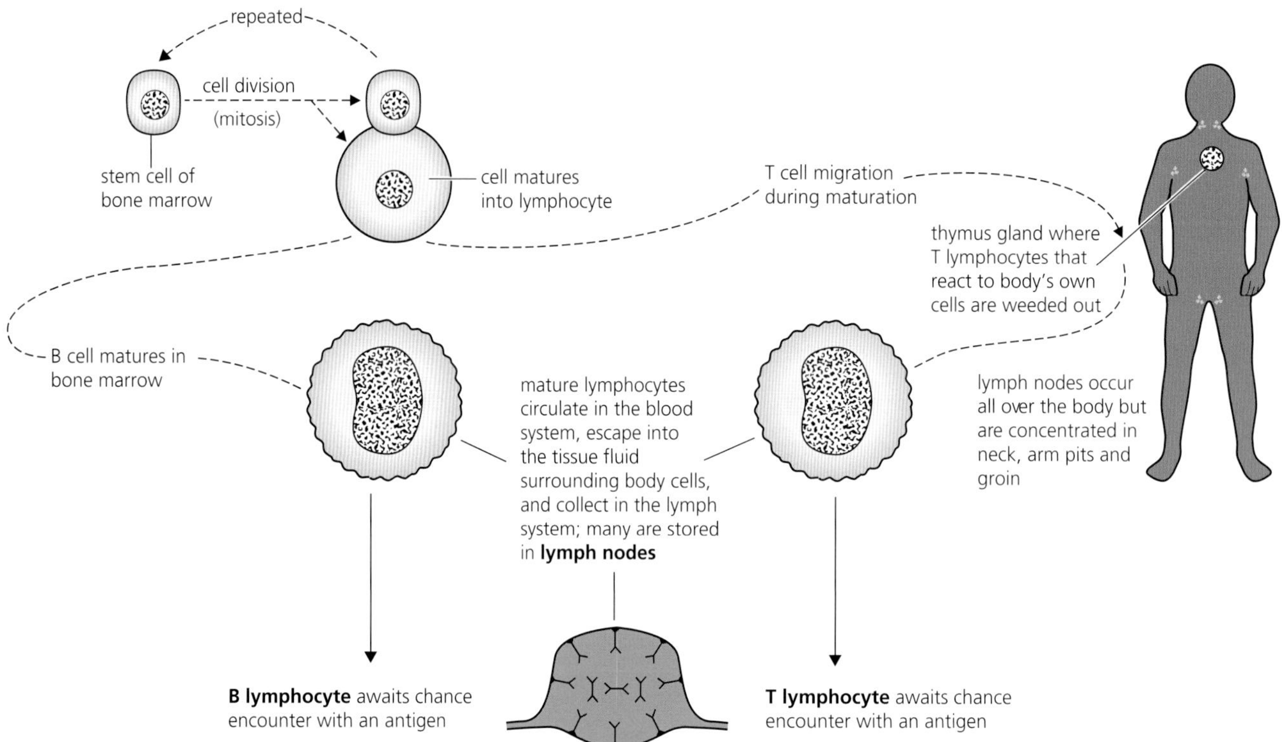

Figure 17.5 The formation of B cells and T cells

A level study, the MHC genes generate almost unbelievable variation in the proteins they encode. To give you a rough idea of this variation, there are at least eight different MHC genes and each gene has multiple alleles, with the number of alleles of a single gene ranging from 13 to 661. Unless you have an identical twin, your MHC proteins are unique.

B cells and T cells both have molecules on their cell surface membranes that are antigen receptors. These receptors are complementary to **antigens** – molecules that trigger an immune response – that might occur on the surface membranes of other cells. Each lymphocyte has only one type of antigen receptor. Consequently, each lymphocyte can 'recognise' only one type of antigen. A conservative estimate is that each of us can produce several million different antigen-receptor molecules. You might wonder how this is possible. Again, the mechanism is too complex for an A level study, but several genes are involved in encoding each antigen-receptor molecule and these genes mutate and genetically cross-over and recombine at a very fast rate.

Tip

Proteins on the surface membrane of any cell act as antigens – either self-antigens or non-self antigens. Consequently, you will often see MHC proteins described as MHC antigens.

Key term

Antigen Any molecule that triggers an immune response. Small molecules, like amino acids, sugars and triglycerides, do not trigger an immune response. Antigens are large molecules, like proteins, glycoproteins and lipoproteins. The surface membrane of cells is coated with antigens.

Tip

It is easy to confuse the complementary fit of antibody to antigen with the induced fit model of enzyme action. In an exam, take care not to refer to the 'active site of an antibody'. It is incorrect terminology and will not gain you marks.

As you will see shortly, the antigen-receptor molecules of a B cell are released as antibodies. Figure 17.6 shows the structure of the two most common antibodies. Both are a type of protein, called an **immunoglobulin** (abbreviated to Ig). You can see that the smaller of the two, called IgG, has four polypeptides linked by disulfide bridges (–S–S–) to form a Y-shape, and that two of these polypeptides are large (the heavy chains) while two are small (the light chains). You can also see that it is only two small parts of the antibody molecule that bind to a complementary antigen. The larger molecule in Figure 17.6 is called IgM. You can see that it is formed by five IgG-like molecules held together.

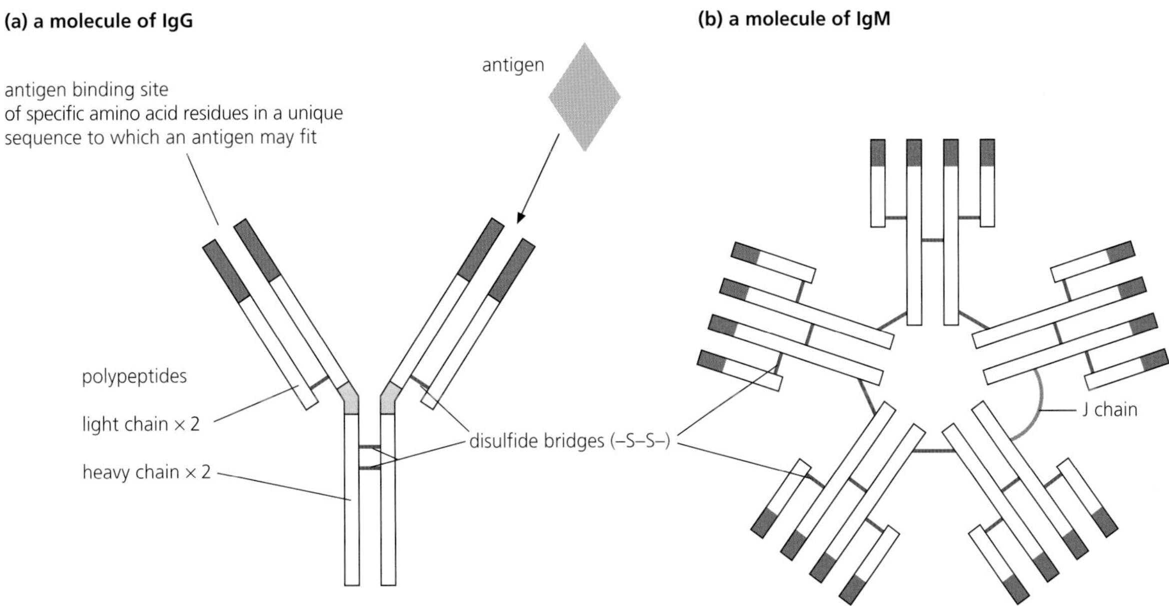

Figure 17.6 The structure of the two most common antibodies: (a) is a molecule of IgG, (b) is a molecule of IgM

The antigen-receptor molecules on the surface of T cells are chemically similar to the Y-shaped IgG immunoglobulin shown in Figure 17.6 but have only two polypeptide chains instead of four. Like those of B cells, these receptors are almost infinitely variable, but each T cell has only one type on its surface. Unlike B cells, T cells do not release their antigen-receptor molecules.

As you saw in Figure 17.5, B cells and T cells mature in different parts of the body. It is during this maturation that any randomly produced cells with antigen-receptor molecules complementary to your own MHC proteins (so-called **self-antigens**) are destroyed. Otherwise, your B cells and T cells might attack your own body cells. That said, Type I diabetes and rheumatoid arthritis are just two examples of human disorders caused by an immune reaction to the body's own cells.

Key term

Self-antigen A glycoprotein on the cell surface membrane of one of the body's own cells. The ability of this glycoprotein to cause an immune response is reduced by the body destroying any randomly produced lymphocytes with a complementary antigen-receptor.

Test yourself

7 The thymus gland is relatively much larger in young people than in adults. Suggest the advantage of a large thymus gland during childhood.

8 Explain how the names of B cells and T cells relate to their development.

9 B cells and T cells are produced by multipotent stem cells. What does 'multipotent' mean?

10 One effect of an IgM antibody is to clump pathogens together. This makes phagocytosis by macrophages easier. Suggest how the structure of IgM molecules enables them to clump pathogens together.

The humoral immune response

The humoral immune response involves the release of antibodies by B cells. It depends, however, on an interaction between B cells, T cells and macrophages. Figure 17.8 demonstrates this interaction. Follow the numbered stages in this diagram as you read the associated steps in the account of the humoral immune response below.

1 A pathogen enters the body; its surface has non-self antigens on it. Completely at random, this pathogen collides with a B cell that has an antigen receptor on its surface membrane that is complementary to a non-self antigen on the pathogen. The antigen binds to the antigen-receptor molecule on the B cell. At the same time, other cells of the pathogen are attacked by non-specific macrophages that engulf cells of the pathogen.

2 The B cell engulfs the antigen and digests it. The B cell then displays fragments of the antigen on its cell surface membrane, bound to its own MHC proteins.

3 Meanwhile, the macrophage (step 1) also digests the antigen-carrying pathogen it has engulfed. It too displays fragments of the antigen bound to the MHC proteins on its cell surface membrane. This is called antigen presentation by a macrophage.

> **Key term**
>
> **Antigen-presenting macrophage** A type of white blood cell, a macrophage, that has engulfed and digested a pathogen and is displaying antigens from the pathogen on its own cell surface membrane.

4 The **antigen-presenting macrophage** comes into contact with a T cell that has an antigen-receptor protein complementary to one of the pathogen's antigens now displayed on the macrophage. The two briefly bind. This activates the T cell, which is now called an **activated T helper cell**.

5 An activated T helper cells now binds to a B cell displaying the same antigen on its cell surface membrane (step 2 above). This, in turn, activates the B cell.

6 Stimulated by the secretion of cytokines from the activated T helper cell, the activated B cell immediately divides very repeatedly by mitosis, forming a clone of cells called **plasma cells**. The transmission electron micrograph in Figure 17.9 shows the plasma cell is packed with rough endoplasmic reticulum. It is here that the antibody is mass-produced, and is then exported from the plasma cell by exocytosis. The antibodies are normally produced in such numbers that the antigen is overcome.

The production of an activated B cell, its rapid cell division to produce a clone of plasma cells, and the resulting production of antibodies that react with the antigen, is called **clonal selection**. Sometimes several different antibodies react with one antigen – this is polyclonal selection.

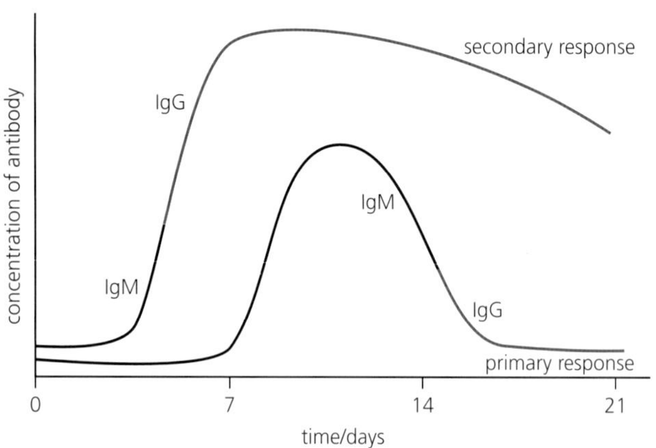

Figure 17.7 Profile of antibody production during infection (primary response) and re-infection (secondary response)

7 After these antibodies have destroyed the foreign matter and the threat of disease that it introduced, the antibodies disappear from the blood and tissue fluid, along with the bulk of the specific B cells and T cells responsible for their formation. However, a few of these specifically activated B cells and T cells are retained in the body as **memory cells**. In contrast to plasma cells and activated T cells, these memory cells are long-lived. In the event of a re-infection of the body by pathogens carrying the same antigen, these memory cells make possible the early and effective response shown in Figure 17.7. This is the basis of natural immunity.

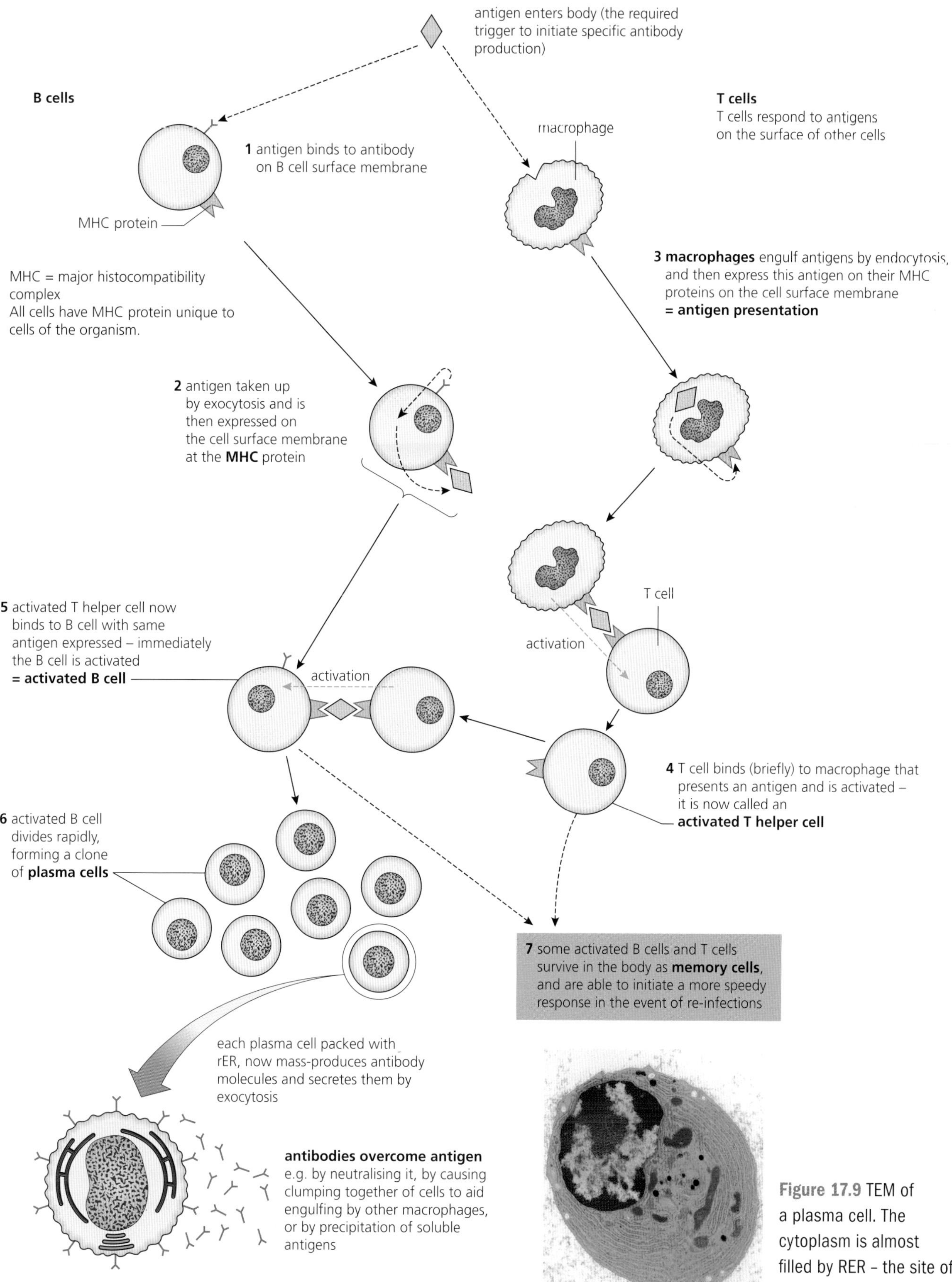

antigen enters body (the required trigger to initiate specific antibody production)
B cells
T cells
T cells respond to antigens on the surface of other cells
macrophage
1 antigen binds to antibody on B cell surface membrane
MHC protein
MHC = major histocompatibility complex
All cells have MHC protein unique to cells of the organism.
3 macrophages engulf antigens by endocytosis, and then express this antigen on their MHC proteins on the cell surface membrane
= antigen presentation
2 antigen taken up by exocytosis and is then expressed on the cell surface membrane at the MHC protein
T cell
activation
5 activated T helper cell now binds to B cell with same antigen expressed – immediately the B cell is activated
= activated B cell
activation
4 T cell binds (briefly) to macrophage that presents an antigen and is activated – it is now called an
activated T helper cell
6 activated B cell divides rapidly, forming a clone of plasma cells
7 some activated B cells and T cells survive in the body as memory cells, and are able to initiate a more speedy response in the event of re-infections
each plasma cell packed with rER, now mass-produces antibody molecules and secretes them by exocytosis
antibodies overcome antigen
e.g. by neutralising it, by causing clumping together of cells to aid engulfing by other macrophages, or by precipitation of soluble antigens

Figure 17.8 The steps involved in antibody release

Figure 17.9 TEM of a plasma cell. The cytoplasm is almost filled by RER – the site of antibody production

The cell-mediated immune response

The cell-mediated immune response is brought about by the activity of T cells. As you saw in Figure 17.8, T cells will bind to an antigen-presenting cell that has antigens from a pathogen on its surface. In doing so, an activated T helper cell is formed that releases cytokines. The release of cytokines stimulates the activated T cell to divide repeatedly to form a clone. Within this clone are three types of T cell:

- T killer cells – destroy body cells infected by viruses.
- T helper cells – release cytokines that stimulate production of B cells.
- Memory cells – remain in the body and bring about the secondary response.

Figure 17.10 provides an overview of the complex roles of B cells and T cells in the immune system.

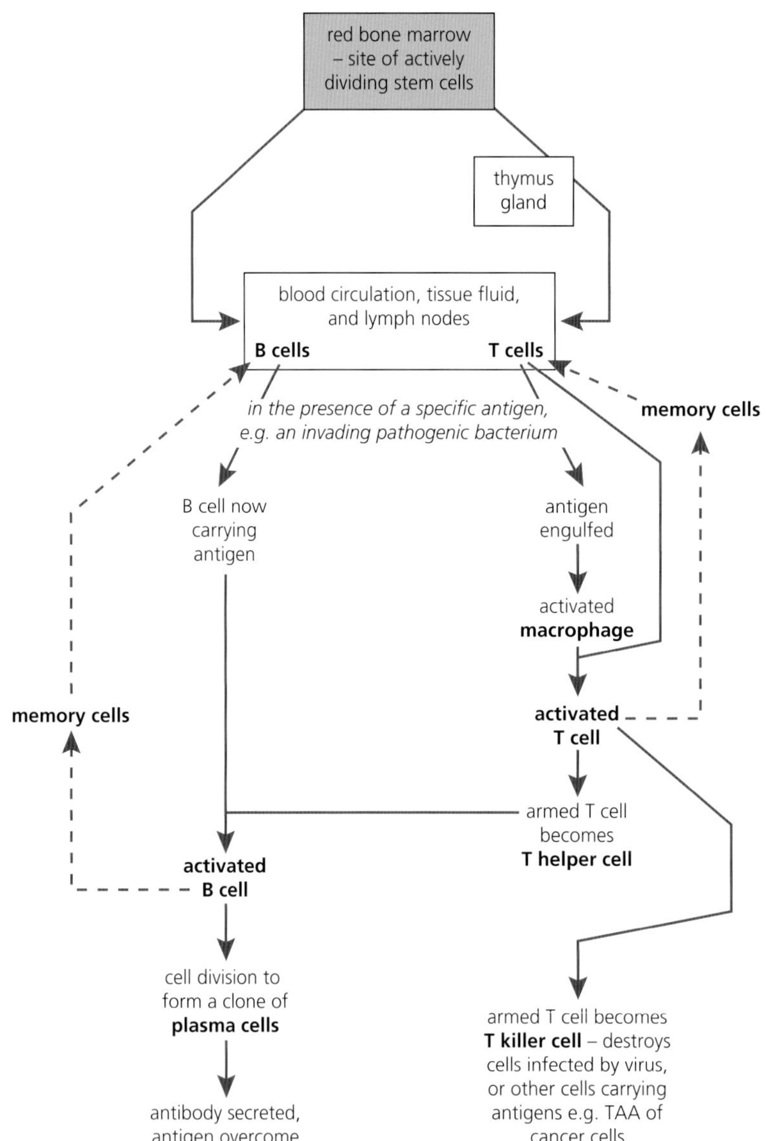

Figure 17.10 A summary of the roles of B cells and T cells in the specific immune response

Test yourself

11 State the importance of antigen-presenting cells in the specific immune response.

12 Give **two** ways in which the antigen-receptor molecules of a T cell differ from those of a B cell.

13 Name **two** processes that enable us to produce millions of different cell-surface antigen-receptor proteins.

14 How does the role of a T helper cell differ from that of a T killer cell?

15 Use Figure 17.8 to suggest why the secondary response is much faster than the primary response to infection.

Activity

Testing the clonal selection hypothesis

Scientists propose explanations for the observations they make. These explanations are referred to as **hypotheses**. In order to test the validity of a hypothesis, scientists use it to make predictions and then devise experiments to test these predictions. If their results are always consistent with their predictions, they become confident in the validity of their hypothesis.

The **clonal selection hypothesis** proposes an explanation for the way that you produce antibodies against non-self antigens. You can summarise this hypothesis in the following way:

- Your immune system randomly produces millions of different types of B and T cells. Each type has a unique protein receptor on its surface membrane. When, and only when, one of these cells binds with a complementary antigen, it is stimulated to produce large numbers of cells that are identical to itself and, consequently, to each other. A group of identical cells is called a **clone**. Thus, in response to the presence of a particular antigen, a B or T cell is selected and it forms a clone. Within the clone, each cell has the identical protein receptor on its surface.

Scientists tested this hypothesis by injecting two rats, **R** and **S**, with antigens from two different strains of pneumococcal bacteria. They injected each rat twice, with the second injection made 28 days after the first.

1 Why do you think the scientists injected each rat twice, with a gap of 28 days between injections?
2 Which type of immune cell do you think the scientists were attempting to stimulate?

The scientists injected rat **R** with antigens from strain **X** of the pneumococcal bacterium (type **X** antigens) and injected rat **S** with antigens from strain **Y** of the pneumococcal bacterium (type **Y** antigens).

3 What do you think the scientists were predicting would happen as a result of these injections?

The scientists now needed a way to find out which cells had been stimulated to produce a clone. The method they chose was rather neat. They coated inert beads with the type **X** antigens and put the beads into two glass columns (labelled 1 and 3 in Figure 17.11 on the next page). They then did the same with type **Y** antigens and put these beads into another two glass columns (labelled 2 and 4 in Figure 17.11). They reasoned that if they washed samples of lymphocytes through these columns, those lymphocytes that had the appropriate complementary protein receptors would bind to the antigens on the inert beads. As a result, they would stay in the glass column and not emerge at the bottom.

4 Why was it important that the beads they used were inert?

One week after the second injection, the scientists removed a sample of blood from each of the two rats and separated the lymphocytes from the rest of the blood. They put half of each sample into a column of inert beads coated with type **X** antigen and half into a column of inert beads coated with type **Y** antigen. They then washed the samples through the columns and collected any lymphocytes that passed through the column.

5 What type of fluid would they have used to wash the lymphocytes through the columns?

Finally, the scientists tested the lymphocytes that had passed through each column to see whether they could make antibodies against either of the two antigens used in the experiment. Figure 17.11 summarises the method they used and their results.

Now look at their results in Figure 17.11 and see if you can interpret them. Start with the results from column 1. First you need to make sure you have understood what they show by describing them.

6 How would you describe the results from column 1?
7 Can you explain both parts of that description?
8 Explain why cells emerging from column 2 give large quantities of anti-X antibody but no anti-Y antibody.

You should be able to use similar arguments to explain the results from columns 3 and 4. You can then **evaluate** the experiment. This means you ask whether the experiment was a valid test of the clonal selection hypothesis. If the results had not been consistent with this prediction, they would have cast serious doubt on the hypothesis. By using two rats injected with different antigens of the same bacterium, and by using columns with only type X antigen or only type Y antigen, the scientists had built a **control** into their experiment. Without further details, you must assume that the scientists made sure that the conditions under which the rats were reared were kept constant. You could criticise the scientists for using only two rats, since this was a small sample size. In fact, they used large groups of rats. This account has been simplified to help you understand what was done. Therefore, you can conclude that the experiment was a valid test of the clonal selection hypothesis.

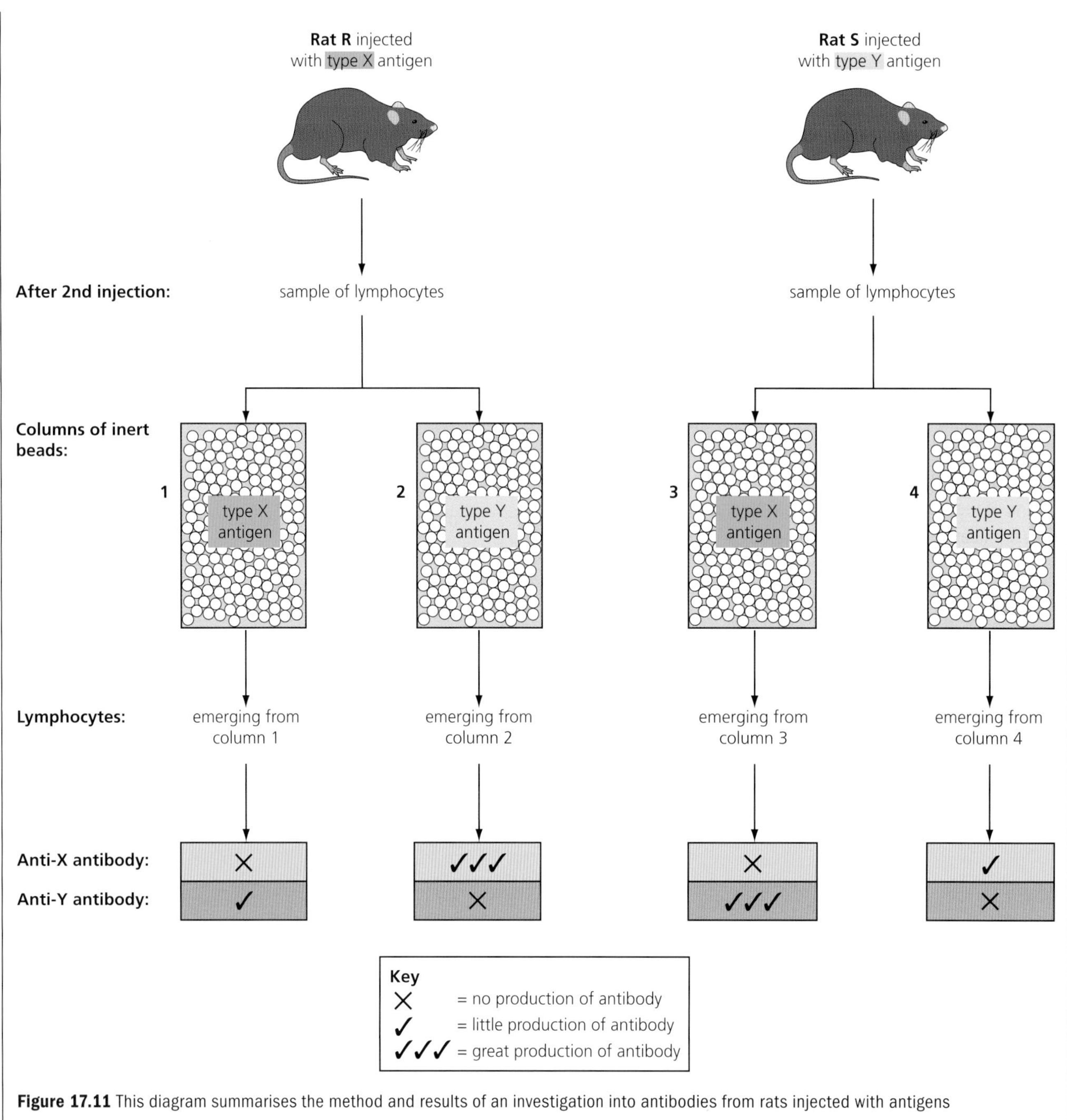

Figure 17.11 This diagram summarises the method and results of an investigation into antibodies from rats injected with antigens

Types of immunity and vaccination

As you have seen, your immune system protects you from the worst effects of many of the pathogens that might infect you. This immunity might be acquired actively or passively and by natural or artificial means. Table 17.2 explains the difference.

Table 17.2 Types of immunity displayed by humans

	Artificial immunity	Natural immunity	Longevity of immunity
Active immunity (antibodies made by subject)	Antibodies made following administration of a vaccine B cells, T cells and memory cells are made	Production of antibodies following infection by, and recovery from, a disease B cells, T cells and memory cells are made	Long-lasting since memory cells are maintained throughout life
Passive immunity (antibodies not made by subject but made by another organism)	Antibodies administered by injection (immunisation)	Mother's antibodies cross placenta to fetus or ingested by baby in mother's breast milk (especially in the colostrum, the first-formed milk)	Fades with time, since the recipient has not made memory cells and the antibodies received are themselves treated as non-self antigens and destroyed by recipient's active immunity

Vaccination

Vaccination is the deliberate administration of antigenic material to stimulate the recipient to develop active immunity against a pathogen. The active agent of the vaccine can be:

- the intact pathogen that has been inactivated (to stop it being able to cause infection) or attenuated (to reduce its ability to cause infection)
- purified components of the pathogen that have been found to have antigenic properties but do not cause disease
- toxoids – modified toxins – to develop active immunity against toxin-based diseases
- genetically engineered DNA – which can be designed to stimulate particular target cells of the immune system.

Vaccines are administered either by injection or by mouth. They cause the recipient's immune system to make antibodies against the pathogen without suffering an infection, and then to retain the appropriate memory cells. Active artificial immunity is established in this way. In terms of antibody production, the response caused by any later exposure to the antigen is exactly the same as if the immunity had been developed after the body overcame an earlier infection.

Vaccination has been so successful that some formerly common and dangerous diseases have become very uncommon occurrences in many human communities. For example, vaccination has led to the worldwide eradication of smallpox and to a great reduction in the incidence of measles, polio and tetanus. You can find the recommended schedule of vaccinations for children brought up in the UK on www.doh.gov.uk.

Herd immunity

Interestingly, it is not essential for everyone in a population to be immunised against a contagious disease in order to control that disease. The **herd immunity** theory proposes that the risk of someone who is susceptible to a contagious disease becoming infected gets less, the greater the proportion of people in that community who are

> **Key term**
>
> **Herd immunity**
> Provided a large enough proportion of a population are immune to a particular contagious disease, the likelihood of the causative pathogen being transmitted to a member of the population who is not immune is negligible.

immune. To take an extreme example, if all but one person in the UK is immune to a contagious disease, the chance of the one susceptible person being exposed to the pathogen within the UK is almost nil.

You might be wondering what proportion of a population could avoid vaccination but still be protected by the majority who have been vaccinated. This depends on the nature of the disease-causing organism and its method of spread. Table 17.3 provides information about a number of contagious diseases with which you might be familiar.

Table 17.3 The threshold percentage of the population needed to achieve herd immunity

Disease	Transmission route	Percentage threshold to achieve herd immunity
Diphtheria	Via saliva	85
Measles	Airborne	83 to 95
Mumps	Droplet	75 to 86
Rubella	Droplet	83 to 85
Smallpox	Social contact	83 to 85

Looking at Table 17.3, you might think it will be safe for you to avoid immunisation or vaccination. Remember, though, you are dealing with a mathematical model concerned with reducing the likelihood of infection. The likelihood of being knocked down by an automobile is low, but you still look both ways before crossing a road. It is best to restrict failure to immunise or vaccinate to those who might be harmed by it, such as people with weakened, or compromised, immune systems.

Given the success of vaccination programmes in eradicating contagious diseases, the public has sometimes become casual about the threat such diseases still pose. During your GCSE science course, you probably studied the effects of a newspaper article suggesting a link between a vaccine to protect against measles, mumps and rubella (the combined MMR vaccine) and autism. As a result of this article, so many parents declined the invitation to have their children vaccinated with the MMR vaccine that the proportion of vaccinated children fell below the herd immunity threshold in some communities. One such community was the area around Swansea, a city in South Wales. Here, it is believed the percentage of vaccinated children fell to almost 80 per cent. The result was the 2013 measles epidemic amongst children in the Swansea area. You might also recall that doctor who proposed this link to autism was subsequently discredited and left the UK.

Test yourself

16 Anti-venom, injected into someone who has been bitten by a snake, does not confer long-lasting protection against further bites by the same species of snake. Suggest why.

17 Suggest **one** factor that determines whether a vaccine is administered by injection or by mouth.

18 It is said that the only smallpox viruses left in the world are in sealed cultures in a few laboratories. Suggest why these laboratories keep samples of this virus.

19 Does vaccination lead to long-term protection against measles? Explain your answer.

20 Define the term 'herd immunity'.

Chapter summary

Non-specific inflammatory response

- Macrophages and neutrophils are phagocytic leucocytes (white blood cells) that are effective in the non-specific inflammatory response. They engulf any foreign cells and destroy them using lysozymes.
- The activation of blood-borne complement proteins attracts macrophages and neutrophils to the sites of infection.
- Some types of activated complement proteins also bind to foreign cells, aiding the phagocytic action of macrophages and neutrophils.

Lymphocytes and antigen-presenting cells

- Lymphocytes are a type of white blood cell produced by multipotent stem cells within bone marrow.
- B lymphocytes, or B cells, mature within the bone marrow in which they were formed.
- T lymphocytes, or T cells, migrate from the bone marrow to the thymus gland where they mature.
- Each B cell and T cell has receptor molecules on its cell surface membrane that are complementary to one specific foreign antigen.
- An antigen-presenting cell (APC) is a cell that has engulfed a pathogen and displays on its surface some of the antigens of the pathogen it has engulfed.

The cell-mediated immune response

- The cell-mediated immune response is brought about by T cells.
- A T cell with complementary surface receptors will bind to the antigens displayed by an antigen-presenting cell. This activates the T cell.
- The activated T cell divides to produce:
  - T killer cells that destroy any pathogen displaying the specific antigen
  - T helper cells that release cytokines that stimulate the production of B cells
  - T memory cells that remain in the blood and bring about a secondary response.

The humoral immune response

- This type of response results when a clone of B cells releases large numbers of an antibody that is complementary to a single antigen.
- A B cell that has engulfed an antigen processes it and displays it on its cell surface.
- A T helper cell with a complementary surface receptor binds to the antigen on the B cell. This activates the T helper cell.
- The activated T helper cell secretes cytokines that stimulate the B cell to proliferate, producing a clone (clonal selection) containing:
  - plasma cells that release one specific type of antibody
  - memory cells that remain in the blood and bring about a secondary response.

Passive and active immunity

- In passive immunity, antibodies are injected into recipients, or cross the placenta from mother to baby. Passive immunity is only temporary.
- In active immunity people make their own antibodies.
- Natural active immunity follows infection by a pathogen.
- Artificial active immunity follows vaccination – injection of harmless pathogens or parts of pathogens – and which triggers the production of T cells, B cells and memory cells.
- Vaccination can help prevent the spread of infectious diseases.
- To be effective, a threshold percentage of the population must be vaccinated, giving so-called herd immunity.
- If a sufficiently large proportion of a population reject vaccination, herd immunity will not be achieved and spread of the disease to susceptible people will result.

Practice questions

1 Antibodies are released by:

A lymphocytes **C** neutrophils

B macrophages **D** plasma cells *(1)*

2 As an emergency treatment, a person who is showing symptoms of rabies can be injected with a rabies immunoglobulin. This is an example of:

A active, artificial immunity **C** passive, artificial immunity

B active, natural immunity **D** passive, natural immunity *(1)*

3 MHC proteins are:

A antibodies **C** antigen receptors

B antigens **D** toxoids *(1)*

4 IgG and IgM are two types of antibody produced by humans.

a) IgG is found in the bloodstream and in body tissues. IgM is found only in the bloodstream. Suggest a reason for this difference in distribution. *(3)*

★**b)** Compare the primary and secondary responses to infection. *(4)*

5 The human immunodeficiency virus (HIV) is a retrovirus that causes autoimmune deficiency syndrome (AIDS). It infects T helper cells that have $CD4^+$ proteins on their cell surface membranes.

a) What is meant by the term 'retrovirus'? *(1)*

b) Suggest why HIV infects only T helper cells that have a $CD4^+$ protein on their cell surface membranes. *(2)*

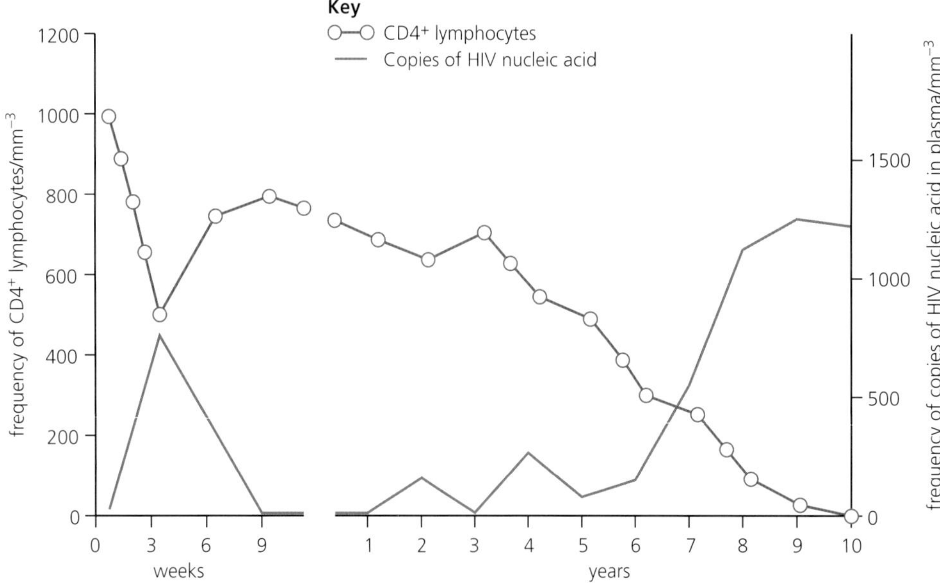

c) The graph shows the frequency of T helper cells with $CD4^+$ proteins and of copies of HIV nucleic acid in the plasma of someone infected with HIV but who receives **no** medical treatment.

i) Suggest an explanation for the data between 9 weeks and 3 years in the graph. Use evidence from the graph to justify your explanation. *(3)*

ii) The person represented in the graph probably died in year 10. Explain why death would occur. *(4)*

6 Dogwhelks are snails that are common on rocky shores around the UK. Their main diet comprises barnacles and mussels.

Dogwhelks show variation in their shell colour. A geneticist investigated a theory that dogwhelks developed coloured shells only if they ate mussels.

A dogwhelk feeds by rasping small particles from its prey, using a file-like tongue. This made it difficult for the geneticist to identify the contents of the guts of dogwhelks by examining them with a light microscope.

Instead he used a technique called the enzyme-linked immunoabsorbent assay (ELISA). The flow chart summarises this technique.

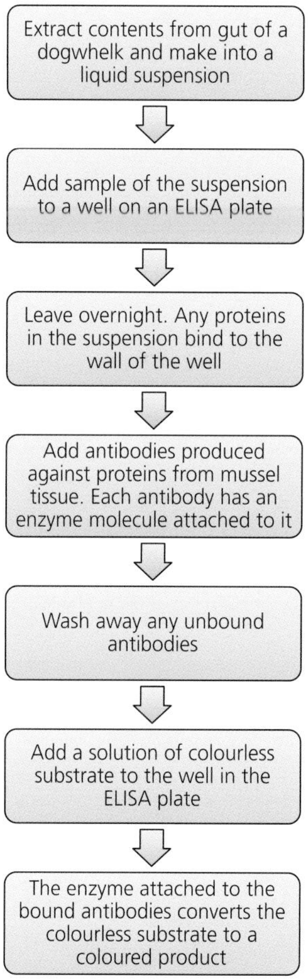

Extract contents from gut of a dogwhelk and make into a liquid suspension
↓
Add sample of the suspension to a well on an ELISA plate
↓
Leave overnight. Any proteins in the suspension bind to the wall of the well
↓
Add antibodies produced against proteins from mussel tissue. Each antibody has an enzyme molecule attached to it
↓
Wash away any unbound antibodies
↓
Add a solution of colourless substrate to the well in the ELISA plate
↓
The enzyme attached to the bound antibodies converts the colourless substrate to a coloured product

a) The antibody against mussel proteins was produced from samples of blood taken from rabbits that had been injected with a suspension of mussel tissue. The geneticist was not allowed to carry out this part of the experimental procedure because he did not hold a UK Home Office licence. Suggest why the UK Home Office has a licensing system. *(1)*

b) The rabbits were injected twice with a 21-day gap between injections. Suggest an explanation for this procedure. *(2)*

c) Explain why the antibodies against proteins from mussels would bind only to these proteins. *(1)*

d) Explain why the unbound antibody was washed away (step 5). *(2)*

e) Describe how the geneticist could tell if a dogwhelk had **not** eaten mussels. *(1)*

f) Suggest an appropriate null hypothesis for the geneticist's investigation. *(1)*

g) How could the geneticist use the ELISA technique to test his null hypothesis? Justify the choice of any statistical test you include in your method. *(4)*

Stretch and challenge

7 Against which diseases are vaccines currently in use, worldwide? Is there a pattern in the distribution of these diseases?

8 Monoclonal antibodies are widely used in biological and medical research.

a) How are monoclonal antibodies made?

b) Outline how they are used.

18 Cell control

Prior knowledge

In this chapter you will need to recall that:

- ➜ after their formation in a multicellular organism, most new cells differentiate, becoming specialised to carry out a particular function. In doing so, the majority lose the ability to divide by mitosis
- ➜ the genetic code comprises 64 different sequences of three nucleotide bases (base triplets), each of which encodes a specific amino acid
- ➜ the genetic material of living organisms consists of one or more molecules of DNA
- ➜ the sequence of bases in an organism's DNA determines the sequence of amino acids in the polypeptides and proteins that the organism is capable of producing
- ➜ the sequence of bases that encodes a polypeptide is called a gene
- ➜ polypeptides are made by ribosomes that assemble amino acids in a sequence that is prescribed by the base sequence of a gene
- ➜ protein synthesis involves transcription and translation
- ➜ whereas all the DNA of prokaryotes encodes polypeptides, much of the DNA of eukaryotes does not encode polypeptides.

Test yourself on prior knowledge

1. State the name given to a group of specialised cells that are derived from a common ancestor and perform the same function.
2. The genetic code is described as universal and degenerate. Explain what this means.
3. Are all genes the same length? Explain your answer.
4. Describe the difference between a polypeptide and a protein.
5. Outline the processes of transcription and translation during polypeptide production.
6. Give **two** locations in a chromosome of DNA that do not code for the amino acid sequence of polypeptides.

Key term

Genome The genetic material of an organism. For a prokaryote, this includes all of its genes; for a eukaryote it includes all of its genes plus the base sequences of DNA that do not encode polypeptides.

Introduction

You saw in Chapter 6 that the zygote of a multicellular animal or plant is a single diploid cell. It contains the organism's **genome** – the complete set of chromosomes that are characteristic of that species – and gives rise to all the somatic cells of that animal or plant. Since the zygote divides by mitosis, you know that all the somatic cells derived from it are clones of the zygote, that is they contain copies of the same genome.

Figure 18.1 Two stages in the life cycle of a dragonfly

Look at Figure 18.1. Unless you are already familiar with these animals, you probably think they are different species. The animal in the photo on the left lives in freshwater, has no wings and, as you can see, is a carnivore (it is eating a fish). The animal in the photo on the right does not live in water, has wings and does not feed on other animals. In fact, they are the same species. The animal on the left is a young stage dragonfly (a larva) and the animal on the right is the adult dragonfly. They look and behave completely differently yet, within one life cycle, have exactly the same genome. A rather less dramatic example of how a single genome can produce different results is shown by the deadly nightshade in Figure 18.2. You can see some of the organs this plant possesses – the stem, leaves, flower and fruit. Although these organs look very different, the cells within them have the same genome.

Figure 18.2 Part of a deadly nightshade plant (*Atropa belladonna*)

These examples present the same puzzle. If their cells contain copies of the same genome, how can animals and plants produce tissues and organs that are structurally and functionally so different? It is this puzzle that this chapter will seek to explain.

Factors affecting gene expression

There are many ways in which the transcription or translation of genes can be regulated in eukaryotes. Here we will examine five:

- DNA regulatory sequences and transcription factors
- post-transcriptional modification of mRNA
- destruction of mRNA
- DNA methylation
- histone acetylation.

(destruction of mRNA, DNA methylation, histone acetylation: epigenetic modifications)

Three of these methods are said to be epigenetic modifications. This means that they are inherited by daughter cells but, in contrast with chromosome and gene mutations, are not the result of changes to the DNA. You will see later how these epigenetic modifications are important in the process of cell differentiation.

> **Key term**
>
> **Epigenetic modification** Stable, long-term changes in the ability of a cell to transcribe its genes. Though these changes are inherited, they are not caused by changes to the base sequence of the DNA.

Regulatory sequences and transcription factors

Biologists used to think that all the DNA in the nucleus of a eukaryotic cell formed genes that encoded polypeptides. One of the many surprises brought about by genome sequencing (considered in Chapter 19) was the realisation that this is not so. Biologists now believe that only about 2 per cent of the DNA in the nuclei of human cells forms genes. Because the function of the other 98 per cent – the non-coding DNA – was not known, it used to be called 'junk DNA'. In fact, nothing could be further from the truth and we now know that this non-coding DNA plays an important role in regulating which of our genes are 'switched on' or 'switched off'.

Key terms

Regulatory sequence A sequence of DNA nucleotides that controls whether its target gene is transcribed or not.

Transcription factor A protein, or assembly of several proteins, that regulate the production of mRNA. A specific transcription factor binds to a promoter region upstream of its target gene and either promotes or inhibits the binding of RNA polymerase to the target gene.

Every gene is associated with short base sequences of non-coding DNA that regulate whether the gene is transcribed ('switched on') or not. There are two types of these **regulatory sequences** that stimulate the transcription of genes:

- **Promoters** – short base sequences that lie closed to their target genes. They initiate transcription by enabling RNA polymerase to bind to the gene they regulate.
- **Enhancers** – short base sequences that lie some distance from their target genes. They stimulate promoters causing an increase in the rate of transcription of the genes they regulate.

Figure 18.3 represents one of these regulatory sequences and its **target gene**, that is, the gene it regulates. The sequence represented in Figure 18.3 is a **promoter**. Notice that it is close to, and 'upstream' of, its target gene.

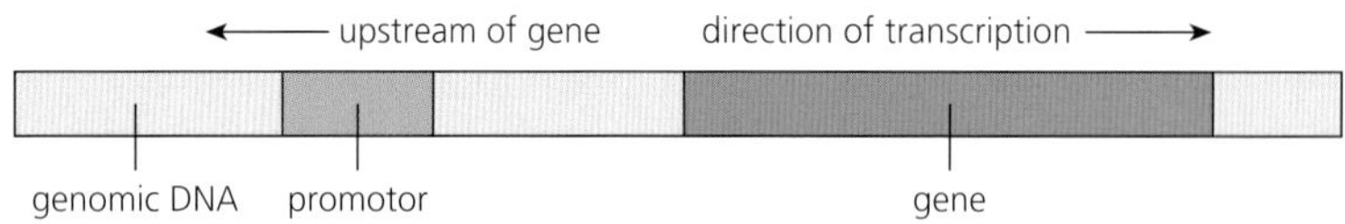

Figure 18.3 In eukaryotes, every gene is controlled by promoters, one or more non-coding sequences of bases. The promoter shown here is close to, and 'upstream' of, its target gene

As you know from Chapter 3, in order for a gene to be transcribed, the enzyme RNA polymerase must be able to attach to it. If this enzyme cannot, the gene will not be transcribed, in other words no mRNA will be produced from it and so none of the polypeptide the gene encodes will be produced. In eukaryotes, RNA polymerase cannot initiate transcription itself. Attachment of RNA polymerase to a gene is regulated by the gene's promoter. Figure 18.4 shows how. One or more, specific proteins, called **transcription factors**, bind to the promoter. Once they have done so, an RNA polymerase binds to the transcription factor complex and becomes activated to begin the synthesis of mRNA from a unique point on the target gene.

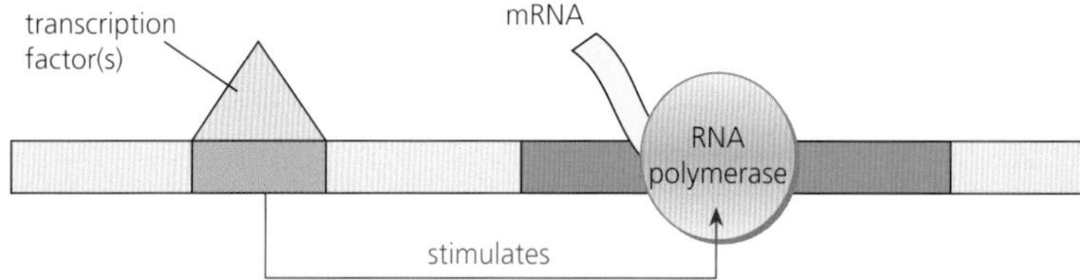

Figure 18.4 How transcription is initiated in a eukaryotic cell. One or more transcription factors bind with a promoter. By binding with the transcription factor complex, a molecule of RNA polymerase is activated and can begin to transcribe the promoter's target gene, producing mRNA

Test yourself

1. Explain why the term 'genome' is applied differently to a bacterial cell and a plant cell.
2. What is meant by the term 'epigenetic'?
3. Explain why the term 'junk DNA' is now thought to be inappropriate.
4. Give the relationship between the direction of transcription and 'upstream'.
5. Describe the role of a promoter in DNA transcription.

Activity

Glucocorticoids as transcription factors

Glucocorticoids are a class of steroid hormones. Steroids are all derived from cholesterol. Figure 18.5 shows how molecules of a glucocorticoid enter human cells.

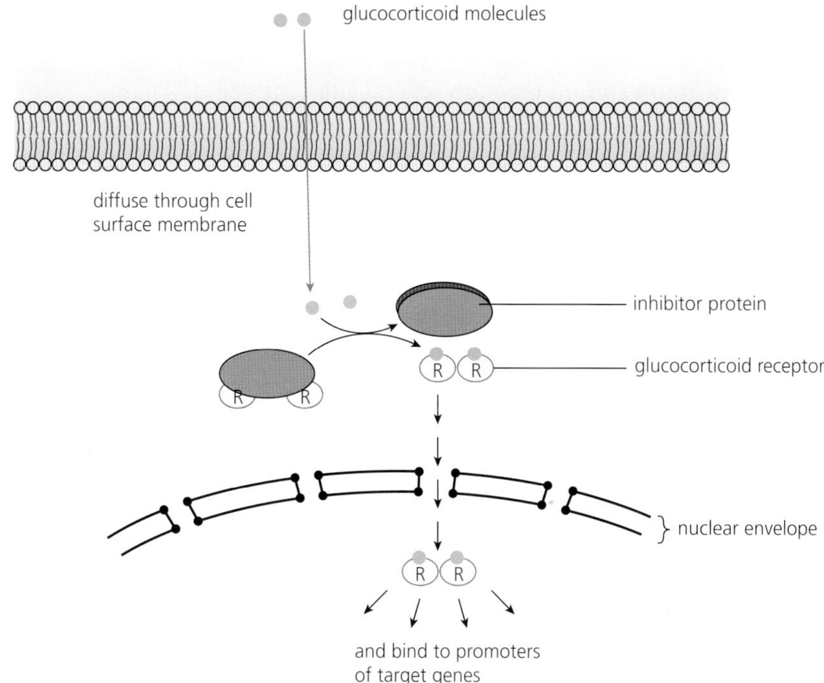

Figure 18.5 The action of glucocorticoids in human cells

1 Explain why molecules of glucocorticoids can diffuse through the surface membranes of human cells.
2 Write a word equation to represent the reaction that forms a glucocorticoid–receptor complex in the cytoplasm.
3 Suggest one advantage of the glucocorticoid receptors normally being bound in the cytoplasm to protein inhibitor molecules.
4 How do molecules of the glucocorticoid–receptor complex get into the nucleus?
5 Once inside the nucleus, the glucocorticoid–receptor complexes activate the expression of their target genes. Outline how they will do this.
6 One effect of glucocorticoids is to up-regulate the expression of genes encoding anti-inflammatory proteins. Use your knowledge from previous chapters to suggest the function of anti-inflammatory proteins.

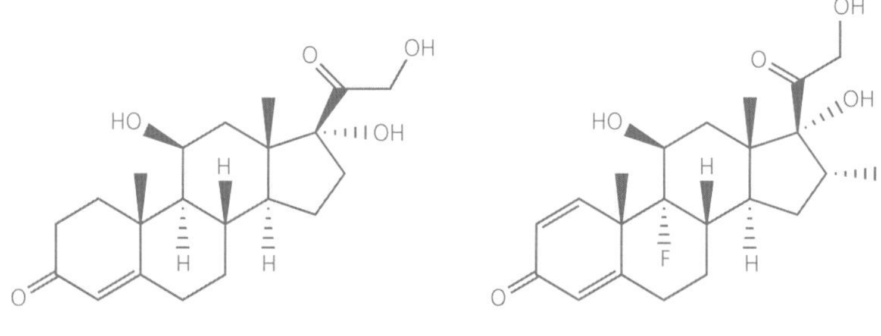

Figure 18.6 The molecular structure of glucocorticoid and the drug, dexamethasone

7 Figure 18.6 shows the generalised structure of a glucocorticoid and of a drug called dexamethasone. This drug binds to glucocorticoid receptors more powerfully than does glucocorticoid itself. Suggest why dexamethasone might be prescribed and use Figure 18.5 to suggest why dexamethasone might bind more powerfully to glucocorticoid receptors.

Post-transcriptional modification of mRNA

An essential feature of science is that when new evidence shows that a long-held hypothesis is not true, we change our ideas. The one-gene-one-polypeptide hypothesis, first proposed by Francis Crick, one of the Nobel prize-winning discoverers of the structure of DNA, is one such hypothesis. We now know that a single gene can give rise to more than one polypeptide.

Tip

It might help you to remember that **e**xons are **e**xpressed regions of DNA whilst **i**ntrons are **i**ntragenic regions that are not expressed.

In organisms with simple genomes, such as bacteria, mRNA molecules can be produced by continuous transcription through several adjacent genes. These organisms then process these 'multigenic transcripts' to generate two or more different polypeptides. This is not common in eukaryotes; the vast majority of eukaryotic genes are transcribed individually. To understand how eukaryotes can produce more than one polypeptide from a single gene, you need to revise your knowledge of the structure of a gene from Chapter 3.

Figure 18.7 reminds you that the genes of eukaryotic cells contain base sequences that do encode mRNA, called exons, and sections that do not, called introns. During transcription, the exons and introns are all copied into the base sequence of an RNA molecule, called pre-mRNA. This molecule is then spliced; the introns are removed and the exons are rejoined, to form mature mRNA. This mRNA migrates to the cytoplasm where its base sequence is translated by ribosomes.

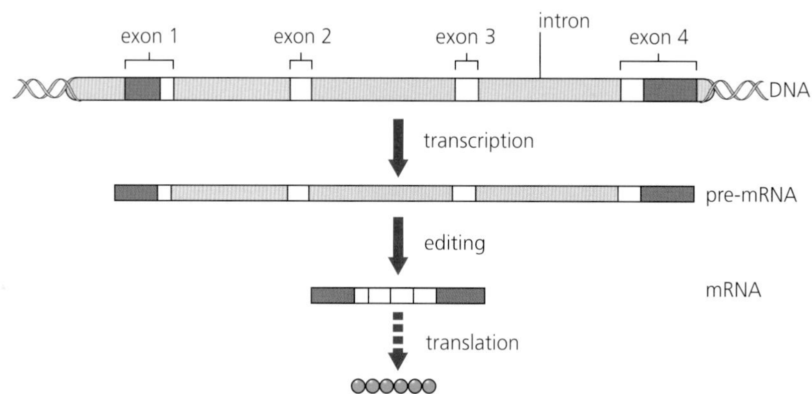

Figure 18.7 Editing of pre-mRNA in eukaryotic cells

Key term

Isoforms Different arrangements of exons in mature messenger RNA transcribed from a single eukaryotic gene. The different isoforms result in different polypeptides being produced from one gene.

Figure 18.8 shows how alternative splicing of pre-mRNA can produce mature RNA with different combinations of exons. Alternative splicing is known to be common in humans. The functions of the different mature mRNA molecules, called **isoforms**, are not always clear. Sometimes, they result in polypeptides that are tissue-specific, as is the case with the gene represented in Figure 18.8. Here, pre-mRNA transcribed from the calcitonin gene is spliced:

- in thyroid tissue to produce the polypeptide **calcitonin**. This polypeptide comprises 32 amino acid residues and acts as a hormone, stimulating a reduction in the concentration of calcium ions in the blood.
- in nervous tissue to produce the polypeptide calcitonin-gene-related peptide (**CGRP**). This polypeptide comprises 37 amino acid residues and is a powerful vasodilator that is involved in the transmission of pain. High levels of CGRP have been associated with migraine.

So, you can see that alternative splicing of pre-mRNA produced from a single gene can result in the production of completely different polypeptides. The one-gene-one-polypeptide hypothesis, at one time a core dogma of cell biology, does not hold true.

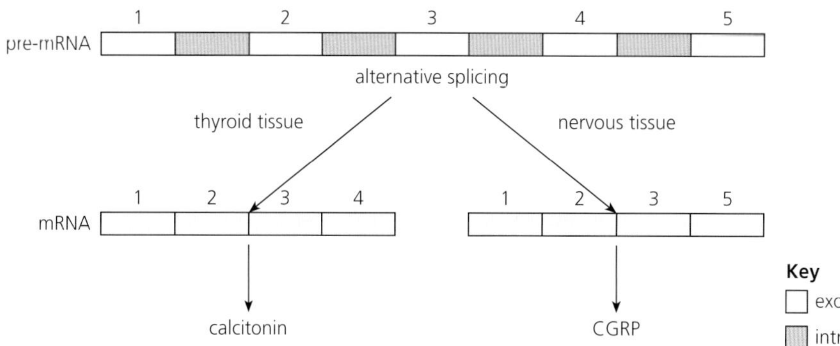

Figure 18.8 Alternative splicing of pre-mRNA results in tissue-specific products of the calcitonin gene

Test yourself

6 Distinguish between an exon and an intron.

7 Several different enzymes are involved in the editing of pre-mRNA. Suggest the different functions of **two** of them.

8 In Chapter 17, you saw that a small number of major histocompatability complex genes encoded a vast number of antibodies. Suggest how they do this.

9 How does a bacterium produce a multigenic transcript and how does it then use it?

10 Suggest the difference in the number of nucleotides in a molecule of mRNA encoding calcitonin and one encoding CGRP. Explain your answer.

Destruction of mRNA

In Chapter 3, you learnt about the roles of three types of RNA during protein synthesis: messenger RNA (mRNA), ribosomal RNA (rRNA) and transfer RNA (tRNA). Recently, RNA molecules have been discovered that were thought to be too small to have any important function. Although these small RNA molecules are non-coding, they have been found to play an important part in gene regulation. They ensure that mRNA can be destroyed, so that it never gets translated.

The destruction of mRNA involves these short regulatory RNA molecules binding to a protein to form a complex called an **RNA-induced silencing complex** (**RISC**). As you might expect, these small RNA molecules are themselves encoded by genes. There are two types of this regulatory RNA:

- **microRNA** (**miRNA**) – short, single-stranded RNA
- **small inhibitory RNA** (**siRNA**) – short, double-stranded RNA.

Let's see how these two types of RNA lead to the destruction of mRNA.

miRNA

In 2013, scientists estimated there to be over 2000 different miRNA molecules in human cells and that they are involved in regulating over 60 percent of the mRNA that encodes polypeptides. Each is produced as a long, precursor molecule in the shape of a hairpin bend. You can see the shape of the precursor molecule, called pri-miRNA in Figure 18.9.

You can also see in Figure 18.9 how, under the action of a RNA hydrolase, one of these molecules is hydrolysed to form much shorter, single-stranded miRNA molecules.

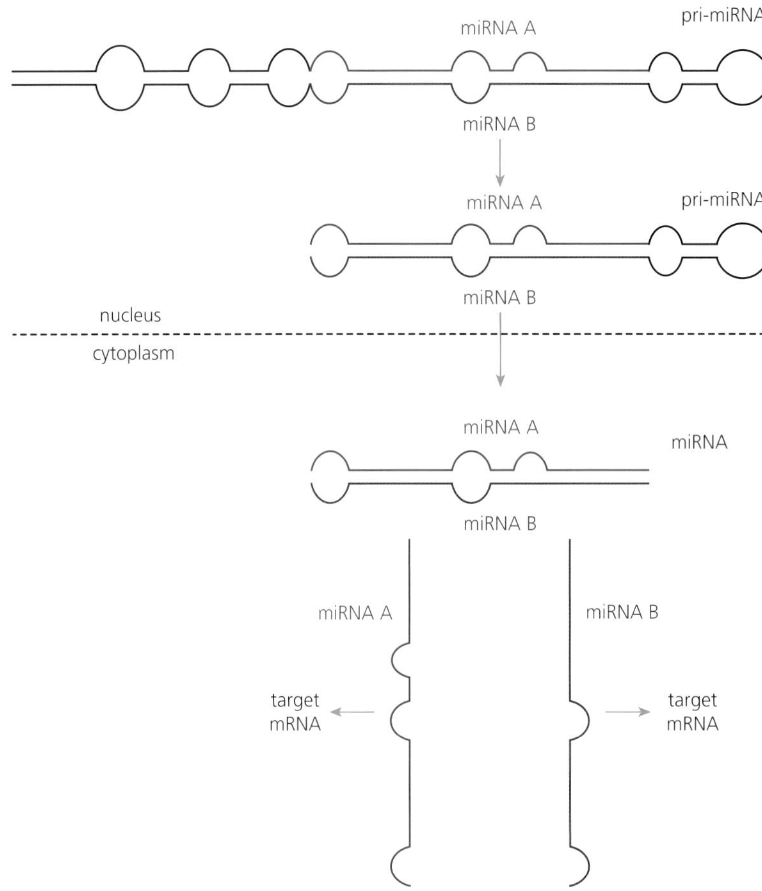

Figure 18.9 The formation of mature microRNA (miRNA) molecules from precursor miRNA (pri-miRNA)

As described above, each miRNA molecule binds to a protein to form a RISC. The miRNA within the RISC will bind to mRNA in the cytoplasm. The two RNA molecules bind by the formation of hydrogen bonds between base pairs – cytosine (C) with guanine (G) and adenine (A) with uracil (U). The sequence of bases in the two strands is not, however, fully complementary. Figure 18.10 shows how 'bulges' appear in the two strands where the bases are not complementary. These bulges prevent the mRNA being transcribed.

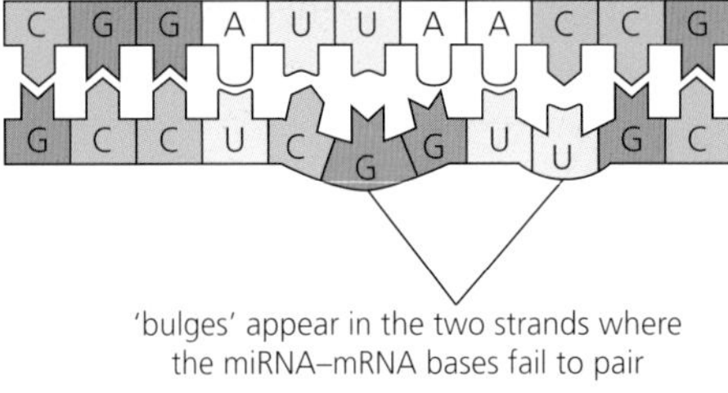

Figure 18.10 'Bulges' appear in the two strands where the miRNA-mRNA bases fail to pair. These 'bulges' prevent the transcription of the mRNA

siRNA

Unlike miRNA, siRNA are formed as molecules of double-stranded RNA (dsRNA). A RNA hydrolase, called a **dicer**, hydrolyses these dsRNA molecules into lengths of about 20 base pairs. These are the siRNA molecules shown as step 1 in Figure 18.11.

Like the miRNA, these double-stranded siRNA molecules bind with a protein complex to form a RISC (step 2 in Figure 18.11). Proteins within the RISC unwind the RNA and remain bound to one of the strands. It is this single-stranded, antisense RNA, bound within the RISC, that binds to the target mRNA (step 3 in Figure 18.11). Again, this binding is by hydrogen bonds between complementary base pairs. Finally, the bound mRNA is hydrolysed by yet another RNA hydrolase.

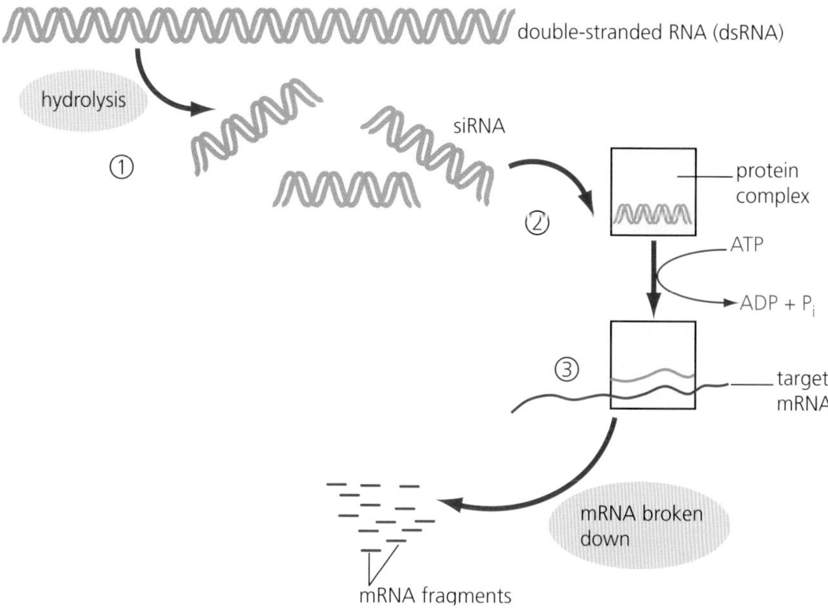

Figure 18.11 Small inhibitory RNA (siRNA) combines with a protein complex, leading to the destruction of messenger RNA (mRNA)

DNA methylation

DNA molecules are very long polymers of nucleotides. Each nucleotide contains the pentose deoxyribose, a phosphate group and a purine or pyrimidine base. Two of these bases – adenine and cytosine – can be methylated, that is a methyl group (CH_3) can be added to one of their carbon atoms. In vertebrate animals, methylation of DNA bases is restricted to the pyrimidine base, cytosine. If you look at Figure 18.12, you can see how a cytosine residue is methylated: the hydrogen atom on carbon-5 is replaced by a methyl group. Only about 3 per cent of the cytosine residues in human DNA are methylated. Most are found where the cytosine is linked by a phosphodiester bond to a guanine residue, represented **CpG**.

Repeated CpG sequences are common in the DNA near promoters. The presence of methylated DNA, especially near promoters, prevents the activation of RNA polymerase, described above. This means that the target genes of these promoters are effectively

Figure 18.12 Methylation – the addition of a methyl group (CH_3) – of a cytosine molecule

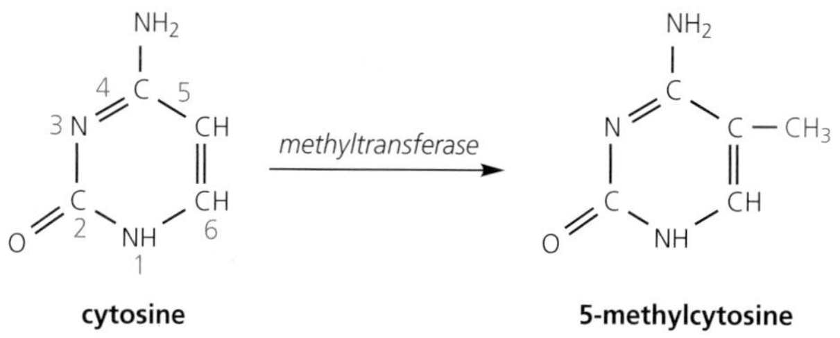

cytosine —*methyltransferase*→ 5-methylcytosine

silenced. Conversely, before any gene that is silenced can be transcribed, its promoter must be demethylated.

Histone acetylation

Eukaryotic DNA is different from prokaryotic DNA in a number of ways. One is that eukaryotic DNA is associated with a protein called histone. You can see this represented in Figure 18.13, in which the 'thread' of DNA is wound around 'beads' of histone.

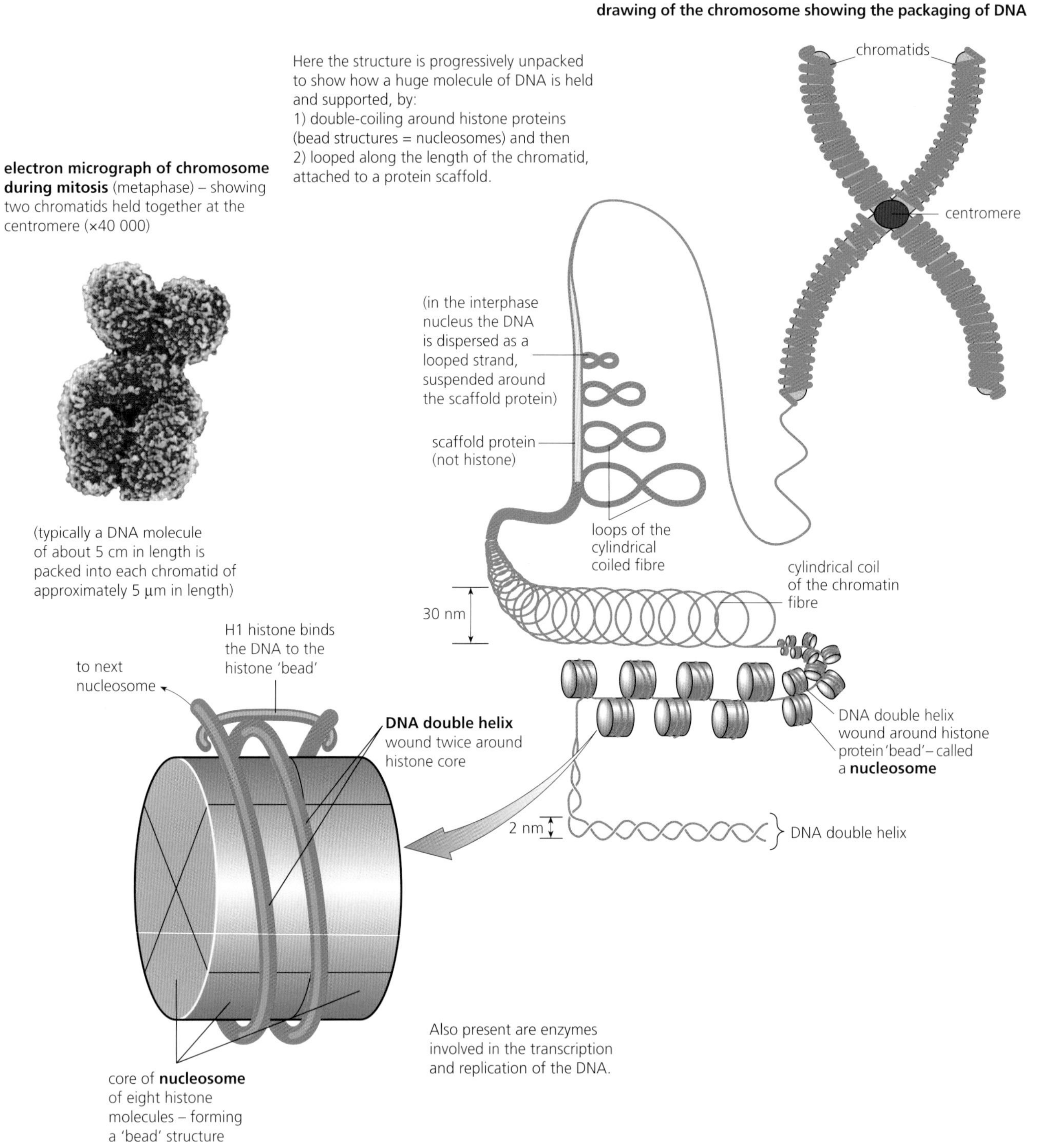

drawing of the chromosome showing the packaging of DNA

Here the structure is progressively unpacked to show how a huge molecule of DNA is held and supported, by:
1) double-coiling around histone proteins (bead structures = nucleosomes) and then
2) looped along the length of the chromatid, attached to a protein scaffold.

chromatids

centromere

electron micrograph of chromosome during mitosis (metaphase) – showing two chromatids held together at the centromere (×40 000)

(in the interphase nucleus the DNA is dispersed as a looped strand, suspended around the scaffold protein)

scaffold protein (not histone)

loops of the cylindrical coiled fibre

(typically a DNA molecule of about 5 cm in length is packed into each chromatid of approximately 5 μm in length)

cylindrical coil of the chromatin fibre

30 nm

H1 histone binds the DNA to the histone 'bead'

to next nucleosome

DNA double helix wound twice around histone core

DNA double helix wound around histone protein 'bead' – called a **nucleosome**

2 nm

DNA double helix

Also present are enzymes involved in the transcription and replication of the DNA.

core of **nucleosome** of eight histone molecules – forming a 'bead' structure

Figure 18.13 The packaging of DNA in the chromosomes of eukaryotic cells

Figure 18.14, represents a tiny part of a chromosome. The 'tails' of the histone molecules contain the amino acid leucine. This amino acid residue can be acetylated, that is an acetyl group ($COCH_3$) can be transferred on to it from acetyl coenzyme A. When this happens, the binding of the histones changes and they become more loosely packed. You can see the change from (a) to (b) in Figure 18.14. In part (a) the histones are so tightly packed that transcription factors and RNA polymerase cannot gain access to this region. After acetylation in part (b), however, the loosening of the histones frees the gene, so that transcription factors and RNA polymerase can now gain access to it.

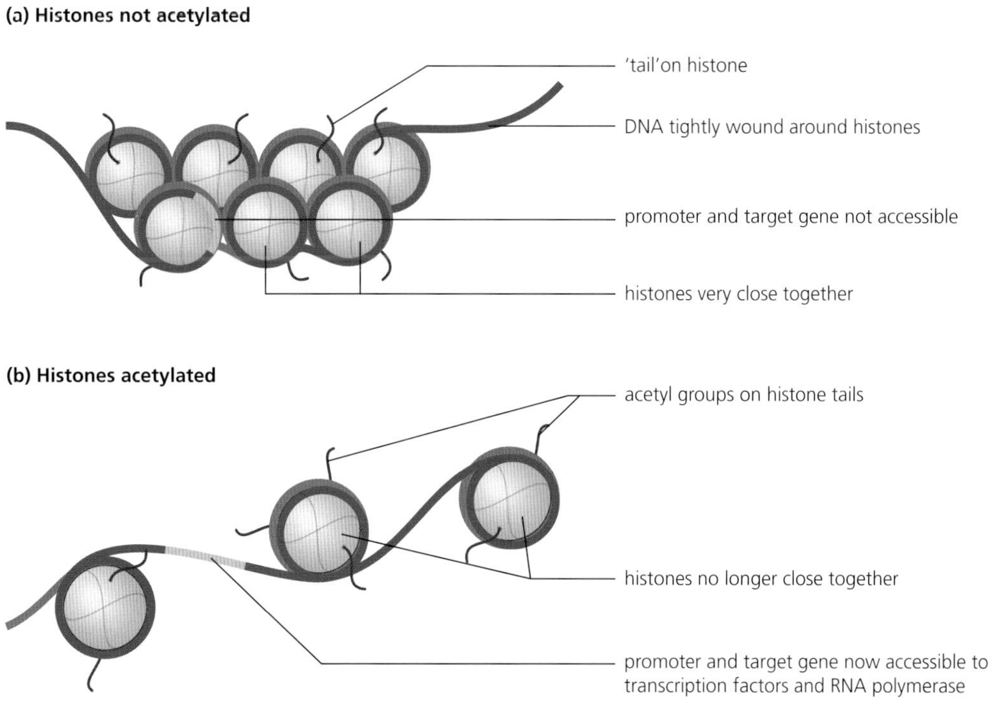

(a) Histones not acetylated

'tail'on histone

DNA tightly wound around histones

promoter and target gene not accessible

histones very close together

(b) Histones acetylated

acetyl groups on histone tails

histones no longer close together

promoter and target gene now accessible to transcription factors and RNA polymerase

Figure 18.14 Acetylation of histones. In (a), the histone 'tails' are not acetylated and the histones are bound tightly together. In (b), the histone 'tails' are acetylated so that the histones are held together more loosely, exposing the gene in this region of DNA

The different patterns of genes 'switched on' and genes 'switched off' that you have seen above are stabilised by DNA methylation and histone acetylation, so that these patterns are passed on to daughter cells formed by division. The stabilisation of these patterns is called **gene imprinting** and, as you will see below, is important both in inheritance and in cell differentiation.

Extension

X chromosome inactivation in mammals

You have seen that individual genes can be 'switched on' or 'switched off'. In mammals, an entire chromosome can be 'switched off'.

In mammals, sex is determined by sex chromosomes. A female has two X chromosomes whereas a male has one X chromosome and a much smaller Y chromosome. Having the 'wrong' number of chromosomes almost always results in abnormal development. So how do mammals avoid abnormal development when the cells of females and males have different numbers of X and Y chromosomes?

Since the Y chromosome contains very few genes, and those that are present are mostly genes regulating male sexual function, it appears that a female can develop normally without a Y chromosome. The X chromosome, however, contains a large number of genes and they are genes that control many processes that are vital to both sexes. You can, therefore, consider that a female mammal has too many X chromosomes for normal development.

The solution is that one of the X chromosomes is inactivated, so that each somatic cell in the body of a female mammal has one activated X chromosome and one inactivated X chromosome. The inactivation occurs early in embryonic development, probably in cells in the inner cell mass of a blastocyst (see Chapter 6, page 131). It also occurs at random in each cell of the blastocyst. In one embryonic cell it might be the paternal X chromosome that is inactivated, and in an adjacent embryonic cell it might be the maternal X chromosome that is inactivated. Whichever, once the inactivation has been established, it is perpetuated. When a cell in the blastocyst divides by mitosis, its daughter cells inactivate the same X chromosome and so on, as they and their daughter cells divide. Consequently, a female mammal is a mosaic of clones derived from these embryonic cells. Within each clone, the same X chromosome (maternal or paternal) is inactivated but between clones the 'choice' is random. The mechanisms involved in X inactivation – how the cell 'counts' the number of X chromosomes and then how it inactivates one of them – remain hotly debated and research in this area is on-going.

This pattern of mosaic clones can be observed in some conditions in which inheritance involves a sex-linked gene, in other words one carried on the X chromosome. One clone might express one allele of a sex-linked gene and another clone might express another allele of the same sex-linked gene. This can result in a female showing patches of tissue that are either affected or unaffected by an inherited disease, such as X-linked hypohidrotic ectodermal dysplasia (XLHED), with symptoms including missing sweat glands.

Test yourself

11 Give the roles of mRNA, rRNA and tRNA.

12 What type of molecule is an RNA-induced silencing complex?

13 Describe how the structure of a molecule of siRNA differs from that of mRNA, miRNA, tRNA.

14 Explain the notation 'CpG'.

15 Ultimately, DNA methylation and histone acetylation have the same effect. Describe that effect.

Stem cells in humans

Textbooks of human histology identify over 200 different cell types in the human body. Like all multicellular organisms, each human starts life as a single-celled zygote. This cell has the ability to produce every one of the different cells identified in textbooks of human histology. In the early stages of development, the human zygote divides to form a ball of cells, the blastocyst (see Chapter 6, page 131). The blastocyst contains an inner mass of cells that will form the embryo and an outer layer of cells that will form part of the placenta. Because the human zygote can form any human cell, including those of the placenta and umbilical cord, it is said to be **totipotent**.

Key term

Totipotent A term used to describe an unspecialised cell that can divide repeatedly to renew itself and to give rise to any cell in the body of an organism including, in mammals, cells of the placenta and umbilical cord.

During development, the zygote repeatedly divides by mitosis. The new cells quickly begin to differentiate to form different tissues. As they do so, their ability to divide and to produce different types of progeny cells becomes restricted. The extent of this restriction is described in Table 18.1.

Table 18.1 The different levels of cell 'potency', i.e. ability to divide and produce different types of progeny cell. Mature cells, such as nerve cells, have no 'potency'

Description of cell	Ability to divide and produce different progeny cells	Human examples
Totipotent	Can divide to replicate itself and produce any cell (including placenta and umbilical cord in mammals)	Zygote
Pluripotent	Can divide to replicate itself to produce any cell (but not placenta or umbilical cord in mammals)	Cell from inner mass of blastocyst
Multipotent	Can divide to replicate itself and to produce the different cells in one type of tissue	Haematopoietic cells in bone marrow that give rise to red blood cells, white blood cells and platelets
Unipotent	Can divide to replicate itself and to produce only one type of cell	Cells in the germinal epithelium of the skin

The cells in mature, fully differentiated tissues generally lack the ability to self-renew. This presents a problem in diseases that involve the death of cells.

Following a myocardial infarction, some of the muscle cells of a sufferer's heart die. These dead muscle cells cannot renew themselves. One way in which this can be treated is by a heart transplant – using surgery, the healthy heart of a dead donor replaces the faulty heart of the recipient. Of course, the heart muscle cells of the donor heart will have non-self antigens, so the recipient must be given immunosuppressant drugs to prevent its rejection.

What if, instead of replacing whole organs, surgeons could transplant cells that have the ability to divide and replace the dead cells? You might be familiar with one way in which this is commonly done. People with cancer of their bone marrow are routinely treated with a bone marrow transplant. Initially, chemotherapy is used to destroy the sufferer's own, faulty bone marrow. They are then given an intravenous transplant of healthy bone marrow from a donor. Again, there is a danger that the new tissue will be rejected, so the donor's bone marrow must be carefully matched to that of the recipient. The new transplanted bone marrow contains haematopoietic cells – multipotent cells that can divide to produce all the blood cell types that the recipient needs (see Table 18.1). Used in this way, the multipotent cells are acting as **stem cells**.

Key term

Stem cells Cells that are capable of self renewal and of producing new cells that differentiate into other specialised types of cell.

Types of stem cell and their uses

You have seen above how stem cells in the bone marrow of a donor can be successfully used to replace those in the bone marrow of a recipient. In theory, this use of transplanted stem cells could be extended to enable sufferers of many diseases to produce new, healthy cells. In reality, the use of stem cells involves moral judgements that have led to governmental restrictions.

Embryonic stem cells

Looking at Table 18.1, you might think that the best type of human stem cell to use in transplants would be pluripotent cells. These cells can produce any type of cell in the body of a child or adult. They are also present in a discrete area – the inner cell mass of a blastocyst – so would be easy to harvest. Since they are found only in the human embryo, these cells are known as **embryonic stem cells**. Herein lies an obstacle to their widespread use; taking embryonic stem cells destroys the embryo. Many people believe that it is unethical to destroy an embryo, since it has the potential to become a human being. Many religious, moral and humanistic organisations also share the same viewpoint.

Governments have to take a balanced view when faced with two conflicting issues, in this case the ability to extend life or relieve suffering by using embryonic stem cells and the understandable objections raised by a large proportion of the population to destroying embryos. In the UK, the use of embryonic stem cells is enshrined in law. Scientists are allowed to use embryonic stem cells only if:

- they are from unused embryos produced by *in vitro* fertilisation (IVF) during the treatment of infertile couples
- the unused embryos are donated specifically for this purpose by both members of the couple receiving fertility treatment
- the use of the stem cells is registered with a professional organisation, called the UK Stem Bank.

An organisation called the Human Fertilisation and Embryology Authority regulates the donation of embryos and, on behalf of the UK government, ensures that the UK law is upheld.

Adult stem cells

Small groups of stem cells are found in the tissues of adults, where their general function is to repair damaged cells or replace lost cells. These cells are called **adult stem cells**. Unlike embryonic stem cells, these cells are either unipotent or, at best, multipotent. As we saw above, the bone marrow is a rich source of adult stem cells but far fewer are found in tissues such as the brain. This makes it much more difficult to harvest adult stem cells from most tissues. One advantage that adult stem cells have over embryonic stem cells, however, is that it is possible to use a patient's own stem cells, removing the risk of rejection.

Induced pluripotent stem cells (iPS cells)

Earlier in this chapter, you saw that epigenetic modifications accompany the progressive restriction of specialised cells to divide. Totipotent cells in the embryo give rise to pluripotent cells in the blastocyst that give rise to multipotent cells in some tissues and fully differentiated somatic cells in most cases. About 10 years ago, scientists working in Japan found they could reverse this process.

Fibroblasts are relatively unspecialised cells found in connective tissue. They are capable of differentiating into adipose tissue (fat), bone, cartilage and smooth muscle (such as that found in arteries and the intestine). The Japanese research scientists reasoned that if they could find the genes that were vital to embryonic stem-cell function, they could induce an embryonic state in adult cells. They identified a number of such genes, all of which encoded transcription factors. One-by-one, they transferred these genes into mouse fibroblasts using retroviruses as vectors. They then devised a technique that enabled them to find which cells had become pluripotent. Eventually they found four genes, called *Oct4*, *Sox2*, *cMyc*, and *KLf4*, that induced the change from an adult fibroblast to a pluripotent stem cell.

Since the 'reverse differentiation' of these fibroblast cells was induced, they called these cells **induced pluripotent stem cells** (**iPS cells**). As these cells have the properties of self-renewal and the ability to differentiate into all adult cell types, but do not involve destruction of an embryo, they are considered to be as useful as, but more ethically appropriate than, embryonic stem cells.

Using pluripotent stem cells to treat medical conditions and test drugs

Pluripotent stem cells have the potential to be used in two ways in medical research.

- They can be used to produce new types of cell that directly replace those affected by disease. Diseases with the potential to be treated in this way include Crohn's disease, Type I diabetes, osteoarthritis and Parkinson's disease.
- They can be used to generate new types of cell that can be used in the laboratory to test the effectiveness and safety of new drugs, reducing the need for animal (and human) experimentation.

Tip

Some of these Test yourself questions rely on you being able to make links between the content of this chapter and other parts of the specification, i.e. they are synoptic.

We must treat the potential uses of pluripotent stem cells with caution, though.

- Scientists do not yet fully understand how to control the differentiation of pluripotent stem cells into the 200-plus cell types catalogued in human histology textbooks.
- Two of the genes that transformed adult fibroblasts to iPS cells (namely *cMyc* and *KLf4*) are oncogenes – genes with the potential to cause cancer.
- The conversion of adult cells to iPS cells is currently slow and the success rate is very low.
- Growing cells for therapies will require specialist systems and research centres, so access to therapies may be limited to areas with suitable facilities.
- The safety aspects of introducing pluripotent stem cells into recipients must be trialled. Clinical trials take a long time and are expensive.

In the meantime, doctors must manage the expectations of their patients suffering diseases that have the potential to be cured using pluripotent stem cells, who read and hear of these 'miracle cures' in the media.

Test yourself

16 Lymphoid cells are found in bone marrow. They are able to divide, producing lymphocytes. Are lymphoid cells totipotent, pluripotent, multipotent or unipotent? Explain your answer.

17 During a myocardial infarction, some of the muscle cells of a sufferer's heart, die. Explain what causes the death of these cells.

18 What is a human stem cell?

19 Explain why immunosuppressant drugs must be given to people who have received a bone marrow transplant.

20 What is an oncogene?

Chapter summary

Factors affecting gene expression

- A gene is expressed when it is transcribed and translated.
- At any one time, a cell does not express all of its genes.
- Each gene is controlled by one or more promotor regions of the chromosome.
- Transcription factors are proteins that bind to the promotor region(s) of a gene. This binding either promotes or inhibits transcription of the controlled gene.
- Gene expression is also controlled by epigenetic modification:
  - Methylation of cysteine bases within the DNA of a gene inhibits its transcription.
  - Acetylation of lysine residues in histones promotes transcription of the associated DNA.
  - Non-coding RNA molecules that are complementary to parts of mRNA base sequences enable RNA-induced silencing complexes (RISCs) to destroy mRNA.
- Epigenetic modification can be inherited and is important in ensuring cell differentiation.
- In eukaryotic cells, transcription of DNA results in the formation of pre-mRNA that contains copies of introns. During post-transcriptional modification, these introns are removed and the exons are spliced together again. Splicing the exons together in different sequences makes possible different products from a single gene.

Stem cells

- A stem cell is a cell that is capable of self-renewal and of producing cells that differentiate into other specialised cells.
- Totipotent stem cells can divide to produce cells that can differentiate into any cell type (including the placenta and umbilical cord in mammals). In humans, only the zygote is totipotent.
- Pluripotent stem cells can divide to produce cells that can differentiate into nearly all cell types.
- Multipotent stem cells can divide to produce cells that can differentiate into cells within a single type of tissue.
- Epigenetic modifications result in embryonic totipotent cells developing into pluripotent stem cells and finally into fully differentiated somatic cells.
- Embryonic stem cells are the cells in the inner cell mass of a blastocyst. They are pluripotent.
- Embryonic stem cells could be used in transplants to extend the life, or reduce the suffering, of a recipient. Since this would result in the destruction, or manipulation, of a pre-implantation-stage embryo, there are legal restrictions on the use of these stem cells.
- A Japanese research team found that the introduction of four genes encoding transcription factors into fully differentiated fibroblasts reprogrammed these cells into induced pluripotent stem cells (iPS cells).
- Since these iPS cells can be made from an adult patient's own fibroblasts, their use does not raise the same ethical considerations as the use of embryonic stem cells.

Practice questions

1 The fertilised egg cell of a multicellular organism is:

A multipotent **C** totipotent

B pluripotent **D** unipotent *(1)*

2 Which one of the following is a form of epigenetic modification?

A alternative pre-mRNA splicing

B continuous transcription

C DNA methylation

D DNA replication *(1)*

3 An exon is:

A a sequence of bases found at the end of a gene

B a sequence of bases found at the end of a molecule of mRNA

C a sequence of bases that is extracted from a pre-mRNA molecule

D a sequence of bases that is copied into a mature mRNA molecule *(1)*

4 Copy and complete the table by placing a tick in each box where the statement is true. *(4)*

Statement	Type of cell		
	Adult stem cell	Embryonic stem cell	Induced pluripotent stem cell
Can be grown in suitable laboratory conditions			
Could be used with patient's own cells			
Use in UK is restricted by law			
Involves removal of epigenetic modification			

5 In mammals, the somatic cells of females have two X chromosomes and those of a male have one X chromosome.

A gene encoding ginger-coloured fur is located on the X chromosome of domestic cats. If an X chromosome carries the gene for ginger fur, the cat will produce ginger fur.

A male cat with ginger fur mated with a female with black fur. The female had four kittens, two male and two female. Neither of the males had ginger fur. Both the females were tortoiseshell, with patches of ginger fur and patches of black fur.

a) What is meant by a 'somatic cell'? *(1)*

b) What name is given to the position of a gene on a chromosome? *(1)*

c) Use the information in the passage to explain why neither of the male kittens had ginger fur. *(2)*

d) Use your understanding of cell regulation to explain why the female kittens had patches of ginger fur. *(4)*

6 The intestinal bacterium, *Escherichia coli*, is able to absorb the disaccharide lactose and hydrolyse it to its constituent monosaccharides. To do this, it uses two enzymes:

- lactose permease, encoded by a gene *lacY*, speeds up the absorption of lactose by the cells of *E. coli*
- β-galactosidase, encoded by a gene *lacZ*, speeds up the hydrolysis of lactose.

(A) No lactose present

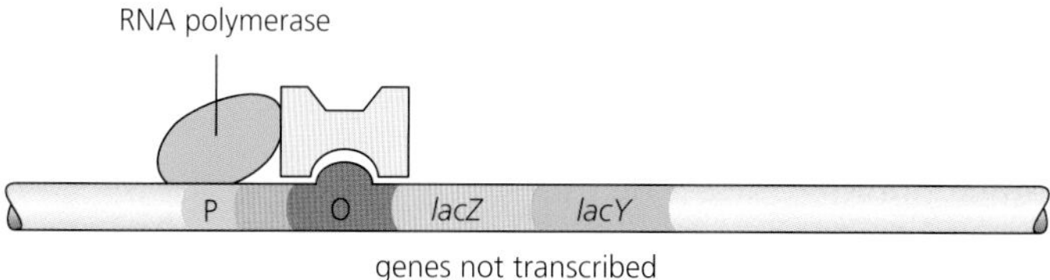

(B) Lactose present

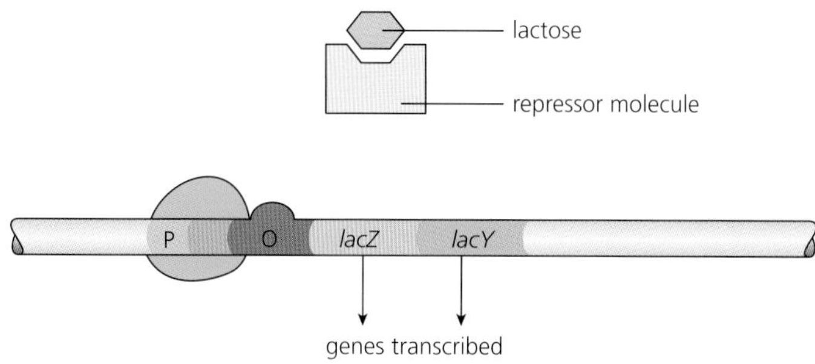

The diagram represents a section of DNA from *E.coli* with these genes and operator (O) and promoter (P) regions. In (A), neither *lacY* nor *lacZ* is transcribed. In (B) both *lacY* and *lacZ* are transcribed.

a) Use the diagram to suggest the function of the operator and promoter regions of DNA. *(3)*

b) Use the diagram to explain why lactose permease and β-galactosidase are produced only when lactose is present. *(3)*

c) Suggest **one** advantage that cells of *E. coli* gain by producing these enzymes only when lactose is present. *(1)*

d) Compare and contrast the method of gene regulation represented in the diagram with gene regulation in eukaryotes. *(3)*

7 Insulin is a peptide, 51 amino acids long, that acts as a hormone. It is produced in small groups of cells in the human pancreas, called the islets of Langerhans. It stimulates the uptake of glucose from the blood by cells mainly in the liver.

a) How many RNA nucleotides would you expect to be present in the mRNA translated to produce insulin? Explain your answer. *(1)*

Type 1 diabetes results from the autoimmune destruction of cells in the islets of Langerhans that normally produce insulin. It has been proposed that human embryonic stem cells could be used to replace the missing insulin-producing cells in the pancreas of a person suffering Type I diabetes.

b) What are the main features of embryonic stem cells? *(2)*

c) Suggest why the method proposed is likely to be more successful than transplanting insulin-producing cells from the pancreas of an adult donor. *(3)*

d) Discuss any ethical issues that are raised by this proposal. *(4)*

Stretch and challenge

8 Huntington's disease is an inherited human disorder caused by the presence of huntingtin protein in brain cells. Its presence causes the progressive death of brain cells and, ultimately, the death of the sufferer.

Outline how the use of siRNA might one day make it possible to provide a treatment for Huntington's disease.

9 Produce a 10-minute presentation in which you provide a balanced view of the use of stem cells in medicine.

19 DNA profiling, gene sequencing and gene technology

Prior knowledge

In this chapter you will need to recall that:

- a nucleotide is formed from three sub-units – a pentose, a phosphate group and an organic base
- a strand of DNA is a polymer of nucleotides, held together by phosphodiester bonds
- a DNA molecule comprises two antiparallel strands of DNA held together by hydrogen bonds between complementary bases, adenine with thymine and cytosine with guanine. Although individually weak, the sheer number of hydrogen bonds in a DNA molecule holds the two strands together very strongly
- during DNA replication, a helicase enzyme separates the two strands in a DNA molecule exposing their bases. Free nucleotides pair with these exposed bases, adenine with thymine and cytosine with guanine, and DNA polymerase catalyses the formation of new phosphodiester bonds in the 5-prime to 3-prime direction of the developing strand
- a DNA molecule contains some base sequences that encode the sequence of amino acids in polypeptides and some that do not. Some of the latter sequences regulate gene expression
- during transcription, part of the DNA base sequence is transcribed into a sequence of bases in a molecule of RNA. In eukaryotes, this sequence is then edited to form mRNA. The mRNA is used by ribosomes during the production of polypeptides
- the genetic code is universal and is based on a combination of three bases encoding one amino acid
- bacteria are prokaryotic. They have a single, circular DNA molecule that is not associated with proteins (in other words is naked) and might have many smaller circular molecules of DNA, called plasmids
- viruses are non-living particles that can infect living cells. During infection, viral nucleic acid is inserted into a host cell. The host cell then replicates the viral nucleic acid, produces the encoded polypeptides and assembles new virus particles
- the DNA sequence that encodes a functional polypeptide is known as a gene and its location is known as its locus.

Test yourself on prior knowledge

1. Name the pentose sugar in a DNA nucleotide.
2. Give the RNA sequence that is complementary to the DNA base sequence AGTCAT and name the bases in your sequence.
3. Identify **two** events that might occur during the editing of newly transcribed RNA in a eukaryotic cell.
4. Explain why mRNA is not edited in prokaryotic cells.
5. During DNA replication, new bases can only be added to a growing DNA strand in a 5-prime to 3-prime direction. What property of DNA polymerase does this exhibit?

Introduction

Some of the content of your A level biology course has changed very little over many years. In complete contrast, this part of the course is one of the fastest changing topics of biology. The techniques that are used have developed, and are continuing to develop, rapidly and most have become automated in the process. The results gained using these new techniques have brought about rapid changes in our understanding of the field of molecular genetics and with it new understanding of how we can better identify and treat diseases.

There are, however, a few techniques that remain at the heart of gene technology. Two of these are used to make multiple copies of DNA and are summarised in Figure 19.1. One, called the polymerase chain reaction (PCR), was originally carried out in glassware (in other words *in vitro*), although glassware has now largely been replaced by plastic; the other involves the use of living cells (*in vivo*) to replicate fragments of DNA that have been inserted into their genomes.

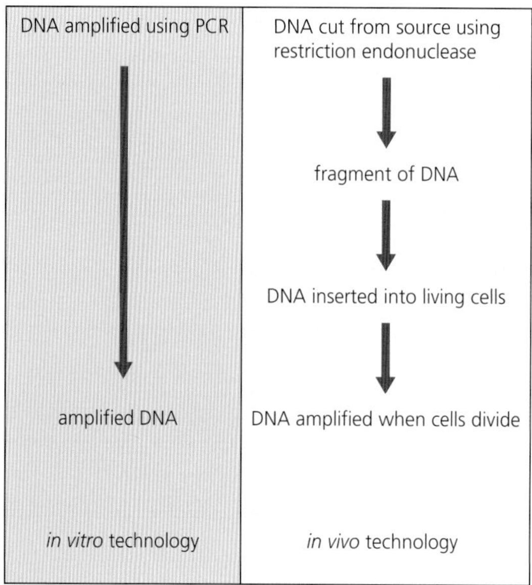

Figure 19.1 Producing multiple copies of DNA fragments can be achieved using *in vitro* and *in vivo* methods

Both techniques are used with purified samples of DNA. Figure 19.2 on the next page, shows how samples of DNA can be extracted from tissue by mechanically breaking up the cells, filtering off the debris, and breaking down cell membranes by treatment with detergents. The protein framework of the chromosomes, often called a scaffold, is then removed by incubation with a protease. The DNA, now existing as long threads, is isolated from this mixture of chemicals by precipitation with ethanol, and is thus 'cleaned'. The DNA strands are then re-suspended in an aqueous, pH buffered medium, ready for use.

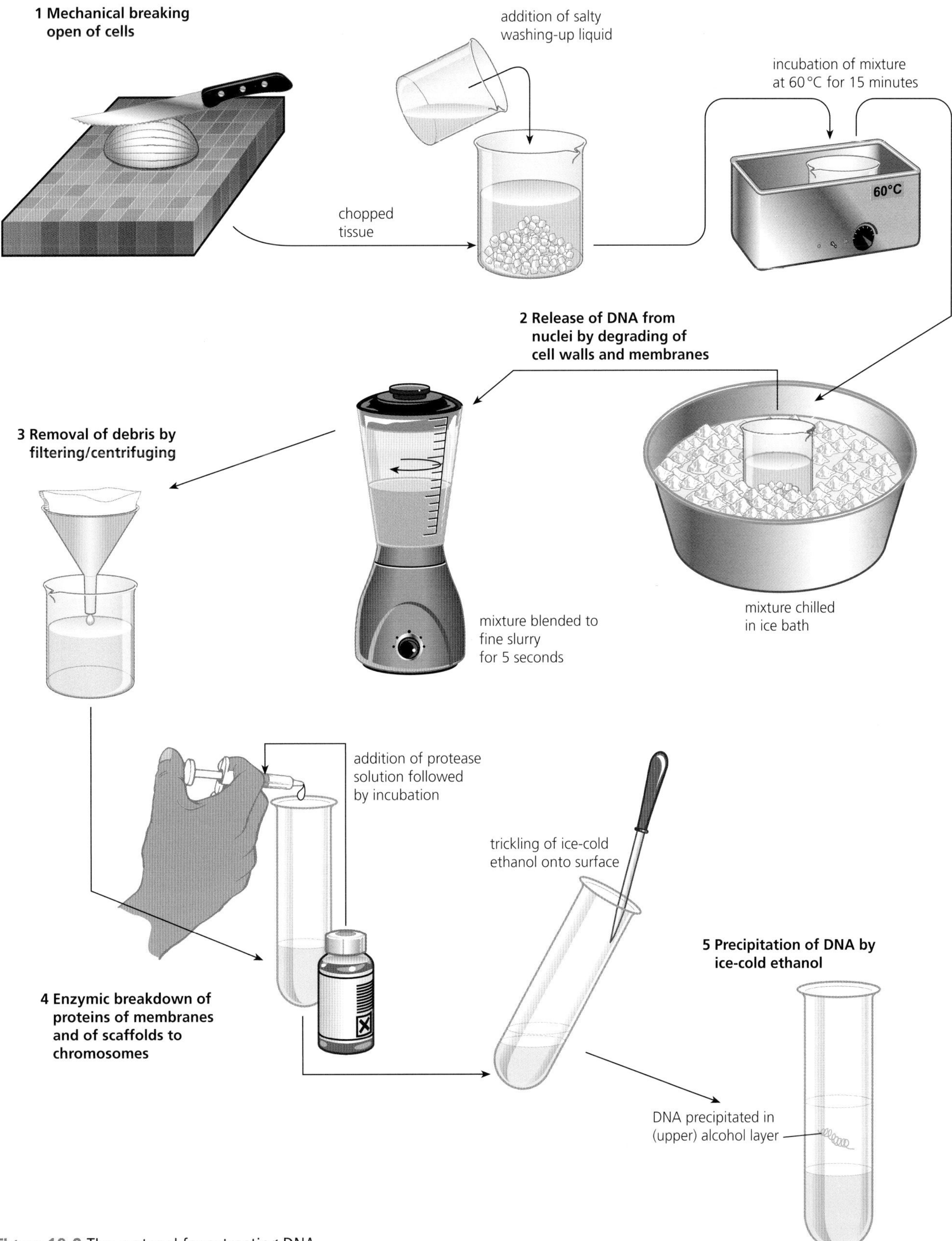
1 Mechanical breaking open of cells
addition of salty washing-up liquid
incubation of mixture at 60 °C for 15 minutes
60°C
chopped tissue
2 Release of DNA from nuclei by degrading of cell walls and membranes
3 Removal of debris by filtering/centrifuging
mixture blended to fine slurry for 5 seconds
mixture chilled in ice bath
addition of protease solution followed by incubation
trickling of ice-cold ethanol onto surface
5 Precipitation of DNA by ice-cold ethanol
4 Enzymic breakdown of proteins of membranes and of scaffolds to chromosomes
DNA precipitated in (upper) alcohol layer

Figure 19.2 The protocol for extracting DNA

In vitro amplification of DNA – the polymerase chain reaction (PCR)

Since the 1980s, the PCR has revolutionised molecular genetics because it allows the rapid analysis and cell-free cloning of DNA. Consequently, it has become a technique that is fundamental to other aspects of gene technology.

The PCR is used to **amplify target DNA sequences** that are present within a DNA source. By amplify, we mean it produces multiple copies. The technique involves mixing DNA containing the target sequence with a mixture of reagents in a plastic PCR tube and placing the tube in a machine called a **thermal cycler**.

The reagents include:

- **primers** – short lengths of single-stranded DNA (called oligonucleotides) that are complementary to the base sequence of part of the 3' (3-prime) ends of the strands of target DNA to be copied
- free DNA nucleotides, each with an adenine, cytosine, guanine or thyme base
- thermostable DNA polymerase.

> **Key terms**
>
> **Amplify target DNA sequences** Produce a very large number of copies of a fragment of DNA. This can be done by transferring the target DNA into bacterial cells and allowing the resulting bacterial culture to produce the new DNA copies - the *in vivo* method. More often, it is done using the polymerase chain reaction (PCR)- the *in vitro* method.
>
> **Primer** A short strand of nucleotides (an oligonucleotide) with a base sequence that is complementary to the short base sequence at the beginning (3' end) of a strand of DNA to be copied. Primers are used as a starting point for the action of DNA polymerase, both in the semi-conservative replication of DNA we considered in Book 1 and in the PCR.

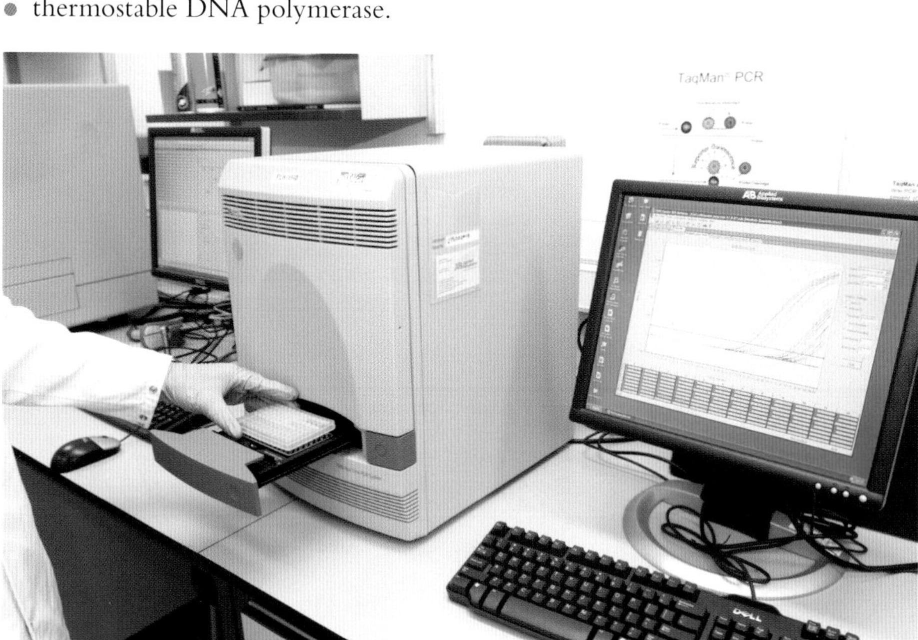

Figure 19.3 Loading a PCR machine. This demonstrates how much of the laboratory work involved in molecular genetics has become automated. The scientist has loaded the contents of each tube. Her next direct involvement will be to interpret the computer printout

You can see a PCR machine being loaded in Figure 19.3. It is a thermal cycler that varies the temperature at which the tubes are incubated in a pre-programmed way. Figure 19.4 on the next page, summarises these temperatures and the reactions that occur during one cycle of the PCR. You can follow these steps in Figure 19.4 as you work through the example that follows.

The polymerase chain reaction involves a series of steps, each taking a matter of minutes.
The process involves a heating and cooling cycle and is automated.
Each time it is repeated in the presence of excess nucleotides, the number of copies of the original DNA strand is doubled.

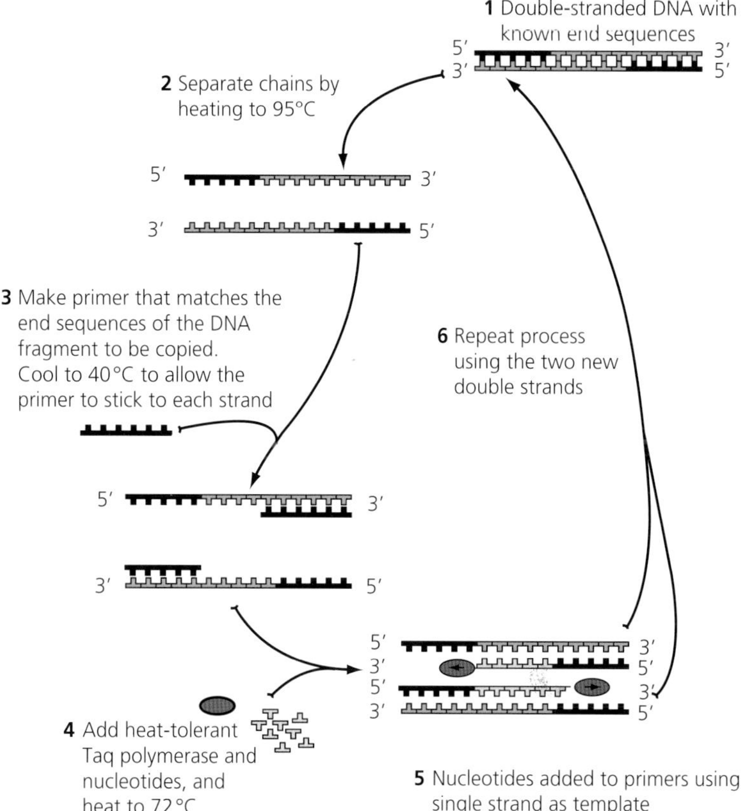

1 Double-stranded DNA with known end sequences
5′
3′
3′
5′
2 Separate chains by heating to 95°C
5′
3′
3′
5′
3 Make primer that matches the end sequences of the DNA fragment to be copied.
Cool to 40 °C to allow the primer to stick to each strand
6 Repeat process using the two new double strands
5′
3′
3′
5′
5′
3′
5′
3′
3′
5′
3′
5′
4 Add heat-tolerant Taq polymerase and nucleotides, and heat to 72 °C
5 Nucleotides added to primers using single strand as template

Note: 'Primers' are short sequences of single-stranded DNA made syntheically with base sequences complimentary to one end (the 3′ end) of DNA.
Remember: DNA polymerase synthesises a DNA strand in the 3′ to 5′ direction.

Figure 19.4 The polymerase chain reaction (PCR). The purine and pyrimidine bases are represented by A (adenine), C (cytosine), G (guanine) and T (thymine). The letter N represents a DNA nucleotide in a satellite repeat sequence

Example

Using the PCR to amplify specific fragments of DNA

The PCR is used to amplify fragments of DNA.

1 Suggest why it might be unhelpful to attempt to amplify the whole of a cell's genome at one time.

At the start of the PCR in Figure 19.4, we have a fragment of double-stranded DNA. In step 1, the two strands of this DNA are separated by heating to 93 °C.

The thermal cycler then cools the separated strands to 55 °C. This enables hydrogen bonds to reform. In theory, the separated strands could join again to reform the original double-stranded DNA.

2 Explain why heating to this temperature causes the two strands to separate.

3 Use information in Figure 19.4 to explain what prevents the two separated DNA strands joining back together.

4 Use your knowledge of DNA structure and replication to explain why the primer is made to be complementary to a base sequence at the 3' end of each template DNA strand.

5 Suggest a disadvantage of using very short primers.

6 Use the information in Figure 19.4 to estimate the distance between any two of these primers on the template DNA.

7 If molecular biologists wish to transfer a human gene to a bacterial cell, they need to amplify the gene plus its promoter. Explain why.

8 Which enzyme, used in natural DNA replication, is missing from the PCR process?

Answers

1 Molecular biologists usually want to amplify only part of a DNA molecule, for example, a gene that they wish to transfer to another organism or store in a gene library. A whole genome contains too much genetic material to be amplified during a single PCR amplification.

2 The two strands are held together by hydrogen bonds between nucleotides with complementary bases – adenine with thymine and cytosine with guanine. Although the very large number of hydrogen bonds in a molecule of DNA strongly holds the two strands together, each individual hydrogen bond is relatively weak. A temperature of 93 °C causes sufficient random thermal motion to break the hydrogen bonds, so that the two strands separate.

3 Figure 19.4 shows that an **excess** of primer is added to the original mixture. If you think back to what you learnt about competitive inhibitors earlier in the course, you will recall that the likelihood of a competitive inhibitor binding to the active site of an enzyme becomes less the more substrate you add. The same principle holds true here as well. If the concentration of primer is very high, the single-stranded DNA is more likely to collide with, and bind to, a primer than it is to its former complementary DNA strand.

You can see in Figure 19.4 that the primer is complementary to part of the base sequence at the 3' end of each template DNA strand.

4 The primer is a sequence of nucleotides that attaches to the end of each strand of DNA that is to be used as a template for the production of a new strand. The enzyme DNA polymerase must attach to such a primer before it can start to build a complementary DNA strand. Like all enzymes, DNA polymerase is specific in the way it binds to its substrate. Here, it can only add a new nucleotide to the 3'–OH end of the growing strand, so must grow the new strand in a 5' to 3' direction. Since the new strand will be antiparallel to the existing strand, the 5' end of the new strand will be complementary with the 3' end of the template strand.

You can also see in Figure 19.4 that the primer is several nucleotides long. Since scientists need to know the base sequence of the template DNA, you might expect it to be easier for them to produce primers that are very short.

5 A primer is a sequence of nucleotides that attaches to template DNA wherever it collides with a base sequence that is complementary to its own. A sequence of, say, only two bases is likely to occur several times within a short length of template DNA.

DNA polymerase starts copying when it attaches to a primer. It then moves along the template DNA but stops when it reaches another primer. With primers only short distances apart, a large number of very short lengths of DNA would be amplified.

6 The primer shown in Figure 19.4 is six nucleotides long. Since there are four different DNA nucleotide bases (A, C, G and T), the sequence shown (ATCCGG) is likely to occur, by chance, every 4^6 nucleotides, in other words every 5120 nucleotides.

The PCR techniques can be used to amplify individual genes. One reason for amplifying a gene is to transfer it into another cell, as described later in this chapter.

7 As you saw in Chapter 18, the promoter region regulates transcription of its target gene. Simply transferring a gene into another cell might not result in that gene being transcribed unless its promoter was also present. Bacteria are prokaryotic and have a method of regulating genes that is different from that of eukaryotic cells, such as human cells. Consequently, the promoter must be transferred along with its target gene.

Figure 19.4 represents a single cycle of the PCR. In one cycle, the two strands of a fragment of DNA are separated and each is used as a template for the production of a new, complementary strand. This mimics the natural semi-conservative DNA replication that you learnt about earlier in the course.

8 In natural DNA replication, the two strands are separated by DNA helicase. In the PCR, the same effect is achieved using a high temperature that 'melts' the DNA.

The thermal cycler is normally programmed to repeat the cycle shown in Figure 19.4 many times. At each cycle the number of DNA copies doubles, so that after n cycles there will be 2^n copies of the DNA.

Test yourself

1 Describe how an *in vitro* technique differs from an *in vivo* technique.
2 Explain the role of a DNA primer.
3 List the groups of reagents used in the PCR.
4 Calculate the number of copies of a single fragment of DNA that will be produced after ten cycles of the PCR.
5 The thermostable enzyme used in the PCR is obtained from certain species of bacteria. Suggest the advantage these bacteria gain by possessing thermostable enzymes.

The PCR is used in DNA profiling

The term **DNA profiling** refers to the general use of DNA tests to establish the identity of an individual or the relationship between individuals. This is possible because, with the exception of clones (including human identical twins), the sequence of bases in the DNA of each sexually reproducing organism is unique.

Key term

DNA profiling The general use of DNA tests to establish the identity of, or relationships between, individuals. The technique involves the production of copies of the DNA fragments, their separation using electrophoresis and a comparison of the location of these fragments on the developed electrophoresis gel.

> **Key term**
>
> **Short tandem repeats** (also known as satellite regions of DNA) In eukaryotes, these are regions of non-coding DNA that contain a particular sequence of nucleotide bases repeated many times over. The number of repeats at a particular locus is unique and so can be used as a genetic marker.

You learnt earlier in the course that most of the DNA in eukaryotes does not code for polypeptides. Some of this non-coding DNA occurs within genes – as introns. There are non-coding sequences between genes as well. Within the latter non-coding regions, we find some short sequences of bases that are repeated many times. They are called **short tandem repeats**, but are often known as 'satellite' regions of DNA. Actually, there are two types of satellite regions:

- **minisatellites** of about 20–50 bases, possibly repeated 50 to several hundred times
- **microsatellites** of 2–5 bases repeated 5 to 15 times.

We all inherit a distinctive combination of these apparently non-functional 'repeat regions', half from our mother and half from our father. The same satellites occur at the same loci on both chromosomes of a homologous pair, but the number of times the sequence is repeated on each chromosome of a homologous pair will differ. It is for these reasons that each of us has a unique sequence of nucleotides in our DNA (except for identical twins). It is the microsatellites that we use as the genetic markers in DNA profiling.

The steps involved in DNA profiling

1 Using the PCR to amplify the desired DNA

A sample of DNA is obtained from cells of the individuals being investigated. The PCR is used to amplify those sections of each DNA sample that are known to contain the desired satellite regions

You have seen above how the PCR can be used to amplify DNA. By choosing appropriate primers, only those parts of the DNA that contain the satellite regions to be used as genetic markers will be amplified. Since these satellite regions from different individuals will contain different numbers of tandem repeats, the amplified sections of DNA will be of different lengths.

> **Tip**
>
> Although here we are looking at the use of electrophoresis to separate fragments of DNA produced by the PCR, the technique is also used to separate fragments of DNA produced by restriction endonucleases, considered later in this chapter.

2 Separating DNA fragments by electrophoresis

Electrophoresis is used to separate these amplified sections and the result is converted into a pattern of bands similar to a bar code.

The process of electrophoresis separates particles according to their charge and size. The apparatus used to do this is shown in Figure 19.5 on the next page. Its major component is a tank. You can see that each end of the tank has an electrode connected to a power source. This generates an electrical field from one end of the tank to the other. Since the phosphate group on each nucleotide gives DNA an overall negative charge (PO_4^{3-}, fragments of DNA will migrate to the positive electrode (anode) of an electrical field. You can also see in Figure 19.5 that the samples containing DNA fragments are placed in wells cut into a sheet of gel that is supported on a glass plate. The gel is made from either agarose (a very pure form of agar) or polyacrylamide. These gels contain tiny pores that allow them to act like molecular sieves. When migrating from the cathode to the anode through these gels, small molecules move faster, and so travel further, than larger molecules.

The small diagram at the bottom right-hand side of Figure 19.5 represents the separated fragments of DNA. The wells are at the top of the diagram so the fragments have migrated down the page. Those fragments with fewer tandem repeats in their satellite regions have travelled further than those with more tandem repeats.

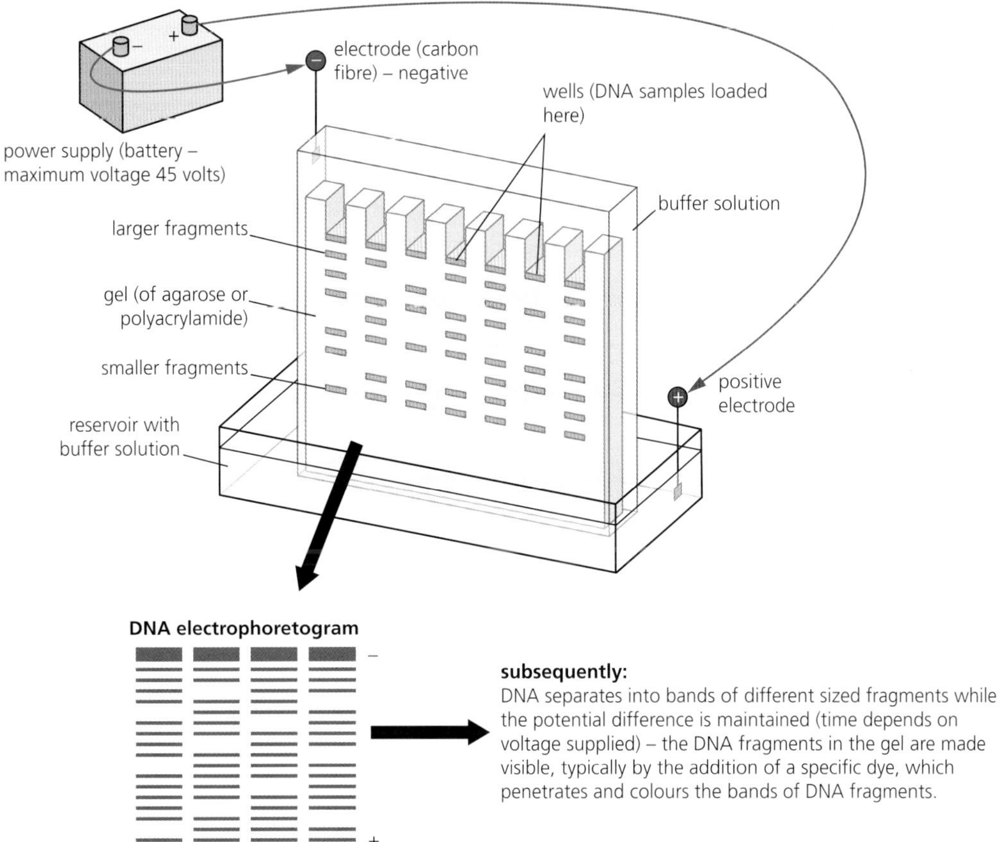

Figure 19.5 Separation of fragments of DNA using electrophoresis

3 Visualising the DNA fragments using Southern blotting

After first separation by electrophoresis, however, none of the DNA bands is visible at all. They must be visualised by, for example, adding a dye that binds only to DNA and is visible in white light. The more commonly used method for visualising the results of electrophoresis uses the Southern blotting technique.

The principles of the Southern blotting technique are shown in Figure 19.6. The gel with the separated DNA fragments is placed on a blotting paper 'wick' fed by alkaline buffer solution. A nylon membrane is placed on the gel and more blotting paper is applied above, topped by a weight.

- As the buffer solution is drawn up through the gel, contact between the alkali and the DNA fragments breaks the hydrogen bonds between complementary bases, so that the DNA fragments become single-stranded.
- The compression caused by the weight, transfers a copy of the DNA fragments from the gel to the nylon membrane, which is much more robust than the gel.

As Figure 19.6 shows, the nylon membrane is then removed, and the distribution of DNA fragments detected by the application of selected **radioactive DNA probes**, followed by autoradiography.

> **Key term**
>
> **Radioactive DNA probe** A short length of DNA (an oligonucleotide) that has been produced with a base sequence that is complementary to that within a DNA fragment you wish to locate. The probe has also been labelled using a radioactive isotope so that it will cause 'fogging' of a photographic plate during autoradiography, allowing its location to be identified.

Southern blotting (named after the scientist who devised the routine):

- extracted DNA is cut into fragments with restriction enzyme
- the fragments are separated on electrophoresis gel
- fragments are made single-stranded by treatment of the gel with alkali.

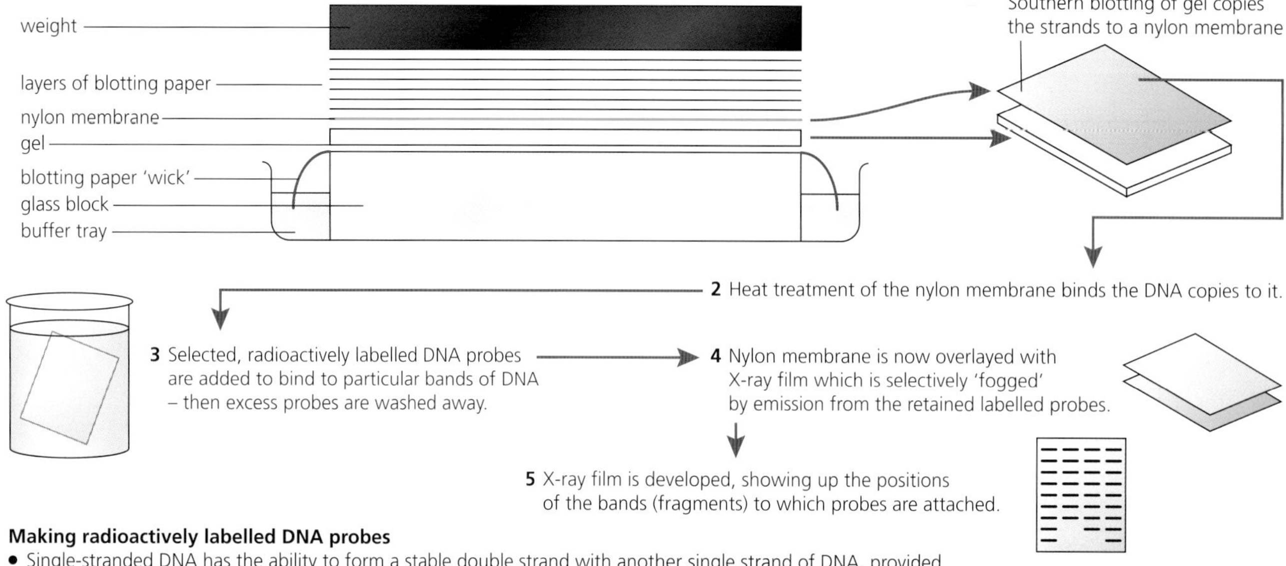

Making radioactively labelled DNA probes

- Single-stranded DNA has the ability to form a stable double strand with another single strand of DNA, provided the bases are complementary (i.e. pair). If one strand is 'labelled', the presence of the paired strands is easily detected.
- Short lengths of single-stranded DNA are made in the laboratory for this purpose, by enzymically combining and then adding selected nucleotides one at a time, in a precise sequence.
- Consequently, the base sequence of probes is predetermined and known.
- All the nucleotides used contain radioactive phosphorus (^{32}P), or carbon (^{14}C) in the ribose of the nucleic acid backbone so the subsequent positions of the probes (and the location of a complementary strand of DNA, e.g. on a nylon membrane) can be located by autoradiography.

What a probe is and how it works

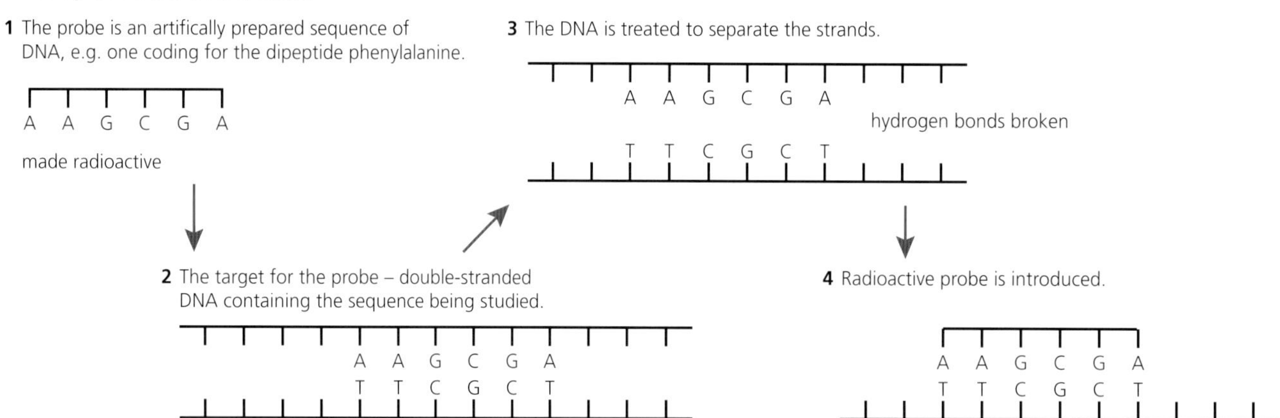

Figure 19.6 Visualisation of separated DNA fragments using Southern blotting and labelled probes

Test yourself

6 Explain why electrophoresis separates fragments of DNA.

7 Why are microsatellites useful in DNA profiling?

8 Explain how scientists can control which part of a genome is amplified by the PCR.

9 The Southern blot technique is used to transfer a DNA profile from a gel to a nylon membrane. Give the advantage of this.

10 Outline how autoradiography is used to show the location of DNA probes in a DNA profile.

The use of DNA profiling

DNA profiles, amplifying several fragments of DNA containing different repeated sequences, result in a unique banding pattern for every individual. There are many uses of these DNA profiles. Here, we will consider just two:

- The identification of family relationships in paternity testing.
- The identification of individuals in forensic science.

1 Identification of family relationships in paternity testing

Scientists can use DNA profiles to judge whether two or more individuals are genetically related. DNA profiles from two members of a clone will be identical – the DNA fragments will be the same size and the bands produced by electrophoresis will be in the same places.

Figure 19.7 shows four DNA profiles. The dark bands show the fragments of DNA that have migrated down the gel during electrophoresis and been visualised using the Southern blotting technique. You can see that the actual bands are less discrete than those represented diagrammatically in Figures 19.5 and 19.6. You can also see that they differ in thickness and in intensity. The first three bands show the DNA profiles of a woman (labelled M) and her two children (labelled C). The final profile is that of the woman's husband (labelled F). The reason the profiles have been produced is to determine whether the woman's husband is the father of the children. You might imagine that it is the husband who is questioning this, but more often paternity tests are carried out at the request of an immigration officer to enable a decision to be made about whether a child should be granted immigration status.

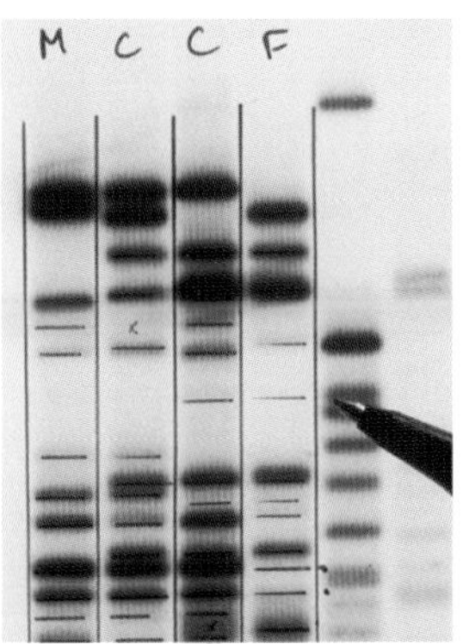

Figure 19.7 DNA profiles used to establish family relationships

Because a child inherits half its DNA from its mother and half from its father, the bands in a child's DNA profile that do not match any of those in its mother's profile must come from the child's father. Look at the DNA profiles in Figure 19.7. Identify those bands in the children's profiles that are **not** present in the mother's profile. Are they present in the profile of her husband? If so, the profiles provide evidence that the husband is likely to be the father of both children. If not, they provide evidence that he is not the father of one or both.

Similar DNA profiling also has applications in studies of wild animals, for example, to ensure that only unrelated animals are used in captive breeding programmes of animals in danger of extinction.

2 Identification of individuals in forensic science

DNA profiles produced from biological specimens taken from the scene of a serious crime, such as a rape attack or murder, can provide reliable evidence. Following amplification by the PCR, samples such as a few hair roots or a tiny amount of blood or semen will provide sufficient DNA to carry out DNA profiling. Specimens might also be collected from people suspected of being present at the crime. The greatest care has to be taken to ensure the authenticity of the samples – there must be no possibility of contamination if the outcome of subsequent testing is to be helpful in a court case.

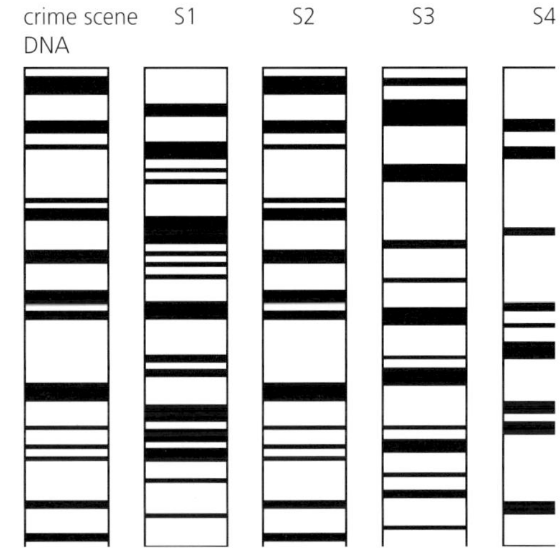

Figure 19.8 DNA profiling in forensic science – profiles from a specimen taken at the scene of a crime and from four different suspects

DNA profiling of these samples can help to eliminate innocent suspects as well as to identify a person, or people, who might be responsible for the crime. You can see an example of this use of DNA profiles in Figure 19.8, in which five DNA profiles are represented.

The one on the left of the diagram is from a crime scene. The others, S1 to S4, are from four people the police suspect might have been at the scene of the crime. Having produced them, the role of a forensic scientist is to advise the police, and then possibly a jury, what these profiles show about the guilt of the suspects.

DNA profiles can also help forensic scientists to identify corpses otherwise too decomposed for recognition, or isolated body parts remaining after bomb blasts or other violent incidents.

Test yourself

11 Which of the DNA fragments in Figure 19.7 is the largest? Explain your answer.

12 Can you conclude from Figure 19.7 that the man (F) is the father of both his wife's children? Explain your answer.

13 TV programmes often show crime scene investigators searching a crime scene for clues dressed in normal clothing. Explain why this is unlikely to happen in reality.

14 What can you conclude from Figure 19.8 about the involvement of the suspects in the crime? Explain your answer.

Using gene sequencing

What is gene sequencing?

Key terms

Gene sequencing Finding the sequence of bases in a DNA molecule. This can be done at the level of an entire genome or at the level of a single fragment of DNA.

Human genome All the genetic material in a human cell. This includes all of the genes plus the base sequences of DNA that do not encode polypeptides.

Gene sequencing involves finding the sequence of bases in a DNA molecule. This can be done at the level of an entire genome or at the level of a single fragment of DNA.

The Human Genome Project was launched in 1990. In 2001, it achieved its objectives when the US National Institutes of Health published the first draft of the base sequence of the entire **human genome**. One of the outcomes of this research was the realisation that much of the genome did not code for polypeptides; something we considered in the last chapter. Another outcome is that scientists can use the known base sequence of a gene to predict the amino acid sequence of the polypeptide it encodes. A third outcome is the ability to screen samples of DNA for links to genetically determined conditions. This has enabled medics to screen DNA from:

- potential parents to find if one of them is a carrier of an inherited disorder and, if so, offer genetic counselling
- fetal cells to find if a child would suffer a debilitating inherited disorder and, if so, the potential to offer the parents an abortion
- embryos prepared for *in vitro* fertilisation (IVF), so that embryos with 'faulty' genes can be rejected and not used for implantation into the mother's uterus
- sufferers of several diseases, including cancer, to help to identify the most suitable drug to alleviate their condition; a science known as pharmacogenomics.

Of course, each of these techniques raises questions about the ethics and cost-effectiveness of these procedures. Since the Human Genome Project began, the techniques used in genetic screening have evolved. The first sequence took 11 years to complete (1990 to 2001) and cost an estimated US$ 2.3 billion. In March 2015, should you have so chosen, you could have had your own genome sequenced in a period of weeks at a cost of £125. Since 2008, a new technique has been developed that enables scientists to sequence the bases of mRNA (called RNA-seq). This has shown that over 90 per cent of human genes contain one or more alternative splicing variants (see page 376).

A method of gene sequencing based on the PCR

In this method, developed by Fred Sanger, the DNA strand to be sequenced is used as a template in the PCR. You have seen that the PCR will, in a short space of time, produce a very large number of copies of the target DNA. The neat trick in this technique is to stop replication when particular nucleotides are incorporated – a process known as **termination sequencing**.

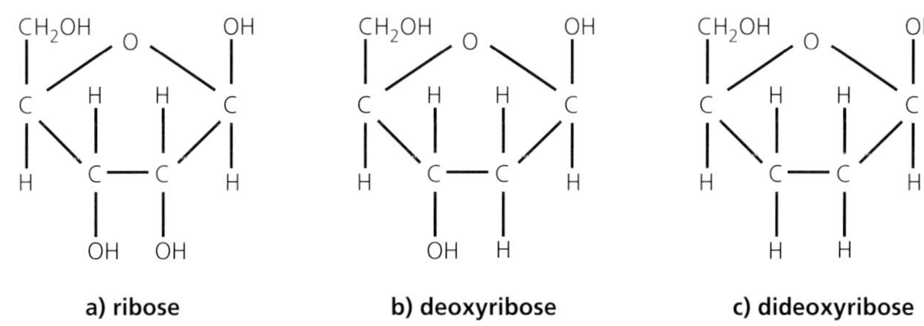

Figure 19.9 A molecule of (a) ribose, (b) deoxyribose and (c) dideoxyribose

Look at Figure 19.9. It shows two pentose sugar molecules you should recognise – ribose and deoxyribose. It also shows a third molecule that you might not have seen before, dideoxyribose. Just as deoxyribose is a ribose molecule with an oxygen atom missing from carbon-2, dideoxyribose is a ribose molecule with two oxygen atoms missing, one from carbon-2 and one from carbon-3. A nucleotide that contains dideoxyribose (a dideoxynucleotide) can pair with a nucleotide that has a complementary base, but because it lacks the OH group on carbon-3, DNA polymerase cannot add another nucleotide to it. This means that the incorporation of a dideoxynucleotide into a developing DNA strand stops the further development of that strand by the PCR.

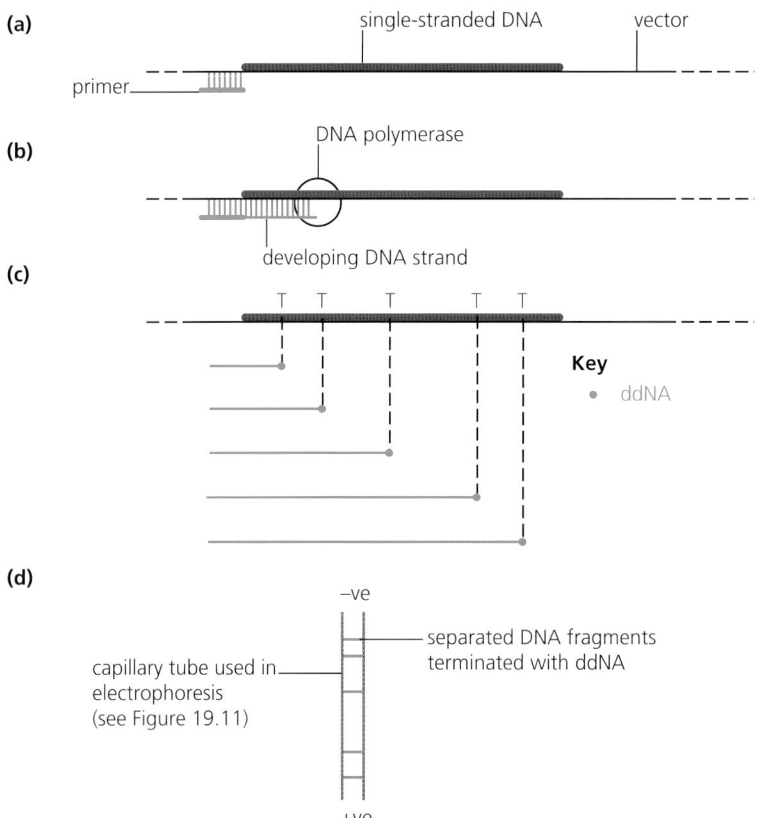

Figure 19.10 The principles involved in one type of gene sequencer. The four stages are described on the next page

Figure 19.10 represents what happens when you use dideoxynucleotides in the PCR. As described earlier, the reagents used include a heat-resistant DNA polymerase, short primers with base sequences complementary to the start of the section of DNA to be copied and an excess of nucleotides, each carrying one of the four bases. This time, however, four reaction mixtures are used, each containing a percentage of dideoxynucleotides carrying adenine, cytosine, guanine or thymine. Each of these dideoxynucleotides is labelled with a different fluorescent dye.

- In Figure 19.10(a) you can see an early stage in one PCR cycle, with a single strand of DNA with a primer attached.
- In Figure 19.10(b), DNA polymerase has attached to the primer and begun to produce a complementary strand, adding nucleotides with bases that are complementary to the bases on the template strand.
- In Figure 19.10(c) the development of five new strands has been terminated when DNA polymerase added a dideoxynucleotide-carrying adenine (ddNA). You can deduce that thymine (T), the base complementary to adenine, must occur at the positions shown on the template strand.
- The fragments of different length are then separated by electrophoresis. Figure 19.10(d) shows one way in which this can be automated. Instead of using gel in a tank, as shown in Figure 19.5 on page 397, gel within a capillary tube has been used. By using a laser, detector and computer, the bands of labelled adenine-carrying dideoxynucleotide can be detected as they migrate through the gel in the capillary and displayed on a screen as shown in Figure 19.11.

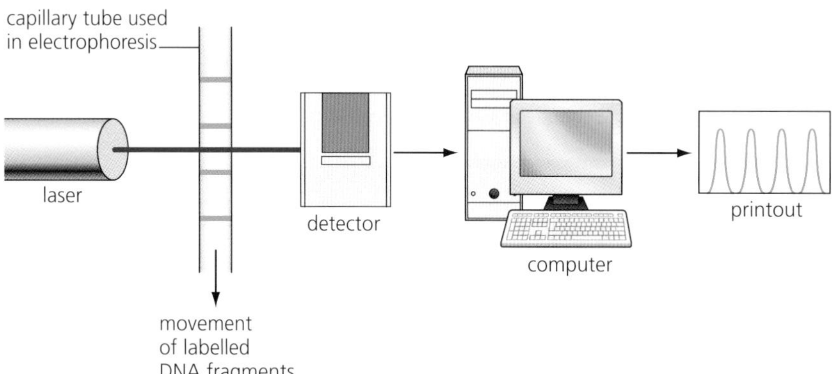

Figure 19.11 Using electrophoresis through a capillary tube allows the automation of electrophoresis. In this case, DNA fragments labelled with green fluorescent dye result in green peaks on a computer screen

By compiling the results of labelled dideoxynucleotide with each of the four bases, an automated sequencer produces results like those in Figure 19.12. Scientists can use this to determine the entire base sequence of the original DNA fragment. Typically, the method described is accurate for sequences up to a maximum of 700–800 base pairs long. Modifications of the same method, in which overlapping fragments are sequenced and the overlaps arranged by computer software, allow sequencing of larger genes and, in fact, whole genomes.

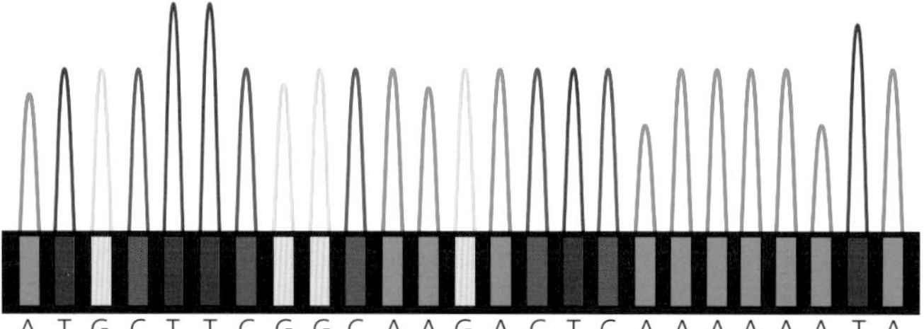

Figure 19.12 Part of the printout of a gene sequencing machine. The bases have been labelled with fluorescent dye: adenine green, cytosine blue, guanine yellow and thymine red

Test yourself

15 Define the term 'genome'.

16 DNA sequencing has found that an intron, 729 base pairs long, found in the *ZFY* gene on the X chromosome was identical in the X chromosomes from a random sample of men. The same intron showed a great deal of genetic variation within samples of X chromosomes from chimpanzees, gorillas and orang-utan. Suggest an explanation for the lack of variation in humans.

17 Does knowledge of the genome enable scientist to predict the proteome (full complement of proteins) that a bacterium and a person can make? Explain your answer.

18 In March 2015, someone in the UK could have had their own genome sequenced in a period of weeks at a cost of £125. Suggest **one** disadvantage that might arise from the knowledge of a person's genome.

19 If a dideoxynucleotide is incorporated into a developing DNA strand, DNA polymerase cannot add further nucleotides to this strand. Explain why.

20 Give the base sequence of the template strand used to obtain the results in Figure 19.12.

In vivo amplification of DNA

As outlined in the introduction on page 390, DNA can be amplified by inserting fragments into the genomes of living cells. Those cells that successfully incorporate the new DNA into their genomes will replicate it and pass it on to their daughter cells when they divide.

The way in which DNA to be replicated is extracted from tissue samples was described in Figure 19.2 on page 391. As Figure 19.13 on the next page shows, the extracted DNA can then be cut into fragments by the addition of a **restriction endonuclease** (often called a restriction enzyme). An endonuclease is an enzyme that hydrolyses the bonds in the sugar-phosphate backbone of both strands in a DNA molecule, producing double-stranded fragments of DNA. Restriction endonucleases occur naturally in bacteria, where they protect against viruses that infect the bacterium (bacteriophages) by cutting the viral DNA into small pieces, thereby preventing the lytic cycle (Chapter 4, page 93). Restriction enzymes were so named because they restrict the multiplication of phage viruses.

DNA may be extracted from tissue samples by mechanically breaking up the cells, filtering off the debris, and breaking down cell membranes by treatment with detergents. The protein framework of the chromosomes is then removed by incubation with a protein-digesting enzyme (protease). The DNA, now existing as long threads, is isolated from this mixture of chemicals by precipitation with ethanol, and is thus 'cleaned'. The DNA strands are then re-suspended in aqueous, pH buffered medium. They are now ready for 'splicing' into fragments.

> **Key term**
>
> **Restriction endonuclease**
> An enzyme (often abbreviated to 'restriction enzyme') that hydrolyses the phosphodiester bonds at a particular base sequence in a DNA molecule, cutting the DNA into double-stranded fragments. The specific base sequence is called the **recognition sequence** of that endonuclease.

Cutting DNA into fragments

Many different restriction enzymes have been discovered and purified, and are widely used to produce DNA fragments. They are named after the species of bacterium from which they are extracted, for example the enzyme *Eco*R1 is extracted from the

Key term

Recognition sequence The specific, short palindromic DNA base sequence to which a restriction endonuclease binds, catalysing hydrolysis of the phosphodiester bonds at that point in the DNA.

bacterium *Escherichia coli*. Where more than one restriction endonuclease has been extracted from the same species of bacterium, roman numerals are added, e.g., *Pvu*II was the second restriction endonuclease to be extracted from the bacterium *Proteus vulgaris*. Like all enzymes, restriction endonucleases are specific in the substrates to which they bind. In this case, each binds only to one particular base sequence, called its **recognition sequence**. You can see the recognition sequences of six different restriction endonucleases in Figure 19.13. One distinctive feature is that they are palindromic, that is they read the same in either direction.

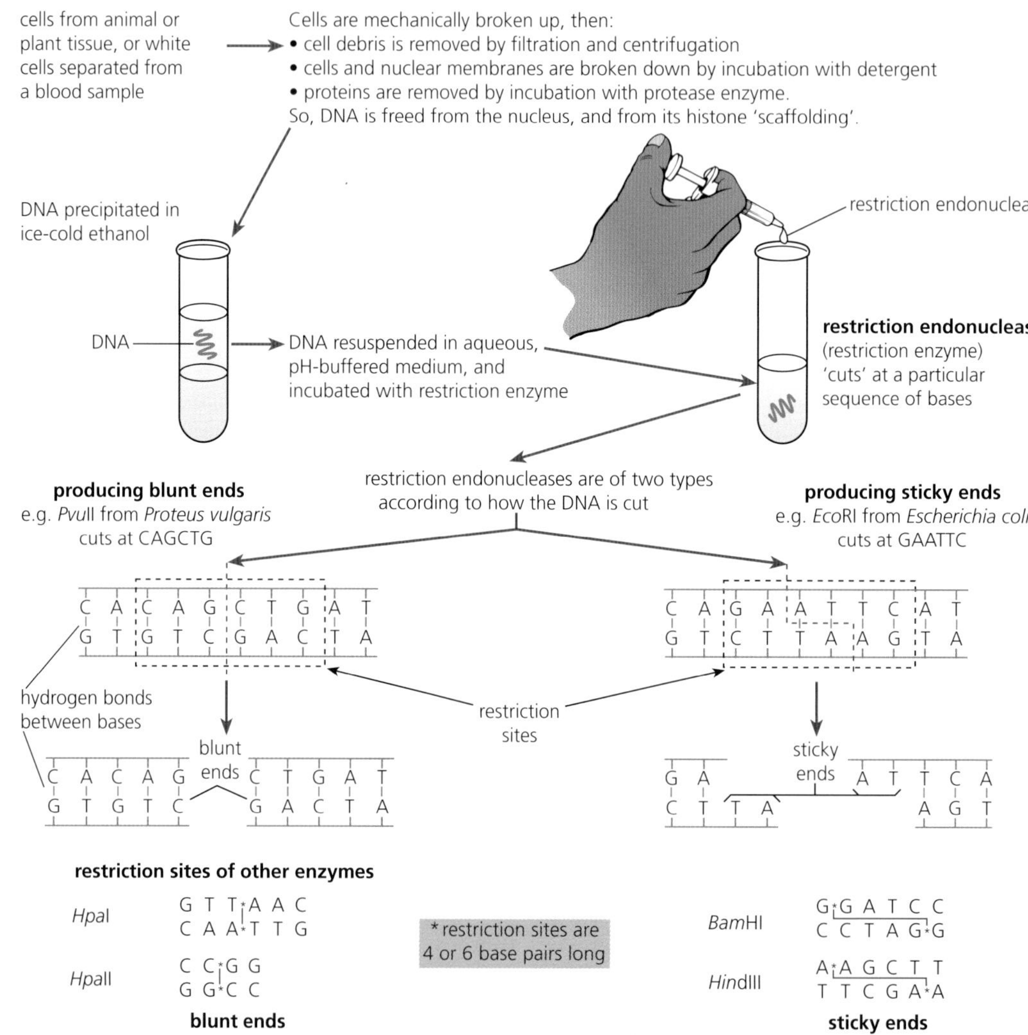

Figure 19.13 Using restriction endonucleases to produce fragments of DNA

Figure 19.13 shows a further property of restriction endonucleases – they produce one of two types of 'cut'. *Pvu*II, *Hpa*I and *Hpa*II make straight cuts, producing so-called '**blunt ends**'. *Eco*RI, *Bam*HI and *Hin*dIII make staggered cuts, producing fragments with overhanging ends, so-called '**sticky ends**'. DNA fragments with 'sticky ends' bind more readily to other DNA molecules. As you will see in the next section, DNA fragments with 'blunt ends' are made into 'sticky ends' when used during *in vivo* methods of DNA amplification.

Producing recombinant DNA

Before a DNA fragment can be cloned using *in vivo* technology, it must be added to a **vector**, which will be used to transfer it into living cells. When considering the transmission of diseases in Chapter 17, we used the term 'vector' to describe an agent that transports between one organism and another. In recombinant DNA technology, a vector is carrier DNA, used to carry a target fragment of DNA into a new organism. One such vector is commonly found in bacteria.

Figure 19.14 reminds you that a bacterium, such as *Escherichia coli*, contains two types of genetic material. One is the long, double-stranded DNA in the form of a ring, called the nucleoid. The other type is the more numerous, and much smaller rings of DNA, called plasmids.

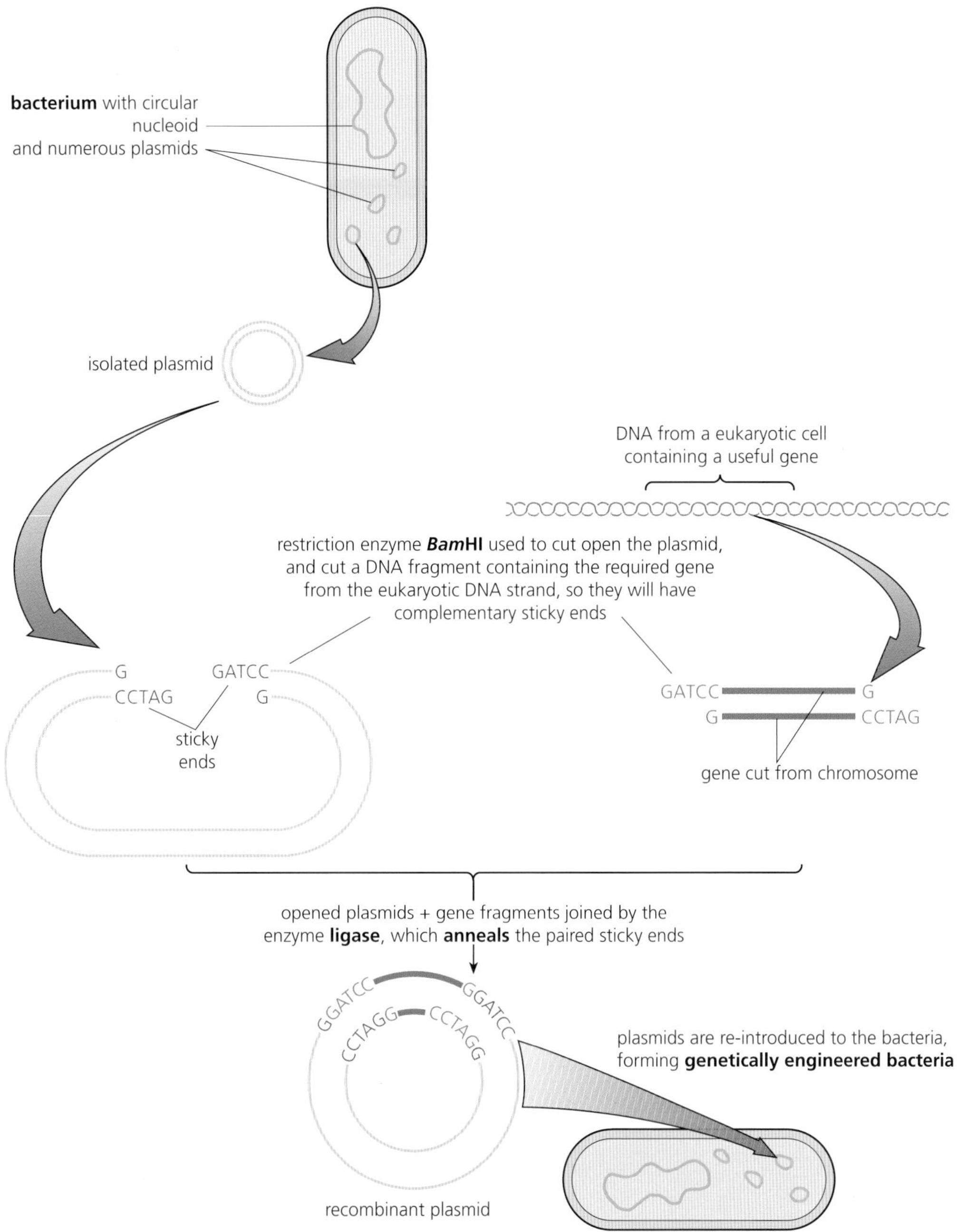

bacterium with circular nucleoid and numerous plasmids
isolated plasmid
DNA from a eukaryotic cell containing a useful gene
restriction enzyme ***Bam*HI** used to cut open the plasmid, and cut a DNA fragment containing the required gene from the eukaryotic DNA strand, so they will have complementary sticky ends
G
GATCC
CCTAG
G
sticky ends
GATCC
G
G
CCTAG
gene cut from chromosome
opened plasmids + gene fragments joined by the enzyme **ligase**, which **anneals** the paired sticky ends
GGATCC
GGATCC
CCTAGG
CCTAGG
plasmids are re-introduced to the bacteria, forming **genetically engineered bacteria**
recombinant plasmid

Figure 19.14 Using bacterial plasmids as DNA vectors

Plasmids are relatively easy to isolate from a bacterial cell and to reintroduce into a bacterial cell. They are, therefore, extremely useful as DNA vectors. In a bacterial cell, the plasmids replicate themselves independently of the nucleoid, so any gene added to a plasmid will be copied many times and will be passed on to the daughter cells when the bacterium divides by binary fission.

As you can see in Figure 19.14, a plasmid is cut open using a restriction endonuclease. If it produces 'sticky ends', the same enzyme is also used to cut the DNA fragment to be inserted. If not, complementary 'sticky ends' are added to the blunt ends of both the plasmid and the DNA fragment. The open plasmids and DNA fragments are then mixed with a **DNA ligase** – an enzyme that catalyses the formation of phosphodiester bonds between the ends of the plasmids and the DNA fragments. Ligase occurs naturally in the nuclei of eukaryotic organisms, where it repairs DNA that has been damaged during DNA replication. Figure 19.15 shows in greater detail how, following the alignment of their complementary base pairs, a ligase joins up the DNA of the plasmid and of the fragment – a process called **annealing**.

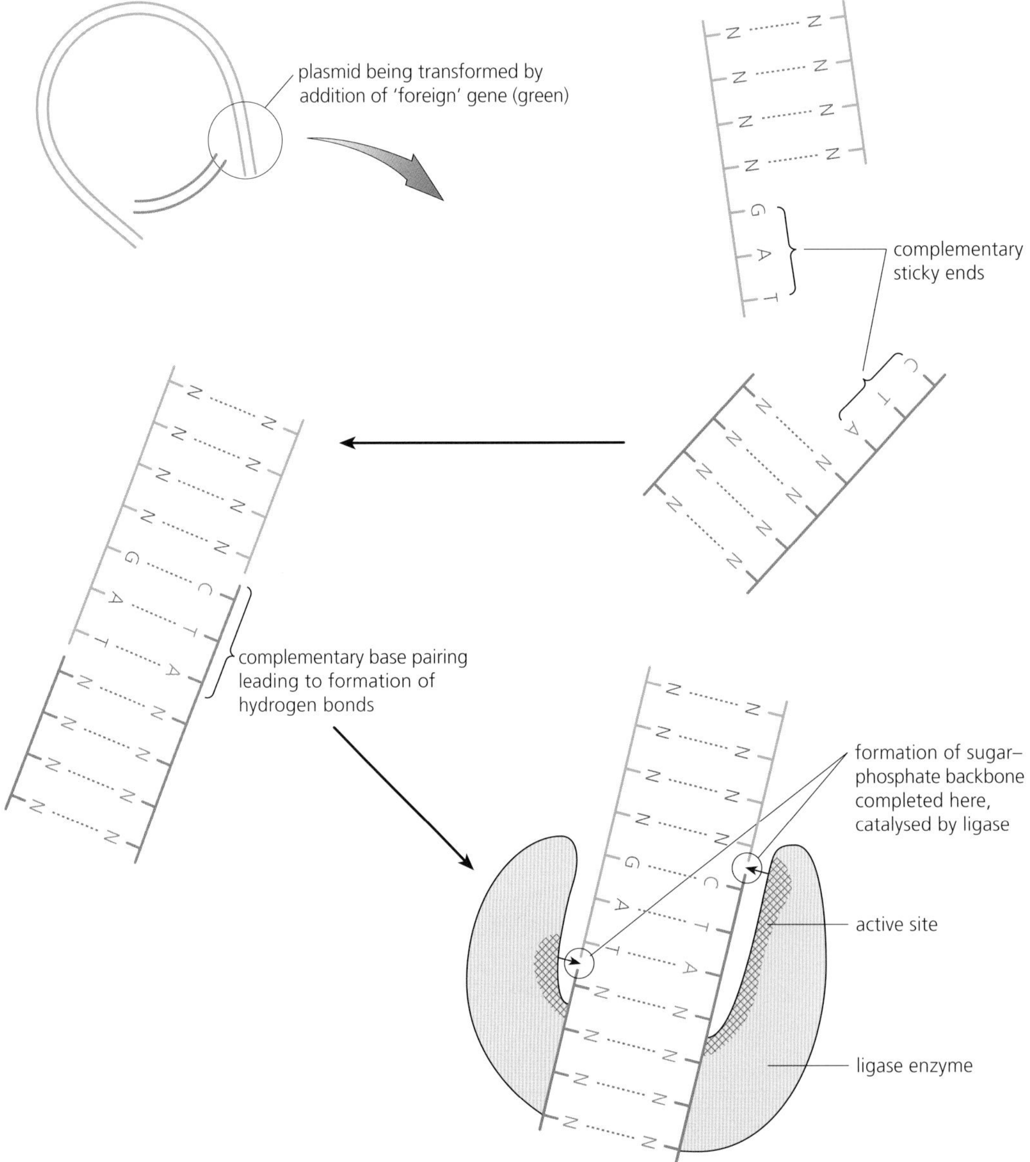

Figure 19.15 Annealing of a cut plasmid and a DNA fragment is catalysed by ligase

Transferring the recombinant DNA into a host bacterium

Most species of bacteria are able to take up plasmids. There are several methods, mostly found by trial and error, which can be used to encourage this. One involves soaking bacterial cells, together with plasmids, in an ice-cold solution of calcium chloride, followed by a brief heat shock at 42 °C for 2 minutes. Bacteria that have taken up these foreign plasmids are said to be **transformed**. If the DNA fragment within the plasmid contains one or more entire genes, they are also described as **transgenic**.

Identifying transformed bacteria

A diagram such as Figure 19.14 makes it easy to see that a bacterium has taken up a plasmid and been transformed. In reality, biologists can see neither the bacteria nor the plasmids. In effect, they carry out the above procedures not knowing whether:

- any plasmids contain recombinant DNA or whether they joined back on themselves (**self-ligated** plasmids)
- any bacteria have taken up plasmids
- any bacterium that has taken up a plasmid has taken up a self-ligated plasmid or a plasmid containing recombinant DNA.

They need methods by which they can identify transformed bacteria so that they can grow these, and only these, in a culture medium. There are several ways in which they can identify transformed bacteria. Most involve the use of marker genes on the plasmids. You are required to recall and understand only one method – the use of antibiotic-resistance marker genes and replica plating.

Figure 19.16(a) shows a plasmid that contains genes conferring resistance to two antibiotics, A and B. This plasmid is used as a vector for transferring a gene from another organism. The recognition sequence for the restriction enzyme used to cut this plasmid is within the gene conferring resistance to antibiotic B.

Figure 19.16(b) shows the appearance of a plasmid into which the 'foreign' gene has been successfully annealed. Using the heat-shock treatment, some bacterial cells will take up these plasmids. But how will we be able to tell which bacteria have taken up the plasmid with the 'foreign' gene?

Initially, we would not know. So we culture all the bacteria on agar plates. Figure 19.17 shows the appearance of one agar plate. Six colonies have grown on it; each colony being a clone of a single cell.

- We now take an imprint of this plate by gently pressing down on it with a piece of sterile velvet (or sterile filter paper). We then press the velvet onto the surface of an agar plate in which the agar contains antibiotic A.
- We repeat this process, this time pressing the velvet onto the surface of an agar plate in which the agar contains antibiotic B.

(a) Normal plasmid

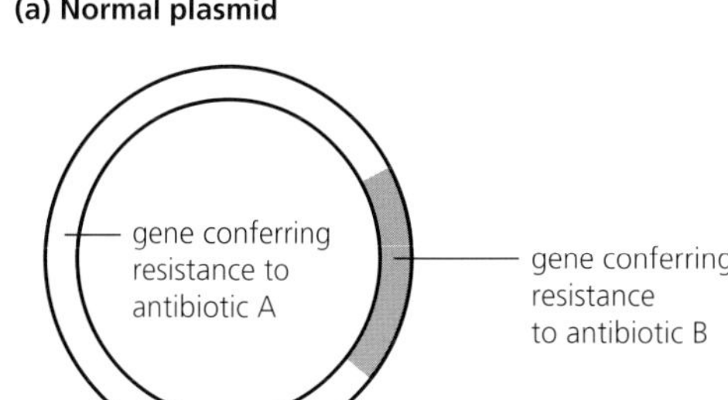

(b) Plasmid with 'foreign' gene

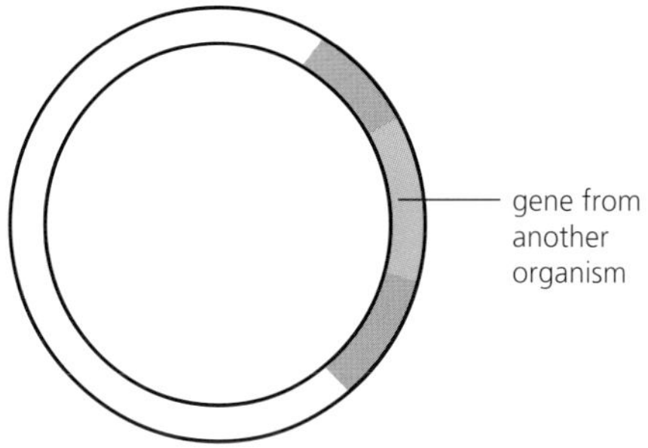

Figure 19.16 Using genes for antibiotic resistance as marker genes

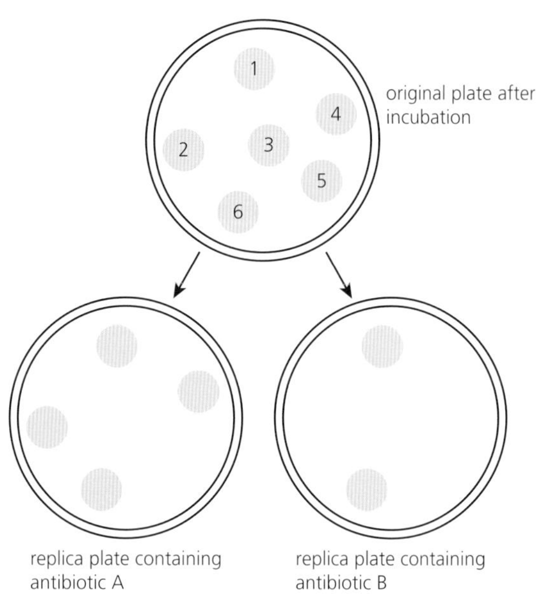

Figure 19.17 The results of the replica plating of six bacterial cultures onto agar plates contain antibiotic A or antibiotic B

The upper plate in Figure 19.17, representing normal agar, has six colonies. The plate containing antibiotic A has only four of these colonies – 1, 2, 4 and 6. Since the bacteria that gave rise to these colonies were able to survive, they must be resistant to antibiotic A. We can, therefore, conclude that they successfully took up the plasmids and that the bacteria that gave rise to colonies labelled 3 and 5 did not.

Of the four colonies that are resistant to antibiotic A, only two showed resistance to antibiotic B – those labelled 1 and 6. Since these bacteria are resistant to antibiotic B, we know that the gene conferring this resistance must be intact. The bacteria forming colonies labelled 2 and 4, however, were not resistant to antibiotic B. The reason for this must be that they contained the 'foreign' gene and it has disrupted their gene for resistance to antibiotic B. The bacteria in these colonies will have plasmids with the structure represented in Figure 19.16(b). We can, therefore, conclude that the bacteria in colonies 2 and 4 are transgenic bacteria – they carry the 'foreign' gene. We would now transfer samples of those colonies from the original agar plate to sterile nutrient medium and allow them to increase in number.

Other methods used to insert DNA into cells

In the above account, you have seen how bacteria can be transformed using recombinant plasmids. This technique can be useful if you wish to amplify the target DNA – the transformed bacteria multiply rapidly and replicate the target DNA at each division.

If scientists wish to transform cells other than bacteria, they can use different vectors to transfer the target DNA. The following four methods are commonly used.

- **Viruses** affect the cells they infect by inserting their own nucleic acid into a host cell. You can remind yourself of this by looking back to Figure 16.14 on page 343. This ability can be exploited by using viruses to transfer recombinant DNA into host cells. Used in this way, however, the virus must be weakened so that it does not cause the death of host cells.
- **Liposomes** are small lipid droplets that can be used to coat plasmids that contain recombinant DNA. The lipid coating enables the droplet, with its recombinant DNA, to cross cell surface membranes. Figure 19.19 on the next page, shows how this technique has been used, with mixed success, to transform epithelial cells in the lungs of human sufferers of cystic fibrosis.
- **Gene guns** use air pressure to enable particles of heavy metals, such as gold or titanium, that are coated with recombinant DNA to be 'fired' through the surface of cells. This technique is often called bioballistics, abbreviated to biolistics. The particles coated with DNA can be fired directly into an organ of the target organism or into a tissue culture containing its cells. Figure 19.18 shows a gene gun being used on a plant organ.
- **Electroporation** uses electricity to create pores in the cell surface membranes of the target organism. The affected cells are then able to take up naked recombinant DNA and incorporate it into their own genomes.

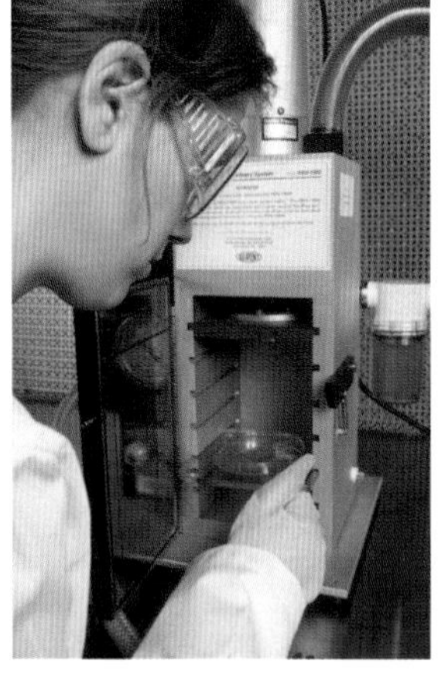

Figure 19.18 A gene gun in use

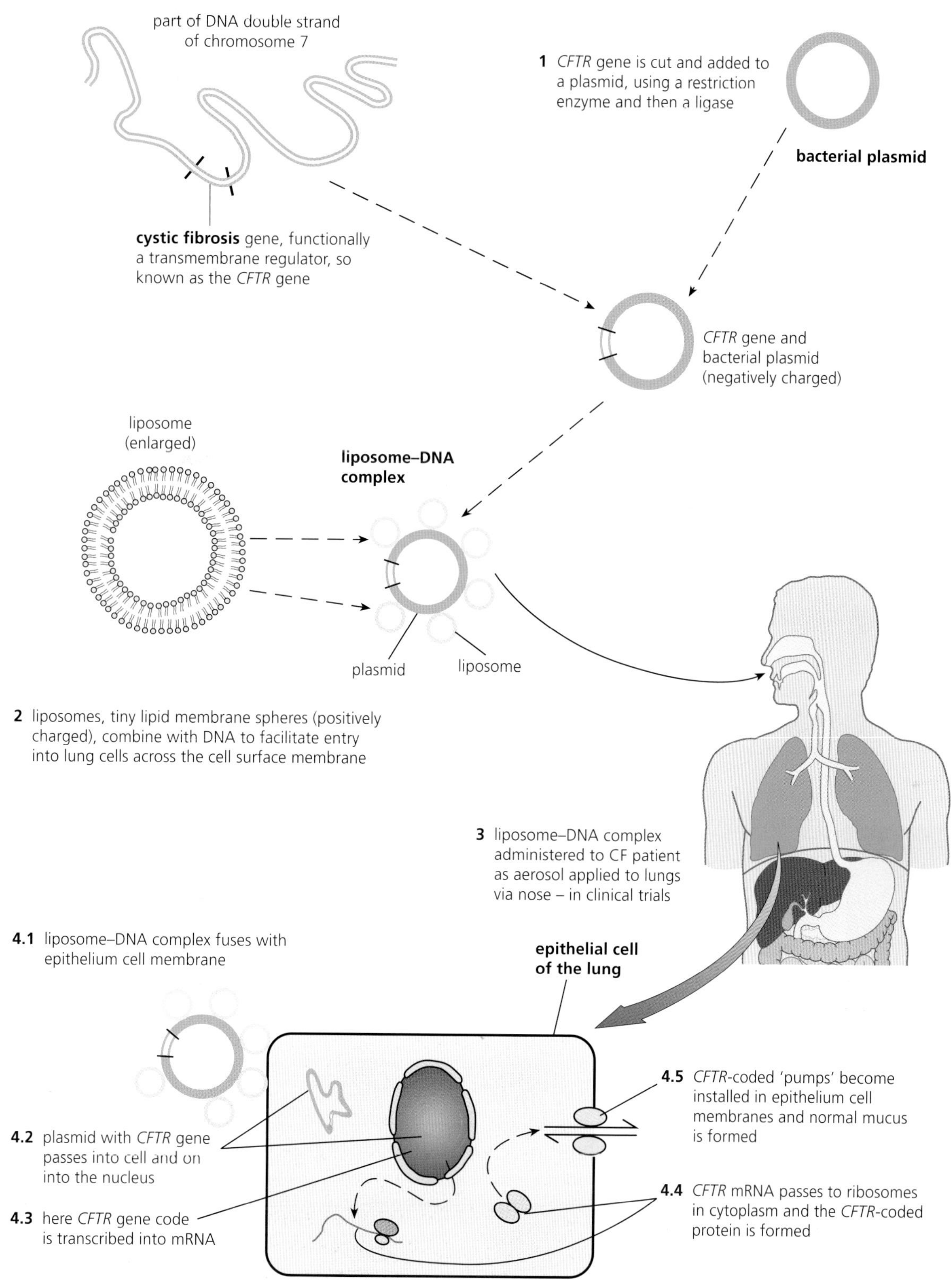

The cystic fibrosis gene codes for a membrane protein that occurs widely in body cells, and pumps ions (e.g. Cl⁻) across cell membranes.
part of DNA double strand of chromosome 7
1 CFTR gene is cut and added to a plasmid, using a restriction enzyme and then a ligase
bacterial plasmid
cystic fibrosis gene, functionally a transmembrane regulator, so known as the CFTR gene
CFTR gene and bacterial plasmid (negatively charged)
liposome (enlarged)
liposome–DNA complex
plasmid
liposome
2 liposomes, tiny lipid membrane spheres (positively charged), combine with DNA to facilitate entry into lung cells across the cell surface membrane
3 liposome–DNA complex administered to CF patient as aerosol applied to lungs via nose – in clinical trials
4.1 liposome–DNA complex fuses with epithelium cell membrane
epithelial cell of the lung
4.5 CFTR-coded 'pumps' become installed in epithelium cell membranes and normal mucus is formed
4.2 plasmid with CFTR gene passes into cell and on into the nucleus
4.4 CFTR mRNA passes to ribosomes in cytoplasm and the CFTR-coded protein is formed
4.3 here CFTR gene code is transcribed into mRNA

In recent clinical trials some 20% of epithelium cells of cystic fibrosis patients were *temporarily* modified (i.e. accepted the *CFTR* gene), but the effects were relatively short-lived. This is because our epithelium cells are continually replaced at a steady rate, and in cystic fibrosis patients the genetically engineered cells are replaced with cells without *CFTR*-coded pumps. Patients would require periodic treatment with the liposome–DNA complex aerosol to maintain the effect permanently.

Figure 19.19 Using liposomes to transfer recombinant DNA into cells lining the lungs of cystic fibrosis sufferers

Two uses of recombinant DNA technology

Recombinant DNA technology can be used in several ways. Food shortage is a worldwide problem. Using traditional breeding techniques, farmers have selectively bred plants and animals to increase the production of crops, milk and meat for centuries. Using recombinant DNA technology, genetic changes can be made to occur much more quickly than these traditional breeding programmes. The transgenic organisms so formed are referred to as genetically modified (GM) organisms. The production of GM organisms is now a major industry, dominated by a small number of manufacturers. Recombinant DNA technology is also used in pure academic research, helping biologists to understand gene function. We will look at one example of each of these uses of recombinant DNA technology.

The use of recombinant DNA technology in the production of genetically modified soya

Beans of the soya plant (*Glycine max*) are a staple food source for humans and livestock and are used worldwide as a source of protein and oils. Although the growth of genetically modified plants (GM plants) within the European Union is banned under EU regulations, well over half the world's soya bean crop is from GM soya plants. Each modification has involved the introduction of recombinant DNA containing a gene that changes the properties of the soya bean plants. In some cases, the recombinant DNA includes a gene that leads to an increase in crop yield, for example by conferring:

- resistance to glyphosate (a commonly used weed killer that would also affect the soya plant)
- resistance to pests, including fungi, nematode worms and insects
- tolerance to drought and to soil salinity.

In other cases, the recombinant DNA includes a gene that changes the biochemical components of the soya beans, for example:

- the balance of the fatty acids, increasing the percentage of oleic acid and reducing that of linoleic acid. The benefit of this is that, during cooking, linoleic acid is more easily oxidised to produce trans fats than is oleic acid. Trans fats are harmful to human health.
- production of active pharmacological ingredients (so-called molecular pharming).

Figure 19.20 Crown gall disease in a chrysanthemum plant. This tumour is caused by a bacterium, *Agrobacterium tumefaciens*, which can infect over 10 000 plant species

Gene guns and electroporation have been used to insert the recombinant DNA into soya plants. In addition, a bacterium, *Agrobacterium tumefaciens*, has also been used. When this bacterium infects plants, it transfers its own DNA into cells of the infected plant, creating tumours (see Figure 19.20). Using restriction endonuclease and ligase enzymes, as described above, it has been possible to insert target genes into non-virulent plasmids of *A. tumefaciens*. These transgenic bacteria have then been used to infect soya tissue cultures, resulting in soya plants in which all the cells contain the desired gene.

The use of recombinant DNA technology in the production of 'knockout' mice

A 'knockout' mouse is a laboratory mouse in which research scientists have inactivated (or knocked out) one of its genes. The scientists do this by adding into the genome of a mouse, a piece of foreign DNA that disrupts transcription of a gene. To ensure that most of the cells of the adult mouse will have the inactivated gene, the scientists begin with embryonic stem cells from an early mouse embryo. Using a virus, or a linear piece of bacterial DNA, scientists insert the artificial gene into these stem cells. They then culture these stem cells in a laboratory before injecting them into new mouse embryos, which they transplant into the uterus of a female mouse. Some of the tissues of the resulting pups will have the target gene inactivated. By cross-breeding these mice, scientists can produced mice in which all the tissues have the target gene inactivated, that is, for this gene they are homozygous knockout mice.

By knocking out the activity of a gene, research scientists can investigate the function of that gene. Since humans and mice have many genes in common, using mice in this way helps us to understand the function of many of our own genes. In turn, this knowledge has enabled us to understand human diseases such as heart disease, cancer and Parkinson's disease and to develop, and test, drugs or other therapies to control them. Knockout mice are not always helpful in this way, however. One gene associated with over half of all tumours in humans is called *p53*. Although *p53* knockout mice do show an increase in the production of tumours, they occur in different tissues from those affected in humans.

The debate about the use of recombinant DNA technology

Although there are many examples of genetic modifications that are beneficial, geneticists are really producing new organisms when they produce transgenic organisms. Consequently, this work is potentially a source of hazards and it certainly generates concerns. These include the following:

- Will a gene added to a genome function in an unforeseen manner, for example triggering some disease in the recipient?
- Might an introduced gene for resistance to adverse conditions get transferred from a crop plant to a species of weed?
- Is it possible that a relatively harmless organism, such as the human gut bacterium, *Escherichia coli*, might be transformed into a harmful pathogen that escapes the laboratory and infects populations?
- Is there an important overriding principle that humans should not 'change nature' in a deliberate way?
- Recombinant DNA technology is costly so it would mainly benefit the health and life expectancy of people in the developed nations. Wouldn't it be better to use these funds to address the more basic problems of housing, health and nutrition in less developed countries?

A short consideration of the potential benefits and possible harmful effects of genetic modification is given in Table 19.1.

Table 19.1 Some pro and cons of genetic manipulation

Reassurances	Potential dangers
The nutritional quality of foodstuffs can be improved much faster than the traditional methods of animal and plant breeding.	GM foods could have a negative impact on human health. A gene for use in genetic modification might be taken from a plant that causes an allergic response in some people. Inserting that gene into another plant could cause the new host plant to express that allergen. Alternatively, the interaction of genes from two species could result in the production of a completely new allergen.
Genes conferring resistance to adverse environmental conditions will enable the use of previously unsuitable land to grow crops or increase the yield in less hostile environments.	Horizontal gene transfer might result in pest plant species gaining the transferred genes, enabling them also to grow in these adverse conditions and, if as a result they are able to compete more strongly, reduce crop yield.
GM organisms are tested in the laboratory and in field trials before they are grown commercially.	When grown commercially, there might be consequences to the environment that did not appear in trials. For example, a product of GM crops could be toxic to beneficial organisms (see Figure 19.21).
People can choose whether or not they eat GM products.	GM crops will eventually pollinate non-GM crops, so that it will become impossible for people to make a choice about whether or not they eat GM foods.
In humans, inherited conditions that are common in a family can be avoided by the careful use of genetic modification.	Many people consider this to be treating humans as commodities that could have serious socio-cultural consequences. It would also lead to social divides as the technology would be available only to the rich.
Only one gene is involved in the transfer so it will have minimal effect on the genome.	Interactions within the genome are currently poorly understood but we do know that promoter genes can regulate a large number of polypeptide-coding genes. In reality, we do not know the impact a single gene change might have on the genome.

Figure 19.21 There is current scientific controversy concerning whether pollen from GM maize plants landing on its natural food source (milkweed plants) has contributed to the dramatic fall in the population of these monarch butterflies

Test yourself

21 Give **two** features of the recognition sequence of a restriction endonuclease.

22 Explain the importance of 'sticky ends' in DNA technology.

23 What is a 'transformed' bacterium?

24 Suggest why 'transferring' a gene directly into affected cells is unlikely to result in the long-term treatment of inherited diseases in adult humans.

25 Explain the term 'homozygous knockout mice'.

Chapter summary

The polymerase chain reaction (PCR)

- The PCR can be used to amplify, i.e. produce multiple copies of, a DNA sample.
- The PCR is carried out in a programmable thermal cycler containing:
  - the sample of DNA
  - primer – short oligonucleotides with a base sequence that is complementary to the 3' ends of the DNA strands to be copied
  - free DNA nucleotides with adenine, cytosine, guanine or thymine bases
  - thermostable DNA polymerase.
- Raising the temperature to 95 °C separates the two strands of the target DNA.
- Cooling to 40 °C allows the primer to attach to the 3' ends of the separated DNA strands.
- Using DNA polymerase and the free DNA nucleotides, each strand acts as a template for the production of a complementary strand.
- At each turn of the cycle, the number of DNA molecules doubles.

Gene profiling and gene sequencing

- In gene profiling, the PCR is used to produce multiple copies of DNA fragments that contain satellite regions.
- Gel electrophoresis is used to separate the DNA fragments, which are then visualised using labelled probes and their locations compared with other, known profiles.
- Gene profiling can be used to test paternity or in forensic science to identify criminals.
- An organism's genome is the sum total of its DNA, coding and non-coding, and includes the DNA located in mitochondria and chloroplasts.
- Gene sequencing is an automated process that finds the DNA base sequence of a fragment of DNA or of the entire genome of an organism.
- The PCR is used in all gene sequencing technologies because large samples of DNA are required.
- Early methods of gene sequencing involved using dideoxyribonucleotides, which stop further amplification of DNA, and deoxyribonucleotides labelled with a fluorescent dye, which can be detected.
- Modern, high-throughput methods allow extremely fast sequencing of entire genomes.
- Gene sequencing can be used to predict the amino acid sequence of encoded polypeptides and, hence, make links to inherited medical conditions.

Gene technology

- Recombinant DNA technology utilises DNA from two different sources combined together, which is then inserted into a target cell, producing a transformed cell.
- To combine two DNA sources, they must be cut using restriction endonucleases and spliced together using DNA ligase.
- Recombinant DNA can be inserted into target cells using vectors, such as viruses or liposomes, and by using gene guns.
- The use of genes conferring antibiotic-resistance as marker genes and replica plating can be used to identify transformed bacteria.
- Recombinant DNA technology has been used to genetically modify soya (*Glycine max*) to improve its productivity and change the balance of fatty acids in its beans.
- Recombinant DNA has also been used to inactivate individual genes of laboratory mice. By following the development of these 'knock-out' mice, scientists can investigate the function of each inactivated gene.
- The unknown consequences of recombinant DNA technology have caused widespread public concern.

Practice questions

1 Which one of the following base sequences is most likely to be a recognition sequence of a restriction endonuclease?

A CCGTAT
GGCATA

B ATCCGC
TAGGCG

C GGGTAT
CCCATA

D GAATTC
CTTAAG *(1)*

2 Replica plating involves:

A making serial dilutions of a bacterial culture

B taking an imprint of bacterial growth on an agar plate and transferring it to a new agar plate

C setting up several repeats of each inoculated agar plate

D other scientists repeating your experiment with bacteria to see if they get the same results *(1)*

3 A transgenic bacterium has:

A gained one or more genes from another organism

B lost one or more genes to another organism

C undergone horizontal gene transfer via conjugation

D many plasmids *(1)*

4 The diagram represents the processes involved in one cycle of the polymerase chain reaction (PCR).

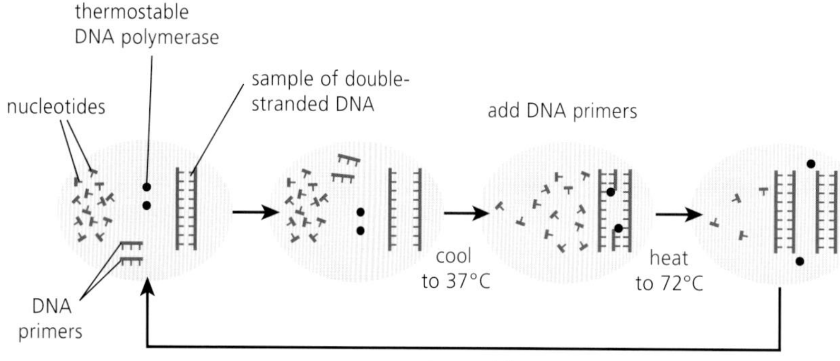

a) Describe the structure of a DNA primer and explain its role in the PCR. *(3)*

b) Explain why the DNA polymerase used in this process must be thermostable. *(2)*

c) How many cycles of the PCR would it take to amplify a single DNA fragment to produce 4000 copies? Explain your answer. *(2)*

5 The diagram shows how enzyme **X** cuts a molecule of DNA.

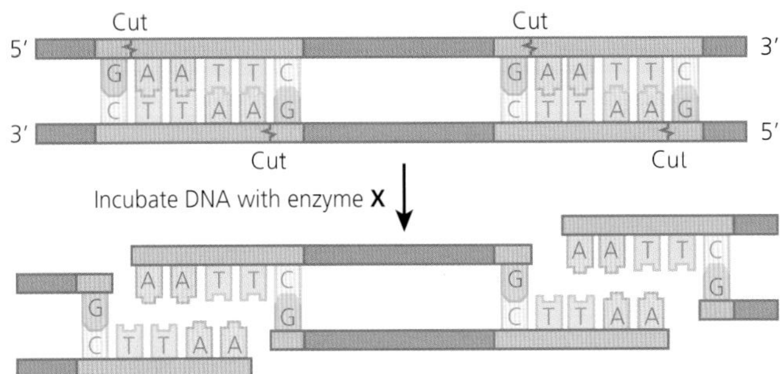

a) What **type** of enzyme is enzyme **X**? *(1)*

b) What is the recognition sequence of this enzyme? *(1)*

c) Explain the importance of the way in which enzyme **X** cuts the DNA. *(3)*

d) Enzyme **X** can be used to cut a gene from a DNA molecule. Suggest why it might be preferable to obtain a gene from mRNA than by cutting it from DNA. *(2)*

6 A scientist used the polymerase chain reaction (PCR) to amplify DNA. She set up four tubes containing the essential ingredients for the PCR to occur. In addition, she added to each tube DNA nucleotides in which the pentose sugar was dideoxyribose. Nucleotides containing this pentose sugar behave in the same way as those in which the pentose sugar is deoxyribose, with one important exception. As soon as a nucleotide containing dideoxyribose is inserted into a developing DNA strand, it terminates further replication.

One of her tubes contained dideoxynucleotides carrying the base adenine (ddNA); the second contained dideoxynucleotides carrying the base cytosine (ddNC); the third contained dideoxynucleotides carrying the base guanine (ddNG); and the fourth contained dideoxynucleotides carrying the base thymine (ddNT).

She then placed samples from each tube into separate wells in an agarose gel and carried out electrophoresis. The diagram shows her results.

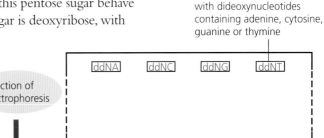

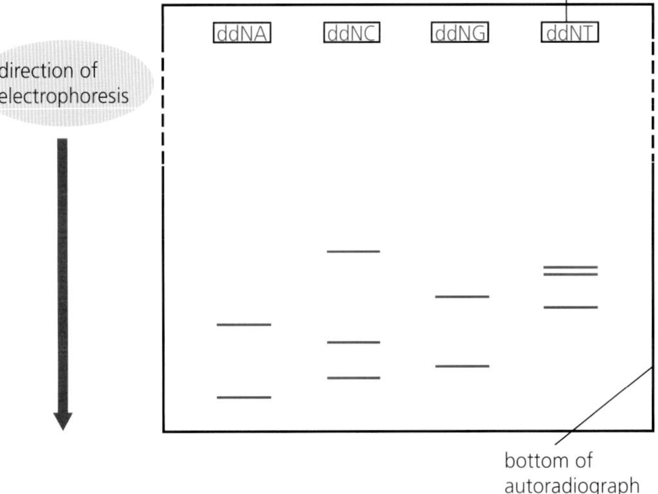

a) Which electrode would she have connected to the gel at the top of the diagram? *(1)*

b) Explain why the fragments of DNA produced the bands you can see in the diagram. *(2)*

c) From the information in the diagram, this scientist was able to deduce the base sequence of the template DNA replicated by the PCR. Explain how she was able to do this and give the base sequence of the template DNA strand. *(4)*

Stretch and challenge

7 Read the following passage and answer the questions that follow it.

A group of scientists wished to insert a gene of interest into the genome of the gut bacterium *Escherichia coli*.

Normal cells of *E. coli* can produce β-galactosidase, an enzyme that hydrolyses the β-glycosidic bond between galactose and another organic residue. This enzyme contains two polypeptide chains, encoded by two genes, *lacZα* and *lacZΩ*. Neither polypeptide is functional alone but, when produced together, the two polypeptides spontaneously form the functional enzyme β-galactosidase.

The scientists chose to work with a mutant form of *E. coli* in which part of the gene encoding β-galactosidase, *lacZα*, is missing.

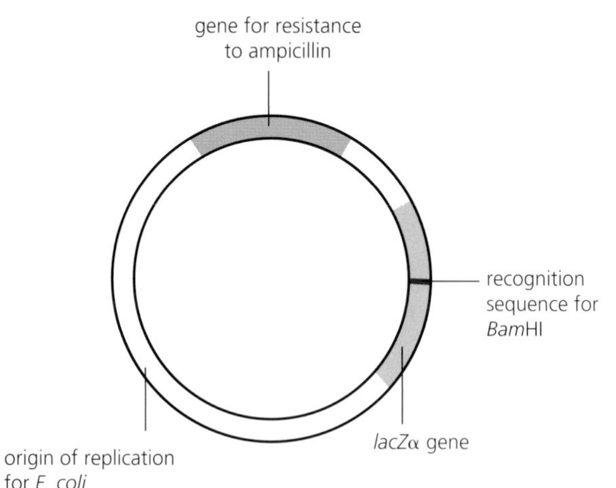

Figure 1 The plasmid pUC used as a DNA vector in this experiment

As a vector, they chose to use a plasmid, called pUC. Figure 1 represents this plasmid, showing some of the genes it carries. The scientists used the restriction enzyme *Bam*HI to insert the gene they were interested in into pUG plasmids. They then mixed these plasmids with heat-shocked mutant *E. coli* and cultured these bacteria on agar plates.

In addition to nutrients and inorganic ions needed for the growth of *E. coli*, the agar contained the antibiotic ampicillin and a lactose analogue, called X-gal. This substance is white but produces a blue-coloured product when hydrolysed by β-galactosidase.

Figure 2 shows the appearance of one of the scientists' plates after incubation for 48 hours.

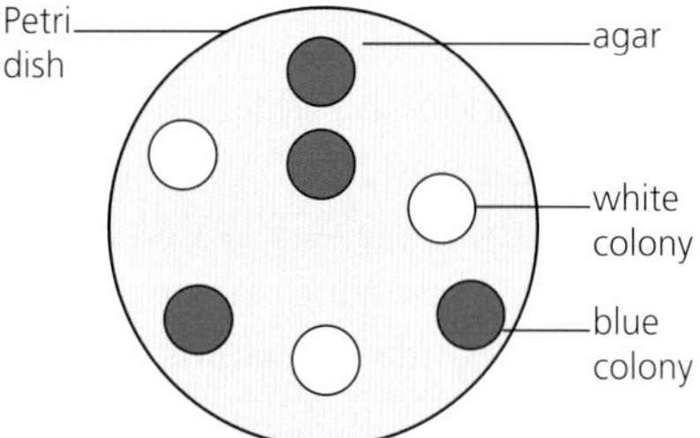

Figure 2 The appearance of one agar plate inoculated with mutant *E. coli* and incubated for 48 hours. Each circle represents a colony of bacteria that had grown from a single cell

a) Explain why β- galactosidase would be able hydrolyse lactose.

b) Suggest the importance of the origin of replication for *E.coli* in the pUC plasmid.

c) Use your knowledge of enzyme activity to suggest the meaning of 'lactose analogue'.

d) Which of the colonies in Figure 2 was formed by cells of *E. coli* that had successfully taken up the gene in which the scientists were interested? Fully explain your answer, using your own knowledge and information within the passage.

e) How would the scientists obtain a pure culture of the transformed bacteria?

8 Developments in molecular genetics have led to the sciences of:

- bioinformatics
- genomics
- pharmacogenomics
- proteomics.

Find out what is involved in each of these branches of biology.

20 Genetics

Prior knowledge

In this chapter you will need to recall that:

- → genes encode the amino acid sequences of polypeptides
- → a gene mutation changes the base sequence of a gene and might involve the deletion, insertion or substitution of one or more bases. Some mutations lead to a change in the amino acid sequence of the polypeptide encoded by a gene
- → alternative base sequences of a single gene are called alleles of that gene
- → chromosome mutations include translocation and non-disjunction
- → meiosis is a source of genetic variation, through the random segregation of homologous chromosomes during anaphase I and crossing over between non-sister chromatids of homologous chromosomes during prophase I
- → the random fusion of gametes during sexual reproduction gives rise to genetic variation in the offspring
- → monohybrid inheritance examines the way in which two or more alleles of a single gene controlling a single characteristic are passed from parents to offspring
- → genetic diagrams and pedigree diagrams can be used to show patterns of inheritance.

Test yourself on prior knowledge

1 Explain what is meant by a 'point mutation'.

2 Explain why some gene mutations have no effect on the amino acid sequence of the polypeptide encoded by the affected gene.

3 Briefly describe chromosome translocation.

4 Humans have 23 pairs of homologous chromosomes. Assuming that no mutations and no crossing over occurs, how many different chromosome combinations could theoretically be present in:

a) the gametes of each of two parents

b) the offspring of these parents?

5 List each of the stages in a genetic diagram representing a monohybrid cross.

Introduction

This chapter builds on the knowledge and understanding you gained in your GCSE science course and in the first year of your A level Biology course. We will re-examine the origins of genetic variation that you studied in Chapter 3, before building on your study of monohybrid inheritance from GCSE.

Origins of genetic variation – a reminder

Gene mutations and chromosome mutations as sources of genetic variation

Gene mutations are the ultimate source of all new genetic variation. Chromosome mutations are simply rearrangements of existing genetic variation.

Gene mutations

Key term

Point mutation A change affecting the base of a single nucleotide in the base sequence of a gene.

In Chapter 3 we defined a **gene** as a sequence of nucleotide bases that encodes the amino acid sequence of a polypeptide. You also saw that a mutation involves a change in the number, or sequence, of bases in a particular gene. The three types of gene mutation you examined are exemplified in Table 20.1. Since they involve a change to a single base in the sequence, they are called **point mutations**.

Table 20.1 Three types of gene mutation

Type of mutation	Effect on base sequence	Encoded amino acid sequence
None	UCC CAG GAG CCA	Serine–Glutamine–Glutamic acid–Proline
Deletion	UCC AGG AGC CA	Serine–Arginine–Serine–
Insertion	UCG **C**CA GGA GCC A	Serine–Proline–Glycine–Alanine–
Substitution	UC**U** CAG GAG CCA	Serine–Glutamine–Glutamic acid–Proline

Gene mutations occur randomly at a rate of about 1 in 10^6 base replications. Agents that increase the rate of mutation, including harmful chemicals and radiation, are called **mutagens**. Although cells possess enzyme-catalysed reactions that identify and correct gene mutations, some can remain uncorrected. If they occur in a somatic cell of an adult, gene mutations will only affect that adult. If they occur in cells producing gametes, gene mutations could be inherited from generation to generation.

Chromosome mutations

You looked at chromosome mutations in Chapter 5, where we reviewed chromosome translocations and chromosome non-disjunction.

Chromosome translocations occur when a chromosome breaks and the resulting fragment joins on to another, non-homologous chromosome. Inheritance of a chromosome that has a translocated fragment can be harmful, for example, about 5 per cent of cases of Down's syndrome are caused by the translocation of part of the long arm of chromosome 21 to chromosome 14.

Chromosome non-disjunction results when members of a homologous pair of chromosomes fail to separate during anaphase I of meiosis. Figure 20.1 shows how this will result in gametes with abnormal chromosome numbers.

- If one of the upper gametes in Figure 20.1 is involved in fertilisation with a normal, haploid gamete, the resulting zygote will have three copies of the long chromosome (known as **polysomy**). Most cases of Down's syndrome result from polysomy involving chromosome 21.

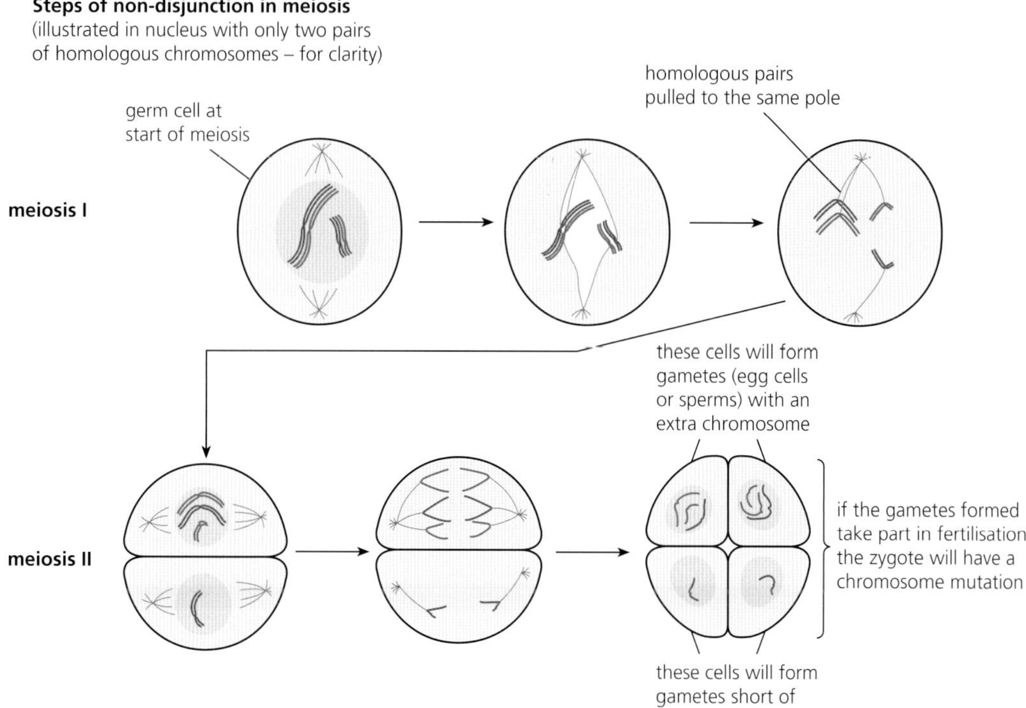

Figure 20.1 Chromosome non-disjunction

- If one of the lower gametes in Figure 20.1 is involved in fertilisation with a normal, haploid gamete, the resulting zygote will have only one copy of the long chromosome (known as **monosomy**). Monosomy is usually lethal. The only example of monosomy in adult humans is Turner's syndrome, in which affected females possess only one X chromosome.

Meiosis and fertilisation as sources of genetic variation

Meiosis was described in Chapter 5. Two nuclear divisions are involved:

Meiosis I separates the two chromosomes in each homologous pair, one to each end of the dividing cell.
Meiosis II separates the chromatids – the two copies of each chromosome.

The result is haploid daughter cells produced by the division of a diploid parent cell.

Figure 20.2 on the next page, shows two possible outcomes of meiosis. For the sake of simplicity it shows just one homologous pair of chromosomes. In the diagram on the left of Figure 20.2, the homologous chromosomes have remained intact. Because the chromosomes had different alleles of genes A and E, they produce two genetically different haploid gametes, with the combinations of alleles of genes A and E of **AE** and **ae**. The configuration contains only dominant alleles or recessive alleles, in other words **AE** and **ae**. These configurations are known as *cis*. In the diagram on the right of Figure 20.2, crossing over has occurred between two non-sister chromatids. This results in four genetically different haploid gametes, with the combinations of the alleles of genes A and E of **AE**, **ae**, **Ae** and **aE**. The configurations **Ae** and **aE** are known as *trans*. So, we can conclude that, because homologous chromosomes have different alleles at many loci, their random assortment during meiosis produces genetic diversity in the daughter cells and that crossing over between non-sister chromatids further increases this genetic diversity.

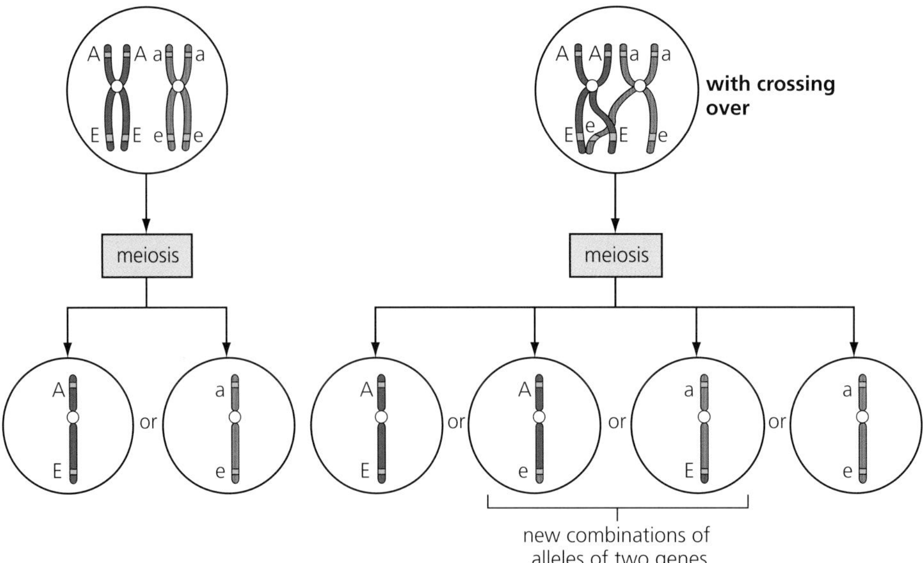

Figure 20.2 Meiosis produces genetic variation amongst the daughter cells. Crossing over further increases the genetic variation

Fertilisation involves the fusion of two haploid gametes to produce a diploid zygote. Meiosis results in genetic diversity in the gametes formed by two adult organisms and which of these different gametes is involved in fertilisation is, again, completely random, further increasing genetic diversity. You saw in Figure 20.2 that even a cell with only one pair of homologous chromosomes involving just one cross-over event can produce four genetically different gametes. The probability of any one of them being involved in fertilisation is 0.25. If the other parent is also able to produce four genetically different gametes, there are 16 possible fusions of any two gametes. The probability of any gamete from one parent fertilising any gamete from the other parent is $0.25 \times 0.25 = 0.0625$ (which we could write as a chance of 1 in 16).

Tip

A probability always has a value between 0 and 1. The expression '1 in 16' refers to chance, not to probability.

Test yourself

1 Define the term 'gene'.
2 What term is used to describe the location of a gene?
3 Identify information in Table 20.1 which shows that the genetic code is degenerate.
4 Which gene mutation, or mutations, in Table 20.1 caused a frame shift? Explain your answer.
5 Describe what is meant by 'polysomy' and explain how it is caused.
6 What is the difference between the *cis* and *trans* combinations of two linked genes?

Key term

Dihybrid inheritance The transfer from generation to generation of two different genes. The two genes might control different features of the phenotype (non-interacting genes) or might both contribute to the control of a single feature of the phenotype (interacting genes). Additionally, they might occur on the same chromosome (linked genes) or on different chromosomes (unlinked genes).

Terminology used in genetics – a reminder

The transfer of genetic information from one generation to the next is known as inheritance. **Genetics** is the study of inheritance. In your GCSE science course, you studied the inheritance of a characteristic controlled by a single gene. This is known as **monohybrid inheritance**. Here, you will study the inheritance of characteristics that are controlled by two different genes, so-called **dihybrid inheritance**.

Some of the expressions used above are rather clumsy. Before going further, we will see how these clumsy expressions can be replaced with technical terms with defined meanings.

Measurable features and combinations of genes

When referring to Figure 20.2 above, we used the expression 'combination of alleles of the genes A and E', which is rather cumbersome. We also used the expression 'inheritance of characteristics' as though every inherited feature could be easily seen. Instead, we use technical terms with exact meanings.

- **Genotype** is the combination of alleles of a particular gene, or genes, present in a haploid gamete or diploid organism. In most of this chapter, we will use the term genotype in the context of two genes considered together.
- **Phenotype** is a measurable feature of an organism. It might be visible, for example, fur colour, or detectable only by chemical or immunological analysis, for example, ABO blood groups. Although the phenotype is affected by the genotype, it is also affected by environmental factors.

  genotype + environmental factors → phenotype

Each member of a pair of homologous chromosomes has the same genes in the same order. If there are two or more alleles of a gene, both homologous chromosomes of a diploid organism might carry the same alleles of that gene or two different alleles of that gene.

- **Homozygous** cells or organisms are diploid and have the **same** allele of a gene under consideration on both copies of a pair of homologous chromosomes. The cell or organism is a **homozygote** for this gene.
- **Heterozygous** cells or organisms are diploid and have **different** alleles of a gene under consideration. The cell or organism is a **heterozygote** for this gene.

The relationship between alleles of the same gene

Although a gene will have an effect on the phenotype, not all alleles have the same ability to affect the phenotypic feature they control.

- **Dominant alleles**, when present in the genotype, always show their effect in the phenotype.
- **Recessive alleles**, when present in the genotype, do not show their effect in the phenotype if a dominant allele of the same gene is also present. Recessive alleles only show their effect in the homozygous condition.
- **Codominant alleles**, when present in the genotype, show their effect in the phenotype regardless of the other allele of the gene.
- **Multiple alleles** occur when there are more than two alleles of a single gene, for example there three alleles of the human ABO blood group ($\mathbf{I^A}$, $\mathbf{I^B}$ and $\mathbf{I^o}$) that you probably studied in your GCSE science course.

Transfer of genetic information

This A level Biology course covers the inheritance of two genes with and without linkage. We will begin by looking at the pattern of inheritance that follows, in the simplest way, from the pattern of monohybrid inheritance you studied during your GCSE science course. Use Figure 20.3 on the next page to refresh your memory of how you can use a genetic diagram to explain the outcome of monohybrid inheritance. The format of Figure 20.3 is that of a genetic diagram and the notes explain the rationale behind its use.

Tip

An organism that is homozygous at a particular locus is sometimes described as **pure-breeding** for that phenotypic feature.

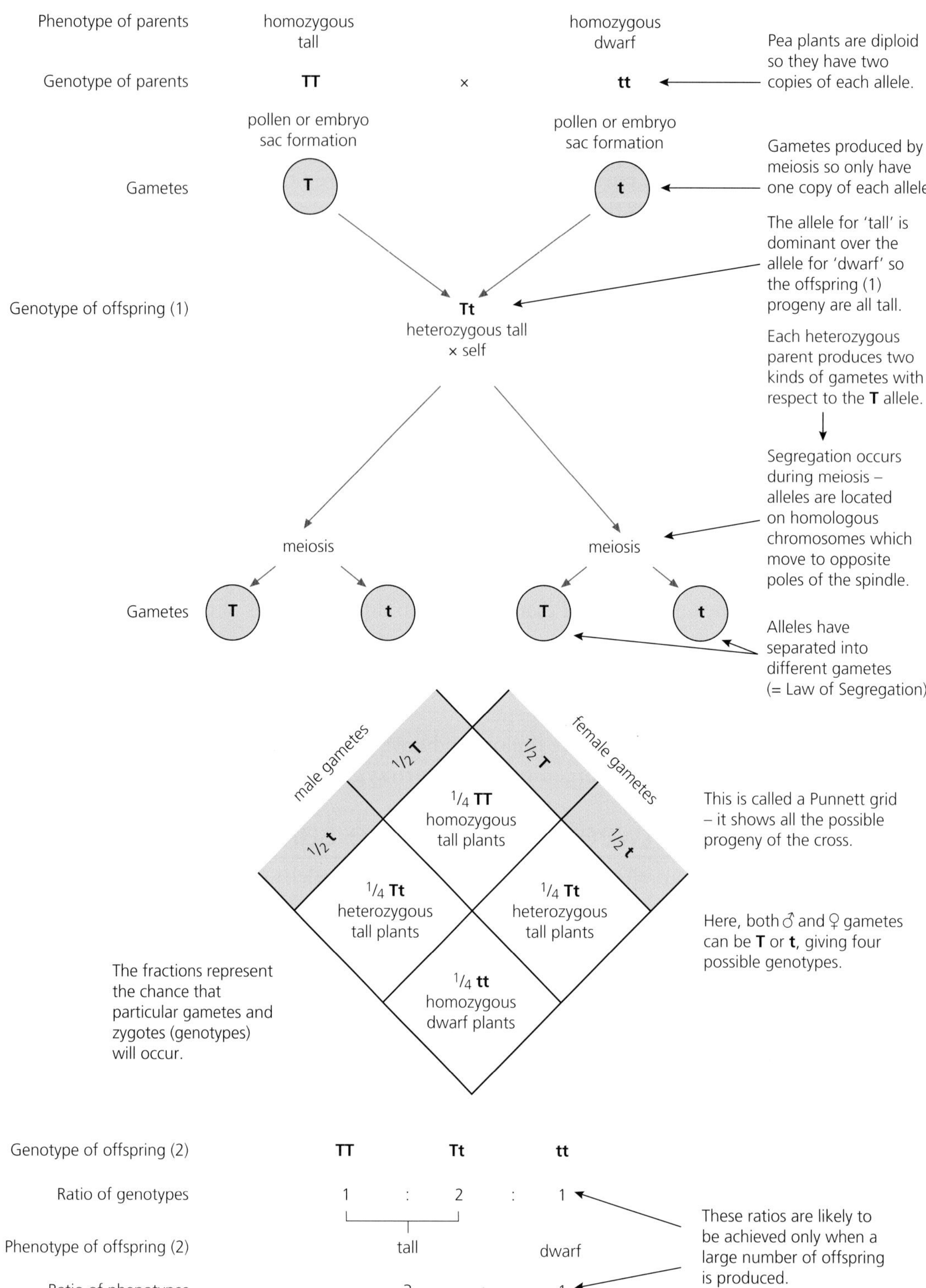
Phenotype of parents
homozygous tall
homozygous dwarf
Pea plants are diploid so they have two copies of each allele.
Genotype of parents
TT
×
tt
pollen or embryo sac formation
pollen or embryo sac formation
Gametes produced by meiosis so only have one copy of each allele.
Gametes
T
t
The allele for 'tall' is dominant over the allele for 'dwarf' so the offspring (1) progeny are all tall.
Genotype of offspring (1)
Tt
heterozygous tall
× self
Each heterozygous parent produces two kinds of gametes with respect to the T allele.
Segregation occurs during meiosis – alleles are located on homologous chromosomes which move to opposite poles of the spindle.
meiosis
meiosis
Gametes
T
t
T
t
Alleles have separated into different gametes (= Law of Segregation).
male gametes
female gametes
1/2 T
1/2 t
1/2 T
1/2 t
1/4 TT homozygous tall plants
1/4 Tt heterozygous tall plants
1/4 Tt heterozygous tall plants
1/4 tt homozygous dwarf plants
This is called a Punnett grid – it shows all the possible progeny of the cross.
Here, both ♂ and ♀ gametes can be T or t, giving four possible genotypes.
The fractions represent the chance that particular gametes and zygotes (genotypes) will occur.
Genotype of offspring (2)
TT
Tt
tt
Ratio of genotypes
1 : 2 : 1
Phenotype of offspring (2)
tall
dwarf
Ratio of phenotypes
3 : 1
These ratios are likely to be achieved only when a large number of offspring is produced.

Figure 20.3 Using a genetic diagram to explain the outcome of monohybrid inheritance

Inheritance with sex-linkage

In Chapter 18 we saw in the Extension *X chromosome inactivation in mammals*, page 380, that mammalian females have two X chromosomes (XX) and males have one X chromosome and one Y chromosome (XY). The larger X chromosome has far more genes than does the Y chromosome, many of which are not related to sexual characteristics. One of these is a gene controlling blood clotting. Since this gene is located on the X chromosome, it is said to be **sex-linked**.

> **Key term**
>
> **Sex linkage** A condition in which the locus of a gene is located on a sex chromosome; the gene itself is described as **sex-linked**. Since there are very few genes on a mammalian Y chromosome, sex linkage in mammals almost always refers to a gene with its locus on an X chromosome.

Blood clotting normally occurs following a break or cut in a blood vessel. A series of enzyme-catalysed reactions produces a fibrous network of a protein called fibrin, which traps red blood cells. The fibrin network and trapped red blood cells form a clot, which reduces the likelihood of both the further loss of blood and of the entry of pathogens. Haemophilia is a relatively rare disease in which the blood fails to clot normally. The result is frequent and excessive bleeding that can be fatal.

Haemophilia is the result of the recessive allele of a gene controlling a step in the blood clotting process. As it is recessive, we will represent it with a lower case letter (**h**) and we will represent the dominant allele with an upper case letter (**H**). Furthermore, since we know that this gene is located on the X chromosome, we will show this in our representation of these alleles: $\mathbf{X^h}$ and $\mathbf{X^H}$.

Figure 20.4 on the next page, represents the inheritance of haemophilia in one family. Both parents show normal blood clotting, but the mother is heterozygous for the blood-clotting gene. The eggs and sperm of these parents are haploid, having been formed by meiosis. At fertilisation, a diploid zygote is formed, which develops into a child.

- Since the father has normal blood clotting, his X chromosome must carry the allele for normal blood clotting, **H**. We can represent his genotype as $\mathbf{X^HY}$.
- Since the mother is heterozygous for this gene, one of her X chromosomes carries the allele for normal blood clotting (**H**) and the other carries the allele for haemophilia (**h**). We can represent her genotype as $\mathbf{X^HX^h}$. Since the allele causing haemophilia is recessive, this woman's blood will clot normally: she does not show the disease but is a 'carrier'.

Half the father's sperm are likely to contain a Y chromosome and half an X chromosome. All the mother's eggs will contain an X chromosome but, as a result of the independent segregation of chromosomes during meiosis, half are likely to carry the $\mathbf{X^H}$ allele and half the $\mathbf{X^h}$ allele. Fertilisation is random, so it is a 50:50 chance which egg is fertilised and a 50:50 chance which sperm fertilises the egg. Figure 20.4 shows how we can represent the formation of gametes, possible fertilisations and the outcome of these fertilisations in the genotypes of the offspring this couple might have. This representation is called a **'genetic cross diagram'** and we will use diagrams like this in most of our explanations of inheritance in the remainder of this chapter.

There are several noteworthy points shown in Figure 20.4.

- The expected ratio of female to male children is 1:1.
- Although neither parent is a **haemophiliac** (suffers haemophilia), they could have a haemophiliac child.
- Any haemophiliac child they might have would be male ($\mathbf{X^hY}$).

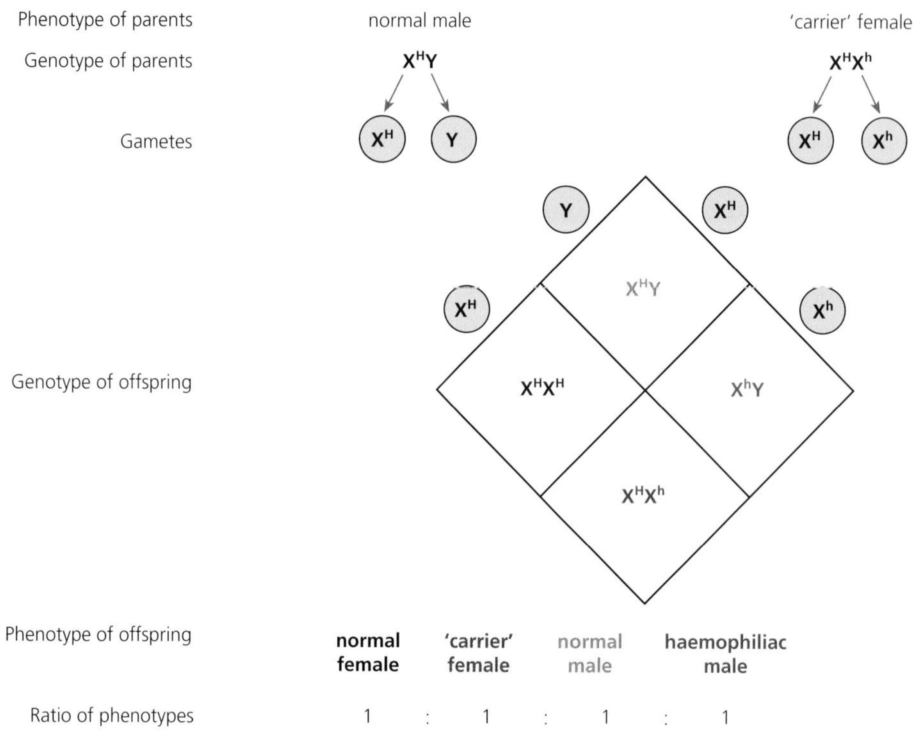

Figure 20.4 Inheritance of haemophilia – an example of sex linkage

Example

Using a pedigree diagram to show the inheritance of haemophilia

Figure 20.5 shows another way in which you can represent the inheritance of a sex-linked gene. It is a **pedigree diagram**. We may investigate the pattern of inheritance of a particular characteristic by researching family pedigrees, where appropriate records of the ancestors exist.

Just as the genetic cross diagram in Figure 20.4 has a fixed layout, so a pedigree diagram involves a set of 'rules'.

- A female is represented as a circle and a male as a square.
- A horizontal line between a circle and a square links two parents.
- A vertical line from the line linking two parents takes us to the offspring from that relationship.
- The offspring from a relationship are shown in birth sequence from left to right of the diagram.

Figure 20.5 also has a key, showing you the phenotype of each individual. Rather than naming them, each individual in Figure 20.5 has been numbered, so you can identify them.

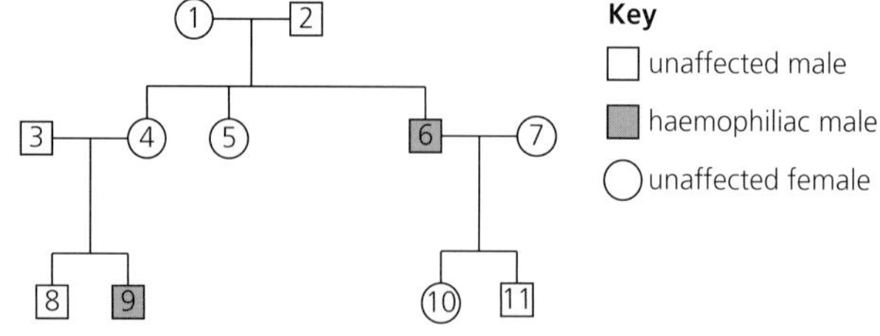

Figure 20.5 A pedigree diagram showing the inheritance of haemophilia in one family

1 How should you interpret a pedigree chart?

2 For which two individuals in Figure 20.5 can you be sure of the genotype?

3 What are the genotypes of individuals 6 and 9?

4 What are the genotypes of individuals 1, 2, 3 and 4?

5 Individual 9 is a haemophiliac. His brother (individual 8) is not. Explain why.

6 What is the genotype of individual 10?

7 Can we be sure of the genotype of individual 7?

8 If individual 7 had been a carrier, what is the probability of her not passing her $\mathbf{X^h}$ chromosome to either of her two children?

Answers

1 When solving an unknown, it is always best to start with something you do know. From your knowledge of the inheritance of haemophilia, you should immediately be able to identify the genotypes of two individuals in Figure 20.5.

2 Since you know that the allele of the gene that causes haemophilia is recessive and you know that females are XX and males XY, you should immediately spot that you can identify the genotypes of individuals 6 and 9 – the haemophiliacs.

3 Individuals 6 and 9 are male (XY). They are both haemophiliacs, so each must have the recessive allele (**h**) on his X chromosome. The genotype of both must be $\mathbf{X^hY}$.

Now you know the genotypes of individuals 6 and 9, you can work backwards from both. Neither of them has a parent who is a haemophiliac. This gives you a big clue to the genotypes of these parents.

4 The fathers (individuals 2 and 3) do not show haemophilia. The genotypes of both must be $\mathbf{X^HY}$. Neither mother (individuals 1 and 4) shows haemophilia but must have passed the haemophilia allele to their sons, in other words they are both carriers with the genotype $\mathbf{X^HX^h}$.

5 Since their father's genotype is $\mathbf{X^HY}$, none of his sperm will carry the $\mathbf{X^h}$ allele. The mother is $\mathbf{X^HX^h}$, so there is a 50 : 50 chance that any one of her eggs will carry the $\mathbf{X^H}$ or $\mathbf{X^h}$ allele. As luck would have it, the egg from which individual 8 was conceived carried the $\mathbf{X^H}$ allele, so his genotype is $\mathbf{X^HY}$.

6 Her father is a haemophiliac, so his X chromosome carries the **h** allele. A girl inherits one of her X chromosomes from her father. As she is not a haemophiliac, her genotype must be $\mathbf{X^HX^h}$.

7 The answer is no. As her children do not show haemophilia, she might be homozygous $\mathbf{X^HX^H}$. On the other hand, she might be heterozygous ($\mathbf{X^HX^h}$) yet, just by chance, neither of her eggs that was fertilised and gave rise to her children carried the $\mathbf{X^h}$ allele.

8 The probability of each child not inheriting the $\mathbf{X^h}$ chromosome from their mother is 0.5, so the probability of neither of them inheriting this chromosome is $0.5 \times 0.5 = 0.25$.

Test yourself

7 Give **two** types of factor that affect the phenotype of an organism.
8 What are 'codominant' alleles?
9 Explain why a son cannot inherit haemophilia from his father.
10 Most haemophiliacs are male. Explain how a female child could inherit haemophilia.
11 What is an 'autosome'?

Figure 20.6 The fruit fly, *Drosophila melanogaster* has been an important animal in genetic research

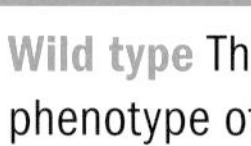

Key term

Wild type The natural phenotype of any particular characteristic, that is, one that is unaffected by any gene mutation.

Dihybrid inheritance with autosomal linkage

An **autosome** is any chromosome other than a sex chromosome, so autosomal linkage describes the condition in which two genes are located on the same chromosome but it is not a sex chromosome. If you look back to Figure 20.2 on page 420, you will see that the alleles of two genes with loci on the same autosome are inherited together, unless crossing over occurs. Bear this in mind as you follow the example of dihybrid inheritance with autosomal linkage given below.

Figure 20.6 shows a fruit fly, *Drosophila melanogaster*. You might have seen flies like this around a bowl of fruit during the summer months. During the early years of the 20th century, an embryologist, named Thomas Hunt Morgan, chose *D. melanogaster* as the organism to use in his research into the mechanisms of inheritance. His work established the science we now call 'genetics' and *D. melanogaster* has continued to be the organism of choice for thousands of geneticists ever since.

D. melanogaster has four pairs of chromosomes – one pair of sex chromosomes and three pairs of autosomes, chromosomes 2, 3 and 4. The fruit fly at the top of Figure 20.7 shows what is called the **wild type** phenotype of *D. melanogaster*. Amongst its features, it has long wings and a yellow body with black stripes. These features are controlled by two genes on chromosome 2: one controlling wing length and the other controlling body colour. The fruit fly at the bottom of Figure 20.7 has vestigial (short) wings and a black body. It is homozygous for a mutant allele of the gene controlling wing length and for another mutant allele of the gene controlling body colour. Table 20.1 shows the effects of these two genes and the two alleles of each gene. It also shows the simple notation we will use in our genetic cross diagram (with the more complex, standard notation used by geneticists to represent the genes in *Drosophila* shown in brackets).

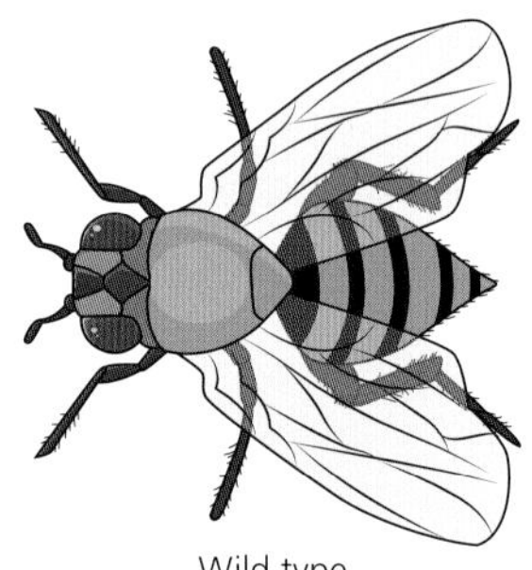

Wild type

Vestigial wings

Figure 20.7 A wild type *Drosophila melanogaster* and a mutant with vestigial wings

Table 20.1 The alleles of two genes on chromosome 2 of *Drosophila melanogaster*

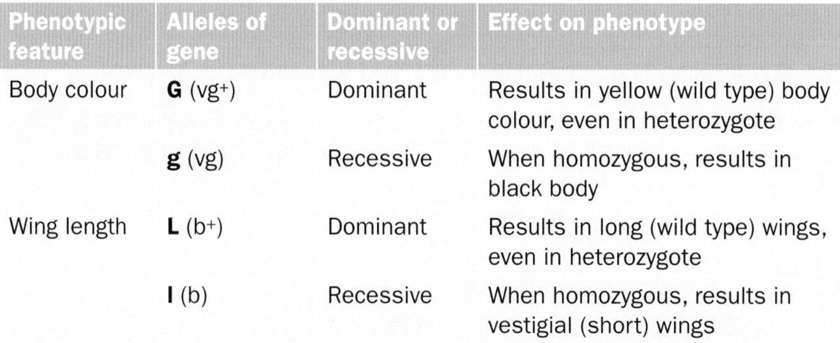

Phenotypic feature	Alleles of gene	Dominant or recessive	Effect on phenotype
Body colour	**G** (vg^+)	Dominant	Results in yellow (wild type) body colour, even in heterozygote
	g (vg)	Recessive	When homozygous, results in black body
Wing length	**L** (b^+)	Dominant	Results in long (wild type) wings, even in heterozygote
	l (b)	Recessive	When homozygous, results in vestigial (short) wings

A dihybrid cross with autosomal linkage in which no crossing over of linked genes occurs

Figure 20.8 represents a cross between two fruit flies. Both are homozygous for the genes controlling body colour and wing length. The female is homozygous dominant (**GGLL**) and the male is homozygous recessive (**ggll**) for these genes. During gamete production, meiosis separates the two copies of chromosome 2 in each diploid cell, so the female adult will produce eggs with the genotype **GL** and the male will produce sperm with the genotype **gl**. All the offspring will be heterozygotes with the genotype **GgLl**.

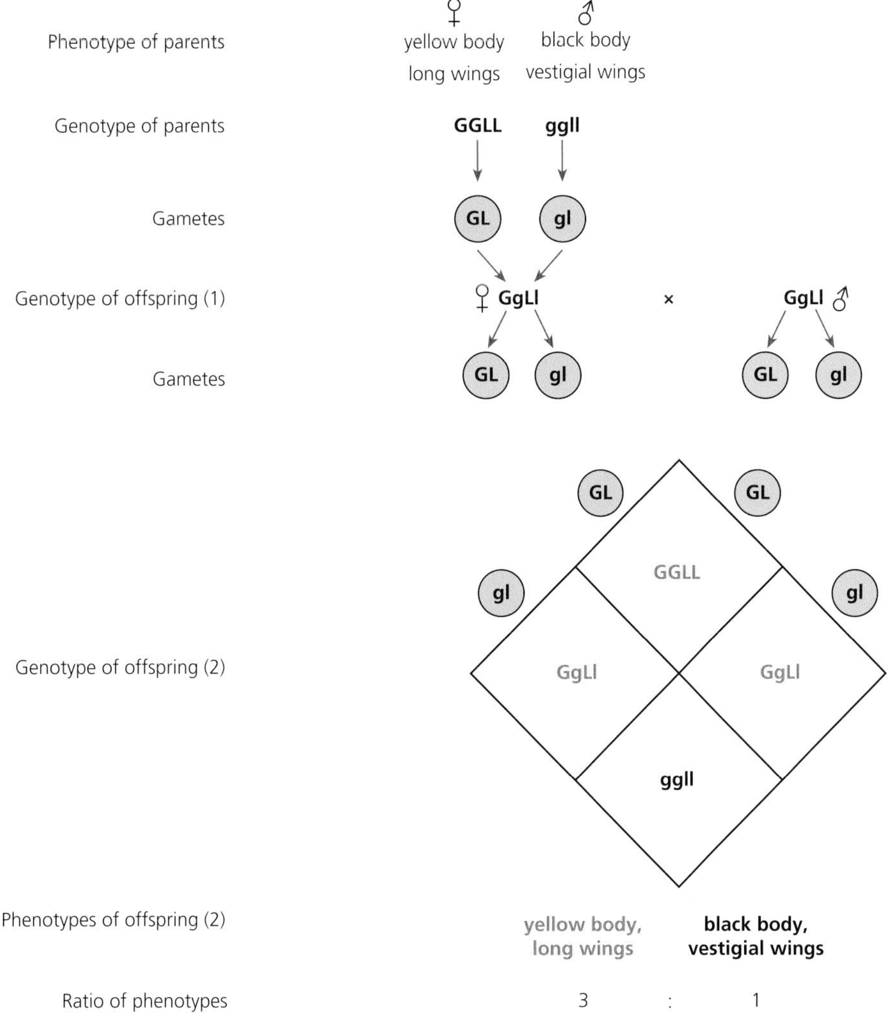

Figure 20.8 A genetic cross between a female fruit fly that is homozygous dominant for the body colour and wing length genes on chromosome 2, with a male that is homozygous recessive for the same genes. One of the female offspring is mated with one of the male offspring to produce a second generation of offspring flies. In this diagram, no crossing over between the two loci has occurred

Tip

Figure 20.8 shows the genotypes of gametes within circles. This makes quite clear to readers, including examiners, how a sequence of letters relates to individual gametes.

It also shows the genotypes of the second offspring generation in the form of a Punnett square. You will find this helpful when constructing your own genetic diagrams.

Tip

When representing genotypes involving linked genes, some students find it helpful to remind themselves which alleles are linked with which by bracketing them together. In Figure 20.8, this would mean representing the genotypes of the parents as (**GL**)(**GL**) and (**gl**)(**gl**).

Since we are dealing with fruit flies, we mate a female and male of this group of brother and sister flies to produce a second offspring generation of flies. You might expect that, since the alleles **G** and **L** are linked on the same chromosome, they will always be inherited together and, similarly, **g** and **l** will always be inherited together. If this were the case, we would only ever get flies that had the same phenotypes as the two parents – wild type and black-bodied with vestigial wings. This is represented in Figure 20.8, where the second offspring generation contains only flies with the original parental phenotypes – yellow bodies with long wings or black bodies with vestigial wings, in an expected ratio of 3 : 1.

Key term

Recombinant An organism with a phenotype that results from the crossing over of linked genes during gamete production in one, or both its parents. The resulting phenotype has a combination of characteristics not shown by either parent.

A dihybrid cross with autosomal linkage in which crossing over of linked genes does occur

Remember, though, that crossing over will sometimes occur. Unusually, crossing over does **not** occur in male *D. melanogaster*. It appears that the males of this species lack the enzyme-catalysed mechanisms that allow close pairing of homologous chromosomes during meiosis, so that chiasmata do not form. Crossing over does, however, occur in female *D. melanogaster*. Sometimes, during meiosis in egg production in a female fruit fly, a crossing over event might occur between the gene for body colour and the gene for wing length, just as is shown for the genes A and E in Figure 20.2 on page 420. If so, we might expect a small number of her gametes to have genotypes of **Gl** and **gL**. You can see from Figure 20.9 that this does occur. As a result, we find a small number of flies in the second offspring generation with new phenotypes – yellow bodies with vestigial wings and black bodies with long wings. These individuals are called **recombinants** and their appearance in the offspring (2) generation shows us that crossing over must have occurred. The number of recombinants will depend on the frequency with which crossing over occurs between the two genes during egg production by the females. This frequency is greater the further apart the two loci are.

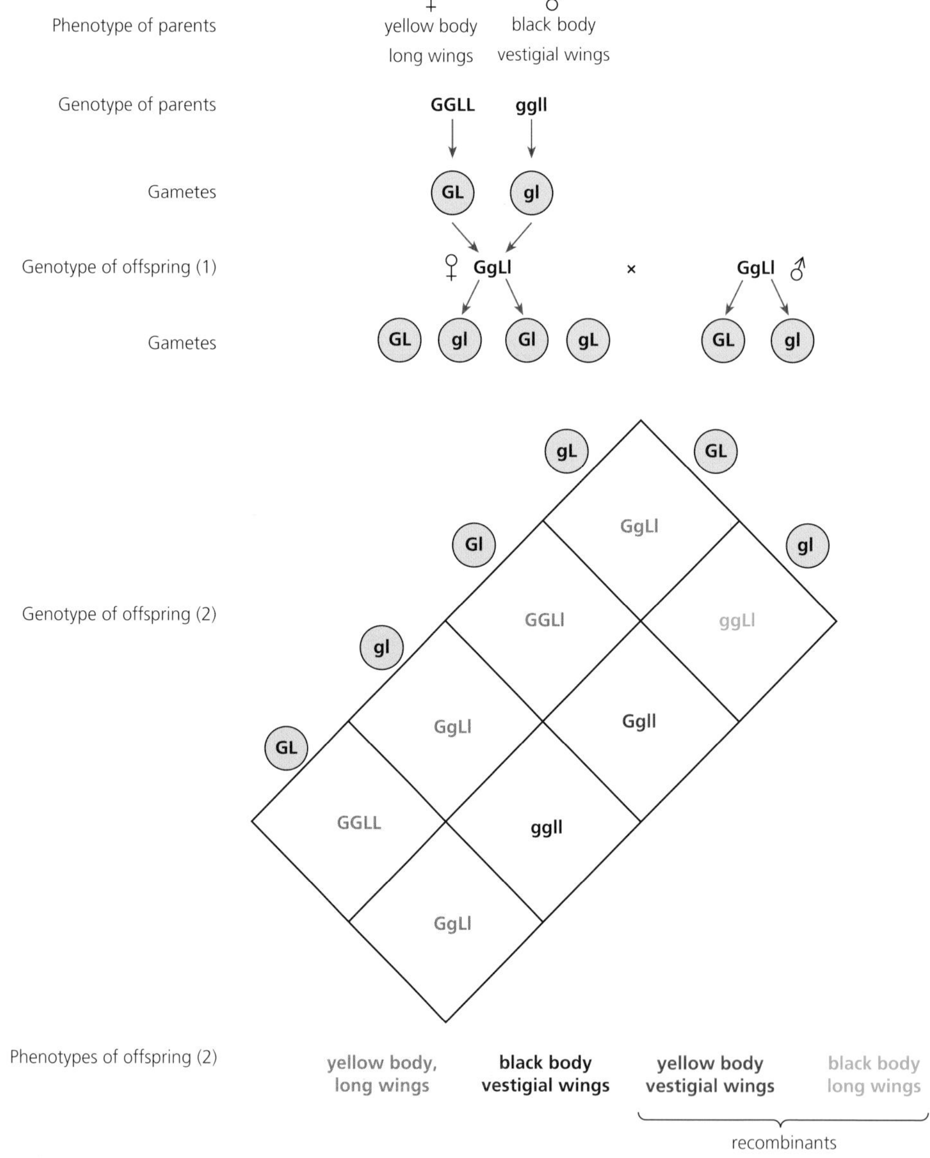

Figure 20.9 The same crosses are shown in Figure 20.8. In this diagram, however, crossing over between the two loci has occurred in the females of the offspring (1) generation

Dihybrid inheritance with non-interacting unlinked genes

Two genes are said to be **unlinked** if they occur on different chromosomes. They are **non-interacting** if they control two different phenotypic features.

Having used humans and fruit flies in the examples above, we will balance the biological examples by using plants here. Gregor Mendel's experiments with pea plants were important forerunners of the science of genetics. We will look at an example of dihybrid inheritance with non-interacting genes using pea plants, *Pisum savitum*, as an example (see Figure 20.10). Table 20.2 shows these two phenotypic features, the notation we will use to represent the two alleles of each of the genes controlling these features and their relationship.

Table 20.2 The alleles of two unlinked genes of *Pisum savitum*

Phenotypic feature	Alleles of gene	Dominant or recessive	Effect on phenotype
Flower colour	**F**	Dominant	Results in violet flowers, even in a heterozygote
	f	Recessive	When homozygous, results in white flowers
Stem length	**T**	Dominant	Results in tall stems, even in a heterozygote
	t	Recessive	When homozygous, results in short stems

Figure 20.11 on the next page represents a cross between two pea plants. Both are homozygous for the genes controlling flower colour and stem length. One plant is homozygous dominant (**FFTT**) and the other is homozygous recessive (**fftt**) for these genes. Since gametes are haploid, one adult will produce gametes with the genotype **FT** and the other will produce gametes with the genotype **ft**. All the offspring will be heterozygotes with the genotype **FfTt** and will be tall plants with violet flowers.

Pea plants are able to self-fertilise – the pollen will germinate if it lands on the stigma within the same flower and fertilise the nuclei within its embryo sac (see Chapter 6). If the offspring (1) plants are allowed to self-fertilise, they will produce an offspring (2) generation. Remember that the two loci are not on the same chromosome, so random segregation of chromosomes will result in all possible combinations of the two sets of alleles – **FT**, **Ft**, **fT** and **ft** – in equal frequencies in female and male gametes. The random fertilisation of these gametes will produce 16 possible fertilisations, all of which are shown in Figure 20.11. The expected ratio of phenotypes of 9 : 3 : 3 : 1 is typical of this type of cross with two, unlinked, non-interacting genes.

Figure 20.10 Pea plants (*Pisum savitum*) showing one of the features we will use in our example of inheritance - short stems and tall stems

Figure 20.11 A genetic cross between a pea plant that is homozygous dominant for the flower colour and stem length genes with another that is homozygous recessive for the same genes. By allowing the offspring plants to self-fertilise, a second generation of offspring pea plants can be produced

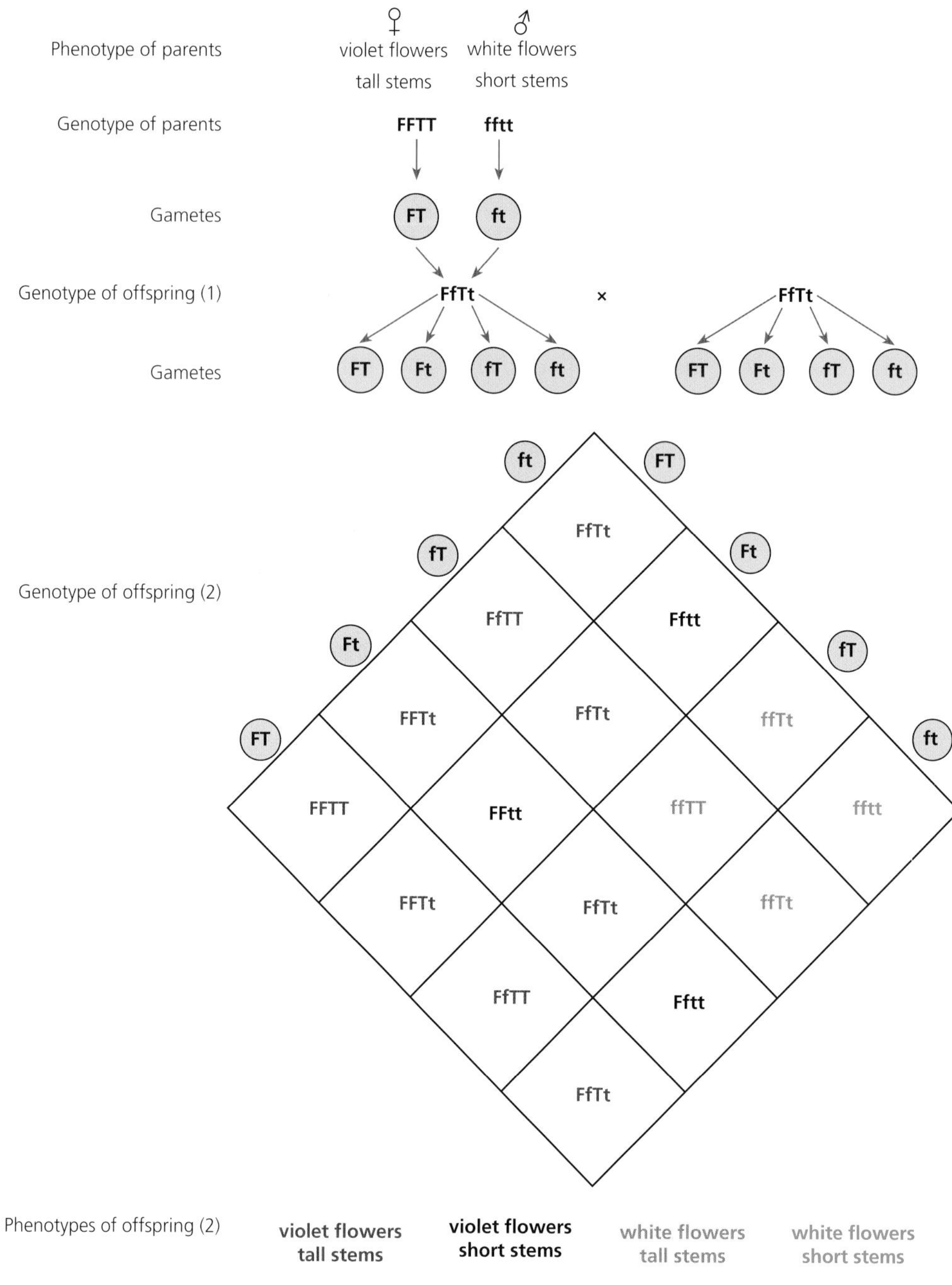

Phenotypes of offspring (2)	violet flowers tall stems		violet flowers short stems		white flowers tall stems		white flowers short stems
Expected ratio of phenotypes	9	:	3	:	3	:	1

Tip

When interpreting dihybrid crosses, the ratio of phenotypes in the offspring (2) generation might give you an immediate clue about whether the two loci are linked or unlinked.

Use of the chi squared (goodness of fit) test in genetics

Once you have a good understanding of the three patterns of inheritance from the previous pages, you will be able to solve genetic puzzles set by your teacher or by examiners. From your genetic diagrams, you will be able to predict the ratio of the different phenotypes resulting from a cross. You will be well aware, though, that random variation is common in biology. In fact, when the results of Gregor Mendel's experiments with pea plants were rediscovered early in the 20th century, the famous statistician R.A. Fisher was highly critical of them – they showed too little random variation from the expected ratios to be believable! However, the underlying mechanisms of these inheritance patterns, hold true.

Table 20.3 The observed results of a genetics experiment with pea plants and the results expected from an understanding of the theory of inheritance

Results	Tall stems with violet flowers	Tall stems with white flowers	Short stems with violet flowers	Short stems with white flowers	Total
Observed	173	55	66	26	320
Expected	180	60	60	20	320

How can you tell whether the results you obtain from a genetics experiment really do match your expectations from theoretical knowledge? Look at the data in Table 20.3. They relate to results from the cross shown in Figure 20.11. From this cross, you would expect the second offspring generation to have the phenotypes: tall with violet flowers, tall with white flowers, short with violet flowers and short with white flowers in a ratio of 9 : 3 : 3 : 1. By dividing the actual number of plants obtained in the second offspring generation into this ratio, you calculate your **expected numbers** of each phenotype. You can compare these with the actual numbers you found – the **observed numbers**.

Since the data shown in Table 20.3 are categoric, you use the chi squared χ^2 test, described in Chapter 27, to find whether your observations are close enough to your expectations for your expectations to be valid. You calculate the value of χ^2 as follows.

$$\chi^2 = \sum \frac{(O - E)^2}{E}$$

Table 20.4 expands on Table 20.3, showing the working to calculate the value of χ^2 from these data.

Table 20.4 Calculation of χ^2 from the data in Table 20.3, using calculated values to three significant figures

	Tall with violet flowers	Tall with white flowers	Short with violet flowers	Short with white flowers
O	173	55	66	26
E	180	60	60	20
$(O - E)$	−7	−5	6	6
$(O - E)^2$	49	25	36	36
$\frac{(O - E)^2}{E}$	0.26	0.42	0.60	1.80
χ^2		3.08		

Now that you have a value for χ^2, you need to interpret what it means. You are testing whether the observed results are a 'good fit' to the expected results. Your assumption is that there is no difference between the observed numbers of each phenotype and the expected numbers of each phenotype (your **null hypothesis**). In your example, you have four categories of data (the four phenotypes), so you have three degrees of freedom. When you check this value against a table of critical values for χ^2, you find:

Degrees of freedom	Significance level		
	0.05	0.01	0.001
3	7.81	11.34	16.27

As your calculated value for χ^2 (3.08) is well below the 0.05 significance level, you can say that the difference between your results and the results you expected is not statistically significant (or, put another way, the probability of the difference between the results you obtained and those you expected being due to chance is greater than 0.95).

Key term

Categoric data Those where only certain values can exist. The values are not continuous, within a range of values, as would be, for example time in an enzyme experiment.

Consequently, you accept your null hypothesis – there is no difference between your results and the results you expected. This means that your interpretation of the pattern of inheritance on which you based your expectation was valid.

Test yourself

12 One of the male yellow-bodied, long-winged fruit flies from the offspring (1) generation in Figure 20.8 is mated with a black-bodied, vestigial-winged female. What ratio of phenotypes would you expect in their offspring? Explain your answer.

13 How could the cross in Question 12 be used to determine the genotype of a yellow-bodied, long-winged fly? Explain your answer.

14 Would it make any difference to your answer to Question 12 if it had been the female that had been yellow-bodied and long-winged? Explain your answer,

15 Here are the genotypes of four pea plants: **FfTT**, **FFTt**, **FfTt**, **fftt**. Which pea plant would be described as 'pure-breeding'?

16 Explain why the chi squared test is the appropriate statistical test to use when comparing the expected outcome of a genetic cross with the observed results.

Chapter summary

Origins of genetic variation

- Gene mutations are the source of new genetic variation, producing new alleles of an existing gene.
- Chromosome mutations, including translocation and non-disjunction, and the random assortment of homologous chromosomes during meiosis result in new combinations of the alleles of genes.
- Random fertilisation of haploid gametes results in genetic variation among the diploid zygotes produced.

Terms used in genetics

- The genotype is the combination of alleles of a gene or of several genes that are present in a haploid gamete or a diploid organism.
- The phenotype of an organism is the detectable characteristic of an organism resulting from the effects of the genotype and the environment.
- A homozygote is a diploid cell or organism that has only one allele of the gene controlling a phenotypic characteristic.
- A heterozygote is a diploid cell or organism that has two different alleles of the gene controlling a phenotypic characteristic.
- When a dominant allele of a gene is present in a genotype, it always shows its presence in the phenotype. It masks the effect of a recessive allele, which only shows its effect in the phenotype if in the homozygous condition.
- Codominant alleles of a gene both show their effect in the phenotype of a heterozygote, e.g., AB blood group.
- Multiple alleles occur when a gene has more than two alleles.

Transfer of genetic information

- A diploid parent has two copies of each gene, one on each homologous chromosome. Following meiosis, only one of these alleles is present in each of the parent's gametes. Fusion of two haploid gametes during fertilisation restores the diploid condition in the zygote.
- A dihybrid cross is one that involves the inheritance of two genes.
- Autosomal linkage occurs when two genes are located on the same chromosome, so the alleles of each gene on one chromosome tend to be inherited together. This can be represented in the example diagram below, in which the alleles **g** and **L** are on the same chromosome in each heterozygous parent fruit fly:

Phenotype of parents	yellow body, long wings		×	yellow body, long wings	
Genotype of parents	**GgLl**		×	**GgLl**	
Genotype of gametes	**Gl**	**gL**		**Gl**	**gL**
Genotype of offspring	**GGll**	**GgLl**		**GgLl**	**ggLL**
Phenotype of offspring	yellow body, short wings	yellow body, long wings			black body, long wings

- In the above diagram, crossing over during meiosis could result in occasional new combinations of alleles, i.e., **GL** and **gl**.
- Sex linkage occurs when a gene is located on one of the sex chromosomes, usually the X chromosome in mammals. This can be represented in the example diagram below, in which the alleles for normal blood clotting (**H**) and haemophilia (**h**) are located on the X chromosome:

Phenotype of parents	female carrier		×	healthy male	
Genotype of parents	X^HX^h		×	X^HY	
Genotype of gametes	X^H	X^h		X^H	Y
Genotype of offspring	X^HX^H	X^HX^h		X^HY	X^hY
Phenotype of offspring	healthy female	carrier female		healthy male	haemophilac male

- Non-interacting, unlinked genes are located on different chromosomes and control different phenotypic characteristics.
- Genetic diagrams can be used to predict the ratio of phenotypes in the offspring of given parents.
- Since the results of a genetic cross are categoric data, the chi squared (χ^2) test is appropriate to test the statistical significance of any difference between the observed and expected results.

Practice questions

1 **Pp** represents:

A an allele **C** a genome

B a gene **D** a genotype *(1)*

2 A cross between two organisms with the genotype **Aa** would produce offspring with genotypes in an expected ratio of:

A 1:1 **C** 2:1

B 1:2:1 **D** 3:1 *(1)*

3 An organism with the genotype for two unlinked genes of **AaBb** could produce gametes with alleles of these genes in the expected ratio of:

A 1:1 **C** 1:2:1

B 1:1:1 **D** 1:1:1:1

4 In humans, the ability to distinguish red and green as separate colours is controlled by a single gene. Red–green colour blindness results from a recessive allele of this gene, represented as **b**. The dominant allele (**B**) results in the ability to distinguish red and green.

The diagram represents the inheritance of red–green colour blindness in one family

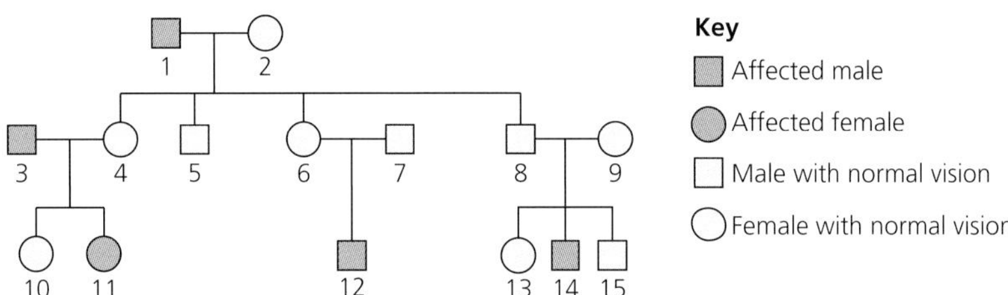

a) Red–green colour blindness is a sex-linked character. Give the evidence from the diagram that supports this statement. *(2)*

b) Give the genotype of person 4. Justify your answer. *(2)*

c) Give the genotype of person 11. Justify your answer. *(1)*

5 Chickens have loose red-coloured skin, called combs, around their heads. The shape of these combs is controlled by two genes, each with two alleles: **P** and **p**, **R** and **r**.

The table shows the phenotypes produced by these genes. The dashes indicate that either of the alleles of a gene could be present.

Genotype	P–R–	P–rr	ppR–	pprr
Phenotype of comb	Walnut	Pea	Rose	Single

The information on the next page shows how a breeder mated a pure-breeding rose-combed chicken with a pure-breeding pea-combed chicken. He then interbred the offspring of these parents to produce an offspring (2) generation.

		♀		♂	
Phenotype of parents		rose comb		pea comb	
Phenotypes of offspring (2)	**walnut comb**	**rose comb**	**pea comb**	**single comb**	
Expected ratio of phenotype	**9** :	**3** :	**3** :	**1**	

a) Draw a genetic cross diagram to explain the phenotypes produced by this cross. *(4)*

b) What can you conclude about the location of the two genes **P** and **R**? *(2)*

6 The diagram shows two characteristics of the flower of a plant called the sweet pea (*Lathyrus odoratus*).

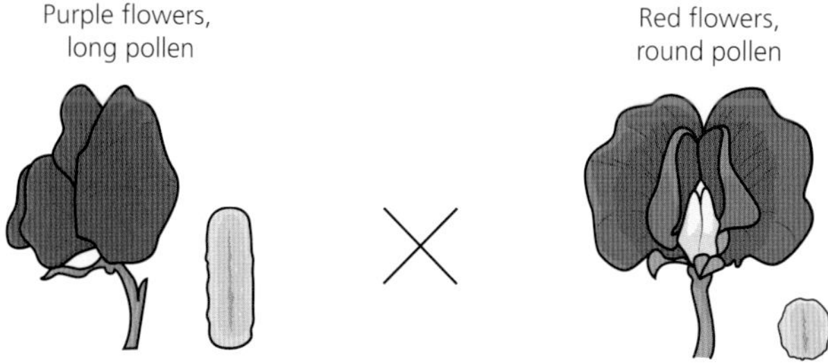

Each of these characteristics is controlled by a gene with two alleles. The gene controlling flower colour has two alleles: the allele for purple flowers (**F**) is dominant and that for red flowers (**f**) is recessive. The gene controlling the shape of the pollen grains also has two alleles: the allele for long pollen grains (**L**) is dominant and that for round pollen grains (**l**) is recessive.

A plant breeder transferred pollen grains from plant 1 that was homozygous dominant for both genes, to plant 2 that was homozygous recessive for both genes.

a) Name the organ of plant 1 from which the plant breeder would take the pollen grains. *(1)*

b) Name the organ of plant 2 onto which the plant breeder would transfer the pollen grains. *(1)*

c) Suggest how the plant breeder would transfer the pollen grains. *(1)*

The plant breeder planted the seed produced by plant 2. After the seeds had germinated and produced adult plants, he ensured these plants self-fertilised. Again, he collected the seeds produced, planted them and recorded the two phenotypes in the offspring (2) generation. He recorded the following number of plants in the offspring (2) generation:

- 284 plants with purple flowers and long pollen grains
- 21 plants with purple flowers and round pollen grains
- 21 plants with red flowers and long purple grains
- 55 plants with red flowers and round pollen grains.

Tip

Question 6 is synoptic, that is, it includes information from another part of your course. It also includes elements of experimental design. Both features are common in Paper 3 questions.

d) Suggest how the plant breeder could ensure that the plants in the offspring (1) generation self-fertilised. *(1)*

e) Explain the results the plant breeder obtained. *(4)*

Stretch and challenge

7 Labrador retrievers are a breed of dog. Their fur can be black, brown or yellow. The colour depends on the inheritance of two unlinked genes.

One gene controls the production of the pigment melanin. This gene has two alleles: a dominant allele, **B**, results in black fur and a recessive allele, **b**, results in brown fur.

A second gene controls whether or not any pigment molecules are deposited in a retriever's fur. This gene has two alleles: a dominant allele, **E**, results in melanin being deposited in the fur (a black or brown dog) and a recessive allele, **e**, results in no melanin being deposited in the fur (a yellow dog).

A dog breeder mated a male dog with the genotype **BBEE** and a female dog with the genotype **bbee**. He then allowed the offspring to mate together to produce an offspring (2) generation.

a) Construct a genetic diagram to show the expected ratio of phenotypes in the offspring (2) generation.

b) Explain why a Labrador retriever might have brown eyes but yellow fur.

c) This cross demonstrates a phenomenon called epistasis. Research the term 'epistasis' and explain what it means.

8 Some human characteristics show continuous variation. Explain the cause of continuous variation in human eye colour.

21 Gene pools

Prior knowledge

In this chapter you will need to recall that:

- a population is a group of organisms of the same species living in the same habitat at the same time
- genetic variation occurs within populations
- mutation is the ultimate source of genetic variation in all populations. In sexually reproducing populations, random assortment of chromosomes and crossing over during meiosis and the random fertilisation of gametes provide further sources of genetic variation
- genetic variation results in differences in the phenotypes of members of a population
- natural selection is the differential reproductive success of phenotypes within a population
- a gene pool is the sum total of all the alleles of all the genes within a population
- natural selection results in a change in the allele frequencies of genes within a population
- under certain circumstances, natural selection can result in the formation of new species.

Test yourself on prior knowledge

1 Give the main stages in the argument for natural selection.

2 What is meant by the 'struggle for existence'?

3 Give **three** sources of evidence that support the theory of natural selection.

4 Distinguish between allopatric and sympatric speciation.

5 Explain how antibiotic resistance in bacteria is an example of directional selection.

Populations – a reminder

Key term

Population A group of individuals belonging to a single species, living together in one habitat. If the organisms reproduce sexually, members of a population are also able to interbreed.

In Chapter 20, you considered genes and their alleles in the context of inheritance. In this chapter you will consider genes in the context of **populations**, both of genes within, and gene flow between populations.

Populations can vary in the number of organisms they contain and in the area or volume they occupy. As you saw in Chapter 15, a population containing millions of bacteria could occupy $10\,cm^3$ of broth culture. A population containing millions of turtles would occupy a much larger volume! The population of garden snails around the compost heap in Figure 21.1 occupies a much smaller area than the population of song thrushes, which might feed on them. In the latter example, the mobility of the animal must be taken into consideration.

In sexually reproducing species, members of a population are able to interbreed. The corollary to this is that if the members of two groups of the same sexually reproducing species are not able to interbreed, they do not belong to the same population. Figure 21.1 illustrates some of the problems in determining whether interbreeding can occur between different groups and, consequently, in defining a population. Garden snails are able to move but only slowly. On this basis, you might consider the garden snails occupying the flower bed on the traffic island in Figure 21.1 as a single population. Snails from this group are unlikely to cross the road safely and mate with the snails living on the compost heap. They probably form a **'closed' population**, that is, one that is completely cut off from neighbouring groups of the same species. Although they move slowly, however, the snails around the compost heap and on the nearby flower bed can probably migrate and interbreed. So these two groups probably form an **'open' population**, that is, a population in which there is considerable movement between members of two or more groups.

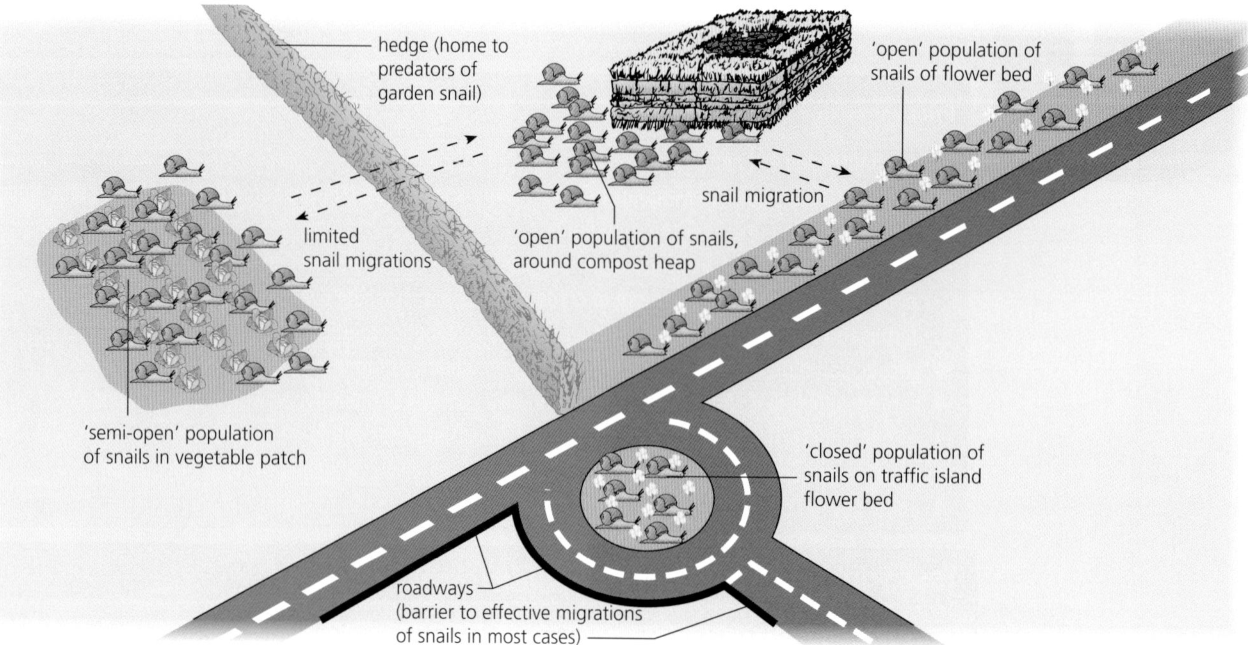

Figure 21.1 Exploring the concept of 'population'

Key term

Gene pool The total of all the alleles of all the genes present in a particular population at a given time. Here, we will use the term to refer only to the alleles of a single gene.

Populations and gene pools

When considering genes within a population, we use the term **gene pool**. As you will see, we normally only consider a single gene at a time. In doing so, we use the term gene pool to refer to the sum of all the alleles of one gene present within a population at a given time. We could, however, use the term to cover the sum of all the alleles of all the genes possessed by members of a particular population at a particular time. Given the complexity of genomes, we would need to use computer software to handle all the data involved.

When breeding occurs between members of a population, a sample of the alleles of each gene in the gene pool will form the genomes (gene sets of individuals) of the next generation – and so on, from generation to generation. In this way, two different populations of the same species might contain different samples of the alleles of the genes forming the genome of this species. Figure 21.2 shows how the gene pools of two populations and the gene pool of the species relate to each other.

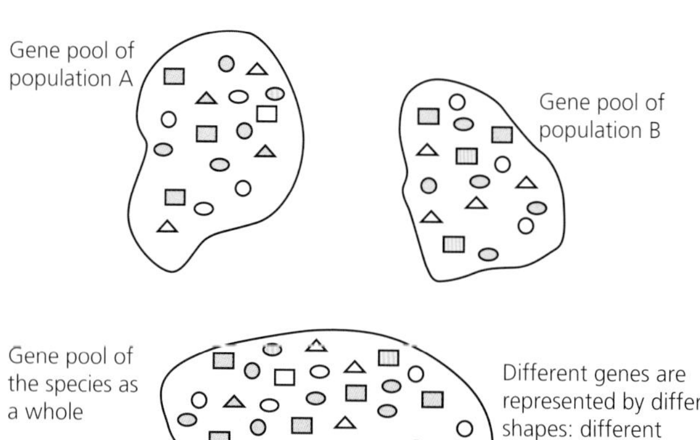

Figure 21.2 The gene pools of two populations of a single species and the gene pool of the entire species

Test yourself

1 Explain the difference between a biological community and a population.
2 Explain what is meant by 'gene flow'.
3 Will gene flow occur between members of open populations or members of closed populations?
4 Define the term 'gene pool'.
5 Are the gene pools of two populations of the same species identical?

Allele frequencies within a gene pool

Consider one gene with two alleles. The frequency with which one of these alleles occurs is the proportion it represents of all the alleles of that gene in a given population. It is called the **allele frequency** and is always expressed as a decimal value less than 1.

Key term

Allele frequency The number of copies of an allele of a single gene within a population divided by the total number of copies of that gene. Since diploid organisms carry two copies of each gene, the total number of copies in a population is two times the number of organisms.

Estimating the allele frequencies when you know the numbers of the different genotypes in a population

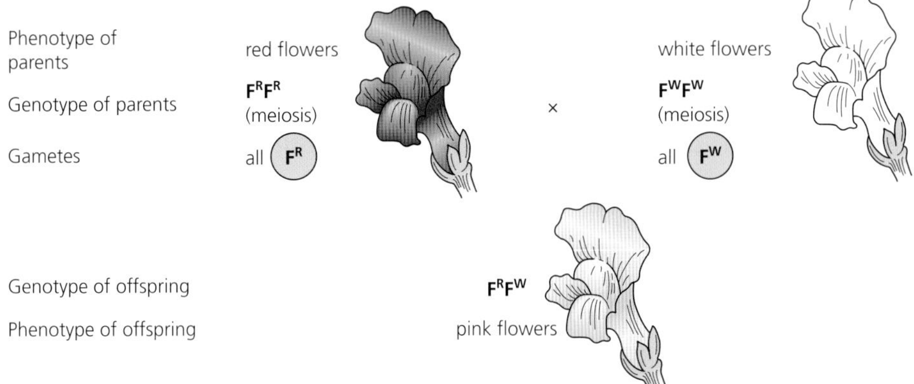

Figure 21.3 Flower colour in snapdragons (*Antirrhinum* sp.) is controlled by two codominant alleles, enabling us to tell all three flower-colour genotypes by observing the phenotypes

Figure 21.3 shows the inheritance of flower colour in snapdragons (*Antirrhinum*). The gene for flower colour has two codominant alleles, $\mathbf{F^R}$ and $\mathbf{F^W}$. Since they are codominant alleles, both show their effect in the phenotype of the heterozygote. As you can see in Figure 21.3, heterozygotes, $\mathbf{F^RF^W}$, have pink flowers. In other words, you can tell the flower-colour genotypes of snapdragon plants just by looking at the colour of their flowers.

Let's suppose that in a particular population of snapdragons:

- there are 1000 diploid plants
- 490 of these individuals are homozygous $\mathbf{F^RF^R}$
- 420 of these individuals are heterozygous $\mathbf{F^RF^W}$
- 90 of these individuals are homozygous $\mathbf{F^WF^W}$.

How can you find the frequencies of allele $\mathbf{F^R}$ *and allele* $\mathbf{F^W}$*?*

You start by realising that there are 1000 plants in the population, each with two alleles of this gene, making a total of 2000 alleles.

You then find the frequency of allele $\mathbf{F^R}$:

- 490 plants in the population carry two $\mathbf{F^R}$ alleles, making 980 $\mathbf{F^R}$ alleles
- 420 plants in the population carry one $\mathbf{F^R}$ allele, making a further 420 $\mathbf{F^R}$ alleles
- this gives 1400 $\mathbf{F^R}$ alleles out of the total of 2000 alleles of this gene
- so the frequency of the $\mathbf{F^R}$ allele $= \frac{1400}{2000} = 0.7$

You now find the frequency of allele $\mathbf{F^W}$:

- 90 plants in the population carry two $\mathbf{F^W}$ alleles, making 180 $\mathbf{F^W}$ alleles
- 420 plants in the population carry one $\mathbf{F^W}$ allele, making a further 420 $\mathbf{F^W}$ alleles
- this gives 600 $\mathbf{F^W}$ alleles out of a total of 2000 alleles of this gene
- so the frequency of the $\mathbf{F^W}$ allele $= \frac{600}{2000} = 0.3$

Hopefully you realised that there was an easier way to calculate the frequency of allele $\mathbf{F^W}$. Common sense should tell you that the frequencies of the two alleles added together must equal 1.0. So, once you had calculated the frequency of allele $\mathbf{F^R}$ as 0.7, the frequency of the only other allele available, $\mathbf{F^W}$, must be $1.0 - 0.7 = 0.3$

Key term

Hardy–Weinberg equation
$p^2 + 2pq + q^2 = 1$, where p is the frequency of the dominant allele (**A**) and q is the frequency of the recessive allele (**a**) of a single gene.

Tip

You will not be asked to prove the Hardy-Weinberg equation, only to use it.

Estimating the allele frequencies when you do not know the numbers of the different genotypes in a particular population

The above example works fine when you can distinguish between the heterozygotes and the homozygotes. But what happens when you can't, that is, when one of the alleles is dominant. To solve this, you need to use an equation independently discovered by two people and so named after them both – the **Hardy–Weinberg equation**.

To use this equation, you:

- give the dominant allele a frequency of p
- give the recessive allele a frequency of q
- since there are no other alleles, $p + q = 1$
- the frequency of the homozygous dominant individuals is p^2
- the frequency of the heterozygous individuals is $2pq$
- the frequency of the homozygous recessive individuals is q^2
- since this accounts for all the individuals, $\mathbf{p^2 + 2pq + q^2 = 1}$

Example

Using the Hardy–Weinberg equation

Let's use the same data as our previous calculation, but this time using dominant and recessive alleles of a gene, **A** and **a**.

As in our previous example with snapdragon plants, let's suppose that in a particular population:

- there are 1000 diploid individuals
- 910 of these individuals show the dominant characteristic (in other words are **AA** or **Aa**)
- 90 of these individuals show the recessive characteristic (in other words are **aa**).

As always when finding an unknown, we start with what we do know.

1 What do we know about the genotypes of any of the individuals in this population?

2 What is the frequency of the **aa** individuals in this population?

3 How can we use the frequency of **aa** individuals to find the frequency of the '**a**' allele in this population?

4 How can we use the frequency of the '**a**' allele to find the frequency of the '**A**' allele in this population?

5 What is the frequency of individuals in this population with the genotype **AA**, **Aa** and **aa**?

6 How many individuals in this population had the genotypes **AA**, **Aa** and **aa**?

Answers

1 In this case, we cannot distinguish between the **AA** and **Aa** individuals – they both show the dominant characteristic. We do know, however, that the 90 individuals showing the recessive characteristics must have the genotype **aa**.

2 Since we know that 90 of the 1000 individuals in this population had this genotype, we can calculate their frequency in the population as: $\frac{90}{1000} = 0.09$

3 In the Hardy–Weinberg equation, the frequency of individuals in a population with the genotype **aa** is represented q^2.

So, we find the value of q, the frequency of the **a** allele, as $\sqrt{q^2} = \sqrt{0.09} = 0.3$

4 Since there are only two alleles to consider, the sum of their frequencies must equal 1.

So, if $p + q = 1$, then $p = 1 - q$, which in our case means:

$p = 1 - 0.3 = 0.7$

Since we used the same numbers, you will not be surprised to find that the frequencies of the two alleles in this example are exactly the same as in our previous example in which we could distinguish all three phenotypes.

5 To solve this, we substitute our values of p and q into the Hardy–Weinberg equation:

AA Aa aa

$p^2 + 2pq + q^2 = 1$

So the frequency of individuals with:

- the **AA** genotype is $0.7^2 = 0.49$
- the **Aa** genotype is $2 \times 0.7 \times 0.3 = 0.42$
- the **aa** genotype is $0.3^2 = 0.09$

6 Since there were 1000 individuals in the population, the number of individuals can be found by multiplying their frequency given above by 1000. So, the number of individuals with the genotype:

- **AA** is $0.49 \times 1000 = 490$
- **Aa** is $0.42 \times 1000 = 420$
- **aa** is $0.09 \times 1000 = 90$

The fact that these values, $490 + 420 + 90 = 1000$, the number of individuals in the population, should reassure us that our calculation is correct.

Tip

When using the Hardy–Weinberg equation to solve problems, always start with the data about homozygous recessive individuals. Their frequency is q^2, enabling you to calculate the value of q ($\sqrt{q^2}$) and of p $(1 - q)$.

Tip

It is always a good idea to check your calculations as you go along. In this case you should expect the sum of the three frequencies to equal 1. Our calculated frequencies are $0.49 + 0.42 + 0.09 = 1.0$, so our calculation is correct.

Tip

Test yourself questions 6 to 8 test your understanding of earlier sub-topics.

Test yourself

6 Look back to Figure 21.3 on page 439. If the offspring had been allowed to interbreed, what ratio of phenotypes would you expect in the offspring (2) generation?

7 Continuing the answer to Question 6, which statistical test would you use to see whether any difference between the actual numbers of phenotypes in the offspring (2) generation and the numbers you predicted, was statistically significant? Explain your answer.

8 Explain what is meant by 'statistically significant'.

9 The rhesus blood group in humans is controlled by two alleles of a single gene. The allele for rhesus positive is dominant and the allele for rhesus negative is recessive. In Europe, 16 per cent of the population is rhesus negative. What percentage of the European population is heterozygous for this gene? Explain your answer.

10 What assumption did you make in your calculation in Question 9?

Key term

Hardy–Weinberg principle Provided several assumptions hold true, the allele frequencies of a gene within a single population will not change from generation to generation.

The Hardy–Weinberg principle (also called the Hardy–Weinberg equilibrium)

G.H. Hardy and Wilhelm Weinberg were independently analysing the behaviour of populations. They both used mathematical models to show that, if certain assumptions are made, the frequency of the alleles of a gene will remain constant from generation to generation in any population.

The seven assumptions underlying the **Hardy–Weinberg principle** are as follows:

- The organisms are diploid.
- The organisms reproduce only by sexual reproduction.
- The generations are discrete, that is, do not overlap.
- Mating is random.
- The population size is infinitely large.
- The allele frequencies are equal in both sexes.
- There is no migration, mutation or selection.

Tip

Do not confuse the Hardy-Weinberg principle with the Hardy-Weinberg equation. The former proposes an equilibrium within a population of the allele frequencies of a single gene. The latter provides a means to estimate the frequencies of alleles and genotypes in a population.

The Hardy–Weinberg principle is of interest because we know that sometimes, in some populations, the composition of the gene pool does change. This can be due to a range of factors, known as **disturbing factors** because they operate to alter the allele frequencies of some genes. Disturbing factors include:

- gene mutation
- migration
- genetic drift
- natural selection.

Gene mutation

Gene mutations are random, rare, spontaneous changes in the base sequence of genes. If they occur during gamete formation in the gonads, they can lead to the possibility of new characteristics in the offspring – for example, the ability to inactivate a pesticide molecule. You examined gene mutations at some length in Chapter 20.

Migration

If you look back to Figure 21.1 on page 438, you can see how two populations could have different frequencies of the alleles of a particular gene. If some individuals leave one population (**emigration**), their alleles will be lost from that population. As a result, the allele frequency of that population will change. Similarly, if those individuals join the second population (**immigration**), their arrival will change the allele frequencies of that population also.

Genetic drift

In much the same way that you are more likely to get a 50:50 split in 'heads' or 'tails' if you toss a coin 1000 times than if you toss a coin ten times, the allele frequencies are more likely to be representative at each generation in a very large population than in a very small one. If a population is very small, chance events will play a big part in determining which organisms survive to reproduce successfully. The random changes in the allele frequencies that result from small population size are known as **genetic drift**. Small population size, leading to genetic drift can occur for a number of reasons.

Key term

Genetic drift Random changes in the allele frequency of a particular gene resulting from 'sampling error' during sexual reproduction in a small population.

Genetic bottleneck

A sudden hostile physical condition (for example, flooding or drought) could sharply reduce a natural population to a very small number of survivors. On the return of a favourable environment, numbers of the affected population might quickly return to normal (as a result of reduced competition for food sources, for example). The new population, however, would be built from a very small sample of the original population, so would contain a small sample of the original gene pool, possibly with some alleles lost altogether (Figure 21.4).

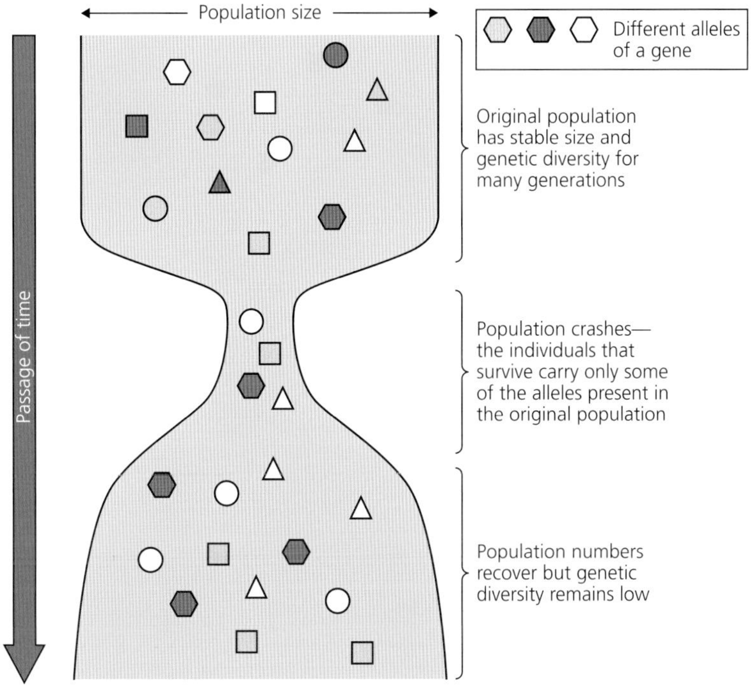

Figure 21.4 A genetic bottleneck results from a sudden reduction in the size of a population and causes a reduction in the genetic diversity of that population

Figure 21.5 There is genetic evidence that the cheetah population went through a genetic bottleneck about 10 000 years ago

Analysis of the human genome suggests that our own species suffered a genetic bottleneck at some stage in our evolution, as did that of the cheetah (Figure 21.5).

Founder effect

A small number of organisms might become isolated in a new environment. As with a genetic bottleneck, the genotypes of these organisms are likely to form a small sample from the original gene pool. When these individuals reproduce to form a larger population, the allele frequencies will remain a small sample of the gene pool of the species. An extreme example of this might occur when a pregnant female mouse is carried on driftwood from the mainland to an unpopulated offshore island (Figure 21.6).

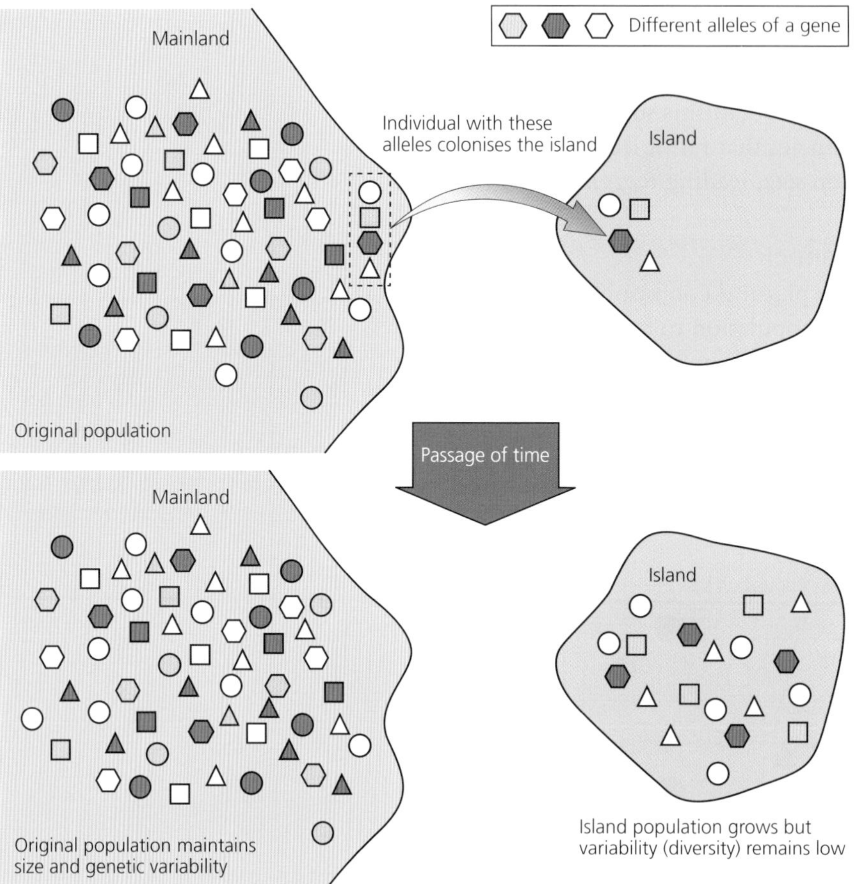

Figure 21.6 The founder effect is shown when a single individual (pregnant or self-fertilising), or small group of individuals, from a mainland colonise an uninhabited offshore island

We can find examples of the founder effect in human populations. On several occasions throughout history, small groups of Europeans emigrated to the USA to escape religious persecution in their own country. On arrival, these people formed self-contained settlements that last to this day. The allele frequencies of many genes in the communities of the Amish and of the Dunkers, for example, are quite different from those of the general population of the USA.

Natural selection

Figure 21.7 The song thrush preys on five-banded snails. It eats more of those that it finds easily, causing pink-shelled snails to be less common in grassland and yellow-shelled snails to be less common in beech woodland

Natural selection acting on a phenotypic feature of members of a population will lead to a change in the allele frequencies of the gene controlling that phenotypic feature. Chapter 8 covered natural selection in some depth. Figure 21.7 provides a reminder of a well-known example – the selective predation by song thrushes (*Turdus philomelos*) on populations of the five-banded snail (*Cepaea nemoralis*) with a particular shell coloration that makes them visible in (say) a woodland habitat, but effectively camouflaged in a grassland habitat.

Natural selection can change the allele frequency in a number of different ways. In Chapter 8, you learnt about stabilising selection and directional selection. Figure 21.8 serves to remind you of **stabilising selection**. The upper graph shows the distribution of a continuous phenotypic feature, such as human body mass at birth. The values follow a normal distribution with a central mode. The lower curve represents the effect of stabilising selection. As you can see from the lower graph, the extreme birth masses have been eliminated; natural selection has favoured the modal birth mass.

Figure 21.9 represents a type of selection you did not cover in Chapter 8 – **disruptive selection**. Here, natural selection has favoured phenotypes at the extremes of the range of values. As a result, the population has two phenotypes, each with a mode that is different from that of the original population. The existence in one population of two or more different phenotypes of the same character is termed **polymorphism**.

Key term

Polymorphism The existence of two or more body forms (morphs) within a single population.

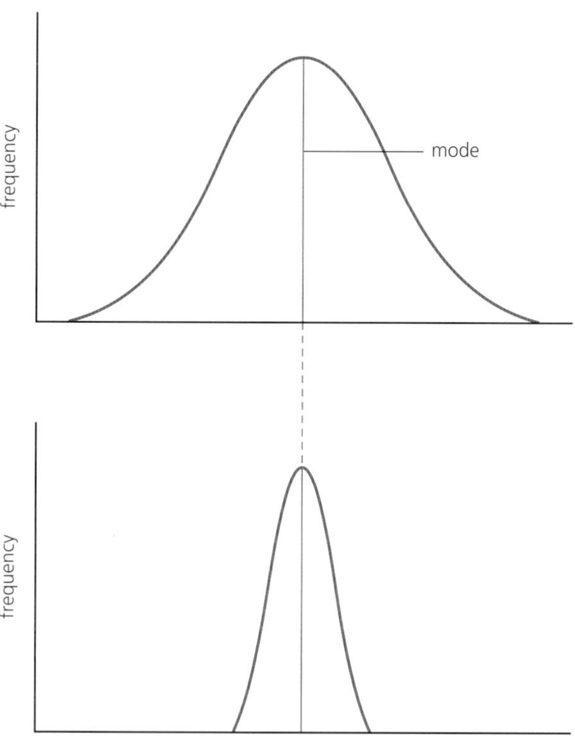

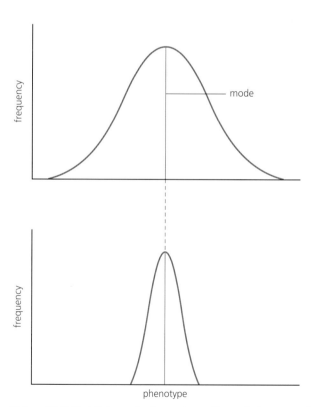

Figure 21.8 Stabilising selection reduces the variation around the mode

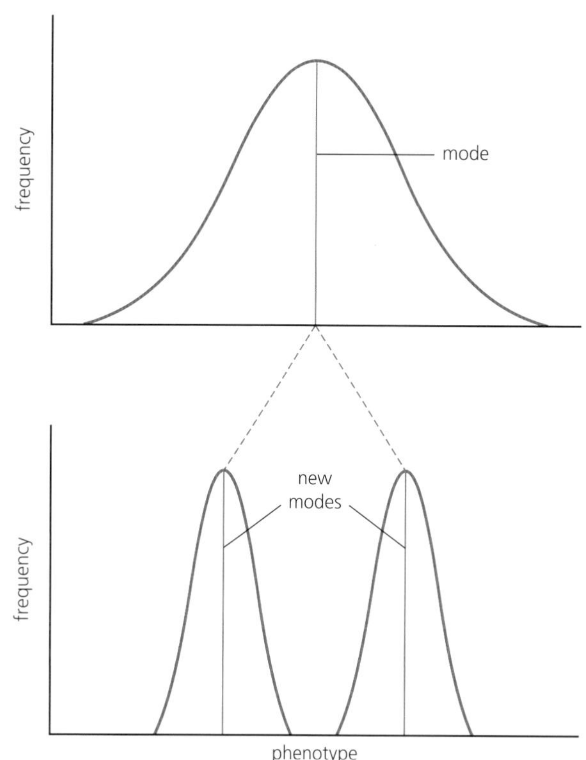

Figure 21.9 Disruptive selection results in two phenotypes (polymorphism) within a population

Test yourself

11 Distinguish between the Hardy–Weinberg principle and the Hardy–Weinberg equation.

12 When asked to calculate allele frequencies in a population, under what circumstances would you **not** use the Hardy–Weinberg equation? Explain your answer.

13 List **four** disturbing factors of the Hardy–Weinberg principle.

14 Analysis of the human genome suggests that our own species suffered a genetic bottleneck at some stage in our evolution. Suggest what this evidence might be.

15 Analysis of several introns in the gene controlling haemophilia showed very little difference between members of the Slavic populations from the European part of Russia and the native ethnic groups of Uzbekistan and Kazakhstan. What can you conclude from this result?

Disruptive selection and polymorphism

The different shell colours of *Cepaea nemoralis* (the five-banded snail) provide an example of a polymorphism. The shell colour that is at a selective advantage is different in different environments.

- In parts of England, where song thrushes prey on these snails, the yellow shell is better camouflaged in grassland than the pink shell but the pink shell is better camouflaged among the beech litter on the floor of a beech woodland than is the yellow shell. Like us, thrushes more readily find the conspicuous shells, so eat more of them. Snails with a yellow shell survive better than snails with a pink shell in grassland but the converse is true in beech woodlands.
- In parts of the Pyrenees, yellow shells reflect more heat than pink shells, so snails with yellow shells are at an advantage in regions with bright sunlight.

In these populations, the polymorphism is stable for many generations, so is called a **balanced polymorphism**.

A **transient polymorphism** is one in which the selective advantage changes over time. An example of this type of polymorphism is industrial melanism. During the industrial revolution in Britain, areas of heavy industry became highly polluted by acidic gases, such as SO_2, which killed the algae and lichens that grew on the surface of trees. The polluting soot also blackened these surfaces.

Like all moths, the peppered moth (*Biston betularia*) rests on surfaces with its wings unfolded. Against the blotchy background caused by lichens, the peppered form shown in Figure 21.10 on the next page had been well camouflaged. In heavily polluted areas, it no longer was and became more susceptible to predation by insectivorous birds. By chance, a gene mutation resulted in a melanic (dark) wing colouration. Moths with this wing colour were much less conspicuous on the blackened, lichen-free trees and so suffered less predation. The result, as you can see in Figure 21.10, was that the lighter, peppered form was more common in unpolluted areas and the melanic form was more common in industrial areas – another example of the effects of disruptive selection.

In the peppered moth (*Biston betularia*), environmental conditions have, at different times, favoured either the pale or the melanic forms.

In these circumstances, the effect of natural selection on the gene pool (in the form of selective predation of moths resting on exposed surfaces by insectivorous birds) has been '**disruptive**'.

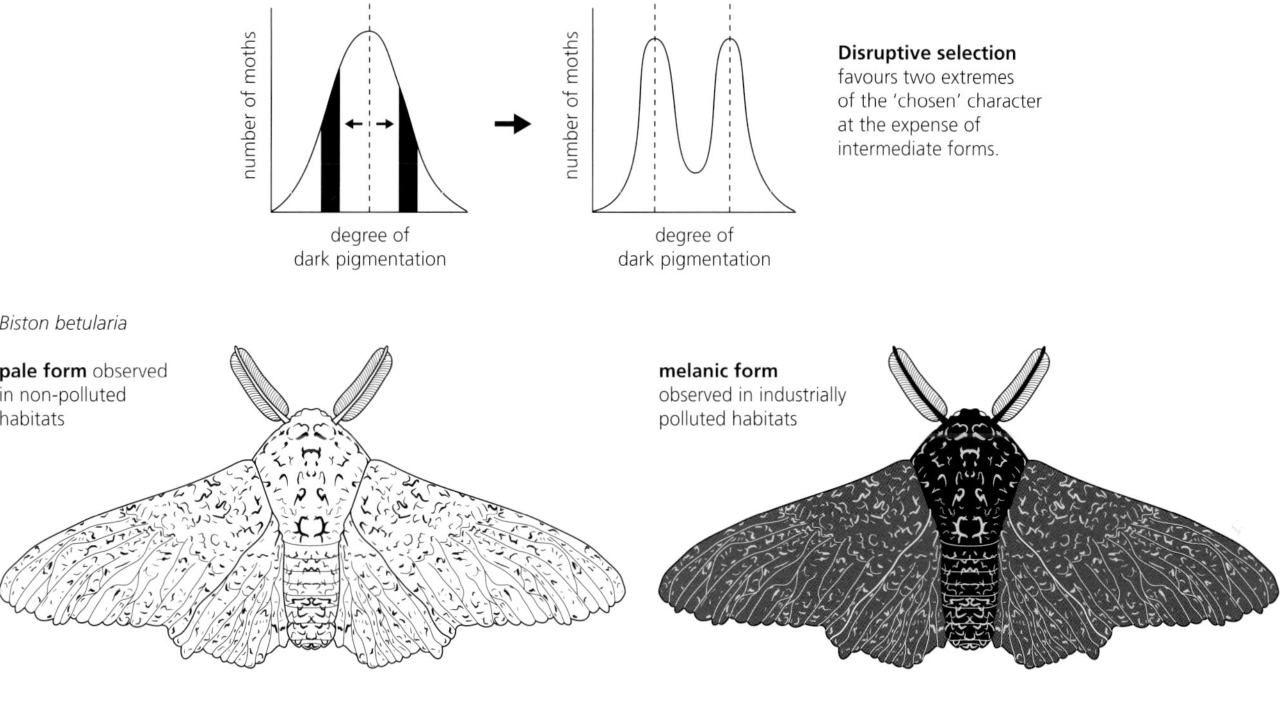

experimental evidence that establishes transient polymorphism

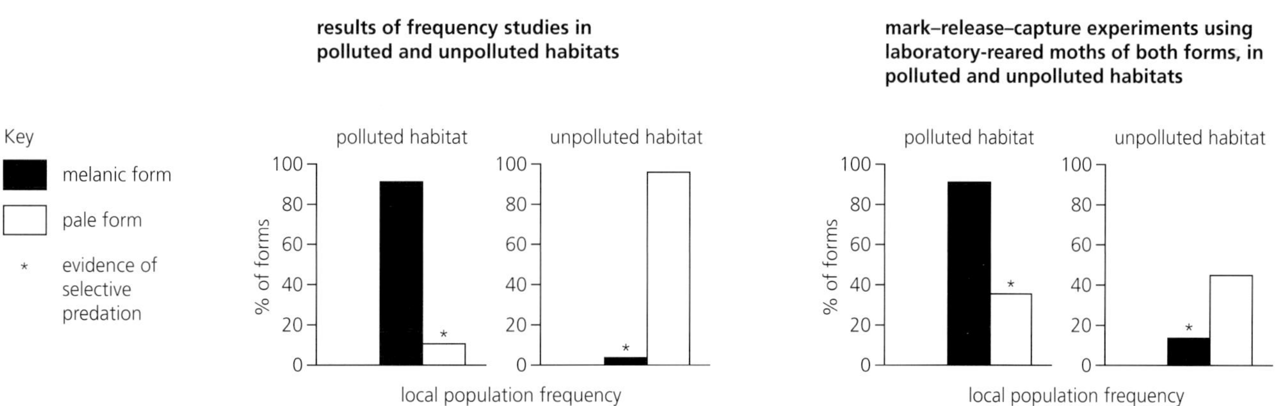

Figure 21.10 The peppered moth (*Biston betularia*) and industrial melanism – a case of a transient polymorphism

Clean Air Acts, passed by the UK government of the 1950s, led to a great reduction in air pollution. As a result, lichens began to grow again in the previously polluted industrial heartlands. As the lichens changed the background on which the peppered and melanic moths rested, insectivorous birds now found the melanic form more conspicuous and ate more of those. Natural selection now favoured the pale, peppered moths and the frequency of these moths increased at the expense of the melanic form.

Balance polymorphisms and speciation

You saw in Chapter 8 how natural selection can lead to speciation. We also differentiated between two models of speciation.

- **Allopatric speciation** might occur following the separation of two populations of the same species by a physical or geographical barrier.
- **Sympatric speciation** occurs without the physical separation of two groups from the same population.

Population geneticists are interested in comparisons between populations of a single species occurring on a mainland and on each of a group of offshore islands. You might recall from Chapter 8 that comparisons between animals on mainland Ecuador and on islands of the Galapagos archipelago were important in the development of Charles Darwin's appreciation of natural selection. Populations on offshore islands could form new species by allopatric speciation.

We can define the term 'species' as a group of organisms that can actually or potentially interbreed to produce fertile offspring. The 'potentially' part of that definition is quite important. We could have two populations of, say, *Cepaea nemoralis*, one in Spain and one in England. They could not naturally interbreed because the distance between them is too great for their migration capability. But if we were to bring them together into the laboratory, they would be able to interbreed and produce fertile offspring. The geographical separation has not led to genetic changes in these two populations that prevent their successful interbreeding; they still belong to the same species.

Balanced polymorphisms are of interest to population geneticists because they might provide opportunities for sympatric speciation to occur. The worked example below provides one example of a balanced polymorphism that might possibly lead to speciation.

Example

Copper tolerance in bent grass

The waste from old copper mines was usually dumped near the mine itself. It formed mounds of soil that have a high concentration of copper ions. Fields around the waste tips of copper mines in North Wales contained populations of the bent grass (*Agrostis tenuis*). But for many years, this plant did not grow on the waste tips, as you can see in Figure 21.11.

Figure 21.11 This hill was formed from waste from a nearby copper mine

1 The seeds from bent grass plants are blown large distances by the wind and some will have landed on the waste tip. Suggest why no bent grass plants grew there.

The waste tip remained plant-free for many years. Eventually, a few plants of bent grass were found growing on the waste tip. Plant biologists from a nearby university found that these plants had become copper-tolerant.

2 Suggest how these plants had become copper tolerant.

3 Did the presence of copper in the waste cause the gene mutation?

4 Although the population of bent grass on the waste tip comprised plants with copper tolerance, the populations in the surrounding areas did not evolve copper tolerance. Suggest why.

5 Explain why the plant biologists were excited that these populations might provide an opportunity for sympatric speciation.

Answers

1 Although copper is a trace element, that is, needed in tiny amounts for healthy plant growth, it is toxic in high concentrations. Consequently, any seeds germinating on the waste tip would be killed by the copper.

2 The copper tolerance resulted from a gene mutation.

3 The answer is no, the gene mutation was a random event. Once it had occurred, however, the mutant plant was able to grow on the copper-contaminated soil and the resulting population contained plants that were copper tolerant.

4 We must assume that a mutation that results in copper tolerance has occurred randomly over the thousands of years that this plant species has existed. In the absence of toxic levels of copper in the soil, this mutation would not confer an advantage and, quite probably, resulted in some selective disadvantage to its possessor. As a result, natural selection would act against the mutation and the allele of this gene would be lost from the population.

5 The copper-tolerant and non-tolerant populations co-exist but any gene flow between them is unlikely to result in successful adults. Plants without copper tolerance will not survive on the waste tips and copper-tolerant plants are likely to be at a selective disadvantage in the unpolluted soil. Effectively, there are closed populations within which changes in allele frequencies could accumulate that would prevent sexual reproduction between them producing fertile offspring.

Test yourself

16 Under what circumstances is genetic drift likely to occur?

17 Of what type of natural selection is the evolution of antibiotic resistance in bacteria an example?

18 Suggest why stabilising selection on human birth mass is of less significance today than in 1950.

19 Following the Clean Air Acts in the UK, the melanic populations of *Biston betularia* became dominated by the lighter, peppered form again. What does this show about the allele of the colour gene causing the melanic body form?

20 What would an unchanging gene pool suggest about a population?

Chapter summary

Allele frequencies within a gene pool

- A gene pool is a collection of all the genes within an interbreeding population.
- We usually consider the frequencies of the different alleles of a particular gene within a gene pool.
- If we know the frequency of each genotype within a population, we can calculate the frequency of the alleles controlling this characteristic.
- The Hardy–Weinberg principle, also known as the Hardy–Weinberg equilibrium, proposes that, in any population of randomly interbreeding organisms, the frequencies of the alleles of a gene and the frequencies of genotypes controlled by that gene will remain constant from generation to generation, in the absence of other evolutionary influences.

What causes changes in allele frequency?

- Natural selection can cause the frequencies of alleles of a gene to change.
- Natural selection occurs when organisms in a population that possess a particular phenotype have more offspring than those with a different phenotype. The allele of the gene that controls the favourable phenotype becomes more common in each subsequent generation.
- Stabilising natural selection favours an optimum phenotype, resulting in the elimination of extreme phenotypes.
- Disruptive selection favours two extreme phenotypes, resulting in polymorphism.
- If polymorphism leads to reproductive isolation, speciation can occur.
- Immigration of new individuals into, and emigration of individuals out of, a population can also lead to changes in allele frequencies.
- Gene mutations can also lead to changes in allele frequencies in a population.
- In very small populations, changes in allele frequency can occur by chance; so-called genetic drift. Genetic drift commonly occurs through:
  - population bottlenecks, e.g., a catastrophe wipes out most members of a population
  - the founder effect, in which a small number of organisms become isolated in a new environment.

Using the Hardy–Weinberg equation

- This equation is useful for estimating allele frequencies when you do not know the frequency of each genotype resulting from two alleles of a gene.
- For example, if a phenotypic character is controlled by a gene with a dominant allele **B** and a recessive allele **b**, individuals with the genotypes **BB** and **Bb** will be indistinguishable. You will only be able to recognise the phenotypes of homozygous recessive genotypes, **bb**.
- The Hardy–Weinberg equation uses symbols to represent the unknown frequencies of alleles and of genotypes:
  - frequency of **B** = p
  - frequency of **b** = q
  - frequency of **BB** = p^2
  - frequency of **Bb** = $2pq$
  - frequency of **bb** = q^2
- Since we can recognise individuals with the **bb** genotype, we:
  - calculate the number of **bb** individuals as a decimal fraction of the total population
  - find the square root of this decimal fraction; this gives us the value of q
  - find p as $1 - q$
  - substitute these values of p and q to find the frequency of **BB** (p^2) and **Bb** ($2pq$) genotypes
  - check that $p^2 + 2pq + q^2 = 1$. If not, we repeat our calculation.

Practice questions

1 Warfarin has long been used as a rat poison. The evolution of resistance to warfarin in rat populations is an example of:

A artificial selection **C** disruptive selection

B directional selection **D** stabilising selection *(1)*

2 A gene has two alleles. If the frequency of the homozygous recessive individuals in a population is 0.5, the frequency of the dominant allele:

A is less than that of the recessive allele

B is the same as that of the recessive allele

C is greater than that of the recessive allele

D cannot be estimated *(1)*

3 Humans are genetically less diverse than gorillas as a result of:

A the founder effect **C** stabilising selection

B a genetic bottleneck **D** transient polymorphism *(1)*

4 A population of *Drosophila melanogaster* contains 640 long-winged flies and 360 vestigial-winged flies. What proportion of the long-winged flies are homozygous for this gene? Show your working. *(4)*

5 Rice is grown in paddy fields throughout the world. In many paddy fields, weeds are removed by hand when the rice plants are young. A species of barnyard grass, called *Echinochloa oryzoides*, is a weed that grows in rice paddies.

The structure of the leaves, colour of the leaf bases and time of flowering of *E. oryzoides* is unlike all other species of *Echinochloa*. Instead, *E. oryzoides* is a rice mimic, that is, its appearance and flowering time closely resemble those of rice plants.

a) What is the advantage to *E. oryzoides* of being a rice mimic? *(3)*

***b)** Suggest how this rice mimicry might have evolved. *(5)*

6 *Mycosphaerella graminicola* is a pathogenic filamentous fungus that causes leaf blotch on wheat. A group of scientists used restriction fragment length polymorphism (RFLP) markers to investigate the DNA of this pathogen from different countries around the world. The table shows their results.

Tip

Question 6 requires you to bring together knowledge and understanding from several chapters and to think about how scientists would carry out an investigation.

Locus	Genetic diversity in samples of fungus from each country						
	Australia	Canada	Denmark	Israel	UK	USA	Uruguay
SS192A	0.77	0.00	0.22	0.02	0.16	0.15	0.22
SS192B	0.00	0.00	0.22	0.48	0.00	0.05	0.00
SS14	0.26	0.53	–	0.36	0.21	0.29	0.22
SS2	0.00	–	0.39	0.50	0.48	0.53	0.50
SL10	0.23	0.61	0.48	0.50	0.56	0.49	0.55
SL53	0.00	0.36	0.47	0.64	0.47	0.70	0.62
SS 43	0.00	0.72	0.65	0.77	0.67	0.49	0.58
SL31	0.24	0.39	0.55	0.74	0.68	0.48	0.79
Mean	0.19	0.37	0.43	0.50	0.40	0.40	0.44

a) Explain the term 'pathogenic'. *(1)*

b) Outline the method by which the scientists would have obtained the data about genetic diversity in the restriction fragments of DNA. *(3)*

c) What causes a restriction fragment length polymorphism (RFLP) at each locus? *(2)*

d) What does a value of 0.00 in the table represent? *(1)*

e) Explain how the data for Australia provide evidence of the founder effect. *(2)*

f) Suggest the origin of the fungus. Use evidence in the table to justify your answer. *(1)*

Stretch and challenge

7 Modelling is an important technique in population genetics. You can model the effects of genetic drift using the diagram. Each of the six individuals in the diagram produces two identical offspring. Each generation, half of these offspring die; the population remains the same size.

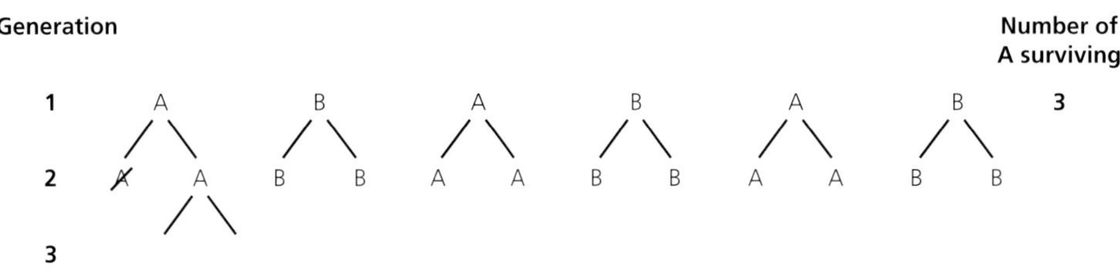

a) Continue the diagram for several generations, deciding which six individuals 'die' by tossing a coin.

b) Plot a graph of the number of surviving **A** offspring against the number of generations.

c) How many generations did it take for either the **A** individuals or the **B** individuals to be lost from the population?

d) Repeat this exercise. Was your answer to question (c) the same? Explain why.

e) Use the internet to find a computer program that will allow you to model genetic drift and use it to explore the effects of different population sizes and starting allele frequencies.

8 How can polyploidy contribute to sympatric speciation in plants?

22 Nervous systems

Prior knowledge

In this chapter you will need to recall that:

- the nervous system of a mammal has two main parts - the central nervous system (CNS) and the peripheral nervous system
- nerve cells are known as neurones and have elongated cell bodies called axons surrounded by insulating myelin sheaths
- there are structural differences between motor and sensory neurones
- motor neurones carry impulses away from the CNS and sensory neurones carry impulses into the CNS
- a nerve impulse is called an action potential, which is a wave of depolarisation caused by ion movements in and out of neurones
- neurones are connected to other neurones and effector organs by synapses
- there is a microscopic gap between neurone membranes at the synapse
- transport across membranes can be by diffusion, facilitated diffusion and active transport (see Chapter 9)
- the simplest connections of the nervous system are reflex arcs
- the brain has distinct parts with individual functions.

Test yourself on prior knowledge

1 Explain why it is important that neurones have insulating myelin sheaths.
2 What type of compound is myelin?
3 Name the **two** ions that are involved in the formation of action potentials.
4 Describe how action potentials cross synapses.
5 Active transport is needed in the conduction of nerve impulses. Explain why.
6 Name **one** human reflex arc.
7 Name the part of the brain that has areas linked with sensory and motor functions of localised parts of the body.

Introduction

As primitive organisms evolved into larger multicellular forms they developed specialised tissues and organs. In this chapter and in Chapters 23 and 24 you will look at how these specialised units are controlled and coordinated to become an efficient living thing. Control generally refers to how instructions are communicated to individual parts; coordination refers to how all the different parts are made to work together efficiently.

A simple example might be attempting to walk. Obviously instructions must be passed to individual muscles to make them contract and move bones using joints. However, this isn't the whole story. If you simply lift your leg to move it forward you will fall over because you have removed one of your supports. Before you lift your leg you must sway your body so that its centre of gravity is over one leg so that you can lift the other off the ground. This needs careful coordination using many other muscles and sense organs. Too much sway and you will fall one way, too little and you will fall the other. Watching a baby learning to walk by taking its first steps will illustrate all these problems very clearly.

The ability to detect changes and respond appropriately is a life-preserving feature of living things, literally. This characteristic, known as sensitivity, is just as much a property of single cells as it is of whole mammals and flowering plants.

Changes that bring about responses are called stimuli. The stimulus is detected by a receptor, and an effector brings about a response. Since the receptor and effector are often in different places in a multicellular organism, mechanisms of internal communication are essential. In animals, internal communication involves both the nervous system and endocrine system, which you will look at in Chapter 23. You will start by examining the nervous system, focusing in particular on the human.

The gross structure of the mammalian nervous system

It is most likely that you are already familiar with the gross structure of your nervous system, consisting as it does of the central nervous system (CNS – brain and spinal cord) and all the peripheral nerves (Figure 22.1).

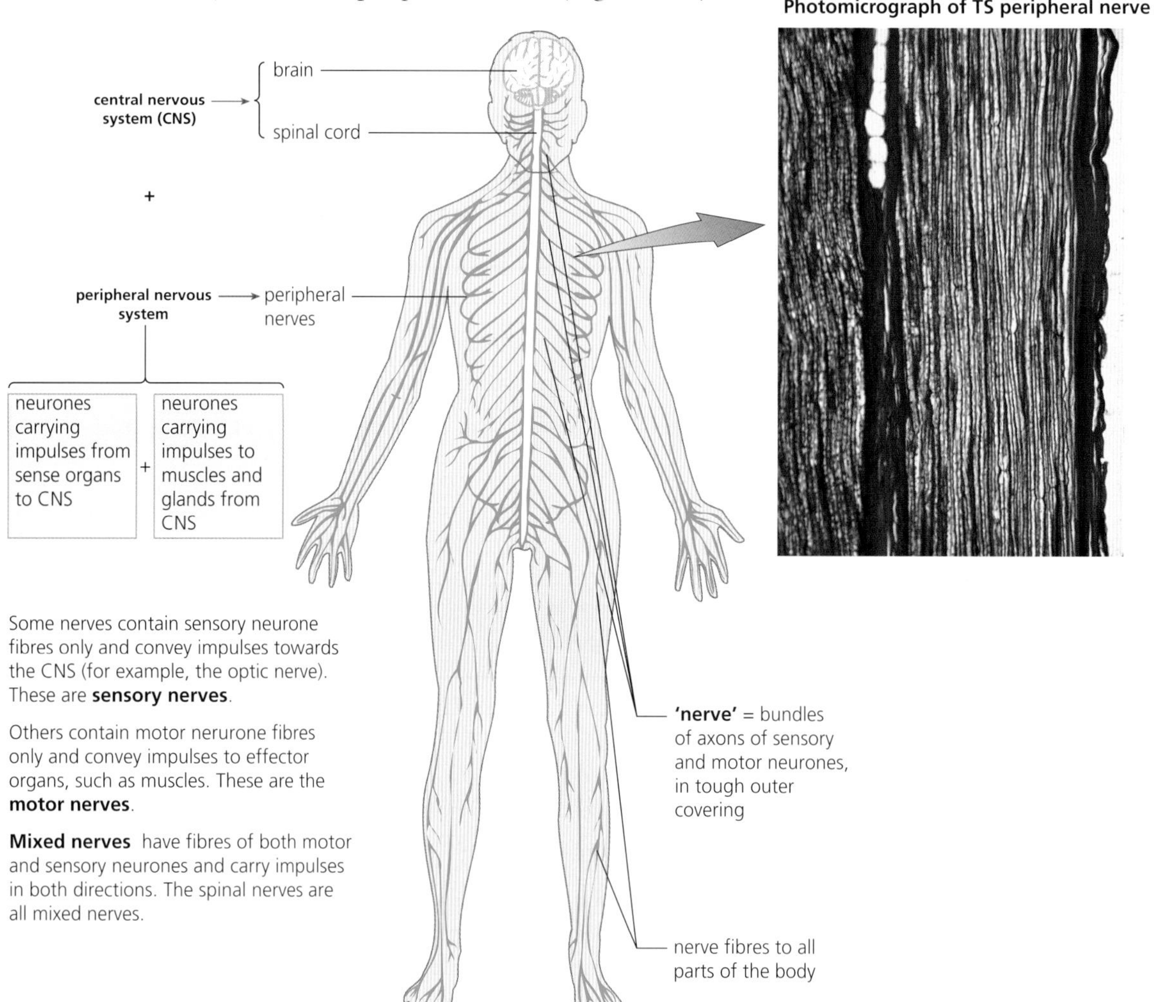

Photomicrograph of TS peripheral nerve
brain
central nervous system (CNS)
spinal cord
+
peripheral nervous system
peripheral nerves
neurones carrying impulses from sense organs to CNS
+
neurones carrying impulses to muscles and glands from CNS
Some nerves contain sensory neurone fibres only and convey impulses towards the CNS (for example, the optic nerve). These are **sensory nerves**.
Others contain motor nerurone fibres only and convey impulses to effector organs, such as muscles. These are the **motor nerves**.
Mixed nerves have fibres of both motor and sensory neurones and carry impulses in both directions. The spinal nerves are all mixed nerves.
'nerve' = bundles of axons of sensory and motor neurones, in tough outer covering
nerve fibres to all parts of the body

Figure 22.1 The organisation of the mammalian nervous system

The role of the brain in coordination and control of the body's responses is summarised in Figure 22.2.

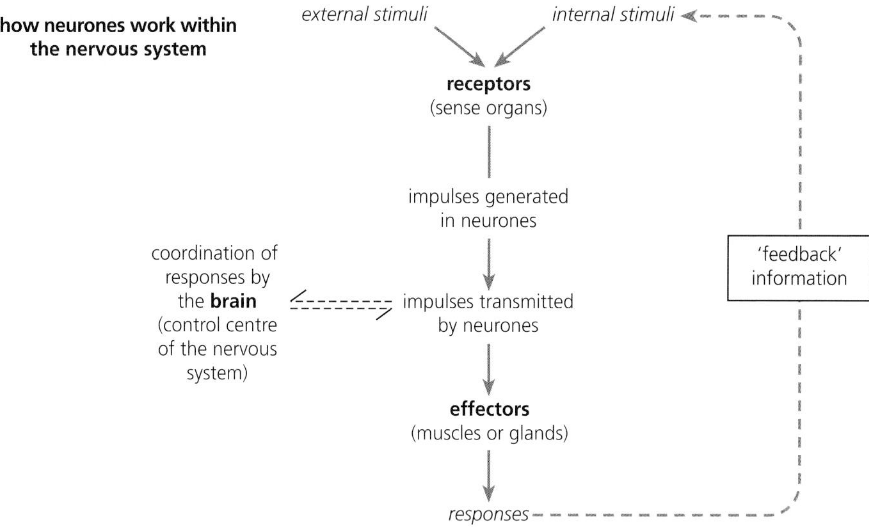

Figure 22.2 Coordination and control by the nervous system

The central nervous system

The spinal cord

The spinal cord is a cylindrical structure with a tiny central canal. The canal contains cerebrospinal fluid and is continuous with the fluid-filled spaces in the centre of the brain. The cord consists of an inner area of **grey matter** (cell bodies and synapses) surrounded by **white matter** (myelinated nerve fibres). You can see a transverse section through the spinal cord in Figure 22.3. The spinal cord is surrounded and protected by the vertebrae of the backbone. In the junction between each pair of vertebrae two spinal nerves leave the cord, one to each side of the body. The role of the spinal cord is to relay action potentials between **receptor organs** and **effector organs** of the body (by reflex action), and between them and the brain. Impulses entering and leaving the spinal cord through the spinal nerves are normally transferred to the brain and back through the neurones it contains.

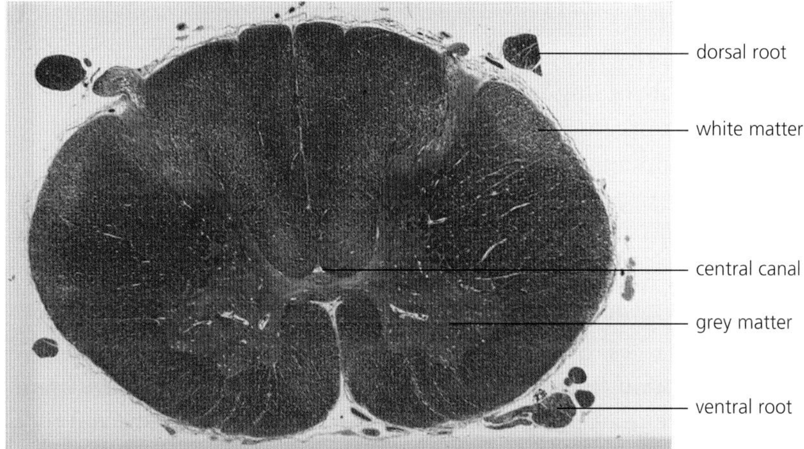

Figure 22.3 Photomicrograph of a transverse section through a spinal cord

Key terms

Grey matter Nervous tissue that is made up largely of the cell bodies of neurones.

White matter Nervous tissue made up largely of axons and their fatty myelin sheaths.

Receptor organs Organs that can detect changes caused by a stimulus and initiate action potentials.

Effector organs Organs that can respond to a stimulus to bring about a particular action.

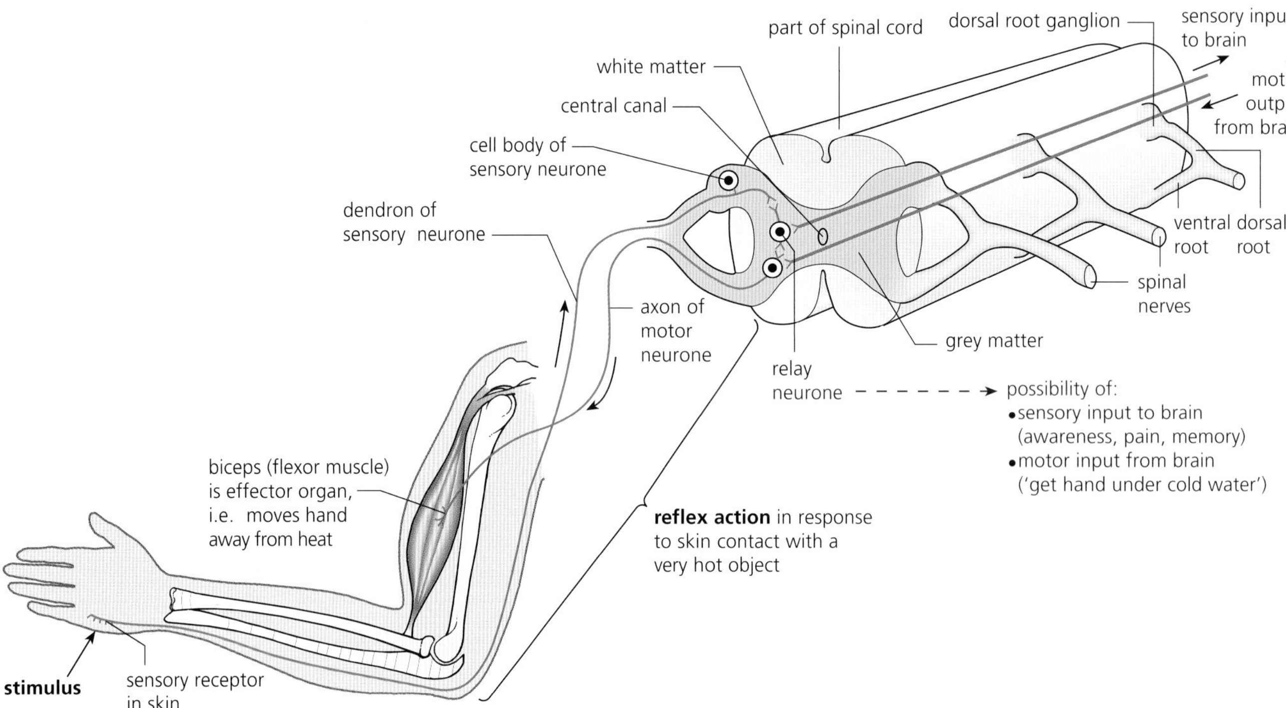

Figure 22.4 The spinal cord with the neurones of a reflex arc, and the associated inputs to, and output from, the brain

> **Key terms**
>
> **Reflex action** A rapid nervous reaction in which there is a direct connection between the sense organ and effector organ, bringing about a similar response to a similar stimulus.
>
> **Interneurones** Short neurones that connect individual neurones to each other.

Very simple **reflex actions** are few in humans but the 'hot hand' reflex shown in Figure 22.4 illustrates how the impulses can be transferred rapidly across the spinal cord. In this reflex action impulses are also sent to the brain, which may override the response, causing the hot object to be tolerated in a dangerous situation or as a test of 'will-power'.

The brain

The brain, a highly organised mass of **interneurones** (see Figure 22.8 on page 462) connected with the rest of the nervous system by numerous motor and sensory neurones, is responsible for complex patterns of behaviour, in addition to many reflex actions. Much activity is initiated by the brain, rather than being mere responses to external stimuli. In summary, the human brain controls all body functions apart from those under the control of simple spinal reflexes. This is achieved by:

- receiving impulses from sensory receptors
- integrating and correlating incoming information in association centres
- sending impulses to effector organs (muscles and glands) causing bodily responses
- storing information and building up an accessible memory bank
- initiating impulses from its own self-contained activities (the brain is also the seat of 'personality' and emotions, and enables you to imagine, create, plan, calculate, predict and reason abstractly).

The vertebrate brain develops in the embryo from the anterior end of a simple tube, the neural tube. This tube enlarges to form three primary structures, known as the forebrain, midbrain and hindbrain (Figure 22.5). The various parts of the mature brain develop from these by selective thickening and folding processes of their walls and roof.

These enlargement processes are most pronounced in mammals, and a striking feature of this group is the enormous development of the cerebral hemispheres, which are an outgrowth of the forebrain.

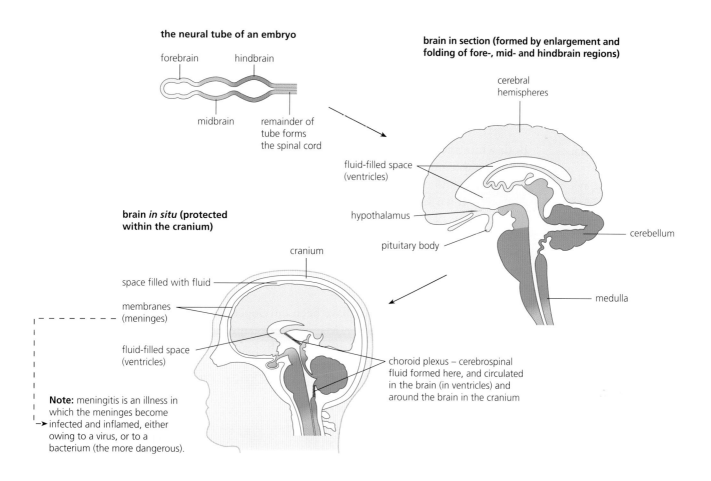

the neural tube of an embryo

forebrain
hindbrain
midbrain
remainder of tube forms the spinal cord

brain in section (formed by enlargement and folding of fore-, mid- and hindbrain regions)

cerebral hemispheres
fluid-filled space (ventricles)
hypothalamus
pituitary body
cerebellum
medulla

brain *in situ* (protected within the cranium)

cranium
space filled with fluid
membranes (meninges)
fluid-filled space (ventricles)
choroid plexus – cerebrospinal fluid formed here, and circulated in the brain (in ventricles) and around the brain in the cranium

Note: meningitis is an illness in which the meninges become infected and inflamed, either owing to a virus, or to a bacterium (the more dangerous).

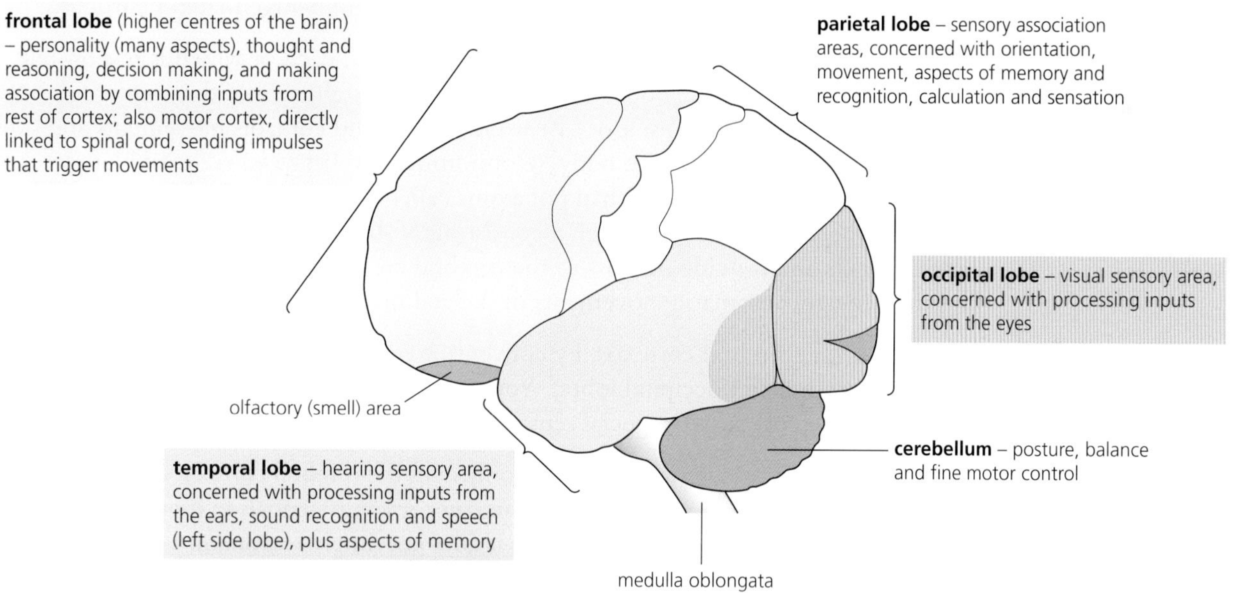

Figure 22.5 The human brain

Key terms

Neuroglia cells Cells found in the brain that are responsible for the support and protection of the neurones of the brain and peripheral nervous system.

Cerebral cortex The thin layer of grey matter covering the cerebral hemispheres.

The human brain contains about 10^{11}–10^{12} interneurones and the same number again of **neuroglia cells**. The majority of these neurones occur in the cerebral hemispheres. There, it is estimated, each interneurone forms synapses with a thousand other neurones. Mammals are the most intelligent of all animals, and their long memory, complexity of behaviour and subtlety of body control are also linked to the development of this brain structure.

Both white and grey matter are present in the brain as in the spinal cord. Grey matter makes up the interior of the brain and white the exterior. However, in the cerebral hemispheres and cerebellum there are additional layers of grey matter (that is, extra neurones). It has long been known, from observation of the effects of brain injury, that different parts of the brain have specific functions. Within the brain as a whole, certain tasks and roles are localised. For example, near the hypothalamus are the thalamus (the 'relay station' for impulses to the cerebral cortex from the rest of the brain and the spinal cord) and the hippocampus (responsible, together with parts of the cerebral hemispheres, for long-term memory).

More recently new techniques have been developed that have dramatically increased our knowledge of brain activity. Magnetic resonance imaging (MRI) uses powerful magnetic fields to detect the positions of hydrogen nuclei, hence it is able to show changes in activity in different parts of the brain without affecting the patient. The functions of some parts of the brain are discussed below.

Cerebrum (cerebral hemispheres)

The cerebral hemispheres, an extension of the forebrain, form the bulk of the human brain. They are positioned above and around the remainder of the brain. Here the body's voluntary activities are coordinated, together with many involuntary ones. The hemispheres have a vastly extended surface, which is achieved by extensive folding so that it forms deep groves. The surface, called the **cerebral cortex**, is covered by grey matter to a depth of 3 mm, and is densely packed with non-myelinated neurones.

The cerebral cortex is divided into right and left halves, each of which is responsible for the opposite half of the body. This means that the right side of the cortex receives information (impulses from sensory neurones) from, and controls movements and other responses in, the left side of the body. (Communication between right and left cerebral cortices occurs via a substantial band of axons called the corpus callosum.) Within the hemispheres are the basal ganglia, consisting of discrete groups of neurones. They receive inputs and provide outputs to the cerebral cortex, thalamus and hypothalamus, and they control automatic movements of skeletal muscle and muscle tone.

Each side of the cerebral cortex is, by convention, divided into four lobes (frontal, parietal, temporal and occipital lobes). You can see from Figure 22.5 (lower image) that the areas of the cortex with special sensory and motor functions have been mapped out.

It is obvious from this description that not only does the cerebral cortex receive large amounts of sensory information but it also initiates action potentials in motor neurones to bring about complex behaviour. To do this it does not simply respond in a pre-determined way as in a reflex action, it uses a whole host of higher mental activities. For example, memory is used to apply reasoning and experience is drawn on when making decisions on what actions to take. It is this ability that makes mammals the most intelligent life-forms yet known.

Cerebellum

The **cerebellum**, part of the hindbrain, has an external surface layer of grey matter. It is concerned with the control of involuntary muscle movements of posture and balance. Here, the precise, voluntary movements involved in hand manipulations, speech and writing are coordinated. Whilst the cerebellum does not initiate motor activity it plays a vital role in ensuring that such actions are carefully coordinated. Damage to the cerebellum does not result in paralysis. The cerebral hemispheres are still able to direct movement but such movements are clumsy and the fine control needed to manipulate a pen or thread a needle is absent. The description of walking given at the beginning of this chapter is also a good example of coordination of movements brought about by the cerebellum.

Medulla oblongata

The **medulla oblongata**, the base of the hindbrain, is a continuation of the uppermost part of the spinal cord. It houses the regulatory centres concerned with maintaining the rate and force of the heart beat and the diameter of the blood vessels. (We will discuss the detailed role of the medulla in the control of heart rate in Chapter 24.) Also, it is here that a respiratory centre adjusts the basic rate of breathing. And it is in the medulla that the ascending and descending pathways of nerve fibres connecting the spinal column and brain cross over (resulting, as already noted above, in the left side of our body being controlled by the right side of the brain, and vice versa).

Hypothalamus

The **hypothalamus** – part of the floor of the forebrain and exceptionally well supplied with blood vessels – is the control centre for the **autonomic nervous system (ANS)**. Here the body monitors and controls body temperature and the levels of sugars, amino acids and ions in **osmoregulation**. Feeding and drinking reflexes, and aggressive and reproductive behaviour, are also controlled here. The hypothalamus works with a 'master gland' called the pituitary gland, to which it is attached, monitoring hormones in the blood, and controlling the release of hormones. So the hypothalamus is the main link between nervous and **endocrine systems**. We shall look in more detail at the role of the hypothalamus and its close links with the hormonal system when discussing osmoregulation in Chapter 24.

Test yourself

1 Explain how a direct connection between sensory neurone and motor neurone is made in a spinal reflex.

2 State where the cell bodies of motor neurones are found.

3 Describe how spinal nerves leave and enter the vertebral column.

4 Describe how the surface area of the cerebral cortex is adapted to increase its size within the cranium.

5 Suggest the symptoms you would expect to see in a patient with a damaged cerebellum.

6 Explain why white matter is white.

7 Name the major endocrine (hormonal) gland that is linked to the hypothalamus.

Key terms

Cerebellum A part of the hindbrain responsible for the fine coordination of motor activity.

Medulla oblongata A part of the hindbrain containing the regulatory centres for breathing and heart rate.

Autonomic nervous system (ANS) The network of motor neurones carrying impulses to smooth muscle and glands, controlling involuntary (unconscious) actions.

Endocrine system A system of glands, in animals, which secrete hormones into the bloodstream.

Hypothalamus A part of the forebrain concerned with control of the autonomic nervous system and maintaining the constant internal environment. It has close links to the endocrine system.

Osmoregulation The process of controlling the concentration of the body fluids.

The peripheral nervous system

The nerves of the peripheral nervous system (PNS) consist of nerve fibres (**axons** and **dendrons**) arranged in bundles, protected by connective tissue sheaths (Figure 22.6). These nerves consist of:

- sensory neurones carrying impulses to the central nervous system
- motor neurones carrying impulses to muscles and glands.

Many of the motor neurones serve the muscles we use in conscious actions to produce voluntary movements, and they form the **somatic nervous system**.

On the other hand, the **autonomic nervous system** controls activities inside the body that are mostly under unconscious (involuntary) control. It consists of motor neurones running to the smooth muscle of the internal organs and to various glands.

The autonomic nervous system (ANS) acts to maintain the body's internal environment (autonomic means 'self-governing'). The detailed role of the ANS in controlling heart rate and osmoregulation are discussed in Chapter 24.

There is a further complication to the ANS, it is divided into two parts:

- the sympathetic nervous system (SNS)
- the parasympathetic nervous system (PNS).

Key terms

Axons Thin, elongated extensions of neurones that carry impulses away from the cell body.

Dendrons Thin, elongated extensions of neurones that carry impulses towards the cell body.

Autonomic nervous system The network of motor neurones carrying impulses to the heart, smooth muscle and glands controlling involuntary (unconscious) actions.

Somatic nervous system The system of motor neurones carrying impulses to muscles controlling voluntary (conscious) actions.

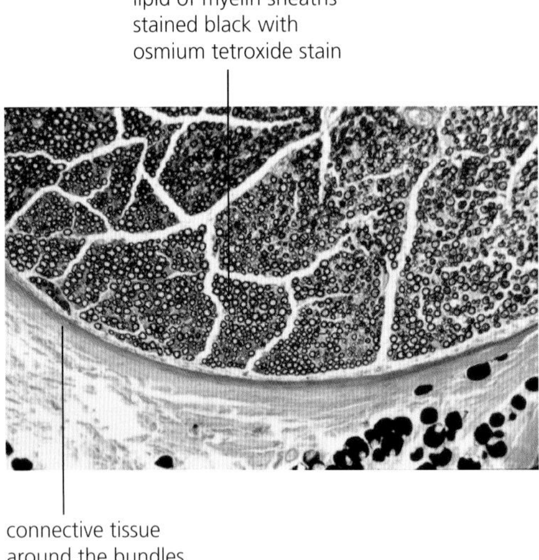

Figure 22.6 A peripheral nerve in TS (×250). The vagus nerve shown here is a mixed nerve having axons of motor neurones and axons and dendrons of sensory neurones

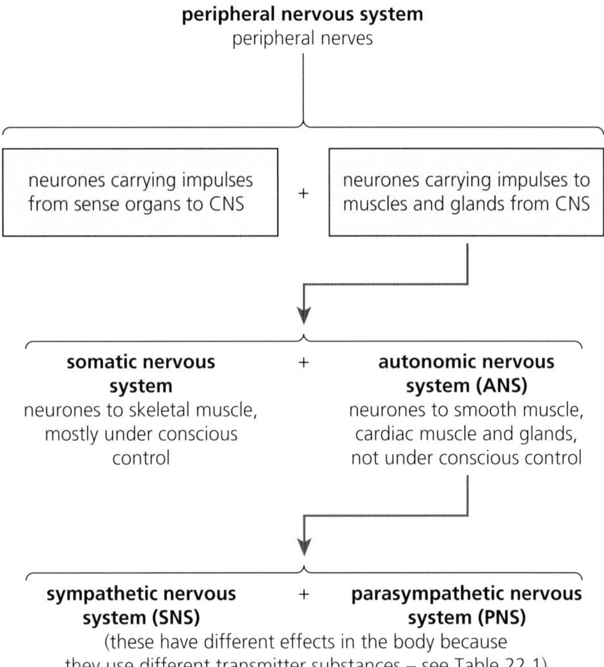

Figure 22.7 Peripheral nerves and conscious/unconscious control

The layout of the peripheral nervous system as a whole is shown in Figure 22.7. In Table 22.1, the key differences between the SNS and the PNS are listed. Note that in some of the functions the two systems are antagonistic in their effects (for example, the SNS causes the heart rate to increase and the PNS causes it to decrease). However, in other cases they may have the same effect on a gland or muscle.

Table 22.1 The autonomic nervous system - roles and responses

Sympathetic nervous system (SNS)	Parasympathetic nervous system (PNS)
More active in times of stress to produce 'fight or flight' responses	Concerned with conservation of energy and the replacement of body reserves
At their junctions with effector tissues (muscles or glands) the neurones release noradrenaline	At their junctions with effector tissues the neurones release acetylcholine
Some of the responses of the two systems	
Increases ventilation rate	Decreases ventilation rate
Causes widening (dilation) of the tissues	Causes constriction (narrowing) of the pupils
Has no effect on the tear glands	Causes the secretion of tears
Has no effect on the salivary glands	Causes the secretion of saliva
Slows peristalsis	Accelerates peristalsis
Constricts bladder sphincter muscles	Causes relaxation of the sphincter muscles of the bladder and contraction of the muscular wall of the bladder (under overall conscious control)

Test yourself

8 Describe the main structural difference between a sensory neurone and an interneurone.

9 Describe the main functional difference between the somatic and autonomic nervous systems.

10 State **two** ways in which the sympathetic and parasympathetic system have antagonistic effects.

Nervous transmission

Neurones – structure and function

You should have already met neurones and their structure in your previous studies but some important details are summarised in this section.

The nervous system is built from specialised cells called neurones. Each neurone has a substantial cell body containing the nucleus and the bulk of the cytoplasm, from which extremely fine cytoplasmic nerve fibres run. The nerve fibres are specialised for the transmission of information in the form of impulses. Most fibres are very long indeed. Impulses are transmitted along these fibres at speeds between 30 and 120 metres per second in mammals, so nervous coordination is extremely fast, and responses are virtually immediate. The three types of neurones are shown in Figure 22.8 on the next page.

- Motor neurones have many fine dendrites, which bring impulses towards the cell body, and a single long axon, which carries impulses away from the cell body.
- Interneurones (also known as relay neurones) have numerous, short fibres.
- Sensory neurones have a single long dendron, which brings impulses towards the cell body, and a single long axon, which carries impulses away.

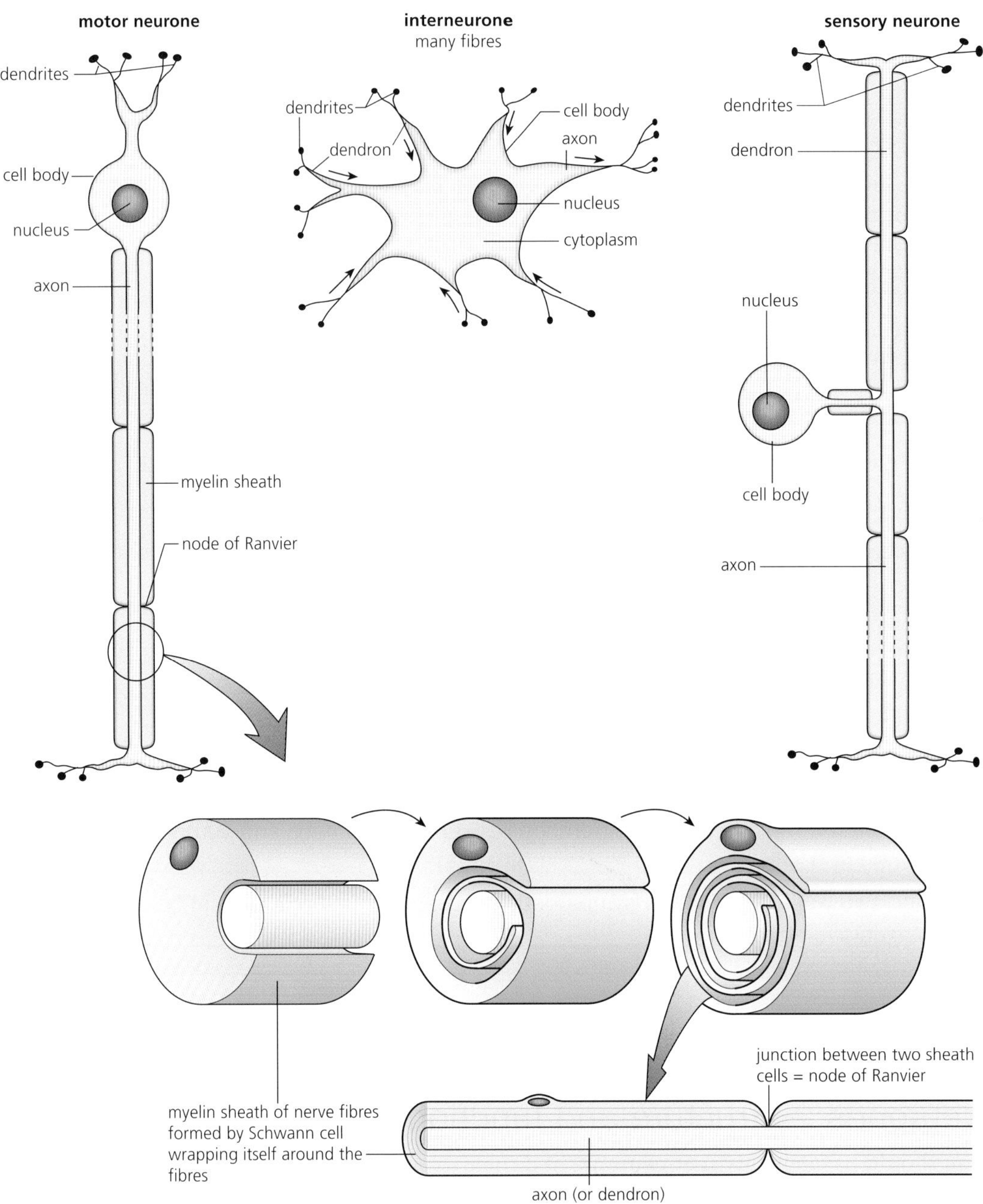

Figure 22.8 Comparing neurones

> **Key terms**
>
> **Schwann cells** Cells found wrapped around dendrons and axons, which produce the myelin sheath.
>
> **Myelin sheath** A layer of fatty tissue secreted by Schwann cells surrounding an axon.
>
> **Node of Ranvier** A small gap in the myelin sheath surrounding an axon.

Surrounding the neurones are different types of supporting cells called neuroglia cells (sometimes shortened to 'glial cells') – also an important part of the nervous system. One type of neuroglia cell is called a Schwann cell. Many of the long fibres (dendrons and axons) are protected by **Schwann cells**. These wrap themselves around the fibres, forming a structure called a **myelin sheath** (Figure 22.8). Between each pair of Schwann cells is a junction in the myelin sheath called a **node of Ranvier**. The myelin sheath and its junctions help increase the speed at which impulses are conducted.

Transmission of an impulse

An impulse is transmitted along nerve fibres, but it is not an electrical current that flows along the 'wires' of the nerves. Rather, the impulse is a momentary reversal in electrical potential difference in the membrane. That is, it is a change in the amounts of positively and negatively charged ions between the inside and outside of the membrane of a nerve fibre (Figure 22.9). This reversal travels from one end of the neurone to the other in a fraction of a second. Between conduction of one impulse and the next, the neurone is said to be resting. Actually, this not the case. During the 'resting' interval between impulses, the membrane of a neurone actively creates and maintains an electrical potential difference between the inside and the outside of the fibre.

How is this done?

The resting potential

Two processes together produce the resting potential difference across the neurone membrane.

- There is **active transport** of potassium (K^+) ions *in* across the membrane, and of sodium (Na^+) ions *out* across the membrane. The ions are transported by a Na^+–K^+ pump, with transfer of energy from ATP. So potassium and sodium ions gradually concentrate on opposite sides of the membrane. However, this in itself makes no change to the potential difference across the membrane.
- There is also facilitated diffusion of K^+ ions *out* and Na^+ ions back *in*. The important point here is that the membrane is far more permeable to K^+ ions flowing out than to Na^+ ions returning. This causes the tissue fluid outside the neurone to contain many more positive ions than are present in the cytoplasm inside. As a result, the inside becomes more and more negatively charged compared with the outside; the resting neurone is said to be **polarised**. The difference in charge, or potential difference, is about −70 mV (the negative sign here is a convention to show the inside is more negative than the outside). This is known as the resting potential. Figure 22.9 summarises how it is set up.

Key terms

Facilitated diffusion The movement of molecules by diffusion across a cell surface membrane, which is assisted by the presence of protein molecules in the membrane forming pores or channels through which the molecule can pass.

Resting potential The potential difference (approx −70 mV) across the axon membrane when no action potential is formed.

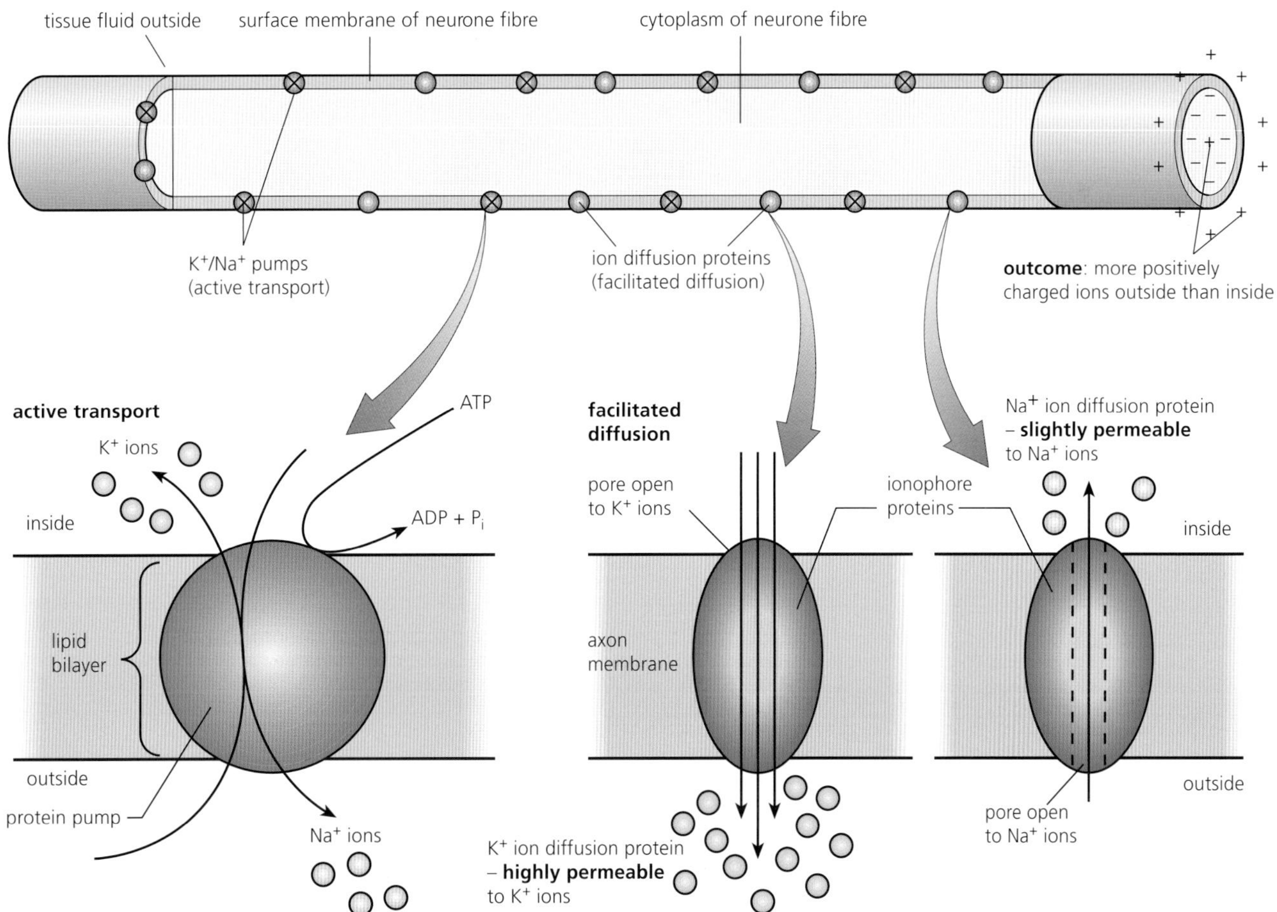

Figure 22.9 The establishment of a resting potential

The action potential

The next event, sooner or later, is the passage of an impulse. An impulse, or action potential, is triggered by a stimulus received at a receptor cell or sensitive nerve ending. The energy transferred by this stimulus causes a temporary and local reversal of the resting potential. The result is that the membrane is briefly depolarised at this point (Figure 22.10).

How does this happen?

The change in potential across the membrane occurs through pores in the membrane, called ion channels because they can allow ions to pass through. One type of channel is permeable to sodium ions, and another to potassium ions. These channels are globular proteins that span the entire width of the membrane. They have a central pore with a gate, which can open and close. During a resting potential, these channels are all closed.

The energy of the stimulus first opens the gates of the sodium channels in the cell surface membrane. This allows sodium ions to diffuse in, down their electrochemical gradient. So the cytoplasm inside the neurone fibre quickly becomes progressively more positive with respect to the outside. This charge reversal continues until the potential difference has altered from −70 mV to +40 mV. At this point, an action potential has been created in the neurone fibre.

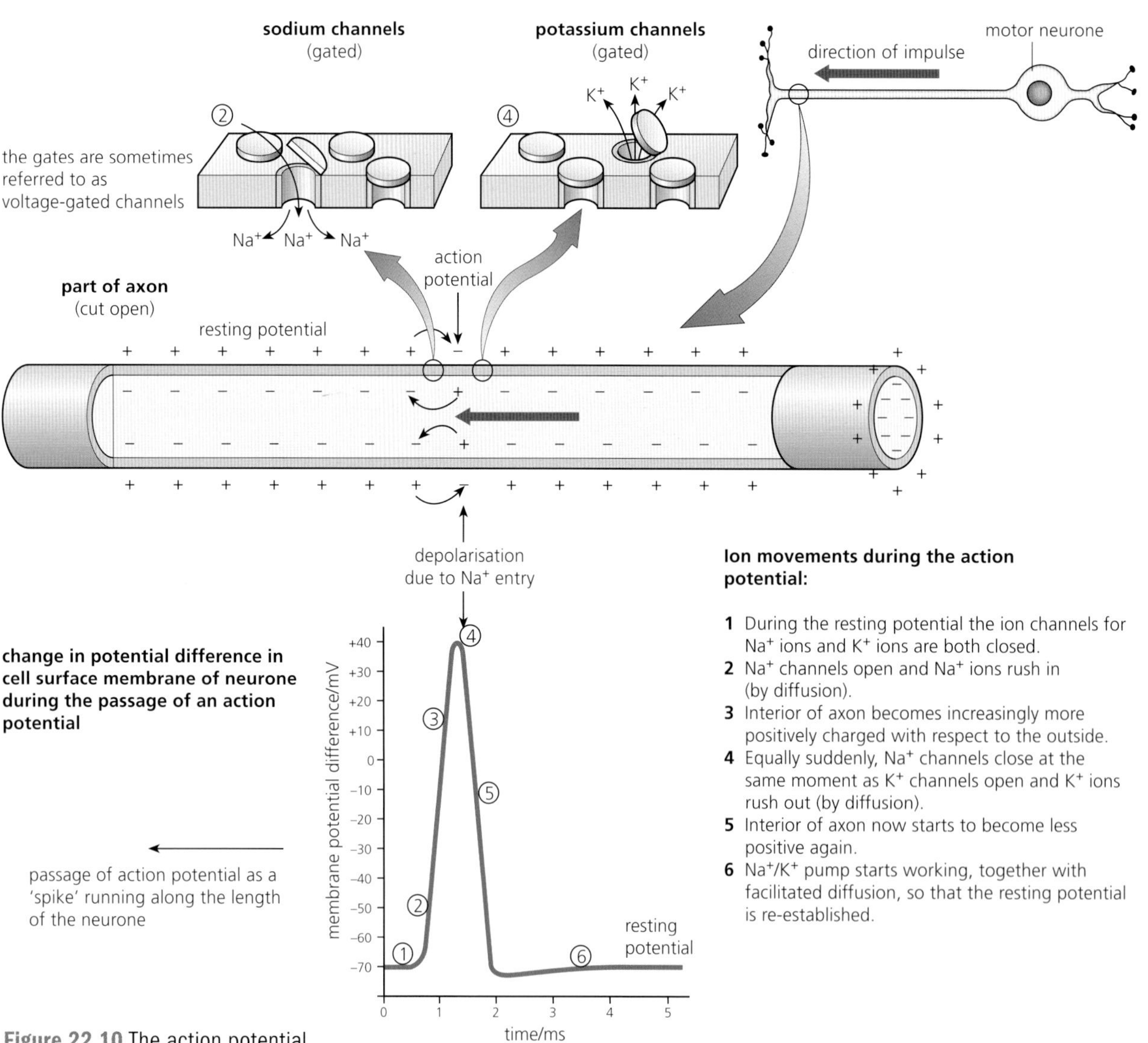

sodium channels (gated)
potassium channels (gated)
motor neurone
direction of impulse
the gates are sometimes referred to as voltage-gated channels
Na^+ Na^+ Na^+
K^+ K^+ K^+
action potential
part of axon (cut open)
resting potential
depolarisation due to Na^+ entry
change in potential difference in cell surface membrane of neurone during the passage of an action potential
passage of action potential as a 'spike' running along the length of the neurone
membrane potential difference/mV
time/ms
resting potential
Ion movements during the action potential:
1 During the resting potential the ion channels for Na^+ ions and K^+ ions are both closed.
2 Na^+ channels open and Na^+ ions rush in (by diffusion).
3 Interior of axon becomes increasingly more positively charged with respect to the outside.
4 Equally suddenly, Na^+ channels close at the same moment as K^+ channels open and K^+ ions rush out (by diffusion).
5 Interior of axon now starts to become less positive again.
6 Na^+/K^+ pump starts working, together with facilitated diffusion, so that the resting potential is re-established.

Figure 22.10 The action potential

The action potential then travels along the whole length of the neurone fibre. At any one point it exists for only two thousandths of a second (2 milliseconds) before the membrane starts to re-establish the resting potential. So action potential transmission is exceedingly quick – an example of positive feedback, in fact.

Almost immediately after an action potential has passed, the sodium channels close and potassium channels open. So potassium ions can exit the cell, again down an electrochemical gradient, into the tissue fluid outside. This causes the interior of the neurone to start to become less positive again. Then the potassium channels also close. Finally, the resting potential of −70 mV is re-established by the sodium–potassium pump, and the process of facilitated diffusion.

The refractory period

For a brief period following the passage of an action potential, the neurone fibre is no longer excitable. This is the refractory period. It lasts only 5–10 milliseconds in total. During this time, firstly there is a large excess of sodium ions inside the neurone fibre and further influx is impossible. As the resting potential is progressively restored, however, it becomes increasingly possible for an action potential to be generated again. Because of this refractory period, the maximum frequency of impulses is between 500 and 1000 per second.

The 'all or nothing' principle

Obviously, stimuli are of widely different strengths – for example, the difference between a light touch and the pain of a finger hit by a hammer! A stimulus must be at or above a minimum intensity, known as the threshold of stimulation, in order to initiate an action potential at all. Either a stimulus depolarises the membrane sufficiently to reverse the potential difference (−70 mV to +40 mV), or it does not. If not, no action potential is generated. With all sub-threshold stimuli, the influx of sodium ions is quickly reversed and the resting potential is re-established.

For stimuli above the threshold, as the intensity of the stimulus increases, the frequency at which the action potentials pass along the fibre increases (the individual action potentials are all of standard strength). For example, with a very intense stimulus, action potentials pass along a fibre at an accelerated rate, up to the maximum possible permitted by the refractory period. This means the effector (or the brain) recognises the intensity of a stimulus from the frequency of action potentials (Figure 22.11).

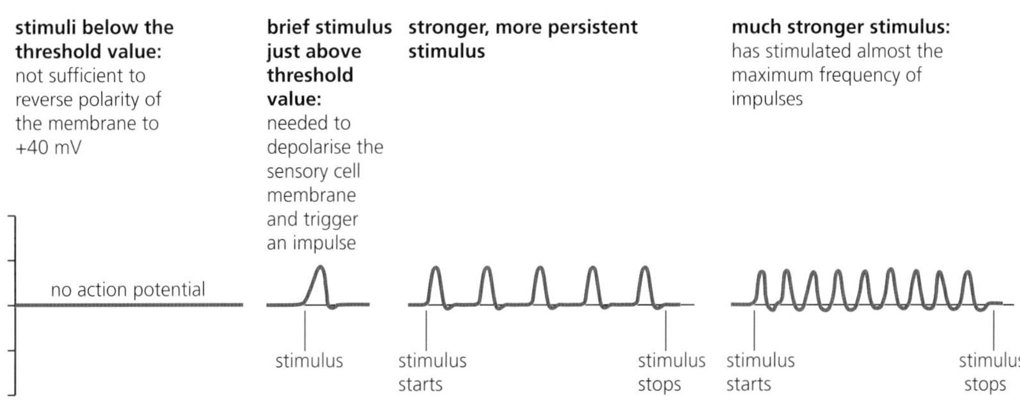
stimuli below the threshold value: not sufficient to reverse polarity of the membrane to +40 mV
brief stimulus just above threshold value: needed to depolarise the sensory cell membrane and trigger an impulse
stronger, more persistent stimulus
much stronger stimulus: has stimulated almost the maximum frequency of impulses
no action potential
stimulus
stimulus starts
stimulus stops
stimulus starts
stimulus stops

Figure 22.11 Weak and strong stimuli and threshold value

> **Key term**
>
> **Saltatory conduction** Conduction of an action potential along a nerve fibre by jumping from node to node, thus increasing the speed.

Speed of conduction of the action potential

The presence of a myelin sheath affects the speed of transmission of the action potential. The junctions in the sheath, known as the nodes of Ranvier, occur at 1–2 mm intervals. Only at these nodes is the axon membrane exposed. Elsewhere along the fibre, the electrical resistance of the myelin sheath prevents depolarisations. Consequently, local depolarisations build up at this point causing them to jump from node to node (Figure 22.12). This is called **saltatory conduction** ('saltation' meaning 'leaping'), and is an advantage, as it greatly speeds up the rate of transmission.

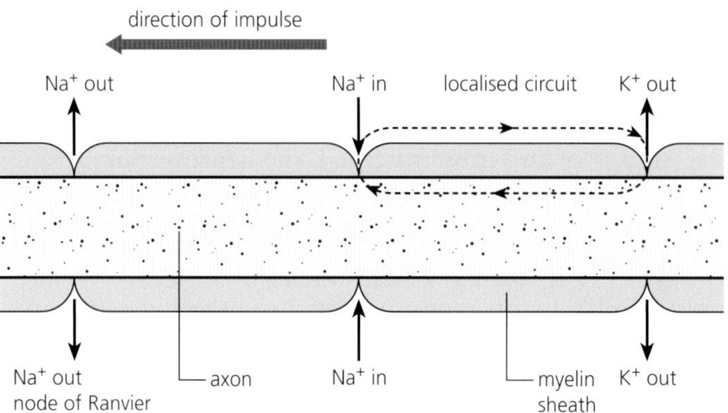

Figure 22.12 Saltatory conduction

Not all neurones have myelinated fibres. In fact, non-myelinated dendrons and axons are common in non-vertebrate animals. Here, transmission is normally much slower because the action potential flows steadily, right along the fibres. However, among non-myelinated fibres it is a fact that large-diameter axons transmit action potentials much more speedily than do narrow ones. Certain non-vertebrates like the squid and the earthworm have giant fibres, which allow fast transmission of action potentials (although not as fast as in myelinated fibres).

Test yourself

11 Name the passive process that accounts for the transfer of Na^+ and K^+ ions to form the resting potential.

12 If Na^+ ions move in and K^+ ions move out by the same pumping mechanism, explain why there is a resting potential difference.

13 State which side of the axon membrane becomes more negatively charged in forming the resting potential.

14 Describe the change in membrane proteins that causes the onset of an action potential.

15 State **two** features of nerve fibres that can affect the speed of nervous transmission.

Synapses – the junctions between neurones

Where two neurones meet they do not actually touch. A tiny gap, called a synapse, is the link point between neurones (Figure 22.13). Synapses consist of the swollen tip (synaptic knob) of the axon of one neurone (pre-synaptic neurone) and the dendrite or cell body of another neurone (post-synaptic neurone). Between these is the synaptic cleft, a gap of about 20 nm.

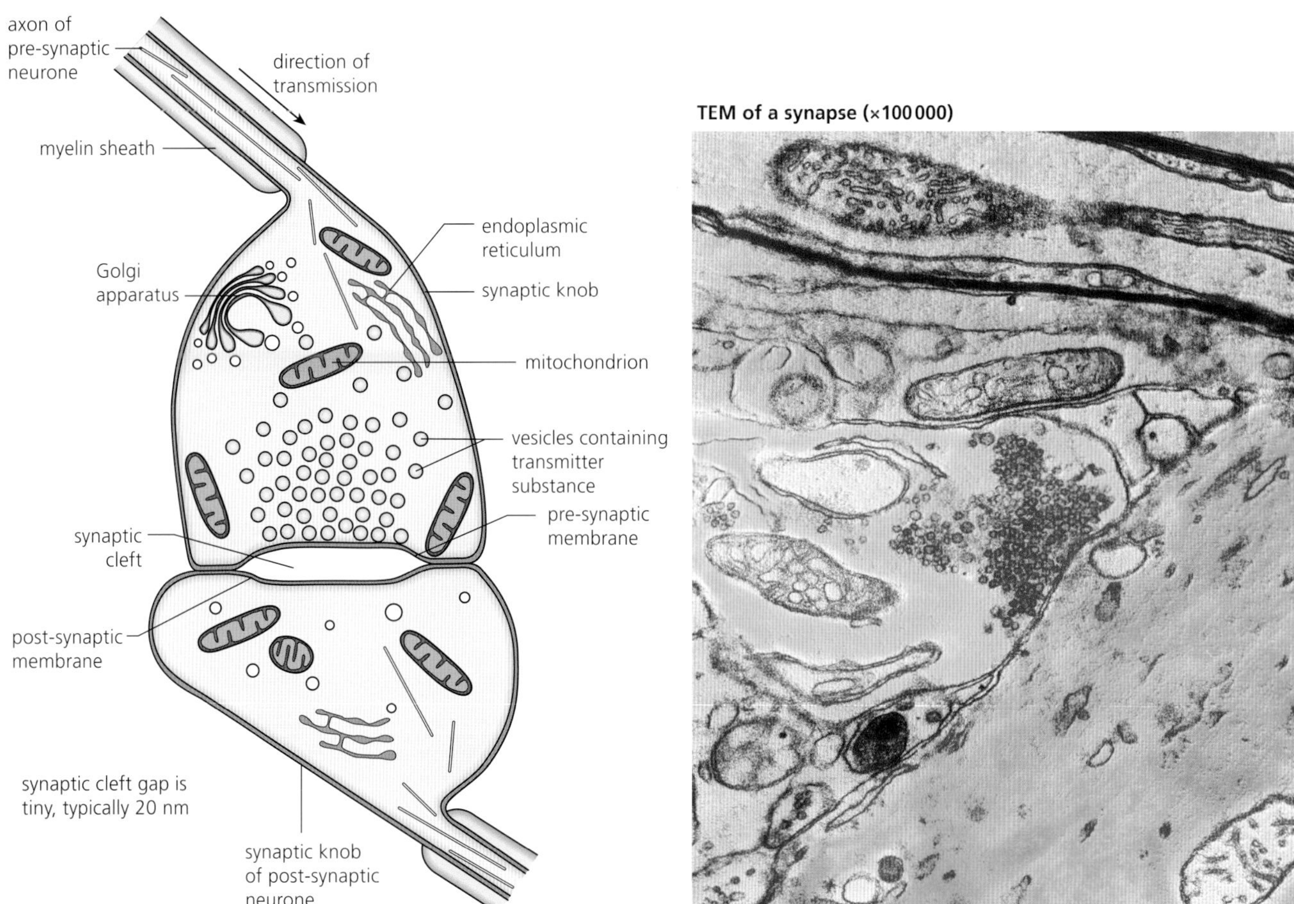

Figure 22.13 A synapse in section

The practical effect of the synaptic cleft is that an action potential cannot cross it. Here, transmission occurs by specific chemicals, known as transmitter substances. These substances are all relatively small, diffusible molecules. They are produced in the Golgi apparatus in the synaptic knob, and held in tiny vesicles prior to use.

Acetylcholine (ACh) is a commonly occurring transmitter substance; the neurones that release acetylcholine are known as **cholinergic neurones**. Another common transmitter substance is **noradrenaline** (released by **adrenergic neurones**). In the brain, the commonly occurring transmitters are glutamic acid and **dopamine**.

Key terms

Acetylcholine (ACh) A commonly occurring transmitter substance at synapses.

Cholinergic neurones Neurones releasing acetylcholine at their synapses.

Noradrenaline A commonly occurring transmitter substance at synapses.

Adrenergic neurones Neurones releasing noradrenaline at their synapses.

Dopamine A neurotransmitter found in the brain.

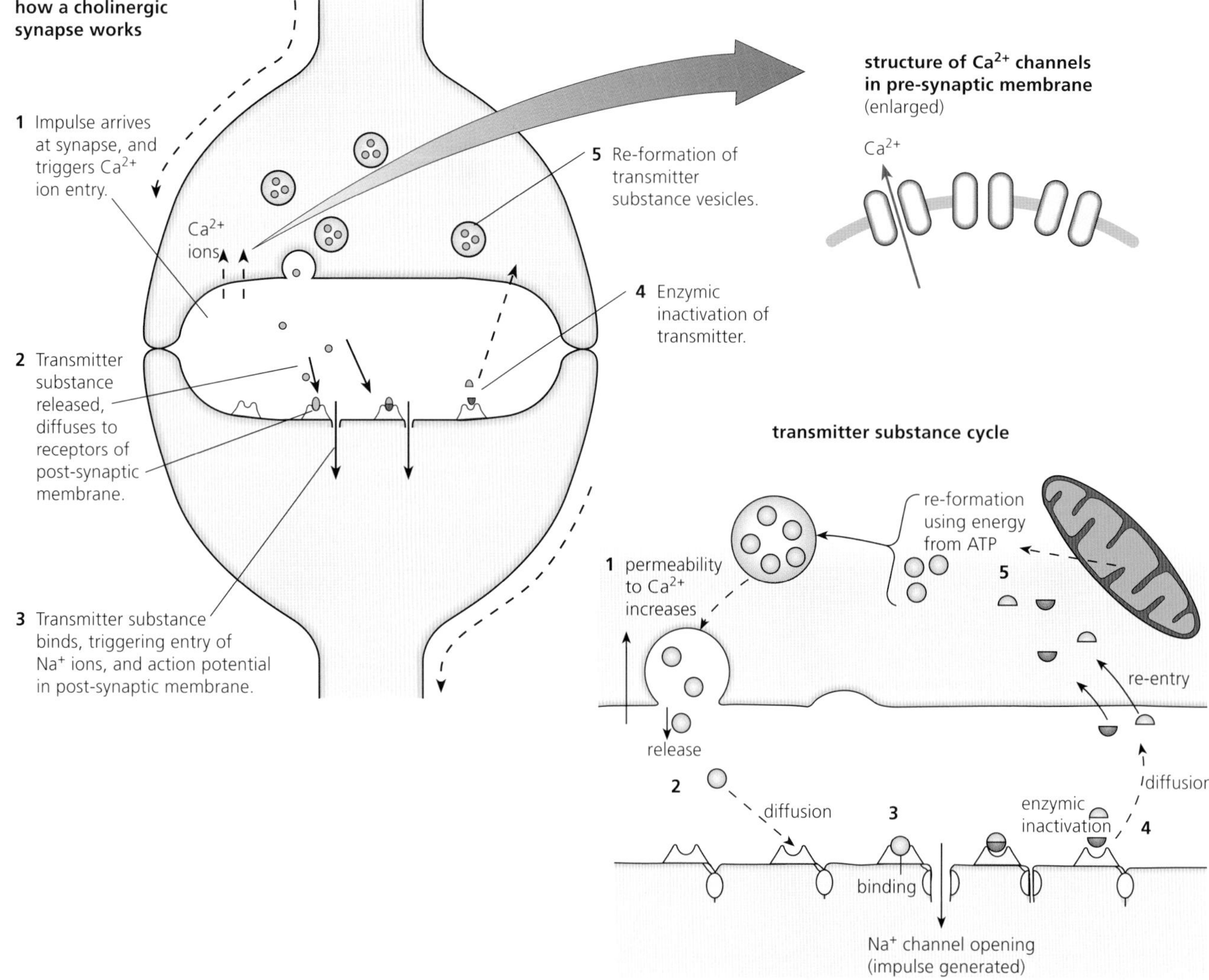
Steps involved in synapse transmission
how a cholinergic synapse works
1 Impulse arrives at synapse, and triggers Ca2+ ion entry.
Ca2+ ions
5 Re-formation of transmitter substance vesicles.
4 Enzymic inactivation of transmitter.
2 Transmitter substance released, diffuses to receptors of post-synaptic membrane.
3 Transmitter substance binds, triggering entry of Na+ ions, and action potential in post-synaptic membrane.
structure of Ca2+ channels in pre-synaptic membrane (enlarged)
Ca2+
transmitter substance cycle
re-formation using energy from ATP
1 permeability to Ca2+ increases
5
re-entry
release
2
diffusion
3
enzymic inactivation
4
diffusion
binding
Na+ channel opening (impulse generated)

Figure 22.14 Chemical transmission at the synapse

You may find it helpful to follow each step in Figure 22.14.

1 The arrival of an action potential at the synaptic knob opens calcium ion channels in the pre-synaptic membrane. Calcium ions flow in from the synaptic cleft.

2 The calcium ions cause vesicles of transmitter substance to fuse with the pre-synaptic membrane and they release a transmitter substance into the synaptic cleft. The transmitter substance diffuses across the synaptic cleft.

3 The transmitter substance binds with a receptor protein on the post-synaptic membrane.

In the post-synaptic membrane, there are specific receptor sites for each transmitter substance. Each of these receptors also acts as a channel in the membrane that allows a specific ion (such as Na^+ or Cl^-, for example) to pass. The attachment of a transmitter molecule to its receptor instantly opens the ion channel.

When a molecule of ACh attaches to its receptor site, a Na^+ channel opens. As the sodium ions rush into the cytoplasm of the post-synaptic neurone, depolarisation of the post-synaptic membrane occurs. As more and more molecules of ACh bind, it becomes increasingly likely that depolarisation will reach the threshold level. When it does, an action potential is generated in the post-synaptic neurone. This process of build-up to an action potential in post-synaptic membranes is called facilitation.

4 The transmitter substance on the receptors is quickly inactivated. For example, the enzyme cholinesterase hydrolyses ACh to choline and ethanoic acid. These molecules are inactive as transmitters. This reaction causes the ion channel of the receptor protein to close, and so allows the resting potential in the post-synaptic neurone to be re-established.

5 Meanwhile, the inactivated products of the transmitter re-enter the pre-synaptic neurone, are re-synthesised into transmitter substance and packaged for re-use.

Excitation and inhibition at synapses

Although many synapses do function with ACh as their transmitter molecule, the post-synaptic membrane has many receptor sites that will respond to other transmitters. Their effect can be to cause the membrane to be more likely to reach the threshold value (that is to make the potential difference less negative), in which case they will be, like ACh, excitatory. If their effect is to cause the membrane to be less likely to reach the threshold value (that is make the potential difference more negative) then they will be inhibitory, as shown in Figure 22.15.

The transmitter glutamate (an amino acid) attaches to receptor sites and causes the opening of Na^+ channels. The influx of Na^+ ions sets up tiny areas of depolarisation, which are called **excitatory post-synaptic potentials (EPSPs)**. These EPSPs make the membrane less negatively charged and more likely to reach the threshold level to trigger an action potential (which is why they are called excitatory potentials).

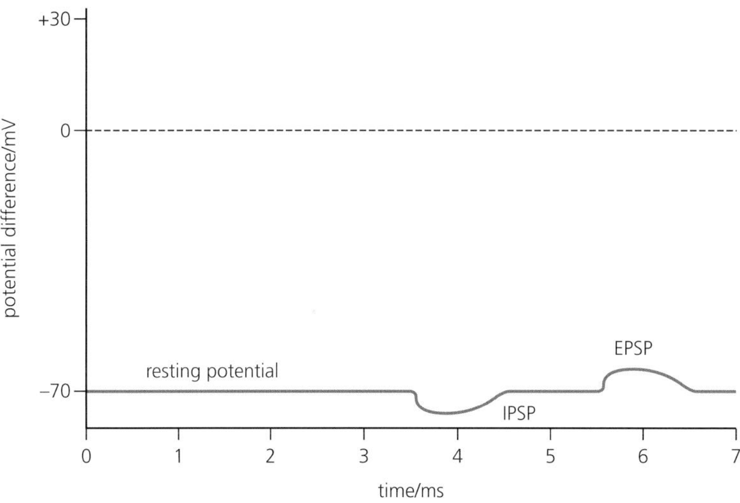

Figure 22.15 The effects of IPSPs and EPSPs on resting potential

The transmitter **gamma-aminobutyric acid (GABA)** is commonly found in the brain. When it attaches to its receptor sites it causes the opening of Cl^- ion channels, which sets up tiny areas of further polarisation that are called **inhibitory post-synaptic potentials (IPSPs)**. These IPSPs make the membrane more negatively charged and less likely to reach the threshold level to trigger an action potential (which is why they are called inhibitory potentials).

Key terms

Excitatory post-synaptic potentials (EPSPs) Small currents making the post synaptic membrane less negative, which makes it more likely to trigger a new action potential.

Gamma-aminobutyric acid (GABA) A neurotransmitter found in the brain.

Inhibitory post-synaptic potentials (IPSPs) Small currents making the post synaptic membrane more negative which make it less likely to trigger a new action potential.

Manipulating synapses using drugs

As synapses use chemical transmitters and are not contained within myelin sheaths, they offer the opportunity for medical intervention, predatory weapons and uncontrolled recreational use. A very common approach is to create artificial molecules that can mimic or block the action of the real transmitters. Some of the most widely prescribed drugs in the world, the benzodiazepines, such as Valium, are used as anti-anxiety medicines due to their ability to bind to GABA receptors in synapses.

Here are some examples of powerful drugs that act through their effects on synapses.

Lidocaine

Although the name may sound unfamiliar it is very likely that you have experienced its effects. Lidocaine is used as a local anaesthetic, especially by your dentist to 'numb' the nerves of your mouth when working on your teeth. This effect is brought about because lidocaine blocks **voltage-gated Na^+ ion channels**. In the synapse this means the post-synaptic membrane is not able to depolarise, so no action potentials can travel to the brain to record pain. In addition, the pain receptors themselves need to depolarise to initiate pain signals, so they never respond. This is also true of motor neurones in the region affected so your lips also feel 'droopy' and you cannot control them for a while. Fortunately lidocaine is quickly metabolised in the liver so the effect begins to wear off after an hour or so.

> **Key terms**
>
> **Voltage-gated channels** Proteins in cell membranes forming channels, which are opened and closed by changes in potential difference.
>
> **Endorphins** Chemicals released by the brain that produce a feeling of pleasurable relaxation.
>
> **Acetylcholinesterase** The enzyme that breaks down acetylcholine within a synapse.

Nicotine

Nicotine from tobacco smoke has widespread effects on the nervous and hormonal systems. Its main effect is brought about by its ability to bind with acetylcholine (ACh) receptor sites in synapses. This blockage causes more ACh to be produced and a feeling of greater alertness as synapses are excited. At the same time it also causes the brain to release another neurotransmitter called dopamine. High levels of dopamine and ACh stimulate the release of **endorphins** in the brain, which are the chemicals that produce a feeling of relaxed pleasure. They are the brain's 'feel good' compounds.

This gives rise to the double effect of nicotine, an initial increase in alertness followed by a relaxed pleasant sensation. Endorphin release is a very powerful response; the brain quickly associates this pleasurable experience with the action preceding it and this naturally leads to addiction. The effect of nicotine is very enjoyable but very short-lived, a classic formula leading to a craving for more.

Cobra venom

Cobra venom is modified saliva containing a mixture of proteins. It is injected into the bloodstream of prey using fangs (Figure 22.16). One of these proteins binds irreversibly to ACh receptors on the post-synaptic membrane. The enzyme **acetylcholinesterase** has no effect on this venom protein. As a result the Na^+ ion channels remain permanently open and after an initial action potential the membrane is unable to repolarise and no further action potentials can be generated. This causes general paralysis, including respiratory muscles, which results in death due to suffocation.

Figure 22.16 Cobra threat posture showing fangs for injection of venom into prey

> **Test yourself**
>
> 16 Name **one** other neurotransmitter apart from acetylcholine.
>
> 17 Name the metal ions that trigger the release of acetylcholine into the synaptic cleft.
>
> 18 The enzyme cholinesterase breaks down acetylcholine. The synapse stops working if this enzyme is not present. Explain why.
>
> 19 Describe the effect of an IPSP on the resting potential.
>
> 20 Suggest why cobra venom victims often suffocate.

Chapter summary

Central nervous system

- The spinal cord is protected by the vertebrae with spinal nerves branching out between them.
- The spinal cord has grey matter made up of cell bodies and synapses and white matter made up of myelinated nerve fibres.
- It forms a relay system between sensory organs and effector organs. The simplest of these is a direct connection in a reflex arc. Hence reflexes are fast, with the same stimulus eliciting the same response.
- The spinal cord swells at one end to form the brain, a mass of highly organised interneurones supported by neuroglia cells.
- The brain not only acts as a coordinating centre but also initiates many impulses directed to effector organs. It is made up of several important areas. The cerebrum is the centre of higher mental activities central to coordination in higher animals. The cerebellum coordinates fine control of motor activity. The medulla oblongata contains the control centre for breathing and heartbeat. The hypothalamus is a centre for homeostatic control such as osmoregulation and temperature, closely linked to the endocrine system.

Peripheral nervous system

- The peripheral nervous system is divided into the somatic system (under conscious control) and the autonomic system (not under conscious control).
- The autonomic system is further divided into sympathetic and parasympathetic systems, which have separate pathways and transmitters to bring about antagonistic actions.

Transmission of a nerve impulse

- The axons of neurones have a resting potential difference of −70 mV across their membrane.
- This is caused by active transport. Na^+ ions are pumped in and K^+ ions are pumped out. Because the membrane is much more permeable to K^+ ions moving out, a potential difference is set up.
- An action potential is a wave of depolarisation of the axon membrane. It is caused by gated channels in the membrane opening to allow Na^+ ions to enter by diffusion, causing the potential difference to change from −70 mV to +40 mV.
- As soon as the action potential passes, the Na^+ channels close and K^+ channels open and the resting potential is restored.
- Axons are surrounded by fatty myelin sheaths with gaps at intervals called nodes of Ranvier.
- Axons with myelin sheaths carry impulses faster than those without because the impulse is able to 'jump' from one node to the next. This is known as saltatory conduction.

Synapses

- Where neurones meet there is a small gap called the synaptic cleft. This means that the action potential cannot pass in the normal way.
- Transmission across a synapse occurs by means of chemical transmitters.
- An action potential arriving at the pre-synaptic membranes causes the opening of Ca^{2+} ion channels.
- The influx of Ca^{2+} ions triggers the release of a transmitter substance into the synaptic cleft.
- This substance diffuses rapidly across the cleft and binds to receptors on the post-synaptic membrane.
- Typically this causes the opening of Na^+ ion gates and Na^+ ions flood in to the post-synaptic neurone by diffusion, causing this membrane to depolarise and a new action potential to form in the next neurone.
- There are many different transmitter substances such as acetylcholine, noradrenaline and dopamine.
- Synapses allow a level of control over the passage of nerve impulses and can be targeted by drugs such as lidocaine, nicotine and snake venom.

Practice questions

1 The maximum number of impulses that can be sent down an axon is about 1000 s^{-1}. This is because:

A there is a gap between axons at the synapse

B Na^+ gated channels cannot open and close faster than this

C nodes of Ranvier cause delays in conduction

D it takes time for the restoration of a resting potential between each action potential *(1)*

2 The part of the brain that forms the main link between the nervous and endocrine systems is called the:

A cerebrum

B medulla oblongata

C hypothalamus

D cerebellum *(1)*

3 The graph shows the changes in potential difference across an axon membrane as an action potential passes.

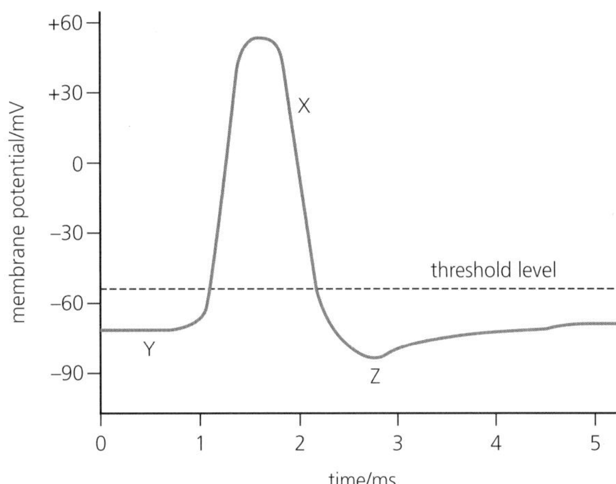

a) What name is given to the potential difference at Y? *(1)*

b) Explain what is meant by the term 'threshold level'. *(2)*

c) Explain how the properties of the axon membrane and the movement of ions account for the changes in membrane potential in region X. *(4)*

d) Explain why the membrane potential at Z becomes lower than that at Y. *(3)*

4 a) Explain how the structure of the spinal cord allows the passage of both simple spinal reflexes and voluntary movements in the somatic nervous system. *(5)*

***b)** Describe how the cerebral cortex and the cerebellum are involved in the initiation and control of voluntary activities. *(5)*

Tip

Question 3 is designed to test your ability to describe processes accurately. It requires some detailed knowledge of action potentials but also tests your understanding of the events in some depth. So, although it is mainly AO1 and straightforward it is not too easy.

Tip

Both sections of Question 4 require a comprehensive explanation in a clear sequence. You will need to know the details involved and also make sure you check exactly what the question is asking. A simple description without emphasis on how the structure and function of the spinal cord and brain are linked will only gain limited credit. Both sections require some application but are mainly AO1.

5 a) The diagram shows a part of a myelinated nerve fibre magnified ×200.

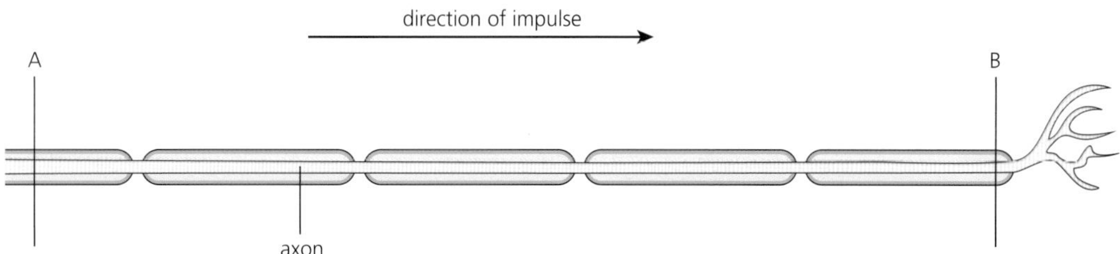

i) The passage of an action potential between the points marked A and B was timed as 0.05 ms. Use the information provided to calculate the speed of the action potential travelling along this fibre. *(3)*

The table below shows the speed of action potentials measured in a number of different nerve fibres.

Nerve fibre	Myelinated/ Non-myelinated	Diameter/μm	Speed of conduction/ms^{-1}
Squid giant axon	NM	500	25
Mammalian type 1	NM	1.5	2
Mammalian type 2	M	17	95
Mammalian type 3	M	9	55
Mammalian type 4	M	3	17

ii) What do these data suggest about the relationship between the myelination and diameter of nerve fibres and the speed of conduction? *(2)*

iii) Comment on the validity of your conclusions based on these data. *(2)*

b) Explain why there is a difference in the speed of conduction in myelinated and non-myelinated nerve fibres. *(4)*

Tip

You will need to revise the magnification formula and your knowledge of standard units such as milliseconds and then apply them to Question 5. In this way it is a synoptic question, a mathematical skills question, a straightforward AO1 question and an AO2 question from this part of the specification. Part (a)(iii) also asks you to apply some judgement in commenting on conclusions so could be classified as AO3. Remember, speed is best expressed as ms^{-1} in your final answer.

Stretch and challenge

6 Research how different neurotransmitters in the brain have enabled pharmacologists to develop treatments for some human disorders.

7 a) i) What is the function of dopamine in the brain and how is it linked to Parkinson's disease?

ii) Why does taking dopamine orally or by intravenous injection have no effect and how is this problem overcome?

b) One function of serotonin is to act as a neurotransmitter in the brain. People suffering from depression are often found to have low levels of serotonin in their brain.

i) One of the world's most prescribed drugs, 'prozac' (fluoxetine), is a SSRI (selective serotonin reuptake inhibitor). Explain how SSRIs are thought to increase serotonin levels in the brain.

ii) What other effects does serotonin have in mammals outside of the brain?

iii) Despite their widespread use, not all doctors accept that they are effective or that depression is simply caused by lack of serotonin. What arguments are used to support their case?

23 Chemical control

Prior knowledge

In this chapter you will need to recall that:

- ➜ mammalian hormones are chemical messengers carried in the bloodstream
- ➜ mammalian hormones affect target organs, often in distant parts of the body
- ➜ hormones are often used to control long-term processes such as growth and reproduction
- ➜ adrenaline produces a 'fight or flight' sequence of actions
- ➜ insulin is used to control blood sugar levels
- ➜ oestrogen and progesterone are important in human reproductive cycles
- ➜ hormones interact with each other to produce a sequence of events
- ➜ many plant hormones are often known as plant growth substances
- ➜ the plant hormone, auxin, is involved in phototropism
- ➜ transcription factors control gene expression (Chapter 18).

Test yourself on prior knowledge

1. State where in the body insulin is produced.
2. Name the target organ for insulin.
3. Describe the effect that auxin has on developing plant cells.
4. State where in the root of a plant auxin is produced.
5. Hormones are carried in the bloodstream but only the target organs respond. Explain why.

You saw in Chapter 22 that the nervous system of mammals is a highly effective and rapid means of controlling and coordinating groups of specialised tissues and organs. The continual need for synthesis of transmitter molecules and the ATP requirements of active transport mean that this is a very energy-demanding means of coordination. This level of energy demand would need to be sustained for the full lifetime of the individual. However, plants do not have nervous systems and they need to exercise control and coordination too.

All of this means that it is an advantage to have other less energy-demanding means of coordination that are better suited to longer and slower processes. Chemical control provides this alternative in both plants and animals. As will be explained further in Chapter 24, both of these means of control need to be carefully coordinated in order to regulate more complex processes in an efficient manner. In this chapter you will look at the details of the principles and individual examples of chemical control in both plants and animals. In Chapter 24 we will explain how these are linked together to bring about control of heart rate, osmoregulation and thermoregulation in mammals.

Homeostasis

Survival of all plants and animals depends upon each cell's metabolism working at its optimum. To achieve this it is essential that the cells' environment, both internal and external is kept at the most favourable level. This process is known as **homeostasis**.

However, the intense activity in all cells means that this environment is constantly changing. The processes of homeostasis therefore need to make adjustments continually, to bring all the different factors back to the correct levels. For this reason there will always be small fluctuations about the optimum level. This is known as a **dynamic equilibrium**. Examples of the many factors that need to be controlled are shown in Figure 23.1.

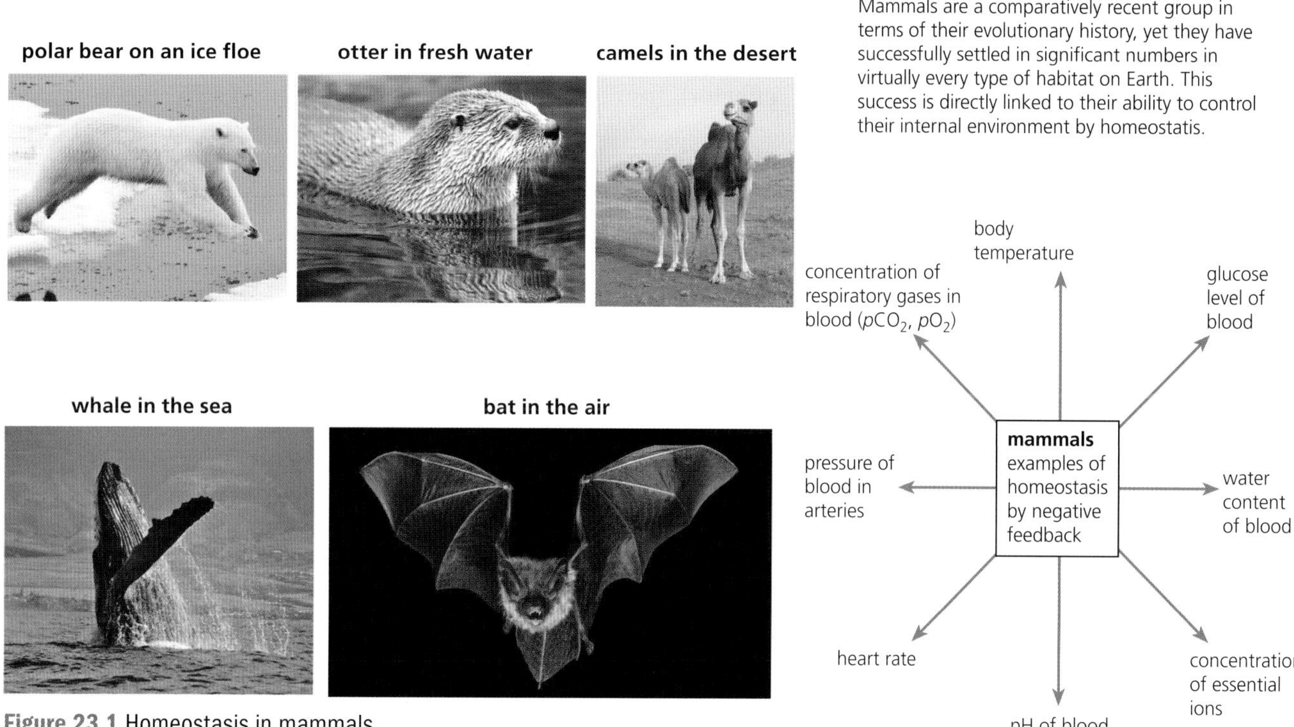

Figure 23.1 Homeostasis in mammals

Negative and positive feedback

An important feature of homeostasis is the use of feedback control. This can be in the form of **negative feedback** or **positive feedback**.

Negative feedback can best be illustrated by taking a simple example of a room, heated by a radiator, whose temperature is controlled by a single thermostat. If the room begins to cool, the thermostat is triggered to switch on the radiator. This causes the temperature to rise and then the thermostat switches off. In other words the more the thermostat is switched on the more it causes an effect that will switch it off. This is therefore **negative feedback**. Negative feedback provides an automatic self-regulating method of control. The process is summarised in Figure 23.2.

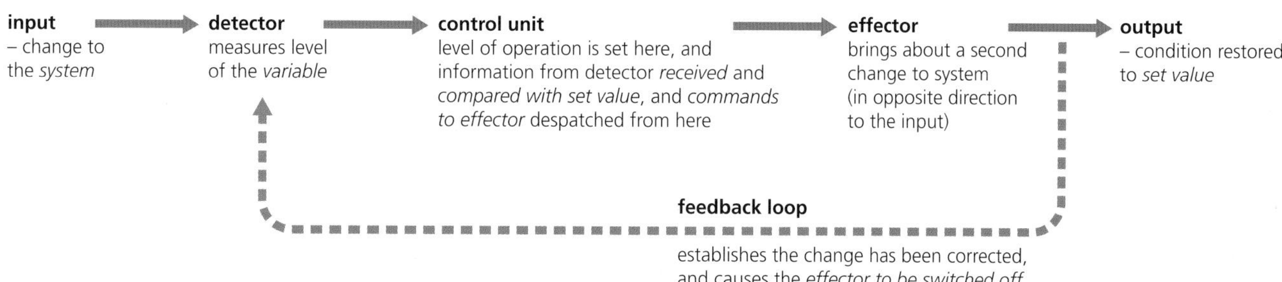

Figure 23.2 The mechanism of negative feedback

This example also illustrates another important principle. With only one heating system and no cooling system then this method will work well in colder weather but in summer the temperature will continue to rise regardless of the thermostat activity. What is needed, of course, is an air-cooling system alongside the radiator heating. As you will see in Chapter 24 the control of body temperature in mammals works in exactly this way.

In mammals the level of blood sugar is partially controlled by the peptide hormone insulin. When the blood sugar levels rise, the β cells of the pancreas (detector) respond by secreting insulin (effector). Insulin stimulates glucose uptake into cells such as muscles and liver by activating glucose transport proteins in the cell membranes. Thus the level of glucose falls and the β cells stop producing insulin (negative feedback). Just as in the room thermostat example there is also a hormone, glucagon, that raises blood sugar levels by a similar negative feedback mechanism. In this way human blood sugar levels are normally maintained between 3.6 and 5.8 mmol dm^{-3} with short-lived peaks after eating starchy or sugary meals.

Positive feedback is the opposite of this. Again, it is useful to consider an example with which you are probably familiar. Playing an electric guitar, attached to an amplifier and speaker, very close to the speakers will often produce an increasingly loud howling noise. Although generally referred to as just 'feedback' it is an example of **positive feedback**. What happens is that the guitar strings vibrate and this is picked up by the guitar sensors and amplified. If the strings are close to the speaker the vibrations in the air can cause the strings to vibrate more. This is again amplified and the speakers stimulate the strings more until the noise is deafening. In other words vibrations of the strings cause them to produce an effect that makes them vibrate even more. The problem with positive feedback is that unless there is some intervention it will spiral out of control. However, it can be useful to initiate actions in the body provided that there are other feedback loops that will bring it under control. Again, you will meet examples in Chapter 24.

Test yourself

1 Describe the main features of a dynamic equilibrium.
2 The action of insulin is an example of negative feedback. Explain why.
3 Suggest why plants do not have the equivalent of a nervous system.

Chemical control in mammals

Hormones are chemical substances produced and secreted from the cells of the **ductless** or **endocrine glands**. In effect, hormones carry messages around the body – but in a totally different way from the nervous system. Hormones are transported indiscriminately in the bloodstream, but they act only at specific sites, called **target organs**. Although present in small quantities, hormones are extremely effective messengers, helping to control and coordinate body activities. Once released, hormones typically cause changes to specific metabolic actions of their target organs. However, hormones circulate in the bloodstream only briefly. When they reach the liver they are broken down and the breakdown products are excreted via the kidneys. So, long-acting hormones must be secreted continuously to be effective.

Key terms

Endocrine (ductless) glands Glands producing hormones that are delivered directly into the bloodstream without the use of specific tubes (ducts) carrying them to their site of action.

Target organ An organ that will respond to a specific hormone.

The positions of all the endocrine glands of the human body are shown in Figure 23.3.

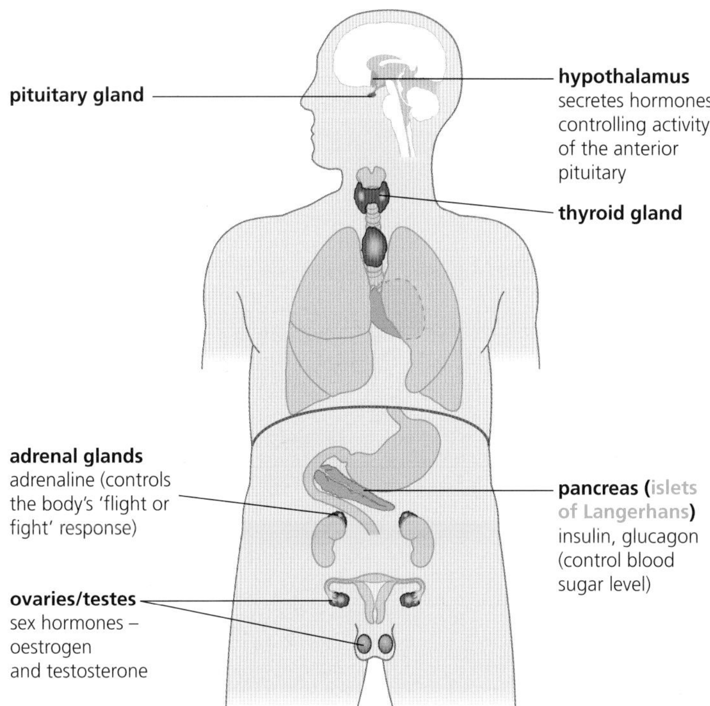

Figure 23.3 The human endocrine system

> **Key terms**
>
> **Islets of Langerhans** Distinct groups of cells found within the pancreas that produce the hormones insulin and glucagon.
>
> **Pituitary gland** An important endocrine gland found attached to the hypothalamus at the base of the brain; it coordinates the functions of other endocrine glands.

The endocrine system and the nervous system work in distinctive and different ways when controlling and coordinating body activities. However, the effects of the endocrine system are coordinated by the **pituitary gland**, a 'master gland' working in tandem with the hypothalamus of the brain. The hypothalamus secretes hormones that regulate the functioning of the pituitary. This is an excellent example of how the two systems are very closely linked.

How hormones bring about their effects

Although hormones are distributed to all tissues by the bloodstream, they only affect their target cells. This is because only the target cells have the correct receptors.

There are two types of hormones, which bring about their effects in slightly different ways:

- **Amides** or **peptides** interact with specific receptors on the outside of the cell surface membrane.
- **Steroids** can pass through the cell surface membrane and interact with specific receptors within the cytoplasm.

In both cases a specific enzyme is needed to bring about the final action of altering structure or function. How this is brought about also differs for each type of hormone, as shown in Figure 23.4.

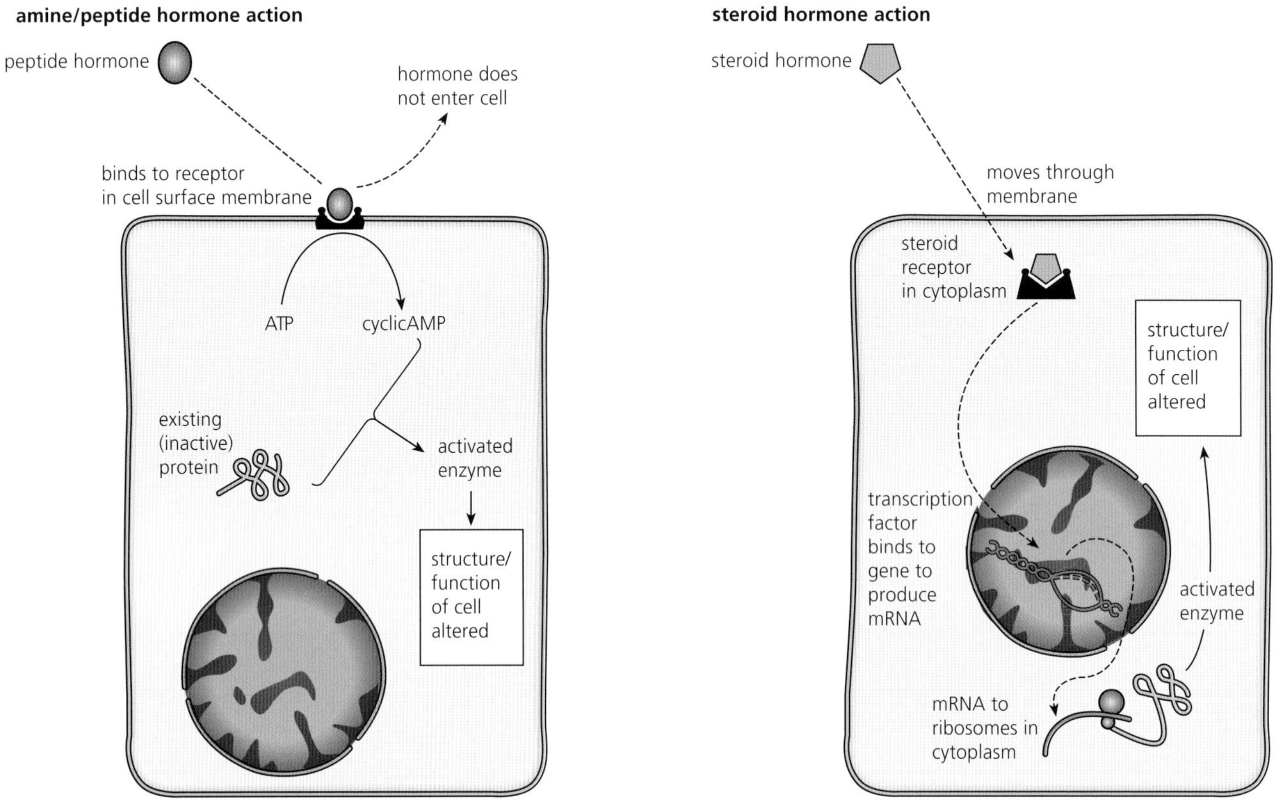

amine/peptide hormone action

peptide hormone

hormone does not enter cell

binds to receptor in cell surface membrane

ATP

cyclicAMP

existing (inactive) protein

activated enzyme

structure/ function of cell altered

steroid hormone action

steroid hormone

moves through membrane

steroid receptor in cytoplasm

structure/ function of cell altered

transcription factor binds to gene to produce mRNA

activated enzyme

mRNA to ribosomes in cytoplasm

Figure 23.4 How the two types of hormones influence target cells

Key terms

Second messenger
An additional molecule that is used to trigger a response when a hormone attaches to receptor sites on a target cell surface membrane.

Cyclic adenosine monophosphate (cAMP)
A cellular molecule often used as a second messenger when cells respond to a stimulus from a hormone.

Peptide/amine hormones such as antidiuretic hormone (ADH) (see Chapter 24) and adrenaline attach to receptors on the cell surface membrane and trigger the release of a **second messenger**, often in the form of a molecule called **cyclic adenosine monophosphate (cAMP)**. This molecule, as its name suggests, is a very close relative of ATP. When the hormone binds to its receptor, cAMP is formed inside the cell and activates existing proteins in the cytoplasm to form enzymes that bring about specific changes. The formation of cAMP continues as long as the hormone binds to the receptor site and in this way the initial signal will be amplified within the cell.

Steroid hormones such as oestrogen and testosterone pass through the membrane before combining with receptors to form **transcription factors**. As we have described in Chapter 18, transcription factors bind to specific genes and as a result protein synthesis is initiated. In this case to produce the enzymes required to bring about specific changes.

Hormones can have multiple effects

Adrenaline (also known as epinephrine)

One advantage of hormonal control is that a single chemical release can have multiple effects in widespread parts of the body. Given that the hormone is already in the bloodstream, all that is required is that a group of cells has the correct receptor sites on its membrane in order to respond. This provides another level of coordination.

The hormone adrenaline (more correctly called epinephrine) is a good example of multiple coordinated responses (Table 23.1 on the next page). It is known as the 'fight or flight' hormone and although this is rather vague it does infer that it brings about several different responses for one purpose. In simple terms the release of adrenaline from the adrenal medulla is triggered by excitement or fear, so prepares the body for a response to what might be causing these sensations. Hence the ability to make muscles contract a little quicker, mobilise stored food reserves and constrict superficial veins (in case of damage), are all useful actions if we wish to defend ourselves or run away. This is likely to be rather less important in humans than in wild mammals, although it is clear that human sports and athletic performance are enhanced by the excitement of a big occasion.

Table 23.1 The multiple effects of adrenaline

Organ	Effect of adrenaline
Heart	Increases heart rate
Lungs	Increases breathing rate
Circulatory	Vasoconstriction
Liver	Increases breakdown of glycogen in liver to increase blood sugar levels
Muscle	Increases readiness to contract (causing shivering in extreme fear or excitement)

You may find some of Table 23.1 rather familiar. In Chapter 22 (Table 22.1) you looked at the effects of the sympathetic and parasympathetic divisions of the autonomic nervous system. The list for the sympathetic system is almost identical to Table 23.1. The explanation for this is that the sympathetic system uses epinephrine as a neurotransmitter and, in fact, the level of this in the blood comes partly from such secretions. So, not surprisingly, their effects are almost identical. Once again we see a very close link between nervous and hormonal control.

Test yourself

4 Explain the term 'steroids'.

5 Describe how amide and peptide hormones operate in a similar way to steroid hormones.

6 Describe how amide and peptide hormones operate in a different way to steroid hormones.

7 Describe the similarities between cAMP and ATP.

8 Suggest why a 'second messenger' is given this name.

9 Name **one** peptide hormone and **one** steroid hormone.

Chemical control in plants

The fundamental differences between plants and animals are reflected in their levels of control and coordination. Lower metabolic rates, a lack of movement and lower internal temperatures all mean that plants require less rapid control systems. Most plant responses are brought about by changes in growth patterns and growth rates. Therefore our definition of hormones is difficult to apply to plants (Table 23.2) and you will often see the compounds involved described as **plant growth substances**. Work on these substances often uses artificial closely related compounds with similar effects as they are more stable and longer-lasting.

Table 23.2 Differences between plant growth substances and animal hormones

Plant growth substances	Animal hormones
Produced in a region of plant structure, e.g. stem or root tips, in unspecialised cells	Produced in specific glands in specialised cells, e.g. islets of Langerhans in the pancreas (producing insulin)
Not necessarily transported widely or at all, and some are active at sites of production	Transported to all parts of the body by the bloodstream
Not particularly specific – tend to influence different tissues and organs, sometimes in contrasting ways	Effects are mostly highly specific to a particular tissue or organ, and without effects in other parts or on different processes

Auxins

Key terms

Meristem A region of actively dividing cells found in plants, often at the root and shoot tips.

Tropism A plant growth response where the direction of movement is determined by the direction of the stimulus.

Auxins are the most widely distributed of all plant growth substances. Auxin has been shown to be the compound indoleacetic acid (IAA), whose formula is illustrated in Figure 23.5. Their primary effect is on plant cell walls. As new cells are produced by mitosis in the meristems of shoot and root tips, they begin to elongate and differentiate in to specialised tissues. The increase in length of these cells is largely brought about by expansion caused by turgor pressure. Auxin increases the plasticity of the cell walls to allow them to expand further. This effect is the mechanism by which stems and roots respond to gravity and light in growth movements called tropisms. However, auxins are also involved in many other aspects of plant physiology as shown in Figure 23.5, both as a separate compound and interacting with other growth substances.

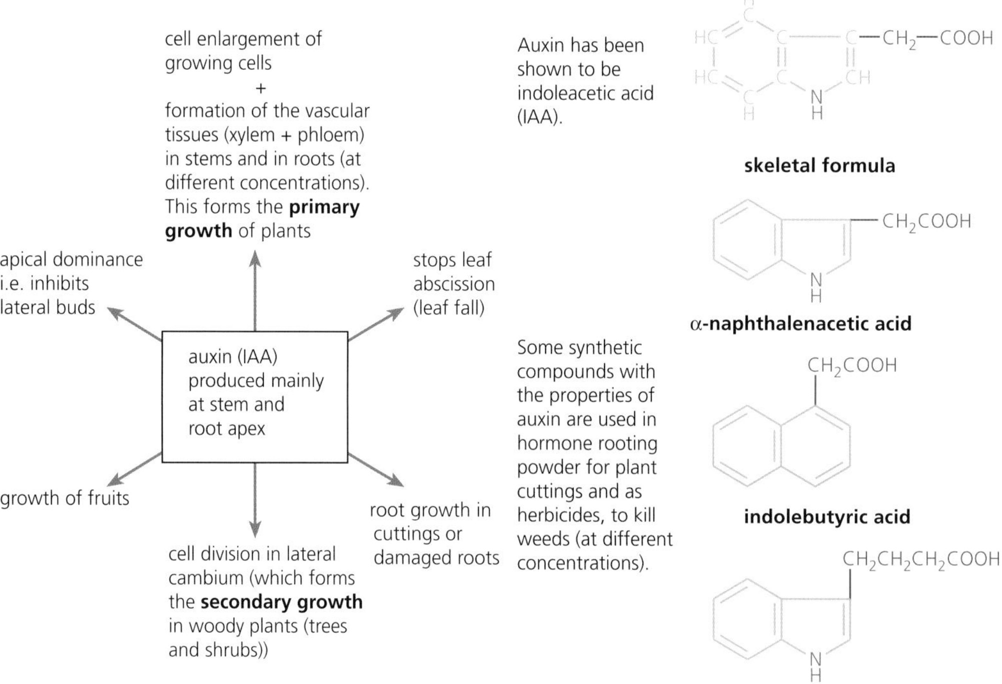

Figure 23.5 The roles of auxin (IAA) in plant growth, and the structure of natural and synthetic auxin

Using coleoptiles to investigate phototropism

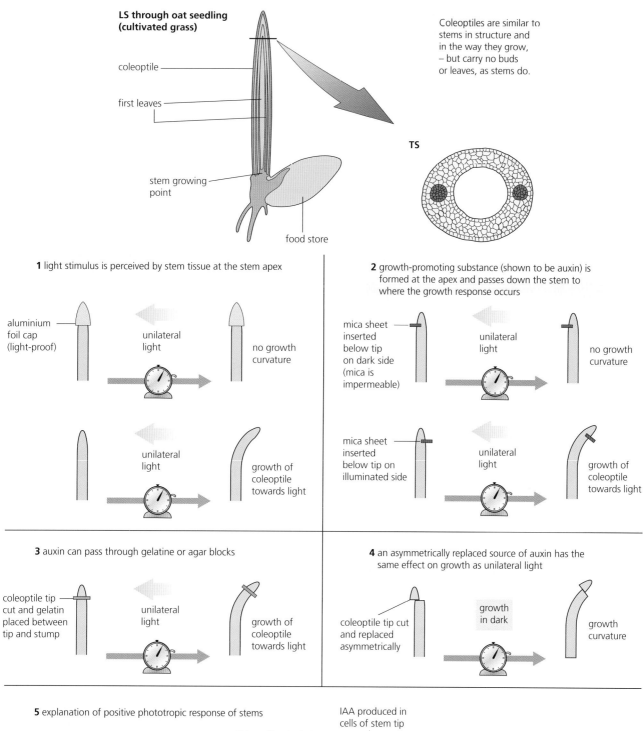

LS through oat seedling (cultivated grass)

coleoptile

first leaves

stem growing point

food store

Coleoptiles are similar to stems in structure and in the way they grow, – but carry no buds or leaves, as stems do.

TS

1 light stimulus is perceived by stem tissue at the stem apex

aluminium foil cap (light-proof)

unilateral light

no growth curvature

unilateral light

growth of coleoptile towards light

2 growth-promoting substance (shown to be auxin) is formed at the apex and passes down the stem to where the growth response occurs

mica sheet inserted below tip on dark side (mica is impermeable)

unilateral light

no growth curvature

mica sheet inserted below tip on illuminated side

unilateral light

growth of coleoptile towards light

3 auxin can pass through gelatine or agar blocks

coleoptile tip cut and gelatin placed between tip and stump

unilateral light

growth of coleoptile towards light

4 an asymmetrically replaced source of auxin has the same effect on growth as unilateral light

coleoptile tip cut and replaced asymmetrically

growth in dark

growth curvature

5 explanation of positive phototropic response of stems

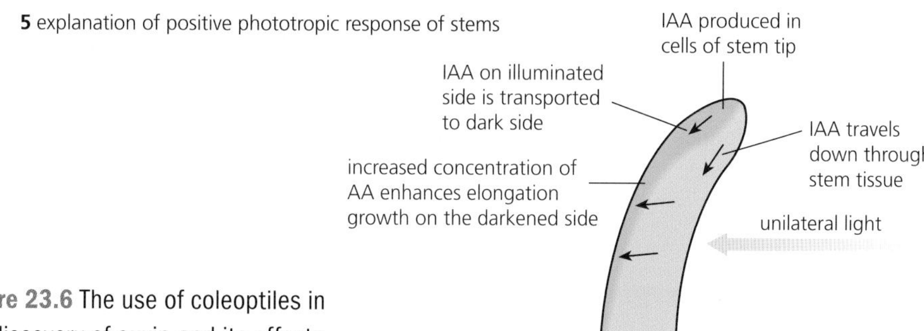

IAA produced in cells of stem tip

IAA travels down through stem tissue

Figure 23.6 The use of coleoptiles in the discovery of auxin and its effects

The **coleoptile** is a sheath of tissue, unique to the grass family, which encloses the shoot of a germinating grass seedling as it grows up through the soil. It grows rather like a stem does, but it is uncluttered by leaves or buds so its growth is easily observed. Experiments have been conducted with oat seedling coleoptiles, the plant organ first used to investigate phototropism (Figure 23.6). In fact, experiments on the responses of oat coleoptiles to unilateral light led to the discovery of 'auxin', later shown to be indoleacetic acid.

Auxin is manufactured by cells undergoing repeated cell division, such as those found at the stem and root tips (and at the tip of coleoptiles). Consequently, the concentration of auxin is highest there. Auxin is then transported to the region of growth behind the tip, where it causes cells to elongate. In the process, the auxin is used up and inactivated.

In one experiment, the tip of the stem or coleoptile is cut off and stood on a gelatine block for a short while. Then the block is placed on a cut stump of stem or coleoptile. Growth in length is found to continue. The explanation is that auxin passes into the gelatine block, so when the gelatine is placed on the stump, the auxin passes down into the tissue and stimulates elongation of the cells. This technique has been used to investigate auxin actions further, as follows.

In stems and coleoptiles exposed to unilateral light, it is the auxin passing down the stem that is redistributed to the darkened side, causing differential growth and the curvature of the stem as shown in part 5 of Figure 23.6.

Cytokinins

Cytokinins are a group of related adenine-based compounds that act as plant growth substances. The basic structure of two of the cytokinins is shown in Figure 23.7. They are produced in meristematic tissues in the roots and shoots. Their principal mode of action is to stimulate cell division by attaching to receptor sites on cell surface membranes and triggering the formation of transcription factors inside the cell.

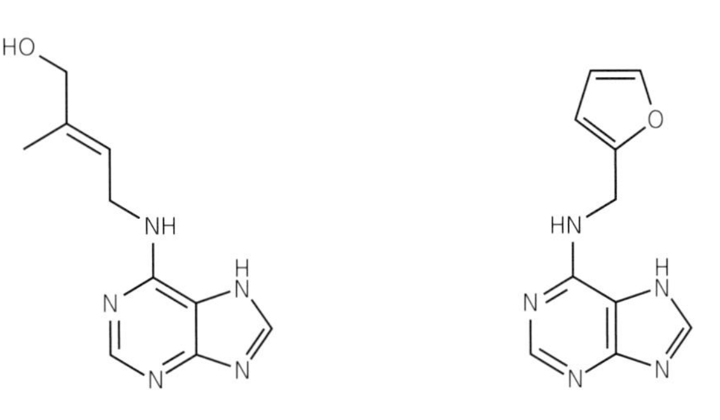

Figure 23.7 The structure of the cytokinins zeatin and kinetin

Like almost all plant growth substances, cytokinins rarely simply stimulate cell division alone, but undergo many interactions with other substances. In the case of cytokinin this is often an interaction with auxin (see Table 23.3).

Table 23.3 A summary of some effects of three plant growth substances

Process	Auxin	Gibberellin	Cytokinin
Stem growth	Promotes cell elongation	Promotes cell elongation only with auxin	Promotes cell-division
Root growth	Promotes root formation in cuttings (rooting powder)	Inhibits root formation	No effect
Apical dominance	Promotes apical dominance	Enhances auxin effect	Promotes lateral bud growth (antagonistic to apical dominance)
Bud dormancy	No effect	Breaks dormancy	Breaks dormancy
Leaf fall (abscission)	Inhibits	No effect	No effect

One important interaction was first demonstrated by Skoog in the 1950s and is an important feature of plant tissue culture today. Plant breeders spend a long time isolating new varieties that may be more colourful or productive. If successful, the time taken to grow sufficient stock to produce seeds or cuttings on a large scale could be many years. This problem is overcome by using **micropropagation**. Micropropagation is a form of tissue culture that starts by carefully breaking down the meristems of young plants into individual cells and then growing the cells on sterile media. Technically only one cell is needed to form each new plant but usually it is a larger number. To ensure the cells begin to differentiate, the mixture of plant growth substances in the medium must be carefully controlled. Skoog found that the ratio of auxin to kinetin was critical.

> **Key term**
>
> **Micropropagation** A form of tissue culture used to grow many copies of a single plant using just a few cells.

Figure 23.8 shows that a high kinetin : auxin ratio results in the cells forming shoots. With an intermediate kinetin : auxin ratio only an undifferentiated mass of cells (a **callus**) is formed and a low kinetin : auxin ratio results in the formation of roots. The inference is obviously that to form the correct balance of roots and shoots for a complete plant then the ratio of the two substances needs to be changed in subtle ways throughout development.

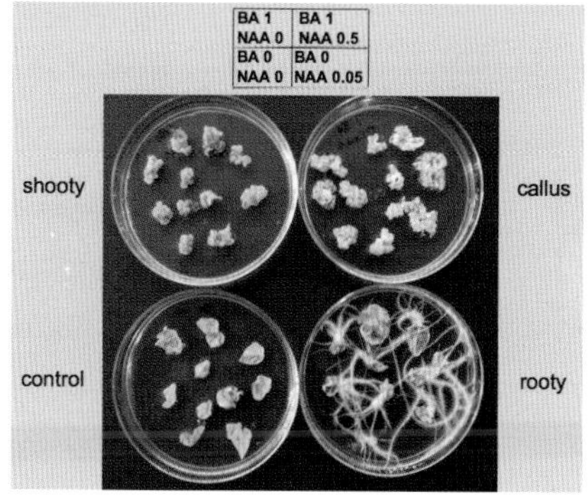

Figure 23.8 The effect of kinetin : auxin ratio on plant tissue differentiation

Gibberellins

As with auxins and cytokinins, there are a number of different chemical variations of gibberellins. These are usually abbreviated as GA with a number, such as GA_3 in Figure 23.9. Chemically gibberellins are complex terpenoids. Their main functions are control of **internode** length and seed development. You will not be surprised to learn that they are also involved with other growth substances in complex interactions (see Table 23.3 on the previous page).

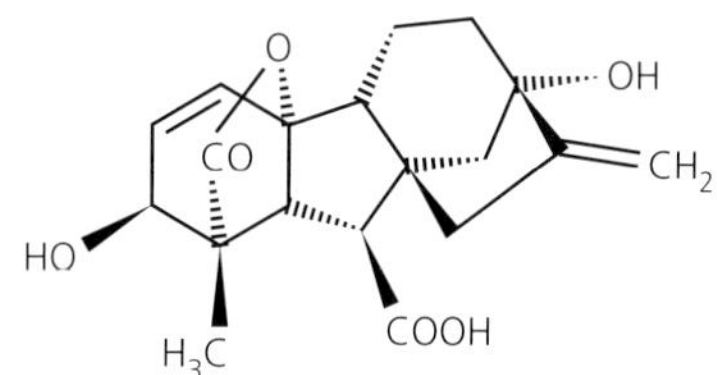

Figure 23.9 The structure of gibberellic acid (GA_3)

> **Key terms**
>
> **Callus** A mass of undifferentiated plant cells.
>
> **Internode** The distance along a plant stem between one side branch and the next.

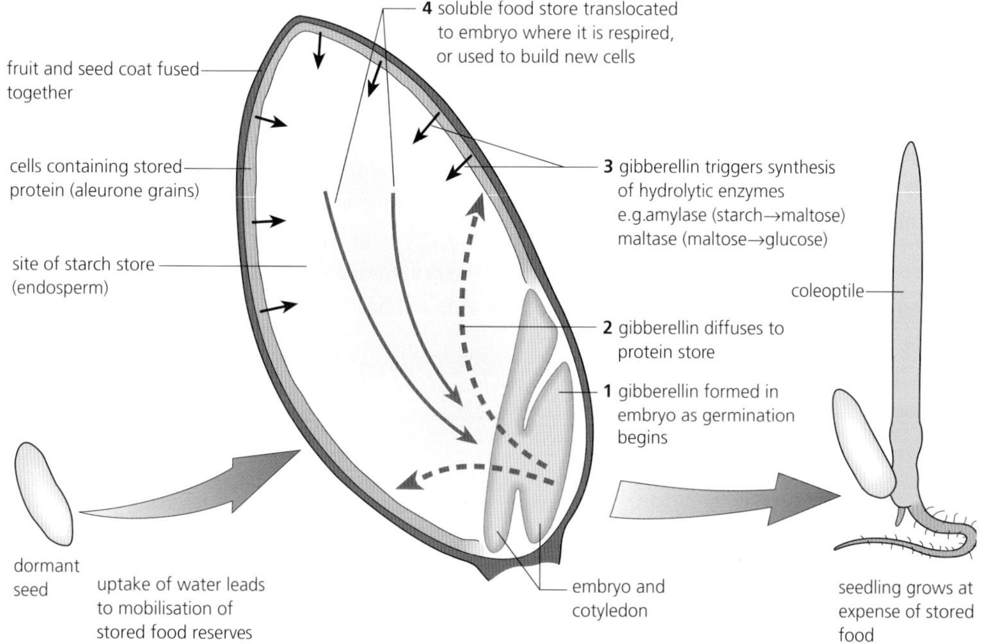

Figure 23.10 The role of gibberellin in the germination of barley fruit

Gibberellins are thought to bring about their effect by controlling transcription factors within the cell. In the cytoplasm they combine with proteins called DELLA proteins. These proteins normally prevent transcription factors from activating several important genes involved in seed germination. When in combination with GA, DELLA proteins no longer prevent these transcription factors from operating and hence the process of germination can begin, as shown in Figure 23.10.

Although there is an important biological difference between a fruit and a seed, and in the case of cereal grains they are a fruit, we will not go into technical details here. However, you might consider the fruits that you eat. The seeds are normally inside the fruit, for example oranges and tomatoes. In the case of cereals the wall of the fruit and the seed are dried out and joined closely together.

Test yourself

10 Name **one** process in plants where cytokinin has:
   a) an antagonistic effect to auxin
   b) a different effect to auxin.

11 Describe the role of a coleoptile in early seedling growth.

12 Suggest the effect on its growth of removing the tip of the coleoptile.

13 Explain how auxin causes an increased elongation of newly formed plant cells.

14 Auxin does not cause elongation in older cells. Explain why.

Core practical 14

Investigate the effect of gibberellin on the production of amylase in germinating cereals using a starch agar assay

Background information

Gibberellins are plant growth substances that have been shown to break dormancy in seeds. Dormancy means that the seeds will not normally begin to germinate until they have received certain treatments, even though all the other conditions may be favourable. This property is particularly important to plants that produce seeds in the autumn. Were the seeds to begin germination immediately, then the small seedlings would not survive the winter. Therefore dormancy delays germination for several months until spring, when the chances of survival are much higher.

The production of gibberellin by the seed embryo triggers the formation of amylases from the aleurone layer. The subsequent hydrolysis of starch to sugars within the endosperm provides the substrate for increased respiration and signals the start of germination (see Figure 23.10).

This assay uses soluble starch suspended in agar gel. When a fruit (seed) containing amylases is inserted into the gel the enzymes will diffuse outwards, hydrolysing the starch. If the plate is then flooded with iodine, any areas containing starch will turn blue-black in colour but any areas of hydrolysed starch will not. The greater the concentration of amylase, the larger the clear area will be.

Carrying out the investigation

Aim: To investigate the effect of increasing concentrations of gibberellin (GA) on the production of amylase in cereal grains.

Risk assessment: The GA solutions are extremely weak and pose no hazard. Many cereal grains will have been treated with anti-fungal seed dressings before sale, so it is essential to handle them with disposable gloves before rinsing them thoroughly before use. Even though bacterial cultures are not used, good sterile technique is needed to avoid contamination. Plain agar, not nutrient agar should be used. Nutrient agar grows bacteria and some fungi, plain agar contains no nutrients and so poses less microbiological risk. The starch agar plates and seeds should be disposed of by wrapping well and placing in the normal refuse immediately after the practical.

1 First of all you will need to make up a suitable range of concentrations of GA solutions. GA is quite expensive but fortunately you need only very dilute solutions. The relative molecular mass of GA is 346 and therefore a 1 M solution would need 346 g dissolved in 1 dm^3. This is far too strong, so a stock solution of 10^{-3}M (or 0.001 M) is advised (0.346 g dissolved in 1 dm^3).
Some research will show that you actually need a good range of concentrations from 10^{-3}M to 10^{-6}M. You can do this by taking 1 cm^3 of your stock solution and adding 9 cm^3 of deionised water. This will dilute the solution ×10 so you will now have a 10^{-4}M solution. Repeating this process of serial dilution will provide you with a range of GA solutions to use. To avoid repeated random errors you must use the most accurate measuring apparatus you have available and mix each dilution well before starting the next.

2 You can use wheat, oat or barley fruits for this investigation. Rinse them several times in distilled water to wash off any dressing and peel the brown outer covering (the husk) off 20 fruits. Cut each one laterally in two as shown in Figure 23.11 and discard the bottom half containing the embryo. It is important that you use only the half without the embryo.

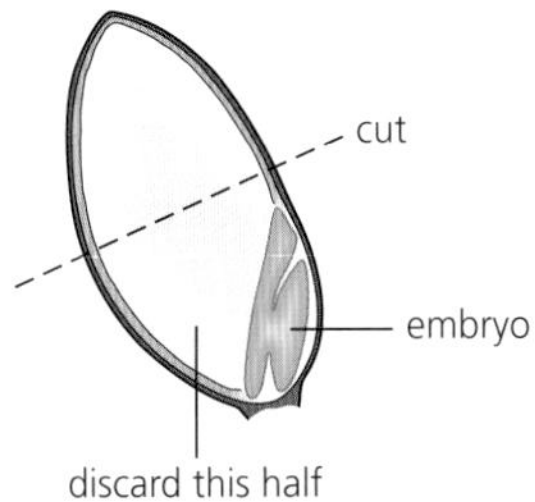

Figure 23.11 Discarding the embryo

3 Soak four halves of fruits in each of your prepared dilutions of GA and four in deionised water, for about 24 hours. During this time, prepare a starch agar (5 g soluble starch, 14 g nutrient agar and 500 cm^3 sterile water) Petri-dish plate for each of the dilutions you have chosen and label them clearly.

4 To prepare each plate, rinse the soaked half fruits in a dilute hypochlorite solution (Milton is fine) to prevent growth of fungi on the plates.

5 Dry the half fruits carefully and push each one gently into the starch agar until it just breaks the surface, spacing them as evenly as possible. Place the lid on the Petri dish and leave it in a warm place for a further 24 hours.

6 Finally, remove the lid and flood the plate with just enough iodine to cover the surface. Leave it until a dark blue colour develops. Rinse off the iodine and measure the diameter of the clear area around each fruit four times, calculating a mean for each one.

7 Record and present your data in a suitable way.

Questions

1 Why are the concentrations written in the form 10^{-3}M rather than 0.001 M?

2 Why do you need to make certain you only use the half fruit that does not contain the embryo?

3 Is it reasonable to assume the diameter of the clear area is proportional to the concentration of amylase in the fruit?

4 Why measure the diameter on one circle four times and take the average?

5 Would it be better to calculate the area of the cleared circles?

6 How can you treat your data to take account of any amylase produced by the distilled water control?

7 If you test your data statistically for a significant correlation (see Chapter 27) would this mean that you have shown that gibberellin does actually stimulate amylase production in cereals?

> **Tip**
>
> This is an excellent opportunity to practise some of the mathematical skills that will make up 10 percent of your final papers (see Chapter 27).

Interactions between plant growth substances

Interactions between substances can be of two main types. When the result of the interaction is that the overall effect is greater than the sum of the effects of the substances acting alone we say that the effect is **synergistic**. When the overall effect is less than the effects of the substances alone we say the effect is **antagonistic**.

One example of antagonistic interaction is seen in the control of **apical dominance** in plants. Apical dominance is a very common feature in the growth of many plants. The main shoot of a plant has a growing point (meristem) at its tip. In most plants this point continues to grow upwards in order to gain more light for photosynthesis while the growth of side shoots, which would keep the plant much lower to the ground, is inhibited. In other words the apex is dominating the growth form. So how is this brought about?

> **Key terms**
>
> **Synergism** When the effect of two substances acting together is greater than the sum of the effects of the substances acting alone.
>
> **Antagonism** When the effect of two substances acting together is less than the sum of the effects of the substances acting alone.
>
> **Apical dominance** The inhibition of lateral bud growth in plants by the presence of a terminal bud at the main growing point.
>
> **Axillary bud** A small dormant bud found in the angle (axil) between a main stem and side shoot of a plant.

The classical model

This suggests that the inhibition of side shoots is a result of the action of auxin produced in the growing tip, which is transported downwards. Side shoots will normally grow from **axillary buds** found in the angle between the branches and the main stem. Note that these are axillary not auxiliary buds as the angle between the stems is called the axil. Auxin is transported downwards, possibly via phloem, and prevents the activation of the genes leading to the production of cytokinins, which would stimulate the axillary buds to begin cell division and the growth of new stems, so the bud remains dormant.

As gardeners will know, one simple way of producing more bushy plants (with more side shoots) is to pinch out the main growing point (terminal bud). This removes the main source of the inhibitory auxin and therefore the axillary buds below begin to grow under the influence of cytokinin. This does not continue for very long since the new side shoots have growing points, which also produce auxin. The upper shoots therefore restore apical dominance. In this example auxin and cytokinin act as antagonists. Careful pruning of trees and shrubs seeks to make use of this idea to produce a desired shape and form.

Many plants have a shape that is wider at the base than it is at the top. This is a consequence of incomplete apical dominance. The buds at the very base of the plant are a long way away from the auxin-producing tip. Therefore the concentration and inhibitory effect of the auxin are much less, so there tends to be more lateral growth lower down the plant. This has the advantage of allowing lower branches to grow outwards further to avoid shading of their leaves by higher branches.

Evidence to support the classical model

There is some evidence that cytokinin levels do rise when terminal buds are removed and that the presence of auxin inhibits the biosynthesis of cytokinin. Application of cytokinin to dormant axillary buds can stimulate them into growth. However, this is not always true.

Evidence lacking or contradictory

The levels of auxin found in axillary buds are not always sufficient to account for inhibition. The predicted effects (such as the effect of applying cytokinin) do not always take place.

Other scientists have suggested different models concerned with the transport of auxin, which is partially contradictory to the classical model.

This is a very good example of the way in which scientific advances are made. Models are suggested and can be used to make predictions. It is these predictions that need to be tested experimentally in order to support (or undermine) the model. As more evidence accumulates in support of the model, it becomes more and more accepted.

In the case of apical dominance the classical theory appears to be such a logical explanation that it has become a very common feature in many text books. However, it is a very long way from becoming a widely accepted 'fact' amongst many plant physiologists and it seems that, at the present time, it must be accepted as only a partial explanation at best. As a scientist a key question is always 'How do I know that?' and at A level it is expected that you will begin to question what you see reported in more depth.

Phytochrome

Phytochrome is a blue–green pigment present in green plants in very low concentrations. The amount of phytochrome is not sufficient to mask chlorophyll, and it has been difficult to isolate and purify the substance from plant tissue, although this has been done. Phytochrome is a very large conjugated protein (protein molecule and pigment molecule, combined) and it is a highly reactive molecule. It is not a plant growth substance, but it is a photoreceptor pigment, able to absorb light of a particular wavelength and change its structure as a consequence. It is likely to react with different molecules around it, according to its structure.

We know that phytochrome exists in two inter-convertible forms. One form, referred to as P_R, is a blue pigment that absorbs mainly red light of wavelength 660 nm (this is what 'R' stands for). The other form is P_{FR}, a blue–green pigment that absorbs mainly far-red (FR) light of wavelength 730 nm. When P_R is exposed to light (or red light on its own), it is converted to P_{FR}. In the dark (or if exposed to far-red light alone), it is converted back to P_R:

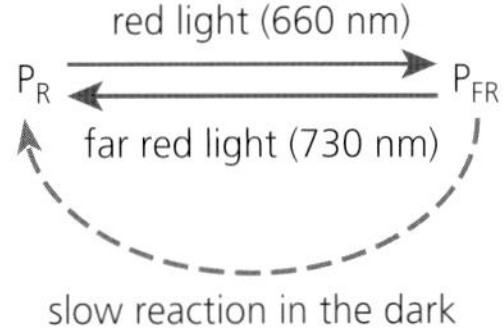

The influence of light on plant growth and development is known as **photomorphogenesis**. Phytochrome is the pigment system involved in photomorphogenesis. We know this because the red/far-red absorption spectrum of phytochrome corresponds to the action spectrum of some specific effects of light on development.

Phytochrome and the control of flowering

It appears that it is P_{FR} that is the active form of phytochrome in photomorphogenesis, stimulating some effects in plant development and inhibiting others.

One effect of light on plant growth and development is its role in determining the switch from vegetative growth to the production of flowers (reproductive growth). You will be aware that most plants flower at different and particular times of the year. In fact, most species have a precise season when flowers are produced. How is flowering switched on by this environmental condition? The answer is that day length provides important signals and these are mediated by phytochrome (Figure 23.13).

Test yourself

15 The effect on stem growth of auxin and cytokinin together can cause a greater effect than the two individually. State the name of this type of effect.

16 Suggest why auxin with cytokinin might cause greater stem elongation than if the two acted alone.

17 The amylase genes are inactive in dormant seeds. Explain why.

Key terms

Phytochrome A conjugated protein in plant cells thought to be responsible for detecting changes in red and far-red light illumination.

Photomorphogenesis The influence of light on plant growth and development.

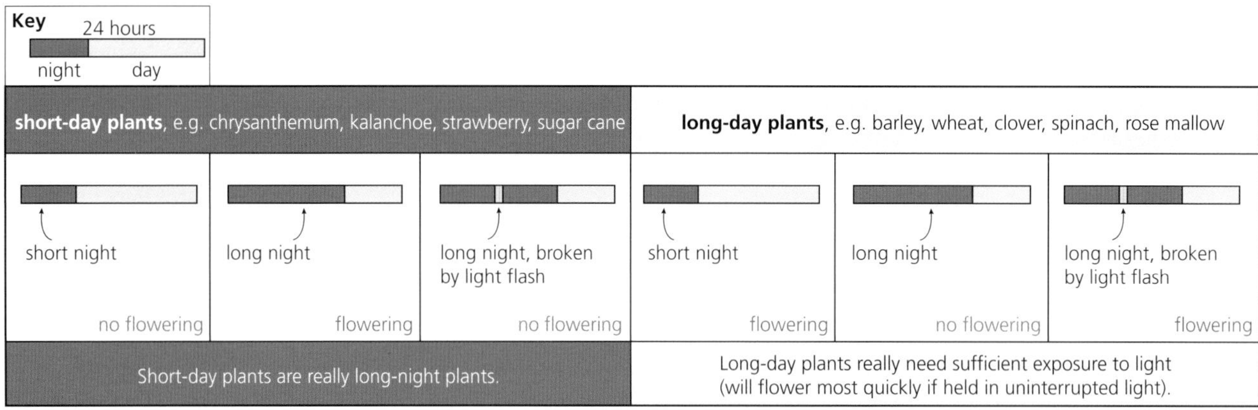

Key
24 hours
night
day
short-day plants, e.g. chrysanthemum, kalanchoe, strawberry, sugar cane
long-day plants, e.g. barley, wheat, clover, spinach, rose mallow
short night
no flowering
long night
flowering
long night, broken by light flash
no flowering
short night
flowering
long night
no flowering
long night, broken by light flash
flowering
Short-day plants are really long-night plants.
Long-day plants really need sufficient exposure to light (will flower most quickly if held in uninterrupted light).

Figure 23.13 Flowering related to day length

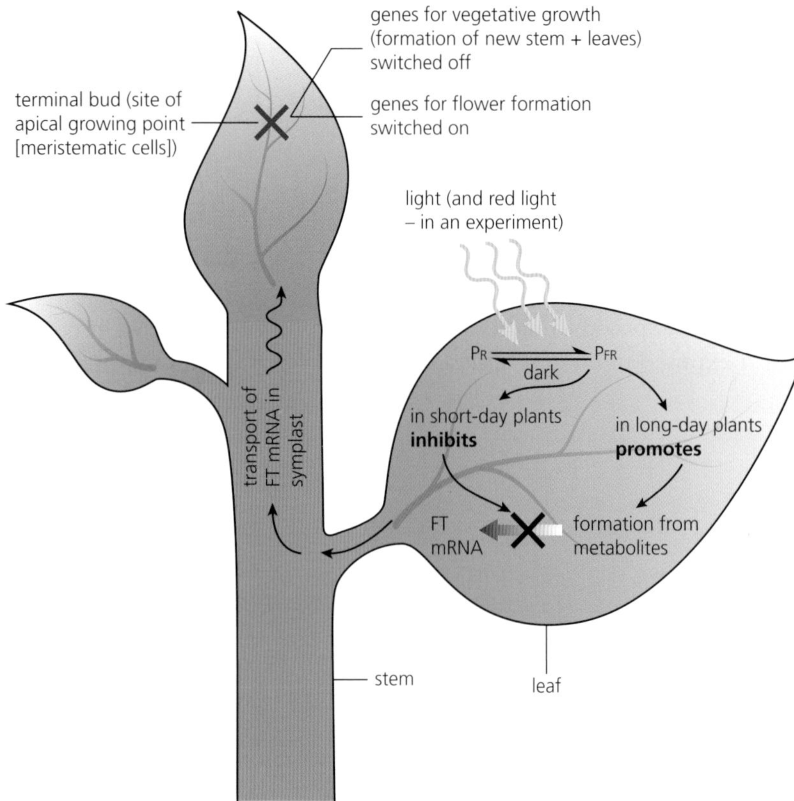

Figure 23.14 Phytochrome and flowering – the suggested model

Figure 23.14 shows the current model of how phytochrome may detect changes in day-length and so influence flowering. It is known that mRNA molecules and proteins, coded for by specific genes, can also function as growth substances. It is molecules of this sort that might be transported about the plant via the plasmodesmata and the symplast pathway. Currently it is suggested that a gene ('flowering locus' – *FT*) is activated in leaves of photoperiodically-induced plants. As a consequence, it is *FT* mRNA that then travels from induced leaves to stem apex. In the cells there, the *FT* mRNA is translated into *FT* protein. This protein, bonded to a transcription factor, activates several flowering genes and switches off the genes for vegetative growth.

Other responses to light are also likely to use phytochrome as their receptor:

- The synthesis of chlorophyll – plants kept in the dark have little chlorophyll but when exposed to light they quickly become green.
- The germination of some seeds is heavily influenced by exposure to red and far-red light.
- Plant leaves of the same species often have different size and shape when grown in low or bright light conditions.

Test yourself

18 What is 'far-red' light?

19 State which form of phytochrome will build up when the nights are much longer than the days.

20 Suggest what will cause shade leaves to have more chlorophyll content than brightly lit leaves.

Chapter summary

Homeostasis

- Homeostasis is the process by which living things control their internal environment at an optimum level. In mammals this involves accurate control of such things as body temperature and concentration of body fluids.
- Homeostasis often involves negative feedback mechanisms where the result of one action has a tendency to inhibit further action, like a heater tending to be switched off by a thermostat.

Chemical control in mammals

- Hormones are chemicals secreted from ductless glands and carried in the bloodstream. They have their effects on target organs that have the correct receptors.
- Hormones are broken down by the liver so need to be continuously secreted to maintain their effect.
- The two main types of hormones are amides/peptides and steroids.
- Amide/peptide hormones attach to receptors on the surface of cell membranes, triggering the release of a second messenger inside the cell, which then activates proteins to form active enzymes. Examples are ADH and adrenaline.
- Steroid hormones pass through membranes and attach to receptors inside the cell. This starts the formation of transcription factors that initiate the production of RNA coding for active enzymes. Examples are oestrogen and testosterone.
- An advantage of hormones is they can stimulate many effects at one time for a specific purpose. For example, adrenaline can increase heart rate, blood sugar levels and muscle tone in response to threats.

Chemical control in plants

- Plants have several 'growth substances' as many of their reactions are slower and often growth is the main form of response. Without a rapid transport system these are often produced close to their sites of action.
- Auxin (indole-3-acetic acid) has many effects. These include cell enlargement, control of leaf fall, fruit formation and promotion of root growth. Many of these effects are brought about in combination with other plant growth substances.
- Auxin formed at the tips of roots and shoots diffuses to the newly-formed meristematic cells, causing them to elongate. When light intensity is greater on one side the auxin is transported to the darker side. This causes the shoot to bend towards the light – positive phototropism.
- Cytokinins attach to receptor sites on meristematic cells and cause the release of transcription factors that stimulate cell division. They too have other effects, such as breaking dormancy and promoting lateral growth. They often interact with auxins.
- Gibberellins are formed in germinating seeds where they combine with DELLA proteins, which normally prevent transcription factors beginning germination. When the DELLA protein is combined with gibberellin this inhibition is released and enzymes such as amylase are synthesised to break down the starch stores in the seed.
- Phytochrome is a photoreceptor pigment in green plants. It exists in two forms, P660 and P730. The two forms are interconvertible as they absorb light of different wavelengths. When P660 is illuminated by red light (660 nm) it changes to P730 and vice-versa. In the dark or if illuminated by far-red light (730 nm) it reverts back to P660. A build up of either form of the pigment then triggers changes in development such as flowering at different times of year, as when nights are long more P660 will build up and when nights are short P730 will build up.

Practice questions

1 Mammals control their internal environment by a process called:

A homiopathy   **C** homozygosity

B homeostasis   **D** homeotrophy *(1)*

2 The actions of insulin and glucagon can be described as:

A agonistic   **C** symplastic

B synergistic   **D** antagonistic *(1)*

3 Which of the following pairs of plant growth substances act synergistically in their effects on cell enlargement?

A auxin and gibberellin   **C** cytokinin and auxin

B cytokinin and phytochrome   **D** gibberellin and phytochrome *(1)*

4 **a)** Explain how plant leaves can detect changes in the relative lengths of day and night. *(4)*

b) Explain why it is an advantage for some plants to flower as the nights become shorter and some plants to flower as nights become longer. *(3)*

Tip

Part (a) of Question 4 is simple recall (AO1) but good practice in organising your explanation to match the marks available. Part (b) asks you to apply your knowledge (AO2) with a little more thought.

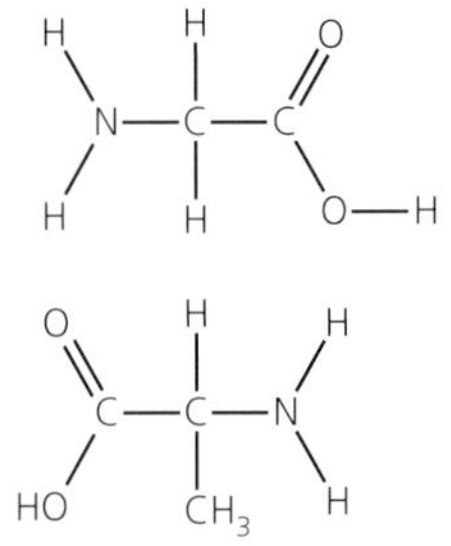

5 **a)** Steroids are compounds closely related to lipids but without their long fatty-acid chain. Explain why steroid hormones are able to pass through cell surface membranes but peptide hormones are not. *(2)*

b) Explain how peptide hormones can exert their effect without passing through the cell surface membrane. *(3)*

c) Insulin is a peptide. The diagram on the right shows two amino acid molecules. Draw a diagram to show how these two molecules would be joined to form a peptide. *(3)*

d) Hormone receptors are integral membrane proteins that are each specific to one molecule.

i) Explain what is meant by 'integral membrane proteins'. *(1)*

ii) Explain how the properties of proteins make them particularly suitable molecules to form large numbers of highly specific receptors. *(3)*

Tip

Question 5 is a synoptic question that illustrates the need for knowledge from all parts of the specification in a single question, and also encourages you to keep refreshing your knowledge of earlier sections of the course rather than relying on the much more difficult task of attempting to revise everything at once.

6 An investigation was carried out to determine the effect of reduced oxygen concentration on the action of gibberellin (GA_3), leading to the metabolism of starch stored in the endosperm of seeds such as oats. Ten identical oat seeds, with their embryos removed, were placed in each of five GA_3 solutions of different concentrations. These solutions were then incubated at 25 °C for 48 hours with a stream of oxygen bubbled through them. Samples of each solution were then taken and analysed for reducing sugar content. The investigation was then repeated with the solutions in a sealed container and no oxygenation. The results of the investigation are shown in the graph.

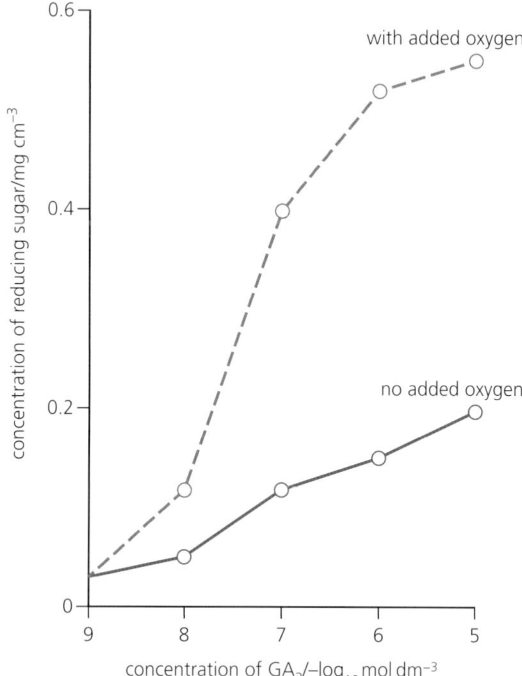

Tip

Question 6 is typical of the type of question you might expect in Paper 3. It requires some knowledge of Core practical 14 from this chapter but also other practical and mathematical skills. It does have a different application and it is less likely that you will get simple recall questions based on core practicals, rather than a test of your understanding of the principles. It is also a synoptic question as knowledge of other parts of the specification are needed for part c) ii). If you are uncertain about logarithms and scale this is also a good opportunity to check the data units in the graph.

a) Explain why it was necessary to remove the embryos from the seeds for this investigation. *(2)*

b) Explain how the action of GA_3 causes an increased concentration of reducing sugar in the solution. *(4)*

c) i) Use the data to calculate the percentage increase in reducing sugar in the solutions of $\log_{10} -5\,\text{mol}\,\text{dm}^{-3}$ GA_3 caused by the addition of oxygen. *(3)*

ii) Explain why a lack of oxygen will have the effect shown by these data. *(3)*

Stretch and challenge

7 Since the discovery of plant growth substances, many variations with similar effects have been produced artificially.

One of the most well-known examples of this is an artificial auxin (IAA) called 2-4,D (2-4 dichlorophenoxyacetic acid). This has been widely used as a selective weedkiller for grassland and lawns.

a i) What similarities are there between the two molecules that could result in similar effects in plants?

ii) Why produce artificial plant growth substances instead of using the original substance?

iii) Why is it important that there are similarities in the molecules if they are to act in a similar way?

iv) Why does watering a lawn with moderate doses of 2-4,D kill off broad-leaved weeds such as plantain and dandelion but not the narrow-leaved grass?

v) What was 'agent orange' and why has it caused concern?

b) i) Over half of the commercial varieties of grapes grown for worldwide consumption are now seedless. This is good for the preference of consumers but how can this be achieved biologically?

ii) 'Thompson' white grapes are the most popular variety found in supermarkets. Why would growers spray their crops with dilute solutions of gibberellins?

O
6
O
5
1
OH
4
Cl
2
Cl
3

2-4,D

O
OH
N
H

IAA

Coordination and control in action

Prior knowledge

In this chapter you will need to recall that:

- ➜ the mammalian eye has three layers – the inner retina, choroid and sclerotic coat
- ➜ the retina is the light-sensitive layer with connections to the optic nerve
- ➜ the retina is made up of rod and cone cells
- ➜ rod cells respond to black and white images, cones to colours
- ➜ rod cells contain a pigment called rhodopsin
- ➜ most images are focused on an area of the retina, opposite the centre of the lens, called the fovea
- ➜ the kidneys are responsible for controlling the concentration of body fluids and the excretion of urea
- ➜ urea is synthesised in the liver but removed by the kidneys
- ➜ kidneys are paired organs with a high-pressure blood supply directly from the main dorsal aorta
- ➜ kidneys are connected to the bladder by a tube called the ureter
- ➜ mammalian heart rate is controlled by nerves and hormones (Chapter 11)
- ➜ countercurrent flow increases total exchange by extending diffusion gradients (Chapter 10).

Test yourself on prior knowledge

1. State the function of the choroid layer of the eye.
2. Name the vitamin important for good vision.
3. State the name given to the point where the optic nerve joins the retina.
4. Explain how the eye is able to regulate the amount of light falling on the retina.
5. State what happens to rhodopsin when it absorbs light.
6. Describe the difference between urine and urea.
7. State the name given to the whole process of adjusting the contents of the blood in the kidney.
8. Suggest why it is important that kidneys are supplied with high-pressure blood.
9. Which hormone has the most important effect of increasing heart rate?
10. Give an example of a countercurrent exchange mechanism in gas exchange.

Introduction

In this chapter you will be looking at how several of the important concepts that you have met in previous chapters are employed to bring about control and coordination of major physiological activities. This relies on your knowledge of the content of Chapters 22 and 23 in this book and it is useful to review these carefully before continuing.

To understand how the kidney selectively reabsorbs substances before they are excreted, discussed at the end of this chapter, you will also need to be familiar with the principles of active transport, osmosis, diffusion and facilitated diffusion from Chapter 9. Once again, this provides an ideal opportunity to reinforce your knowledge of all of the course material in easy stages.

Detection of light by mammals

All control and coordinating mechanisms require information if they are to be effective. Sense organs are needed to detect any need for change and to monitor the results of any actions. This may be a need to respond extremely quickly to a threat from a predator or to coordinate long-term growth and development. You will look at examples of different types of sense organs later in this chapter but first you will consider the way in which mammals detect light.

Our example will be the human eye but it is important to remember that the eyes of other animals have even more remarkable adaptations according to their niche. Birds of prey, such as eagles, are able to focus on small prey from a height of several hundred metres and nocturnal animals have eyes adapted to the detection of very low light levels (but even they cannot 'see' in total darkness!).

Apart from obvious functions such as reading and navigating, vision is also a vital part of other functions such as balance. Just try balancing on one leg with your eyes closed!

Detection of light by the retina

The structure of the retina

Sense organs respond to certain stimuli and need to initiate action potentials if they are to communicate via the nervous system. This is the function of the retinal cells.

The retina of each eye is sensitive to light in the wavelength range 380–760 nm – that is, the visible range of the electromagnetic spectrum (the radiation from the Sun). The retina has two types of light-sensitive cell, the rods and cones, shown in Figure 24.1. These very elongated cells have an outer part called the outer segment. This consists of flattened membranous vesicles housing a light-sensitive pigment. An inner segment contains many mitochondria (the site of ATP formation).

Rods are far more numerous than cones; the human retina contains about 120 million rods compared with 6 million cones. Rods are distributed evenly throughout the retina, while cones are concentrated at and around a region called the **fovea**. This is an area where vision is most accurate – here there is the greatest density of photoreceptors. (Note that light passes through the neurones, synapsing with the rod and cone cells before reaching the outer segments of these cells. Because of this feature, the retina is described as 'inverted' (Figure 24.1).)

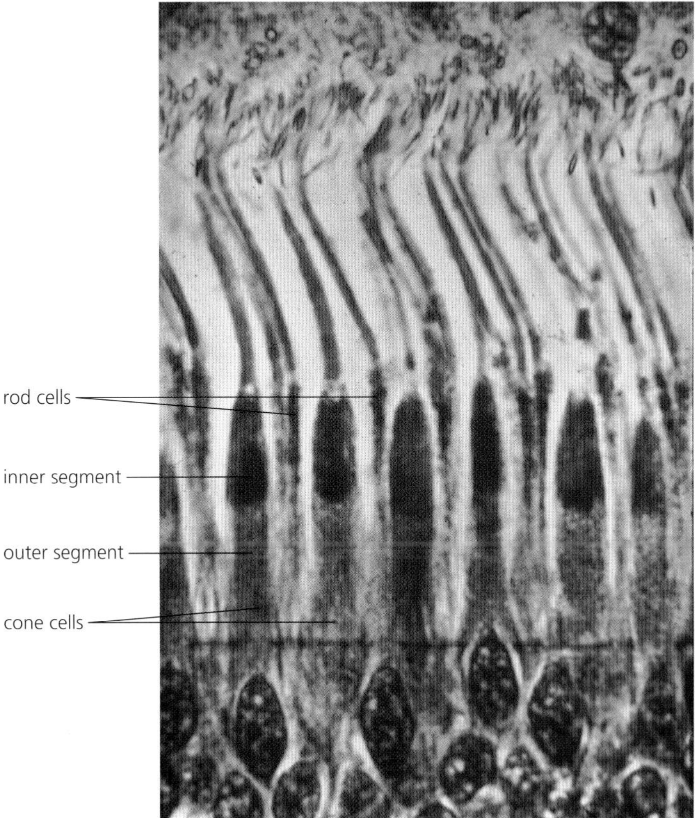

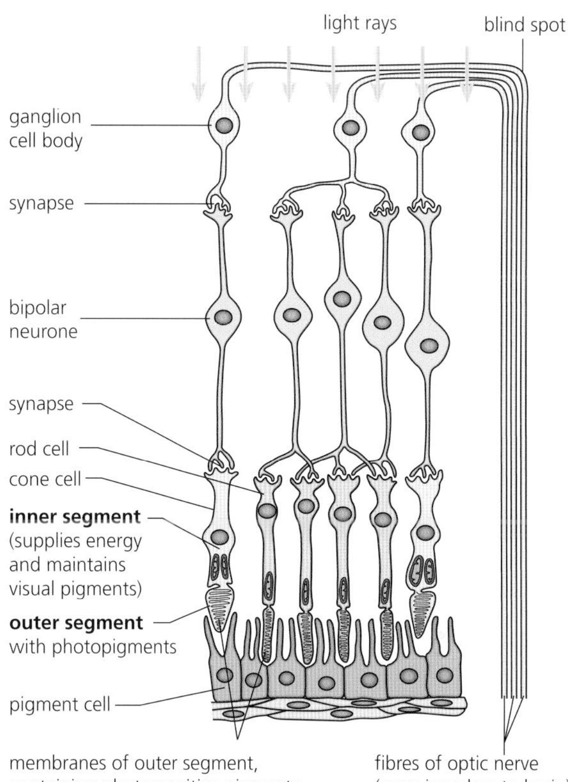

Figure 24.1 The structure of the retina

Rod cells are extremely sensitive to light, much more sensitive than the cones, but rod cells do not discriminate colours. Since they respond to lower light intensities than cones, they are principally used for dim light and night vision. The type of visual pigment molecules housed in the rods is called 'visual purple' or **rhodopsin**. This molecule is a combination of a protein (**opsin**) and a light-absorbing compound derived from vitamin A, called **retinal**. Remember, a diet deficient in vitamin A causes 'night blindness' – the inability to see in low light intensities. Figure 24.1 also shows that each cone cell synapses with only one optic nerve fibre whereas a single optic nerve fibre has synapses connecting it to several rod cells, a phenomenon known as **convergence**. This means that in bright light, cone cells can not only provide a coloured image but also a much more accurate image. However, convergence does have advantages as it means that light can be gathered from a larger area to produce an action potential in dim light.

The accuracy of the image is expressed as **visual acuity**. This is the ability of the eye to distinguish between two points close together. The visual acuity of the cones is much higher than that of rods. As points become increasingly closer and closer, there comes a time when they are so close that despite stimulating two different rods, these rods share the same optic nerve fibre so only one signal is sent to the brain, which interprets this as one point. Stimulation of two cones will always result in two separate impulses until the points are so close that they cover the same cone cell. This, and the tightly packed cones in the fovea, account for the sharp image formed in bright light.

Test yourself

1 Describe the position of the fovea on the retina.
2 Explain the term 'convergence'.
3 Suggest why convergence produces a low visual acuity.
4 State the breakdown products of rhodopsin.
5 If trying to observe a very faint star at night, it is a good idea to look to one side of the star, not directly towards it. Explain why.

Initiating action potentials in rod cells

The ways in which a rod cell responds to stimulation by light, and to its absence, are detailed in Figure 24.2.

Figure 24.2 The working rod cell

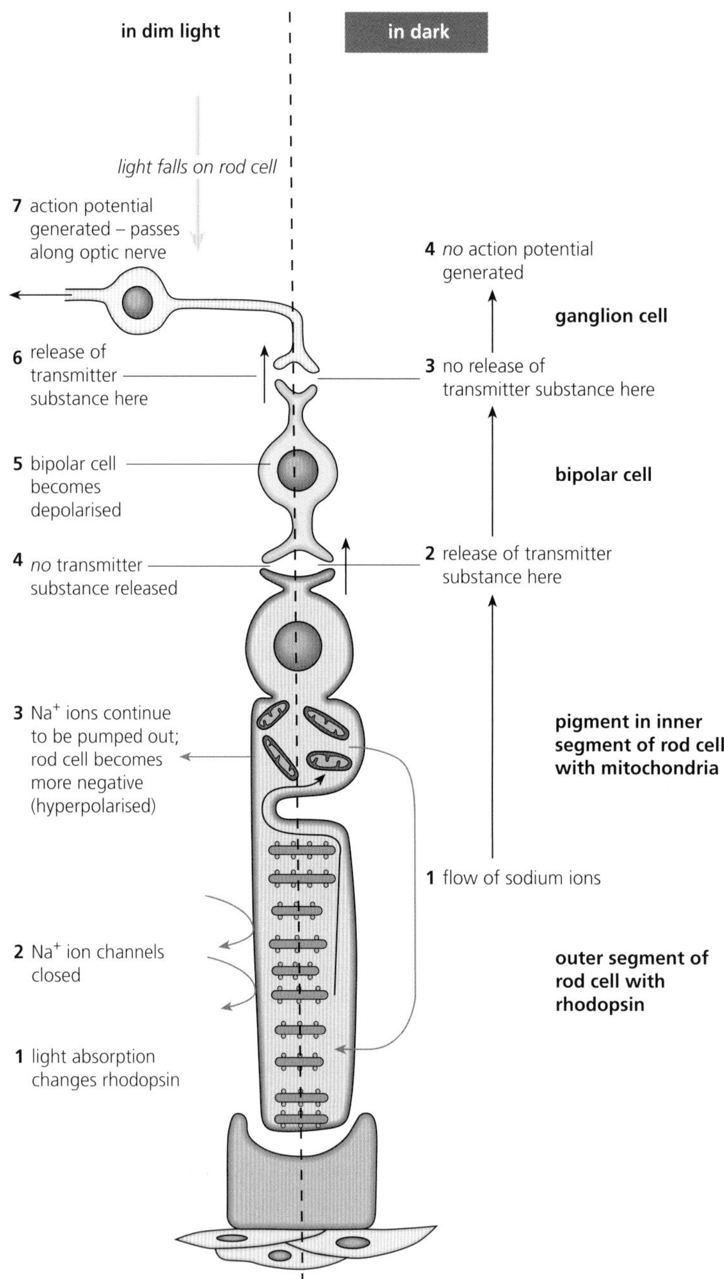

Follow the numbered steps in Figure 24.2 carefully as you read the text below.

Rod cells in the dark

In the dark, there is a steady flow of sodium ions into the outer segment, through open cation channels, located in the cell surface membrane. At the same time, the cell surface membrane of the inner segment reverses this movement of ions – sodium ions are continuously pumped out of the cell at this point. This efflux occurs at the expense of ATP formed in the mitochondria of the inner segment. Consequently a concentration gradient is maintained between outer and inner segments, down which the sodium ions flow. Meanwhile, the influx of sodium ions at the inner segment slightly depolarises the cell, and the potential difference across the cell surface membrane is about −40 mV (compared with a resting potential of −70 mV).

Under these conditions, the rod cell releases a neurotransmitter substance (glutamate) that binds to the bipolar cell and prevents its depolarisation. The consequence is that no action potential is generated in the optic nerve that synapses with that bipolar cell.

Rod cells in the light

When light falls on the retina, it causes reversible structural change in rhodopsin (called 'bleaching'), breaking it down into retinal and opsin. Opsin now functions as an enzyme that activates a series of reactions resulting in the closing of the cation channels of the outer segment, and so the influx of sodium ions is blocked. Meanwhile the inner segment continues to pump out sodium ions. This causes the interior of the rod cell to become more negative – a state described as **hyperpolarisation**. In this condition, no neurotransmitter is released by the rod cell, and the bipolar cell becomes depolarised.

The bipolar cell releases a transmitter substance. An action potential is generated in a neurone of the optic nerve serving the rod cell. This action potential is transmitted to the visual cortex of the brain.

Meanwhile, the structure of rhodopsin is rebuilt, using energy from ATP. In very bright light, all the rhodopsin is bleached. In these conditions you are using cone cells, and the state of the visual pigment in rod cells is not of immediate consequence. In fact, you are not aware your rods cells are temporarily non-functional. But if you move suddenly from bright to very dim light it takes time for sufficient reversing of bleaching to occur, and you are temporarily blinded. We say your eyes are 'adapting to the dark'.

The presence of both rods and cones means that the brain is able to form an image in a wide range of light intensities. Even though the image in low-light conditions is less accurate and not coloured, a retina of cones only would leave you blind in anything other than bright daylight so this is a good compromise.

The role of cone cells

Animals that have cone cells in their retinas are able to distinguish colours. It is not the case for all mammals, but the human eye does contain cones, concentrated in the fovea where light is most sharply focused. Cone cells operate on the same principle as the rod cells, but with a different pigment, called **iodopsin**. This is less readily broken down; it needs more light energy. Cones work only in high light intensities; we cannot see colours in dim light.

According to the **trichromatic theory** of colour vision, there are three types of cone cell present in the retina, each with a different form of iodopsin. These absorb different wavelengths of light – in the blue, green and red regions of the spectrum. White light stimulates all three types equally, but different colours are produced by the relative degree of stimulation of the three types of cone.

Processing action potentials from the retina

Observations of the three-dimensional world around you are reduced to two-dimensional images on the surface of the retina. As a consequence, action potentials generated in the rods and cones are carried by neurones of the optic nerves to the visual cortex of the brain. While each eye views left and right sides of the visual field, the brain receives and interprets action potentials from the right and left visual fields on the opposite side of the visual cortex. This is known as **contralateral processing** (Figure 24.3).

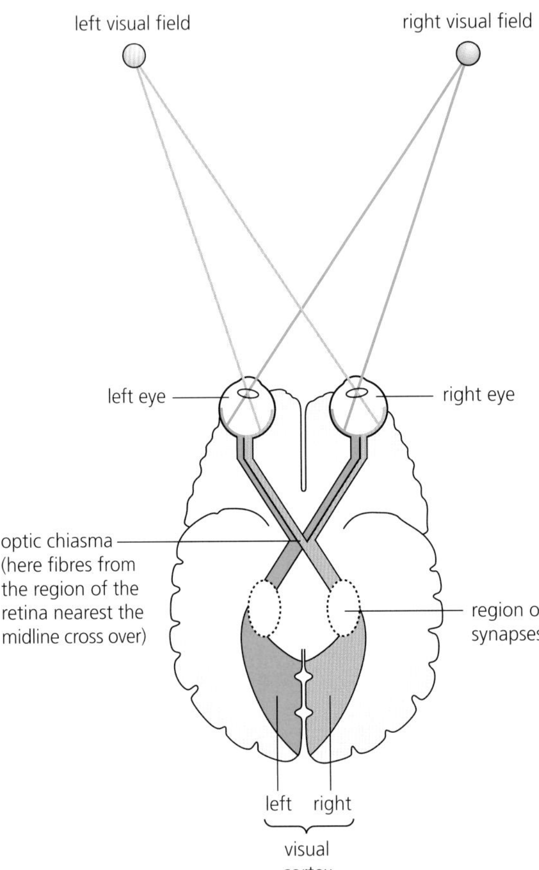

Figure 24.3 The eye and the visual cortex – the pathways of impulses

The messages from interpretation of these action potentials are combined by the brain to produce a single impression – your sight. 'Seeing', therefore, occurs largely in the brain, and the seeing process, known as **perception**, is complex. This is because perception involves the interpretation of sensory data from the retina in terms of existing and past experiences and your expectations. The phenomenon of perception has implications for the nature and reliability of visual sense data, too (and, therefore, for the processes of science).

Test yourself

6 Glutamate binds to receptors to produce small IPSPs (inhibitory post synaptic potentials) (see nervous transmission, Chapter 22). Explain why these IPSPs prevent depolarisation of the bipolar cell.

7 Name the breakdown product of iodopsin that triggers reactions which block the influx of Na^+ ions into the outer segment.

8 In normal daylight almost all visual information received by the brain comes from cones in the fovea. Explain why this is.

9 Suggest why iodopsin is more difficult to break down than rhodopsin.

Control of heart rate in mammals

The control of heart rate is an example of control using the autonomic nervous system. You have looked at the detailed structure of this system in Chapter 22 of this book and this is a good time to refresh your memory.

The heart beats rhythmically throughout life, without rest, apart from the momentary relaxation between beats. Even more remarkably, the origin of each beat is within the heart itself – we say that heart beat is **myogenic** in origin.

The heart beat originates in a structure in the muscle of the wall of the right atrium, called the **sino-atrial node** (**SAN**), also known as the natural pacemaker. Muscle fibres radiating out from the SAN conduct impulses to the muscles of both atria, triggering atrial systole (contraction).

Then a second node, the **atrio-ventricular node** (**AVN**) situated at the base of the right atrium picks up the excitation and passes it to the ventricles through modified muscle fibres, called the **Purkyne fibres** (Figure 24.4). Ventricular systole is then triggered.

After every contraction, cardiac muscle has a period of insensitivity to stimulation, known as a **refractory period** (in effect, a period of enforced non-contraction, which we may call a 'rest'), when the heart refills with blood. This period is a relatively long one in heart muscle, and doubtless an important feature, enabling the heart to beat throughout life.

The heart's own rhythm, set by the SAN, is about 50 beats per minute, but it is essential that this can be modified according to the ever-changing demands of the body. In humans this can vary from about 70 beats per minute at rest, to about 200 beats per minute during very strenuous exercise.

Tip

Although we shall give a brief summary of the transmission of impulses through cardiac muscle by the SAN and AVN here, more details of this process and the sequence of events in one heartbeat have been discussed in Chapter 11. This is another ideal opportunity to revise work covered earlier in your course and to make links with other parts of the specification in preparation for synoptic questions in the examination papers.

Key term

Myogenic Activity that originates within muscles rather than through the nervous system.

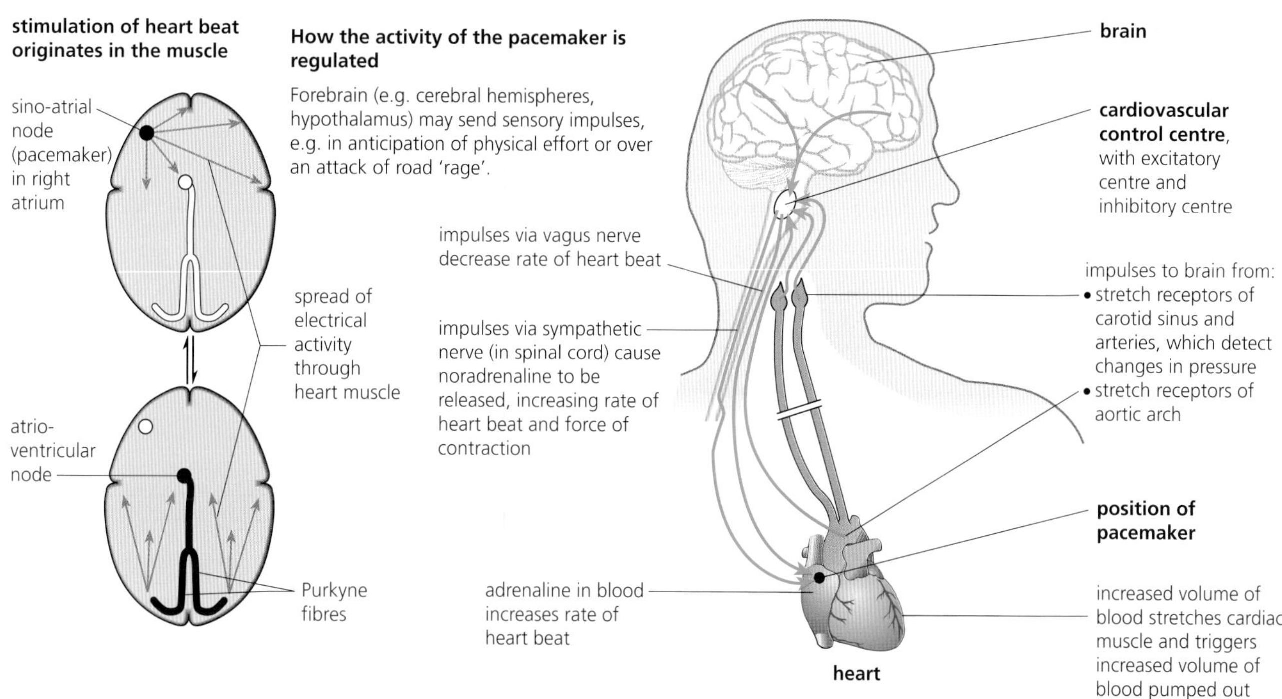

stimulation of heart beat originates in the muscle
sino-atrial node (pacemaker) in right atrium
spread of electrical activity through heart muscle
atrio-ventricular node
Purkyne fibres
How the activity of the pacemaker is regulated
Forebrain (e.g. cerebral hemispheres, hypothalamus) may send sensory impulses, e.g. in anticipation of physical effort or over an attack of road 'rage'.
impulses via vagus nerve decrease rate of heart beat
impulses via sympathetic nerve (in spinal cord) cause noradrenaline to be released, increasing rate of heart beat and force of contraction
adrenaline in blood increases rate of heart beat
brain
cardiovascular control centre, with excitatory centre and inhibitory centre
impulses to brain from:
• stretch receptors of carotid sinus and arteries, which detect changes in pressure
• stretch receptors of aortic arch
position of pacemaker
increased volume of blood stretches cardiac muscle and triggers increased volume of blood pumped out
heart

Figure 24.4 Control of heart rate

The main centre for control of heart rate is situated in the **cardiovascular centre** in the **medulla** of the hindbrain (see Chapter 22). This has both a cardiac inhibitory region and a cardiac accelerator region.

The heart receives impulses from the cardiovascular centre via two nerves:

- a sympathetic nerve, part of the sympathetic nervous system, from the accelerator centre
- a branch of the **vagus nerve**, part of the parasympathetic nervous system, from the inhibitory centre.

Since the sympathetic nerve and the vagus nerve have opposite effects in this matter of regulation of heart beat, we say they are **antagonistic** – a typical feature of the sympathetic and parasympathetic systems.

Key terms

Stretch receptors Sensory receptors that initiate action potentials in response to changes in tension. Also called baroreceptors.

Chemoreceptors Sensory receptors that initiate action potentials in response to changes in their chemical environment.

In order to respond correctly the cardiovascular centre needs information from sense organs. For example, it receives impulses from **stretch receptors** (baroreceptors) located in the walls of the aorta, in the carotid arteries and in the wall of the right atrium, when changes in blood pressure occur at these positions.

When blood pressure is high in the arteries, the rate of heart beat is lowered by impulses from the cardiovascular centre, via the vagus nerve. When blood pressure is low, the rate of heart beat is increased.

The oxygenation of the blood is also a strong factor in controlling heart rate. **Chemoreceptors** in the main arteries also provide information to the cardiac centre through sensory nerves. These are sensitive to pH levels. Rising carbon dioxide levels in the blood lower the pH during exercise and trigger impulses, which stimulate the cardiac accelerator centre and increase impulses in the sympathetic nerve.

The rate of heart beat is also influenced by impulses from the higher centres of the brain. For example, emotion, stress and anticipation of events can all cause impulses from the sympathetic nerve to speed up heart rate.

As was suggested in Chapter 23, there is a close link between nervous and endocrine control to bring about a coordinated response. The peptide hormone **adrenaline** (**epinephrine**) produced by the adrenal medulla has a powerful effect on raising heart rate. This link is also underlined by the fact that a very closely related chemical **noradrenaline** (**norepinephrine**) is produced by sympathetic neurones and has the same effect as adrenaline on the heart. The parasympathetic vagus nerve releases the neurotransmitter **acetylcholine** in bringing about its inhibitory effect.

Both acetylcholine and noradrenaline are released by their respective autonomic neurones at the SAN.

Test yourself

10 Explain why the stimulation of the heart is said to be 'myogenic'.

11 State which division of the autonomic nervous system increases heart rate.

12 Which part of the brain contains the cardiovascular centre?

13 Describe the sensory information received by the cardiovascular centre.

Temperature regulation

The regulation of body temperature, known as **thermoregulation**, involves controlling the amount of heat lost and heat gained through the skin surface. Heat may be transferred between an animal and the environment by **convection**, **radiation** and **conduction**. These processes are summarised in Figure 24.5.

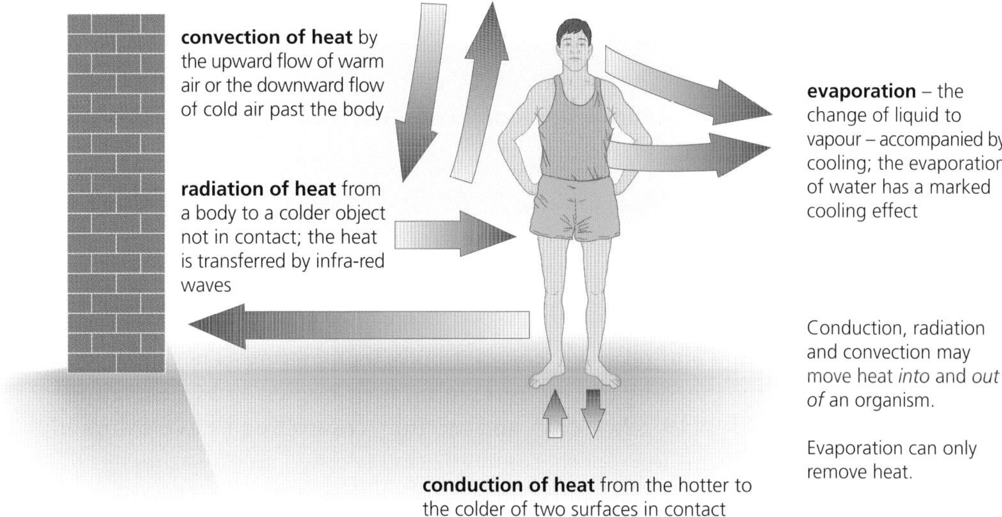

Figure 24.5 How heat is transferred between an organism and its surroundings

Body temperature of fish and reptiles

Fish are unable to regulate their body temperature. The huge gill surface area over which water moves continuously for gaseous exchange (see Chapter 10) is also an efficient heat exchanger! In fish, the temperature inside the body is approximately the same as the temperature of their surroundings. This is because any body heat is quickly lost to the surroundings. In relation to thermoregulation, fish are good examples of 'non-regulators'.

On the other hand, the air-breathing land animals, reptiles, do have a crude form of body temperature control, at least when they are active and alert. Lizards and snakes are good examples (Figure 24.6).

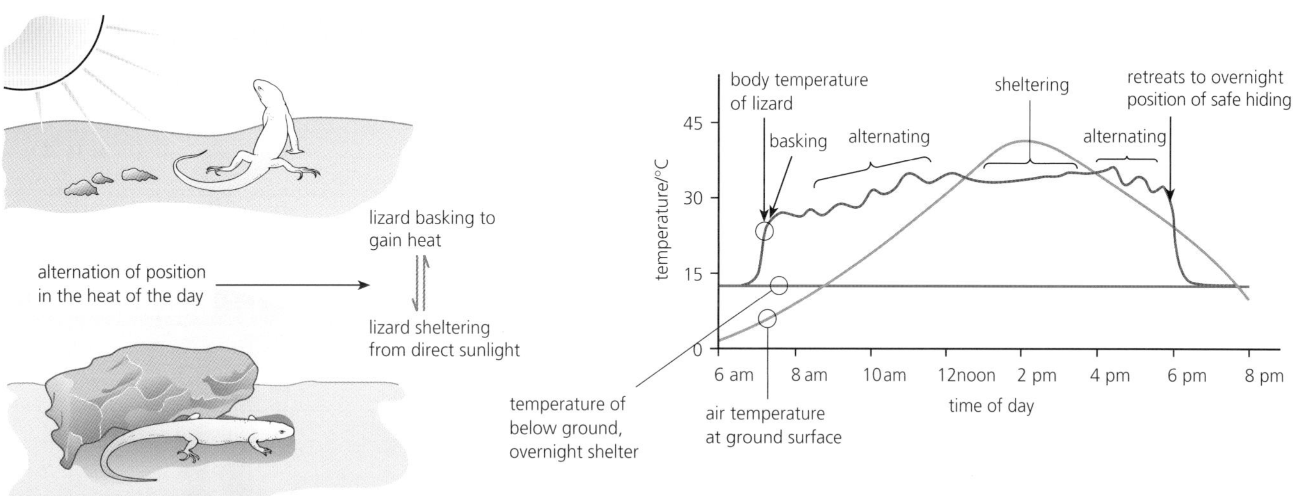

Figure 24.6 Thermoregulation in an ectotherm

Here, control is exercised by behavioural changes to take in heat as needed, exploiting any heat available in the external environment. In the morning, the animals 'bask' in sunlight to warm up. Then, for the remainder of the day, they move into and out of sunlight to absorb more or less heat according to their need. At night and over winter, their body temperature drops with that of the environment, and they become sluggish or even totally inactive.

Key term

Ectotherm An organism that relies on external heat sources for thermoreguation.

An animal with this form of thermoregulation is called an **ectotherm**, meaning 'outside heat'. During warm days an ectotherm may achieve a closely regulated body temperature. However, the kind of places where ectotherms can typically live is more restricted, as is their lifestyle. They are also very vulnerable to mammal and bird predators during cold times. Reptiles are found commonly in only a few of the wide range of habitats that mammals have mastered.

(Note: the old term 'cold blooded' to describe fish and reptile body temperature is now avoided, as is the term 'warm blooded' for birds and mammals.)

Thermoregulation in mammals

Key term

Endotherm An animal that relies on heat energy generated by internal metabolism for thermoregulation.

Mammals maintain a high and relatively constant body temperature. They achieve this by using heat energy generated by metabolism within their bodies, or by generating additional heat in their muscles when cold, and carefully controlling heat loss through the skin. An animal with this form of thermoregulation is called an **endotherm**, meaning 'inside heat'. Birds as well as mammals have perfected this mechanism. For example, humans hold their inner body temperature ('core temperature') just below 37 °C. In fact, in a human who is in good health the body's inner temperature varies only between about 35.5 and 37 °C within a 24 hour period (Figure 24.7). When the external temperature is low, however, only the temperature of the trunk is held constant. The body temperature falls progressively from the trunk towards the end of the limbs.

Body temperature over a 48 hour period
The body temperatures shown were taken with the thermometer under the tongue. Although this is a region close to the body 'core', temperatures here may be altered by eating/drinking, and by the breathing in through the mouth of cold air, for example. More accurate values are obtained by taking rectal temperature.

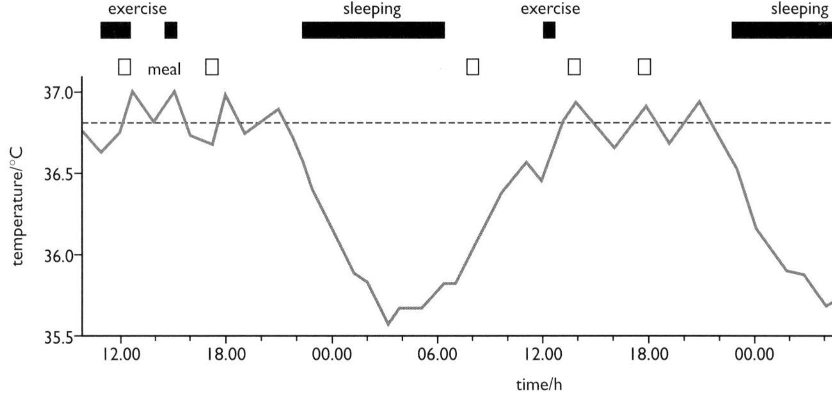

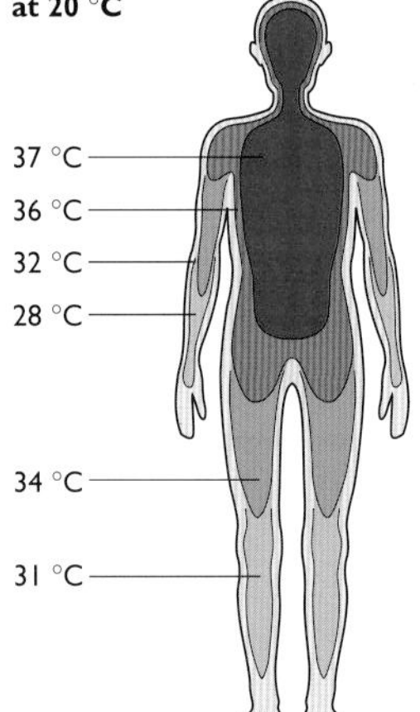

Temperature distribution in environments at 20 °C and at 35 °C
The lines, **isotherms**, connect sites of equal temperature. The shaded area is the core, and around this the temperatures varies according to the temperature of the surrounding air (**ambient temperature**).

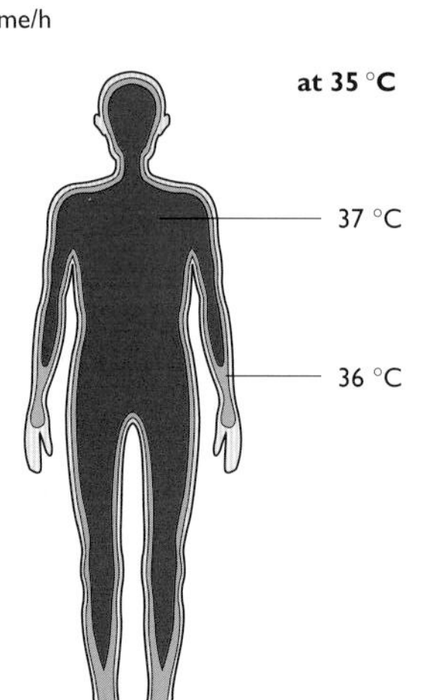

Figure 24.7 Body temperature of a human

Heat production in the human body

The major sources of heat in endotherms are the biochemical reactions of metabolism, which generate heat as a waste product. From the site of production, this heat reaches the rest of the body through the blood vessels. The organs of the body vary greatly in the amount of heat they produce. For example, the liver is extremely active metabolically, but most of its metabolic reactions require an input of energy (that is, they are endothermic reactions), so little energy is lost as heat. In consequence, the liver is more or less thermally neutral.

The bulk of your body heat (over 70 per cent) comes from other abdominal organs – mainly from the heart and kidneys, but also from the brain and lungs. In contrast, when the body is at rest, the skeleton, muscles and skin, which make up over 90 per cent of the body mass, produce less than 30 per cent of the body heat (Figure 24.8).

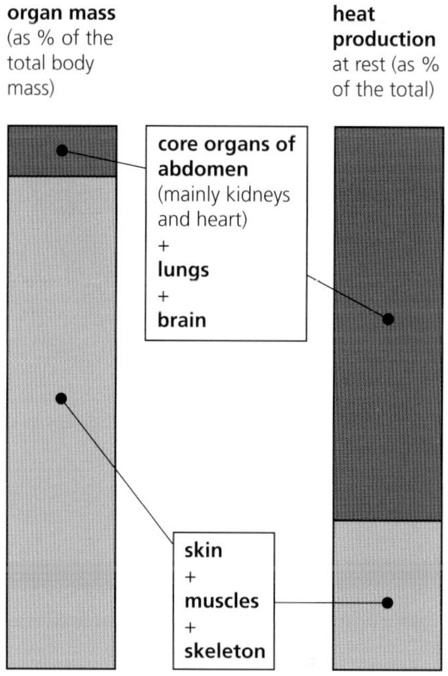

Figure 24.8 Heat production in the body at rest

The role of the skin in thermoregulation

Heat exchanges occur at the skin. The outer layer of the skin, the epidermis, consists of stratified epithelium. The cells in its basal layer (called the **Malpighian layer**) constantly divide, pushing the cells above them towards the skin surface. These upper cells are progressively flattened and the cell contents turn into keratin. The outermost layer of cells is continuously being rubbed off, but replaced from beneath so it does not wear away.

Below this layer is the dermis. This is a much thicker layer that consists of elastic connective tissue. In the dermis are blood capillaries, the hair follicles with hair erector muscles and the sweat glands. The sense receptors and sensory nerve endings are also found in this layer, and these are especially numerous in certain parts of the skin, which are consequently very sensitive.

At the base of the dermis is **adipose tissue**. In a mammal this is one of the major sites of fat storage. This tissue has a limited blood supply and is a poor conductor of heat, so it insulates internal organs against heat loss. Aquatic mammals that inhabit cold waters, such as whales and seals, have an extremely thick layer of fat stored below the skin (known as blubber), which they maintain throughout life. Terrestrial mammals that remain active through the unfavourable season of the year also tend to build up their fat here, mostly as a food store but also to provide insulation.

The amount of heat loss through the skin can be varied to control body temperature, for example:

- **at capillary networks:** the arterioles supplying them are widened (**vasodilation**) when the body needs to lose heat, but constricted (**vasoconstriction**) when it needs to retain heat
- **by the hair erector muscles:** these contract when heat must be retained, raising the hairs to trap a thicker layer of insulating air, but relax when more heat needs to be lost
- **by the sweat glands:** these produce sweat only when heat needs to be lost. The evaporation of the liquid sweat into vapour requires significant amounts of heat energy (specific latent heat of vaporisation), which is taken from the skin.

These mechanisms are shown in Figure 24.9 on the next page.

Key terms

Malpighian layer The basal layer of the epidermis of the skin, in which cells are constantly dividing by mitosis.

Adipose tissue Groups of cells containing large fat stores.

Vasodilation The widening of arteries and arterioles in the circulatory system.

Vasoconstriction The narrowing of arteries and arterioles in the circulatory system.

structure of the skn

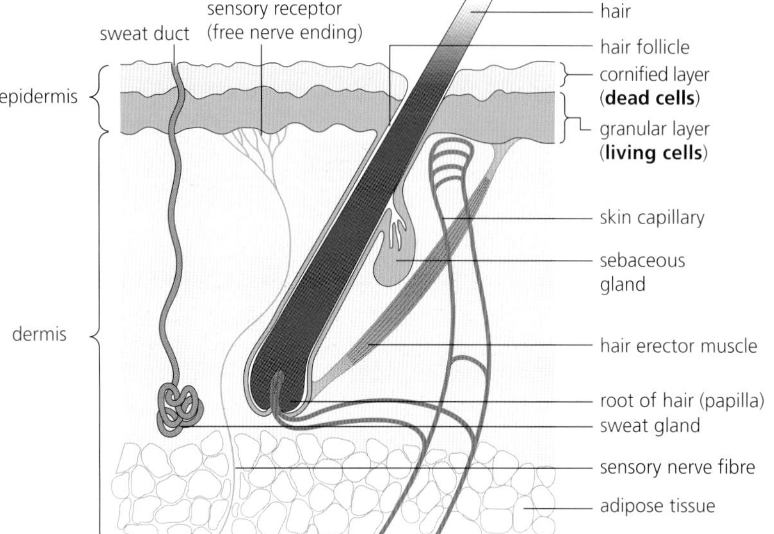

role of the sweat glands in regulating heat loss through the skin

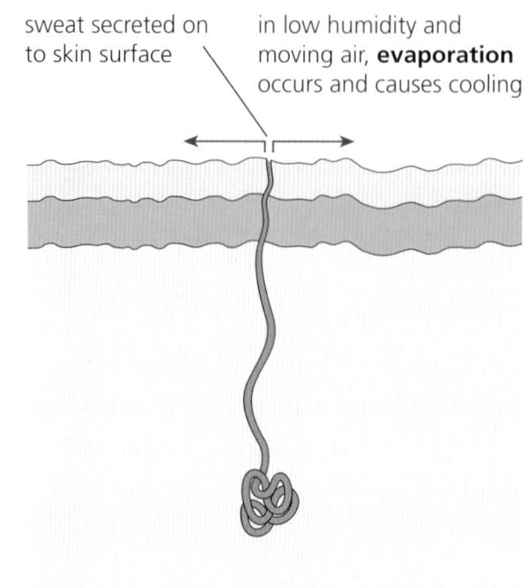

role of capillaries in regulating heat loss through the skin

In skin that is especially exposed (e.g. outer ear, nose, extremities of the limbs) the capillary network is extensive, and the arterioles supplying it can be dilated or constricted.

warm conditions

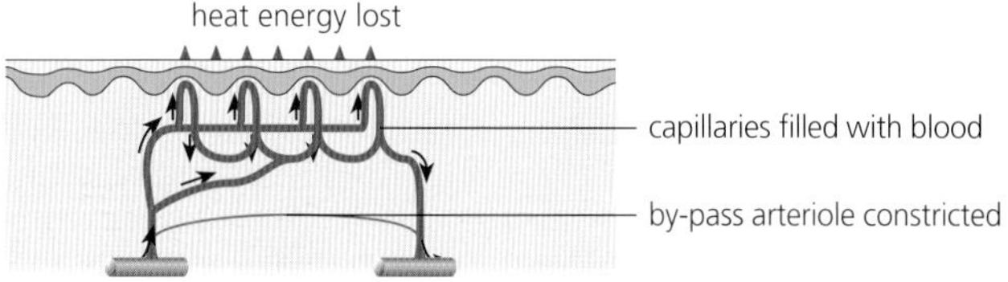

cold conditions

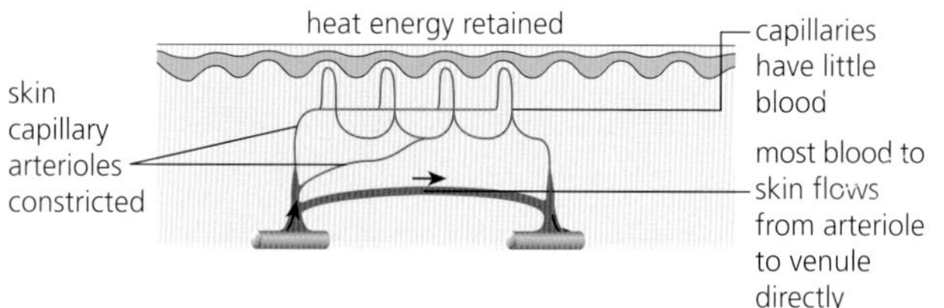

role of the hair in regulating heat loss through the skin

warm conditions

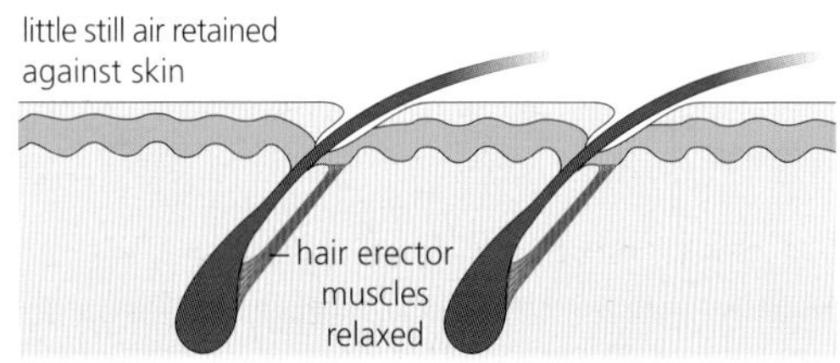

The hair erector muscles may be contracted or relaxed.

Still air is a poor conductor of heat.

cold conditions

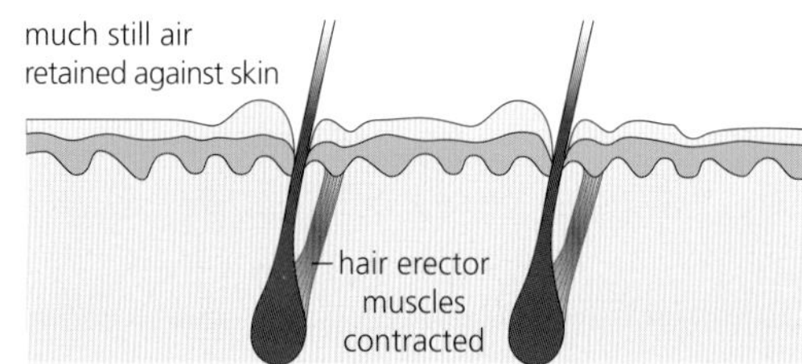

Figure 24.9 The skin and temperature regulation

Test yourself

14 Suggest why 'cold blooded' is a poor scientific term to describe ectotherms.

15 State the source of heat for endotherms.

Other mechanisms of thermoregulation

Changing metabolic rate

If a mammal's body experiences persistently cold conditions then its heat production is increased. The rate of heat release by an organism at rest is dependent on its basal metabolic rate (BMR). This is under the control of two hormones. In the short term it is regulated as another of the roles of the hormone adrenaline. In the longer term it is controlled by the actions of the hormone thyroxine, which is secreted by the thyroid glands (see Figure 23.3, page 477).

A specialised site of metabolic heat production is tissue known as brown fat, which is found in patches in the thorax of many mammals. The role of brown fat is to generate heat. When tissue is stimulated by sympathetic nerves, respiration of glucose formed from surrounding fat reserves is speeded up. The ATP formed in the brown fat cells is immediately hydrolysed to ADP and P_i, and all the free energy of this reaction is released as heat and circulated by the blood.

If conditions are persistently hot the metabolic rate is reduced.

Behaviour changes

Under chilly conditions, heat output from body muscles increases. Live muscle has a firm solid feel, which is known as muscle tone. This is caused by many tiny contractions within the muscle and is normally used to maintain posture. These contractions are distinct from those used to move the skeleton and can be speeded up to increase the production of heat all over the body. Further uncontrolled contractions, known as shivering, are also triggered in cold conditions. This shivering can raise muscle heat production to about five times its resting value.

In contrast, panting is a very efficient method of losing heat. It is used by mammals such as dogs, which have a pronounced snout to make it effective and have fur, which prevents effective sweating. In this method air is drawn in through the nose and mouth and expelled over the moist tongue. As with sweating, the evaporation of moisture requires heat, which is taken from the blood vessels in the tongue, to cool the body.

Other behavioural changes used to regulate heat include simply moving to a hotter or colder place, huddling together with other individuals, or becoming vigorously active to generate even more muscle heat. In addition, humans carefully adjust the type of clothing they wear to match the prevailing environmental conditions.

Key terms

Basal metabolic rate (BMR) The rate of heat release by metabolic reactions when an organism is at rest.

Thyroxine A hormone produced by the thyroid gland that regulates basal metabolic rate and therefore has a long-term effect on growth and development.

Brown fat cells Groups of cells around the thorax of mammals capable of releasing heat using very high rates of respiration.

The hypothalamus as a control centre

In a direct parallel to the role of the medulla in control of heart rate, a region of the forebrain called the hypothalamus contains the thermoregulatory centre. The hypothalamus has a 'heat loss centre' and a 'heat gain centre'. The thermoregulatory centre receives information from temperature-sensitive nerve endings monitoring blood temperature in the hypothalamus itself, as well as others found in the skin and many major organs.

The hypothalamus communicates with the rest of the body using the autonomic nervous system with its antagonistic divisions of sympathetic and parasympathetic neurones. These effects are shown in Figure 24.10 on the next page.

Key term

Hypothalamus A region of the forebrain controlling many important autonomic functions. Closely connected to the pituitary gland.

If the body temperature is lower than normal, the heat-gain centre inhibits the activity of the heat loss centre. Impulses are sent down sympathetic nerves to skin, hair erector muscles, sweat glands and elsewhere to initiate actions to decrease heat loss (for example vasoconstriction, shivering and increased brown fat respiration). When the body temperature is higher than normal the heat-loss centre inhibits the heat-gain centre and impulses are sent to the same organs but through parasympathetic nerves, which initiate actions to increase heat loss (for example vasodilation, sweat production and inhibiting brown fat respiration).

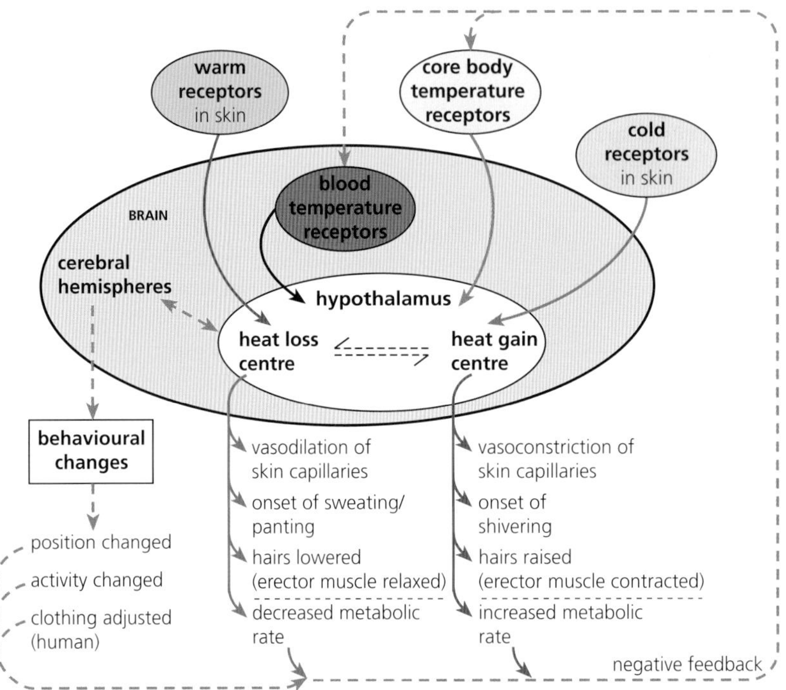

Figure 24.10 Temperature regulation by the hypothalamus

Test yourself

16 Respiration produces ATP. What is the fate of ATP in brown fat cells.

17 Explain why sweating causes cooling.

18 State which division of the autonomic system initiates heat gain.

Activity

How do we know that there are hot and cold receptors in the skin?

Carrying out the investigation

Aim: To demonstrate the effect of hot and cold skin receptors.

This is a very simple method but an excellent demonstration of both detection and perception of stimuli.

Take three small beakers. Fill each about three quarters full of water at different temperatures. Fill the first one with iced water containing an ice cube, the second with water as hot as a hot bath and the third with tepid water that feels just very slightly warm.

Place your left index finger in the cold water and your right index finger in the hot water for 1 minute.

Then quickly transfer both fingers into the tepid water and record the sensation from each one.

Question

1 Why do both fingers give different sensations when in water at the same temperature?

Osmoregulation and excretion in the kidneys

Urea formation in the liver

In animals, excess proteins and amino acids cannot be stored as they would be too disruptive. Instead they are broken down by a process called **deamination** (because the first step is the removal of the amino groups). This process must happen without the release of free ammonia within the tissues. This is because ammonia is both very toxic and very soluble. To achieve the breakdown safely, cells in the liver convert amino groups into **urea**, which is a relatively harmless product that can be safely transported in the blood to the kidneys, where it is excreted. The deamination process is summarised in Figure 24.11.

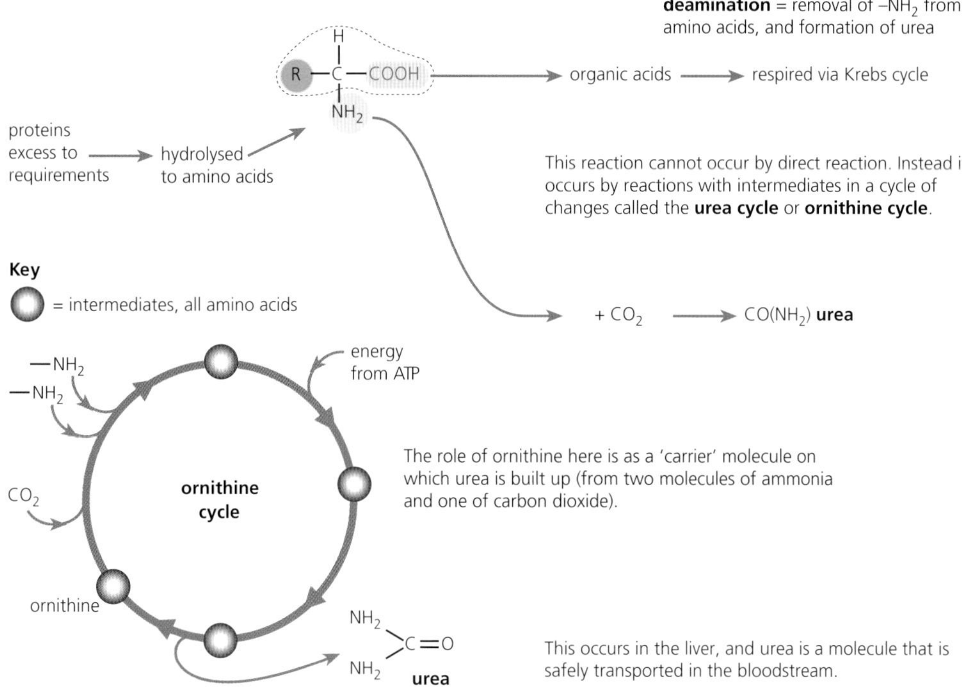

Figure 24.11 Deamination of excess amino acids

Key terms

Deamination The biochemical process of breaking down excess amino acids by removal of amino groups , ultimately producing urea.

Urea An excretory nitrogen-containing compound of low-toxicity produced by deamination of amino acids in the liver of mammals and some other animals (not to be confused with urine).

Urine A solution of urea, mineral ions and some other metabolic wastes excreted by the kidneys (not to be confused with urea).

Ureter The tube carrying urine from the kidney to the bladder (not to be confused with the urethra).

Urethra The tube carrying urine from the bladder to the exterior (not to be confused with the ureter).

Structure and function of the kidneys

The kidneys regulate the internal environment by constantly adjusting the composition of the blood. The waste products of metabolism are transported from the metabolising cells by the blood circulation, removed from the blood in the kidneys, and excreted in a solution called **urine**. The concentration of inorganic ions such as Na^+ and Cl^- are also regulated by the kidneys.

The position of the kidneys in humans is shown in Figure 24.12. Each kidney is served by a renal artery and drained by a renal vein. Urine from the kidney is carried to the bladder by the **ureter**, and then, at intervals, to the exterior by the **urethra**, when the bladder sphincter muscle is relaxed.

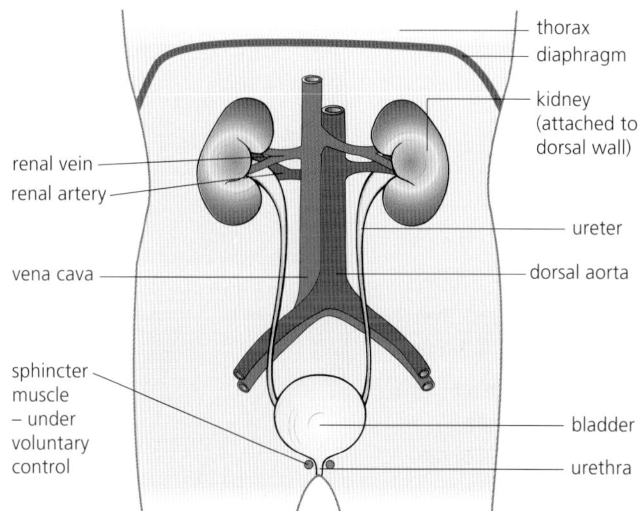

Figure 24.12 The human urinary system

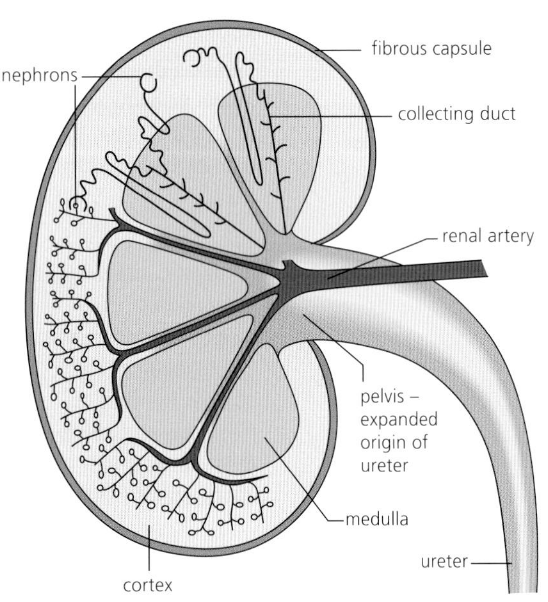

Roles of the parts of the nephron:

1 Bowman's capsule + glomerulus = ultrafiltration
2 proximal convoluted tubule = selective reabsorption from filtrate
3 loop of Henle = water conservation
4 distal convoluted tubule = pH adjustment and ion reabsorption
5 collecting duct = water reabsorption

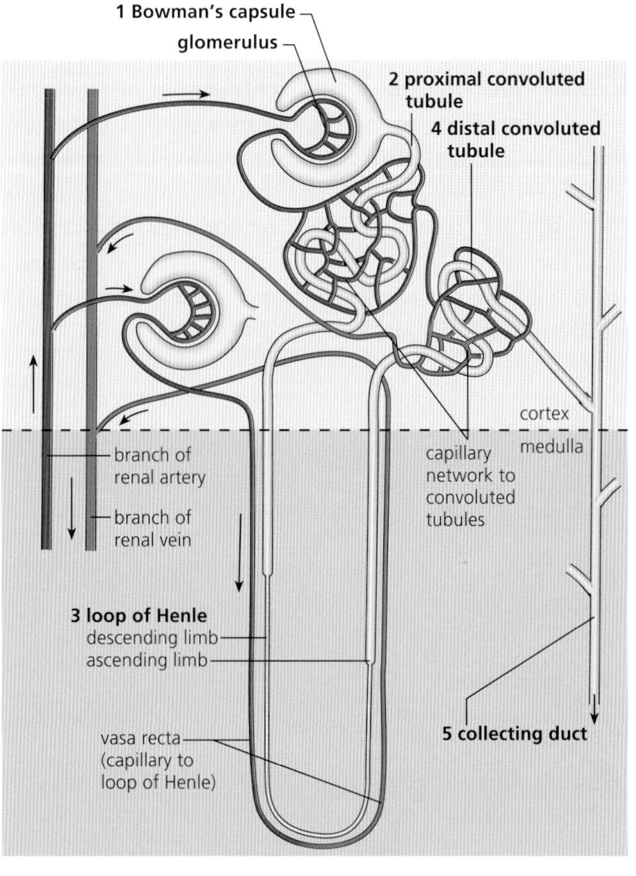

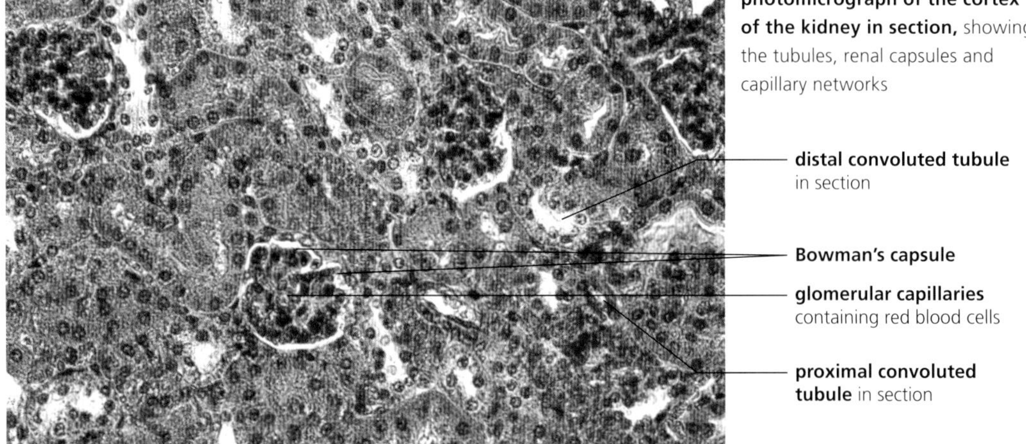

Figure 24.13 The kidney and its nephron – structure and roles

Key terms

Cortex (kidney) The outer part of the kidney.

Medulla (kidney) The inner part of the kidney.

Nephrons Fine tubules that make up the functional units of the kidney.

In section, a kidney can be seen to consist of an outer **cortex** and inner **medulla**. These are made up of more than a million tiny tubules called **nephrons**, together with their blood supply. Part of the nephron is in the cortex and part is in the medulla (see Figure 24.13). A nephron is a thin-walled tube about 3 cm long. Capillary networks associated with the nephron are crucial to its function.

The formation of urine

In humans, about 1.0–1.5 litres of urine is formed each day, typically containing about 40–50 g of solutes, of which **urea** (about 30 g) and **sodium chloride** (up to 15 g) make up the bulk. The nephron produces urine in a continuous process, which can be conveniently divided into five steps to show how the blood composition is so precisely regulated.

Step 1: Ultrafiltration in the renal capsule

In the glomerulus, water and relatively small molecules of the blood plasma, including useful ions, glucose and amino acids, are forced out of the capillaries, along with urea, into the lumen of the capsule. This is described as **ultrafiltration** because it is powered by the pressure of the blood, which drives substances through an extremely fine sieve-like structure.

> **Key term**
>
> **Ultrafiltration** The process by which small molecules are forced out of the capillaries in the capsule of the kidney by high blood pressure.

The **blood pressure** here is high enough for ultrafiltration because the input capillary (afferent arteriole) is wider than the output capillary (efferent arteriole). The 'sieve' is made of two layers of cells (the endothelium of the capillaries of the glomerulus and the epithelium of the capsule), between which is a basement membrane. You can see this arrangement in Figure 24.14.

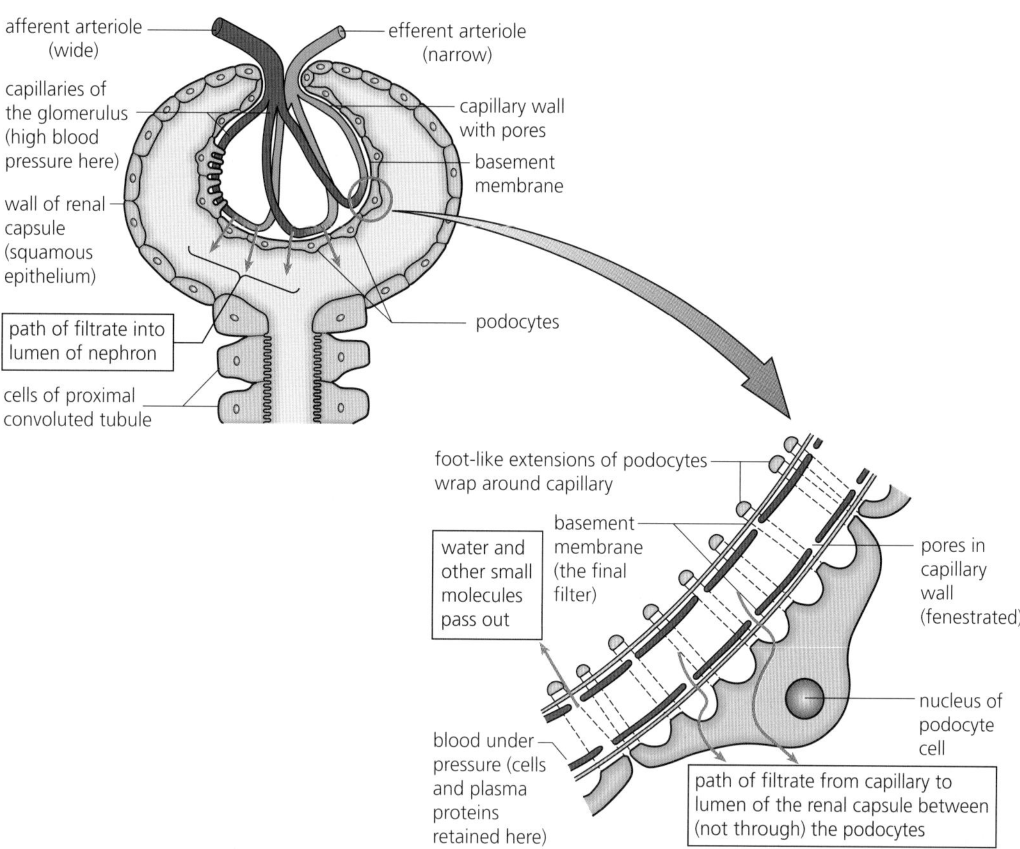

Figure 24.14 The site of ultrafiltration

Notice that the cells of the capsule wall are called **podocytes** because they have foot-like extensions that form a network with tiny slits between them (a situation we call **fenestrated**). Similarly, the endothelium of the capillaries has pores, too. This detail has only become apparent from studies using the electron microscope – these filtration gaps are very small indeed.

> **Key term**
>
> **Podocytes** Specialised cells found in the wall of the kidney capsule.

The entire contents of blood are not forced out. Not only are blood cells retained, but the majority of blood proteins and polypeptides dissolved in the plasma are also retained in the circulating blood. This is because of the presence of the **basement membrane**.

Step 2: Selective reabsorption in the proximal convoluted tubule
The proximal convoluted tubule is the longest section of the nephron. The walls are one cell thick and are packed with mitochondria (ATP is required for the active transport). The cell membrane in contact with the filtrate has a brush border of microvilli which enormously increase the surface area for reabsorption. A large part of the filtrate is reabsorbed into the capillary network here (Figure 24.15).

The individual mechanisms of transport are:

- movement of water by **osmosis**
- **active transport** of glucose and amino acids across membranes
- movement of mineral ions by a combination of **active transport**, **facilitated diffusion**, and some **exchange of ions**
- **diffusion** of urea
- movement of proteins by **pinocytosis**.

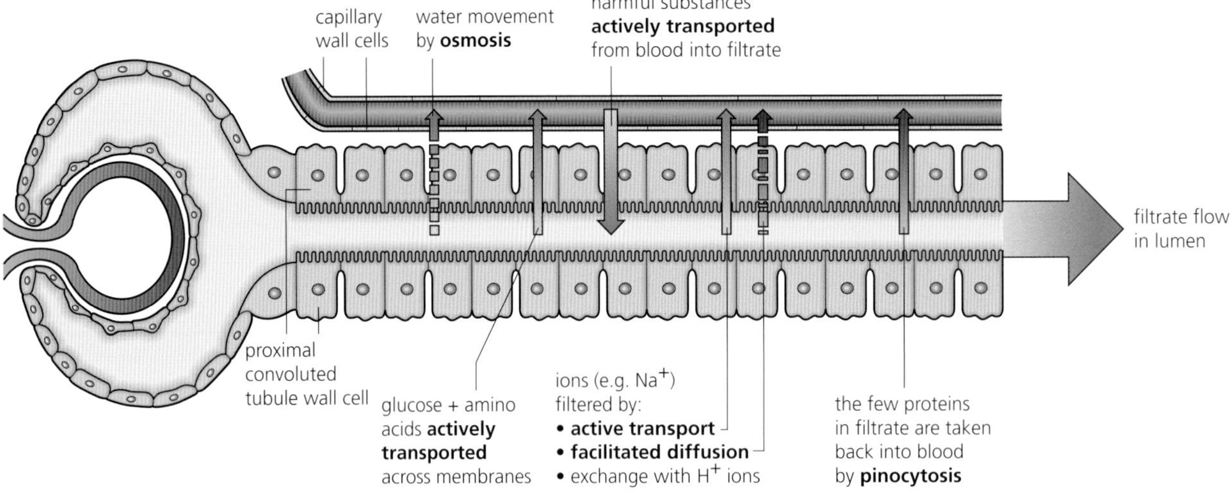

Figure 24.15 Selective reabsorption in the proximal convoluted tubule

Step 3: Water conservation in the loop of Henle
Urea is expelled from the body in solution, so water loss in excretion is inevitable. However, mammals are able to form urine that is more concentrated than the blood (when necessary), thereby reducing the water loss to a minimum. The role of the loop of Henle with its **descending** and **ascending limbs**, together with a parallel blood supply, the **vasa recta**, is to create and maintain a high concentration of salts in the tissue fluid in the **medulla of the kidney**. This is brought about by a **countercurrent multiplier mechanism**. It is the building up of a high concentration of salts in the tissue of the medulla that causes water to be reabsorbed from the filtrate in the collecting ducts. The collecting ducts run through the medulla.

Key terms

Vasa recta Blood vessels found adjacent to the loop of Henle in the kidney.

Kidney medulla The inner part of the kidney.

The roles of the vasa recta are to:

- absorb water that has been absorbed into the medulla at the collecting ducts
- remove carbon dioxide and deliver oxygen to the metabolically active cells of the loop of Henle without removing the accumulated salts from the medulla.

Figure 24.16 explains how the countercurrent mechanism works. Notice that the descending and ascending limbs lie close together.

Look first at the second half of the loop, the ascending limb.

Here, sodium and chloride ions are pumped out into the medulla but water is retained inside the ascending limb. Opposite, the descending limb is permeable here, so sodium and chloride ions diffuse in. Water passes out into the medulla tissue, due to the salt concentration in the medulla. As the filtrate flows down the descending limb, this water loss increases the salt concentration in the loop, making the filtrate more concentrated.

Consequently, sodium ions and chloride ions diffuse out down their concentration gradient, around the 'hairpin' zone at the base of the descending limb, adding to the concentration of ions in the medulla. How this concentration helps in the formation of concentrated urine is explained in step 5 on the next page.

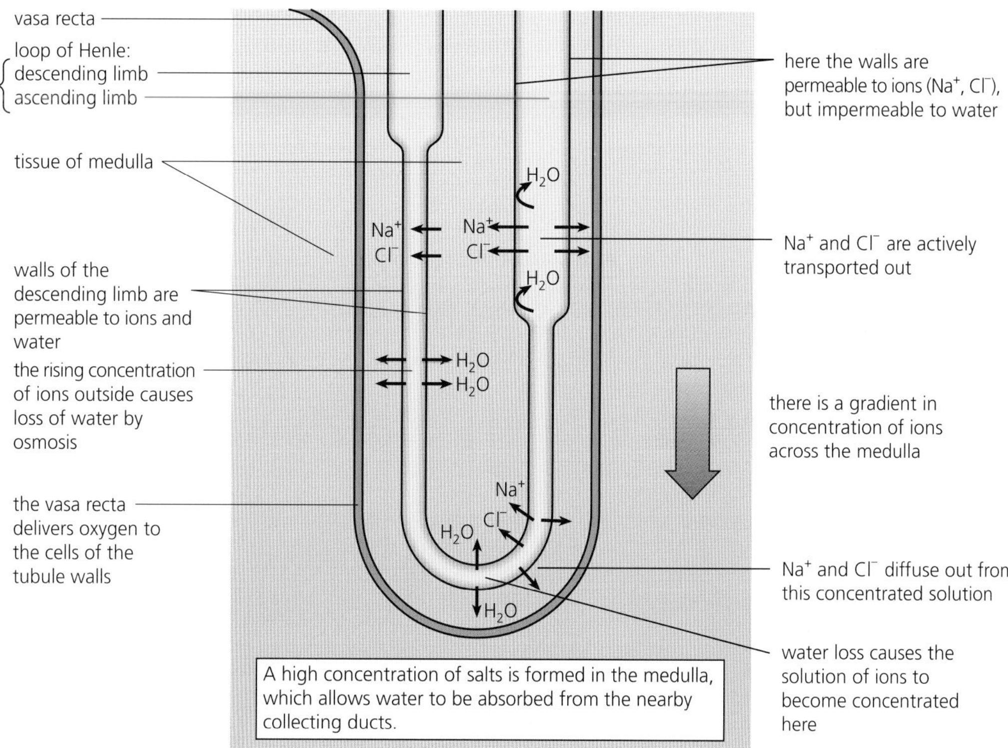

Figure 24.16 Countercurrent mechanism

Step 4: Blood pH and ion concentration regulation in the distal convoluted tubule

Here the cells are of the same structure as those of the proximal convoluted tubule, but their role is to adjust the composition of the blood, and in particular the **pH**. An initial tendency for the pH of the blood to change is buffered by the blood proteins, but if the blood does begin to deviate from pH 7.4, then the concentration of hydrogen ions and hydroxyl ions in the blood is adjusted, along with the concentration of hydrogencarbonate ions. Consequently, blood pH does not vary outside the range pH 7.35–7.45, but the pH of urine varies from pH 4.5 to pH 8.2.

Also in the distal convoluted tubule, the selective reabsorption of ions useful in metabolism occurs from the filtrate.

Key term

Antidiuretic hormone (ADH) A hormone synthesised in the hypothalamus and released by the posterior pituitary gland, which increases the permeability of the walls of the collecting ducts in the kidney.

Step 5: Water reabsorption in the collecting ducts

The collecting ducts are where the **water content of the blood** (and therefore of the whole body) is regulated (Figures 24.17 and 24.18). When the water content of the blood is low, **antidiuretic hormone (ADH)** is secreted from the posterior pituitary gland. When the water content of the blood is high, little or no ADH is secreted.

The permeability of the walls of the collecting ducts to water is variable (a case of facilitated diffusion) – the presence of ADH causes the walls of the collecting ducts to be fully permeable. This allows water to be withdrawn from the filtrate of the tubule into the medulla, due to the high concentration of sodium and chloride ions there (see step 3 on page 510). This water is taken up and redistributed in the body by the blood circulation, and only small amounts of concentrated urine are formed. Meanwhile, the ADH circulating in the blood is slowly removed at the kidneys.

When no ADH is secreted, the walls of the collecting ducts become less permeable. The result is that large quantities of very dilute urine are formed.

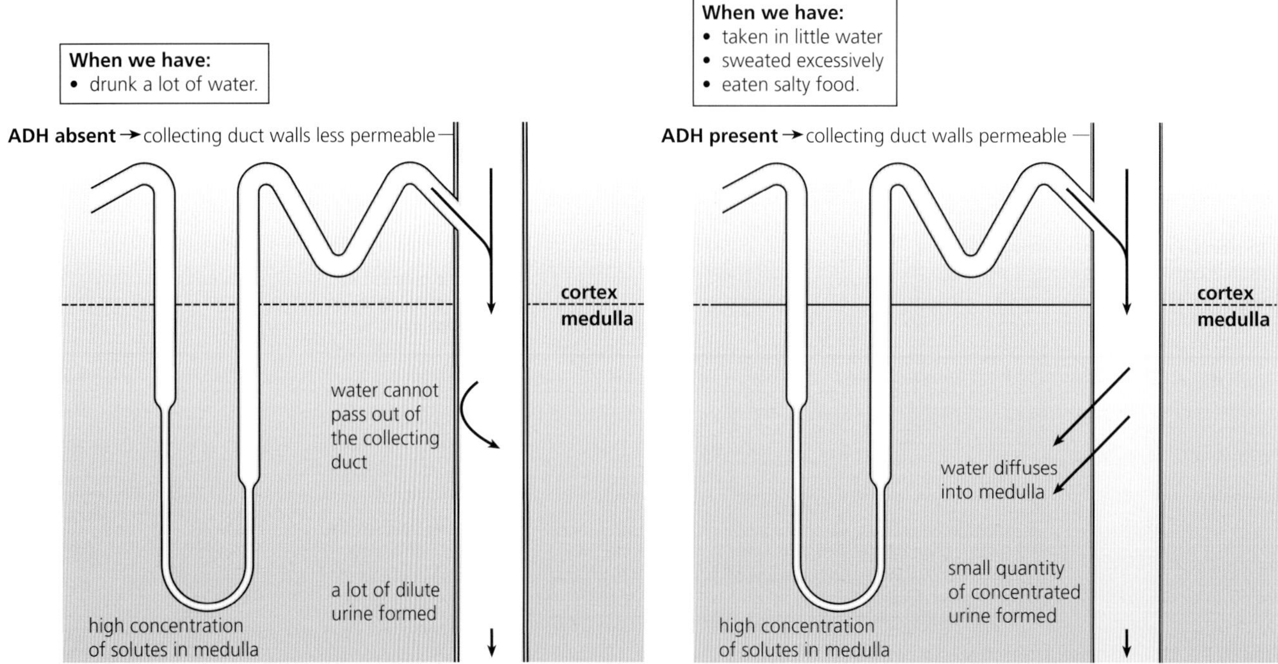

Figure 24.17 Water reabsorption in the collecting ducts

Test yourself

19 Cells of the walls of the proximal convoluted tubule have a brush border. Describe what this means, and explain how it helps in tubule function.

20 Predict in what circumstances in the body ADH is released.

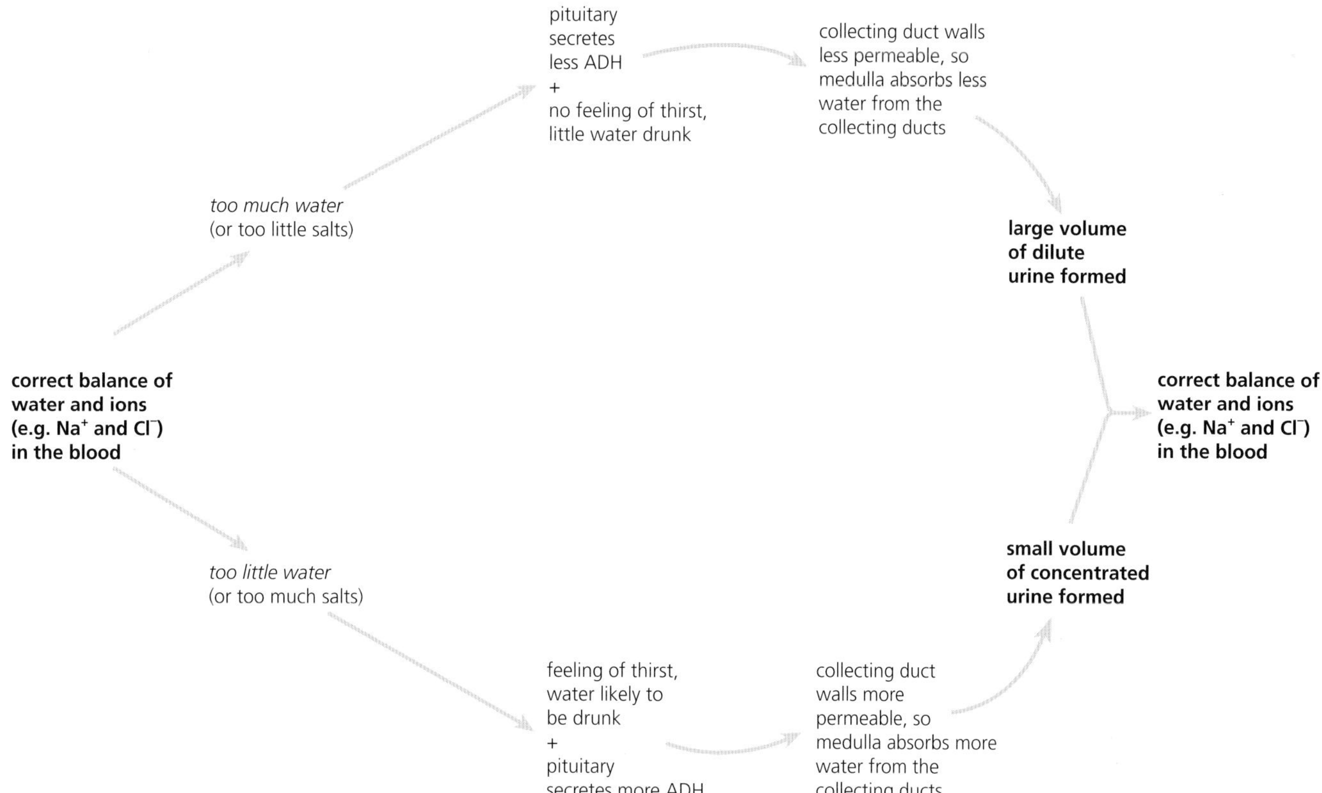

Figure 24.18 Homeostasis by osmoregulation and regulation of ion content in the kidneys – a summary

Hypothalamus, pituitary and neurosecretion

The control of osmoregulation provides us with another excellent example of the close coordination between the nervous and endocrine system. This is shown very clearly by the links between the **pituitary gland** and the hypothalamus. The hypothalamus is part of the floor of the forebrain. It is exceptionally well supplied with blood vessels and is the site of specialised neurones. The hypothalamus has a key role in monitoring and control of many aspects of homeostasis and information from the composition of the blood as it flows through its capillary networks provides important sensory information. This information, and that which comes from sensory neurones via the spinal cord enables the hypothalamus to regulate many body activities concerned with homeostasis, such as thermoregulation discussed in the earlier part of this chapter.

The pituitary gland is situated below the hypothalamus but is connected to it. This gland consists of two parts, the anterior and posterior lobes. Just like the hypothalamus, the pituitary has a key role in homeostasis but its actions are mediated through release of hormones. It is sometimes referred to as the 'master gland' because, not only does it release hormones that have a direct effect, it also releases hormones that stimulate other endocrine glands. However, systems do not work well with two different managers and it is the hypothalamus, with its superior sensory information, that controls the activity of the pituitary by releasing a number of controlling hormones from its special **neurosecretory cells** into the portal vein that supplies the anterior lobe of the pituitary as shown in Figure 24.19 on the next page.

Key terms

Pituitary gland An endocrine gland attached to the hypothalamus at the base of the forebrain. Often known as the 'master gland' because it produces and releases many hormones controlling growth, development and homeostasis.

Neurosecretory cells Modified neurones producing and transporting hormones.

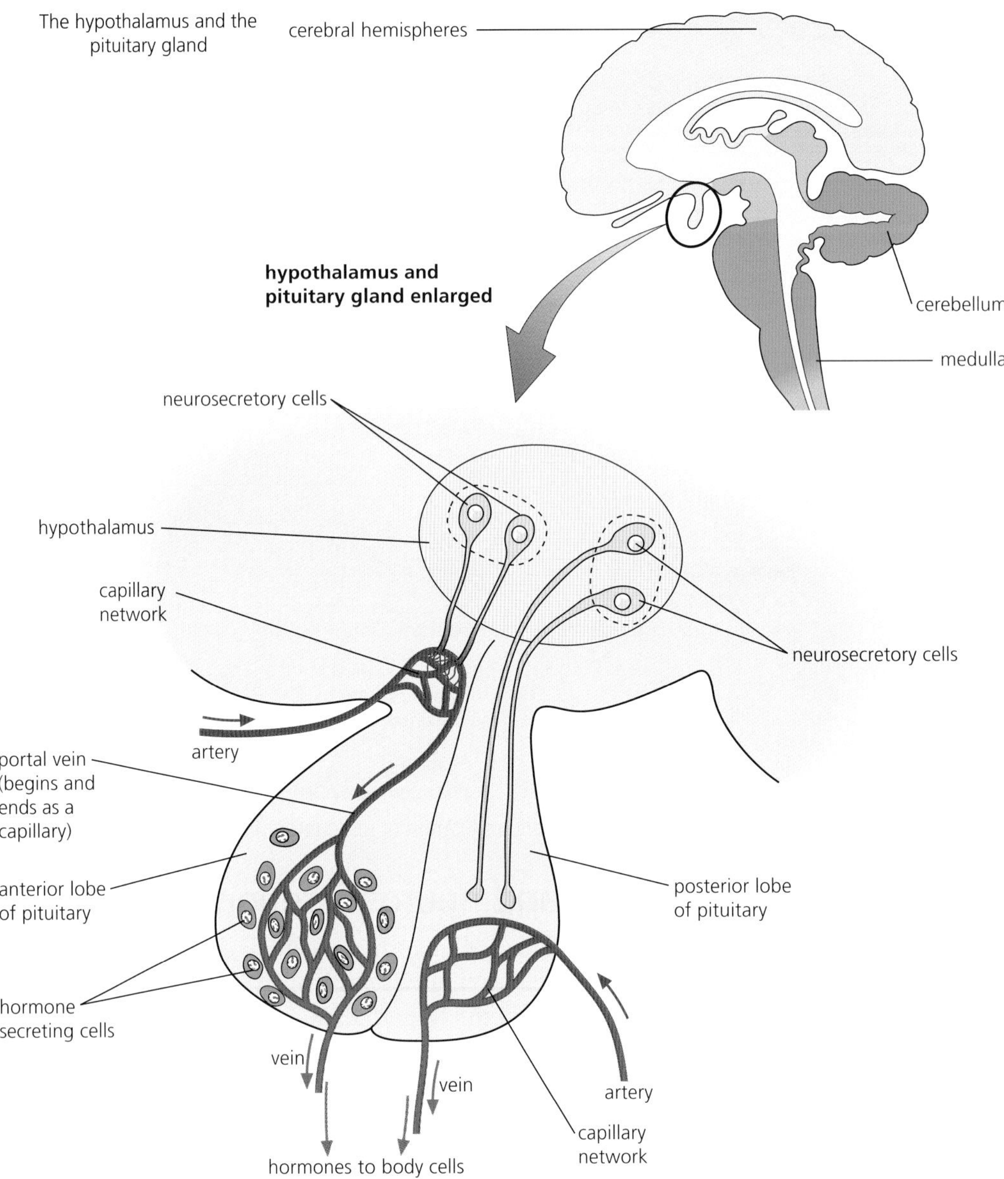

Figure 24.19 The hypothalamus and the pituitary gland

The posterior lobe of the pituitary does not synthesise hormones but stores and releases hormones synthesised by the hypothalamus. These hormones are transported to the posterior pituitary along modified neurones and stored in the vesicles found at the end of these specialised neurosecretory fibres within the gland (Figure 24.20). Impulses from the hypothalamus cause the release of specific hormones into the blood in the capillary network in a process very similar to the release of neurotransmitters from the presynaptic membrane of synapses.

The secretion of ADH and its mode of action

You have seen that osmoregulation by negative feedback is brought about by the secretion of ADH and its action on water reabsorption in the collecting ducts (Figure 24.18). This is yet another example of the nervous and endocrine systems working in harmony, and you can illustrate this using your knowledge of the links between the hypothalamus and pituitary shown in Figure 24.19.

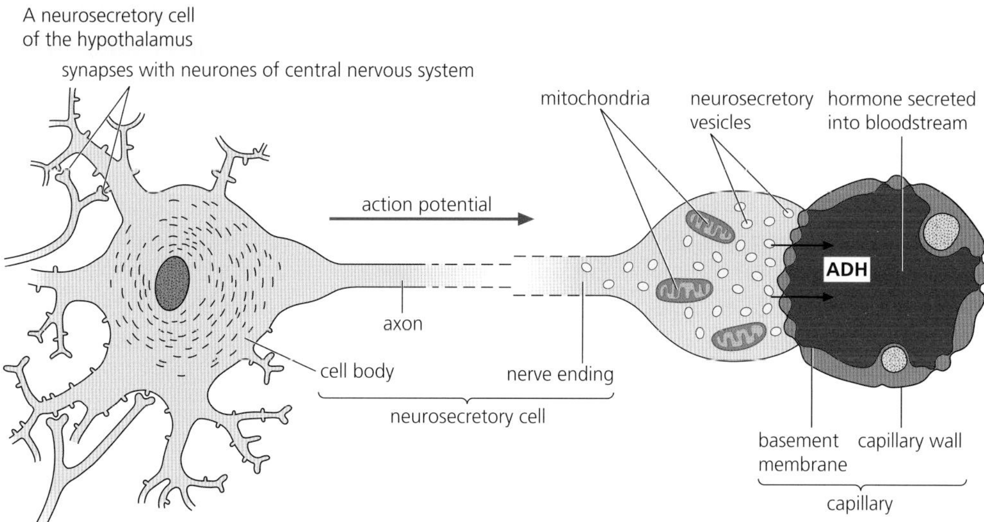

Figure 24.20 The working neurosecretory cell of the hypothalamus

ADH is one of the hormones synthesised in the hypothalamus and transported by neurosecretory cells to the posterior pituitary as shown in Figure 24.20.

ADH is a peptide hormone and therefore acts by binding to receptor sites on the cells of the collecting ducts (as you saw in Chapter 23) and by the use of a second messenger triggers the insertion of integral membrane protein channels called **aquaporins**. Aquaporins are selectively permeable to water molecules and therefore increase the rate of water diffusion (osmosis) through the membrane. This is because the water molecules no longer have to pass through the lipoprotein membrane structure that restricts their flow. In this way the presence of ADH ensures that a maximum volume of water can be reabsorbed into the medulla of the kidney and back into the bloodstream.

> **Key term**
>
> **Aquaporins** Integral membrane proteins that form channels to allow the free passage of water molecules through the phospholipid bilayer.

Hormones such as ADH are removed from the bloodstream and broken down into inactive compounds by the liver. This means that continual secretion is needed to retain its effect on the kidney and allow the hypothalamus to retain accurate control. Figure 24.18 also shows you that the action of ADH is another example of a negative feedback control system, which was described at the beginning of Chapter 23.

Adaptations of the kidney to dry environments

Mammals are a successful group of animals that have been able to colonise many different habitats. Extremely dry environments, such as deserts, pose particular challenges, and there are only a limited number of mammals that can survive the high temperatures and arid conditions.

Excretion of urea inevitably involves water loss that a desert mammal can ill-afford, and to survive, adaptations are needed to keep this to a minimum.

One mammal that is able to thrive in arid conditions is the kangaroo rat, *Dipodomys* sp., shown in Figure 24.21.

Figure 24.21 A kangaroo rat – *Dipodomys* sp.

Dipodomys is able to survive because of a number of water-conservation features, both behavioural and physiological. It does not have sweat glands, nor does it evaporate moisture off the tongue in panting to cool itself. It lives in burrows which, in addition to providing a shelter, allow it to modify its behaviour to avoid the hottest times of day.

It forages for seeds, mainly at night, to further limit exposure to the hot sun, and it has large eyes with good nocturnal vision to find food and to escape predators, using its speed and agility provided by long hind legs and a balancing tail.

The kidneys of *Dipodomys* are able to reduce water loss by producing a very concentrated urine, approximately 20 times more concentrated than humans. To achieve this by active transport would be far too energy-demanding, so *Dipodomys* utilises the counter-current multiplier effect (see Gas exchange in fish, Chapter 10) of the loop of Henle to raise the concentration of the medulla to very high levels. As you can see from Figure 24.16 (page 511), Na^+ and Cl^- ions are lost from the fluid inside the descending limb of the loop of Henle as it passes into the medulla. The further into the medulla the descending limb passes, then the more ions are lost from the fluid and the more concentrated the medulla becomes. The proximity of the ascending limb to form a **counter-current system** means that there are always ions available to do this. A very highly concentrated medulla is just what is needed to draw water from the collecting ducts by passive osmosis. Examination of the kidneys of *Dipodomys* shows that they have, comparatively, very long loops of Henle that pass deep into the medulla to enhance this effect.

Key term

Counter-current system
An arrangement of two fluid movements in opposite directions, which maintains a diffusion gradient along its whole length.

Test yourself

21 State in which part of the nephron, glucose is reabsorbed.
22 Explain why proteins are not found in the capsule of the glomerulus.
23 Name **three** substances that are transported by active transport in the reabsorption process.
24 State the **two** ions that are responsible for the high concentration in the medulla.
25 In which part of the kidney is most water reabsorbed back into blood capillaries?
26 State which part of the kidney is extended in length in a kangaroo rat.

Chapter summary

Detection of light by mammals

- There are two types of cell in the retina, rods and cones.
- Rods are much more numerous and are distributed evenly around the retina. Cones are found concentrated around the fovea.
- Connecting neurones are layered on the surface of the retina so light must pass through them to reach the sensitive parts of rods and cones.
- Rods are sensitive to dim light and contain the pigment rhodopsin, which is formed from opsin and retinal.
- Cones respond to different wavelengths of bright light and contain the pigment iodopsin.
- Rod cells have an inner and outer segment, a bipolar cell and a ganglion cell.
- Light falling on the rhodopsin breaks it down to retinal and opsin. Na^+ ion channels in the outer segment close, causing hyperpolarisation. This causes the bipolar cell to depolarise and set off an action potential in a neurone of the optic nerve. In darkness this process is reversed.
- Cones operate in a similar way but it is thought different cones respond to different wavelengths of light to give colour vision.
- Action potentials from the optic nerve are processed in the visual cortex of the brain to give a perception of 'seeing'.

Control of heart rate in mammals

- The basic heart rate is set by the activity of the sino-atrial node (myogenic in origin).
- The rate can be altered according to demand by the cardiovascular centre in the medulla of the brain.
- This receives information on blood pressure from stretch receptors in the aorta and CO_2 levels from chemoreceptors in main arteries.
- Heart rate can be accelerated by impulses from the sympathetic nerve or slowed by impulses from the vagus nerve (antagonistic control).
- The hormone adrenaline also has a powerful effect of increasing heart rate.

Temperature regulation

- Heat is lost and gained by conduction, convection and radiation.
- Many animals cannot control body temperature and so rely on behavioural methods such as basking in the sun or hiding in the shade.
- In mammals the hypothalamus controls body temperature by antagonistic actions of the sympathetic and parasympathetic nerves.
- In mammals heat is conserved by a layer of insulating fat under the skin (adipose tissue).
- Superficial capillaries can be widened to increase heat loss or constricted to retain heat.
- Hairs on the skin can be raised to trap insulating air or lowered to increase heat loss.
- Mammals are endotherms, generating most of their body heat internally. Adjusting basal metabolic rate using the hormone thyroxine also controls body temperature.

Osmoregulation and excretion

- Urea is a breakdown product of proteins formed in the liver. Toxic amino groups are removed from amino acids and combined with carbon dioxide in the liver to form urea.
- Urine is a weak solution of urea and many other ions in water.
- The functional unit of the kidney is a nephron consisting of the Bowman's capsule, convoluted tubules, the loop of Henle and collecting ducts.
- Ultrafiltration takes place in the Bowman's capsule when pressure of the blood forces out small molecules, ions and water into the tubule.
- Selective reabsorption in the proximal convoluted tubule ensures many vital substances such as glucose and amino acids are returned to the blood capillaries.
- The loop of Henle acts as a counter-current multiplier to maintain a high concentration in the kidney medulla. This allows a great deal of water to be retained as it is drawn out of the urine in the collecting ducts by osmosis before being passed to the bladder. Mammals in extremely dry environments have very long loops of Henle producing very high concentrations in the medulla and very highly concentrated urea.
- The distal convoluted tubule is concerned with pH adjustments and ion control of the body fluids.
- Fine control of osmoregulation is brought about by the hormone ADH. The release of ADH from the anterior pituitary is controlled by neurosecretion from the hypothalamus.

Practice questions

1 Antidiuretic hormone is produced in the:

A anterior pituitary gland

B medulla

C posterior pituitary gland

D hypothalamus *(1)*

2 When there is no light shining on the retina:

A rod cells release a transmitter substance

B bipolar cells release a transmitter substance

C rhodopsin forms retinal and opsin

D Na^+ ion channels in the outer rod segment close *(1)*

Tip

Despite being multiple choice, Question 2 is a good test of your detailed knowledge of the events taking place on the retina.

Tip

Question 3 is a simple question that is largely AO1. However, take care to read it carefully. This is about showing you understand negative feedback, not about detailed descriptions of the methods mammals use to increase or decrease heat loss, so make sure you keep to the point. You don't get marks knocked off for irrelevant material but neither do you gain any credit. You do, however, penalise yourself by wasting a lot of precious time.

3 **a)** Explain what is meant by the term 'negative feedback control'. *(3)*

b) Explain how negative feedback control plays an important part in thermoregulation by the autonomic nervous system in mammals. *(4)*

4 **a)** Explain why the structure of the retina is described as 'inverted'. *(1)*

b) During periods of low light intensity, the iris of the eye causes the pupil to dilate. This allows the image on the retina to expand over the surface of the retina. Explain how this helps to provide better low light vision. *(3)*

***c)** Explain how light falling on a rod cell in the retina can produce an action potential in an optic nerve fibre. *(6)*

Tip

Question 4 is a mixed question where you need to apply your knowledge of the retina and show that you know all the details of the events leading up to the formation of an action potential in the optic nerve. A good exercise in testing your revision and emphasising the level of detail you will need in the examination papers.

5 The table below shows the relative concentration of the blood plasma and urine in a number of different mammals.

Mammal	Habitat	Urine concentration mmol dm^{-3}	Urine concentration : blood plasma concentration ratio
Common brown rat	Temperate	2900	9
Kangaroo rat	Desert	5500	16
Beaver	Freshwater/land	520	1.7
Human	Temperate	1400	4.5
Camel	Desert	2800	8

a) Estimate the approximate blood plasma concentration in these mammals and explain why this might be an expected trend in mammals. *(3)*

b) Explain why the beaver might be expected to have the lowest urine concentration:blood plasma concentration ratio compared to the other mammals. *(2)*

c) Drugs that cause an increase in urine production are called diuretics. A trial was conducted to test the effects of two different diuretics, acetazolamide and frusemide on urine production in patients. Two groups of 50 patients were each given identical concentrations of the drugs and the total volume of urine produced was measured for 24 hours. A third group of 50 patients were given identical doses of isotonic saline solution as a control. Isotonic saline is a dilute salt solution of exactly the same concentration as the blood plasma. All groups had exactly the same water and food intake throughout the investigation.

The results of this investigation are shown in the graph below.

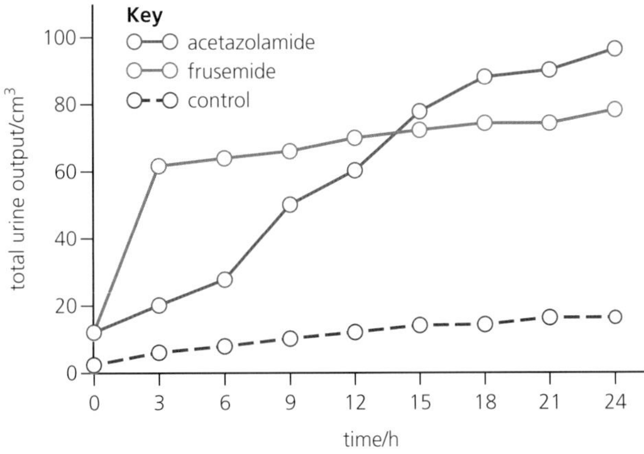

i) Explain why it was important that the control group were given an isotonic solution. *(2)*

ii) Diuretics are sometimes used to help control blood pressure. Analyse the data to explain why frusemide might reduce high blood pressure and be a more effective treatment. *(5)*

d) Sailors stranded at sea without drinking water are sometimes tempted to drink seawater. Explain why drinking sea water will neither reduce thirst nor aid survival. *(3)*

Tip

Question 5 is a very common type of question that you are likely to face. Not only are you expected to understand the working of the kidney but also apply your knowledge to a novel situation by interpreting data and carrying out some simple calculations. Note: 'estimate' means you do not have to carry out all the calculation, just mentally check the approximate values.

*6 It has been suggested that chemical control in living things is concerned with long-term processes such as growth and development whilst nervous control is concerned with short-term responses. Assess the validity of this suggestion. (9)

Stretch and challenge

7 Seals are extremely well-adapted to life in cold water and they are capable of diving to great depths for periods of up to an hour. As mammals, they breathe through lungs and maintain a high body temperature. One adaptation is known as the 'dive reflex' and this can also be demonstrated in humans. The strongest dive reflexes occur when the face is fully immersed in cold water.

What is the 'dive reflex', how is it controlled and how can it benefit the seal on a long dive?

8 Humans and other animals use urea as a nitrogenous excretory product but this is by no means the only compound used in this way.

The table below shows some different excretory products and their properties.

Animal	Habitat	Excretory compound	Chemical properties
Trout	Freshwater	Ammonia	Highly soluble and highly toxic
Locust	Desert	Uric acid	Almost insoluble in water
Cod	Salt water	Trimethylamine oxide	Very soluble; less toxic than ammonia
Human	Terrestrial	Urea	Moderately soluble

Explain how each nitrogen-containing compound can be excreted and how this is an adaptation to the environment of the animal.

9 The temperature of the Arctic and Antarctic oceans is below the freezing point of fish blood. Many species, including the Arctic cod, have 'antifreeze' in their blood.

a) If fish blood is likely to freeze, why does the sea water not freeze?

b) The relative molecular mass (RMM) of these antifreeze agents is between 5000 and 30 000. The glomerular membrane is normally impermeable to compounds with a RMM of greater than about 50 000+. What problems does this pose to these fish and how might they be overcome?

Tip

Question 6 is first of all a synoptic question where you will need to use your knowledge of control and coordination. It also requires that you compose your answer carefully in continuous prose and make sure that you make comparisons using examples from plants and animals that are well-explained, not just a few words, as this is marked using a 'levels' marking scheme (see further details in the 'Preparing for the exams' chapter at the end of this book). The question asks you to 'Assess the validity' so you must come to some conclusion but remember there is no 'right' or 'wrong' answer; it is your balanced argument that gains the credit.

25 Ecosystems

Prior knowledge

In this chapter you will need to recall that:

- → food chains and food webs can be used to represent relationships in ecosystems
- → most food chains and food webs start with energy from sunlight trapped by photosynthesis
- → food chains represent the transfer of energy from organism to organism
- → the number and total mass of organisms gets smaller as you move down the food chain
- → pyramids of number show the decrease in organisms as you move down a food chain
- → quadrats and transects can be used in ecological investigations
- → ecosystems are groups of plants and animals that live together in fixed area, interacting to form a balanced system
- → organisms can be divided into feeding types such as producers, consumers, herbivores, carnivores, detrivores and decomposers
- → autotrophs are able to synthesise food molecules from simpler substances whilst heterotrophs cannot
- → carbon and nitrogen cycles recycle nutrients within the ecosystem.

Test yourself on prior knowledge

1. Name an example of an ecosystem.
2. Food chains contain less and less organisms as you move down them. Explain why.
3. Explain the term 'quadrat'.
4. List **three** ways in which organisms interact with each other in an ecosystem.
5. State the reason why nitrogen is so important to living organisms.
6. Explain how food chains and webs show that an ecosystem is 'balanced'.
7. State the most common method of autotrophic nutrition.
8. Describe the difference between an autotroph and a heterotrophy.

Key terms

Biosphere The total area of the Earth and its atmosphere that is inhabited by living organisms.

Population A group of members of the same species that interact with each other.

Habitat A division of the biosphere with its own unique characteristics and conditions.

Community A group of populations of different species living together in one habitat.

Ecosysytem A collection of communities and their non-living surroundings, which form a stable, self-perpetuating system in which there is an energy flow and nutrients are recycled.

What is an ecosystem?

The whole area of the Earth that can be inhabited by living organisms is quite limited. If we simply consider its height above and below sea level then it extends for approximately 30 km, forming a sphere known as the **biosphere**. Living within the biosphere are lots of individual organisms. Members of one species are usually found living together in groups called **populations** and each species has a particular set of adaptations and behavioural patterns. The whole biosphere has countless different smaller areas known as **habitats** and within each habitat there will be a number of populations forming a **community**.

An **ecosystem** is more than just a collection of communities. It also concerns how these communities are linked to each other and to their surroundings to form a balanced system.

It is much more difficult than you might think to give undisputed examples of single ecosystems if you are to meet all the conditions of the definition. First of all, most ecosystems are influenced by organisms that have links to many ecosystems. For example, a small isolated lake forms a separate ecosystem, but predation of fish by birds such as herons is an important factor, yet the herons almost certainly have this effect on several different lakes and streams. Swallows and other migratory birds play an important role in different ecosystems many thousands of miles apart.

However, one thing is certain, and that is, that ecosystems can vary in size enormously. Large areas of desert or semi-arid scrub can form ecosystems of thousands of square kilometres, with animals needing to roam widely to find scarce food. In contrast they can be small, isolated pools of less than 1 square metre. The important part is that most of the organisms are present for a significant period of time and that nutrients and energy can flow freely throughout.

Unusual ecosystems

Key terms

Hydrothermal vents Fissures on the deep ocean floor where the formation of tectonic plates causes hot water, minerals and gases to escape.

Chemosynthesis The use of chemical energy from the oxidation of inorganic compounds to synthesise organic compounds.

For many years ecologists considered that solar energy was the start point of energy flow in all ecosystems. The discovery of deep-sea **hydrothermal vents** and their associated ecosystems necessitated a revision of this model.

Hydrothermal vents are formed in the deep ocean at mid-ocean ridges where the tectonic plates diverge and new plates forming the Earth's crust are made from the magma beneath. At these points, hot water and minerals leak out onto the ocean floor. The minerals solidify as they come into contact with the cold water, forming large chimney-like structures. Many of the minerals are sulphides, which are dark in colour and their escape from vents gives rise to their common name 'black smokers' (Figure 25.1). Others have mixtures of gases such as carbon dioxide and are known as 'white smokers'.

These vents are found at depths of more than 3000 m and the gases emerging from them can have temperatures as high as 300 °C. Remarkably, they are often surrounded by ecosystems of previously unknown species, with extreme adaptations that allow them to survive in an environment with no light, enormous pressure and temperatures varying from 200–300 °C. Even more surprising was the discovery that the energy within these ecosystems is not linked to sunlight but to a special type of bacteria. These bacteria are able to use chemicals such as the sulfide minerals as a substrate for **chemosynthesis** to gain the energy they need to grow and begin new food chains.

Food chains

Figure 25.1 A 'black smoker' hydrothermal vent with associated ecosystem

A feeding relationship in which a carnivore eats a herbivore, which itself has eaten plant matter, is called a **food chain**. Of course, light is the initial energy source in most food chains (except our example of hydrothermal vents). Note that in a food chain, the arrows point to the consumers, and so indicate the direction of energy transfer.

oak leaf → caterpillar → beetle → shrew → owl

A food chain tells us about the feeding relationships of organisms in an ecosystem, but they are shown as entirely qualitative relationships (we know which organisms are present as prey and as predators) rather than providing quantitative data (we do not know the numbers of organisms at each level). In a whole ecosystem food chains are interconnected in many different ways to form a complex **food web**. There are also significant drawbacks to simple food webs. In most cases they tell us only a very limited part of the story. In Figure 25.2 on the next page for example, there are literally hundreds of different insects or their larvae that feed on oak leaves. Similarly, the fox and the shrew

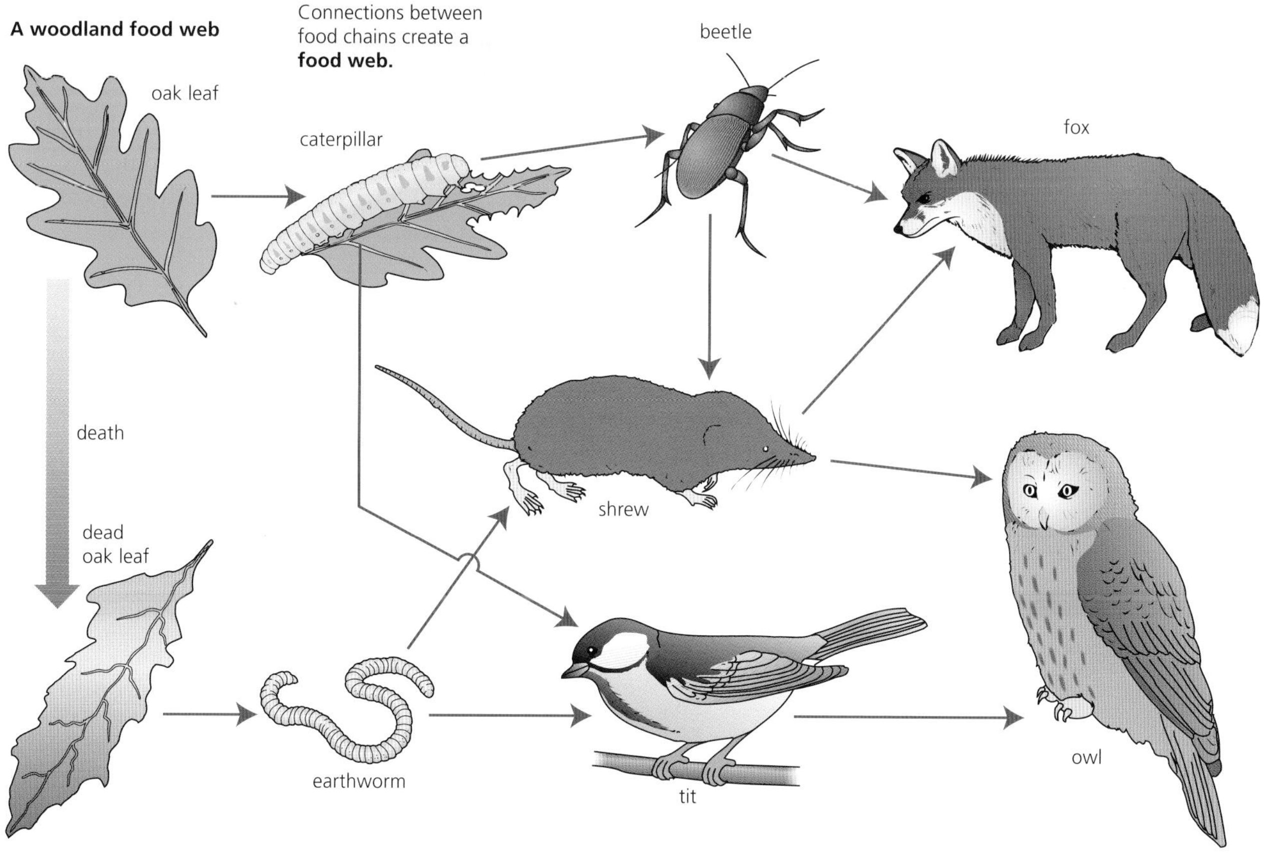

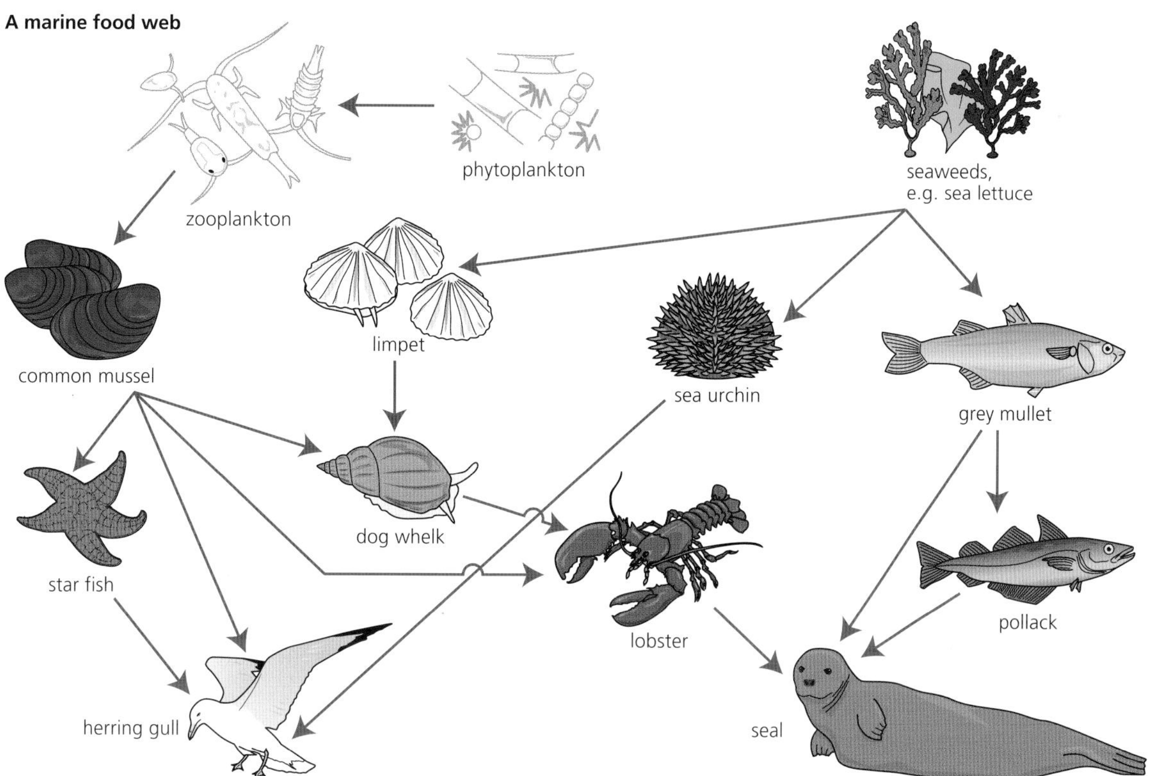

Figure 25.2 Examples of food webs

have very varied diets, often determined by what food they can find. Figure 25.2 shows two different food webs but these are only a tiny portion of the ecological relationships in these ecosystems.

Key term

Trophic level A level in a food chain defined by the number of energy transfers an organism is from the primary energy source.

The level at which an organism feeds in a food chain is called its **trophic level**. In this way of classifying feeding relationships, the producers are designated as trophic level 1 because their energy has been transferred once, from Sun to plant. All herbivores are in level 2, because here energy has been transferred twice, and so on.

The trophic levels of some woodland organisms are classified in Table 25.1. Note that there is no fixed number of trophic levels to food chains, but rather they are typically of three, four or five levels only. There is an important reason why stable food chains remain quite short, which we shall consider later.

Table 25.1 An analysis of trophic levels

Trophic level	Woodland	Rainforest	Savannah
Producer	Oak	Vines and creepers on rainforest trees	Grass
Primary or first consumer	Caterpillar	Silver-striped hawk moth	Wildebeest
Secondary consumer	Beetle	Praying mantis	Lion
Tertiary consumer	Shrew	Chameleon lizard	
Quaternary consumer	Fox	Hook-billed vanga-shrike	

Test yourself

1. Explain why a lion feeding on an antelope is described as the third trophic level.
2. Suggest what eventually happens to the energy in any animal at the top of a food chain.
3. Use Figure 25.2 to suggest three possible effects on the marine ecosystem if the zooplankton were to be severely reduced by a pollution incident.
4. State the main difference between a population and a community.

Energy flow through ecosystems

The productivity of photosynthesis

Only about half the energy emitted by the Sun and reaching the Earth's outer atmosphere gets through to soil level and to plant life – the remainder is reflected into space as light or heat energy. Of the radiation reaching green plants, about 45 per cent is in the visible wavelength range (400–700 nm) and can be used by the plant in photosynthesis. Much of the light energy reaching the plant is reflected from the leaves or transmitted through them, however. Furthermore, of the energy absorbed by the stems and leaves of plants, much is lost in the evaporation of water (Figure 25.3).

A small quantity of the energy reaching a green leaf is absorbed by the photosynthetic pigments and used in photosynthesis; only one quarter of this light energy ends up as chemical energy in molecules like glucose. The remainder is lost as heat energy in the various reactions of the light-dependent and light-independent reactions. In green plants, the total amount of light energy fixed through photosynthesis in a given period of time is known as the **gross primary productivity** (**GPP**). GPP is usually expressed as units of energy per unit area per year, typically either $kJ\,m^{-2}\,y^{-1}$, or $MJ\,ha^{-1}\,y^{-1}$.

Finally, much of the energy in glucose is lost as heat energy in cellular respiration and other reactions of metabolism. The remainder is retained in new materials, either in the form of new structures (cells and tissues) or as stored food, and represents the **net primary productivity** (**NPP**) of the plant. The value given in Figure 25.3 for net primary productivity of about 5.5 per cent applies to a fully grown crop plant. It is achieved for only a short period in the growth cycle of the crop plant – for a significant part of the year agricultural land is uncultivated.

Key terms

Gross primary productivity (GPP) The total amount of light energy fixed by photosynthesis in a given area and fixed time, usually expressed as $kJ\,m^{-2}\,y^{-1}$.

Net primary productivity (NPP) The total amount of light energy fixed by photosynthesis in a given area and fixed time, which remains available to the next trophic level after losses and uses by a producer, usually expressed as $kJ\,m^{-2}\,y^{-1}$.

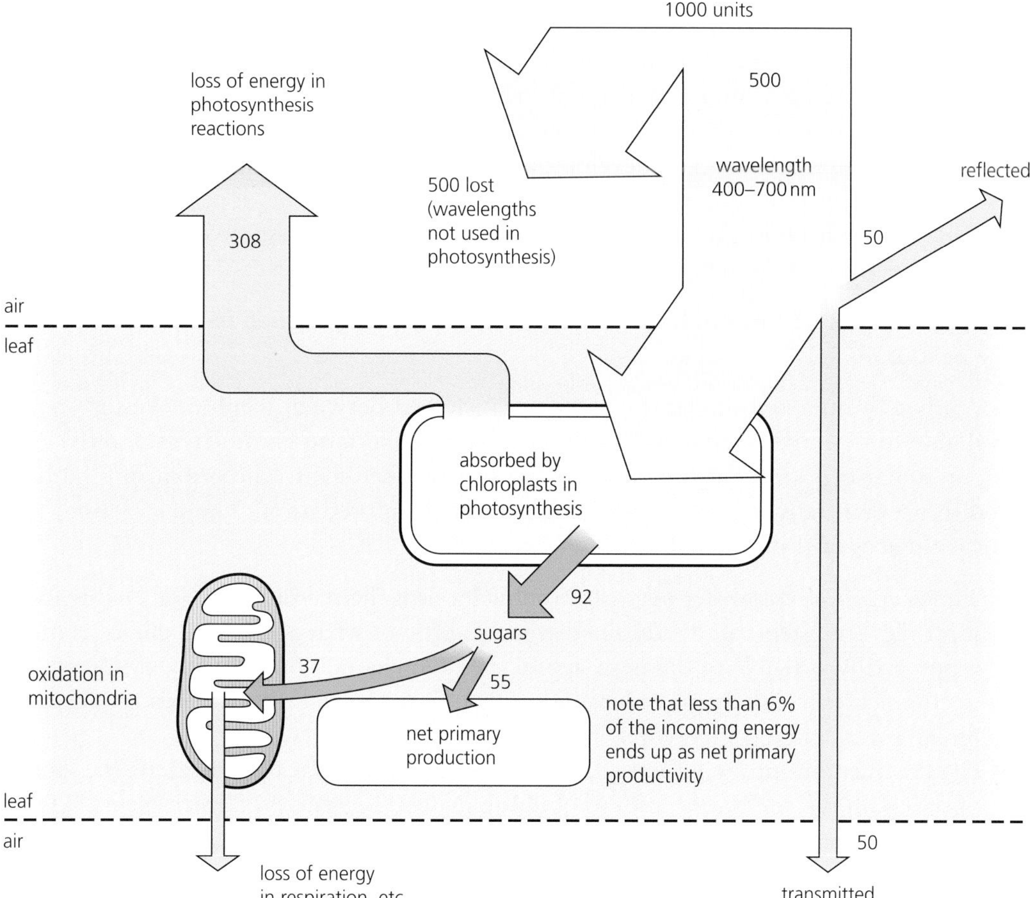

Figure 25.3 The fate of light energy that reaches the green leaf of a crop plant (taken as 1000 units per unit time)

Of course, in many natural habitats you might study, a part of the organic matter that makes up 'net primary productivity' is directly available to sustain browsing herbivores, and indirectly available to other organisms in the environment around the plant. We will examine energy transfer between organisms in a food chain shortly. Meanwhile, the relationship between net primary productivity (NPP), gross primary productivity (GPP) and respiration (R) is summarised in the equation:

$$NPP = GPP - R$$

Applying this equation to data from a temperate ecosystem where GPP was found to be $43\,510\,kJ\,m^{-2}\,y^{-1}$, and R to be $23\,930\,kJ\,m^{-2}\,y^{-1}$, then NPP here was $9580\,kJ\,m^{-2}\,y^{-1}$.

The fate of energy within and between trophic levels

At the base of the food chain, green plants transfer light energy to the chemical energy of sugars, in photosynthesis. Of this, while some is transferred in the reactions of respiration that drive metabolism (and is then lost as heat energy), much is transferred to essential metabolites used in the growth and development of the plant. In these reactions, energy is locked up in the organic molecules of the plant body. Then, when parts of the plant are consumed by herbivores (or parasites), energy is transferred to other organisms. Finally, on the death of the plant, the remaining energy passes to detritivores and saprotrophs when dead plant matter is broken down and decayed. We will describe the activities of these microorganisms later in this chapter (page 530).

Similarly, energy is transferred in the consumer when it eats, digests and then absorbs nutrients. The consumer transfers energy in muscular movements by which it hunts and feeds, and as it seeks to escape from predators (and is then lost as heat energy). Some of the food eaten remains undigested and is lost in the faeces. Also, heat energy – a waste product of the reactions of respiration and of the animal's metabolism – is continuously lost as the consumer grows and develops, and forms body tissues. If the consumer itself is caught and consumed by another, larger consumer, energy is again transferred. Finally, on the death of the consumer, the remaining energy passes to detritivores and saprotrophs when dead matter is broken down and decayed.

Energy transfers within and between trophic levels are summarised in Figure 25.4 on the next page.

So, only a limited amount of the energy transferred between trophic levels is available to be transferred to the next organism in the food chain. In fact, only about 10 per cent of what is eaten by a consumer is built into the organism's body, and so is potentially available to be transferred on in predation. There are two consequences of this:

- The energy loss at transfer between trophic levels is the reason why food chains are short. Few transfers can be sustained when so little of what is eaten by one consumer is potentially available to the next step in the food chain. Consequently, it is very uncommon for food chains to have more than four or five links between producer (green plant) and top carnivore.
- Feeding relationships in a food chain may be structured like a pyramid. At the start of the chain is a very large amount of living matter (**biomass**) of green plants. This supports a smaller biomass of primary consumers, which in turn supports an even smaller biomass of secondary consumers.

Key term

Biomass The total mass of a living organism in a given area.

Test yourself

5 Name **three** ways in which energy in any one trophic level is lost so that it is not available to the next level.

6 The GPP for an area of grassland in a fixed time is $100\,kJ\,m^{-2}$ and losses of energy are $71\,kJ\,m^{-2}$. Calculate the NPP of the grassland.

7 Suggest why it is more efficient to produce protein from soya beans than it is to produce beef from cattle.

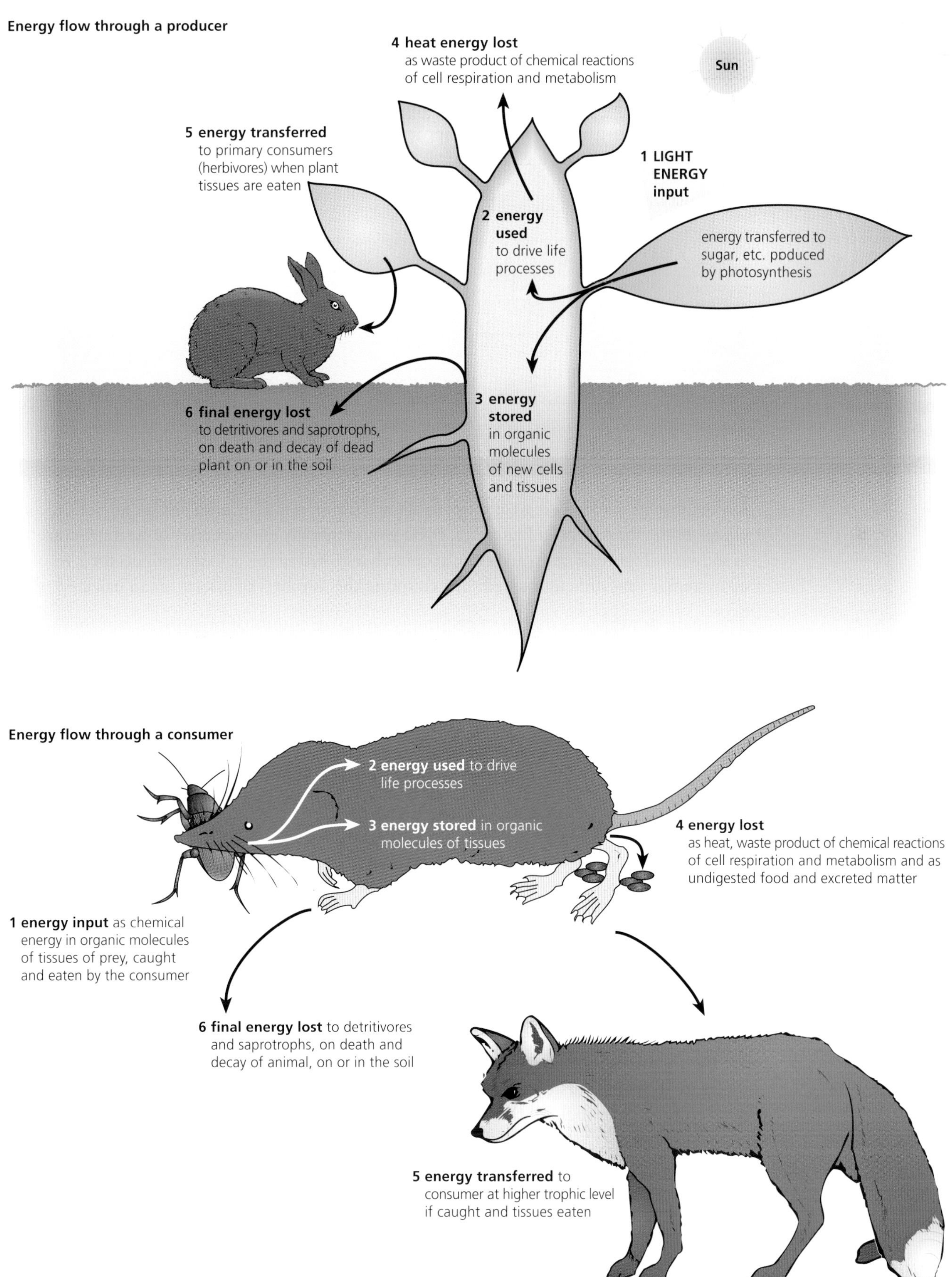

Energy flow through a producer
4 heat energy lost
as waste product of chemical reactions of cell respiration and metabolism
Sun
5 energy transferred
to primary consumers (herbivores) when plant tissues are eaten
1 LIGHT ENERGY input
2 energy used
to drive life processes
energy transferred to sugar, etc. pdduced by photosynthesis
6 final energy lost
to detritivores and saprotrophs, on death and decay of dead plant on or in the soil
3 energy stored
in organic molecules of new cells and tissues
Energy flow through a consumer
2 energy used to drive life processes
3 energy stored in organic molecules of tissues
4 energy lost
as heat, waste product of chemical reactions of cell respiration and metabolism and as undigested food and excreted matter
1 energy input as chemical energy in organic molecules of tissues of prey, caught and eaten by the consumer
6 final energy lost to detritivores and saprotrophs, on death and decay of animal, on or in the soil
5 energy transferred to consumer at higher trophic level if caught and tissues eaten

Figure 25.4 Energy flow through producers and consumers

Illustrating feeding relationships quantitatively

Pyramids of numbers

The simplest way to illustrate the feeding relationships in a whole ecosystem is to count the number of organisms at each trophic level and represent them by horizontal bars on top of each other (Figure 25.5). This is known as a pyramid of numbers.

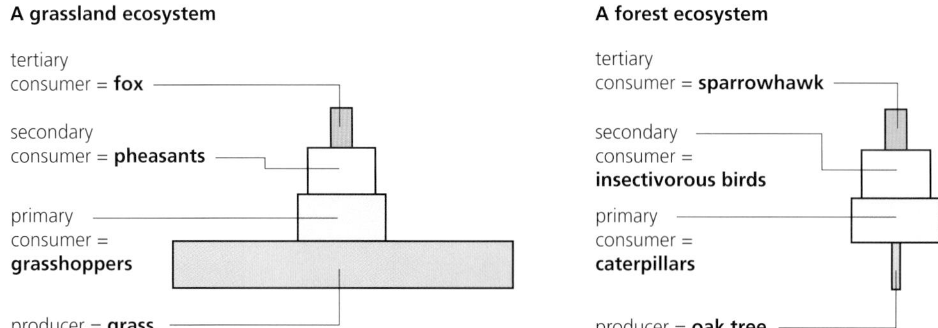

Figure 25.5 Examples of ecological pyramids of numbers

Unfortunately, if you were to attempt to draw a real pyramid of numbers for any of the food chains or the food webs in Figure 25.2 you would quickly encounter a confusing picture as shown in Figure 25.5. In addition, accurately estimating the actual numbers for a whole ecosystem is very difficult indeed. Try counting the numbers of insects on an oak tree!

The main drawback is that the bars simply compare counts of organisms, but these organisms are of very different sizes and therefore they distort the actual picture. In this case 'one oak tree = one caterpillar' which is obviously not representative of the real ecosystem. To add to this confusion, trees such as oaks live for many years and build on previous growth year after year, whilst almost all the insects will have life cycles lasting less than one year. In addition, the scale would be impossible to select on one axis as you would have to cope with one oak tree and many thousands of primary consumers.

Pyramids of biomass

To solve the problems of simply counting numbers you can measure the total biomass (Figure 25.6). Biomass is simply the mass of all the organisms at any one trophic level. But this, too, has its major drawbacks. The biomass of almost all living organisms is made up of over 80 per cent water and this is not helpful in illustrating relationships. Water content can also vary enormously over relatively short periods of time. To overcome this problem it is important to find the dry biomass in each trophic level. Even then you still have a further problem in that different components of biomass have very different energy contents per kilogram. For ecologists, studies finding dry biomass are highly undesirable as all the organisms need to be killed. Fortunately there are tables to allow conversion from fresh to dry biomass in different organisms but you still need to find and weigh all the organisms concerned.

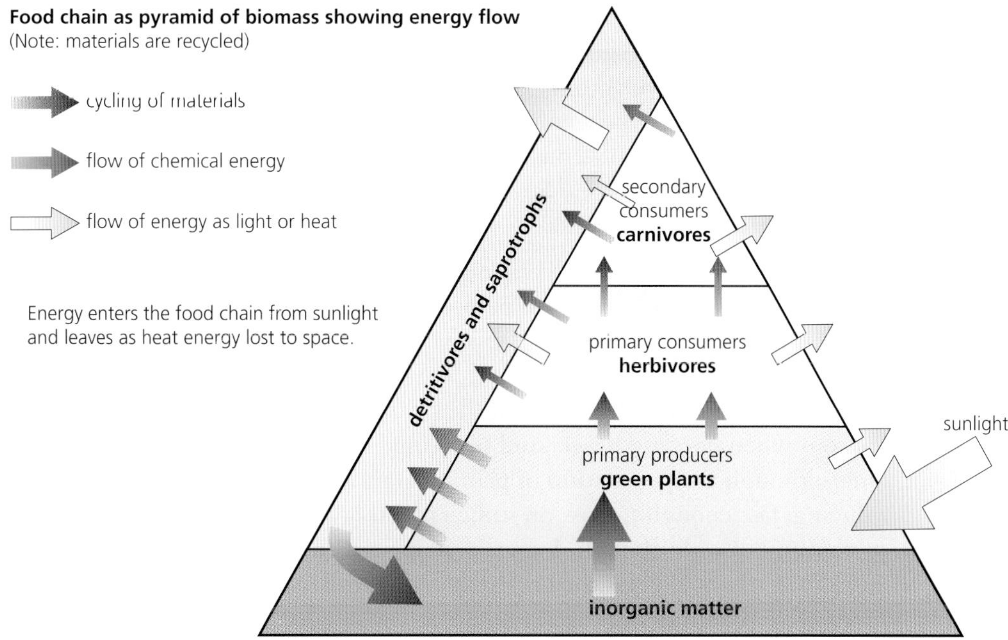

Figure 25.6 Energy flow through a food chain – the pyramid of biomass

Pyramids of energy

Given the problems of pyramids of biomass then the next logical step is to estimate the amount of energy available in each trophic level and to draw a pyramid of energy (Figure 25.7). Once again there are tables that will convert simple dry biomass measurements into energy content for each organism. The units for energy are expressed as $\mathrm{kJ\,m^{-2}\,yr^{-1}}$ and you will notice that the final term includes a time element, in this case $\mathrm{yr^{-1}}$. This is a vital part of the total energy calculation and overcomes the difficulties of different life-spans, even though it makes accurate measurement even more difficult.

Only energy taken in at one trophic level and then built in as chemical energy in the molecules making up the cells and tissues is available to the next trophic level. This is about 10% of the energy.

The reasons are as follows.

- Much energy is used for cell respiration to provide energy for growth, movement, feeding, and all other essential life processes.
- Not all food eaten can be digested. Some passes out with the faeces. Indigestible matter includes bones, hair, feathers, and lignified fibres in plants.
- Not all organisms at each trophic level are eaten. Some escape predation.

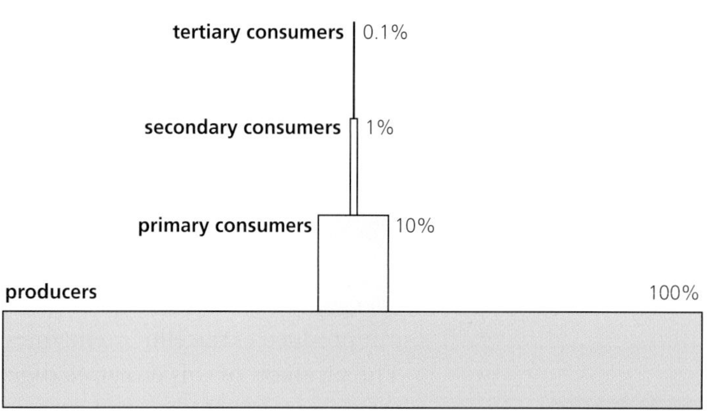

Figure 25.7 A generalised pyramid of energy

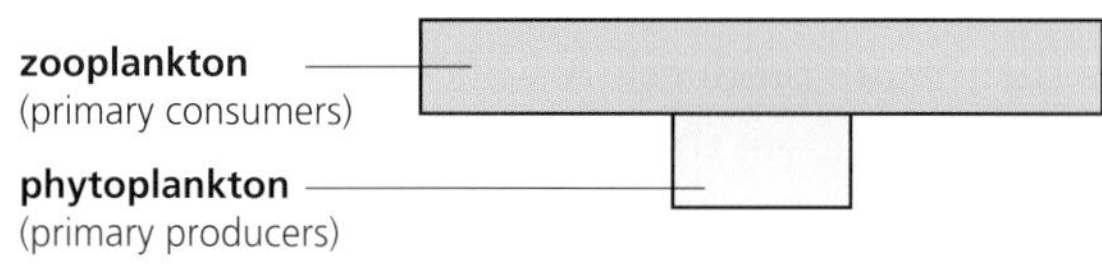

Figure 25.8 Phytoplankton and zooplankton – an inverted pyramid

Why this is so important can easily be demonstrated by considering another difficulty with pyramids. A single set of measurements only gives us a snapshot at one instant in time, but we know that ecosystems are subject to many fluctuations. We can show the problem by looking at yet another pyramid. Figure 25.8 shows the pattern of a very simple pyramid (dry biomass) obtained from data measured in the sea just off the coast of the British Isles.

Phytoplankton are the microscopic algae found in the oceans that photosynthesise and are therefore primary producers. Although often overlooked, they play a vital part in maintaining oxygen balance in the atmosphere as two thirds of the Earth's surface is ocean. Zooplankton are a diverse group of tiny marine invertebrates that feed off the phytoplankton, so are classic primary consumers. Zooplankton are a crucial step in a large number of marine food chains. The data have repeatedly been shown to be accurate, but why are things upside down?

The explanation is simple but a cautionary reminder that you must think carefully about exactly how data have been collected before you jump to conclusions. It is quite true that the biomass of the consumers is higher than that of the producers in this sample. However, this is just a single sample at one time. If we study things more carefully we find that the reproduction rate of the plankton is very high, especially in summer conditions when days are longer and sea temperatures are higher. Therefore at any one time, although the population of plankton appears to be too small, they are rapidly reproducing, fast enough to pass on sufficient energy to maintain a very high population of consumers, even though, logically, it appears that the ecosystem is about to collapse. However, if you express the energy content available in a fixed time you return to a predictable pyramid shape.

Test yourself

8 State the main drawback of using pyramids of numbers to illustrate feeding relationships.

9 Explain why it is essential to consider dry mass of organisms.

10 Suggest why simple dry mass or energy content of an oak tree is not directly comparable with that of the insects living upon it.

11 Explain how ecologists overcome the problem of having to kill organisms in order to determine their dry mass.

The role of microorganisms in an ecosystem

Microorganisms and the recycling of energy

All organisms in all trophic levels produce waste and eventually die. Although, as you have seen, a good deal of the energy contained within each trophic level is lost during transfer to the next, significant amounts of energy remain in the organic molecules, such as cellulose, lignin, lipids, carbohydrates and proteins of dead organisms. Much of this energy is recycled by microorganisms, especially bacteria and fungi. Microorganisms can produce extracellular enzymes that break down dead tissues in decay processes. The products of this enzymic digestion are then reabsorbed into the cells of the microorganisms to be used as respiratory substrates or raw material for synthesis. This method of nutrition is known as saprotrophic (or saprobiontic) nutrition.

Key term

Saprotrophs Mainly fungi and bacteria; feed by secreting extracellular enzymes to break down dead organic matter and reabsorb the products; also known as saprobionts.

You may not be aware of the activities of **saprotrophs**, but without them our world would be covered in a layer many hundreds of metres thick, consisting of leaf litter and woody tissue mixed with dead animal remains and their waste products. A walk in woodland during the autumn will provide you with some clues about the activities of many fungi. At this time of year it is possible to see many different mushroom-like growths. This is the 'tip of the iceberg' as these are only the spore-producing bodies of the fungus. What lies beneath is a large network of fine threads, known as **hyphae**, forming a network called a **mycelium**, and it is these hyphae that secrete the enzymes and reabsorb the products. The activities of countless bacteria are even less visible to the naked eye.

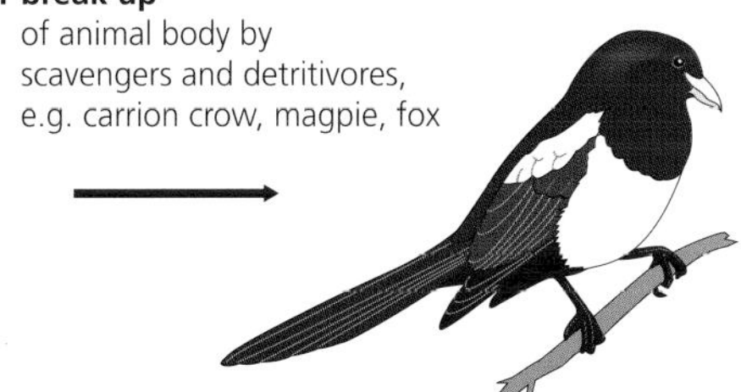

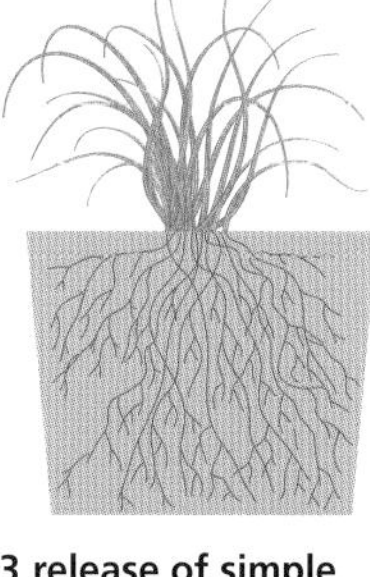

• firstly on simple nutrients such as sugars, amino acids, fatty acids
• secondly on polysaccharides, proteins, lipids

1 break up
• firstly on simple nutrients such as sugars, amino acids, fatty acids
• secondly on polysaccharides, proteins, lipids
• thirdly on resistant molecules of the body, such as keratin and collagen
of plant body by detritivores, e.g. slugs and snails, earthworms, wood-boring insects

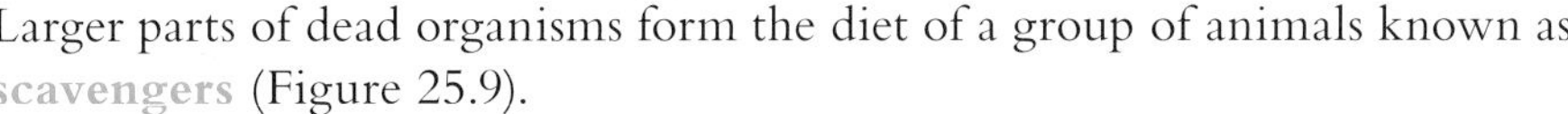

Figure 25.9 The sequence of organisms involved in decay

Figure 25.10 A detrivore – *Gammarus pulex*

Larger parts of dead organisms form the diet of a group of animals known as **scavengers** (Figure 25.9).

Dead organisms, especially plants, become broken down or decay and form a valuable food source, which is also recycled by a whole range of animals known as **detrivores**. For example, the enormous numbers of leaves that fall into streams and rivers are often broken down by the water flow and rocks under the surface. The particles formed are the main food supply for very large numbers of the freshwater shrimp, *Gammarus pulex* (Figure 25.10). This small shrimp is a vital part of freshwater ecosystems as it is the major food source for many freshwater fish. Earthworms, and slugs and snails are also described as detrivores and they play an important part in the physical breakdown of dead materials as well as recycling them. All ecosystems have their unique pattern of saprotrophs, scavengers and detrivores.

Key terms

Scavengers Opportunist feeders on the remains of dead animals.

Detritivores Animals that feed off dead and decaying organic materials. They are important recyclers in all ecosystems.

Microorganisms and the recycling of nutrients

Recycling is essential for the survival of living things because the available resources of many elements are strictly limited. The activities of bacteria and microorganisms in decay not only make some of the energy in dead organisms available to other food chains, but also release many of these elements locked up within them. These become part of the soil solution, and some may react with chemicals of soil or rock particles before becoming part of living things again when they are reabsorbed by plants.

Nitrogen is a particularly important element. It is a component of proteins and nucleic acids. There is an abundance of nitrogen in the biosphere since it makes up almost 80 per cent of the atmosphere. However, nitrogen molecules in the air are not directly available to plants and animals. This is because the bonds in molecules of nitrogen (N_2 or dinitrogen) are very strong and a great deal of energy is required to break them. Plants and animals cannot do this. Instead, plants take up nitrogen from the soil in the form of compounds such as nitrate and ammonium ions. From these nitrogen compounds plants are able to manufacture the amino acids they require.

Animals take in 'ready-made' proteins in their diet, digest them to amino acids and absorb them. The amino acids are then used to rebuild the animal's own specific proteins. This is a fundamental difference between plant and animal nutrition.

The cycling processes by which essential elements are released and reused are called biogeochemical cycles, and the nitrogen cycle (Figure 25.11) is one of the most important.

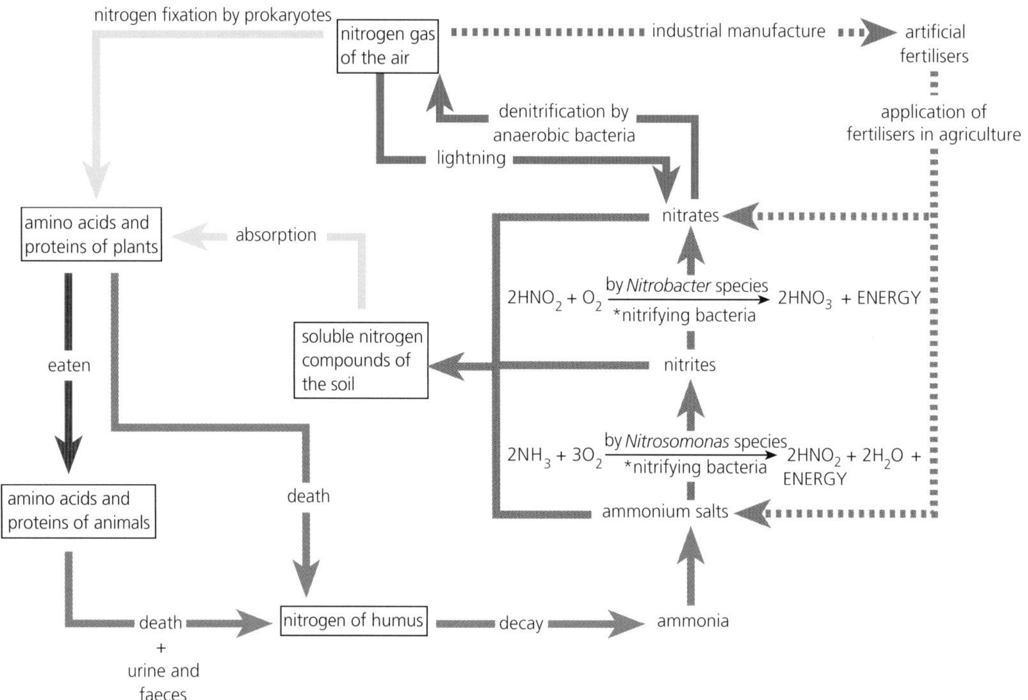

Figure 25.11 The nitrogen cycle

The process of converting ammonium compounds released by the decay of plant and animal materials into nitrates (nitrification), which can be absorbed by plant roots, is an excellent example of the role of bacteria in these cycles. Notice that these are oxidation reactions, which take place inside the bacterial cells (intracellular) where the enzymes are located, and these reactions are the way in which the bacteria gain their energy. A look back at the description of the bacteria in the hydrothermal vent ecosystems will remind you that this is **chemosynthesis** and that it is different from the saprotrophic nutrition involved in the decay process.

A careful look at the nitrogen cycle will also reveal that, because ammonium and nitrate compounds are very soluble, they can often be washed out of the soil and lost to the ecosystem by **leaching**. Terrestrial ecosystems cannot thrive without some means of replacing this loss. **Nitrogen-fixing bacteria**, often of the genus ***Rhizobium***, are found in root nodules of leguminous plants. They are able to convert nitrogen gas from the atmosphere into ammonium compounds and therefore play a vital role in maintaining levels of nitrogen available to the ecosystem.

The natural nitrogen cycle cannot keep pace with the demands of modern agriculture, where intensive farming of high yields of a single crop (monoculture) removes large quantities of nitrogen-containing ions from the soil. To compensate, the addition of industrially produced nitrogen-containing compounds is essential.

Key terms

Leaching The loss of soluble materials in soil caused by water flow.

Nitrogen-fixing bacteria Bacteria capable of converting atmospheric nitrogen in to ammonium ions using ATP.

***Rhizobium* sp.** An important group of nitrogen-fixing bacteria found in the root nodules of leguminous plants.

Test yourself

12 Describe the difference between chemosynthesis and saprotrophic nutrition.

13 Explain why nitrogen is such an important element to living organisms.

14 What is meant by 'nitrogen fixation'?

15 Nitrogen-fixing bacteria are essential to maintain levels of nitrogen circulating in an ecosystem. Explain why.

Estimating population size and distribution in a habitat

Unlike a highly controlled laboratory investigation, ecological investigations often involve many variables that cannot all be adequately controlled. This means they need even more careful planning and cautious interpretation.

We will begin here by considering how you might, first of all, obtain accurate data about what organisms are present in a habitat and what is the pattern of their distribution. This will give you many clues about the complex interrelationships within this habitat and the whole ecosystem. The very first problem you encounter is exactly what method would be suitable to count your chosen organisms. Your choice will need to be very different if you wish to include mobile animals such as mice and voles as opposed to the plants in some grassland. Ecologists use several methods of actually recording abundance, which are selected according to the organism being counted. The methods chosen must be both reliable and practical. For example, it is easy to count the number of individual crabs found on a rocky shore within a few square metres but an almost impossible, and extremely time-consuming task to assess the huge number of barnacles in the same way.

Methods of assessing abundance

- **Individual counts** – the simplest method to use provided numbers are reasonably low and each individual is easily distinguished.
- **Percentage cover** – used where individual organisms form continuous cover on a surface, for example lichens covering a rock surface or dense grass cover.
- **ACFOR scales** (Table 25.2) – these are used for more approximate assessments where abundance is measured on a five-point scale. There are tables defining how these scales might be applied to different organisms to make data comparable across different investigators. ACFOR data are useful in displaying comparative overall patterns but cannot be used statistically. A very similar DAFOR scale is often used for plant species (D = Dominant here).

Table 25.2 An example of an ACFOR scale for small barnacles

ACFOR rating	Numbers per unit area
Abundant	100+ 0.1 m^{-2}
Common	10–99 0.1 m^{-2}
Frequent	1–9 0.1 m^{-2}
Occasional	1–99 m^{-2}
Rare	<1 m^{-2}

Sampling

It is normally impossible to measure everything in a whole habitat or ecosystem, therefore samples of smaller areas are taken from which inferences can be drawn. This is useful because it makes the investigation possible, but might not tell the whole story. Sampling can also introduce bias. For example, if you are measuring the heights of some plants you are more likely to select taller plants than to search for shorter examples. If you are sampling coloured molluscs you are much more likely to select brightly coloured examples that catch your eye.

Quadrats

A **quadrat** is simply a frame that outlines an area of known size for sampling purposes. The size of the quadrat used is determined by the actual habitat and organisms to be counted. The most common sizes are square quadrats of 1 m × 1 m or 0.5 m × 0.5 m (remember, this is a 0.25 m^2 not a 0.5 m^2 area, so be careful how you record it!). However, much smaller quadrats may be needed, as shown in the barnacle ACFOR scale in Table 25.2.

A **gridded quadrat** is a frame quadrat modified by adding strings to form extra squares within the frame as shown in Figure 25.13 on the next page. This helps in ensuring organisms are not counted twice and is particularly useful when making estimates of percentage cover.

A **point frame** (Figure 25.12) is a adaptation of the same idea which is used where there is particularly dense vegetation that makes estimation of numbers in a whole frame very difficult. It consists of a frame with 10 pointed metal pins. The frame is placed at the chosen sampling points and only the plant touching the ten points of the metal pins is recorded.

Sand deposited by the sea and blown by the wind builds into small heaps around pioneer xerophytic plants, such as marram and couch grass, at coasts where the prevailing wind is on-shore. The tufts of leaves growing through the sand accelerate deposition, and gradually drifting sands gather a dense cover of vegetation. Fixed sand dunes are formed.

point frame quadrat in use

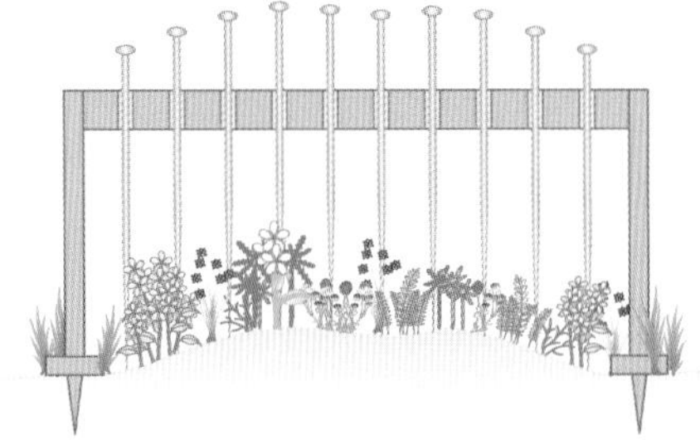

The frame is randomly placed a large number of times, the 10 pins lowered in turn onto vegetation and the species (or bare ground) recorded.

Figure 25.12 A point frame

Random sampling

Having decided upon your method of actual counting you must now think about exactly where to count your samples. This is where you will need to use your planning skills and some thought. Habitats are so varied that you must select the most appropriate type of sampling according to the area you are studying and the hypothesis you are investigating.

One of the most common approaches is to compare two fairly large areas to discover if there are any significant differences between them. In this case we often use a large marked area as a grid and select points to sample within it using a table of random numbers or a random number function on a calculator as shown in Figure 25.13.

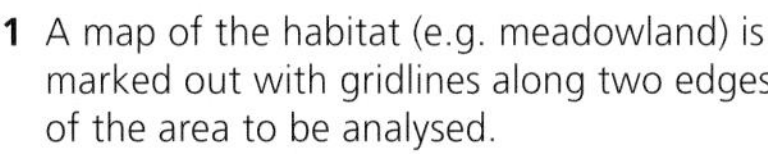

1 A map of the habitat (e.g. meadowland) is marked out with gridlines along two edges of the area to be analysed.

2 Coordinates for placing quadrats are obtained as sequences of random numbers, using computer software, or a calculator, or published tables.

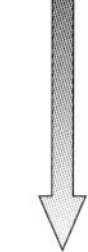

3 Within each quadrat, the individual species are identified, and then the density, frequency, cover or abundance of each species is estimated.

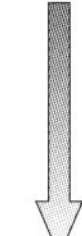

4 Density, frequency, cover, or abundance estimates are then quantified by measuring the total area of the habitat (the area occupied by the population) in square metres. The mean density, frequency, cover or abundance can be calculated, using the equation:

$$\text{population size} = \frac{\text{mean density (etc.) per quadrat} \times \text{total area}}{\text{area of each quadrat}}$$

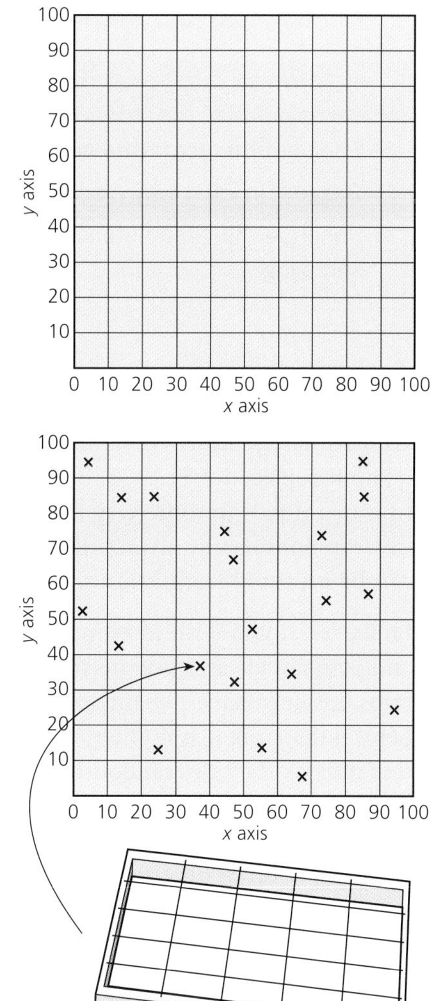

Figure 25.13 Random locating of quadrats

A second very common method of random sampling is to use a **transect**. Transects are simply a graduated line across the area you wish to study. Quadrats or point frames are placed at regular intervals along the line to make the required counts. Transects are most useful when you are investigating the effect of a gradient of factors across the habitat, for example changes in a sand dune system as you move inland, or as you move away from wetter areas on the banks of a river towards drier areas up a slope.

If the transect is short then you might use intervals where the quadrats touch each other; this would form a **continuous belt transect**. For much longer transects you would select intervals that give you a sensible number of quadrats to assess but do not miss any obvious ecological changes along the line. This is an **interrupted transect**.

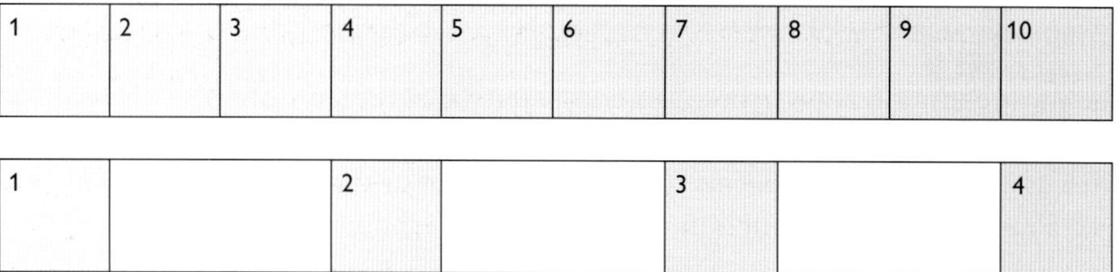

Figure 25.14 Continuous and interrupted transects

Test yourself

16 Spell out the acronyms ACFOR and DAFOR in full.

17 Suggest in what way a scale such as ACFOR is inaccurate.

18 Describe the circumstances in which it is advisable to use a transect method of sampling.

Assessing abundance of mobile populations

The methods described so far depend heavily on the organisms being sedentary. Unfortunately most wild animals are not so cooperative and do not sit around whilst a quadrat is placed over them or a transect line passes by. Therefore it is usually necessary to trap animals in some way in order to count them. Nocturnal insects can be trapped in large numbers by attracting them with a bright light, whilst others such as butterflies can be captured using large soft nets.

However, if you wish to estimate the populations of ground animals that move quickly and over a wide area you need to employ other techniques. There are many designs of traps but most have a chamber where suitable bait is placed and a trapdoor that closes behind the animal as it enters, without injuring it. The most common method of doing this is to set the traps randomly over a wide area, mark any animals caught and release them. This is repeated over a long period and careful records kept of the numbers of marked and unmarked animals recaptured. The principle of the method is that after a suitable period of time the marked animals will mix with the unmarked animals. The results will be that further trapping will give you data where the ratio of marked to unmarked that you recapture will be the same as that in the whole population. Since you know precisely how many you have marked, then the only unknown will be the number in the whole population, so you can calculate that as shown in the equation below. For obvious reasons this is known as the **mark-release-recapture** (MRR method).

$$\frac{N}{n} = \frac{K}{k}$$

Where N = total number of animals in the population

n = total number of animals recaptured

K = total number of animals marked

k = total number of recaptured animals that were marked

Since we know how many we marked it is possible to calculate the number in the whole population as follows:

$$N = \frac{nK}{k}$$

There are a lot of mathematical assumptions in making this calculation that can lead to significant errors, but if carried out over a reasonably short time, many are acceptable.

- The population must be large to make this fraction representative.
- All of the animals must mix randomly and stay together in the test area.
- The marking must not make the animals unacceptable to their population.
- There is no death, migration or births to change the numbers you are using.

Safety and ethics in ecological investigations

Risks

As with all investigations the first consideration in planning must always be, is this safe to perform? There needs to be a serious review in order to answer this question, not just a casual, subjective decision. This review takes the form of a **risk assessment**.

As the name suggests this must be an assessment that reaches conclusions, not just a simple listing of possible dangers. There are many forms of risk assessment but they tend to follow a common pattern.

- What are the principle risks involved?
- How can I plan my investigation to eliminate all risks?
- If I cannot eliminate all risks, what measures must I take to reduce these risks to an acceptable level?

When making final decisions, the level of risk will depend on two things: (a) the likelihood of it happening and (b) the consequences if it were to happen.

If both these are high, then the investigation should not be undertaken unless the likelihood can be reduced to a very low level.

Field investigations mean you will encounter very different and often more serious risks than in the laboratory. First and foremost, personal safety should be a priority, as many habitats such as rocky shores and exposed locations such as moorland mean that there are significant dangers. Obvious precautions, such as not working alone, and consulting weather forecasts and tide tables, are vital. Similarly, having a means of communication is important should help be required. Mobile phones are very useful but make sure their batteries are fully charged!

Field study centres often use numbers to quantify the dangers and likelihood of risks, where the totals for any investigation can indicate the need for more precautions or refusal of permission to go ahead.

Ethical issues

Ethical issues are not simply about deciding between right and wrong; they very often include complex decisions to which there is more than one obvious logical answer. Above all, there are many different and often very logically argued, ethical viewpoints, which are justifiably held by different people.

In any ecological study you would at least expect biologists to adhere to two main ethical ideas:

1 Any investigation should do minimal harm to the environment.

2 All living things should be treated with respect.

Therefore, planning an ecological investigation should always involve both these principles, ensuring that such damage as trampling or sampling is kept to the absolute minimum and that simple measures such as removing all litter are strictly adhered to.

Just to illustrate how complicated things can become, what do we mean by treating all living things with 'respect'? The criminal law lays down some strict guidelines about the use of animals in scientific investigations. Special licences are needed to carry out investigations using mammals for example, but this does not apply to many other animals, generally ectotherms. So you can be prosecuted for using inhumane traps for wild animals that may cause them suffering, but Britain's most popular outdoor sport, angling, involves hauling fish from the water by a hook through the sensitive tissues in their mouth. So why should a fish be treated differently from a vole? You may be an angler and argue that the fish suffer no significant harm, or you may dislike the practice and hold different views.

This type of dilemma and differing ethical stances are very common subjects for debates.

Test yourself

19 In assessing a population using a method involving marking organisms, it is important that the marking does not stimulate a response from other members of the population. Suggest why.

20 Describe an instance when you might consider using an interrupted transect rather than a continuous transect.

21 Describe a situation when you would use a point frame in preference to an open quadrat.

22 State what fraction of $1\,m^2$ is covered by the area of a $0.5\,m \times 0.5\,m$ quadrat.

Core Practical 15

Investigate the effect of differing sampling methods on estimates of the size of a population, taking into account the safe and ethical use of organisms

Background information

Whilst this practical (and Core practical 16) are designed to give you practice in using the ecological techniques described, this is not their main purpose. This practical aims to give you the opportunity to plan a whole investigation and to analyse your data statistically. You will find a simple summary of some of the important points about statistics at the end of this chapter, but the mathematical skills section (Chapter 27) gives much more detail.

The suggested method on the next page is given as an illustration, as the investigation you will perform will depend on the habitat that is available and the apparatus you can use. The principles, however, will be exactly the same no matter what populations you assess.

Remember that you are trying to compare two methods to see if they give the same result or, if they differ, is this statistically significant or simply expected variation?

In this method you are using any area of mown grassland and comparing assessment by a transect with assessment by random sampling, but you can also try comparing the effect of using a large quadrat with using a small quadrat (say 1 m × 1 m vs 0.5 m × 0.5 m) or compare using a quadrat with using a point frame. Comparing the methods of counting individuals and assessing percentage cover can also be interesting. The plants you are using are common to most grassland – plantains or dandelions.

If you are using plantains you need to be able to identify the two main species (Figure 25.15) that you are likely to find and make sure you count only one species. You can find many sources to help you identify these on the web, but remember to check the sites you use carefully. Many of the websites originate in the USA or other countries and whilst they are often very good, they do not always describe the same species you might find in this country. The Science and Plants in Schools website (SAPS) is a good place to start. The illustrations below will help you.

Figure 25.15 The two common species of plantain. Left: greater plantain (*Plantago major*); right: ribwort plantain *(Plantago lanceolata)*

Dandelions are much easier to identify but do make sure that you can distinguish them from the plantains, especially the ones without flowers. (Check the edges of the leaves and the main veins in the leaf if you are not sure.)

Carrying out the investigation

Aim: To compare the assessment of population numbers using random sampling and a transect.

Risk assessment: If you use the school field then the risks will probably be very limited, but there are possible dangers that need very simple checks. Are there any groups practising athletic field events? Has the field been treated recently with fertilisers (or weedkillers). If you are using any other habitat you must check with your teacher. Always wash your hands thoroughly after working outside, and before any hand to mouth contact.

1 First of all, make sure that you and any partners are confident in identifying your chosen plants. Then start with some basic observations of the whole area. Make sure that you select an area where there are plenty of plantains and that the area you select does not have any other obvious factors that could affect their distribution, for example large trees giving big patches of light and shade, a large slope that might be far wetter at one end, a part of a football field that gets heavy wear or has large bare patches. In other words, try to make sure you select your large sample area to mitigate the effect of other variables.
2 The next step is to decide on a sensible number of samples for each method. You might make a quick trial to see how long it takes for each quadrat reading and match your sampling to the time you have available.

3 To test random sampling, use two tapes, about 100 m long, at right angles and set up a grid system as shown in Figure 25.13. If you do not have tapes this long then lay a metre ruler on the ground at a suitable start point to indicate your first axis, and generate a random number. (You can generate random numbers on most scientific calculators or use printed copies of random number tables.) Walk the number of paces indicated by the first two random digits along this axis then turn 90 degrees and walk the number of paces shown by the second two random digits. At this point lay the quadrat in front of you and count the plantains inside. Repeat this at least 10 times.
4 Using the same start point, lay out a single tape in one direction and count the plantains in another 10 quadrats at points along the tape indicated by random numbers.
Remember, you can choose to investigate other interesting variables, as indicated in the background information, in which case you would simply use the grid system for both.

Data processing

- Make sure that you have at least 10–15 measurements for each method of assessment. If time is short, consider pooling your data with other groups.
- Calculate the mean and standard deviation for each of your two data sets.
- Use a suitable graph to display your data.
- Try to make a subjective judgement to decide if you think the two data sets show there is a difference or are about the same.
- Use your data to test for a significant difference at the 5% significance level (see Chapter 27). You will need to use either a *t*-test or a Mann-Whitney U test.

Questions

1 How do I count a plantain that is partly inside and partly outside the quadrat?
2 What is the easiest way to tell the different between *Plantago lanceolata* and *Plantago major*?
3 Is there any scientific reason why a transect should give a different result from a random sample?
4 Could I just throw the quadrat in a random manner in the area?
5 What would be a null hypothesis for this investigation?
6 What does a '5% confidence level' mean?

Example

A worked example of a *t*-test

Most biologists use computers to carry out the detailed calculations needed to arrive at the test statistic necessary to find the overall probability. You are likely to do the same, but you will be required to carry out some part of a calculation and interpret the results in examination papers. A full detailed calculation such as this will take some time and it is unlikely this amount of time will be available, but you will certainly need to be familiar with substituting values in parts of an equation and be able to manipulate a formula.

Don't panic!

The *t*-test is, by far, the most complicated calculation of any of the main statistical tests; others are much more straightforward (see the correlation test in Chapter 26).

Make sure you learn the principles of statistical testing outlined in Chapter 27, Mathematics for biology. An understanding of these will assist you in gaining a good proportion of the marks available in this type of question. Don't simply switch off because it contains a little more mathematics. Use your core practical work and other examples to become familiar with the calculations.

Try the specimen examination question at the end of this chapter and, as you will see, such questions are often well-structured to guide you through.

Table 25.3 A worked example of a t-test based on some typical results of Core practical 15

	Numbers of plantains in transect quadrats (x_1)	Numbers of plantains in random quadrats(x_2)	
	10	8	
	3	9	
	9	7	
	7	11	
	5	3	
	8	5	
	5	4	
	6	7	
	4	9	
	7	9	
Σx	64	72	Total (= sum of the 10 quadrat values)
n	10	10	sample number
$\bar{x}$	6.4	7.2	Mean (= $\frac{\text{total}}{n}$)
Σx^2	454	576	Sum of the squares of each quadrat value
$(\Sigma x)^2$	4096	5184	Square of the total (Σx). It is not the same as Σx^2
$\frac{(\Sigma x)^2}{n}$	409.6	518.4	
Σd^2	44.4	57.6	$\Sigma d^2 = \Sigma x^2 - \frac{(\Sigma x)^2}{n}$
σ^2	4.9	6.4	$\sigma^2 = \frac{\Sigma x^2}{(n-1)}$
$\sigma d^2 = \frac{\sigma_1^2}{n_1} = \frac{\sigma_2^2}{n_2}$	4.9 + 6.4 = 11.3	σd^2 is the variance of the difference between the means	
σd	3.36	σd^2 (the standard deviation of the difference between the means)	
$t = \frac{\bar{x}_1^2 - \bar{x}_1^2}{\sigma d}$	$\frac{6.4 - 7.2}{3.36}$ = 0.238	ignore minus sign	

So you now have a *t* value which you can use to check how likely it is that your results come from the same population.

To do this you look up the value in *t*-test tables as shown in Table 25.4.

Table 25.4 Table of critical values of *t*

Degrees of freedom	Significance level					
	20% (0.20)	10% (0.10)	5% (0.05)	2% (0.02)	1% (0.01)	0.1% (0.001)
1	3.078	6.314	12.706	31.821	63.657	636.619
2	1.886	2.920	4.303	6.965	9.925	31.598
3	1.638	2.353	3.182	4.541	5.841	12.941
4	1.533	2.132	2.776	3.747	4.604	8.610
5	1.476	2.015	2.571	3.365	4.032	6.859
6	1.440	1.943	2.447	3.143	3.707	5.959
7	1.415	1.895	2.365	2.998	3.499	5.405
8	1.397	1.860	2.306	2.896	3.355	5.041
9	1.383	1.833	2.262	2.821	3.250	4.781
10	1.372	1.812	2.228	2.764	3.169	4.587
11	1.363	1.796	2.201	2.718	3.106	4.437
12	1.356	1.782	2.179	2.681	3.055	4.318
13	1.350	1.771	2.160	2.650	3.012	4.221
14	1.345	1.761	2.145	2.624	2.977	4.140
15	1.341	1.753	2.131	2.602	2.947	4.073
16	1.337	1.746	2.120	2.583	2.921	4.015
17	1.333	1.740	2.110	2.567	2.989	3.965
18	1.330	1.734	2.101	2.552	2.878	3.922
19	1.328	1.729	2.093	2.539	2.861	3.883
20	1.325	1.725	2.086	2.528	2.845	3.850
21	1.323	1.721	2.080	2.518	2.831	3.819
22	1.321	1.717	2.074	2.508	2.819	3.792
23	1.319	1.714	2.069	2.500	2.807	3.767
24	1.318	1.711	2.064	2.492	2.797	3.745
25	1.316	1.708	2.060	2.485	2.787	3.725
26	1.315	1.706	2.056	2.479	2.779	3.707
27	1.314	1.703	2.052	2.473	2.771	3.690
28	13.13	1.701	2.048	2.467	2.763	3.674
29	1.311	1.699	2.043	2.462	2.756	3.659
30	1.310	1.697	2.042	2.457	2.750	3.646
40	1.303	1.684	2.021	2.423	2.704	3.551
60	1.296	1.671	2.000	2.390	2.660	3.460
120	1.289	1.658	1.980	2.158	2.617	3.373
∝	1.282	1.645	1.960	2.326	2.576	3.291

When you do so you will find another term that you need to understand. The left-hand column is entitled '**degrees of freedom**', so what does this mean? When checking what your *t*-value means in terms of the probability of the two sets of measurements coming from the same population, it is very important to know just how many samples you took. The probability will change if you had taken 100 samples and not 10. So you need to look at the row that corresponds to the total number samples, but for reasons not important here, you subtract one from each set of samples.

So, in your example, degrees of freedom = (10 – 1) + (10 – 1) = 18.

The general expression for this is $(n_1 - 1) + (n_2 - 1)$.

If you have consulted the principles of statistical testing in Chapter 27, you will know that biologists use a 5% significance level as the benchmark for deciding whether to accept or reject the null hypothesis. If there are less than 5 chances in one hundred that your data could come from the same population then you will reject the null hypothesis (and be able to state that there is a significant difference).

At last, we reach the final stage. You know that you are looking for the 5% column and that you want the row for 18 degrees of freedom.

The critical value here is 2.101, but your *t* value is only 0.238. To reject your null hypothesis your value must be *greater* than this critical value. Hence, you must accept your null hypothesis and your conclusion from the *t*-test is 'There is **no significant difference** between the density of plantains measured using random quadrats and the density of plantains using quadrats on a line transect.'

Notice we have been quite precise to include exactly what the hypothesis was all about.

We have deliberately chosen an example here where there is no significant difference. This is partly because there is a tendency to dismiss such conclusions as a failure or, 'it didn't work!' Scientifically, nothing could be further from the truth. Showing there is no difference can be just as valuable, when amassing evidence to support or challenge a suggested model, as any other conclusion.

Two other technical points

Most biologists now carry out calculations like these on computers and there are many programmes to allow you to do this. However, they will require you to choose exactly which variation of the *t*-test you want to use and therefore it is important you understand what to select.

- **Paired or unpaired test?** – paired data means that the samples you take are always linked together because by taking one of the samples you always determine the position of the other. For example, if you wish to compare the lichen cover on a tree trunk on the north and south facing sides, you can place a small quadrat on the north side and count the lichens. If you then simply take a second reading at exactly the same position but move around to the south side you will have paired data where the position of one determines the position of the other. This is quite rare so you would normally select 'unpaired'.
- **One- or two-tailed test?** – almost all of the tests you are likely to perform will be two-tailed tests. Therefore choose this option. The technical reasons behind this are not essential for you to look at in detail here.

Chapter summary

Energy flow in ecosystems

- Members of one species living together are a population. A community is a group of populations living together.
- The biosphere is the total area of the Earth inhabited by living things. Within it are numerous smaller suitable areas called habitats.
- An ecosystem is a group of communities, their links with each other and their surroundings.
- The simplest links are food chains but these rarely exist in isolation as organisms normally have several sources of food, which are better represented by food webs.
- Levels of feeding relationships are trophic levels. Producers are autotrophic organisms, producing food from simple molecules in the surroundings (often photosynthetic). Consumers are named according to their position in the chain, primary, secondary, tertiary and so on.
- Ecosystems depend on energy flow between all the different levels. Gross primary productivity (GPP) is the amount of energy per unit area per year that is fixed by producers. Net primary productivity (NPP) is the amount of energy actually available to the next trophic level.
- Typically only about 5% of GPP ends up as NPP so food chains are usually quite short as there is not enough energy flowing through to sustain another level.
- The main loss of energy at each level is from respiration of substrates and the subsequent use of ATP. Active animals lose large amounts of energy as heat to the atmosphere and in moving around. This can be summarised as NPP = GPP – R, where R = energy lost in respiration.
- The classic model of ecosystems starts with sunlight energy trapped in photosynthesis. But recently thriving ecosystems have been found around mid-ocean vents in total darkness where the starting point is chemosynthesis of minerals released from deep in the Earth's crust.

Microorganisms in ecosystems

- In all ecosystems animals and plants die. The energy and materials locked up in them are released by fungi and bacteria known as saprophytes.
- Other scavengers such as vultures or detrivores such as earthworms and freshwater shrimps also recycle materials.
- Some of the most important ions that are recycled are nitrates. This is because they are used to form the amino groups for protein synthesis and are readily soluble in soil water for uptake by plants. During the nitrogen cycle bacteria convert the ammonia released in decay to ammonium compounds and then it is oxidised by other chemosynthetic bacteria to nitrites and nitrates.

Ecological investigations

- Ecology provides biologists with excellent opportunities to design their own investigations because ecosystems are so varied that you are almost certain to be finding some original answers and not demonstrating some textbook 'fact'.
- Working with real living things often means there are many variables that cannot be controlled and so provides excellent training in realising exactly what conclusions can and cannot be drawn from the data collected.
- Sampling is a vital part of ecology so the use of quadrats and point frames is common but their application needs to be carefully thought out using truly random sampling. You will be expected to have experience of such techniques from your core practicals.
- As a biologist you will also be expected to carry out any investigations with respect for the habitats you are using and apply basic risk assessments to ensure your own safety.
- Ecological investigations always show the inherent variability of living things. This means that significant differences can often be hidden and that statistical testing is the only way to make valid conclusions. This is an obvious place to familiarise yourself with the different types of statistical test, starting with the example of a *t*-test in this chapter and using the further details in the 'Mathematics for biology' chapter (Chapter 27).

Practice questions

1 An ecosystem can be described as a balanced, self-regulating system because:

A the numbers of plants and animals within it do not change

B there are always more producers than consumers

C photosynthesis will always provide the same input of energy

D natural cycles and feeding relationships normally interact to keep things stable *(1)*

2 In statistical testing, a 5% confidence level indicates:

A there are 5 chances in 100, or less, that the samples might come from the same population

B there are 95 chances in 100, or less, that the samples might come from the same population

C there is a probability of 0.95, or less, that the samples might come from the same population

D there is a probability of 0.05, or less, that the samples are from exactly the same population *(1)*

3 In the nitrogen cycle, ammonium ions are oxidised to nitrates. This process is known as:

A denitrification

B nitrogen fixation

C nitrification

D nitration *(1)*

4 **a)** Decay processes are often brought about by fungi. Describe the process of saprophytic nutrition from the synthesis of enzymes to the absorption of products. *(4)*

b) What will be the end products of the enzyme digestion of:

i) lipids

ii) cellulose

iii) muscle? *(3)*

5 **a)** **i)** Explain what is meant by chemosynthesis. *(2)*

ii) Explain how chemosynthesis is used by soil bacteria to oxidise ammonium ions to nitrate ions. *(4)*

***b)** Explain how green plants can synthesise amino acids using NADPH $+H^+$ and ATP from the light-dependent stage of photosynthesis and nitrate ions absorbed from soil. *(5)*

Tip

As Questions 1–3 show, multiple-choice questions are not all about simple recall. You need to think carefully, but don't spend too much time puzzling over one mark.

Tip

Question 4 is a straightforward AO1 question, mainly testing knowledge of saprotrophic nutrition. However, it is partially synoptic as you will need to consider the transport of highly active enzymes.

Tip

Question 5 is a typical synoptic question. Whilst part a) is concerned with this chapter, part b) requires you to apply your knowledge of Chapter 14 material on photosynthesis in a slightly different way. You need to be aware that synoptic questions will ask you to switch your concentration from one part of the specification to another quite quickly, and that lots of basic knowledge from earlier in the course will also be needed to answer many questions.

6 A student carried out an investigation into the effect of different light intensities on the length of bracken (*Pteridium aquilinum*) stems. She selected two different areas of woodland; one area that had been cleared in the past year so there was little foliage to block out the light, and a second area where the trees had been allowed to grow for 10 years and was therefore well-shaded.

She randomly sampled each area and measured the height of 10 plants in each.

a) i) Describe **one** method of random sampling that would be appropriate in this investigation. *(3)*

ii) Name **three** other abiotic factors that would need to be controlled or monitored in this investigation. *(1)*

b) The results of this investigation are shown in the table below.

	Height of plant/cm	
	In shaded woodland	**In unshaded woodland**
	47	59
	56	68
	55	39
	32	55
	49	63
	60	40
	45	67
	39	45
	56	42
	44	51
Mean ($\bar{x}$)	48.3	52.9
Standard deviation (σ)	± 8.72	± 11.13
Variance (S^2)	76.03	123.87

The student decided to test if there was a significant difference in height of the two samples using a *t*-test.

i) Calculate the value of *t* using the formula: *(3)*

$$t = \frac{|\bar{x}_1 - \bar{x}_2|}{\sqrt{\frac{s_1^2}{n_1} + \frac{s_1^2}{n_2}}}$$

$\bar{x}$ = mean

s = standard deviation

n = number of entries in a set of data

s^2 = variance

$|\bar{x}_1 - \bar{x}_2|$ = the positive difference between two means

Tip

Question 6 is one of the ways in which your wider practical skills can be tested. You may be asked to make judgments or comment on experimental design for AO3 marks. This is also included to allow you to become familiar with questions involving statistical analysis.

ii) Use your calculated value of *t*, and this extract from a table of critical values of *t*, to explain what conclusions can be drawn from this statistical analysis. *(3)*

Degrees of freedom	Significance level					
	20%	10%	5%	2%	1%	0.1%
17	1.333	1.740	2.110	2.567	2.898	3.965
18	1.330	1.734	2.101	2.552	2.878	3.922
19	1.328	1.729	2.093	2.539	2.861	3.883
20	1.352	1.725	2.086	2.528	2.845	3.850

c) i) Explain what is meant by the term 'standard deviation'. *(2)*

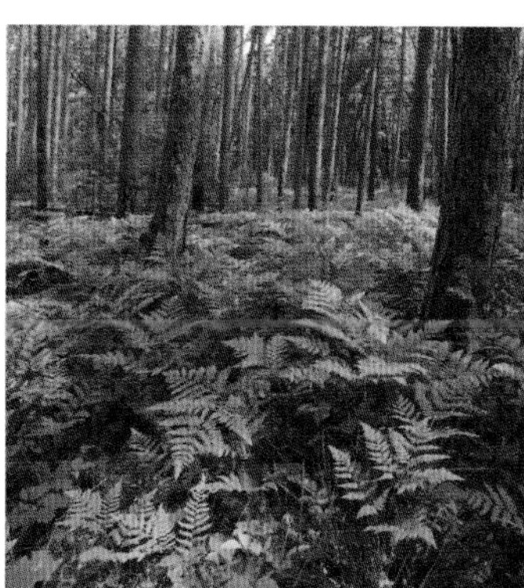

ii) The photograph shows bracken, *Pteridium aquilinum*, growing in a woodland habitat.

Use the information in the photograph and the table of results to comment on the reliability of the conclusions made from these data. *(3)*

Stretch and challenge

7 The nitrogen-fixing bacterium *Rhizobium* sp. is found in the root nodules of leguminous plants.

a) What are root nodules?

b) The relationship between these bacteria and the host plant is known as 'mutualism'. What is meant by 'mutualism' and why is this relationship a good example?

c) The genes involved in nitrogen fixation are known as 'nif' genes.

i) Which enzymes are coded by nif genes?

ii) How do low nitrogen levels affect the expression of nif genes?

iii) The artificial transfer of nif genes into common crop plants is apparently an excellent way of reducing agricultural use of artificial fertilisers, but this has caused great concern. Why might biologists be very concerned about the effect of such crops on ecosystems?

d) Apart from those found in root nodules, what other nitrogen-fixing bacteria are thought to play an important role in nutrient cycles?

26 Changing ecosystems

Prior knowledge

In this chapter you will need to recall that:

➜ populations of living organisms are affected by living and non-living factors in their surroundings
➜ climate, soil and temperature are important factors in determining the distribution of living things
➜ competition between organisms is a constant feature of ecosystems
➜ newly established ecosystems change over time to form stable communities
➜ global warming is causing significant changes to ecosystems
➜ the greenhouse effect is due to increased concentrations of gases such as carbon dioxide in the atmosphere
➜ burning of fossil fuels is a major source of atmospheric carbon dioxide
➜ melting of polar ice and glaciers are indicators of global warming
➜ many countries are attempting to reduce carbon dioxide emissions
➜ solar power, wind power and tidal power are important sources of renewable energy
➜ over-exploitation of natural resources can cause ecosystems to break down.

Test yourself on prior knowledge

1 Name **two** greenhouse gases other than carbon dioxide.
2 Explain why the presence of a greenhouse gas warms the atmosphere.
3 Describe **two** ways in which temperature can affect living cells.
4 State the major way in which carbon dioxide is removed from the atmosphere.
5 Explain what is meant by 'renewable' energy.
6 State the main difficulty in relying on wind or solar power as a main energy source.
7 Explain why tropical rainforests are such an important ecosystem.
8 Explain why tropical rainforest ecosystems are under threat.

Ecosystems – abiotic and biotic factors

We have defined an ecosystem as a stable unit of nature consisting of a community of organisms interacting between themselves and the physical and chemical environment. The living things known as the **biota** form the biotic environment and the physical, non-living factors form the **abiotic** environment. These aspects of ecosystems are so closely related as to be almost inseparable, as you will see shortly. To learn about the working of the ecosystem, however, we need to look at both aspects in more detail. While we do, keep in mind examples of ecosystems you are familiar with, such as woodland or seashore.

Key terms

Biota All of the living things found within an ecosystem.

Biotic factors All of the living influences within an ecosystem.

Abiotic factors All the non-living aspects of an ecosystem.

Introducing abiotic factors

The physical and chemical components of an ecosystem more-or-less determine the physical conditions in which populations live (Figure 26.1).

Abiotic factors of a terrestrial habitat are of three types, relating to:

- climate – factors such as solar radiation, temperature, rainfall and wind
- soil – factors such as the parent rock, soil water and soil chemistry, and the mineral nutrients available (**edaphic factors**)
- topography – factors such as slope and aspect of the land, and altitude.

> **Key term**
>
> **Edaphic factors** Factors that influence an ecosystem that are linked to the soil.

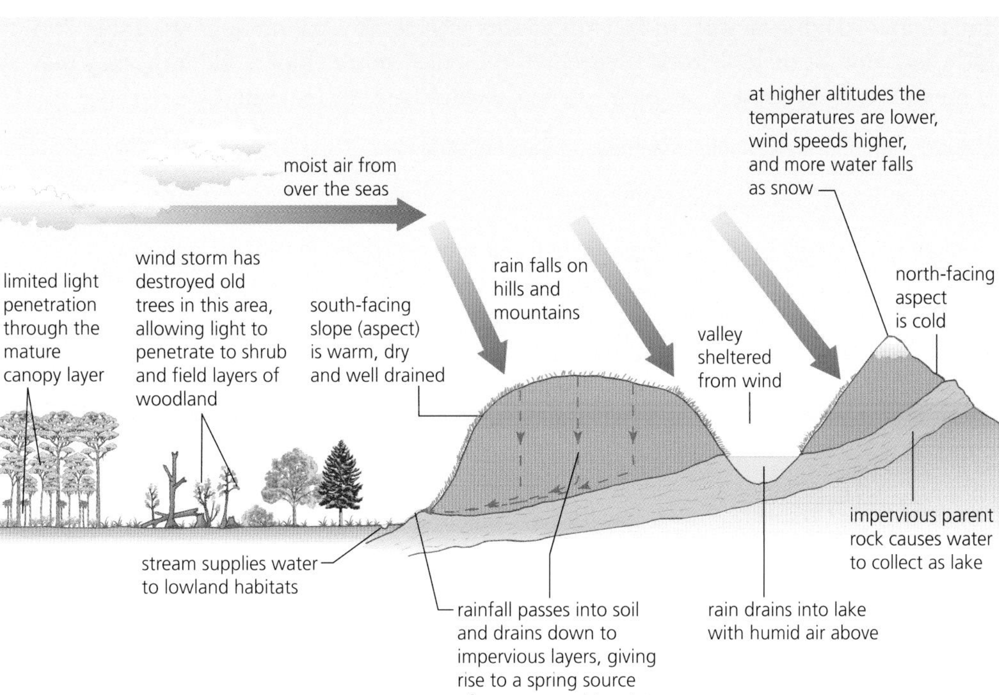

Figure 26.1 Interaction of climate, soil and topography in terrestrial ecosystems

We can illustrate the far-reaching impact of abiotic factors by looking at the effects of solar radiation. Light is the ultimate source of energy for the ecosystem; green plants grow only where there is sufficient light for their autotrophic nutrition. This need for light by green plants has an effect on the structure of plant communities. For example, an area of woodland is stratified into layers from the canopy above to the shrub layer below, the field layer (herbaceous plants) and ground layer (mosses). Each layer has particular plant life adapted to the light regime, and its own fauna. In aquatic habitats, plant life is largely confined to a region close to the surface.

The duration of illumination is the environmental trigger for inducing flowering of many plants, and in the timing of reproduction, migration and hibernation of animals. Light enables animals to see and be seen.

Sunlight is the major source of heat. Very few organisms grow if the temperature of their environment falls outside the range 0–40 °C. The effect of temperature on organisms is direct, as temperature influences the rate of all biochemical reactions. At low temperatures, ice crystals may form in cells, disrupting the cytoplasm. High temperatures denature enzymes, although certain bacteria found in hot springs have evolved tolerance of temperatures above 100 °C.

The length of daily illumination and the intensity of the light are determined by latitude, season, aspect (slope), time of day and the extent of cloud cover. Through its effects on temperature, light intensity also influences humidity.

The measurement of abiotic factors

Which abiotic factors will most strongly influence distribution of particular organisms within a habitat under investigation? We have already noted that the important abiotic factors are climatic factors (light, temperature, water availability and wind) and edaphic factors (the soil, its texture, nutrient status, acidity and moisture content). Topographic factors (angle and aspect of slope, and altitude) operate by their influence on local climate and edaphic factors. In fact, all factors interact to varying degrees. Table 26.1 lists a selection of these factors, their chief influences on the biota, and how they may be measured in a terrestrial habitat, such as a woodland, or in a pond.

Table 26.1 Introducing key abiotic factors and their measurement

Factor		Chief influence on biota	Measurement
Climatic	light	the ultimate source of energy	dedicated digital sensor linked to a sensor meter
	temperature	directly influences rates of biochemical reactions, and has indirect effects on other factors e.g. evaporation	dedicated digital sensor linked to a sensor meter, or a permanently mounted maximum and minimum thermometer
	relative humidity	influences rate of water loss by evaporation, and rate of transpiration in plants	dedicated digital sensor linked to a sensor meter, or a whirling hygrometer
Edaphic	pH	affects availability of nutrient ions that otherwise exist in unavailable forms	dedicated digital sensor linked to a sensor meter, or colorimetrical measurement using a soil test kit
	temperature	affects root growth, microorganism activity, and seed germination	dedicated digital sensor linked to a sensor meter
	texture	relative proportions of different-sized particles affect, among other things, aeration and drainage	hand assessment of soil
Topographical – terrestrial	slope aspect	indirect effects on illumination, temperature, drainage and so on	survey methods, as in profile transect
Topographical – pond	water supply, or flow	ponds with 'spring' source are permanent with relatively stable communities, whereas ponds raised by surface drainage tend to have ephemeral communities	direct observation and measurements of seasonal changes in water levels
	O_2 availability	low or non-existent concentrations of O_2 trigger anaerobic respiration, and favour obligate anaerobic organisms – otherwise, small changes in percentage O_2 concentration in an environment may have little impact on life under generally aerobic conditions	dedicated digital sensor linked to a sensor meter

Introducing biotic factors

The organisms of an ecosystem affect each other (Figure 26.2). Interactions between organisms, known as **biotic factors**, are between members of the same species (**intraspecific competition**) and between members of different species (**interspecific competition**). Of course, the impact of biotic factors depends upon the numbers of organisms present in relation to resources available, within a given environment. So we say that biotic factors are **density dependent**. Furthermore, we can recognise that biotic factors must be highly influential since most species occupy only a small part of the environment in which they are equipped to live.

> **Key terms**
>
> **Intraspecific competition** Competition between members of the same species.
>
> **Interspecific competition** Competition between members of different species.

Herbivory – caterpillars of the monarch butterfly feeding on milkweed leaves

Predation – African lion at the moment of capture of prey (kudo – a savannah herbivore)

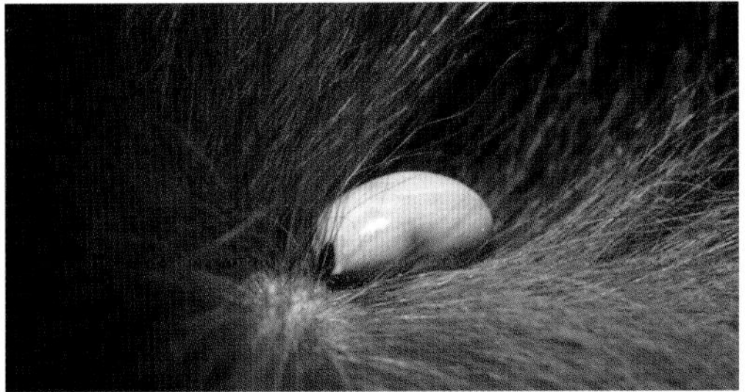

Parasitism – sheep tick (an ectoparasite) attached to the skin of a cat where it has fed on a blood meal

Mutualism – mushroom of the fly agaric fungus takes sugars and amino acids from the tree's roots in return for essential ions, via its hyphae attached below ground

Figure 26.2 Interactions between species

Competition

Plants compete for space, light and mineral nutrients. Animals compete for food, shelter and a mate. To lose out in competition for resources means the individual grows and reproduces more slowly or, in extreme cases, dies. When the fastest growing competitor eliminates a slower growing competitor, it takes over the area completely. This is known as the principle of competitive exclusion.

Predation, grazing and symbiotic relations

Interactions between individuals of different species may also take the form of predation, grazing or symbiosis.

A predator is an organism that feeds on other living species. Predators are normally larger than their prey, and they tend to kill before they eat. The predator's prey is another animal – the eating of plants by herbivorous animals is a very similar process, but is referred to as grazing or browsing. All food webs show numerous examples of both predation and grazing.

Predator–prey relationships may be studied in the laboratory. Experiments show that both populations oscillate naturally. Predators feed on their prey and the population of prey starts to decline. Meanwhile the well-fed predators breed more so their numbers increase. Eventually their food source starts to become scarce and some die through lack of food. As their numbers decline so the number of prey begins to rise and the cycle begins again.

This simple relationship is much more difficult to demonstrate in natural populations, where individual species are part of more than one food chain so changes are not as clear-cut. The numbers of predator and prey pelts received by the Hudson Bay Trading Company of Canada from trappers over a 100 year period was carefully recorded and appears to be a clear example. (Figure 26.3), but the data were not collected by any scientifically organised random trial and could be affected by other factors.

1 *Paramecium* feeding on yeast (*Saccharomyces*)

yeast cells (×300)

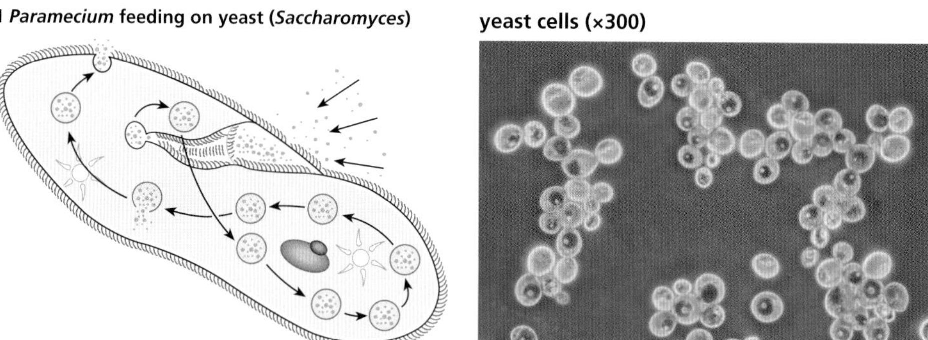

The results of a laboratory study of *Paramecium* and *Saccharomyces* populations over several days

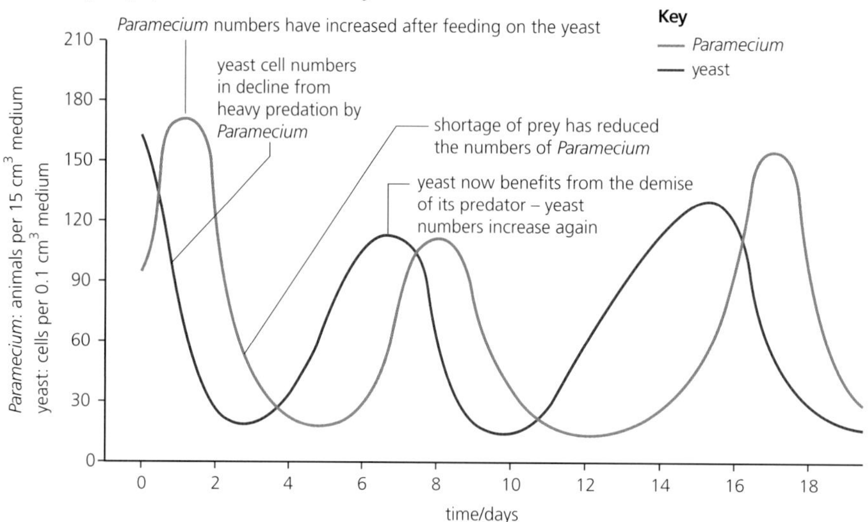

2 Evidence for prey–predator oscillations in nature: the fluctuations in numbers of pelts that hunters were able to trap, 1845–1945, of snowshoes hare (prey) and lynx(predator)

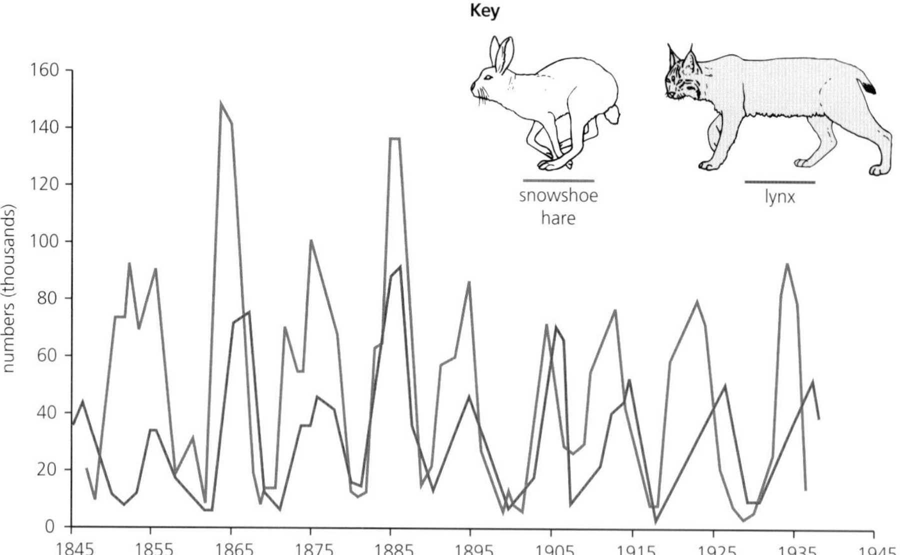

Figure 26.3 Feeding relationship between *Paramecium* and yeast (1) and predator-prey oscillation (2)

Symbiosis (sometimes known as **mutualism**) is the name we give to a relationship between two or more organisms living in intimate association. It simply means 'living together'. Parasitism is one form of symbiosis, in which the parasite lives on or in another organism, the host, for all or much of its life cycle. The parasite depends on the host for food and the host receives no benefit at all. **Endoparasites** live in the body of their host, like the human tapeworm and the malarial parasite. **Ectoparasites** live on the body of their host, like the aphids that tap the phloem sieve tubes of plants.

A parasite may affect the growth and reproduction of its host and in these cases the parasite is a limiting factor for the host species. In fact, parasitic associations show a gradation from those that normally kill the host (like the *Myxoma* virus on the rabbit, causing the fatal disease myxomatosis), to associations so bland that the parasite leaves its host virtually unharmed.

Key terms

Symbiosis A close and often obligatory association between two or more organisms, often, but not necessarily, to mutual advantage.

Parasitism A mutualistic partnership between two living organisms where one partner gains benefit and the other does not.

Test yourself

1 State the name given to abiotic factors related to the soil.
2 Suggest why biotic factors are density dependent.
3 Name **two** factors for which members of the same species may compete.
4 State the difference between a parasite and other symbionts.
5 Explain why many parasites are adapted to do only limited damage to their hosts.
6 In a theoretical predator–prey cycle, suggest why the prey population will peak before the predator population.

Niche – distribution and abundance of species

Competition between organisms is an ecological 'force' resulting in the establishment of distinct niches, and distinct differences in distribution and abundance of related species in particular habitats. The concept of ecological niche is not just some tiny place in which an organism is found, it encompasses everything the organism does and how it interacts with its living and non-living surroundings. In other words, its whole lifestyle that makes it particularly successful in that part of the habitat.

Key term

Niche An ecological term used to describe the exact role that an organism plays within an ecosystem. This includes many features of the lifestyle of the organism including its interaction with the living and non-living environment.

We can illustrate this with two examples:

1 Barnacle distribution

Two species of marine crustaceans, the barnacles *Chthamalus* and *Semibalanus*, are common creatures of seashore habitats. These sedentary animals release their gametes into sea water, where fertilisation occurs. From the fertilised eggs, free-living larvae emerge, which feed and grow before attaching to a surface, thereby adopting the sessile mode of life of the adults. Attachment occurs randomly on firm, submerged surfaces (typically rocks) of the intertidal region of the shore. However, one species (*Chthamalus*) is able to withstand prolonged exposure when the tides recede, whereas these same conditions slow the growth or actually kill off the other species (*Semibalanus*). As a result, as the degree of exposure is experienced by the growing barnacles, *Chthamalus* barnacles become less abundant in lower zones of the shore, and *Semibalanus* barnacles are similarly crowded out from upper (exposed) zones (Figure 26.4 on the next page).

So the distribution of *Chthamalus* in the upper intertidal zones, and of *Semibalanus* in the lower intertidal zones, is a function of differences in their respective niches. That is, behavioural and structural differences in resistance to periodic desiccation and endurance of prolonged submersion have determined where each species survives best.

2 Marine alga distribution

Another illustration of the evolution of distinctive niches between related species that has lead to differences in distribution and abundance is found on the rocky shore among common species of brown algae (Figure 26.5). All seaweeds have a covering of mucilage over their plant 'body' (thallus), and this acts as a reservoir of water. Differences in mucilage production and other differences appear to account for differences in species distribution. The algal species of the upper shore are shown to be better able than others to withstand desiccation – they contain more water when hydrated and they lose it more slowly when exposed.

the degree of exposure determines the distinctive distribution pattern of these two species of barnacle

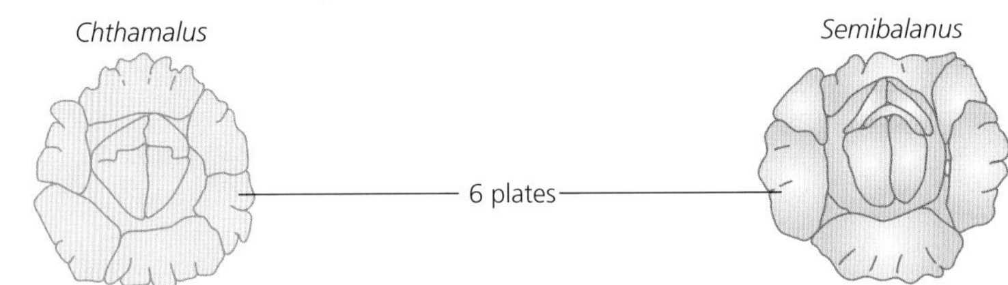

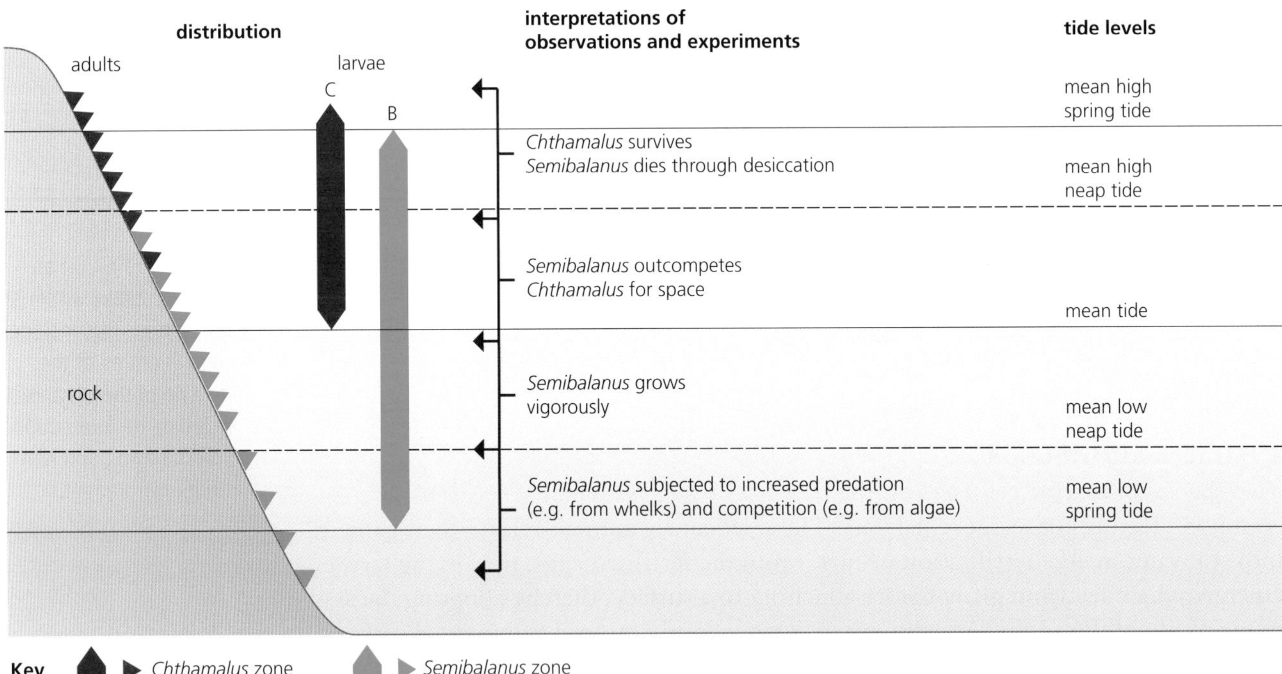

Figure 26.4 The growth of two species of barnacle on the seashore

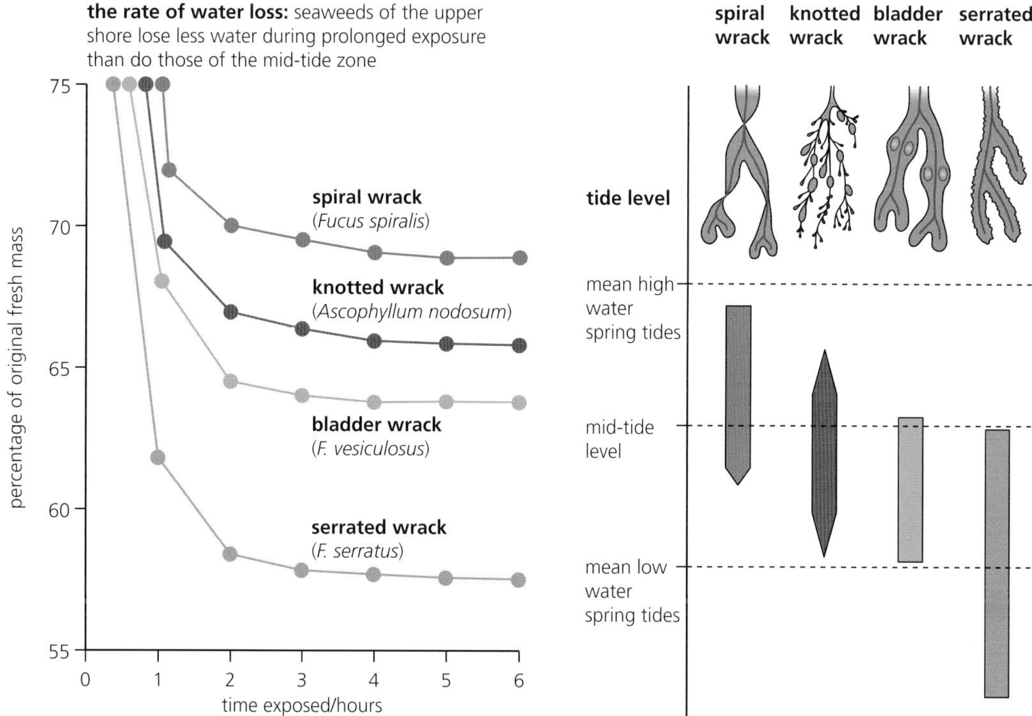

Figure 26.5 The resistance to desiccation of related species of brown algae

Ecological succession

When new land is exposed, it is quickly invaded and colonised by organisms. In fact, a sequence of communities develops with time by a process known as ecological succession. The stages in a succession are a series of plant and animal communities of increasing complexity, which develop as the abiotic factors operating change with succeeding communities. These stages are called **seral stages**, and the whole process is termed a sere. A climax community finally results, characteristic of the area.

> **Key terms**
>
> **Ecological succession** Sequences of different ecological communities developing in a habitat over time.
>
> **Sere** All of the stages in a complete seral succession.
>
> **Humus** The dead and decaying remains of plants and animals, which form an important part of fertile soil structure.

Primary succession

When the succession sequence starts on entirely new land without soil, the process is known as a **primary succession**. New land is formed on the Earth's surface at river deltas, at sand dunes and from cooled volcanic lava, for example. Primary successions also develop in aquatic habitats, such as in a pond formed and fed by a spring.

In all cases, the first significant development is the formation of soil, as at the initial site of a primary succession all that may be present is parent rock, from which the bulk of the soil is formed by erosion. However, mineral particles may also be blown or washed in from elsewhere, and the resulting mineral skeleton is of particles of a wide range of sizes.

Soil, when fully formed, has organic matter called humus, wrapped around the particles of the mineral skeleton. Humus is a substance derived from dead plant and animal remains, together with animal faeces, that have been decomposed by the actions of microorganisms. Humus contributes mineral nutrients as it continues to be decayed, and it also helps soil to hold water and to retain heat. Between mineral particles and humus are innumerable pockets of air.

Key terms

Pioneer species Plants and animals that have adaptations to enable them to become the first colonisers of an empty habitat.

Climax community The final stable stage in an ecological succession.

Humus is first added by plant invaders of the primary succession, known as **pioneer plants**, as shown in Figure 26.6. Since the first-formed soil retains little water, plants able to survive there (called xerophytes) have drought-resistant features. When a sere starts from dry conditions, then the sere is called a xerosere.

The growth and death of the early plant communities continue to add humus, so more soil water is retained. Nutrients are added to the soil when organisms die and the range of nutrients available to plants increases steadily. Different plants now grow – various herbaceous weeds, for example, may start to shade out the pioneers. Herbaceous plants are followed by shrubs and small trees, all growing from seeds carried in by wind, water or the activities of animals. If the site remains undisturbed, a **climax community** such as a stable woodland will result.

So, succession can be seen as a directional change in a community with time. Initially abiotic factors have the greater influence on the survival and growth of organisms. Later, as the numbers of living organisms build up, biotic factors increasingly affect survival too, especially as they come to modify the abiotic factors operating.

An important feature of a succession is the progressive increase in the number of species present. As more species occur in a habitat, the food webs diversify. Now, in the event that one population crashes (such as when a disease sweeps through, or predators have a temporary population explosion), then alternative food chains may be sufficient to supply the higher trophic levels.

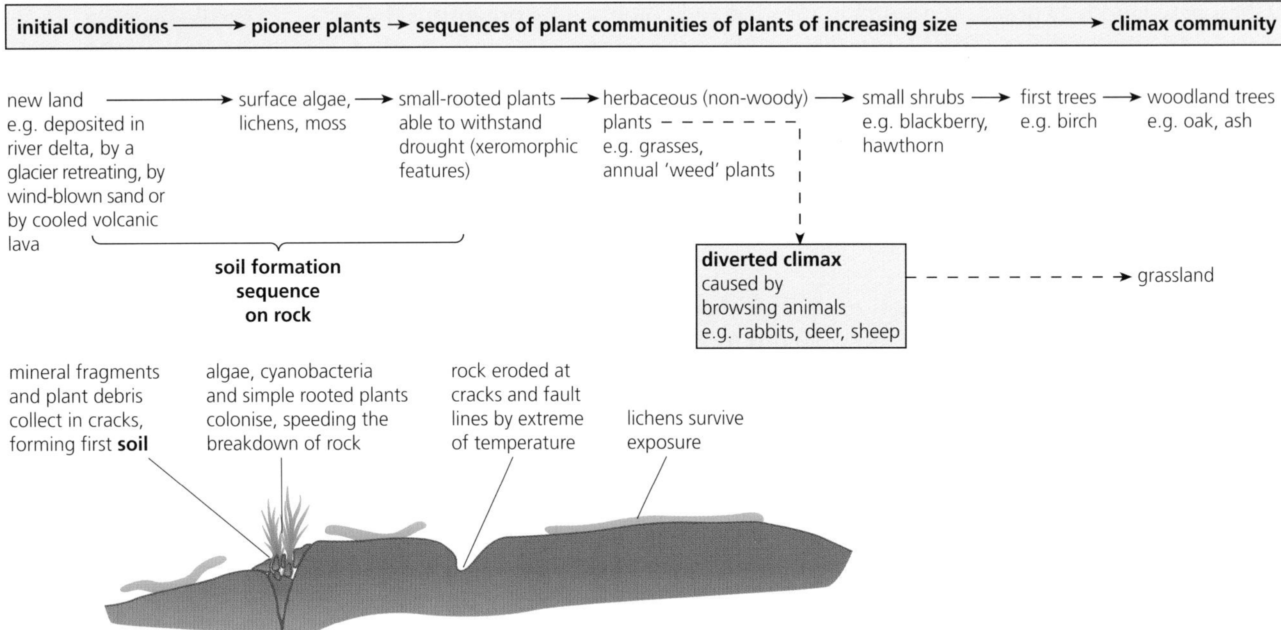

Figure 26.6 A primary succession on dry land – a xerosere

Secondary succession

Sometimes established communities are suddenly disrupted and totally destroyed. This occurs, for example, when fire destroys a large area of vegetation; occasionally it occurs as a result of human activities. In these situations, soil is already formed and present – it is just the existing biota that has been abruptly removed. A succession that starts from existing soil is known as a **secondary succession**.

Secondary successions normally happen quite quickly, since the necessary soil for plant life is already present. Plant communities are established in succession, as spores and seeds are blown in, or carried in by visiting animal life, or as they grow in from the surrounding, unharmed climax communities. After forest fires, for example, the soil is quickly covered by moss species that favour scorched soil habitats. The carpet of moss reduces soil erosion, starts to contribute to the supply of humus to the soil, and provides conditions favourable to the lodging and germination of seeds of higher plants.

Changes in climax communities

There are several types of climax communities.

- **Climatic climax** – a natural climax brought about by prevailing climatic conditions, such as deciduous woodland in temperate wet conditions. In uplands where temperatures are lower and rainfall higher, soils become saturated and more acidic. The low pH inhibits the breakdown of plant material and large areas of peat bog or moorland will become the climax community.
- **Deflected climax** – a change from the climatic climax brought about by the activities of humans, such as farming.

Seral changes do, in theory, lead to stable climax communities. In Great Britain the most likely outcome is the formation of a deciduous woodland ecosystem. Centuries ago this would have meant primarily oak woodland. However, at one time oak was of extreme military importance as the material for building warships and for structural timber. Not surprisingly a great deal of the oak woodland was cut down and today only small, ancient remnants remain.

In the 15th century, wool was an extremely important source of great wealth. This meant that more and more woodland was turned into pasture. The activities of sheep can still be seen today as the green hills of the Lake District are largely due to the effects of their grazing preventing the development of a climatic climax.

Climax communities can change, as we are witnessing in parts of the world where average temperatures are rising. For example, large areas on the fringes of the Sahara desert have become permanent arid desert rather than simply arid scrubland.

Key terms

Climatic climax
The final stage of an ecological succession, which is determined by the prevailing climate.

Deflected climax
The final stage of an ecological succession, which has been determined by human activity rather than natural forces.

Test yourself

7 Explain what is meant by a 'xerosere'.

8 Suggest the most likely climatic climax ecosystem in lowland UK.

9 Explain what changes a climatic climax into a deflected climax.

10 A secondary succession will develop much faster than a primary succession. Explain why.

Core practical 16

Investigate the effect of one abiotic factor on the distribution or morphology of one species, taking into account the safe and ethical use of living organisms

Background information

The exact nature of this investigation will depend upon the habitats available to you and you will need to discuss this with your teacher. In this example we will consider one example but the choice available to you is extremely wide. This practical is closely linked to Core practical 15 in Chapter 25. In particular, you will almost certainly need to consider such aspects as random sampling, which are also covered in Chapter 25. For this example we will look at an investigation that considers a gradual change in an abiotic factor along a transect and we will show how the data may be analysed using a correlation test.

Whatever you choose to investigate it is important that you plan carefully. In this practical you are investigating the effect of one abiotic factor. This will be your main independent variable so naturally it is vital that it should be measured or monitored as precisely and as reliably as possible. This is not always an easy task in field investigations so you must think very carefully. One common abiotic factor is light, and this poses many problems if you are to measure it carefully. Readings will obviously change throughout the day due to weather conditions and movement of the Sun, so if you are considering light and shade, what might be in bright sunlight in the morning will possibly be in deep shade in the afternoon. If the day is cloudy there might be bright, sunny intervals alternating with dull, cloudy conditions. What might be the best measurement in these circumstances? There are no simple answers to this so some thought and trial are needed.

Exactly the same problems occur with the dependent variable. Imagine you were investigating the effect of light intensity on leaf morphology; what would you measure and why – length, width, area, thickness or simply number? All will provide different information, so consider the biology behind your hypothesis and select the parameter which would provide most information. Remember that often a ratio such as width : length will give more information about overall shape, even though each leaf may not be exactly the same size.

The investigation below was carried out on sand dunes, which are a good example of succession in action. At the edge of the sea only pioneer species that can grow in loose, yellow, free-draining sand with little humus and a saline environment are found. Marram grass (*Ammophila arenaria*) is often dominant here. As the dunes become more stable and humus accumulates, the soil darkens to grey dunes. More and more plants are able to colonise the better soils and finally a climax community of woodland develops. Grasses such as red fescue begin to colonise the grey dunes and higher. This investigation is designed to find out if this was because there was a greater humus content.

NOTE: If red fescue is not present on the dunes you are visiting, you can simply choose another plant that is common across the section you study.

If you wish to find out more about dune transects before you read on, then there are a number of excellent photographic sequences showing real transects on the web. These can be found by simply searching for 'virtual sand dune transect' in your chosen browser.

Carrying out the investigation

Aim: To investigate the effect of soil humus content on the distribution of red fescue grass (*Festuca rubra*).

Hypothesis: There will be a significant positive correlation between the humus content of the grey dune and the abundance of red fescue.

Risk assessment: Read the section describing 'safety and ethics in ecological investigations' in Chapter 25. As with any outdoor activity, do not undertake this in isolated areas unless in a group with good communications. You will be working in exposed areas so check weather forecasts carefully and never swim in the sea without some supervision. Many dune systems have lifeguards and safety equipment nearby. Always wash your hands thoroughly after working outside, and before any hand to mouth contact. If you choose to investigate humus content of soil, you should burn off the humus in a fume cupboard, as the chemicals released into the air are similar to those released from burning cigarettes.

1. First of all make an initial survey of the area you are to work in. Make sure that you can identify red fescue easily. It does have a reddish tinge to the leaves but its typical grass spikelets (flowers) and seeds have a more pronounced red colour, which make it easy to spot.
   Find an area of the dunes where red fescue begins to be obvious and continues inland for at least 20 m. You will now need to use some judgment according to what you find.
2. To investigate, use a transect (Chapter 25) and take not less than seven measurements for your correlation test; ideally 10–15. To sample the dune, lay out a tape stretching inland and decide whether to take samples each metre or at longer intervals. Make sure that your transect crosses a typical section of dune but avoid introducing other variables

such as deep dips in the dunes known as 'slacks', where the conditions will change a great deal.

3 The next step is to decide how to record abundance of red fescue. This will depend on what you find on your dune. If the grass is quite sparse and only in small tufts you might simply count these within an open 1 m^2 quadrat. If the tufts are large and merge into each other you might choose a gridded quadrat to estimate percentage cover. If the grass forms a dense turf with other plants then you might choose a point frame. The latter can easily be improvised by drilling 10 holes in a 40 cm piece of wood and using one or two knitting needles (see Figure 25.12).

The process of planning a field investigation in this way is quite common. As habitats vary so much you must adapt your methods to take account of exactly what you find by initial observations, and not expect a rigid idea to be appropriate each time.

4 You now need to sample the soil at your selected sites and determine its humus content. To do this, take a soil sample at the bottom right-hand corner of each of your quadrats or each sample site. To ensure this is the same depth each time, a small empty can or rigid plastic yogurt pot can be pushed firmly into the soil and then removed with the help of a small trowel to prevent the soil spilling out. Place each sample into a polythene bag and mark this with the quadrat number.

5 Back in the laboratory, remove the sample and place it in a small beaker in an oven at 50 °C for several hours to dry it thoroughly. You can check that it is dry by weighing it at intervals until it loses no more mass.

6 The humus content of the dry soil can now be found by weighing a small sample (about 5–10 g) and placing this in a crucible or other heatproof container. Humus can be burned off at high temperature by using a Bunsen burner directly on the sample or using an oven at high temperature (250 °C+) for several hours. The mineral content of the soil will not be affected. Finally, weigh the sample again carefully and calculate the percentage loss in mass. This will be the humus content.

Analysis of the data using Spearman's rank correlation test

The formula you need to calculate your test statistic, known as the Spearman's rank correlation coefficient (r_s), is:

$$r_s = 1 - \frac{6\sum d^2}{n(n^2-1)}$$

Where r_s = Spearman's rank correlation coefficient

d = the difference in ranks of the two measurements

n = the number of pairs of measurements.

Here is a typical set of data from an investigation such as yours.

Sample number	% cover of *F. rubra*	% soil humus
1	20	1.9
2	23	2.2
3	18	2.1
4	15	1.6
5	19	1.8
6	25	2.4
7	15	1.7
8	21	2.1

First you have to rank each set of data from highest to lowest and subtract them to find the difference (d).

Then square each difference (d^2) (notice you lose the minus signs by doing this) and find the total Σd^2.

Sample number	% cover of *F. rubra*	Rank of % cover	% soil humus	Rank of % humus	Difference in ranks (d)	d^2
1	20	4	1.9	5	−1	1
2	23	2	2.2	2	0	0
3	18	6	2.1	3.5	2.5	6.25
4	15	7.5	1.6	8	−0.5	0.25
5	19	5	1.8	6	−1	1
6	25	1	2.4	1	0	0
7	15	7.5	1.7	7	0.5	0.25
8	21	3	2.1	3.5	−0.5	0.25
					Sum of d^2 (Σd^2)	9

When two measurements are the same, add together the two ranks and divide by two, for example samples 4 and 7 have 15 per cent cover. The two ranks would be 7 + 8, which you simply divide by two to give rank 7.5 as shown in the table. If there were three of the same value you would add together the three available rankings and divide by three.

For the formula $6\Sigma d^2 = 54$

$n(n^2 - 1) = 8(64 - 1) = 504$

$r_s = 1 - (54 \div 504)$

$r_s = 1 - 0.107 =$ **0.893**

You now look up the **critical value for eight pairs of measurements** at the 5% confidence level in a statistical table for the Spearman's rank test to find this is 0.738.

Your conclusions would be: There is a significant correlation between percentage cover of *Festuca rubra* and soil humus content at the 5% significance level as our value of r_s is greater than the critical value.

Correlations and causation – a cautionary note

Be very careful when interpreting a correlation, even where this has been shown to be significant by a statistical test.

A correlation does not tell you that one thing causes another. It simply tells you that when one changes so does the other. This might be a strong hint but it does not prove causation.

In the example it shows that as the humus content of the soil increases so does the percentage cover of *Festuca*, but it does not show why or if it causes this effect.

Scientific investigations often come up with this type of result but there may be other linked but very different reasons why this is the case. Your investigation took samples by working inland from the sea. It could be true that the humus content increases, but what if the salinity of the soil also decreased as you moved inland? You would get the same result even though it had nothing at all to do with humus. This problem is very widespread and therefore you need to be very careful when interpreting correlation data.

Questions

1 Why is it necessary to dry the soil before burning off the humus?

2 Why express humus content as a percentage?

3 Why is it important to keep burning the humus until I have a constant final mass?

4 Why is there likely to be more humus as I move inland?

5 How would I display my data?

Human effects on ecosystems

Humans are the dominant animals on the Earth. They have used their intellectual capacity to overcome many of the ecological forces that would bring about a balance in other populations, and to manipulate their environment in unprecedented ways. The effects of their ingenuity and exploitation of resources have influenced the whole of the biosphere.

In this section you will be looking at several aspects of how human activities have affected ecosystems and the difficulties associated with striking a balance between meeting human needs and conserving ecosystems.

Human population growth

Central to the problems of human influences on the biosphere is the enormous growth in human populations throughout the world. This began in earnest following the Industrial Revolution some 200 years ago. Since that time advances in medical knowledge and increased food availability have dramatically decreased death rates and birth rates have increased. The net result is that average life-expectancy has nearly doubled in this time (Figure 26.8). The inevitable result is shown in Figure 26.7. Human pressures on both natural resources and other populations have increased in the same way.

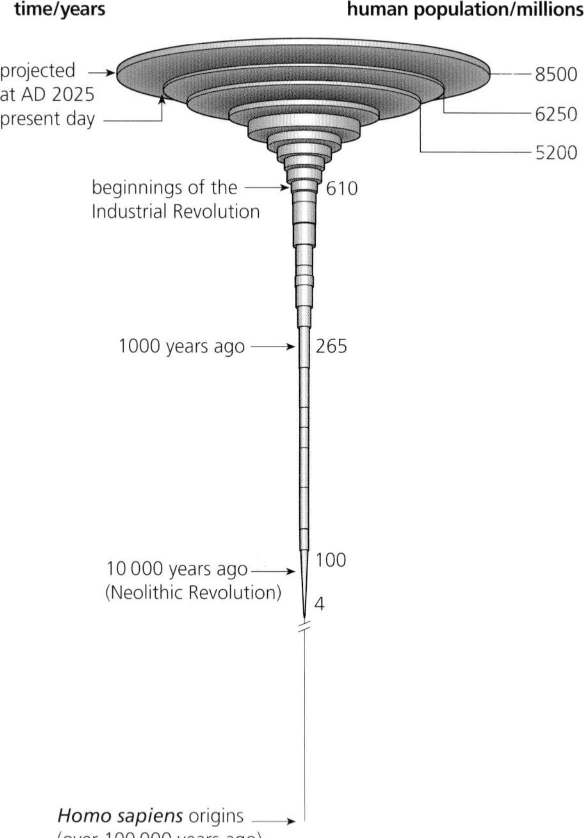

Figure 26.7 The changing pattern of the estimated world human population

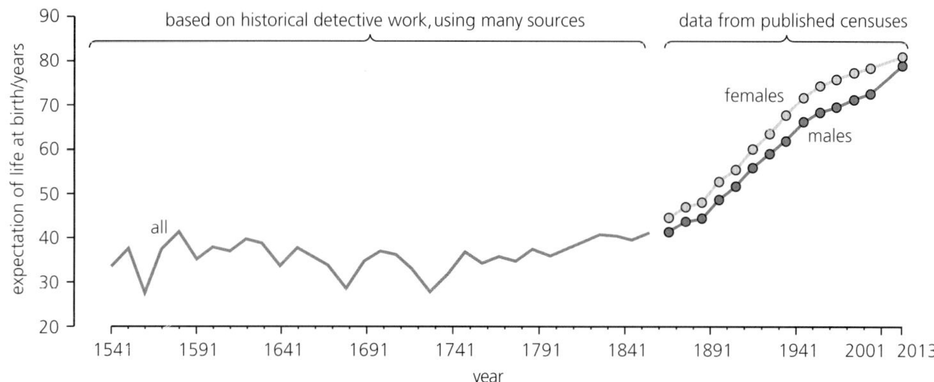

Figure 26.8 Expectation of life at birth in England over approximately the past 500 years

Test yourself

11 Describe the mathematical relationship that illustrates the current trend of human population growth.

12 State **two** factors that have contributed to the increase in human population.

Human pressures on resources – a case study

Abundant supplies of natural resources of food depend upon thriving ecosystems. You have seen that ecosystems have an inbuilt tendency to remain in balance and often a remarkable ability to adjust to changing conditions. However, there are strict limits, which if exceeded result in the complete breakdown of the system.

An understanding of the ecosystem and balancing the needs of humans with good management of the natural environment is the aim of conservation throughout the world. Unfortunately, there are many pressures, which mean that this is not always successful. Conservation of fish stocks is an example of how these efforts have failed in many parts of the world and also provides good lessons for the future.

As you will see in the examples that follow, conservationists need to come to terms with the many different influences on decisions and actions, even though the simple scientific logic may seem obvious.

The cod fisheries of Newfoundland

As scientists, the first thing we need to think about is the undisputed background to the case history. In this example we need to know more about the Atlantic cod (*Gadus morhua)* before looking at the problem.

The Atlantic cod, like many marine fish, reproduces by relying upon strength in numbers. By this we mean that there is almost no parental care of the offspring and only a tiny number will develop into fertile adults, so this drawback is overcome by producing very large numbers of offspring.

At certain times of year cod gather together in large shoals of many hundreds of thousands of individuals. A mature adult female cod will release well over 1 million eggs at this time. Older, larger females may release 10 times this number. These are fertilised by the sperm of the males in open water. Newly fertilised eggs are buoyant and float to the surface, where they are easy prey to many fish species. In fact, only about 1 in a million will develop into an adult cod.

The developing cod larvae use the yolk in the egg (Figure 26.9) to grow into tiny fish, which then feed off zooplankton and small crustaceans. Shallow water and marine algae are ideal places for young cod to escape predators and find enough food to grow. As they increase in size they begin to prey upon larger shrimps and other marine life, until as adults they will feed off larger fish and almost all other smaller species such as crabs. At this stage they have few predators and become one of the top carnivores within their ecosystem.

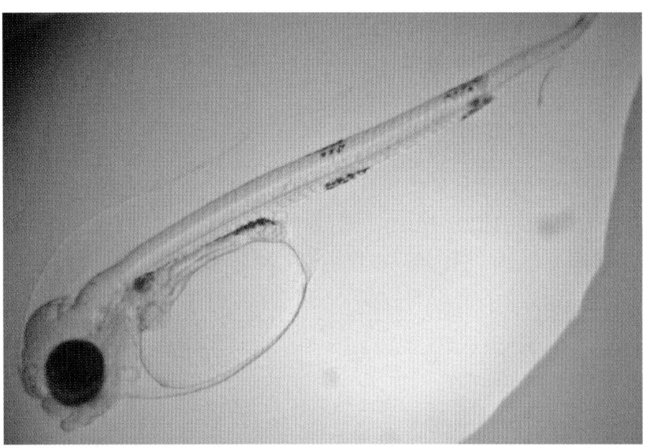

Figure 26.9 Atlantic cod (*Gadus morhua*) larval and adult stages

An adult cod is a large fish about 80 cm in length, weighing about 4 kg and with a life span of at least 10–15 years. Females become fully mature at about 5–6 years of age. However, this average hides the fact that shoals used to contain older cod of more than 1 m in length and a mass of over 50 kg.

Atlantic cod are cold-water species, thriving in Arctic waters. The ideal conditions in the North Western Atlantic, and especially in the shallow waters off the coast of Newfoundland in eastern Canada known as the Grand Banks, mean that historically there were huge populations of fish.

The collapse of the cod stock

The Atlantic cod population on the grand banks of Newfoundland had been recognised for hundreds of years. Native Canadians and early English and French settlers were able to exploit this population without affecting its enormous size. After the Second World War, commercial fishing increased dramatically and catches began to decline. Finally, in 1992 the cod population collapsed completely (Figure 26.10), forcing the Canadian government to ban cod fishing in the area completely. Over 40 000 Canadians in Eastern Canada lost their livelihood and the government introduced special pensions and benefits to prevent mass poverty.

It was hoped that this extreme measure would allow the cod stock to recover in a few years but 20 years later this had not happened.

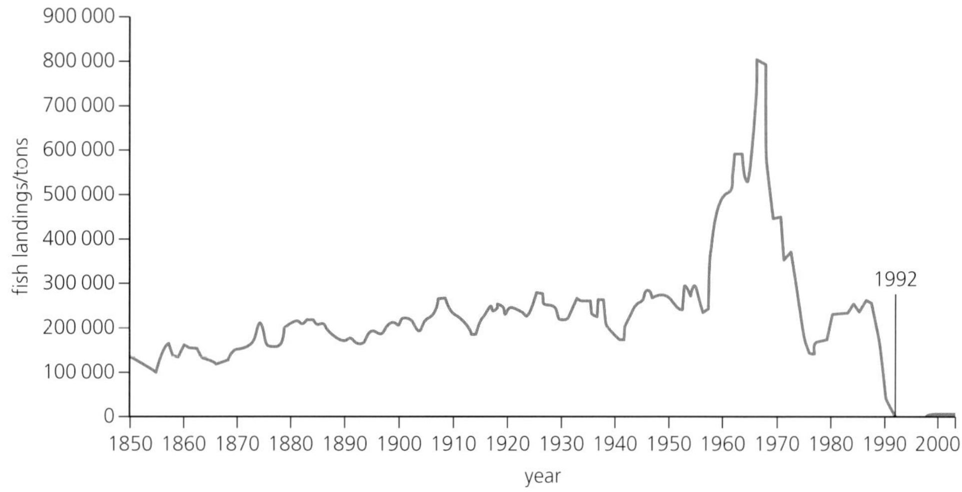

Figure 26.10 Total fish landings in Newfoundland 1850–2005

What caused the collapse of the cod stock?

In hindsight it seems very obvious what happened, but the story also illustrates the problems of reconciling human demands and the conservation of whole ecosystems.

1850–1950

During this time fishing was largely controlled by the limitations of fishing technology and limited international trade in fish. Local fisherman relied on human effort to haul nets and row boats. Even the introduction of sailing boats and the first steam-driven trawlers had little effect on the huge populations of cod.

Figure 26.11 Fishing schooner on the Grand Banks circa 1900

1950–1960

Big international companies from Europe introduced large factory ships (Figure 26.12), which froze their catch on board. These were able to fish day and night for many days using very large trawl nets, which were dragged across the sea bottom where most cod were found. The number of fishing boats increased enormously and their nets caused irreparable damage to the ocean floor and its ecosystem (Figure 26.13 on the next page), which was essential for the young cod to grow. Bottom trawling also results in an enormous 'bycatch', which is a large collection of organisms deemed to be unsaleable and simply dumped back into the sea, destroying many food webs in the process. Amongst this 'bycatch' were large numbers of fish called capelin. These small fish are not commercially valuable but crucially are a very important food source for young cod, so the disruption was compounded. Increasing use of sonar to locate fish meant that, even though the population was declining, the remaining fish were easily found. Taking so many fish from the population also meant that the large female fish were no longer available to produce vast numbers of eggs each breeding season. Between 1955 and 1968 the total catch of fish increased from an average of around 250 000 tons to just over 800 000 tons per year.

Figure 26.12 A modern factory-fishing vessel

1960–1992

In 1968 international treaties allowed the Canadian government to extend its jurisdiction to 200 miles offshore and it was able to take control of fishing on the Grand Banks. Sadly, what proved to be the last opportunity to conserve the fish stocks was

Figure 26.13 The damaging effects of repeated bottom trawling on the ocean floor

not fully implemented, as Canadian vessels partially replaced international competitors. Total fish landings did reduce dramatically but largely as a result of diminishing stocks as the damage had already been done. Despite a brief recovery in the early 1980s, there was a dramatic collapse in 1992 to such a low level that the government was forced to close the fishery completely.

1992–present day

Despite initial optimism, cod stocks on the Grand Banks have not recovered. Even with government support, the population of Newfoundland suffered severe hardship and many people emigrated. Whilst the original ecosystem has not returned, a new balance has established itself. This is now dominated, not by a large carnivorous fish, but by millions of crustacea such as snow crabs and prawns, which are essentially scavengers. Surprisingly, there is a large international market for such crustaceans and now there is a developing fishing industry again. Worryingly, for many ecologists, this industry is dominated by large industrial-sized fishing vessels.

Conflict and conservation

So what can we learn from the demise of the Atlantic cod fishery of Newfoundland?

First and foremost we can see that the whole story is a complex mixture of scientific prediction, political will, international agreement, national interests, commercial interests and a dash of greed. Above all we can see that any conservation effort is bound to fail unless there is local support and assistance.

Commercial companies, both internationally and in Canada, invested heavily in new ships and technology, obviously to make a profit but at the same time providing jobs and prosperity to the local economy. A large proportion of the Newfoundland population was employed in this way, not only as fishermen, but also whole families working in shore-based factories. Local and national politicians are unlikely to support measures that would severely restrict their constituents' incomes.

Even ecologists employed by the government would be subject to extreme pressures. Predicting the future of natural populations often involves complex computer models, which were far less developed in the 1970s. Even then, some theoretical assumptions had to be made and this means any predictions will have a margin of error. In an attempt to get some actions approved, selecting more optimistic predictions was a much more attractive option.

Sovereign countries have only a limited amount of jurisdiction beyond their coastline and this highlights the need for international agreements.

It is easy to think that these events are far removed from one's home country but nothing is further from the truth. Almost every country in the world has some issues of overfishing. In the UK we have lost the whole of an enormous North Sea herring fishery because of exactly the same problem as that experienced by the cod industry.

There are lessons to be learnt from successes too. There still remains a viable cod-fishing industry in the eastern part of the North Atlantic. This is largely because of strong policies put in place by Norway and Iceland to protect fish stocks as increased fishing threatened to overcome them. Here, too, large populations were dependent upon the fish stocks. This was not achieved without controversy as, at one point, UK and Iceland aggressively confronted each other with naval vessels to protect their fishing fleet from arrest in what became known as the 'cod war'. Eventually, in 1976, agreement was reached and the UK accepted that Iceland could enforce a 200 mile zone around their island in which they alone controlled the fishing. But, just as in Newfoundland, many British trawlermen lost their jobs in the years that followed and the fishing ports of Grimsby and Hull suffered severe decline – a better outcome for conservation but not for diplomatic relations or individual fishermen.

Conserving fish stocks in the 21st century

By far the most influential development in recent years has been the raising of public awareness of conservation issues on a local and international scale. Public support for the implementation of difficult conservation measures has meant that their influence on consumer demand and political decisions has increased.

Figure 26.14 The MSC logo

The problems of overfishing have been highlighted by large international organisations such as Greenpeace and The World Wide Fund for Nature. This has led to independent bodies such as The Marine Stewardship Council (MSC) establishing codes of practice for fisheries.

The MSC standard consists of three core principles that each fishery must demonstrate it meets:

- **Principle 1: Sustainable fish stocks.** The fishing activity must be at a level that is sustainable for the targeted fish population. Any certified fishery must operate so that fishing can continue indefinitely and is not overexploiting the resources.
- **Principle 2: Minimising environmental impact.** Fishing operations should be managed to maintain the structure, productivity, function and diversity of the ecosystem on which the fishery depends.
- **Principle 3: Effective management.** The fishery must meet all local, national and international laws and must have a management system in place to respond to changing circumstances and maintain sustainability.

The crucial point about such standards is that they influence consumers when they purchase fish. There are now very encouraging signs that this is happening. Conservation and sustainable fishing are increasingly in the minds of shoppers, and large retailers are keen to show their 'green' credentials. Logos such as the MSC (Figure 26.14) are now increasingly familiar and have helped to change fishing habits throughout the world.

Increasing awareness amongst consumers of the origins and methods of fish production has also had a strong influence on conservation.

Demand for tuna has increased worldwide but consumer awareness is influencing fishing methods. Tuna are large fish and can be caught in huge nets. Unfortunately this also means that large numbers of other animals such as dolphins are trapped and killed. A glance at supermarket shelves will today show prominent labelling indicating only tuna caught with the less damaging line and pole method is now stocked – a good step forward but there is still concern about the numbers of tuna being harvested worldwide.

Atlantic salmon, like the cod, are a severely threatened species. Here, biologists have devised enclosed fish farms in sheltered bays and inlets where specially bred fish can be produced to meet consumer demand without further pressure on depleted wild stocks. The large majority of salmon found on supermarket shelves is now farmed.

Even though fish farming helps to solve the problem of consumer demand, it also creates important biological problems of its own, such as the escape of farmed fish into wild populations and the increase of pests and diseases in concentrated numbers of near-identical individuals.

Other developments

- Many countries are setting up marine nature reserves. In these reserves all fishing is banned and they are chosen to include areas that will provide protected breeding grounds for fish.
- Satellite imaging means that vast areas of the ocean can be monitored to prevent illegal fishing.

Test yourself

13 Explain why the advent of 'factory ships' meant that more cod were landed.

14 Repeated bottom trawling was extremely damaging to the cod stock. Explain why.

15 Give **two** reasons why it was difficult for the Canadian government to prevent overfishing in the 1960s.

16 Explain what a 'bycatch' is.

17 Pole and line fishing is less damaging to the ecosystem than trawling. Explain why.

Human influences on ecosystems – endangered species

Many ecosystems worldwide are threatened, not only by exploitation of resources for food but also by the removal of key animals and plants from their natural habitats. Animals such as the rhinoceros and tiger are seriously endangered. In part this is due to loss of habitat but they are also under great pressure from poaching. In both cases, misinformed traditional belief in the medicinal power of body parts of these animals, means they command extremely high prices, making poaching a profitable enterprise.

A similar threat is posed by the value of elephant ivory.

Key term

CITES The Convention on International Trade in Endangered Species of wild fauna and flora. An important milestone in international cooperation on conservation.

Apart from local anti-poaching initiatives and the support of international wildlife charities, one of the most important international agreements on conservation and trafficking in endangered species is the Convention on International Trade in Endangered Species of wild fauna and flora (**CITES**). This is one of the oldest international agreements on conservation. Established in 1973, it has 180 member-countries.

The purpose of CITES is to licence and control the movement of endangered species and their products throughout the world. Each country has a government body responsible for issuing licences for the import and export of any species or product listed on a large agreed database. By restricting such movements, the transfer of plants and animals out of their natural habitat for commercial purposes is prevented and damage to indigenous ecosystems by other countries avoided.

The CITES website and database will give you a clear indication of the wide range of plants and animals that are protected under this scheme.

We shall look at other international agreements later in this chapter.

Climate change

Carbon dioxide is present in the atmosphere at about 0.038 per cent by volume (which represents 0.057 per cent by mass). Atmospheric carbon dioxide is added as a waste product of respiration by all living things, by combustion, and from the decay of organic matter by microorganisms. Much carbon dioxide is removed by fixation during photosynthesis – an interrelationship illustrated in the **carbon cycle** (Figure 26.15). About as much carbon dioxide is withdrawn from the atmosphere during the daylight each day as is released into the air by all the other processes, day and night – or nearly so.

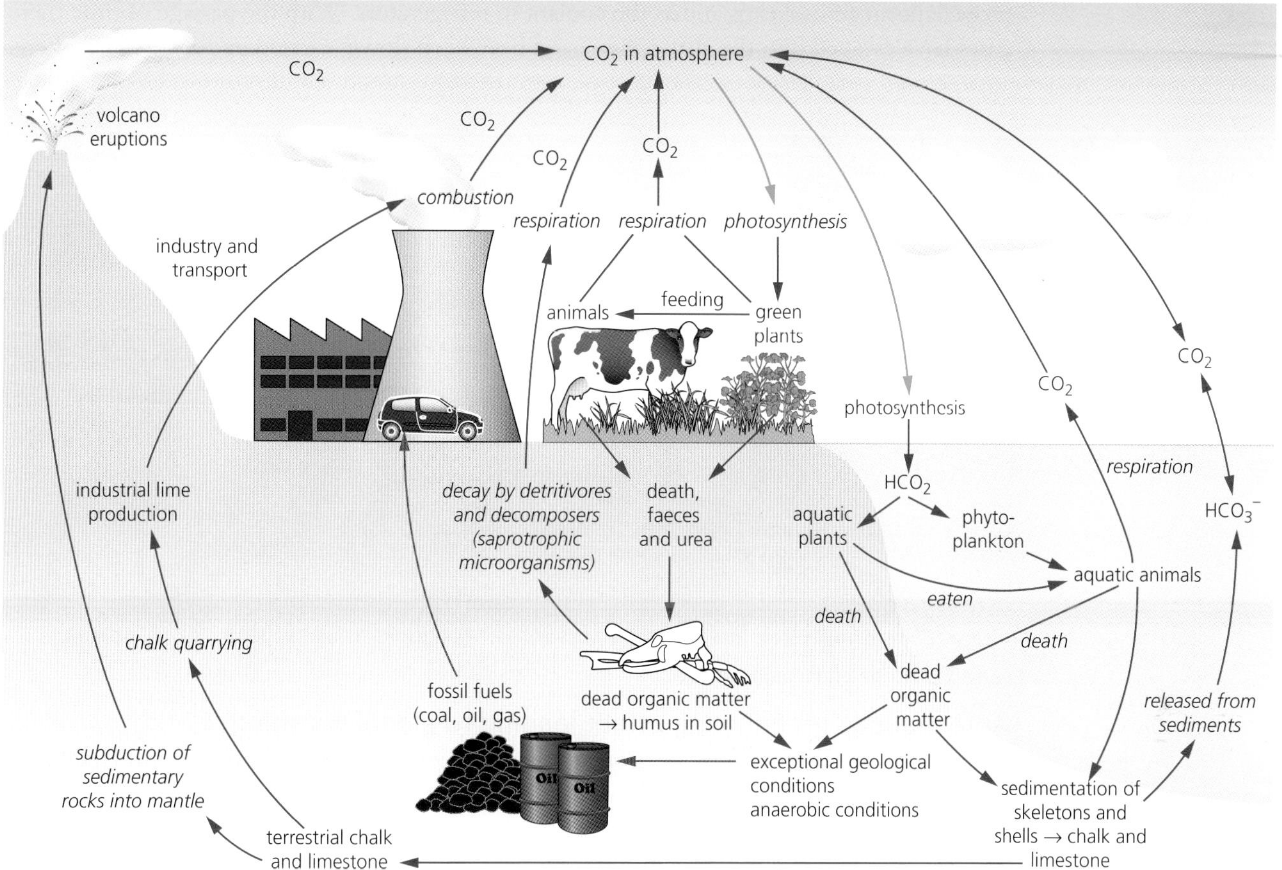

Figure 26.15 The carbon cycle

The effect of a low level of atmospheric carbon dioxide is to maintain a favourable environmental temperature on Earth – a phenomenon known as the **greenhouse effect**. Actually, the level of atmospheric carbon dioxide is now rising, for reasons we will investigate shortly.

> **Key term**
>
> **Greenhouse effect**
> Atmospheric warming caused by the absorption of re-radiated solar energy by gases such as carbon dioxide and methane.

The mechanism of the greenhouse effect

The radiant energy reaching the Earth from the Sun includes visible light (short wave radiation) and infrared radiation (longer wave radiation – heat), which warms up the sea and land. As it is warmed, the Earth radiates infrared radiation back towards space. However, much of this heat does not escape from our atmosphere. Some is reflected back by clouds and much is absorbed by gases in the atmosphere, which are warmed. In this respect, the atmosphere is working like the glass in a greenhouse, which is why this phenomenon is called a 'greenhouse effect' (Figure 26.16 on the next page). It is vitally important, as without it, surface temperatures would be too cold for life to exist on Earth.

Any gas in the atmosphere that absorbs infrared radiation is referred to as a **greenhouse gas**. Carbon dioxide is neither the only component of our atmosphere with this effect, nor the most 'powerful'. Both water vapour and methane are also naturally occurring greenhouse gases, and the latter is much more efficient at heat retention than carbon dioxide, although not present in the same proportions (so far).

In addition, purely anthropogenic atmospheric pollutants – such as oxides of nitrogen (particularly nitrous oxide), and chlorofluorocarbons (CFCs) – have 'greenhouse' properties, too. Oxides of nitrogen are waste products of the combustion of fossil fuels (oil and coal), and so occur in the exhaust fumes of vehicles. CFCs, on the other hand, are unreactive molecules that were deliberately manufactured by the chemical industry to use as propellants in aerosol cans and as the coolant in refrigerators. With the passage of time these gases have escaped into the atmosphere, and have been slowly carried up to the stratosphere.

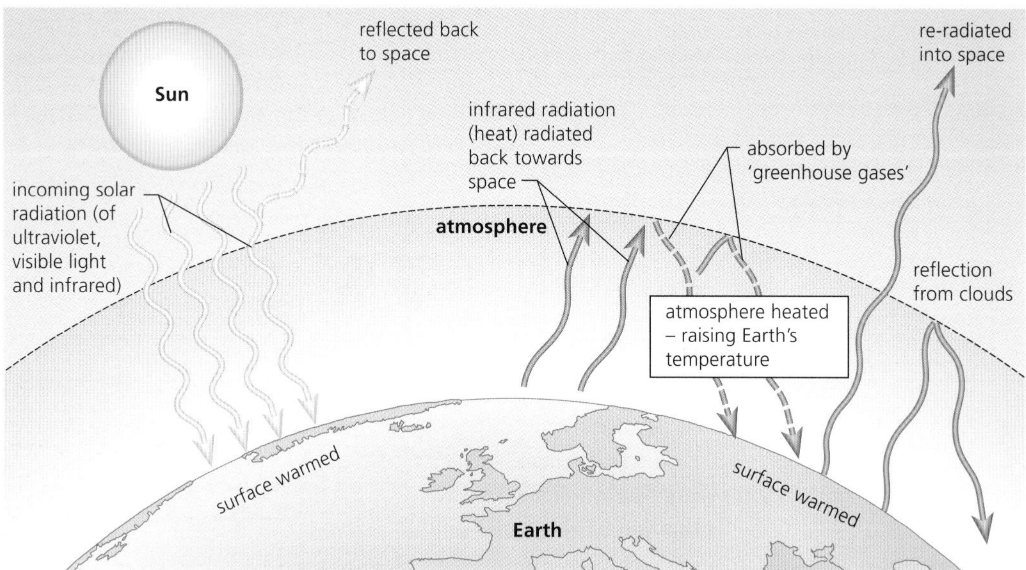

Figure 26.16 The greenhouse effect

An enhanced greenhouse effect leading to global warming?

Increases in the atmospheric concentrations of greenhouse gases will have inevitably enhanced the greenhouse effect. In order to assess how the composition of the atmosphere has changed over time, current and historic levels of atmospheric carbon dioxide and methane must be known. How are such records obtained?

The best long-term records of changing levels of these greenhouse gases (and associated climate change) are based on evidence obtained from ice cores drilled in the Antarctic and Greenland ice sheets. As water freezes, bubbles of air from the surrounding atmosphere become trapped within the ice. For example, data from the Vostok ice core in East Antarctica (that is, the composition of the bubbles of gas obtained from these cores) show us how methane and carbon dioxide levels have varied over no less than 400 000 years. Similarly, variations in the concentration of oxygen isotopes from the same source indicate how temperature has changed during the same period (Figure 26.17).

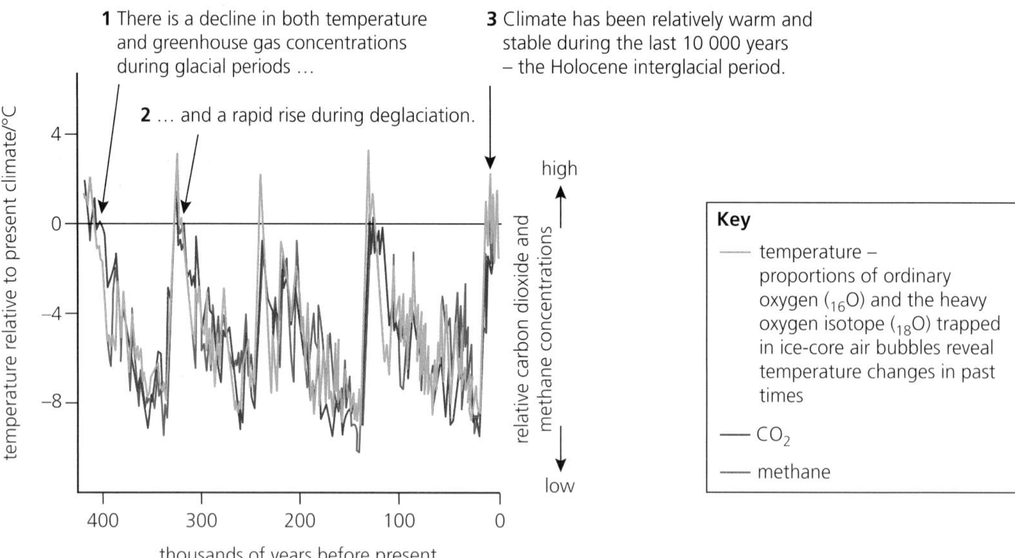

Figure 26.17 Three types of data recovered from the Vostok ice cores over 400 000 years of Earth history

Clearly, here the levels of greenhouse gas in the atmosphere can be closely correlated with global temperature. Environmental conditions on Earth have changed as a consequence. In fact, the Earth's climate has varied greatly over its billions of years of existence. Even over the 100 000 years of human presence, ice ages have come and gone! However, since the beginning of agriculture and the formation of city communities (about 8000 years ago) Earth conditions have been atypically steady. This stability can be correlated with steady atmospheric levels of carbon dioxide and methane (Figure 26.18).

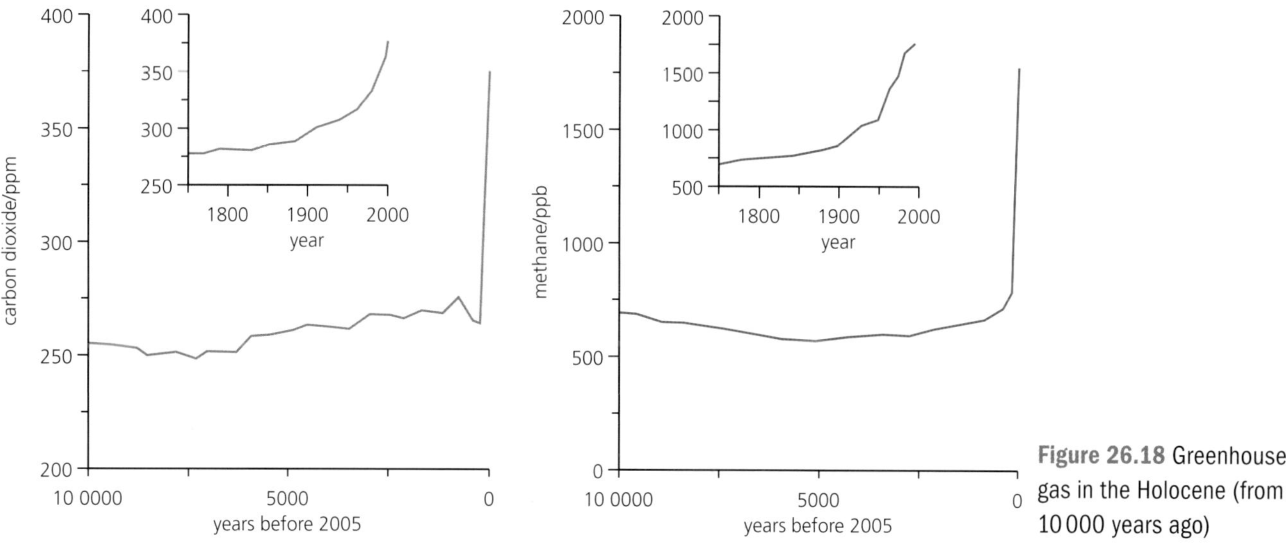

Figure 26.18 Greenhouse gas in the Holocene (from 10 000 years ago)

Since the Industrial Revolution in the developed countries of the world (about 200 years ago), there have been sharp rises in the levels of greenhouse gases, attributed to the burning of coal and oil (Table 26.2). These 'fossil fuels' were mostly laid down in the Carboniferous Period. So, we are now adding to our atmosphere, carbon that has been locked away for about 350 million years. This is an entirely new development in geological history. The effect has been a recent, accelerating rate of global warming. Many climate scientists argue that this development poses a major environmental threat to life as we know it.

Table 26.2 Changing levels of atmospheric CO_2

	CO_2 (in ppm)
pre-Industrial Revolution level	280 (± 10)
by mid 1970s	330
by 1990	360
by 2007	380
by 2050 (if current rate maintained)	**500**

The evidence for global warming – environmental change

The report of the Intergovernmental Panel on Climate Change (IPCC) of 2007 estimated global warming would be in the range 2.4–6.4 °C by 2100. This would generate the warmest period on Earth for at least 100 000 years, with highly significant environmental impacts. The paragraphs that follow describe in outline various theatres of environmental change attributed to global warming. These changes (and others) are already evident in part, and will have disastrous consequences if they continue unabated.

Figure 26.19 The retreat of the famous Fox glacier in New Zealand

Polar ice melt

The Arctic is a highly sensitive region – ice cover varies naturally. However, since 1979 the size of the summer polar ice cap has shrunk more than 20 per cent. In this period, the decline in the ice has been, on average, more than 8 per cent per decade. At this rate, there may be no ice in the summer of 2060. The associated Greenland ice is similarly in decline.

In Antarctica the picture is less clear. The Antarctic Peninsula has warmed, and 13 000 km^2 of ice have been lost in the past 50 years. Also, major sections of the Antarctic ice shelf have broken off. Meanwhile, at times the interior ice has become cooler and thicker – due to circular winds around the land mass preventing warmer air reaching the interior. Warmer seas may be eroding the ice from underneath, but IPCC predicts that the Antarctic's contribution to rising sea levels will be small.

Glacier retreats

Retreat by glaciers is worldwide and rapid – since 1980, glacier retreat has become ubiquitous. Mid-latitude mountain ranges such as the Himalayas, the Tibetan plateau, Alps, Rockies, and the southern Andes, plus the tropical summit of Kilimanjaro, show the greatest losses of glacier ice. Rivers below these mountain ranges are glacier-fed, so the melting of glaciers will have increasing impact on the water supplies for a great many people. The photographs in Figure 26.19 show the rapid retreat of the Fox Glacier in New Zealand from 2005 to 2015.

Rising sea levels

The impact of global warming on sea levels is due to thermal expansion of sea water and the widespread melting of ice. The global average sea level rose at an average rate of 1.8 mm per year in the period 1960–2003, but during the later part of that period the rate was far higher than at the beginning. If this acceleration continues at the current rate, sea levels could rise by at least 30 cm in this century. This phenomenon will threaten low-lying islands and countries (including Bangladesh), and major city communities such as London, Shanghai, New York and Tokyo.

Changing weather and ocean current patterns

At the poles, cold, salty water sinks and is replaced by surface water warmed in the tropics. Now, melting ice decreases ocean salinity, which then slows the great ocean currents that convey heat energy from warmer to colder regions through their pattern of convection. So, for example, as the Gulf stream (which to date, keeps temperatures in Europe relatively warmer than in Canada) slows down, more heat is retained in the Gulf of Mexico. Here, hurricanes get their energy from hot water, and become more frequent and more severe.

Also, alteration in the patterns of heat and rainfall distribution over continental land masses are predicted to cause Russia and Canada to experience the largest mean temperature rises, followed by several Asian countries and already drought-ridden countries in West Africa. Least warming is anticipated in Ireland and Britain in the northern hemisphere, and New Zealand, Chile, Uruguay and Argentina in the south. The most immediately vulnerable populations are already impoverished communities in parts of Africa; the least vulnerable is the wealthy population of Luxembourg.

Coral bleaching

Microscopic algae live symbiotically in the cells of corals, giving them their distinctive colouration, but when under environmental stress (for example, high water temperatures), the algae are expelled (causing loss of colour) and the coral starts to die. Mass bleaching events occurred in the Great Barrier Reef in 1999 and 2002. The effects from thermal stress are likely to be exacerbated under future climate scenarios, threatening biodiversity in coral communities. A photo of bleached corals can be seen in Figure 26.20.

Figure 26.20 Bleached corals

Other bio-indicators of climate change

Evidence of past climate changes may also be deduced from the remains of organisms that survived in habitats in the past. For example, in ancient peat deposits are found the 'fossilised' pollen grains of the once dominant vegetation. Alternatively, the study of tree rings (known as **dendrochronology**) indicates climatically favourable and less favourable years for tree growth, for as far back as preserved ancient timbers go.

> **Key term**
>
> **Dendrochronology** The dating of wooden artefacts by analysis of their unique pattern of tree rings formed from xylem vessels.
>
> **Extrapolation** The practice of extending conclusions, or graphical presentation, beyond that shown by data to make predictions about future trends and patterns.

The evidence for global warming – the debate continues

Global warming as an issue is seldom out of the news. Many scientists believe that the trends shown by average temperatures and the evidence from polar ice caps and glaciers make a very strong argument that this is an important and possibly long-term effect. However, there are many others who claim that this is simply natural climatic variation, which the Earth has seen many times before. One problem with the argument is that many predictions are based upon **extrapolation** of existing data. This means simply analysing the current trend and assuming that this is going to continue in the same pattern for many years to come. All scientists are very wary of extrapolation along with its assumptions, however the data keeps building and it could be that current estimates may even underestimate the effect.

Even if we accept the fact of global warming, there are problems in explaining its causes. Figure 26.21 shows the correlation between rising temperature and rising atmospheric CO_2.

Even simple observation shows a clear correlation between the two and it is possible to show that this is statistically significant. But, as we have discussed earlier in this chapter, showing a correlation does not demonstrate causation. You cannot automatically say that the rise in carbon dioxide levels is the main cause of global warming. Many vested interests who are opposed to limiting carbon emissions are quick to seize upon this dilemma. As scientists, you must also look carefully at the data. For example, carbon dioxide levels in the atmosphere are extremely low, so just where and how accurately were they measured in 1860? What other secondary causes might give a false correlation?

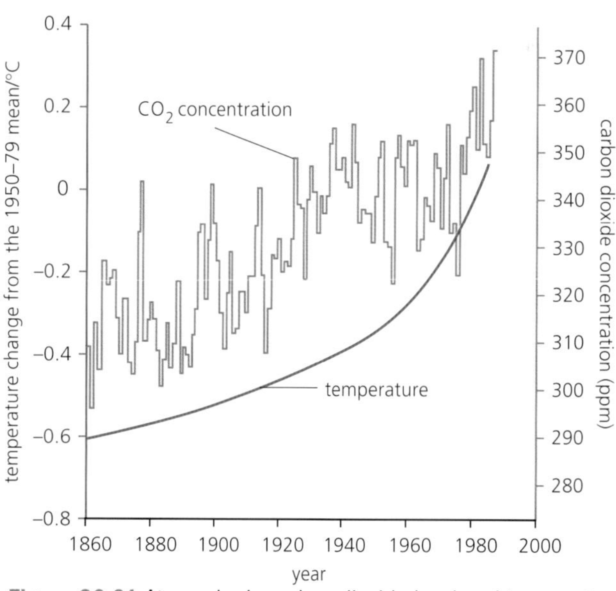

Figure 26.21 Atmospheric carbon dioxide level and temperature

Test yourself

18 Name the type of radiation that is absorbed by greenhouse gases.

19 Describe how evidence of ancient atmospheric composition is provided by ice cores.

20 Scientists are very wary of making conclusions based on extrapolation. Explain why.

To prevent the most severe impacts of climate change, the international community agreed, in 2014, that global warming should be kept below 2 °C compared to the temperature in pre-industrial times. That means a temperature increase of no more than around 1.2 °C above today's level.

To stay within this ceiling, the scientific evidence shows that the world must stop the growth in global greenhouse gas emissions by 2020 at the latest, reduce them by at least half of 1990 levels by the middle of this century and continue cutting them thereafter.

At the present time there is a strong consensus amongst scientists that rising carbon dioxide levels are at least very strongly implicated as the causative agent of global warming. So how do scientists come to a consensus and discuss the various lines of evidence pointing to the effect of carbon dioxide?

Communication and validation of evidence by scientists

At this point it is a good idea to refresh your memory on how scientists communicate and discuss their findings to build a body of reliable evidence. You have met this before in Chapter 7 when discussing the debate concerning the three-domain classification model. The main methods of communication and validation are listed below.

1 Scientific journals

All scientists publish full details of their investigations in well-known scientific journals. Their reports must contain full details of their methodology, the original data and an analysis of their findings, following some strict rules. These journals are available to scientists worldwide who can read about the work of others and the latest developments in their field.

2 Peer review

Before a scientific journal will accept work for publication it must be verified by senior scientists in the place where it was carried out. It is then scrutinised by an independent panel of scientists who are experts in the same field. They check the details of the method, the data collected and the validity of conclusions. Peer reviewers often ask for more details or a revision of conclusions before approving its publications. The process of peer review and publication of scientific papers is quite strict and therefore ensures that the information contained in the papers is very reliable. In this way a large body of scientific knowledge and understanding has been built up over many years.

3 Conferences (symposia)

Most important fields of research are carried out by many scientists in many parts of the world. Universities and other institutions often host meetings of scientists from around the world specialising in one particular area of research. At these meetings invited participants often present their latest findings before they have been published. However, the most important function of these meetings is to allow individuals to share ideas, discuss common problems and argue their case where different models are proposed.

Finally, it is important to realise that scientists are also human. Debates on the merits of different models can become very heated as proponents defend their ideas.

Action to limit carbon dioxide emissions – the need for international cooperation

Agreeing that carbon dioxide might be the problem is one thing; doing something about it is quite another. Global warming is a problem of the Earth's atmosphere. The atmosphere knows no national boundaries and the activities of one country affect all. Any action that is not agreed by most countries of the world is bound to have very limited effect.

The first stages of an attempt to gain international agreement on reducing emissions of carbon dioxide and other greenhouse gases were begun in 1992 by the United Nations and resulted in what is known as the **Kyoto Protocol**. What followed is shown in the timeline below.

- **1992:** The UN Conference on the Environment and Development is held in Rio de Janeiro. It results in the Framework Convention on Climate Change (FCCC or UNFCCC) among other agreements.
- **1995:** Parties to the UNFCCC meet in Berlin (the 1st Conference of Parties (COP) to the UNFCCC) to outline specific targets on emissions.
- **1997:** In December the parties conclude the Kyoto Protocol in Kyoto, Japan, in which they agree to the broad outlines of emissions targets.
- **2002:** Russia and Canada ratify the Kyoto Protocol to the UNFCCC, bringing the treaty into effect on 16 February 2005.
- **2011:** Canada becomes the first signatory to announce its withdrawal from the Kyoto Protocol.
- **2012:** On 31 December the protocol expires.

The principles of the Kyoto Protocol are simple. Each country would sign the agreement and commit themselves to reducing greenhouse gas emissions to about 8 per cent lower than those of their country in 1990. This agreement was to run from 2008 to 2012 and took over 5 years to agree and a further 5 years to begin implementation.

To illustrate the enormous problems that need to be overcome in achieving agreement with so many countries, we need to look at one of the major obstacles. Poorer underdeveloped countries felt that imposing targets would be unfair as richer countries had already developed their industries and economies without restraining carbon emissions. These developed countries, in turn, felt that restrictions on them would give unfair advantage to others. To meet both these arguments a compromise scheme was devised. The carbon credit was introduced. A carbon credit is simply a licence to emit 1 tonne equivalent of carbon dioxide. All countries were assigned a fixed quota of emissions; if measures taken meant that less than this was emitted then they would gain credits. If they exceeded their target then they would need to purchase credits from another country. As most of the underdeveloped countries were unlikely to breach their target they would have credits to sell, to finance their changes with the money coming from the richer countries.

Like all compromises this had drawbacks. Principally the poorer countries were never going to reach their limit, so by selling off their carbon credits they allowed others to emit more, with the result that there would be no reduction overall. Nevertheless the protocol was up and running and action to reduce emissions was put in place on a large scale.

Despite the slow progress, the Kyoto Protocol was the very first large-scale international treaty to address global warming. In all, more than 180 countries were involved and it was a great testimony to patience and diplomatic skill. It has resulted in many countries implementing far-reaching carbon-emission policies and setting challenging targets.

Sadly, although initially signing the agreement, the USA never ratified their acceptance and, as the country that produces about a third of global emissions, this was a major weakness. Its neighbour Canada also withdrew its participation in 2011.

There is hope that a new Protocol will be agreed to cover the period 2013–2020 with a major conference in 2015 but the signs are not promising. Three of the world's largest countries – China, India and the USA – have already declared that they will not enter into any legally binding agreement but at least they are open to voluntary reduction measures and there is hope for some positive outcome.

Key term

Kyoto protocol An international treaty signed by 180 countries to reduce carbon emissions between 2008 and 2012.

Test yourself

21 Give **two** reasons why it is so difficult to reach international agreement on climate control.

22 Describe what the Kyoto protocol aimed to achieve.

Chapter summary

Factors affecting ecosystems

- Ecosystems depend on the interaction between the living things (biotic factors) and the non-living environment (abiotic factors).
- Abiotic factors include sunlight, temperature and wind.
- Abiotic factors linked to soil such as parent rock, water and mineral ions are called edaphic factors.
- Altitude, slope and aspect also have effects by changing these abiotic factors.
- In aquatic environments water flow and oxygen levels also become important.
- A powerful biotic factor is competition with others, either of the same species (intraspecific) or different species (interspecific).
- Competition can be for space, light, mineral resources, food or mates.
- Food webs show how these biotic factors may apply in predator–prey relationships and how the numbers of each may regulate the other. Fewer predators means more prey survive, which provides more food for the predators. As predator numbers increase the number of prey decreases, meaning less food for predators, and this continues in a cycle.
- Some biotic relationships have mutual benefits and are known as symbiosis. For example, many fungi in soils use carbohydrates from plant roots but supply essential ions in return.
- Other organisms are parasites where the relationship is one-sided, but even here most parasites are highly adapted to using nutrients from their host without taking so much that the host is killed.
- Competition forces most organisms to become very specialised in order to be successful. They develop a specific ecological niche, which is a term used to describe not just the limited area in which they might live but also their whole lifestyle, including such things as behaviour and reproduction.

Ecological succession

- When bare land is colonised a sequence of different communities develops over time. This is ecological succession and the process is called a sere.
- The first plants are known as pioneer species. As conditions improve more species appear and eventually a stable climax community is formed.
- Climax communities depend on where they form and are such areas as tropical rainforests, temperate oak woodland or peat bogs.
- A natural climatic climax is determined by climate alone. A deflected climax is changed by other events, especially human activities.

Human effects on ecosystems

- Human populations have increased tenfold in the last 300 years, placing huge demands on many resources.
- You will find many examples in current newspapers. The case study of the Newfoundland fishery has many identical features to recent problems.
- There is continued debate about global warming amongst scientists and politicians. Whilst there is much evidence from around the world that this is happening, there is less conclusive proof that it is directly linked to carbon emissions, even though these are rising.
- The greenhouse effect is caused when solar radiation enters the atmosphere and warms the Earth, which then radiates energy back outwards. Any gases in the atmosphere that absorb infrared radiation will prevent this energy escaping. In addition to CO_2, water vapour and methane are powerful greenhouse gases, especially methane, which comes from decay and from the digestive systems of cattle and sheep.
- You will see some of the evidence from ice cores, retreating glaciers and changing weather patterns in this chapter.
- As in the case of overfishing, it is proving very difficult to gain international agreement to take action and then monitor compliance with the agreement despite possible severe consequences.
- This chapter also illustrates the foolishness of assuming that a correlation can be used to demonstrate a causal link, even when the correlation is shown to be significant using a statistical test.

Practice questions

1 The exact role that an organism plays within an ecosystem is known as its:

A habitat **C** niche

B community **D** sere *(1)*

2 Greenhouse gases only absorb radiation that has been reflected from the Earth's surface because:

A the wavelength of the radiation is changed on reflection

B the energy of direct radiation from sunlight is too high

C the destruction of the ozone layer has allowed more radiation into the atmosphere

D greenhouse gases are only found in lower levels of the atmosphere *(1)*

3 Which of the following would be described as a secondary succession?

A The colonisation of a newly-formed volcanic island.

B The activities of sheep maintaining a grassland ecosystem rather than woodland.

C The development of new communities following a severe forest fire.

D The build up of non-decayed mosses to form a peat bog. *(1)*

4 The coastal waters of Peru are home to very large shoals of small fish called anchovies (*Engraulis* sp.). Anchovies are an extremely important part of the marine ecosystem as primary consumers, and different species are common throughout the world's oceans. Whilst anchovies are consumed directly because of their strong flavours, most of the catch is processed into fish oils and dried as animal feed.

Overfishing has meant that in recent years the stocks of anchovies have shown periods of significant decline followed by partial recovery. The Peruvian government has been compelled to take action to try to prevent a total collapse of the anchovy population.

a) Explain how overfishing can result in long-term damage to the whole marine ecosystem. *(3)*

b) Explain why using anchovies as food for intensively reared animals such as pigs is an inefficient use of animal protein. *(3)*

c) What action might the Peruvian government take to protect fish stocks? *(3)*

5 Scientists are able to study the temperature and the carbon dioxide content of the Antarctic atmosphere, in the Vostok area, by analysis of air trapped in the ice over many thousands of years. Long cores of ice are extracted from the ice by drilling. The deeper the core, the older the air trapped within it. The nature of the analysis meant that there were far fewer readings for carbon dioxide concentration than there were for temperature.

Tip

Although in Question 4 you will need to apply your knowledge to a new situation to some extent, this is a very straightforward question based on specification material.

Tip

Question 5 has a mixture of demands. Part c) is quite simple AO1 material, which you will have met both earlier in the book and in this chapter. However, part a) requires you to look very carefully at the data and understand clearly what conclusions might be drawn from it.

An extract from the data obtained in this way is shown in the graph.

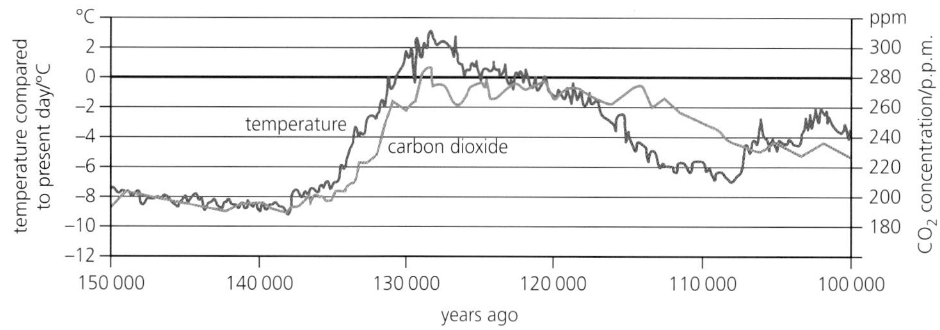

a) Analyse the data in the graph between 110 000 and 105 000 years ago to explain why some scientists might argue that this evidence does not support the idea that a rise in carbon dioxide levels actually causes a rise in atmospheric temperature. *(3)*

b) Other scientists have argued that the overall pattern of changes between 150 000 and 130 000 years ago displays such a strong correlation that this must show that carbon dioxide levels were the cause of the temperature rise. Evaluate this conclusion. *(4)*

c) Describe how these data would be communicated to the scientific community, and debated within it. *(4)*

6 A student carried out an investigation to test the hypothesis that there would be a correlation between light intensity and the number of different plant species (species richness) growing in an area of grassland. He placed a belt transect across a region of grassland that covered a shaded area and a sunlit area. He then measured the light intensity using a light meter at three random points in each of ten 0.5 m × 0.5 m quadrats along the transect and calculated the mean. Finally, the number of different plant species in each quadrat was counted.

a) i) State **two** precautions that should be taken when measuring light intensity using a light meter in this way. *(2)*

ii) Describe **two** ways in which measurement of light intensity could be made more representative of the actual exposure of the plants to light. *(2)*

b) The student decided to test the strength of the correlation between light intensity and number of species found by applying a Spearman's rank correlation test.

i) State a suitable null hypothesis for this investigation. *(1)*

ii) Complete the table of results shown on the next page and calculate the value of Σd^2. *(2)*

Tip

Question 6 has been extended to include 16 mark points. This has been done to give examples of how you may be asked to deal with statistical testing and practical skills. It is unlikely that you will meet such a long question in an examination paper but you will need to be able to deal with all the types of question that it contains.

Mean Light Intensity/lux	Number of plant species found	Rank Light intensity	Rank number of plants	Difference in ranks (d)	d^2
6350	0	1	1	0	0
7033	2	2	5.5	−3.5	12.25
7560	2	3	5.5	−2.5	6.25
7780	2	4	5.5	−1.5	2.25
10276	1	5	2.5	2.5	6.25
10773	3	6			
12090	1	7	2.5	4.5	20.25
13010	3	8			
13596	2	9	5.5	3.5	12.25
17566	4	10	10	0	0
				$\Sigma d^2 =$	

iii) Calculate Spearman's rank correlation coefficient (r_s) for these data using the formula

$$r_s = 1 - \frac{6\sum d^2}{n(n^2 - 1)}$$

Where n= the number of pairs of data in the sample. *(3)*

iv) The critical value of r_s for 10 pairs of measurements at the 5% confidence level is 0.648. Using this information and your calculated value of r_s, what conclusions can be drawn about this relationship? *(2)*

v) Use the information on methods and the collected data to explain why this conclusion could be regarded as unreliable. *(4)*

Stretch and challenge

7 The data from the Vostock ice cores, such as that shown in Question 5 on the previous page, has caused some debate amongst scientists investigating the model that it is atmospheric carbon dioxide that is causing global warming.

a) Research these data further and find out exactly how the information on temperature and atmospheric composition were found.

b) Explain how scientists argue that it can be used to both support and challenge this model.

8 The European Common Fisheries Policy is typical of many inter-governmental attempts to conserve fish stocks.

One recent example of the conflict that this can cause was the restriction of fishing in an area known as the 'Irish Box'. Make a list of the typical arguments that might be put forward by

a) fishermen and

b) conservationists

to argue for and against such restrictions.

27 Mathematics for biology

At least 10 per cent of the total marks in the two AS examination papers and 10 per cent of the total marks available in the three A level papers will be awarded for mathematics at Level 2 or above. 'Level 2 mathematics' means the standard of the higher tier of GCSE mathematics.

This is obviously a significant part of each qualification, which will make a big difference to your final grade. If you are not studying mathematics beyond GCSE level then it is important to continue to practise your mathematical skills throughout the course. Even if you have achieved a good grade in mathematics you cannot assume that you will retain your skills one or two years later. If you are less confident with mathematics you must continue to develop your skills further. The mathematical skills required are not something that can be developed in a short period of intensive revision at the end of your course.

How will mathematical skills be tested?

Mathematical skills will be tested in many different types of questions and these will change from year to year. Remember, your papers will contain synoptic questions so it is possible that they may introduce some mathematical requirement at any time. However, as you will see from the examples in this book and the following sections, many are linked to data in both a theoretical and a practical context. This means you should take every opportunity to practise your skills when you are carrying out practical investigations. It has the added advantage that you will become familiar with using your skills in many different ways and this is what is expected in the examination.

To help you to do this you will find specific examples of the use of mathematical skills throughout this book. They have been included in chapters where you are most likely to meet practical applications of mathematics. They will help you to understand why mathematics is relevant to a biology course and give you examples to show what might be required in written examinations.

This chapter does not repeat all of these skills but reinforces some of the most important requirements. It also explains some of the more difficult ideas, such as statistics, in a little more detail.

Basic units

All the units that you meet will be based on the SI system. This is an international standard used by all scientists. Those you will meet most often are shown in Table 27.1.

Table 27.1 SI units

Measure	Unit	Symbol	Note
Length	Metre	m	
Mass	Kilogram	kg	
Time	Second	s	
Temperature	Degree Kelvin	K	1 degree Kelvin = 1 degree Celsius but their scales are different (0 °C = 273 °K)
Amount of substance	Mole	mol	

There are many scientific reasons to use these units but scientists also use common sense when applying them. For example, it would be very awkward to keep recording in seconds when an investigation continued for several days.

Other common units are derived from these basic beginnings. The simplest way to do this is to represent fractions of the basic SI unit. Chapter 4 explains how units of length are divided to give units appropriate to a wide range of sizes. The common prefixes for decreasing values in steps of 1000 are milli-, micro- and nano-. So a millimetre is a thousandth of a metre, a micrometre is a millionth of a metre and so on.

Time is more awkward because historically 1 minute is divided into 60 seconds and there are 60 minutes in an hour. The advent of digital stopwatches means you will need to take care. A common error is to take a stopwatch reading of say 1:56 min and record this as a decimal fraction, 1.56, rather than 1 min 56 s.

Other units

Concentration

Controlling or measuring concentration is a very common feature of many practical investigations. The concentration is the amount of substance in a given volume. It is correctly expressed as moles per decimetre cubed ($mol\,dm^{-3}$). Here a decimetre cube (dm^3) is a derived unit of $1000\,cm^3$ or a litre. We shall consider indices in the next section but the minus sign indicates 'per'. Problems arise when we stray away from the mole as the SI unit of amount. It is much easier to make up percentage solutions where a 1% solution simply has 10 g of the substance made up in $1\,dm^3$ of the solvent. This can lead to large errors. For example, a 1% solution of glucose and a 1% solution of sucrose do not have the same concentration, simply because a sucrose molecule has twice the mass of a glucose molecule. Therefore 1 gram of the sucrose solution will only contain half the number of molecules, and the number of particles in a given volume is what we really mean by concentration.

Tip

The only way to become comfortable with units and with standard form is to practise simple examples. Using very dilute solutions of gibberellic acid in Core practical 14 is a useful exercise for practising this.

Standard form (scientific notation)

You will find numerous examples in this book and in examination papers where numbers are written in standard form. Any number can be written in standard form but it is often used for very large or very small numbers. It will always be in the form $a \times 10^b$, where a is a number >1 and <10 and b a power of 10. For example, 1500 is written as 1.5×10^3 and 11 500 as 1.15×10^4.

If we have very small numbers of less than 1 then the power of 10 becomes negative, meaning the same as 'divide by'. For example, 0.0015 is written as 1.5×10^{-3} and 0.000015 as 1.5×10^{-5}.

A simple rule for calculating using standard form numbers is, if you are dividing then the powers of 10 are subtracted and if you are multiplying then the powers of 10 are added. For example, $\frac{10^5}{10^2} = 10^3$ and $10^5 \times 10^2 = 10^7$.

Significant figures

A significant figure in a number adds to its precision. If you find the mass of a substance using a digital balance that has an accuracy of 0.01 g, then you would record the mass as, say, 1.00 g to indicate its precision. This means that writing 1 and 1.0 are not the same. '1' simply indicates that the value is 1 or more but not 2. '1.0' means it is 1 or more but not 1.1.

Similarly, you must be careful not to introduce additional significant figures that are not justified by your precision.

Example

You find the final mass of four results using a balance of 0.01 g accuracy and then calculate the mean.

Readings: 1.21 g, 1.33 g, 1.30 g, 1.27 g

Mean = 1.2775 (the result on your calculator)

Here we have suddenly introduced five significant figures when our balance can only justify three, so our mean should be limited to three significant figures, 1.28 g.

Graphs

Remember, graphs are pictorial representations of trends and patterns in data. When accurately drawn they can be used to make mathematical calculations and express relationships in algebraic form. The simplest relationship is a **straight line graph**, which can be expressed as:

$$y = mx + c$$

Here, x and y are the values on the coordinates, m is the gradient of the line and c is the value where the line cuts the y-axis.

Main graphical formats

1 Line graph

Both axes are continuous variables. In Figure 27.1, this means that it is possible to have any measurement on the temperature scale between 20 °C and 50 °C or any volume measurement up to 7 cm³.

It is advisable to join points with a straight line, as attempting to draw acceptable curves freehand is very difficult and you do not know exactly what happens between each point.

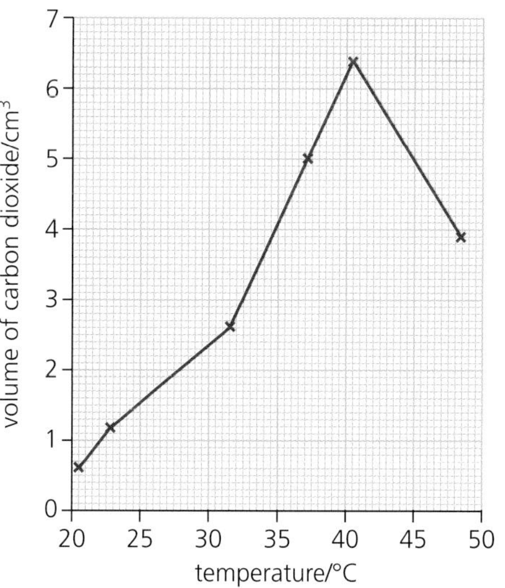

Figure 27.1 A line graph

2 Bar chart

Bar charts are used where the independent variable on the horizontal axis is not a continuous scale but is made up of distinct categories. To show this, the columns must not touch each other (Figure 27.2). A bar chart can also be the simplest way to display the means for two sets of data.

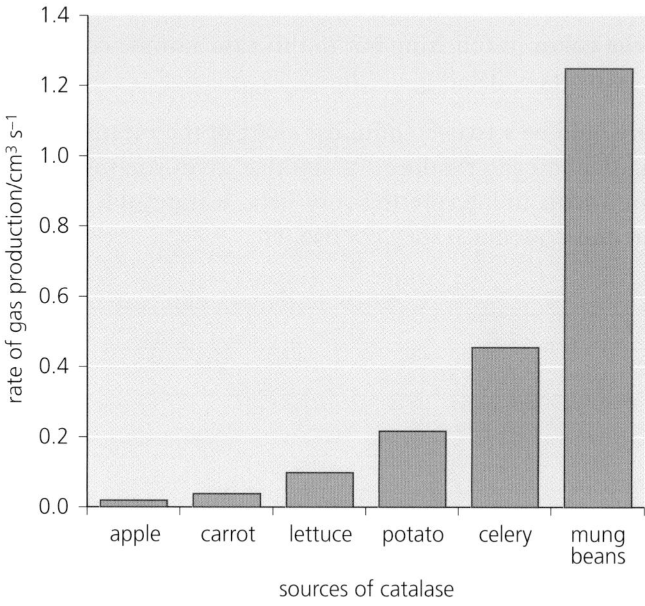

Figure 27.2 A bar chart

3 Histogram

A histogram is also drawn with columns, but the horizontal axis often shows the data from the dependent variable measurements organised into size classes. In Figure 27.3 the range of holly leaf sizes is divided into ten size classes having 5 mm in each. You simply count how many leaves come into each size category to produce the number on the vertical axis (Figure 27.3).

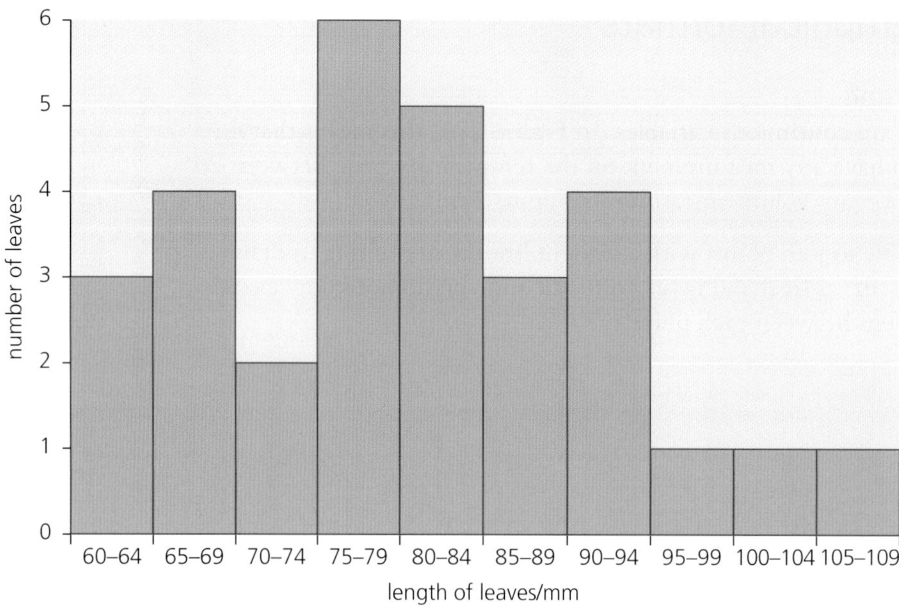

Figure 27.3 A histogram

If two sets of data are plotted on one graph it is possible to produce a comparison such as the example in Figure 27.4. Here, the sizes of dog whelks on an exposed and a sheltered shore are being compared, as you might meet in a Core practical.

Note: a histogram normally has the columns touching but in this case a single column is split into two to give space for two sets of data.

A simple presentation of the data would be a two-column bar chart of the means for each shore. By working a little harder you can produce a graph that gives you much more information, which you can discuss in interpreting your data. It is possible to see how much the data are spread out and how much they overlap, etc.

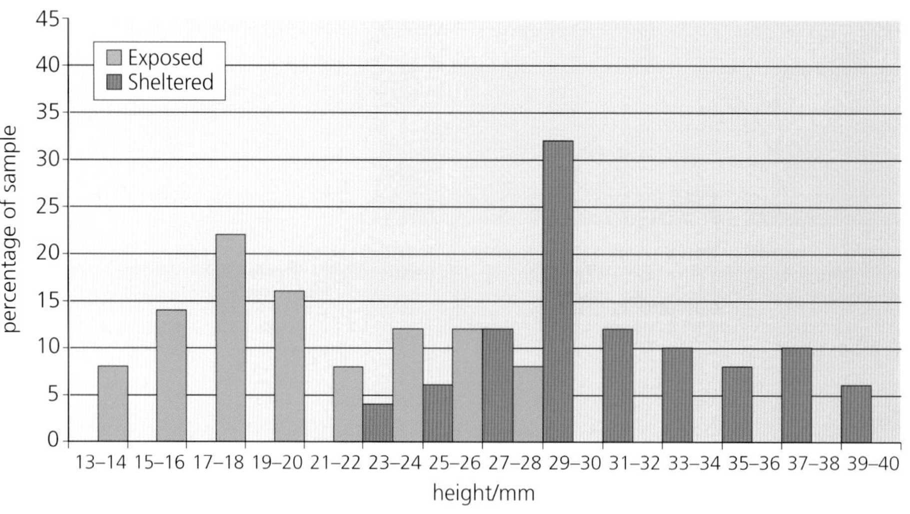

Figure 27.4 A comparative histogram showing variation in shell height in dog whelks on sheltered and exposed shores

4 Scatter graph

Scatter graphs (sometimes called scattergrams) are used when investigating a correlation between two variables. The data are simply plotted as individual points. This can often highlight possible anomalies for further investigation, such as the low diameter at pH 4.2 in Figure 27.5.

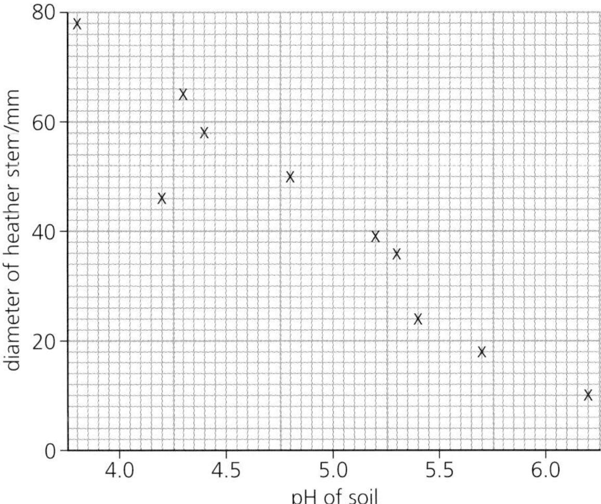

Figure 27.5 A scatter graph

The pattern of points will also indicate the general trend of any correlation present, as shown in Figure 27.6.

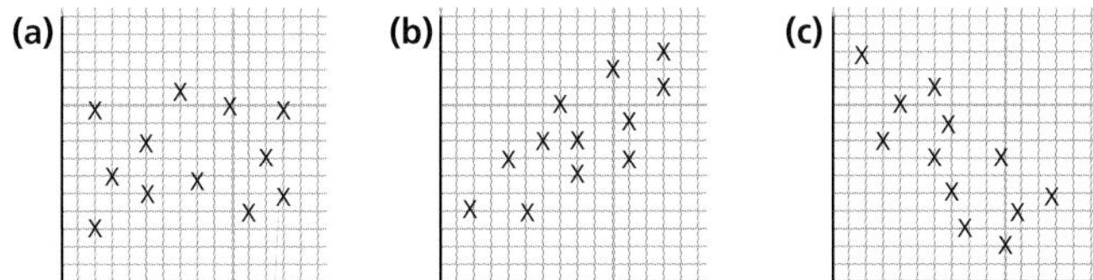

Figure 27.6 Three possible trends on a scattergram: a) no correlation; b) positive correlation; c) negative correlation

5 'Box and whisker' plot

Box and whisker plots (Figure 27.7) are most often used to represent skewed data but they are very useful for showing lots of information about the data. Plotting two box and whiskers side by side can also be advantageous when comparing data sets.

To find the values to plot, all the measurements are ranked in one list. The list is then divided into quartiles. The lower quartile boundary is the measurement that has 25 per cent of the sample. If there were 16 readings then this would mean moving up the rank order until you have 4th measurement. Similarly, the upper quartile boundary is when you have 75 per cent of the sample (the 12th measurement). The 'box' is now drawn as a column using the upper and lower quartiles on the vertical scale. The 'whiskers' are added as lines with a small cross-bar to indicate the highest and lowest measurements, and the median is drawn as a line in the box.

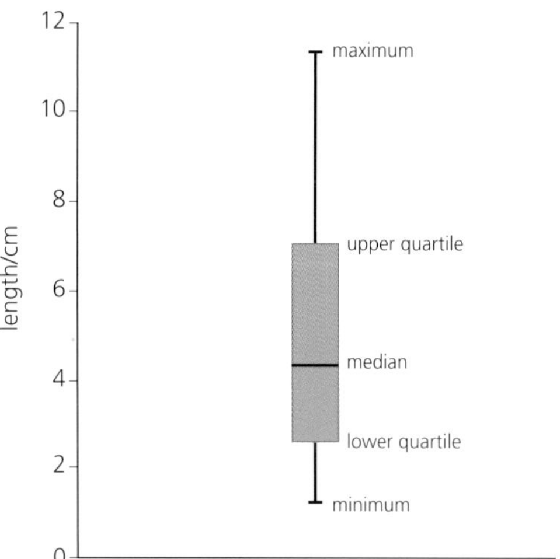

Figure 27.7 A 'box and whisker' plot

> **Tip**
>
> Don't rush into graphically-based questions without taking a few moments to check exactly what the data on each axis actually show. What is the title? What are the units on the scales?

Graphs and examination questions

Graphs are extremely common in examination papers. They are used to test several skills but often they are linked to calculations and data interpretation.

The two graphs in Figure 27.8 show how important it is to be very clear about what data are actually plotted.

Both graphs show ion uptake into carrot root tissue. Graph A shows data recording the concentration of ions in the carrot tissue over time. Graph B shows data recording the rate of ion uptake over time.

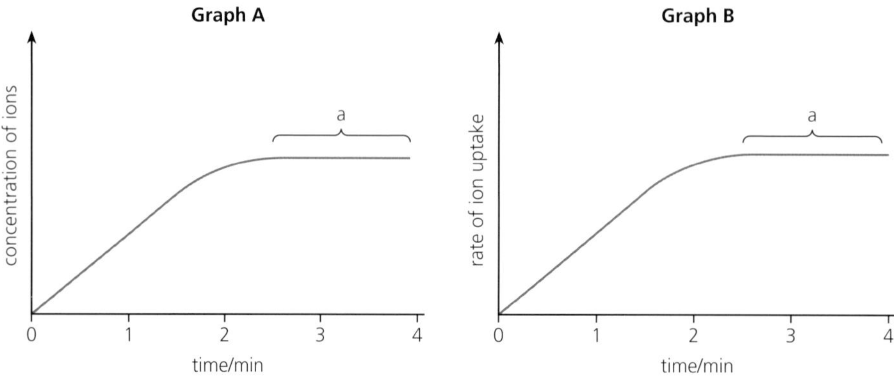

Figure 27.8 Different axes mean different trends

The graphs appear identical, but if we look at section 'a' on each then they mean very different things. In A, the horizontal line labelled 'a' shows no increase in concentration so transport has stopped. In B the horizontal section 'a' shows the rate has not changed but transport continues at a high level. So a lack of care in checking axes can lead to large mistakes.

Calculating rates from graphs

This is again a very common examination question, so you need to practise until you are confident with the methods used. You will find more examples of calculating rates in Core practicals 9 and 10 (on pages 281 and 300). Calculations might include drawing a tangent to a curve in order to find the gradient, or taking readings from graphs and using these to find the change in value and the time taken.

Ratios and percentages

Chapter 10 introduces the concept of surface-area-to-volume ratio and demonstrates the comparative value of ratios. Knowing that a mouse might have a smaller surface area than an elephant is rather obvious, but calculating that it has a much larger surface-area-to-volume ratio leads you to some important biological conclusions.

Ratios can also be used to give a more meaningful description of shape. The example in Figure 27.9 compares the shape of two limpets (*Patella vulgata*). Limpets are cone-shaped molluscs found attached to rocky shores. They have different shell shapes when living on exposed shores compared with very sheltered shores.

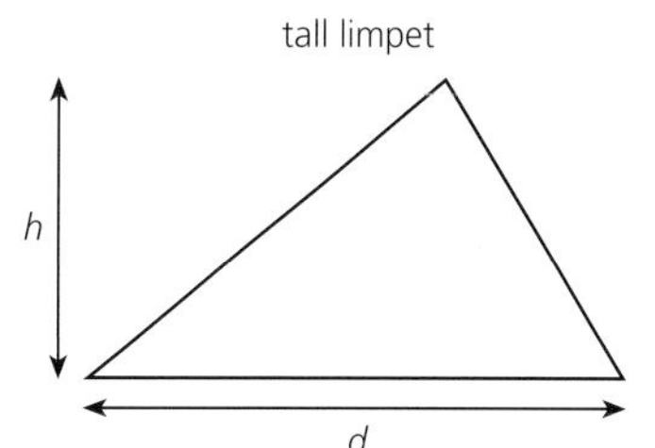

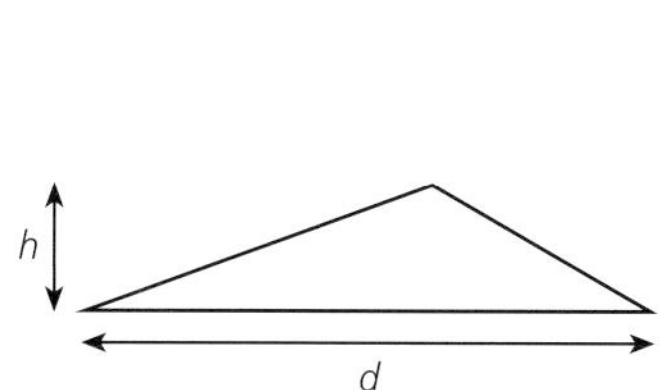

Figure 27.9 Using a ratio to describe shape

Individual measurements of height and diameter can vary, but if we use the ratio $h:d$ to describe the shape it is independent of these variations. Hence the 'tall' limpet will always have a much larger $h:d$ ratio compared with the 'flat' limpet, regardless of its overall size.

Percentage changes have very similar uses when comparing the magnitude of an overall change. A loss of mass of 1 g for the mouse could be catastrophic, but for an elephant it might be a tiny scratch on a toenail. Converting to percentage change would show this clearly, as 1 g would be 30–40 per cent loss of mass for the mouse but far less than 0.01 per cent for the elephant.

Tip

When calculating percentage change, make sure you divide the change by the initial value not the final value, and always add a plus or minus sign to indicate the direction of the change.

Calculating percentage change

This is a fairly simple calculation but a surprising number of students make basic errors when answering examination questions.

$$\% \text{ change} = \frac{\text{change in value}}{\text{initial value}} \times 100$$

Formulae

Whilst the number of equations you will need to memorise is very small, you do need to be confident in manipulating them to change the subject of the formula or to substitute values in them to calculate the final figure.

The simplest example is the magnification formula from Chapter 4. It is very useful to learn the three variations of this relationship:

$$\text{magnification} = \frac{\text{size of image}}{\text{size of specimen}}$$

$$\text{size of specimen} = \frac{\text{size of image}}{\text{magnification}}$$

$$\text{size of image} = \text{size of specimen} \times \text{magnification}$$

Some other specification formulae

In Chapter 8 you met more complex equations such as the index of diversity (D), which is calculated using the following formula:

$$D = \frac{N(N-1)}{\Sigma n(n-1)}$$

Where N = total number of individuals of all species and n = the number of individuals of each separate species. The symbol Σ means 'sum of' so that in this case it is the sum of all the calculations of $n(n-1)$ for each separate species found in the habitat.

Some specific formulae will be required for statistical testing but as you will see in Chapters 25 and 26, you will not need to memorise all of them.

In Chapter 21 you will have met the Hardy–Weinberg relationship, which gives us the allele frequencies in a population. Usually written as:

$$p^2 + 2pq + q^2 = 1$$

Where p and q are the allele frequencies written as probabilities.

This is quite straightforward and you will be expected to learn this. As with other equations you will be expected to be able to substitute a range of values into the equation and find values for p or q.

Logarithms

Look back at Core practical 14 in Chapter 23. Here you will find good examples of the use of logarithms and of their usefulness.

- Technically speaking, the logarithm of a number is the power to which the base must be raised to give that number.
- Sounds complicated, so just take out your calculator and try a few simple examples.
- For many uses the base we use is base 10 as it is very convenient.
- Remember, your base is 10. If you enter 1000 and press 'log' the answer you will see is 3.
- Obviously this is 10^3 exactly as our definition states. $\text{Log}_{10}\ 100 = 2$ in exactly the same way.

The example in Chapter 26 shows how this is useful in a simple way. Here, you wished to plot a scale where the values increased rapidly and this was very difficult to organise with the usual scales. So, for example, values such as 10, 100, 1000, 10000, 100000 would be almost impossible to plot accurately on a linear scale, but as a log scale the numbers become 1, 2, 3, 4 and 5. This is not only easy to plot but also turns a curve of ever increasing gradient into a straight line, which is much easier to manipulate further mathematically too.

Logarithmic growth

In Chapter 15 Core practical 12 you met an obvious example in bacterial growth. Not only does the number of microorganisms increase rapidly, but also the rate at which it increases goes up dramatically. If you wish to calculate how many organisms might be produced you need to make use of logarithms. It would be useful to check this idea by looking back at the worked example and the Exam practice question in Chapter 15, but you should be able to use your calculator to estimate the size of a bacterial population (N_x) after time (t), knowing its growth rate constant (μ) and the initial population number (N_0) from the formula:

$$\mu = \frac{2.303(\log N_x - \log N_0)}{t_x - t_0}$$

Statistical testing

Why do we use statistics?

Up until this point in your biology courses you may well have come across investigations and data from which you have been asked to draw conclusions. Although you will have had to apply your biological knowledge, these conclusions will have been based largely on your opinion. The trouble with opinions is that everyone has their own and this isn't good enough if we are to have reliable scientific progress.

Many investigations collect data to discover the answer to simple questions such as:

- Is there a difference between these two sets of results?
- Is there a correlation between these two variables?

Very often, the data collected do not make the answer to these questions obvious. So you need some rules on how you are to decide. These rules must be agreed before the data are collected, not selected later, as this makes it tempting to choose the rules just to fit your ideas, and they must be recognised by all other scientists.

The basic rule is all about chances or probability. Probabilities can be written in several ways (Table 27.2) but you are much more likely to meet them in decimal format.

Table 27.2 Probabilities

	Fraction	Percentage	Decimal fraction
Probability of tossing a fair coin and it falling as heads	$\frac{1}{2}$	50%	0.5

So a probability of 0 will indicate no probability and 1 or 100% will indicate total certainty.

Imagine that you are trying to investigate if there is a difference between the height of plants in two different areas. You measure the heights of random samples in each area. But is there a difference?

The problem is that, as with most living things, the height of a plant varies in each area, so it could be possible that more smaller plants than average were measured in one area and more slightly taller plants were measured in the other. This would mean you might think that the plants in the two areas had different heights when in fact they were the same.

Most of the statistical tests you might choose will calculate the probability that your results could occur purely by chance.

The rule that scientists apply to the type of data you are likely to collect is that there must be less than a probability of 0.05 (5% or 5 chances in every 100) that your results could arise simply by random sampling two areas where there was really no difference. This is called the **5 per cent significance level**.

If you can show that the probability is less than this then you are entitled to claim that there is a **significant difference** between your two sets of data.

Tip

Always make sure you use the word 'significant' if your statistical test demonstrates this. 'Different' and 'significantly different' are not the same thing. Exactly the same argument is true for tests for a **significant correlation** and **significant association**.

Null hypotheses

In order to test a hypothesis using the 5 per cent significance level several steps are needed. In most cases this will be done by following the instructions for your chosen test but you do need to understand what is meant by a null hypothesis. These are the basic steps in hypothesis testing using the same example of plant heights as above.

1 Start by assuming that there is no difference in the height of plants in both areas. (This is the null hypothesis.)

2 Measure the height of sample plants from both areas.

3 Use the statistical test to find the probability of getting the results that you have measured if there was no difference.

4 If the probability of getting results like yours if there was no difference in heights is very low (less than $p = 0.05$) then you can reject your idea (null hypothesis) and accept that there is a significant difference (the alternative hypothesis).

A null hypothesis is usually given the symbol H_0 and the alternative hypothesis the symbol H_1.

Key terms

Correlation A relationship between two variables where it can be shown that as one increases so does the other (positive correlation) or as one increases the other decreases (negative correlation).

Categorical data Categorical data measurements are counts of numbers that fall into distinct groups or categories such as round/wrinkled, has/has not, blue eye/brown eye, etc.

Interval level measurement This type of measurement covers almost all the data you collect by measuring something, such as volume of gas, time taken, length, etc. You can always quantify any differences between interval level measurements.

Types of statistical test

Almost all the investigations you might undertake will be covered by three types of tests (Table 27.3).

Table 27.3 Statistical tests

Type of test	Common tests	Notes
Testing for a significant difference	*t*-test	Only for normally distributed data. See worked example in Chapter 25 of the book, page 540.
	Mann-Whitney U test	Can be used for different types of data.
Testing for a significant correlation	Spearman's rank test	Simple to apply and understand. See Core practical 16, Chapter 26, page 551.
Testing for an association or 'goodness of fit'	Chi-squared test	Only for categorical data not interval level measurements. See Chapter 20, page 430.

You are not expected to know the more technical details of all the tests. However, do make sure you understand the principles and avoid basic errors when making your choice.

Chi-squared tests are often misused. They can only be used for categorical data. Investigations where this test is applicable are very rare at this level, so check carefully if you are thinking about using this test. You will be familiar with this type of data from genetics, for example where 'red-eye' and 'white-eye' are typical categorical counts in *Drosophila* investigations. In such cases you may form a hypothesis that there will be a fixed ratio, such as 3:1, in the results. It is rare for this to be exactly 3:1, so you can use a Chi-squared test with a 5 per cent confidence limit to test the 'goodness of fit' of your hypothesis. Are your data close enough to this predicted ratio?

An association might be tested in some cases. If you formed a hypothesis that rose bushes are more likely to suffer from black spot disease in rural areas compared with urban areas, then this could be an association. If the independent variables were rural and urban and the dependent variables were 'has black spot' and 'does not have black spot', then these would be categorical measurements. If you decided to measure the area of sample rose leaves affected by black spot then you would not have categorical data so would need to use one of the tests for a significant difference.

Take care to use the word 'correlation' correctly. Using it inaccurately often reveals a poor understanding of what is being tested.

Accepting or rejecting a null hypothesis

For each statistical test you will need to calculate a test statistic. In most tests you will use a formula to do this. It is unlikely that you will need to learn the formulae for each test as these will normally be provided, but you do need to practise calculating the test statistic. Core practical 16 (see Chapter 26) will provide you with an ideal opportunity to do this. Following this calculation you need to know the critical value of your chosen test statistic that matches your chosen level of confidence (0.05 or 5%). This involves a lot of calculations but fortunately the work will have been done for you and published in tables. If you do not have access to copies then they are freely available by typing the name of your test and 'table' into an internet search. Some are more complicated than others, so if you find one too complex, simply look up another. How you interpret the table is slightly different for each common test, and is shown in Table 27.4.

Table 27.4 Interpreting common statistical tests

Name of test	Name of test statistic	Rejecting null hypothesis
t-test	*t* value	Reject if your *t* value is higher than the critical value
Mann-Whitney U test	U1 and U2 values	Reject if the lowest U value is equal to or less than the critical value
Spearman's rank test	r_s (Spearman's correlation coefficient)	Reject if r_s is greater than or equal to the critical value
Chi-squared test	χ^2 (chi-squared)	Reject if value of χ^2 is greater than the critical value

You will find worked examples in this book of a *t*-test (Chapter 25), a correlation test (Chapter 26) and Exam practice questions to help you become familiar with statistical tests.

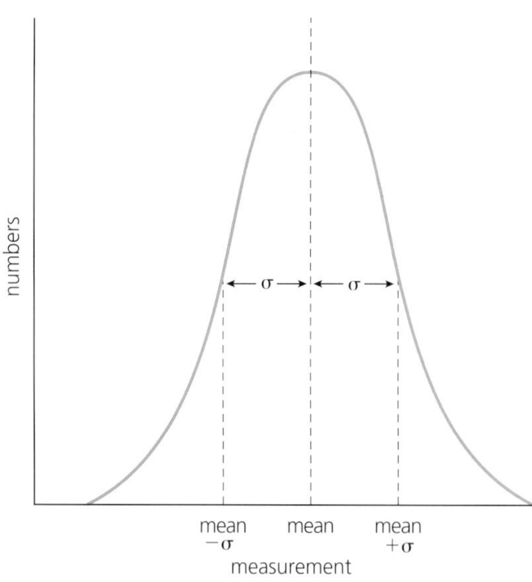

Figure 27.10 A normal distribution. The standard deviation is shown as σ

Descriptive statistics

As the name implies, descriptive statistics are used to describe the data you collect. Several important descriptive statistics are part of the mathematical requirements of the specification. An understanding of their meaning is important when describing data.

Normal distribution

Living things often show variation. It is a vital element of natural selection. If you measure one feature of a large sample of individuals you often find the pattern shown in Figure 27.10.

In simple terms this shows that the 'average' measurement is the one shown by most individuals and that the distribution is a symmetrical bell-shaped curve. This is what is meant by a 'normal' distribution.

The word 'average' is used in lots of different ways, so the term **mean** is better as it has a clearly defined scientific meaning.

If you look carefully at the graph in Figure 27.10 you will see that it can tell you something else about your data, namely how much the data are spread out. If all the data are in a narrow range then the curve will be tall and thin, but if the data are well spread out then the curve will be much wider and flatter. This is a really important feature if you are trying to decide if two populations are different, so it is calculated precisely. The calculation gives us a **population standard deviation**. This is given the sign σ (sigma). In a normal distribution we know that 68 per cent of all our values will lie within +/- one standard deviation of the mean and 98 per cent of our data will lie between +/- two standard deviations from the mean.

The formula for population standard deviation is:

$$\sigma = \sqrt{\frac{1}{N}\sum_{i=1}^{N}(x_i - \mu)^2}$$

This looks complicated, but if you break it down it becomes much simpler. You can use data from a number of your core practicals to practise substituting into the formula.

The standard deviation is actually the square root of the variance. So what is variance?

To calculate the variance you simply subtract each reading from the mean and square your answers. Then add up all the values and divide by the number of readings (N). In the formula above this is shown by the part of the expression under the square root sign, where x_i is the measurement and μ is the mean.

This is best illustrated by a simple example, as given on the next page.

Key terms

Mean The average value of a set of measurements calculated by adding all the measurements and dividing by the sample number.

Population standard deviation A measure of how much the sample data are spread out from the mean value in a whole population.

Example

A student measures the mass of five seeds, in grams, as shown below.

1.2, 1.5, 1.3, 1.7, 1.7

What will be:

a) the mean

b) the variance

c) the population standard deviation of these data?

Answers

a) Mean = 1.48 (This is one more significant figure than we can justify from our original data but we tend to keep this when using it in further calculations.)

b) To calculate variance find the sum of (Σ) the squared differences from the mean:

$(-0.28)^2 + (0.02)^2 + (-0.18)^2 + (0.22)^2 + (0.22)^2$

= 0.208 (to 3dp)

Now divide by the number in the population ($N = 5$)

So, variance = 0.0416

c) The population standard deviation shown by the formula is the square root of this: = 0.204 (to 3dp)

Note: the units of standard deviation are those of the original values (g) and it is usually written as +/− 0.204 g.

Lots of statistical formulae that you will meet contain squared numbers and square roots. You may have wondered why this is the case. The answer is shown in the calculations in the example. Trying to add differences from a mean is an obvious way to check the variability of data. However, lots of data have a nice even distribution about the mean so the plus values and the minus values tend to be even and we always end up with a total of zero, which is not very helpful. Squaring a number gets rid of the minus values as minus times minus equals plus. Now we can simply add up the differences, but since they are all squared numbers we need to take the square root to get them back to their real value. In other words a neat mathematical trick to get a total!

Just to add to the complication you might also meet a **sample standard deviation** that is exactly the same as the population standard deviation except that, for technical reasons, the sum of the squares of the differences from the mean is divided by $N - 1$ to find the variance.

Be careful when interpreting a standard deviation. This may be a small or large number but you need to compare it with the mean. A standard deviation of 0.1 may sound very small but if the mean was 0.05 then it would represent a very large variability in your data.

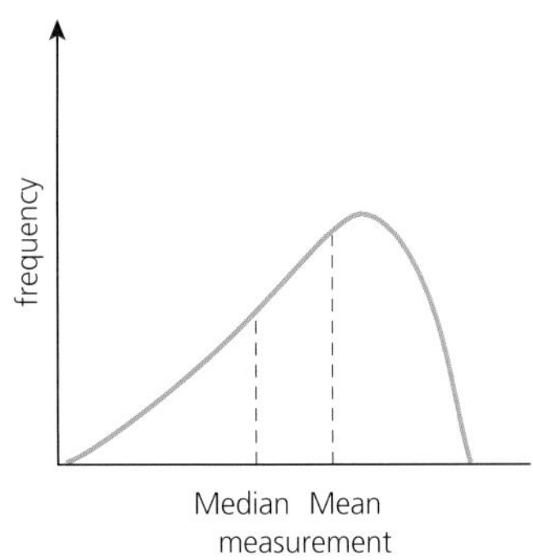

Figure 27.11 The distribution of skewed data

Skewed data

Not every set of measurements you might take are evenly spread out like a normal distribution. Sometimes there are a lot more readings at one end of the scale. For example, if you wished to investigate the percentage cover of heather on a moorland you would quickly find that it was very common and the majority of your measurements would be in the 80–100 per cent range. This would certainly not give you a symmetrical curve. It would look more like the graph in Figure 27.11.

In this case the mean as a measure of the average value would be misleading and would not represent the data very well. Therefore for skewed data, such as this, the **median** value would be more useful.

Another way of expressing an 'average' value is to use the **mode** or **modal** value of your data. With normally distributed data the mean, median and mode are likely to be the same but for skewed data they could all be different values.

Key terms

Median A measure of 'average' value for skewed data, using the middle value of the range of readings rather than the mean.

Mode A measure of 'average' value of data, which is found by identifying the measurement that occurs most often in a set of results.

Error bars

In many ways error bars are not well-named as they do not show errors. They are used to show the variability of your data on graphs, to enable you to analyse your data in an objective way. If you are measuring some natural feature such as the area of a leaf you would expect your data to vary over a range of values. If the error bars show a lot of variability in a laboratory investigation where you intended to control many variables carefully, they may indicate a flaw in your planning.

To calculate the lengths of error bars you would normally calculate the mean of your data and then the standard deviation (to be strictly accurate this ought to be standard error but again the difference goes a little beyond A level). This could be represented as shown in Figure 27.12, using some data comparing the length of rats' tails in the wild with those kept as pets.

A much simpler way could be to use a range bar, where the bar simply represents the highest and lowest values above and below the mean.

A simple way of showing variation in skewed data is by using a 'box and whisker' plot, as shown in Figure 27.7.

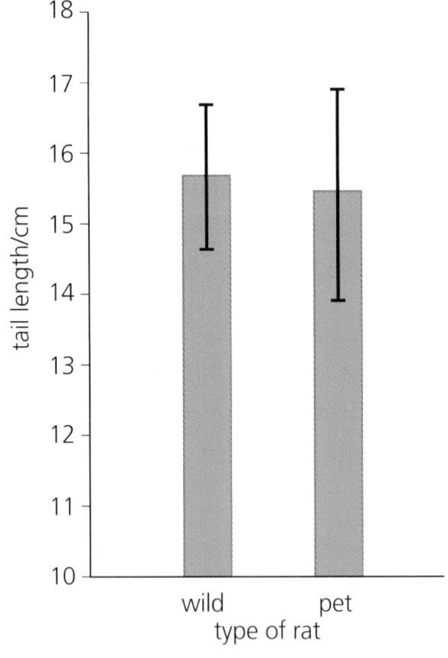

Figure 27.12 Errors bars – the mean and standard deviation of the tail lengths of wild and pet rats are shown. The error bars rise one standard deviation above and one below the mean

28 Preparing for the exams

The book covers the content of Pearson Edexcel's Advanced Level Biology B specification. Although some of the advice in this chapter is relevant only to the full Advanced Level examination papers, most is also relevant to the AS Biology B examinations.

Key term

Specification The document from the examination board that shows the content and skills that will be tested in an A Level examination. You can, and should, download a copy for your own reference from the Pearson Edexcel website.

Why should I read this chapter early in my course of study?

Let's assume that your ambition is to gain a grade A*. Looking at the national picture over the past few years, this means your ambition is to be in the top 9 per cent or so of candidates who started a two-year A level course. How do you turn this ambition into reality?

Perhaps most important of all, you need to accept responsibility for your own learning. The best students do not simply rely on their teachers and the work they do in class to drive their learning. They know what is needed in order to achieve their ambition and ensure they develop the skills to achieve it. Accepting responsibility for your own learning is a mindset – an attitude – that you need to develop early. You cannot do it a few weeks before your examinations start.

Tip

Throughout the academic year, you should continue practising your best skills as well as improving your weakest skills if you are to achieve a high grade.

Let's take an example from sport. Serena Williams is a tennis player, high in the world rankings. How has she achieved this? Clearly, she needs to know the 'rules' of tennis and to know what physical attributes successful tennis players develop. Then, she needs to train. This means she recognises her own skills and practises them. She practises her best strokes to maintain them and practises her weak strokes to improve them. For her, tennis is a full-time job – you do not need to train with the same intensity she does. But **practise** is a key to her success just as it will be to your success.

Figure 28.1 Serena Williams is a tennis player high in the world rankings. How has she achieved this?

What do I need to practise?

By now, you have realised that examinations test more than just recall of facts. As a consequence, preparation for your examination cannot be just a case of 'swotting facts' for a few weeks before the examinations. Although the A level Biology examination includes tests of factual recall (memory), it tests many more skills than that. These are the skills you need to practise.

The skills tested in each A level Biology examination are called **assessment objectives**. Table 28.1 summarises these objectives. Notice the heading of the second column in the table. It states 'the skills that will be tested'; not might, but *will*.

Table 28.1 The skills (assessment objectives) that will be tested in your A level Biology exams

Assessment objective	Description of the skills that will be tested
AO1	Demonstrate knowledge and understanding of scientific ideas, processes, techniques and procedures.
AO2	Apply knowledge and understanding of scientific ideas, processes, techniques and procedures: • in a theoretical context • in a practical context • when handling qualitative data • when handling quantitative data.
AO3	Analyse, interpret and evaluate scientific information, ideas and evidence, including in relation to issues, to: • make judgements and reach conclusions • develop and refine practical design and procedures.

Table 28.2 shows the balance of marks awarded for each of the assessment objectives in the A level Biology examination papers. Notice that the balance of marks is given as a percentage of the overall marks for the examinations. The percentages are not just rough guides – examiners have to ensure the papers have this balance of marks, every year.

Table 28.2 The percentage weighting for each assessment objective in Pearson Edexcel's A level Biology exams

Exam paper	Raw marks	Percentage weighting of each assessment objective			
		AO1	AO2	AO3	All
1	90	11–13	12–14	5–7	30
2	90	11–13	12–14	5–7	30
3	120	8–10	16–18	13–15	40
Total for A level	**300**	**31–33**	**41–43**	**25–27**	**100**

Suppose you rely on 'swotting facts' just before your A level Biology examinations. What is the maximum mark you can expect to gain on this skill alone? Look again at Table 28.1. Recall of facts is part of AO1 – not all of it, just a part (demonstrating knowledge). Now look at Table 28.2. The maximum weighting for the whole of AO1 is 31–33 per cent of the total raw marks. Even if recall (without understanding) earns half those marks, the maximum marks for recall will be about 15–17 per cent of the total raw marks. If you are guessing that would earn you the lowest grade possible (grade U), you are correct. You need to develop *all* the skills in Table 28.1.

Tip

The weighting of assessment objectives means that relying solely on memorising facts is unlikely to earn you the high grade you hope to gain in your A level Biology exams.

Do I really need to practise these skills throughout the year?

Perhaps you are hoping to pass your driving test soon, or can remember how you felt before you passed it. What did you do to prepare for that? The chances are you regularly went over the information you needed for the theory test, just to make sure you still remembered it. You might have asked someone to test you with random questions or even tried the practice test papers on the Driver and Vehicle Standards Agency website. You also probably pestered a parent, sibling or friend who had a full driving license to sit in the passenger seat, enabling you to drive the family car. If you are not learning to drive, you have probably practised a different skill recently – a performance piece on a musical instrument, a dance routine, preparing a favourite meal or reaching a new level in your favourite computer game. If so, just as with the example of learning to drive, your behaviour will have shown two key aspects of learning:

- Repetition improves performance.
- All the skills that will be tested must be repeated.

You might still be unconvinced. Look at Figure 28.2. It shows the results of an experiment performed in 1885 by a German psychologist called Hermann von Ebbinghaus. In his experiment, Ebbinghaus learnt a list of nonsensical three-letter 'words'. He then tested how well he recalled them until he could remember none of the words from the list. As you can see from curve A in Figure 28.2, he forgot the list pretty quickly. He then repeated the same experiment but this time he re-learnt his list after 2 weeks and, in a further repeat, he re-learnt his list after 2 weeks and again after 4 weeks. You can see the improvement in his ability to recall the list when he re-learnt it after 2 weeks (curve B) and even more improvement when he re-learnt it after 2 weeks and after 4 weeks (curve C). These results are generally accepted as showing how we all lose the ability to recall unless we keep revising what we have learnt.

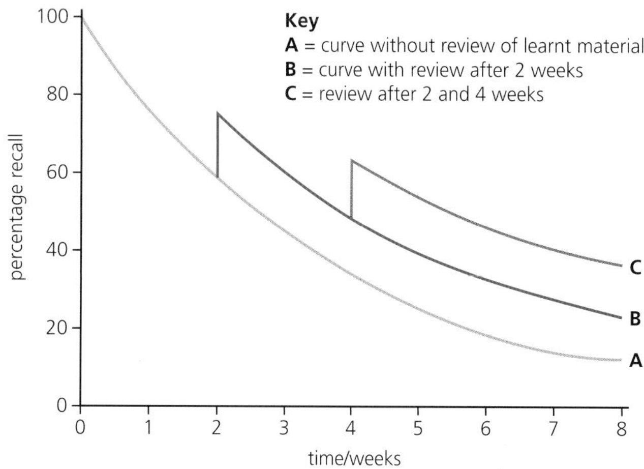

Figure 28.2 The 'Ebbinghaus forgetting curve' shows how reviewing what we learn aids memory and slows forgetting

How can I practise these skills?

Firstly, it is important that you understand what you have been taught each week. If you do not, you will find it difficult not only to recall information but also to be able to apply it. There are probably long periods of time when you are in college or school but not timetabled for classes. Use some of this time to visit the learning centre and go over your notes. If you find something you do not understand, make a note of it and plan to deal with that straight away. You could:

- ask your teacher for help
- ask others in your class for help
- use the relevant chapter in this book
- type a question into your favourite search engine. The web is full of animations, presentations and answers to students' questions that might be helpful to you. Take care, though, to use trustworthy sources.

In addition, you might choose to set aside a regular time each week to practise your skills. Research shows that an intense but short period is more effective than a prolonged period of practice. You will know best the period of time you can concentrate for; it is likely to be between 20 and 40 minutes. This is the maximum time you should plan for your practice session.

Look back to Table 28.1. It shows the skills you need to practise. Decide in advance which skills you will practise that week. Remember that the weighting of these skills, shown in Table 28.2, means you cannot afford to leave any skill as a weakness. Be prepared to plan practice sessions for skills that you find tough.

Tip

You must not stay in your comfort zone by practising only those skills you find easy.

Practice is an active process – you must be doing something. Simply reading your notes is not an active process. So, your final act of preparation is to find material that you will use to practise your chosen skill.

Practising AO1 skills

These are perhaps the easiest of all skills to practise. Think of how often you are alone and idle, for example, standing in a queue or sitting on a bus. How long would it take you to pick a topic and remind yourself of the key facts, principles or terminology? You could, for example, decide to recall the definitions of key ecological terms, to recall the events in the light-dependent and light-independent stages of photosynthesis or to explain to yourself the second messenger model of hormone action. It would take minutes. And these minutes are not 'time you will never get back' – you weren't doing anything useful in the first place.

For a more structured practice session, you need test questions. Most of the 'Test yourself questions' in this book are simple tests of recall or of recall with understanding. This is also true of some of the 'Exam practice questions' in this book. Being able to spot what skill a question is testing is an important part of preparing for your examination. The best way to do this is to look at the **command word** – the wording that tells you what the examiners want you to do. Table 28.3 shows you the command words used in questions that test AO1 skills (recall and recall with understanding). There is no point in writing an answer that does not do what the command word asks. Writing a description when asked for an explanation, for example, will not gain the marks you need.

Key term

Command word The verb or phrase used by examiners to tell you what is required in your answer, e.g. describe, explain, calculate.

Table 28.3 The command words used to test AO1 skills

Command word	Description of what is required
Add/Label	Requires the addition of labelling to stimulus material given in the question, for example labelling a diagram or adding units to a table.
Complete	Requires the completion of a table/diagram.
Describe (in absence of stimulus material)	To give an account of something. Statements in the response need to be developed as they are often linked but do not need to include a justification or reason.
Draw	Produce a diagram either using a ruler or using freehand.
Explain	An explanation requires a justification/exemplification of a point. The answer must contain some element of reasoning/justification; this can include mathematical explanations.
Give/state/name	All of these command words are really synonyms. They generally all require recall of one or more pieces of information.
Plot	Produce a graph by marking points accurately on a grid from data that is provided and then draw a line of best fit through these points. A suitable scale and appropriately labelled axes must be included if these are not provided in the question.
Sketch	Produce a freehand drawing. For a graph this would need a line and labelled axes with important features indicated, the axes are not scaled.
State what is meant by	When the meaning of a term is expected but there are different ways of how these can be described.
Write	When the questions ask for an equation.

Practising AO2 and AO3 skills

Questions testing AO2 and AO3 skills contain **stimulus material**, in other words text, artwork or tabulated data that you are expected to use. Consequently, you need to have questions ready for use during practice sessions for these skills. They are easy to spot because they contain lots of information that you need to use. Usually you will not have seen this information before. Do not worry; neither has anyone else. If examiners wish to test your ability to use information, it is important that they provide stimulus material that none of the candidates taking the examination is likely to be familiar with or be able to recall. You will need to understand the underlying biology, but will not have seen the context before. So, in addition to the skills being tested in the question, you need to develop a further skill during your course, namely the confidence to deal with something new.

Key term

Stimulus material The written, diagrammatic or tabulated information given in an examination question that you must describe, explain, analyse, interpret or evaluate.

Table 28.4 shows the command words by which you can recognise questions testing AO2 and AO3 skills. Notice that, in each case, reference to one or more aspects of the stimulus material is required. If you do not refer to the stimulus material, you cannot show AO2 or AO3 skills and, consequently, will not gain many marks.

Table 28.4 The command words used to test AO2 and AO3 skills

Command word	Description of what is required
Assess	Give careful consideration to all the factors or events that apply and identify which are the most important or relevant. Make a judgement on the importance of something, and come to a conclusion where needed.
Calculate	Obtain a numerical answer, showing relevant working. If the answer has a unit, this must be included.
Comment on	Requires the synthesis of a number of variables from data/information to form a judgement.
Compare and contrast	Look for the similarities **and** differences of two (or more) things. Should not require the drawing of a conclusion. Answer must relate to both (or all) things mentioned in the question. The answer must include at least one similarity and one difference.
Criticise	Inspect a set of data, an experimental plan or a scientific statement and consider the elements. Look at the merits and faults of the information presented and support judgements made by giving evidence.
Deduce	Draw/reach conclusion(s) from the information provided.
Describe what the information shows	Translate the stimulus material from one form to another, e.g., from a graph into words.
Determine	The answer must have an element that is quantitative from the stimulus provided, or must show how the answer can be reached quantitatively. To gain maximum marks there must be a quantitative element to the answer.
Devise	Plan or invent a procedure from existing principles/ideas.
Discuss	• Identify the issue/situation/problem/argument that is being assessed within the question. • Explore all aspects of an issue/situation/problem/argument. • Investigate the issue/situation, etc. by reasoning or argument.
Evaluate	Review information then bring it together to form a conclusion, drawing on evidence including strengths, weaknesses, alternative actions, relevant data or information. Come to a supported judgement of a subject's qualities and relation to its context.
Explain	An explanation requires a justification/exemplification of a point. The answer must contain some element of reasoning/justification; this can include mathematical explanations.
Give a reason/ reasons	When a statement has been made and the requirement is only to give the reasons why.
Identify	Usually requires some key information to be selected from a given stimulus/resource.
Justify	Give evidence to support (either the statement given in the question or an earlier answer).
Predict	Give an expected result.
Show that	Verify the statement given in the question.

Tip

If you find you are using six lines of text to answer a 1-mark question, you are probably wasting valuable examination time. If you are answering a 4-mark question with a few words, you are probably not fully answering the question.

Using the mark allocation

Understanding the meaning of command words will increase your chances of answering the question in the way the examiners intended. It is important that you also take a note of, and use intelligently, the mark allocation for each question. Look at the mark schemes for the specimen examination papers, available on the Pearson Edexcel website. The marks are not awarded subjectively by examiners. Instead, with the exception of extended prose questions, each mark is awarded for a single term, fact, concept, definition, principle or process. If a question has a tariff of 1 mark, you should offer the one appropriate term, fact, concept, definition, principle or process. If a question offers 4 marks, your answer should include four appropriate components.

You should also bear in mind that mark schemes contain no marks for re-writing the question. For example, when identifying a structure labelled on a drawing, the answer 'The name of the structure labelled A is a mitochondrion' wastes time when the mark is awarded for the answer 'mitochondrion'.

What do I need to know about the examination papers?

There is little point in developing your skills throughout your course unless you know how you will be asked to demonstrate them in an examination paper. This involves knowing:

- what content will be tested in each paper
- the types of question that will be used in each paper, and where within that paper.

Let's deal with these in turn.

Tip

The final A level examinations will test the content of your first year, as well as your second year, of A level study, so you must practise recall of the content of Topics 1 to 4 of the specification as well as Topics 5 to 10.

The content of each paper

Even if you have already taken the AS Biology exams, at the end of your Advanced Level course you will have to sit all three A level examinations, covering the content of the entire specification.

Table 28.5 shows the specification content that is tested in each of the three examination papers at A level, and links the tested content to the relevant chapters in this book. Because much of its content is fundamental to what you will study in your second year, all three papers will include content from your first year of study. You can, though, gear your final preparation to the content of your second year topics. Paper 1 will test only three of the topics from your second year – Topics 5, 6 and 7. Paper 2 will also test only three topics from your second year – Topics 8, 9 and 10.

Only Paper 3 can include questions from *any* part of the specification. This means that this paper is the one that is most likely to contain **synoptic questions**. Synoptic questions will test your ability to bring together knowledge and understanding from different topics, for example when:

- developing an argument or explanation using extended prose
- explaining data provided from the experimental work of other scientists
- relating practical processes and procedures to the experimental work of others.

Key term

Synoptic questions
These test your ability to bring together knowledge and understanding from different topics within the specification, often shown by developing an argument or interpreting the work of other scientists.

Table 28.5 The specification content that is tested in each A level exam paper

Exam paper	Exam time/ minutes	Total raw marks	Specification topics tested in the examination paper	Relevant chapters in this book
1	105	90	Biological molecules	1, 2 and 3
			Cells, viruses and reproduction of living things	4, 5 and 6
			Classification and biodiversity	7 and 8
			Exchange and transport	9, 10, 11 and 12
			Energy for biological processes	13 and 14
			Microbiology and pathogens	15, 16 and 17
			Modern genetics	18 and 19
2	105	90	Biological molecules	1, 2 and 3
			Cells, viruses and reproduction of living things	4, 5 and 6
			Classification and biodiversity	7 and 8
			Exchange and transport	9, 10, 11 and 12
			Origins of genetic variation	20 and 21
			Control systems	22, 23 and 24
			Ecosystems	25 and 26
3	150	120	All of 1 to 10	1 to 26
			Practical principles in Biology	1 to 26

Types of examination question

As Table 28.5 shows, Papers 1 and 2 each last for 105 minutes and carry 90 marks; Paper 3 lasts for 150 minutes and carries 120 marks. You could regard that as 1 mark per minute plus some 'reading and thinking time'. It does not leave you with time to spare or time to waste.

You might wonder why Paper 3 seems to allow you 30 minutes of 'reading and thinking time' while Papers 1 and 2 allow only 15 minutes. To explain this, we have to look at the type of questions that will occur in the three papers. All three papers will include the following types of question:

- **multiple choice**, in which you choose the correct response from four alternatives; these usually form the first one or two parts of a structured, short-answer question
- **short open**
- **open-response**
- **calculation**, targeting mathematics at Level 2 or above
- **extended writing**, carrying up to 6 marks.

Tip

The way you use time during an examination is crucial. Regard the examination papers as allowing some reading and thinking time and a work rate of 1 mark per minute. During an examination, ask yourself, 'In the last minute, did I gain 1 mark or did I waste time?'

In addition, Paper 3 will include synoptic questions and questions that test your conceptual and theoretical understanding of experimental methods. These questions will require some thought and planning. To answer these questions you must:

- carefully read the information given in the question, identifying which information you must use in your answer
- ensure you understand what is required by the question
- select any information from across the entire specification that is relevant to the question
- organise this information into a logical sequence
- write your answer.

All of this takes time: hence the additional 'reading and thinking time' in Paper 3.

Extended writing questions and 'levels of response' mark schemes

An extended writing question with 6 or 9 marks will normally have a mark scheme that is different from other types of question. This mark scheme will set out a range of possible information that, from your own knowledge of the specification content, you *might* include in your answer. Your answer will then be assessed in one of three levels and given a mark accordingly. Obviously, it is important that you use all of the information provided in the question, and a wide range of your own knowledge, but don't be tempted to add lots of superficial comments at the expense of a logical, well-organised discussion. It is quite possible to achieve very high marks without including everything that the examiners have listed in the mark scheme.

To gain high marks when examiners use a 'levels of response' mark scheme, it is even more important that you carefully organise your answer for these questions. A few minutes listing all the things you think might be included and then grouping them into a logical sequence will be a very profitable exercise.

Questions with 9 marks will often include phrases such as 'Assess the ...' or 'Discuss the validity of ...'. These are a clear indicator that your answer must not only contain logical arguments or reasoning, but must lead to some form of conclusion. If you do not follow your arguments through in this way, your marks will be severely limited.

In this book we have used the same device that Pearson Edexcel uses in exam papers, i.e., an asterisk, to indicate questions that will be marked using a 'levels of response' mark scheme.

Preparing your examination strategy

Examination papers are usually designed with the following features:

- The early questions are more accessible than the later questions.
- Within each structured question, the earlier parts are usually more accessible than the later parts of the same question.

You will also remember from your previous experience that examinations are stressful.

Let's put these two ideas together.

- It is highly unlikely that you will obtain full marks in an examination; few students ever do. What you do need to do, though, is ensure that you gain all the marks that you are capable of gaining.
- Early in the examination, you need to reduce your anxiety levels. The best way to do this is by doing something that plays to your strengths, thus reassuring yourself that you have gained marks.

Rather than leaving it for the day on which the examination paper lands on your desk, the best way to achieve these two objectives is to plan how you will answer the examination paper well in advance. This plan is your examination strategy. So, how do you make this plan?

Firstly, remember that the order of questions in the examination paper is not designed with you in mind. You do not need to answer them in numerical order. Secondly, ask yourself what your favourite topics are on each paper. Thirdly, ask yourself in which of your skills you have the most confidence. Finally, look through the specimen question papers and, if available, past examination papers. Is there a particular place where types of question occur? For example, if you love extended prose questions that allow you to show your writing skills, and gain 6 marks in the process, is there a place in the examination paper where such a question always crops up? Once you have the answers to those questions, you can start your strategy. Remember that, since it plays to your strengths, your strategy will be unique to you; don't be put off if someone else has a different approach.

Table 28.6 outlines some of the general features that your examination strategy might contain.

Table 28.6 A possible examination strategy

I plan to ...	Reason(s)
• spend 5 minutes skimming through the examination paper	• I need to ensure that I have seen every question, so that I don't miss any that I can answer. • I need to find those that are easy for me to ensure I gain marks by answering them and don't waste valuable time by getting stuck on a harder question. • I need to plan the order in which I answer the questions to ensure that, early on, I get all the marks that are 'easy' for me.
• pick one or two questions that play to my strengths and answer those first	• I will gain valuable marks early in the examination. • Knowing I have been successful will give me confidence and reduce my stress levels. This will help me to feel in control.
• answer the other questions by picking those parts I find straightforward and, when a question is not easy, move quickly to the next question or part of a structured question	• I am now 'harvesting' marks, ensuring I gain all the ones that are easy to get and avoiding wasting time on those I find harder. I can come back to those once I have gained my 'easy marks'.
• go back through the paper, filling in the gaps I have left, again without wasting too much time on any part of a question	• Having built up my confidence by gaining many marks, I am now ready to tackle the parts of questions I found less accessible on the first run-through.
• make an intelligent 'guess' rather than leave a gap	• There is no point in leaving gaps in the paper since I know that a gap gains no marks.
• go back through the paper to check my answers and correct any errors	• Under the pressure of an examination, it is easy to make a silly mistake – an exam howler. I will just check that I haven't made any and correct any that I find.

Sources you might find useful

In addition to the materials you gain in class and this textbook, there are many other helpful sources that are readily available. They include:

- the examination board's website for the specification and specimen examination papers:
  http://qualifications.pearson.com/en/qualifications/edexcel-a-levels/biology-b-2015.html#/tab-1
- the intranet in your college or school
- your favourite search engine – key in your question, topic area, or 'biology animations'. Do take care, though, to use sources that are academically reliable
- Edexcel A level Biology Teaching and Learning Resources
- *Biological Sciences Review* for articles of interest, including structured examination-style questions about some of them:
  https://www.hoddereducation.co.uk/magazines
- your classmates.

Figure 28.3 Whilst the examination is a solo effort, solving problems or revising in a group can be rewarding

Index

C

O

P

Q

R

Acknowledgements

The Publisher would like to thank the following for permission to reproduce copyright material.

Photo credits:

p.7 © enskanto – Fotolia; **p.11** *both* © Andrew Lambert Photography/Science Photo Library; **p.14** *both* © Andrew Lambert Photography/Science Photo Library; **p.15** © Biophoto Associates/ Science Photo Library; **p.16** © Biophoto Associates/Science Photo Library; **p.19** © molekuul. be / Alamy; **p.21** © Steve Gschmeissner/Science Photo Library; **p.32** © Steve Gschmeissner/ Science Photo Library; **p.73** *l* © J.C. Revy, Ism/Science Photo Library, *r* © Gene Cox; **p.75** © Gene Cox; **p.77** © Power And Syred/Science Photo Library; **p.78** © George Chapman/Visuals Unlimited/Getty Images; **p.79** © Sinclair Stammers/Science Photo Library; **p.80** *t* © Dr. Kevin S. Mackenzie, Institute of Medical Sciences, Aberdeen University, *r* © Eye Of Science/Science Photo Library; **p.82** *l* © Steve Gschmeissner/Science Photo Library, *r* © Dr. Jeremy Burgess/Science Photo Library; **p.83** © Biophoto Associates/Science Photo Library; **p.84** *t* © CNRI/Science Photo Library, *r* © Dr. Kari Lounatmaa/Getty Images; **p.85** *t* © Medimage/Science Photo Library, *b* © Omikron/Science Photo Library; **p.86** © Carolina Biological Supply Co/Visuals Unlimited, Inc. /Science Photo Library; **p.87** © Dr. Kevin S. Mackenzie, Institute of Medical Sciences, Aberdeen University; **p.88** © Dr. Jeremy Burgess/Science Photo Library; **p.89** © Kwangshin Kim/Science Photo Library; **p.100** *l* © James Cavallini/Science Photo Library, *r* © BSIP SA / Alamy; **p.103** *all* © Michael Abbey/Science Photo Library; **p.106** © Wim Van Egmond/Visuals Unlimited, Inc. /Science Photo Library; **p.115** © Pr. Philippe Vago, Ism/Science Photo Library; **p.119** © Science VU/B. John, Visuals Unlimited /Science Photo Library; **p.126** © Jean-Claude Revy-A. Goujeon, Ism/Science Photo Library; **p.127** © Gene Cox; **p.129** © Edelmann/Science Photo Library; **p.133** © Gerry Cambridge/NHPA/Photoshot; **p.135** © Dr. Keith Wheeler/ Science Photo Library; **p.139** © CNRI/Science Photo Library; **p.145** *l* © idp wildlife collection / Alamy, *m* © Lip Kee / http://www.flickr.com/photos/lipkee/5657636385/sizes/o/in/pool-42637302@N00/ http://creativecommons.org/licenses/by-sa/2.0, *r* © FLPA / Alamy; **p.154** *l* © Springfield Gallery – Fotolia, *r* © C. J. Clegg; **p.171** © Sally A. Morgan/Ecoscene; **p.175** © Tony Watson / Alamy; **p.181** © kjorgen/iStock/Thinkstock; **p.186** © Robert Bird / Alamy; **p.190** © Frans Lanting Studio / Alamy; **p.194** *both* © Don W. Fawcett/Science Photo Library; **p.202** *both* © Biophoto Associates/Science Photo Library; **p.216** © Biodisc/Visuals Unlimited, Inc./Science Photo Library; **p.223** © PHOTOTAKE Inc. / Alamy; **p.224** © Ned Therrien/Visuals Unlimited, Inc./Science Photo Library; **p.225** © Gene Cox; **p.237** © PHOTOTAKE Inc. / Alamy; **p.246** © CNRI/Science Photo Library; **p.247** © BSIP/Vem/Science Photo Library; **p.258** *l* © Dr. Keith Wheeler/Science Photo Library, *r* © Ed Reschke/Getty Images; **p.259** *both* © Gene Cox; **p.260** *t* © Gene Cox, *b* © Dr. David Furness, Keele University/Science Photo Library; **p.292** © Dr Kari Lounatmaa/Science Photo Library; **p.293** © Dr Kenneth R. Miller/Science Photo Library; **p.307** © Dr Jeremy Burgess/Science Photo Library; **p.311** © Dr Linda Stannard, Uct/Science Photo Library; **p.312** © Doncaster And Bassetlaw Hospitals/Science Photo Library; **p.313** *both* © Trevor Clifford Photography/Science Photo Library; **p.315** © John Durham/Science Photo Library; **p.319** © Amelie-Benoist/Bsip/Science Photo Library; **p.320** © Martyn F. Chillmaid/Science Photo Library; **p.323** © Amelie-Benoist/Bsip/Science Photo Library; **p.332** © Kwangshin Kim/ Science Photo Library; **p.333** *t* © Juergen Berger/Science Photo Library, *b* © CNRI/Science Photo Library; **p.334** *t* © Eye Of Science/Science Photo Library, *b* © Simon Fraser/Science Photo Library; **p.339** © Dr Linda Stannard, Uct/Science Photo Library; **p.342** © Yue Jin/US Department Of Agriculture/Science Photo Library; **p.343** © Nick Gregory / Alamy; **p.345** © Dr. Pete Billingsley, University Of Aberdeen/Sinclair Stammers/Science Photo Library; **p.354** © Steve

Gschmeissner/Science Photo Library; **p.355** © Steve Gschmeissner/Science Photo Library; **p.361** © Steve Gschmeissner/Science Photo Library; **p.371** *tl* and *tr* © Gary Meszaros/Science Photo Library, *br* © Gilles Mermet/Science Photo Library; **p.378** © Biophoto Associates/Science Photo Library; **p.392** © UK Crown Copyright Courtesy Of Fera/Science Photo Library; **p.399** © David Parker/Science Photo Library; **p.408** © Matt Meadows/Photolibrary/Getty Images; **p.410** © Nigel Cattlin/Science Photo Library; **p.412** © Janice and Nolan Braud / Alamy; **p.426** © Solvin Zankl/Visuals Unlimited, Inc. /Science Photo Library; **p.444** © Imagestate Media (John Foxx); **p.445** © Dave Watts / Alamy; **p.448** © Peter Falkner/Science Photo Library; **p.454** © Gene Cox Estate; **p.455** © Gene Cox Estate; **p.460** © Gene Cox Estate; **p.467** © Prof S. Cinti/Science Photo Library; **p.470** © Daniel Heuclin/NHPA/Photoshot; **p.475** *tl* © Vladimir Melnik – Fotolia, *tm* © Nazzu – Fotolia, *tr* © ZambeziShark/iStock/Thinkstock, *bl* © Marcelo Sanchez – Fotolia, *br* © Faultier/iStock/Thinkstock; **p.483** © Ross Koning; **p.495** © Gene Cox Estate; **p.508** © P&R Fotos - www.superstock.com; **p.515** © Jim Zipp/Science Photo Library; **p.522** © Noaa Pmel Vents Program/Science Photo Library; **p.531** © Christian GUY/imageBROKER - www.superstock.com; **p.539** *l* © G A Matthews/Science Photo Library, *r* © Glenis Moore/Science Photo Library; **p.547** © Marshall Ikonography / Alamy; **p.551** *tl* © Marvin Dembinsky Photo Associates / Alamy, *tr* © Martin Harvey / Alamy, *bl* © Premaphotos / Alamy, *br* © RM Floral / Alamy; **p.552** © Biophoto Associates/Science Photo Library; **p.562** *l* © Greg Arthur, *r* © Nature Picture Library / Alamy; **p.563** *t* © CAP/Roger Viollet/Getty Images, *b* © Pierre Gleizes / Greenpeace; **p.564** © Greenpeace; **p.565** © Marine Stewardship Council; **p.570** *all* © Dr Ian Fuller, Massey University; **p.571** © Georgette Douwma/Science Photo Library; **p.585** © Stiggg/iStock/Thinkstock; **p.593** © Actionplus / TopFoto; **p.602** © Rido – Fotolia.

t = top, *b* = bottom, *l* = left, *r* = right, *m* = middle

Every effort has been made to trace all copyright holders, but if any have been inadvertently overlooked, the Publisher will be pleased to make the necessary arrangements at the first opportunity.